Handbook of Lipoprotein Testing
Second Edition

Edited by:

Nader Rifai
G. Russell Warnick
Marek H. Dominiczak

AACC Press
2101 L Street, NW, Suite 202
Washington, DC   20037-1526

GARY L. MYERS

Library of Congress Cataloging-in-Publication Data

Handbook of lipoprotein testing / edited by Nader Rifai, G. Russell Warnick,
Marek H. Dominiczak.—2nd ed.
    p.;cm.
  Includes bibliographical references and index.
  1. Blood lipoproteins—Analysis. I. Rafai, Nader. II. G. Russell Warnick
III. Marek H. Dominiczak
  [DNLM: 1. Lipoproteins—blood—Laboratory Manuals. 2. Hematologic
Tests—Laboratory Manuals. 3. Lipids—metabolism—Laboratory Manuals.
4. Lipoproteins—chemistry—Laboratory Manuals. QY 25 H236 2000]
  RB46 .H36 2000
616.07′561—dc21   00-031313

1 2 3 4 5 6 7 8 9 0 P C P 02 01 00

ISBN 1-890883-35-2 (alk. paper)

Dedication

We dedicate this book to all those individuals behind the scenes who have contributed to its publication: to numerous scientists, many unrecognized, who have diligently added to the body of knowledge from which this book draws; to our mentors, who inspired us to contribute; to our technical and administrative staff members, for their assistance; and to our editors and publisher. With this, the fourth book in the series, we wish to especially acknowledge the inspiration of Dr. Gerald Cooper, who for decades at the Centers for Disease Control and Prevention has kept the focus on standardization and improvements in laboratory methods. And we wish to express our gratitude to our respective spouses, children, and other family members who have supported us in this time-consuming endeavor throughout the years. Thanks to all those who have contributed in any way to the publication of this book.

Contributors

Joseph D. Artiss, PhD
Associate Professor, Department of Pathology
Wayne State University School of Medicine
Detroit, MI

Paul S. Bachorik, PhD
Professor (Retired)
The Johns Hopkins University School of Medicine
Baltimore, MD

Stefan Barlage, MD
Assistant Lecturer, Institute for Clinical Chemistry and
        Laboratory Medicine
University of Regensburg
Regensburg, Germany

Carol C. Benson, MA
Scientific Reviewer, Office of Device Evaluation
Center for Devices and Radiological Health
Food and Drug Administration
Rockville, MD

Deepak Bhatnagar, MBBS, PhD, FRCP, MRCPath
Consultant in Metabolic Medicine and Clinical Biochemistry
The Royal Oldham Hospital, and
Honorary Senior Lecturer and Consultant Physician
University of Manchester Department of Medicine
Manchester Royal Infirmary
Manchester, United Kingdom

Alfred Böttcher, PhD
Assistant Lecturer, Institute for Clinical Chemistry and
    Laboratory Medicine
University of Regensburg
Regensburg, Germany

Muriel J. Caslake, PhD
Research Fellow, Department of Pathological Biochemistry
University of Glasgow
Glasgow Royal Infirmary University NHS Trust
Glasgow, United Kingdom

V. Michelle Chenault, PhD
Associate Director for Science, Office of Science and Technology
Center for Devices and Radiological Health
Food and Drug Administration
Rockville, MD

Marian C. Cheung, PhD
Research Associate Professor, Department of Medicine
University of Washington School of Medicine
Seattle, WA

Thomas G. Cole, PhD
Research Professor of Biochemistry in Medicine
Department of Medicine
Director, Core Laboratory for Clinical Studies
Lipid Research Center
Washington University School of Medicine
St. Louis, MO

Gerald R. Cooper, MD, PhD
Research Medical Officer
Special Activities Branch
Division of Laboratory Sciences
National Center for Environmental Health
Centers for Disease Control and Prevention
Atlanta, GA

Ian N.M. Day, BA, MB BChir, PhD, MRCPath
Lister Institute Professor of Human Genetics
Director of Research Division of Human Genetics
Southampton University Hospital NHS Trust
Southampton, United Kingdom

Sridevi Devaraj, PhD
Assistant Professor, Division of Clinical Chemistry
Department of Pathology
University of Texas Southwestern Medical Center
Dallas, TX

Marek H. Dominiczak, MD, PhD, FRCPath, FRCP (Glasg)
Head, Biochemistry Department
Western Infirmary and Gartnavel General Hospital, and
Physician, The Lipid Clinic and Cardiovascular Risk Factor Clinic
West Glasgow Hospitals University NHS Trust, and
Senior Lecturer, University of Glasgow
Glasgow, United Kingdom

D. Robert Dufour, MD
Chief, Pathology and Laboratory Medicine
VA Medical Center, and
Professor of Pathology
George Washington University Medical Center
Washington, DC, and
Clinical Professor of Pathology
Uniformed Services University of the Health Sciences
Bethesda, MD

Patrick Duriez, PhD
Professor, Department of Physiology
Faculty of Pharmacy, University of Lille II, and
Assistant, Department of Research on Atherosclerosis
Pasteur Institute, Inserm U325
Lille, France

Paul N. Durrington, BSc, MD, FRCP, FRCPath
Professor, Department of Medicine
University of Manchester, and
Honorary Consultant Physician
Manchester Royal Infirmary
Manchester, United Kingdom

Christopher J. Fielding, PhD
Professor, Department of Physiology
Cardiovascular Research Institute
University of California San Francisco Medical Center
San Francisco, CA

Jean-Charles Fruchart, PhD
Professor, Department of Clinical Biochemistry
Faculty of Pharmacy, University of Lille II, and
Head, Department of Research on Atherosclerosis
Pasteur Institute, Inserm U325
Lille, France

Valentin Fuster, MD, PhD
Director, The Zena and Michael A. Wiener Cardiovascular Institute
Richard Gorlin, MD/Heart Research Foundation, and
Professor of Cardiology
The Mount Sinai Medical Center
New York, NY

David J. Galton, MD, DSc, FRCP
Professor, Department of Human Metabolism and Genetics
St. Bartholomew's Hospital
London, United Kingdom

Deborah Gersony, MD
The Zena and Michael A. Wiener Cardiovascular Institute
The Mount Sinai Medical Center
New York, NY

Neil Greenberg, PhD, DABCC
Product Manager, Regulatory Affairs
Ortho-Clinical Diagnostics
Rochester, NY

David J. Hassemer, MS
Assistant Director, Outreach Programs
State Laboratory of Hygiene
University of Wisconsin
Madison, WI

Richard J. Havel, MD
Emeritus Professor, Cardiovascular Research Institute
University of California, San Francisco
San Francisco, CA

John E. Hokanson, MPH, PhD
Assistant Professor, Department of Preventive Medicine
    and Biometrics
University of Colorado Health Science Center
Denver, CO

Seijin Hosaki, MD, PhD
Professor, Faculty of Human Life Sciences
Jissen Women's University
Hino-shi, Tokyo, Japan

Steve E. Humphries, PhD, FRCPath
British Heart Foundation Professor of Cardiovascular Genetics
University College London Medical School
London, United Kingdom

Ishwarlal Jialal, MD, PhD, DABCC, FRCPath
The C. Vincent Prothro Chair in Human Nutrition Research
Professor, Departments of Pathology and Internal Medicine
Director, Division of Clinical Biochemistry and Human Metabolism
Senior Investigator, Center for Human Nutrition
University of Texas Southwestern Medical Center
Dallas, TX

Andrea Kay, BA, MSc
Research Scientist, Department of Human Metabolism and Genetics
St. Bartholomew's Hospital
London, United Kingdom

Mary M. Kimberly, PhD
Coordinator, Cholesterol Reference Method Laboratory Network
Special Activities Branch
Division of Laboratory Sciences
National Center for Environmental Health
Centers for Disease Control and Prevention
Atlanta, GA

Sigrid G. Klotzsch, MS
Senior Chemist
Biomedical Data Company
Irvington, NY

Marlys L. Koschinsky, PhD
Associate Professor, Department of Biochemistry
Queen's University
Kingston, Ontario, Canada

Christine Labeur, PhD
Labo Lipoproteine Chemie
Universiteit Gent
Gent, Belgium

Karl J. Lackner, MD
Lecturer, Institute for Clinical Chemistry and Laboratory Medicine
University of Regensburg
Regensburg, Germany

Clodagh M. Loughrey, MD, MRCP, MRCPath
Specialist Registrar in Clinical Pathology
Royal Group of Hospitals
Belfast, N. Ireland

Santica M. Marcovina, PhD, DSc
Research Professor, Department of Medicine
Division of Metabolism, Endocrinology and Nutrition
Director, Core Laboratory, Northwest Lipid Research Laboratories
University of Washington School of Medicine
Seattle, WA

Judith R. McNamara, MT (ASCP)
Senior Research Assistant, Lipid Metabolism Laboratory
Jean Mayer USDA Human Nutrition Research Center on Aging
Tufts University, and
Research Associate, Lipid Research Laboratory
New England Medical Center
Boston, MA

W. Greg Miller, PhD
Professor, Department of Pathology
Director, Pathology Information Systems
Co-Director, Clinical Chemistry Laboratory
Medical College of Virginia Hospitals at
Virginia Commonwealth University
Richmond, VA

Gary L. Myers, PhD
Chief, Special Activities Branch
Division of Laboratory Sciences
National Center for Environmental Health
Centers for Disease Control and Prevention
Atlanta, GA

Matthias Nauck, MD
Department of Clinical Chemistry
University Hospital Freiburg
Freiburg i. Br., Germany

Mitsuyo Okazaki, PhD
Professor, Laboratory of Chemistry
College of Liberal Arts and Sciences
Tokyo Medical and Dental University
Ichikawa-shi, Chiba, Japan

Gunilla Olivecrona, PhD
Professor, Department of Medical Biosciences
Section on Medical Biochemistry
Umeå University
Umeå, Sweden

Thomas Olivecrona, MD, PhD
Professor, Department of Medical Biosciences
Section on Medical Biochemistry
Umeå University
Umeå, Sweden

James D. Otvos, PhD
Professor, Department of Biochemistry
North Carolina State University
Raleigh, NC

Christopher J. Packard, DSc, FRCPath
Top Grade Biochemist and Professor, Department of
    Pathological Biochemistry
University of Glasgow
Glasgow Royal Infirmary University NHS Trust
Glasgow, United Kingdom

Henry J. Pownall, PhD
J. S. Abercrombie Professor of Atherosclerosis and
    Lipoprotein Research
Chief, Section of Atherosclerosis and Lipoprotein Research
Department of Medicine
Baylor College of Medicine and The Methodist Hospital
Houston, TX

P. Haydn Pritchard, PhD
Professor, Department of Pathology, and
Director, Atherosclerosis Specialty Lab
Healthy Heart Program
St. Paul's Hospital
The University of British Columbia
Vancouver, British Columbia, Canada

Paul M. Ridker, MD, MPH
Associate Professor of Medicine
Harvard Medical School, and
Director, Center for Cardiovascular Disease Prevention
Brigham and Women's Hospital
Boston, MA

Nader Rifai, PhD
Associate Professor, Department of Pathology
Harvard Medical School, and
Director, Clinical Chemistry Laboratory
Children's Hospital
Boston, MA

Maryvonne Rosseneu, DSc
Labo Lipoproteine Chemie
Universiteit Gent
Gent, Belgium

Ernst J. Schaefer, MD
Professor, Departments of Medicine and Nutrition, and
Director, Lipid Research Laboratory and Lipid and Heart Disease
    Prevention Clinic
New England Medical Center School of Medicine, and
Director, Lipid Metabolism Laboratory
Jean Mayer USDA Human Nutrition Research Center on Aging
Tufts University
Boston, MA

Françoise Schiele, PhD
Associate Lab-Director
Center for Preventive Medicine
Nancy, France

Alexandra Schlenck, PhD
Scientific Co-worker
Center for Preventive Medicine
Nancy, France

Gerd Schmitz, MD
Professor, Institute for Clinical Chemistry and Laboratory Medicine
University of Regensburg
Regensburg, Germany

Gérard Siest, PhD
Professor, Director of the Research Center for
    Preventive Medicine, and
Université Henri Poincaré
Nancy, France

Anne K. Soutar, PhD
Lipoprotein Group
MRC Clinical Sciences Centre
Imperial College School of Medicine
Hammersmith Hospital
London, United Kingdom

Marjorie Starck
PhD Student
Center for Preventive Medicine
Nancy, France

Papasani V. Subbaiah, PhD
Professor, Departments of Medicine and Biochemistry
Rush Medical College
Chicago, IL

Shinichi Usui, MT
School of Allied Health Science
Tokyo Medical and Dental University
Bunkyo-ku, Tokyo, Japan

Monique Vincent-Viry, PhD
Senior Clinical Chemist
Center for Preventive Medicine
Nancy, France

Sophie Visvikis, PhD
Team 4 Director, Cardiovascular Genetics
Center for Preventive Medicine, and Université Henri Poincaré
Nancy, France

G. Russell Warnick, MS, MBA
President
Pacific Biometrics Research Foundation
Seattle, WA

Parvin P. Waymack, PhD
Chief, Lipid Reference Laboratory
Special Activities Branch
Division of Laboratory Science
National Center for Environmental Health
Centers for Disease Control and Prevention
Atlanta, GA

Philip R. Wenham, MSc, PhD, FRCPath, MCB
Clinical Scientist
Department of Clinical Biochemistry
Lothian University Hospitals NHS Trust
Western General Hospital, and
Honorary Senior Lecturer
Department of Clinical Biochemistry
University of Edinburgh
Edinburgh, United Kingdom

Donald A. Wiebe, PhD
Associate Professor, Department of Pathology and Laboratory
    Medicine
University of Wisconsin Hospital & Clinics
Madison, WI

Ian S. Young BSc(Hons), MD, FRCP, MRCPath
Professor of Medical Biochemistry
The Queen's University of Belfast, and
Consultant Chemical Pathologist
Royal Group of Hospitals
Belfast, N. Ireland

Bennie Zak, PhD
Emeritus Professor of Pathology
Wayne State University School of Medicine, and
Consultant
DMC University Laboratories
Detroit, MI

Contents

LABORATORY ASPECTS OF LIPIDS, LIPOPROTEINS, AND APOLIPOPROTEINS

Foreword

The transport of cholesterol and triglycerides in blood plasma lipoproteins is now of daily interest to the primary care physician and to most of his or her patients. Armed with national guidelines for diagnosis and goal setting in the management of lipoprotein disorders, and with truly effective therapies for achieving these goals, it is possible to make important contributions to reducing the risk of death and disability from cardiovascular disease. The crucial role of the laboratory in supporting this effort has become clear as clinical trials have documented the value of identifying elevated low-density lipoprotein cholesterol and lowering it 10 to 40 percent. The application of this information would be a futile exercise without the marked improvement in precision and accuracy achieved by clinical laboratories in the assessment of blood plasma lipoprotein concentrations.

This Handbook represents a highly focused and distilled compilation of the knowledge of many experts who have helped bring about this successful application of techniques to clinical medicine. Valid assessment of total plasma cholesterol, triglycerides, and of the cholesterol content of low-density and high-density lipoproteins remains a concern of the first order for any clinical laboratory, and this book offers information to laboratory personnel, at any level of training that should prove useful in setting up or improving assessment methods. The material is enriched by clearly written chapters on the fundamentals of lipoprotein metabolism and of the clinical disorders that cause the lipoproteins to be of interest to the clinician.

This book goes far beyond the now routine lipoprotein measurements and represents a valuable resource for the research laboratory as well. Lipoprotein metabolism is complicated, involving at least nine apolipoproteins and a series of other plasma and cell surface proteins with enzymatic and lipid transfer functions. We are in the process of learning to assess these components and to use this new knowledge to better assess risk of related clinical disorders. This Handbook contains a series of chapters that provide a state-of-the-art description of our current understanding of these various biochemical and physiologic systems as well as clear and complete descriptions of the latest in relevant measurement techniques. Even the assessment of specific genes as potentially important measures is presented.

Every laboratory with a serious interest in assessing lipoprotein composition, structure, or function should have a copy of this Handbook available for use by all of its staff: from the beginning students, to senior technicians, to the laboratory director.

W. Virgil Brown, MD
Charles Howard Candler Professor of Internal Medicine
Emory University School of Medicine
Chief of Medicine, Atlanta VA Medical Center

Introduction

Diseases of the vascular system, which represent the major cause of morbidity and mortality throughout the world, have been a high-profile target for public health efforts. In recent decades, national and international efforts to combat cardiovascular diseases, especially coronary heart disease (CHD), have gained substantial momentum, and consequently laboratory measurements of lipoproteins and their constituents have played a critical and highly visible role in research investigations and in clinical practice. The greatest contribution of laboratory medicine to public health might well be in the characterization of CHD risk by reliable measurements of lipoprotein risk factors. This book, the fourth in a series of books on lipoprotein measurement, and its three predecessors, can certainly claim some credit for facilitating improvements in laboratory practice.

Clinical studies clearly demonstrate that lipid-lowering therapy decreases CHD morbidity and mortality. Just 16 years ago, the Lipid Research Clinics Program reported the findings of its Coronary Primary Prevention Trial: that decreasing serum cholesterol concentration reduced the incidence of CHD. Subsequently, a consensus conference sponsored by the National Heart, Lung, and Blood Institute recommended launching a national intervention program. In time, the result—the National Cholesterol Education Program (NCEP)—became a template for many other similar intervention programs worldwide. The most recent studies show that lipid-lowering treatment decreases CHD risk not only in those with the highest lipid levels but also throughout the population.

Laboratory measurements of lipids and lipoproteins underpin all the clinical studies and are essential to assessing cardiovascular risk and monitoring treatment. The American Association for Clinical Chemistry (AACC), primarily through its Lipids and Lipoproteins Division, has made a major contribution to the development and clinical utilization of these tests.

The AACC's Lipids and Lipoproteins Division itself grew out of the activities of the Lipid Research Clinics Program, which fostered a highly successful laboratory collaboration among scientists in academia and industry, and especially with the Centers for Disease Control and Prevention, which has long promoted standardization and method improvement. Division members, in fact, were involved in various expert panels of the NCEP, and division-sponsored educational workshops and symposia for practicing laboratorians and industry scientists also contributed to the evolution of lipoprotein testing, and hence, the genesis of this book.

The first predecessor of this book, *Methods for Clinical Laboratory Measurement of Lipid and Lipoprotein Risk Factors,* was published in 1991 amid the atmosphere of method improvement stimulated by the NCEP. Members of ad hoc committees previously convened by the Division to recommend improvements in laboratory methods wrote the book's key chapters, which covered basic lipid and lipoprotein measurements. We published the text in softcover to keep it affordable and to signal our intent to update it as measurement technologies evolved.

The second book in what would become a series, *Laboratory Measurement of Lipids, Lipoproteins, and Apolipoproteins,* was published three years later and built on foundations laid in the first. Content was considerably expanded to cover topics of increasing clinical interest and newer research tests that demonstrated clinical utility. This effort became international in scope when it was translated to Russian by Professor Alexander Sigalov and published by Pharmarus Print.

The third book, *Handbook of Lipoprotein Testing,* was published in 1997 and expanded on the methodological and clinical interface aspects of lipoprotein measurement. Content evolved to include research methodologies, and several internationally recognized lipidologists, including Dr. Marek Dominiczak as co-editor, were added to the roster of contributors.

In keeping with the book's international scope, Professor Sigalov will also translate this newest edition of the *Handbook* for publication in Russian. For this, the fourth book in the series, all chapters have been updated and supplemented with additional, new chapters that discuss the latest lipoprotein risk factors and even some of the emerging non-lipid risk factors, consistent with evolving trends in cardiovascular research. Furthermore, recognizing the essential role of clinical trials and regulatory clearances for laboratory methods, we have included chapters that contain guidelines for conducting clinical studies and explanations of the U. S. Food and Drug Administration's clearance process for diagnostic tests.

We trust that the book will continue to be of value to laboratorians, national and international, involved in both the service and research aspects of lipidology and cardiovascular disease prevention. We hope it will be particularly useful to those who are involved in, or responsible for, the standardization of laboratory methods. Thanks to all who have contributed their time, knowledge, and experience to this exciting project.

Nader Rifai
G. Russell Warnick
Marek H. Dominiczak

Apolipoproteins and Lipoproteins in Human Plasma

1

Marek H. Dominiczak

✧   This chapter provides an overview of lipoprotein metabolism. The reader will find a fascinating earlier report on this topic by Fredrickson published in 1993.[1]

Because lipids are both a source of energy and structural components of cells, it is essential to regard lipoprotein metabolism not as a separate entity, but as an integral part of the body energy metabolism.

Cholesterol and phospholipids are essential for the structure of cell membranes. Cholesterol serves as a precursor of bile acids, vitamin D, and other steroids. Fatty acids, esterified to form triacylglycerols (triglycerides [TG]), are a high-energy metabolic fuel and the most efficient form of energy storage.

The main sites of fatty acid metabolism are liver and muscle, adipose tissue being the principal storage depot. Such tissue distribution of fuel requires an efficient inter-organ transport system. However, hydrophobic lipids cannot be transported in a free form in the aqueous environment of plasma: thus fatty acids are transported bound to plasma albumin, and other lipids as components of amphipathic lipoprotein particles.

Lipoproteins are globular (or sometimes discoid) particles of varying size and composition, configured so that their outer surface is hydrophilic and their inner core, which contains immiscible lipids, hydrophobic. The surface of lipoprotein particles contains an amphipathic phospholipid bilayer, non-esterified cholesterol, and apolipoproteins. The core consists of cholesteryl esters and TG. One can characterize lipoproteins by their size, density, flotation constant, and electrophoretic mobility (see Table 1–1).

During their transport in plasma, lipoprotein particles can exchange components; if the transferred components are bulky, the size of the lipoproteins can change. For instance, acquisition of TG increases particle size, and their removal decreases it. During the life of the TG-rich particles, TG are successively digested by lipases: the lipoprotein lipase (LPL) and hepatic triglyceride lipase (HTGL).[2] In this process, liberated free fatty acids are taken into cells. Another enzyme, lecithin:cholesterol acyltransferase (LCAT),[3] esterifies cholesterol in the high-density lipoproteins (HDL); the newly formed cholesterol esters move into the core of the particles, increasing their size. Thus, the lipoprotein population in plasma is both complex and interchangeable.

Today, the main systems of lipoprotein classification are based on their hydrated density, which is determined mainly by the TG content, or on their electrical

Table 1–1 ✧ The Apolipoproteins

Apolipoprotein	Main Functions	Association with CHD Risk
Apo A-I	Accepts cholesterol. Structural for HDL. Ligand for HDL binding. LCAT cofactor.	Yes
Apo A-II	Structural for HDL. Ligand for HDL binding. LCAT cofactor. Modulator of LPL and HTGL activity(?)	No
Apo A-IV	Ligand for HDL binding. LCAT activator.	No
Apo (a)	Structural for Lp(a). Structural analogy with plasminogen.	Yes
Apo B-48	Structural for chylomicrons.	No
Apo B-100	Structural for VLDL, IDL, and LDL. LDL receptor ligand.	Yes
Apo C-I	LCAT and LPL activator.	No
Apo C-II	LCAT and LPL activator.	No
Apo C-III	LPL inhibitor; HTGL inhibitor. Modulator of uptake of triglyceride-rich lipoproteins by LRP.	No
Apo D	Unknown. Increased in some malignant tumors.	No
Apo E	Ligand for B/E receptors, LRP, and apo E2 receptor.	Phenotype, yes
Apo F	Unknown.	No
Apo G	Unknown.	No
Apo H	Affects platelet function(?)	No
Apo J	Membrane protection(?)	No

HDL=High-density lipoprotein. LCAT=Lecithin:cholesterol acyltransferase. LPL=Lipoprotein lipase. HTGL=Hepatic triglyceride lipase. VLDL=Very-low-density lipoprotein. LDL=Low-density lipoprotein. IDL=Intermediate-density lipoprotein. LRP=LDL receptor-related protein.

charge. However, these classification systems assume the existence of discrete structures in what are populations of constantly interchanging particles.

Ultracentrifugation separates lipoproteins in plasma into five main classes: chylomicrons, very-low-density lipoproteins (VLDL), intermediate-density lipoproteins (IDL), low-density lipoproteins (LDL), and HDL.[4,5,6] Further subspecies are present within each class.[7,8,9] Particle density increases, and particle size decreases, from

Table 1–2 ✧ The Lipoproteins

Lipoprotein	Density (kg/L)	Particle Diameter (nm)	Flotation Rate (Sf)	Electrophoretic Mobility
Chylomicrons	<0.95	80–1200	>400	Origin
VLDL	0.95–1.006	30–80	60–400	Pre-beta
IDL	1.006–1.019	23–35	20–60	Broad beta
LDL	1.019–1.063	18–25	0–20	Beta
HDL	1.063–1.21	5–12	0–9	Alpha

VLDL=Very-low-density lipoprotein. LDL=Low-density lipoprotein. IDL=Intermediate-density lipoprotein. HDL=High-density lipoprotein.

chylomicrons to HDL. Agar electrophoresis separates lipoproteins on the basis of electrical charge, and the observed bands are designated as pre-beta, beta, and alpha fractions, which correspond approximately to VLDL, LDL, and HDL respectively.[1]

Still another classification of lipoproteins is based on their protein components, i.e., apolipoproteins (apo). Lipoprotein particles always contain one or more apoproteins. Apolipoproteins control lipoprotein metabolism by binding to specific cell membrane receptors, and by acting as cofactors for enzymes that participate in lipoprotein metabolism. Apolipoproteins are also essential for the structural integrity of lipoprotein particles. The diverse functions of apolipoproteins are summarized in Table 1–2. As in other components, there is a constant traffic of apolipoproteins between different particles. Changes in particle size mentioned above affect the conformation of apoproteins on the lipoprotein surface, and their ability to bind to receptors.

Particles with different apoprotein composition may be separated by affinity chromatography[10] (see also Chapter 27). Recently it became clear that the composition of lipoproteins might change during ultracentrifugation: this was clearly shown in the case of HDL. An alternative technique based on gel filtration and sequential immunoaffinity separation can yield lipoproteins with a composition closer to that present *in vivo* (for review, see reference 11).

LIPOPROTEIN METABOLISM

Lipoprotein metabolism (Figure 1–1) is traditionally described as consisting of the exogenous pathway, the endogenous pathway, and the pathway of reverse cholesterol transport. The exogenous pathway involves transport of dietary lipid from the intestine to the liver. The endogenous pathway involves transport of lipids synthesized in the hepatocytes to peripheral tissues. The two pathways overlap at the stages of hydrolysis by LPL in the periphery, and by HTGL in the liver. Reverse cholesterol transport is the pathway of cholesterol removal from peripheral tissues to the liver.

A new way of describing lipoprotein metabolism was introduced in the previous

Figure 1–1 ✧ An Overview of Cholesterol Metabolism

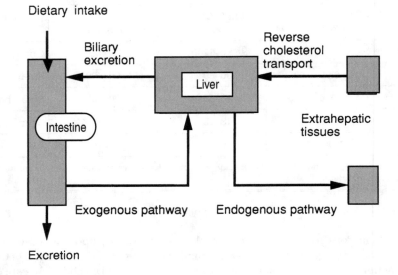

edition of this book.[12] The emphasis is on lipoprotein metabolism as a component of body fuel metabolism, and divides the lipid transport system into a high rate "fuel transport pathway," central for tissue energy supply and storage, and "the overflow pathway," which is primarily related to maintenance of the tissue cholesterol balance. The overflow pathway draws its substrates from the fuel transport pathway and is particularly important in atherogenesis. This concept is illustrated in Figure 1–2.

The state of the lipid transport system is determined by the availability of TG. Fatty acids are provided as components of TG in the diet. In the fed state they are primarily sent to the adipose tissue for storage. In the post-absorptive and fasting states, free fatty acids are supplied from storage depots by lipolysis. They are taken up by muscle and liver and, depending on cell energy status, are either oxidized to yield energy or re-esterified to form TG.[13]

Thus in the fuel transport pathway, lipoproteins are generated by the intestine and liver. Dietary cholesterol is absorbed in the intestine, mostly as cholesteryl esters. These are hydrolyzed by cholesterol esterase to release free cholesterol and fatty acids. TG are hydrolyzed by pancreatic and intestinal lipases and absorbed mainly as free fatty acids and monoglycerides. Long-chain fatty acids and cholesterol are then re-synthesized in the intestinal epithelial cells. The fatty acids are re-assembled within cells into TG and then, on the backbone of apo B-48, a variant of apolipoprotein B,[14] into large, TG-rich, chylomicron particles (see below). The fatty acid composition of TG in chylomicrons mirrors fatty acid composition of the diet. Enterocytes secrete chylomicrons into the thoracic duct from where they enter plasma.

In contrast to enterocytes, hepatocytes incorporate TG into VLDL particles, which are smaller than chylomicrons and are assembled on the backbone of apo B-100.[15] VLDL are also TG-rich. Apart from transporting lipids, both chylomicrons and

Figure 1–2 ✧ The Secondary Remnant Concept of Lipid Metabolism

LPL = Lipoprotein lipase

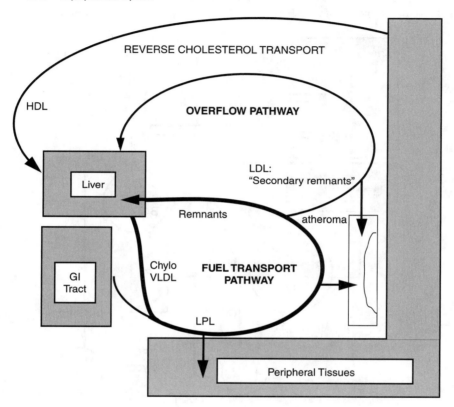

VLDL are key vehicles for the transport of fat-soluble vitamins.[16] The chylomicron and VLDL pathways converge when particles containing both apo B-48 and apo B-100 undergo partial hydrolysis by LPL present on the vascular endothelium (see Chapter 22). LPL digests TG, allowing fatty acids to be taken up by the cells. The particles that remain are known as remnants (chylomicron remnants, or VLDL remnants, depending on their origin). When characterized by hydrated density, most remnants belong to IDL. The definition of a remnant particle is functional rather than structural; the remnant is "a stage in the metabolism of the TG-rich lipoproteins that diverts the particles from LPL to catabolic sites."[17] A continuous spectrum of remnants with regard to size and composition exists in plasma, and the plasma concentration of IDL cholesterol is in the range of 5–15 mg/dL (0.13–0.39 mmol/L). (see chapters 19 and 28 for details and reference 18 for a recent review).

Because apo B-48 and apo B-100 have different receptor-binding properties, the metabolism of chylomicrons and VLDL remnants differs, with a degree of overlap. VLDL remnants are taken up for metabolism primarily by a hepatic apo B/E receptor

Figure 1–3 ✧ The Metabolism of Chylomicrons

CHYLO = Chylomicrons   LPL = Lipoprotein lipase   FFA = free fatty acids
HTGL = Hepatic triglyceride lipase   LRP = LDL receptor-related protein

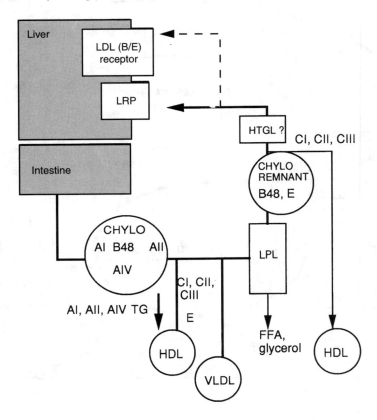

(the classical LDL receptor). Approximately 35% of chylomicron remnants are also metabolized through this pathway.[19] The rest of the chylomicron remnants bind to a different, although structurally related, receptor known as LDL-receptor-related protein (LRP).[20] The metabolism of chylomicrons is summarized in Figure 1–3, and the metabolism of VLDL in Figure 1–4.

A small proportion (10%–20%) of VLDL remnants, instead of being taken up by B/E receptors, are further delipidated by HTGL and transformed into LDL.[21] LDL particles, depleted of TG and rich in cholesterol, enter the overflow pathway. One could view the LDL particle as a "secondary remnant" of fuel-carrying lipoproteins. However, in contrast to "primary" remnants mentioned above, LDL is much less efficiently removed from the circulation.

LDL particles are taken up by the peripheral cells and by hepatocytes after binding to the apo B/E receptor[22,23] in much the same way as VLDL remnants. LDL is internalized and cholesterol esters liberated intracellularly, which regulates both the rate of

Figure 1–4 ✧ The Metabolism of VLDL

LPL = Lipoprotein lipase   FFA = free fatty acids   HTGL = Hepatic triglyceride lipase

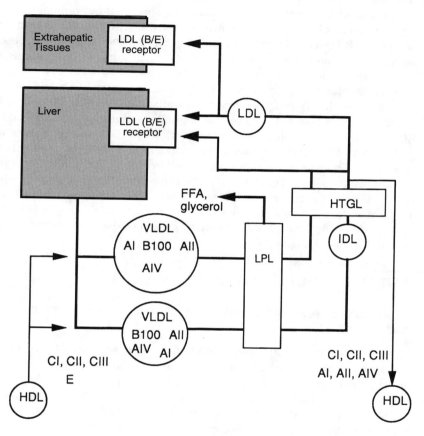

cell cholesterol synthesis (the rate-limiting enzyme, 3-hydroxy-3-methylglutaryl-CoA [HMG-CoA] reductase) and the expression of LDL receptors.[24,25] Thus, the receptor controls the amount of cholesterol entering cells.

The liver requires cholesterol for the synthesis of primary bile acids, cholic and chenodeoxycholic, with 7-alpha hydroxylase being the rate-limiting enzyme. Bile acids become bile components and are secreted into the intestine. There, they are converted into secondary bile acids, deoxycholic and lithocholic acid. Bile acids emulsify fats in the gastrointestinal tract and are subsequently re-absorbed and taken up again by the liver.[26,27] Approximately 0.5g of bile acids derived from hepatic cholesterol are lost with feces every day.

Recent data suggest that the level of expression of 7-alpha-hydroxylase also influences the rate of cellular lipid synthesis.[28] It might contribute to the control of VLDL assembly by activation of SREBP-mediated genes (see below).

The LDL in plasma, with their relatively long half-life, constitute a pool of cholesterol that can be used for either synthetic or structural purposes. Only a small proportion of LDL is normally incorporated in non-hepatic tissues. Approximately 80% of cholesterol secreted by the liver with lipoproteins returns to the hepatocytes. Excess LDL is undesirable, because when it leaves an antioxidant environment of plasma, it becomes a target for chemical modifications such as oxidation. When modified by oxidation, apo B, instead of binding to the B/E receptor, binds to scavenger receptors on macrophages, and initiates foam cell formation. Thus, low CHD risk status would require maximally low activity of the overflow pathway.

In addition to the mechanisms regulating the entry of cholesterol into cells, there is a separate system for removal of cellular cholesterol and its transfer back to the liver. This is known as the reverse cholesterol transport pathway and involves HDL, which are assembled both in the liver and in the intestine. Earlier work suggested that HDL shuttled between the periphery and the liver, changing its shape, size, and composition while removing cholesterol from membranes. Previous data indicated that it off-loaded cholesterol in the liver without internalizing the whole particle.[29,30] However, recent results obtained with HDL tracers prepared by gel filtration and sequential immunoaffinity separation challenge the concept of HDL shuttles: it appears that HDL particles are taken up by cells once they have delivered the cholesterol to the liver[11] (Figure 1–5).

COMPONENTS OF THE LIPID TRANSPORT SYSTEM

Assembly of Apo B-Containing Particles (Chylomicrons and VLDL)

Apo B-100, the main apolipoprotein of VLDL and LDL, and apo B-48, the main lipoprotein of chylomicrons, are encoded by a single gene. Apo B-100 is a large amphipathic protein consisting of 4536 amino acids. Its molecular mass exceeds 550 kDa (Chapter 14). Twenty-seven amino acid residues are cleaved from the N-terminal end of this molecule before secretion, leaving the protein with a molecular mass of 513 kDa. Apo B has a globular N-terminal domain, (probably the site of interaction with the microsomal TG transfer protein; MTP), and contains amphipathic beta-sheets and short amphipathic alpha-helices (which serve as anchors for lipids). The domain that recognizes the LDL receptor is located at residues 3359–3367 (a mutation at residue 3500 results in defective binding to the receptor). There are 16 disulfide bonds throughout the molecule and multiple potential glycosylation sites (for a review see reference 28).

In apo B-48, the mRNA codon 2153 is a stop codon, which prematurely terminates the translation of the apo B gene. Thus apo B-48 is in effect an N-terminal 48% portion of apo B-100.[31]

Apo B-100 is synthesized in the rough endoplasmic reticulum and is the backbone for the assembly of VLDL in the hepatocytes. Newly synthesized apo B can either enter the lipoprotein assembly pathway or be degraded by an ubiquitin-dependent proteasome.[31,28] This is regulated by the availability of lipids that affect expression of intraluminal MTP, a protein that mediates the transfer of TG, cholesterol esters, and

Figure 1–5 ✧ The Metabolism of HDL: Reverse Cholesterol Transport

LCAT = Lecithin:cholesterol acyltransferase   TG = Triglycerides
HTGL = Hepatic triglyceride lipase   CETP = Cholesteryl ester transfer protein

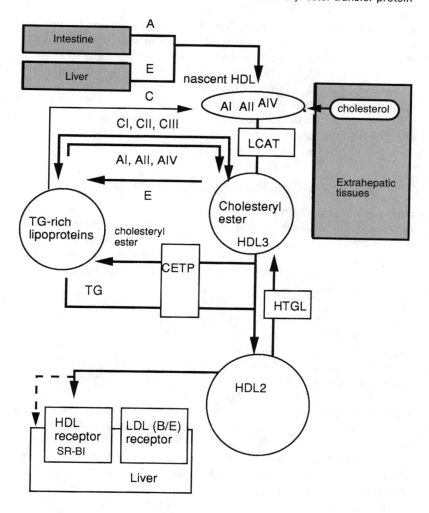

phospholipids between membranes and lipoproteins.[32] Entering the assembly pathway, the newly synthesized apo B translocates from the cytosolic to the luminal side of the endoplasmic reticulum.[15] This process is facilitated by MTP and also by the presence of TG or fatty acids and probably cholesterol esters and phosphatidyl choline.[15,33] Hydrophobic sequences in the apo B-100 molecule play a role in lipid recruitment.[34] Apo B-100 appears to be synthesized in excess of what is required for lipid transport with the excess degraded in the hepatocyte.

Chylomicrons are assembled in the enterocytes in a similar way, using the shorter apo B-48 polypeptide. A model of chylomicron assembly has been recently proposed by Hussain: first the partially lipidated (primordial) lipoproteins are synthesized in the rough endoplasmic reticulum by minimal lipidation of the apo B-48 using MTP. Independently of the apo B synthesis, triglyceride-rich lipid droplets form in the smooth endoplasmic reticulum. The final step is expansion of the lipoprotein core, which involves the fusion of primordial lipoprotein with the lipid droplet. This occurs at the junction of the smooth and rough endoplasmic reticulum.[16]

In studies of lipoprotein assembly, it is important to take into account species differences in hepatic lipoprotein secretion. Human and rabbit hepatocytes secrete apo B-100 that contains only VLDL.[35] Rat hepatocytes secrete both apo B-48 and apo B-100.[36] Human hepatoma cells (HepG2) secrete particles in the density range of LDL and HDL, rather than VLDL.[37]

The Fate of TG-Rich Particles: Apolipoproteins B and C

Particles participating in the fuel transport pathway—chylomicrons, VLDL, VLDL remnants, and IDL—all contain multiple apoproteins. Chylomicrons are normally present in plasma in the postprandial state only. They are composed of more than 90% TG and therefore their presence in plasma is reflected by an increased plasma TG concentration. If large numbers of chylomicrons are present, there is also a considerable increase in plasma cholesterol.

Chylomicrons contain apo B-48;[14] its concentration in plasma is low, in the range of 0.6 mg/L.[38] Nascent chylomicrons also contain apo A-I, apo A-II, and apo A-IV.[39] When they reach plasma, chylomicrons receive apo C (C-I, C-II, and C-III-1 and C-III-2) and apo E from HDL and VLDL.[40–42] Apo E and apo C control further chylomicron metabolism. The C apolipoproteins also control the activity of LPL; apo C-II activates and apo C-III inhibits LPL[2,43] and probably HTGL (see also Chapters 19 and 28).

LPL hydrolyses chylomicrons TG to glycerol and free fatty acids, which are then taken up by cells. Interestingly, the recently discovered VLDL receptor appears to bind LPL, and thus may play a role in the metabolism of this enzyme in the endothelium.[44] The off-loading of TG results in an approximate 20-fold decrease in chylomicron mass. Such change in size changes the conformation of its apolipoproteins, and the degree of exposure of receptor-binding domains of apo B and apo E. Some of the surface components such as phospholipids and apo A are lost from the particles at this stage;[45] they may serve as a substrate for intravascular HDL formation.[46] At this point the chylomicron transforms into a chylomicron remnant. However, apo B-48 cannot bind to the LDL receptor because the receptor-binding domain that was present in the C-terminal of the apo B-100 molecule was cleaved off. Apo B-48 binds to the LRP. On the surface of the hepatocyte, LRP functions in concert with heparan sulfate proteoglycans.[47]

VLDL are assembled in the hepatocytes as a range of differently sized TG-rich particles, each containing one apo B-100 molecule. In common with chylomicrons, VLDL exchange components with HDL. Cholesteryl esters, apo C (C-I, C-II, and C-III), and apo E are transferred from HDL to VLDL in exchange for TG.[42] VLDL enriched in apo C and apo E undergo hydrolysis by LPL.[2,17] This generates smaller VLDL remnants. At this stage apo A-I and A-IV are transferred back to HDL.

Importantly, VLDL remnants have higher affinity towards the LDL receptor than LDL itself. They may either be directly taken up by the liver or further hydrolyzed in plasma, probably by HTGL, to yield IDL.[48] (When HTGL is deficient,[49] VLDL remnants accumulate in plasma.) As lipolysis progresses, remnants lose TG, phospholipids, apo C, and apo E. This results in the formation of LDL.[17]

The metabolic fate of VLDL also depends on their size. Remnants of large VLDL are metabolized directly, whereas remnants of small VLDL enter the IDL-LDL route.[50,51] VLDL remnants and IDL are closely related: essentially, IDL are partially hydrolyzed VLDL remnants that are present in a range of particle sizes[9] and contain apo E and apo B-100.[17] The IDL particles either bind to the LDL receptor or are transformed into LDL (the latter process, as noted, involving loss of TG, apo C, and apo E, probably through interaction with HDL). In LDL receptor defects, less VLDL remnants are removed directly and more are available for transformation into LDL.[50]

Remnant metabolism might be affected by the cholesterol content of cell membranes. In human HepG2 cells, an increase in the cholesterol content of the hepatocyte membrane reduced the binding of beta-VLDL, probably by affecting the membrane receptor pattern.[52]

Because of their low concentration and similarity to other lipoprotein particles, the measurement of remnant particles has been notoriously difficult. A recently introduced method of separation of remnant-like particles is based on immunoaffinity chromatography with anti-apo A-I and anti-apo B-100 antibodies.[53] The remnant lipoprotein (RLP) cholesterol concentration correlated with plasma triglyceride level. Also, RLP-cholesterol was shown to be increased in patients with CHD.[54] For more information on remnant particles refer to Chapter 28.

Apolipoprotein E

Compared to apo B, apo E is a small molecule: a single polypeptide containing 299 amino acids. Its C-terminal end has lipid-binding determinants.[55,56] The N-terminal contains the receptor-binding region and the heparin-binding site.[56] Plasma apo E levels correlate with plasma TG levels.[57] In one population study, apo E concentration in plasma ranged between 16 and 169 mg/L.[58]

Apo E is produced in the liver; it is also synthesized in extrahepatic tissues, kidney, adrenals, and spleen[68] and is present in the amyloid plaque.[69,70] In the liver, Apo E mediates the uptake of chylomicron remnants, VLDL remnants, and IDL. It also mediates the interactions of lipoproteins with the apo B/E receptor and with LRP[59,60] and through this process, targets remnants towards the liver.[59] Apo E has a greater affinity for the apo B/E receptor than does apo B. The binding of apo-E-containing remnants to the receptor involves heparin sulphate proteoglycans[17] (for review see references 61 and 56).

Apo C-I alters how apo E binds to liver receptors and may inhibit clearance of TG-rich lipoprotein particles. On the other hand, apo E probably displaces apo C-II from LPL, and thus slows down the lysis of VLDL. Data from experiments involving apo E-deficient mice and apo E3 transgenic mice indicate that apo E affects VLDL triglyceride production: Apo E is continuously synthesized in the liver, however, VLDL cannot receive apo E directly from hepatocytes. As much as 58% of apo E in plasma is present in the HDL fraction.

There are several genetically determined apo E isoforms that differ in their affinity for the LDL receptor.[59,62] Apo E4 and E2 are products of different alleles at one locus, and differ from apo E3 in their patterns of amino-acid residues. Less common apo E variants also exist. The most common E3/3 phenotype is present in 60% of the population and the E2/3 phenotype is present in approximately 25%. Apo E seems to play a major role in determining the plasma cholesterol level. In one study, 47% of variance in cholesterol levels was explained by apo E polymorphism.[63] (For additional information on this subject refer to Chapters 19 and 28.)

Persons who have the E4 allele also metabolize Apo B more slowly,[63,64] and absorb cholesterol more efficiently; they also have enhanced apo B production.[62] Individuals with apo E4/4 and E4/3 have higher cholesterol levels than those with E3/3 and E2/2.[65,66] Individuals with apo E2/3 and E2/4 have lower cholesterol levels than those with E3/3.

The E2/2 phenotype results in apo E with the lowest affinity for LDL receptors and is characteristic of individuals with familial dysbetalipoproteinemia. E2/2 is associated with a Type III hyperlipidemic pattern in plasma, which is characterized by an increased IDL concentration, broad beta band on electrophoresis, and an increase in TG and total cholesterol. Interestingly, although up to 1% of the population possess the E2/2 phenotype, the overt type III hyperlipidemia occurs in only 1 in 10,000 individuals: diabetes, hypothyroidism, or genetic dyslipidemia must be present for type III hyperlipidemia to express in these persons.[67] The association of apo E polymorphism with the response to dietary cholesterol has been intensively investigated with conflicting results.[62]

The elucidation of apo E's role in neurobiology is a subject of a major research effort. The brain contains high levels of apo E: these concentrations are second only to those found in the liver.[56] In the brain, apo E is synthesized and secreted by brain astrocytes.[71] Apo E, particularly apo E3 and to a lesser extent apo E4, probably promote repair and remodeling of neurons. Specifically, apo E3 stimulates the polymerization of beta-tubulin and stabilizes microtubule formation in Neuro2a cells. This effect is isoform-specific, as the E4 isoform actually destabilizes the microtubules.[72]

Apo E3 and E2 accumulate in neurons to a greater extent than does apo E4.[73] Human brain expresses the apo E receptor 2, which is related to the VLDL receptor.[23] Apo E is also secreted by macrophages.[74]

The ε4 allele has been found to occur more frequently in familial and late-onset Alzheimer disease.[75,76] A meta-analysis of studies related to genetic variation of apo E and Alzheimer disease has been recently published.[77] The results suggest that 60% of Alzheimer disease over the age of 65 and 92% of cases below age 65 can be attributed to apo E.

LDL

LDL is the main cholesterol-containing particle in plasma. The major component of LDL is cholesteryl ester; LDL contain very little TG and free cholesterol. Each particle contains one molecule of apo B-100 and no other apolipoproteins. In normolipidemic individuals, about half of LDL is metabolized through the apo B/E receptor pathway.[22,24,25,78]

The LDL receptor controls the rate of LDL metabolism and, through this, its plasma concentration. The rates of receptor synthesis and LDL clearance are inversely related to the amount of intracellular free cholesterol.[79] Many genes that encode cholesterol synthetic enzymes, and the LDL receptor gene, are responsive to a family of transcription factors known as sterol regulatory element-binding proteins (SREBPs; for review see references 80,81,82). This includes HMG-CoA reductase and the genes involved in fatty acid and phospholipid synthesis. SREBP1 also affects expression of 7-alpha-hydroxylase, a key enzyme in the synthesis of bile acids mentioned above. Depletion of hepatic sterols activates SREBPs. When the cell is replete with sterols, the SREBP activation is suppressed by proteolytic cleavage.

Mutations of the LDL receptor affect both LDL binding and receptor processing (see chapter 29). Plasma LDL are heterogeneous.[83] The degree of cholesterol enrichment of LDL particles is determined at the stage of their precursors' formation.[21,84] This is influenced by cholesteryl ester transfer protein (CETP) activity and a transfer of cholesteryl esters from HDL to VLDL. When CETP[85,86] or LCAT[87] activity is high, the cholesterol content of LDL increases.

Several LDL subclasses have been identified by gradient gel electrophoresis. One scheme defines four LDL subclasses[88] within the LDL density band. LDL1 is the largest and most buoyant, whereas LDL3 and LDL4 are small and dense. For additional information on this refer to Chapters 16 and 31.

Lipolysis of core TG in LDL1 and LDL2 may lead to the formation of LDL3.[89] The predominance of LDL1 and LDL2 in plasma, which occurs in 75% of subjects, is known as pattern A; the predominance of LDL3 is designated pattern B.[90] The LDL subclass phenotype is influenced by an allele with an autosomal-dominant inheritance. Individuals with pattern B have higher plasma VLDL cholesterol (VLDL-C) concentration and VLDL mass, increased IDL-C, and low HDL-C concentrations. Apo B concentration is higher and apo A-I lower. Changes associated with pattern B are known as atherogenic lipoprotein phenotype (ALP).[91,92] TG above 1.7 mmol/L are associated with ALP.[93]

ALP could be particularly important in diabetes. A study from Kaiser Permanente demonstrated that 15% of non-diabetic women, and 67% of women with non-insulin dependent diabetes (NIDDM), had pattern B. Pattern B is also common in women with glucose intolerance (33%). It is also associated with insulin resistance syndrome.[94,95]

Apoproteins A and HDL

Apoprotein A

Apoprotein A-I is an acceptor of cell cholesterol, serves as cofactor for LCAT, and may be a ligand for the putative HDL receptor (for review see reference 61). It is synthesized in the liver and intestine as pre-pro apo A-I. Its form of apo A-I contains 243 amino acids.

Apo A-I has internal repeat units of 11–22 amino acids that can assume an amphipathic helical structure. The C-terminal end is implicated in binding to lipid structures[96] and to receptors.[97] Other domains are involved in LCAT activation[98] and cholesterol efflux from membranes.[99]

The expression of apo A-I is affected by another family of transcription factors, peroxisome proliferator-activated receptors (PPARs). The entire A-I /C-III/A-IV gene cluster seems to be subject to PPAR regulation. This increases the expression of apo A-I and apo A-II, and reduces the expression of the apo C-III gene.[100] One of the PPARs, PPAR-alpha, can be activated by fibrates (see chapter 27).

HDL

Collectively, apoproteins A (A-I, A-II, and A-IV) are the main apolipoprotein constituents of HDL.[29] HDL also contains apo C, and, in particular, apo E. Approximately 60% of HDL particles contain both apo A-I and A-II; the rest contain only apo A-I.[101] A-I and A-I:A-II particles include HDL particles across the entire HDL size range.[102] Apo A-I and A-II modulate HDL metabolism. In the absence of A-II, A-I catabolism is more rapid. Conversely, apo A-I is required for normal apo A-II catabolism.

HDL is the smallest and most dense lipoprotein particle with alpha, or sometimes pre-beta, electrophoretic mobility. Because, together with LCAT and CETP, HDL is involved in bi-directional exchange of components with other lipoproteins, it plays a controlling role in lipoprotein metabolism. Apart from its function in reverse cholesterol transport, HDL could be regarded as a chaperone, an overseer of lipoprotein metabolism.

Ultracentrifugation separates HDL into two main HDL subclasses, HDL2 and HDL3, but at least seven further subfractions have been identified by gradient polyacrylamide gel electrophoresis (for more details see Chapters 15, 27, and 30).[103] HDL2 is larger and richer in lipids than HDL3. HDL3 is smaller and denser.[29] The most important other subfractions, in order of decreasing size, are 2b, 2a, 3a, 3b, and 3c.[103]

Liver accounts for 72% of the clearance of HDL cholesterol esters.[104] The liver and intestine secrete nascent, discoid HDL containing apo A and apo E. Some apo C-containing discoid forms are generated from VLDL and chylomicrons during TG hydrolysis. Free cholesterol released from cells is taken up by nascent HDL and converted into cholesteryl ester by LCAT.[87] This increases the size of the particles and changes their shape to spherical. Apo A-I and apo A-II are cofactors of LCAT, which is inhibited by its product, cholesteryl esters. LCAT deficiency leads to a decrease in HDL through increased metabolism of A-I and A-II.[105]

Cholesteryl esters carried by HDL are either transported to the liver or transferred to VLDL and chylomicrons. This is facilitated by CETP[106] in exchange for TG, phospholipids, apo A-I, apo E, and apo C.[107] CETP activity tends to be high in conditions associated with low HDL.[108–111] Transfer of TG to HDL further increases its size.[110] CETP deficiency increases HDL concentration through slower catabolism. It seems that high cholesteryl ester content of HDL stabilizes the particle and protects it from degradation.[30] Due to their apo E content, some particles in the HDL range may be taken up by either the LDL receptor or the remnant receptor.

Most reverse cholesterol transport occurs without the need to internalize HDL. This so-called selective uptake of cholesteryl ester is the predominant way of delivering cholesterol ester to the liver: it does require binding of HDL to the receptor, but does not involve cellular uptake of HDL particles.[112]

The scavenger receptor BI (SR-BI) is the first physiologically relevant receptor for HDL and it seems that SR-BI is responsible for cholesterol flux into the liver. SR-BI is also capable of binding LDL and modified LDL and VLDL.[113]

Recent kinetic HDL studies have used gel filtration and sequential immuno-affinity separation, instead of ultracentrifugation, to prepare intact large and small HDL tracers[114,115] (small HDL are particles with diameter 7.2–8.2 nm, medium particles have diameter of 8.2–9.8 nm; and large particles 9.8–12.2nm[11]). These studies have shown that large HDL were actually not converted to small or medium HDL. It seems that small HDL acquire cholesterol from membranes either by diffusion or by binding to cell membrane receptors[116] and are then converted, outside the plasma compartment, to medium and large HDL which, instead of becoming small particles again, are removed from plasma.

HDL also has functions unrelated to lipid transport, for example, decreasing LDL oxidation. In addition, paraoxonase, an enzyme present on HDL, prevents the accumulation of lipoperoxides in LDL.[117,118] HDL may have an antioxidant function.[119,120] Also, it appears to decrease the expression of adhesion molecules[121] such as VCAM-1, ICAM-1 and E-selectin induced by TNF-alpha.[29]

Lipoprotein (a)

Apo(a) is a highly polymorphic protein.[122] Lp(a) links lipid metabolism with the blood coagulation system.[123] On electrophoresis, Lp(a) primarily migrates as pre-beta lipoprotein. Lp(a) is synthesized in the liver and comprises an apo B-100 molecule linked by a disulfide bridge to apo(a). Apo(a) is highly glycosylated and because of the presence of multiple isoforms, its mass varies between 200 and 800 kDa.[123,124] Its plasma levels range from 0.1 to above 200mg/dl (for review see reference 125).

Lp(a) concentration is controlled by a series of autosomal alleles, at a single locus, designated Lp(a)F, Lp(a)B, Lp(a)S1, Lp(a)S2, Lp(a)S3, Lp(a)S4, and Lp(a)0. Phenotypes S3 and S4 are associated with low Lp(a) concentrations in plasma, and phenotypes B, S1, and S2 with high concentrations.[126] Ninety percent of variation in Lp(a) levels is determined by the apo(a) gene.[127,122] More than 38 isoforms have been identified.[125]

There is a structural homology between apo(a) and plasminogen. The Lp(a) sequence includes a copy of plasminogen kringle 5 and multiple copies of kringle 4, the latter being the most polymorphic region of apo(a).[4,128] However, the protease activity of Lp(a), unlike that of plasminogen, is minimal. There is also an antigenic similarity between plasminogen and apo(a).[129] Lp(a) binds to the LDL receptor, although with lesser affinity than apo B.[130,131]

Apo(a) synthesis occurs in the liver. It is most probably first secreted to the surface of the hepatocytes, and there it is assembled with LDL to form Lp(a). In rodents Lp(a) is removed by the liver,[132] but the kidney probably plays a significant role in man;[133] kidney disease has been reported to affect the Lp(a) level.[134] Menopause is associated with a 10%–30% rise in Lp(a) and the levels decrease on hormone replacement therapy.[72] Apo E is present in 20% of Lp(a) particles. For additional information on Lp(a) refer to Chapter 17.

MINOR APOLIPOPROTEINS

There are several other apolipoproteins, the function of which in lipid transport and metabolism remains unknown.[135,136] Apo J, a highly sialylated glycoprotein,[137] is associated with HDL and may be involved in inhibition of complement-mediated cell lysis and in sperm maturation.[138] Due to its capacity to interact with hydrophobic molecules, apo J has a membrane-protective role. Apo J has been detected in plasma and urine and also in cerebrospinal fluid, breast milk, and seminal fluid. It also has been identified in the intima and media of atherosclerotic human aortas, with a pattern of distribution similar to Apo A-I and apo E.[139]

Apo D, similarly to apo J and apo E, is expressed in a variety of extrahepatic tissues such as spleen, adrenal, lungs, brain, and testes.[140,141] Apo D is present in benign and malignant human tissues.[142,143] It was expressed in a high percentage of breast tumors in men and its expression was associated with relapse-free survival.[142]

Apo H, a 43–54 kDa protein also known as beta-2-glycoprotein, is present in all major lipoprotein fractions and has been reported to affect platelet response to ADP. It is a carbohydrate-rich protein of molecular weight approximately 50kDa.[144] In humans, its level correlates with cholesterol concentration in female but not male patients.[145] The functions of apo F and apo G remain unknown.

LIPOPROTEIN PARTICLES AND ATHEROGENESIS

The concentrations of the components of the fuel transport pathway—chylomicrons, VLDL, and remnant particles—may exceed the critical level, above which there is a deposition of some particles in the arterial wall.[10,14]

It was previously reported that there was no excess cardiovascular risk in LPL deficiency, in which chylomicron concentrations are extremely high. This has been contradicted by case reports.[146] It seems that although chylomicrons cannot enter the arterial wall, the remnant particles, including chylomicron remnants, can.[147]

The arterial clearance of VLDL is less than that of IDL and LDL. The ability of these particles to penetrate the vessel wall is inversely related to their size.[148] Also, postprandial lipemia may affect the HDL level.[149] It was suggested that an impairment of TG transport, affecting either chylomicrons or both chylomicrons and VLDL, may increase the risk of atherogenesis.[95] This was described as the "triglyceride intolerance hypothesis."[150]

IDL particles are directly atherogenic. Remnant-like particles (RLP) promote lipid accumulation in mouse peritoneal macrophages[151] and impair endothelium-dependent relaxation.[152] LPL-mediated generation of remnants yields lipolytic products that are toxic to macrophages and increase the permeability of the endothelium.[153,154] Patients with type III hyperlipidemia and high IDL concentration are prone to coronary heart disease (CHD). Diabetic individuals, whose CHD risk is two to three times that of non-diabetic individuals, also have increased IDL.[155,156] It was also demonstrated, using human cholesteryl-ester-rich VLDL from hypertriglyceridemic, but not normotriglyceridemic, patients, that VLDL can form foam cells.[157,158] However, Apo E itself may be antiatherogenic. This concept is strengthened by the fact that apo-E-deficient mice develop premature atherosclerosis. Apo E also facilitates cholesterol efflux from cholesterol-loaded macrophages to HDL.[159]

A high concentration of LDL-C, whatever the cause, leads to an increased cardiovascular risk.[160,161] The LDL is atherogenic because it can accumulate in the extracellular matrix and in cells in the arterial intima. While the LDL receptor-mediated cellular uptake is carefully controlled, the uncontrolled uptake mediated by the macrophage scavenger receptor results in cellular cholesterol overload and the generation of foam cells.[162] As mentioned above, modification of LDL is required before this can take place.

The most important modification is LDL oxidation[163,164] (see chapters 20 and 21), although non-enzymatic glycation of LDL may also play a role.[165] LDL oxidation mostly occurs after the particle has penetrated the endothelial barrier. Oxidized LDL is present in the arteriosclerotic plaque[166] but the presence of plasma auto-antibodies to oxidized LDL suggests that LDL modification may also occur in plasma.[167] Notable, CHD is more prevalent in patients with smaller, denser LDL.[168] These species can more easily penetrate the endothelial barrier and are more susceptible to oxidation than larger, more buoyant LDL1.[169]

High levels of LDL-C may result from defects in the LDL receptor, as in familial hypercholesterolemia (FH);[170] from defects in apo B, as in familial defective apo B-100 (FDB), where glutamine has been substituted by arginine at position 3500 of apo B-100;[171,172] or from increased apo B synthesis or secretion as in familial combined hyperlipidemia (FCHL).[173,174] Importantly, hyperapobetalipoproteinemia due to overproduction of apo B-100 may occur at relatively low plasma cholesterol concentrations[175–177] and is also associated with increased cardiovascular risk. Permeability of the endothelial layer to LDL may be an important factor in atherogenesis.[178]

Apolipoprotein B and CHD Risk

As is discussed elsewhere in this book, the assessment of cardiovascular risk is most commonly based on the measurements of total serum or plasma cholesterol, which is used as a surrogate marker of LDL-C. Data on the significance of apo B in CHD risk prediction are not consistent, but most studies suggest that apo B is a very good discriminator of patients with CHD (see also Chapter 14).

Apo B measurement was the best discriminator for men with early-onset CHD.[179] Apo B also predicts the risk of myocardial infarction[180] and of angiographically defined CHD.[181] The Quebec Heart Study results suggest that apo B was the best predictor of the risk of vascular disease. There, the risk was increased in both hyperlipidemic and normolipidemic individuals who had an increased apo B concentration, but not in hyperlipidemic patients with normal apo B.[182] In the same study, the presence of small, dense LDL was associated with increased CHD risk.[183] The results of large studies on concentrations of apo B and apo A-1 in American[184] and Swedish[185] populations have been recently published and provide extensive data on these apolipoproteins.

HDL and CHD Risk

It is well established that a high concentration of HDL-C is cardioprotective, and that a low HDL-C is associated with an increased risk of cardiovascular disease.[186–188] The protective effect of HDL is primarily associated with the HDL2 subfraction.[189,190] There is also an inverse correlation between HDL-C and plasma TG concentration. Obesity, smoking, and type 2 diabetes lower HDL-C, while exercise and ethanol consumption raise HDL-C.[187,188] Apo A-II deficiency does not cause premature atherosclerosis. In apo A-I deficiency, the association with CHD was observed to be greater if LCAT activity was also impaired.[189]

HDL particles can remove cholesterol from lipid-rich macrophages through either scavenging the released lipids or through receptor-mediated cholesterol efflux.[190] Also, HDL may impede LDL oxidation.[191] It now becomes clear that the role of HDL in reverse cholesterol transport may not be the only function related to its cardioprotective effect.[24] Controversy still exists as to whether measurements of apo A-I add much discriminatory value to HDL-C measurement in the assessment of cardiovascular risk (see also Chapters 14 and 15).[192,193]

Lipoprotein (a) and CHD Risk

The majority of the available studies confirm that Lp(a) is an independent risk factor for CHD. Also, there are suggestions that the risk associated with a high level of Lp(a) demonstrates itself only when LDL is also elevated[194] or when HDL is low.[195]

The role of Lp(a) in atherosclerosis has recently been reviewed.[196,122] The ability of Lp(a) to deposit in the extracellular matrix, together with its possible interference with the fibrinolytic mechanism, suggest a direct role in atherogenesis. There is also evidence that Lp(a) is deposited in the arterial intima and in atherosclerotic plaques.[197] Apo(a) was located intracellularly in the endothelium in early lesions, and extracellularly in mature lesions.[122] An increased fatty streak formation was observed in a transgenic mouse line expressing human apo(a).[198] Lp(a) binds to fibronectin in aortic plaques.[199] It stimulates proliferation of human smooth muscle cells in culture[200] and also inhibits clot lysis in plasma. By competing with plasminogen for its binding sites on the cell surface, it decreases plasminogen activation by tissue plasminogen activator.[201–203] In *in vitro* experiments, Lp(a) competed with plasminogen for binding to fibrin.[204] Lp(a) may also play a role in the early stages of the wound-healing process.[205,122]

There is considerable clinical and epidemiological evidence linking Lp(a) concentrations to CHD; apo(a) isoforms predict the risk of CHD.[206] There is also a relationship between Lp(a) concentration and the risk of peripheral vascular disease and stroke,[207] and Lp(a) concentration is also higher in asymptomatic men who have carotid plaques.[208] There is also a link between Lp(a) concentration and parental history of premature CHD.[209,210]

Lp(a) is an independent risk factor for CHD in women younger than age 65.[211] In the Framingham Heart Study, the presence of sinking pre-beta lipoprotein, a surrogate marker of Lp(a), predicted fatal and nonfatal CHD.[212] Lp(a)-associated risk increases in the presence of elevated LDL-C.[213] There is an additive effect of LDL and Lp(a) in producing angiographically detectable CHD.[214] Lp(a) concentration appears to lose its predictive power after intensive cholesterol lowering.[215] (Refer to Chapter 17 for additional information on this subject.)

SUMMARY: PRACTICAL CONSEQUENCES FOR THE LABORATORY

The lipid transport system exists primarily to transport energy-rich lipids from intestine and liver to the adipose tissue. TG are transported as a component of lipoprotein particles. Cholesterol-rich lipoproteins are generated from the TG-transport particles. The cholesterol-rich particle that resides the longest in plasma is LDL. LDL enters the arterial wall and plays a central role in the formation of atherosclerotic plaque.

At present, we rely either on total concentrations of cholesterol and TG in plasma, or use selected components of lipoproteins, such as cholesterol or apoproteins, as markers of concentration of lipoprotein particles. Much has been achieved in understanding the role of the lipoproteins as a risk factor for CHD using these surrogate measurements.

The present challenge for laboratory medicine is to further develop measurements of components of the lipoprotein transport system in order to identify more accurately individual patients who remain at risk for cardiovascular disease. ◈

Acknowledgments: This work was partially supported by grants from the Research into Aging and the Chest Heart and Stroke Association (Scotland). The author is grateful to Ms. J. Gardiner and Ms. Anne Cooney for excellent secretarial assistance.

REFERENCES

1. Fredrickson DS. Phenotyping: on reaching base camp (1950–1975). Circulation 1993; 87(Suppl III):III-1–15.
2. Olivecrona T, Bengtsson-Olivecrona G. Lipoprotein lipase and hepatic lipase. Curr Opin Lipidol 1990;1:222–30.
3. Applebaum-Bowden D. Lipases and lecithin:cholesterol acyltransferase in the control of lipoprotein metabolism. Curr Opin Lipidol 1995;6:130–5.
4. Havel RJ, Eder HA, Bragdon J. Distribution and chemical composition of ultracentrifugally separated lipoproteins in human serum. J Clin Invest 1955;34:1345–53.
5. Lipid Research Clinic Program manual of laboratory operations, revised. Washington DC: U.S. Government Printing Office, 1982:63–77.
6. Cathcart S, Dominiczak MH. The measurement of lipoprotein subfractions in plasma using a tabletop ultracentrifuge. Ann Clin Biochem 1990;27:459–64.
7. Austin MA, Hokanson JE, Brunzell JD. Characterization of low-density lipoprotein subclasses: methodological approaches and clinical relevance. Curr Opin Lipidol 1994;5: 395–403.
8. von Eckardstein A, Huang Y, Assman G. Physiological role and clinical relevance of high-density-lipoprotein subclasses. Curr Opin Lipidol 1994;5:404–16.
9. Musliner TA, Giotas C, Krauss RM. Presence of multiple subpopulations of lipoproteins of intermediate density in normal subjects. Arteriosclerosis 1986;6:79–87.
10. Fruchart JC, Ailhaud G. Apolipoprotein-A-containing particles: physiological role, quantification, and clinical significance. Clin Chem 1992;38:793–7.
11. Colvin PL, Parks JS. Metabolism of high-density-lipoprotein subfractions. Curr Opin Lipidol 1999;10:309–14.
12. Dominiczak MH. Apolipoproteins and lipoproteins in human plasma. In: Rifai N, Warnick GR, Dominiczak MH (eds.). Handbook of lipoprotein testing. Washington: AACC Press 1997:2–8.
13. Dominiczak MH. Glucose homeostasis and fuel metabolism. In: Baynes J, Dominiczak MH (eds.). Medical Biochemistry. Mosby, London 1999:243–66.
14. Powell LM, Wallis SC, Pease RJ, Edwards YH, Knott TJ, Scott J. A novel form of tis-

sue-specific RNA processing produces apolipoprotein B-48 in intestine. Cell 1987; 50:831–40.

15. Pease RJ, Leiper JM. Regulation of hepatic apolipoprotein-B-containing lipoprotein secretion. Curr Opin Lipidol 1996;7:132–8.

16. Hussain MM. A proposed model for the assembly of chylomicrons. Atherosclerosis 2000;148:1–15.

17. Eisenberg S, Sehayek E. Remnant particles and their metabolism. In: Baillieres Clin Endocrinol Metab 1995;9:739–53.

18. Cohn JS, Marcoux C, Davignon J. Detection, quantification, and characterization of potentially atherogenic triglyceride-rich remnant lipoproteins. Arterioscler Thromb Vasc Biol 1999;19:2474–86.

19. Thuren T, Wilcox RW, Sisson P, Waite M. Hepatic lipase hydrolysis of lipid monolayers. Regulation by apolipoproteins. J Biol Chem 1991;266:4853–61.

20. Herz J. The LDL-receptor related protein: portrait of a multifunctional receptor. Curr Opin Lipidol 1993;4:107–13.

21. Packard CJ. Plasma lipid and lipoprotein metabolism in the 1990s: what we know and what we need to know. In Betteridge DJ (ed.). Lipids: current perspectives, Vol. 1. London: Martin Dunitz 1996:1–14.

22. Schneider WJ, Nimpf J. Lipoprotein receptors: old relatives and new arrivals. Curr Opin Lipidol 1993;4:205–9.

23. Yamamoto T, Bujo H. Close encounters with apoprotein E receptors. Curr Opin Lipidol 1996;7:298–302.

24. Brown MS, Goldstein JL. A receptor-mediated pathway for cholesterol homeostasis. Science 1986;232:34–47.

25. Brown MS, Goldstein JL. Lipoprotein receptors in the liver. Control signals for plasma cholesterol traffic. J Clin Invest 1983;72:743–7.

26. Wikvall K. Conversion of cholesterol into bile acids. Curr Opin Lipidol 1990;1:248–54.

27. Stravitz RT, Hylemon PB, Vlahcevic ZR. The catabolism of cholesterol. Curr Opin Lipidol 1993;4:223–9.

28. Davis RA. Cell and molecular biology of the assembly and secretion of apolipoprotein-B-containing lipoproteins by the liver. Biochimica et Biophysica Acta 1999;1440:1–31.

29. Barter PJ, Rye K-A. High-density lipoproteins and coronary heart disease. Atherosclerosis 1996;121:1–12.

30. Rader DJ, Ikewaki K. Unraveling high-density lipoprotein-apolipoprotein metabolism in human mutants and animal models. Curr Opin Lipidol 1996;7:117–23.

31. Cartwright IJ, Higgins JA. Intracellular events in the assembly of very-low-density-lipoprotein lipids with apolipoprotein B in isolated rabbit hepatocytes. Biochem J 1995; 310:897–907.

32. Fielding CJ. Lipid transfer proteins: catalysts, transmembrane carriers, and signaling intermediates for intracellular and extracellular lipid reactions. Curr Opin Lipidol 1993;4:218–22.

33. Watts G, Naumova R, Cummings MH, Umpleby AM, Slavin BM, Sonksen PH, Thompson GR. Direct correlation between cholesterol synthesis and secretion of apolipoprotein B-100 in normolipidemic subjects. Metabolism 1995;44:1052–57.

34. McLeod RS, Wang Y, Wang S, Rusiñol A, Links P, Yao Z. Apolipoprotein B sequence requirements for hepatic very-low-density lipoprotein assembly. Evidence that hydrophobic sequences within apolipoprotein B-48 mediate lipid recruitment. J Biol Chem 1996;271:18445–55.

35. Arbeeny CM, Meyers DS, Berquist KE, Gregg RE. Inhibition of fatty acid synthesis decreases very-low-density lipoprotein secretion in the hamster. J Lipid Res 1992;33: 843–51.

36. Cartwright IJ Hebbachi AM, Higgins JA. Transit and sorting of apolipoprotein B within the endoplasmic reticulum and Golgi compartments of isolated hepatocytes from normal and orotic acid fed rats. J Biol Chem 1993;268:20937–52.

37. Gibbons GF. A comparison of *in vitro* models to study hepatic lipid and lipoprotein metabolism. Curr Opin Lipidol 1994;5:191–99.

38. Karpe F, Bell M, Bjorkegren J, Hamsten A. Quantification of postprandial triglyceride-rich lipoproteins in healthy men by retinyl ester labeling and simultaneous measurement of apolipoproteins B-48 and B-100. Arterioscler Thromb Vasc Biol 1995;15:199–207.

39. Beisiegel U, Utermann G. An apolipoprotein homolog of rat apolipoprotein A-IV in human plasma: isolation and partial characterization. Eur J Biochem 1979;93:601–8.

40. Eisenberg S. Metabolism of apolipoproteins and lipoproteins. Curr Opin Lipidol 1990;1:205–15.

41. Blum CB. Dynamics of apolipoprotein E metabolism in humans. J Lipid Res 1982;23:1308–16.

42. Huff MW, Breckenridge WC, Strong WLP, Wolfe BM. Metabolism of apolipoproteins C-II, C-III and B in hypertriglyceridemic men: changes after heparin-induced lipolysis. Arteriosclerosis 1988;8:471–9.

43. Ginsberg HN, Le N-A, Goldberg IJ, Gibson JC, Rubinstein A, Wang-Iverson P et al. Apolipoprotein B metabolism in subjects with deficiency of apolipoproteins CIII and A-I. J Clin Invest 1986;78:1287–95.

44. Argaves KM, Battey FD, MacCalman CD, McCrae KR, Gafvels M, Kozarsky KM et al. The very-low-density lipoprotein receptor mediates the cellular catabolism of lipoprotein lipase and urokinase-plasminogen activator inhibitor type I complexes. J Biol Chem 1995;270:26550–7.

45. Schaefer EJ, Jenkins LL, Brewer HB. Human chylomicron apoprotein catabolism. Biochem Biophys Res Commun 1978;80:405–12.

46. Tall AR, Small DM. Plasma high-density lipoproteins. N Engl J Med 1978; 299:1232–6.

47. Mahley RW, Ji Z-S. Remnant lipoprotein metabolism: key pathways involving cell-surface heparan sulfate proteoglycans and apolipoprotein E. J Lipid Res 1999;40:1–16.

48. Havel RJ. The formation of LDL: mechanisms and regulation. J Lipid Res 1984; 25:1570–6.

49. Clay HA, Hopkins GJ, Ehnholm C, Barter PJ. The rabbit as an animal model of hepatic lipase deficiency. Biochim Biophys Acta 1989;1002:173–81.

50. Grundy SM. Multifactorial etiology of hypercholesterolemia. Arterioscler Thromb 1991;11:1619–35.

51. Packard CJ, Boag DE, Clegg RJ, Bedford DK, Shepherd J. Effects of 1,2-cyclohexanedione modification on the metabolism of VLDL apoprotein B: potential role of receptors in IDL catabolism. J Lipid Res 1985;26:1058–67.

52. Mas-Oliva J, Velasco-Loyden G, Haines TH. Receptor pattern formation as a signal for the capture of lipoproteins. Biochem and Biophys Res Comm 1996;224:212–8.

53. Nakajima K, Okazaki M, Tanaka A, Pullinger CR, Wang T, Nakano T et al. Separation and determination of remnant-like particles in human serum using monoclonal antibodies to apoB-100 and apo A-I. J Clin Ligand Assay 1996;19:177–83.

54. Leary ET, Wang T, Baker DJ, Cilla D, Zhong J, Warnick GR et al. Evaluation of an immunoseparation method for quantitative measurement of remnant-like particle-cholesterol in serum and plasma. Clin Chem 1998;44:2490–8.

55. Westerlund JA, Weisgraber KH. Discrete carboxyl-terminal segments of apolipoprotein E mediate lipoprotein association and protein oligomerization. J Biol Chem 1993;268:15745–50.

56. Mahley RW. Huang Y. Apolipoprotein E: from atherosclerosis to Alzheimer's disease and beyond. Curr Opin Lipidol 1999;10:207–17.

57. Huang Y, Li XQ, Rall SC, Jr., Taylor JM, von Eckardstein A, Assmann G et al. Overexpression and accumulation of apolipoprotein E as a cause of hypertriglyceridemia. J Biol Chem 1998;273:26388–93.

58. Vincent-Viry M, Schiele F, Guegen R, Bohnet K, Visvikis S, Siest G. Biological variations and genetic reference values for apolipoprotein E serum concentrations: results from the STANISLAS cohort study. Clin Chem 1998;44:957–65.

59. Mahley RW, Innerarity TL, Rall JSC, Weisgraber KH, Taylor JM. Apolipoprotein E: genetic variants provide insights into its structure and function. Curr Opin Lipidol 1990;1:87–95.

60. Beisiegel U, Weber W, Ihrke G, Herz J, Stanley KK. The LDL-receptor-related protein, LRP, is an apolipoprotein E-binding protein. Nature 1989;341:162–4.

61. Sirtori CR, Calabresi L, Franceschini G. Recombinant apolipoproteins for the treatment of vascular diseases. Atherosclerosis 1999;142:29–40.

62. Kesäniemi YA. Genetics and cholesterol metabolism. Curr Opin Lipidol 1996;7: 124–31.

63. Gylling H, Kontula K, Miettinen TA. Cholesterol absorption and metabolism and LDL kinetics in healthy men with different apoprotein E phenotypes and apoprotein B Xba I and LDL receptor Pvu II genotypes. Arterioscler Thromb Vasc Biol 1995;15:208–13.

64. Kesaniemi YA, Miettinen TA. Metabolic epidemiology of plasma cholesterol. Ann Clin Res 1988;20:26–31.

65. Utermann G. Apolipoprotein E polymorphisms in health and disease. Am Heart J 1987;113:433–40.

66. Enholm C, Lukka M, Kaussi T, Nikkila E, Utermann G. Apoprotein E polymorphism in the Finnish population: gene frequencies and relation to lipoprotein concentrations. J Lipid Res 1986;27:227–35.

67. Brewer HB, Zech LA, Gregg RE, Schwartz D, Schaeffer EJ. Type III hyperlipoproteinemia: diagnosis, molecular defects, pathology, and treatment. Ann Int Med 1983; 98:623–40.

68. Blue ML, Williams DL, Zucker S, Khan SA, Blum CB. Apolipoprotein E synthesis in human kidney, adrenal gland, and liver. Proc Natl Acad Sci USA 1983;80:283–7.

69. Strittmatter WJ, Saunders AM, Schmechel D, Pericakvance M, Enghild J, Salvesen GS et al. Apolipoprotein E: high-avidity binding to β–amyloid and increased frequency of type 4 allele in late-onset familial Alzheimer disease. Proc Natl Acad Sci USA 1993; 90:1977–81.

70. Strittmatter WJ, Weisgraber KH, Huang DY, Dong LM, Salvesen GS, Pericakvance M et al. Binding of human apolipoprotein E to synthetic amyloid β peptide: isoform-specific effects and implications for late-onset Alzheimer disease. Proc Natl Acad Sci USA 1993;90:8098–102

71. Boyles JK, Pitas RE, Wilson E, Mahley RW, Taylor JM. Apolipoprotein E associated with astrocytic glia of the central nervous system and with nonmyelinating glia of the peripheral nervous system. J Clin Invest 1985;76:1501–13.

72. Nathan BP, Chang K-C, Bellosta S, Brisch E, Ge N, Mahley RW et al. The inhibitory effect of apolipoprotein E4 on neurite outgrowth is associated with microtubule depolymerization. J Biol Chem 1995;270:19791–9.

73. Ji Z-S, Pitas RE, Mahley RW. Differential cellular accumulation/retention of apolipoprotein E mediated by cell surface heparan sulfate proteoglycans. Apolipoproteins E3 and E2 greater than E4. J Biol Chem 1998;273:13452–60.

74. Mazzone T. Apolipoprotein E secretion by macrophages: its potential physiological functions. Curr Opin Lipidol 1996;7:303–7.

75. Saunders AM, Schmader K, Breitner JCS, Benson MD, Brown WT, Goldfarb L et al. Apolipoprotein ε4 allele distributions in late-onset Alzheimer's disease and in other amyloid-forming diseases. Lancet 1993;342:710–11.

76. Weisgraber KH, Roses AD, Strittmatter WJ. The role of apoprotein E in the nervous system. Curr Opin Lipidol 1994;5:110–6.

77. Rubinsztein DC, Easton DF. Apolipoprotein E genetic variation and Alzheimer's disease. A meta-analysis. Dement Geriatr Cogn Disord 1999;10:199–209.

78. Shepherd J, Packard CJ. Lipid transport through the plasma: the metabolic basis of hyperlipidaemia. [Review]. In: Shepherd J (ed.). Lipoprotein metabolism. Baillieres Clin Endocrinol Metab 1987;1:495–514.

79. Havel RJ, Hamilton RL. Hepatocytic lipoprotein receptors and intracellular lipoprotein catabolism. Hepatology 1988;8:1689–704.

80. Horton JD, Shimomura I. Sterol regulatory element-binding proteins: activators of cholesterol and fatty acid biosynthesis. Curr Opin Lipidol 1999;10:143–50.
81. Brown MS, Goldstein JL. The SREPB pathway: regulation of cholesterol metabolism by proteolysis of a membrane-bound transcription factor. Cell 1997;89:331–40.
82. Briggs MR, Yokoyama C, Wang X, Brown MS, Goldstein JL. Nuclear protein that binds sterol regulatory element of low-density-lipoprotein receptor promoter. I. Identification of the protein and delineation of its target nucleotide sequence. J Biol Chem 1993;268:14490–6.
83. Griffin BA. Low-density lipoprotein heterogeneity. [Review]. In: Betteridge DJ (ed.). Dyslipidemia. Baillieres Clin Endocrinol Metab 1995;9:687–703.
84. Roheim PS, Asztalos BF. Clinical significance of lipoprotein size and risk for coronary atherosclerosis. Clin Chem 1995;41:147–52.
85. Hesler CB, Swenson TL, Tall AR. Purification and characterization of a human plasma cholesterol ester transfer protein. J Biol Chem 1987;262:2275–82.
86. Inazu A, Brown ML, Hesler CB, Agellon LB, Koizumi J, Takata K, et al. Increased high-density lipoprotein levels caused by a common cholesteryl-ester transfer protein gene mutation. N Engl J Med 1990;323:1234–8.
87. Glomset JA. The plasma lecithin: cholesterol acyltransferase reaction. J Lipid Res 1968; 9:155–67.
88. Krauss RM, Burke DJ. Identification of multiple subclasses of plasma low-density lipoproteins in normal humans. J Lipid Res 1982;23:97–104.
89. Austin MA, Edwards KL. Small, dense low-density lipoproteins, the insulin resistance syndrome and noninsulin-dependent diabetes. Curr Opin Lipidol 1996;7:167–71.
90. Kraus RM. Low-density lipoprotein subclasses and risk of coronary artery disease. [Review]. Curr Opin Lipidol 1991;2:248–52.
91. Austin MA, King M-C, Vranizan KM, Krauss RM. Atherogenic lipoprotein phenotype: a proposed genetic marker for coronary heart disease risk. Circulation 1990;82:495–506.
92. Nishina PM, Johnson JP, Naggert KJ, Krauss RM. Linkage of atherogenic lipoprotein phenotype to the low-density-lipoprotein receptor locus on the short arm chromosome 19. Proc Natl Acad Sci USA 1992;89:708–12.
93. Chapman MJ, Bruckert E. The atherogenic role of triglycerides and small, dense, low-density lipoproteins: impact of ciprofibrate therapy. Atherosclerosis 1996;124 (Suppl):S21–8.
94. Selby JV, Austin MA, Newman B, Zhang D, Quesenberry CP Jr, Mayer EJ, Krauss RM. LDL subclass phenotypes and the insulin resistance syndrome in women. Circulation 1993;88:382–7.
95. Byrne CD. Triglyceride-rich lipoproteins: are links with atherosclerosis mediated by a procoagulant and proinflammatory phenotype? Atherosclerosis 1999;145:1–15.
96. Ji Y, Jonas A. Properties of an N-terminal proteolytic fragment of apolipoprotein A-I in solution and in reconstituted high-density lipoproteins. J Biol Chem 1995;270: 11290–7.
97. Allan CM, Fidge NH, Morrison JR, Kanellos J. Monoclonal antibodies to human apolipoprotein A-I: probing the putative receptor-binding domain of apolipoprotein A-I. Biochem J 1993;290:449–55.
98. Meng QH, Calabresi L, Fruchart JC, Marcel YL. Apolipoprotein A-I domains involved in the activation of lecithin:cholesterol acyltransferase. Importance of the central domain. J Biol Chem 1993;268:16966–73.
99. Rothblat GH, Mahlberg FH, Johnson WJ, Phillips MC. Apolipoproteins, membrane cholesterol domains, and the regulation of cholesterol efflux. J Lipid Res 1992;33: 1091–7.
100. Schoonjans K, Martin G, Staels B, Auwerx J. Peroxisome proliferator-activated receptors, orphans with ligands and functions. Curr Opin Lipidol 1997;8:159–66.
101. Cheung M, Albers JJ. Distribution of high-density-lipoprotein particles with different apoprotein composition: particles with A-I and A-II and particles with A-I but no A-II. J Lipid Res 1982;23:747–53.

102. Ikeda Y, Ohta T, Matsuda I. Interaction between apo-A-I-containing lipoproteins and lecithin:cholesterol acyl-transferase. Biochim Biophys Acta 1994;1215:307–13.

103. Blanche PJ, Gong EL, Forte TM, Nichols AV. Characterization of human high-density lipoproteins by gradient gel electrophoresis. Biochim Biophys Acta 1981;665:408–19.

104. Patel SB, Salen G, Hidaka H, Kwiterovich PO, Stalenhoef AFH, Miettinen TA et al. Mapping a gene involved in regulating dietary cholesterol absorption. The sitosterolemia locus is found at chromosome 2p21. J Clin Invest 1998;102:1041–4.

105. Barter PJ, Hopkins GJ, Gorjatschko L. Lipoprotein substrates for plasma cholesterol esterification: influence of particle size and composition of the high-density-lipoprotein subfraction-3. Atherosclerosis 1985;58:97–107.

106. Cholesteryl ester transfer protein. [Editorial]. Lancet 1991;338:666–7.

107. Tall AR. Plasma cholesteryl transfer protein and high-density lipoproteins: new insights from molecular genetic studies. J Internal Med 1995;237:5–12.

108. Ruhling K, Zane-Langhenning R, Till U, Thielmann K. Enhanced net mass transfer of HDL cholesteryl ester to apo-B-containing lipoproteins in patients with peripheral vascular disease. Clin Chim Acta 1989;184:289–96.

109. Yamashita S, Hui DY, Wetterau JR, Sprecher DL, Harmony JAK, Sakai N et al. Characterization of plasma lipoproteins in patients heterozygous for human plasma CETP deficiency: plasma CETP regulates high-density-lipoprotein concentrations and composition. Metabolism 1991;40:756–63.

110. Bagdade JD, Ritter MC, Subbaiah PV. Accelerated cholesteryl ester transfer in plasma of patients with hypercholesterolemia. J Clin Invest 1991;87:1259–65.

111. Bagdade JD, Ritter MC, Subbaiah PV. Accelerated cholesteryl ester transfer in patients with insulin-dependent diabetes mellitus. Eur J Clin Invest 1991;21:161–7.

112. Williams DL, Connelly MA, Temel RE, Swarnakar S, Phillips MC, de la Llera-Moya M, Rothblat GH. Scavenger receptor B1 and cholesterol trafficking. Curr Opin Lipidol 1999;10:329–39.

113. Acton SL, Scherer PE, Lodish HF, Krieger M. Expression cloning of SR-B1, a CD-36-related class B scavenger receptor. J Biol Chem 1994;269:21003–9.

114. Colvin P, Moriguchi E, Barrett H, Parks J, Rudel L. Production rate determines plasma concentration of large high-density lipoprotein in non-human primates. J Lipid Res 1998;39:2076–85.

115. Colvin PL, Moriguchi E, Barrett PH, Parks JS, Rudel LL. Small HDL particles containing 2 apoA-I molecules are precursors *in vivo* to medium and large HDL particles containing three and four apoA-I molecules in nonhuman primates. J Lipid Res 1199;40:1782–92.

116. Rothblat GH, de la Llera-Moya M, Atger V, Kellner-Weibel G, Williams DL, Phillips MC. Cell cholesterol efflux: integration of old and new observations provides new insights. J Lipid Res 1999;40:781–96.

117. Mackness MI, Arrol S, Abbott CA Durrington PN. Protection of low-density lipoprotein against oxidative modification by high-density lipoprotein associated paraoxonase. Atherosclerosis 1993;104:129–35.

118. Mackness MI, Arrol S, Durrington PN. Paraoxonase prevents accumulation of lipoperoxides in low-density lipoproteins. FEBS Lett 1991;286:152–4.

119. Decossin C, Tailleux A, Fruchart J-C, Fievet C. Prevention of *in vitro* low-density lipoprotein oxidation by an albumin-containing LpA-I subfraction. Biochim Biophys Acta 1995;1255:31–8.

120. Kilimov AN, Gurevich VS, Nikiforova AA, Shatilina LV, Kuzman AA, Plawinsky SL, Teryukova NP. Antioxidative activity of high-density lipoproteins in vivo. Atherosclerosis 1993;100:13–8.

121. Cockerill GW, Rye KA, Gamble JR, Vadas MA, Barter PJ. High-density lipoproteins inhibit cytokine-induced expression of endothelial cell adhesion molecules. Arterioscler Thromb Vasc Biol 1995;15:1987–94.

122. Hobbs HH, White AL. Lipoprotein(a): intrigues and insights. Curr Opin Lipidol 1999;10:225–36.

123. Loscalzo J. Lipoprotein(a): a unique risk factor for atherothrombotic disease. Arteriosclerosis 1990;10:672–9.
124. Seed M. Lipoprotein(a): its role in cardiovascular disease. In: Betteridge DJ (ed.). Lipids: current perspectives. Lipids and lipoproteins, Vol. 1. London: Martin Dunitz, 1996:69–88.
125. Uterman G. Genetic architecture and evolution of the lipoprotein(a) trait. Curr Opin Lipidol 1999;10:133–41.
126. Utermann G, Menzel HJ, Kraft HG, Duba HC, Kemmler HG, Seitz C. Lp(a) glycoprotein phenotypes. J Clin Invest 1987;80:458–65.
127. Boerwinkle E, Leffert CC, Lin J, Lackner C, Chiesa G, Hobbs HH. Apolipoprotein(a) gene accounts for greater than 90% of the variation in plasma lipoprotein(a) concentrations. J Clin Invest 1992;90:52–60.
128. McLean JW, Tomlinson JE, Kuang W-J, Eaton DL, Chen EY, Fless GM et al. cDNA sequence of human apolipoprotein(a) is homologous to plasminogen. Nature 1987; 330:132–7.
129. Karadi I, Kostner GM, Gries A, Nimpf J, Romics L, Malle E. Lipoprotein(a) and plasminogen are immunochemically related. Biochim Biophys Acta 1988;960:91–7.
130. Floren C-H, Albers JJ, Bierman EL. Uptake of Lp(a) by cultured fibroblasts. Biochem Biophys Res Commun 1981;102:636–9.
131. Krempler F, Kostner GM, Rascher A, Haslauer F, Bolzano K, Sandhofer F. Studies on the role of specific cell surface receptors in the removal of lipoprotein(a) in man. J Clin Invest 1983;71:1431–41.
132. Ye S, Keling J, Stein O, Stein Y, McConathy WJ. Tissue distribution of [3H]cholesteryl linoeyl ether-labeled human Lp(a) in different rat organs. Biochim Biophys Acta 1988; 963:534–40.
133. Kronenberg F, Trenkwalder E, Lingenhel A, Friedrich G, Lhotta K, Schober M et al. Renovascular arteriovenous differences in Lp(a) plasma concentrations suggest removal of Lp(a) from the renal circulation. J Lipid Res 1997;38:1755–63.
134. Kronenberg F, Utermann G, Dieplinger H. Lipoprotein(a) in renal disease. Am J Kidney Dis 1996;27:1–25.
135. Bhatnagar D, Durrington PN. Does measurement of apolipoproteins add to the clinical diagnosis and management of dyslipidemias? Curr Opin Lipidol 1993;4:299–304.
136. Jordan-Starck TC, Witte DP, Aronow BJ, Harmony JAK. Apolipoprotein J: a membrane policeman? Curr Opin Lipidol 1992;3:75–85.
137. Ghosh P, Hale EA, Lakshman R. Long-term ethanol exposure alters the sialylation index of plasma apolipoprotein J (Apo J) in rats. Alcohol Clin Exp Res 1999;23:720–5.
138. Gelissen IC, Hochgrebe T, Wilson MR, Easterbrook-Smith SB, Jessup W, Dean RT, Brown AJ. Apolipoprotein J (clusterin) induces cholesterol export from macrophage-foam cells: a potential anti-atherogenic function? Biochem J 1998;331: 231–7.
139. Ishikawa Y, Akasaka Y, Ishii T, Komiyama K, Masuda S, Asuwa N et al. Distribution and synthesis of apolipoprotein J in the atherosclerotic aorta. Arterioscler Thromb Vasc Biol 1998;18:665–72.
140. Provost PR, Villeneuve L, Weech PK, Milne RW, Marcel YL, Rassart E. Localization of the major sites of apolipoprotein D gene transcription by in situ hybridization. J Lipid Res 1991;32:1959–70.
141. Navarro A, Tolivia J, Astudillo A, del Valle E. Pattern of apolipoprotein D immunoreactivity in human brain. Neurosci Lett 1998;254:17–20.
142. Diaz CS, Vizoso F, Lamelas ML, Rodriguez JC, Gonzalez LO, Baltasar A, Medrano J. Expression and clinical significance of apolipoprotein D in male breast cancer and gynaecomastia. Br J Surg 1999;86:1190–7.
143. Zhang SX, Bentel JM, Ricciardelli C, Horsfall DJ, Haagensen DE, Marshall VR, Tilley WD. Immunolocalizatiion of apolipoprotein D, androgen receptor, and prostate-specific antigen in early stage prostate cancers. J Urol 1998;159:548–54.
144. Saxena A, Gries A, Schwarzenbacher R, Kostner GM, Laggner P, Prassl R. Crystalliza-

tion and preliminary X-ray crystallographic studies on apolipoprotein H (beta2-glyco-protein-I) from human plasma. Acta Crystallogr D Biol Crystallogr 1998;54:1450–2.

145. Crook MA, Ch'ng SI, Lumb P. Serum apolipoprotein H and its relationship to lipids and other apolipoproteins in normal human men and women. Blood Coagul Fibrinolysis 1999;10:197–200.

146. Benlian P, de Gennes JL, Foubert L, Zhang HF, Gagne SE, Hayden M. Premature athero-sclerosis in patients with familial chylomicronemia caused by mutations in the lipopro-tein lipase gene. New Engl J Med 1996;335:848–54.

147. Zilversmit DB. Atherogenesis: a postprandial phenomenon. Circulation 1979;60:473–85.

148. Zilversmit DB. Atherogenic nature of triglycerides, postprandial lipidemia, and triglyceride-rich remnant lipoproteins. Clin Chem 1995;41:153–8.

149. Kirchmair R, Ebenbichler CF, Patsch JR. Postprandial lipemia. In: Betteridge DJ (ed.). Dyslipidemia. Baillieres Clin Endocrinol Metab 1995;9:705–37.

150. Miesenbock G, Patsch JR. Postprandial hyperlipidemia: the search for atherogenic pro-tein. Curr Opin Lipidology 1992;3:196–201.

151. Tomono S, Kawazu S, Kato N, Ono T, Ishii C, Ito Y et al. Uptake of remnant like particles (RLP) in diabetic patients from mouse peritoneal macrophages. J Atheroscler Thromb 1994;1:98–102.

152. Kugiyama K, Doi H, Motoyama T, Soejima H, Misumi K, Kawano H et al. Association of remnant lipoprotein levels with impairment of endothelium-dependent vasomotor function in human coronary arteries. Circulation 1998;97:2519–26.

153. Chung BH, Segrest JP, Smith K, Griffin FM, Brouillette CG. Lipolytic surface remnants of triglyceride-rich lipoproteins are cytotoxic to macrophages but not in the presence of high-density lipoprotein: a possible mechanism of atherogenesis? J Clin Invest 1989;83:1363–74.

154. Rutledge JC, Woo MM, Rezai AA, Curtiss LK, Goldberg IJ. Lipoprotein lipase increases lipoprotein binding to the artery wall and increases endothelial layer permeability by formation of lipolysis products. Circ Res 1997;80:819–28.

155. Winocour PH, Durrington PN, Ishola M, Anderson DC. Lipoprotein abnormalities in in-sulin-dependent diabetes mellitus. Lancet 1986;1:1176–8.

156. American Diabetes Association. Consensus statement. Role of cardiovascular risk fac-tors in prevention and treatment of macrovascular disease in diabetes. Diabetes Care 1989;12:573–9.

157. Koo C, Wernette-Hammond ME, Innerarity TL. Uptake of canine β-very-low-density lipoproteins by mouse peritoneal macrophages is mediated by a low-density-lipopro-tein receptor. J Biol Chem 1986;261:11194–201.

158. Huff MW, Evans AJ, Sawyez CG, Wolfe BM, Huff MW. Cholesterol accumulation in J774 macrophages induced by triglyceride-rich lipoproteins: comparison of very-low-density lipoproteins from subjects with type II, IV and V hyperlipopro-teinemia. Arterioscler Thromb 1991;11:221–32.

159. Mazzone T, Reardon CA. Expression of heterologous human apolipoprotein E by J774 macrophages enhances cholesterol efflux to HDL3. J Lipid Res 1994;35:1345–53.

160. The Expert Panel. Summary of the second report of the National Cholesterol Education Panel (NCEP) Expert Panel on Detection, Evaluation, and Treatment of High Blood Cho-lesterol in Adults (Adult Treatment Panel II). JAMA 1993;269:3015–23.

161. European Atherosclerosis Society, International Task Force for Prevention of Coronary Heart Disease. Prevention of coronary heart disease: scientific background and new clinical guidelines. Nutr Metab Cardiovasc Dis 1992;2:113–56.

162. Badimon JJ, Fuster V, Chesebro JH, Badimon L. Coronary atherosclerosis: a multifactorial disease. Circulation 1993;87 (suppl II): II-3–16.

163. Steinberg D, Parthasarathy S, Carew TE, Khoo JC, Witztum JL. Beyond cholesterol: modifications of low-density lipoprotein that increase its atherogenicity. [Review]. N Engl J Med 1989;320:915–22.

164. Navab M, Berliner JA, Watson AD, Hama SY, Territo MC, Lusis AJ et al. The yin and

yang of oxidation in the development of the fatty streak. Arterioscler Thromb Vasc Biol 1996;16:831–42.

165. Witztum JL, Mahoney EM, Branks MJ, Fisher M, Elam R, Steinberg D. Nonenzymatic glucosylation of low-density lipoprotein alters its biologic activity. Diabetes 1982;31: 283–91.

166. Yla-Herttuala S, Palinski W, Rosenfeld ME, Parthasarathy S, Carew TE, Butler S et al. Evidence for the presence of oxidatively modified low-density lipoprotein in atherosclerotic lesions of rabbit and man. J Clin Invest 1989;84:1086–95.

167. Salonen JT, Yla-Herttuala S, Yamamoto R, Butler S, Korpela H, Salonen R et al. Auto-antibodies against oxidized LDL and progression of carotid atherosclerosis. Lancet 1992;339:883–7.

168. Austin MA, Breslow JL, Hennekens CH, Buring JE, Willett WC, Krauss RM. Low-density-lipoprotein subclass patterns and risk of myocardial infarction. JAMA 1988;260: 1917–21.

169. De Graaf J, Hak-Lemmers HLM, Hectors MPC, Demacker PNM, Hendriks JCM, Stalenhoef AFH. Enhanced susceptibility to *in vitro* oxidation of the dense low-density-lipoprotein subfraction in healthy subjects. Arteriosclerosis 1991;11:298–306.

170. Bild DE, Williams RR, Brewer HB, Herd JA, Pearson TA, Stein E. Identification and management of heterozygous familial hypercholesterolemia: summary and recommendations from an NHLBI workshop. Am J Cardiol 1993;72:1D–5D.

171. Innerarity TL, Mahley TL, Weisgraber KH, Bersot TP, Krauss RM, Vega GL et al. Familial defective apolipoprotein B-100: a mutation of apolipoprotein B that causes hypercholesterolemia. J Lipid Res 1990;31:1337–49.

172. Tybjaerg-Hansen A, Gallager A, Vincent J, Houlston R, Talmud P, Seed AM et al. Familial defective apolipoprotein B-100: detection in the United Kingdom and Scandinavia, and clinical characteristics of 10 cases. Atherosclerosis 1990;80:235–42.

173. Goldstein JL, Schrott HG, Hazzard WR, Bierman EL, Motulsky AG. Hyperlipidemia in coronary heart disease. II. Genetic analysis of lipid levels in 176 families and delineation of a new inherited disorder, combined hyperlipidemia. J Clin Invest 1973;52:1544–68.

174. Kissebah AH, Alfarsi S, Evans DC. Low-density-lipoprotein metabolism in familial combined hyperlipidemia: mechanism of the multiple lipoprotein phenotypic expression. Arteriosclerosis 1984;4:614–24.

175. Teng B, Sniderman AD, Soutar AK, Thompson GR. Metabolic basis of hyperapobetalipoproteinemia: turnover of apolipoprotein B in low-density lipoproteins and its precursors and subfractions compared with normal and familial hypercholesterolemia. J Clin Invest 1986;77:663–72.

176. Sniderman A, Shapiro S, Marpole D, Skinner B, Teng B, Kwiterovich PO. Association of coronary atherosclerosis with hyperapobetalipoproteinemia (increased protein but normal cholesterol levels in human plasma low-density [beta] lipoprotein). Proc Natl Acad Sci USA 1980;77:604–8.

177. Teng B, Thompson GR, Sniderman A, Forte TM, Krauss RM, Kwiterovich PO Jr. Composition and distribution of low-density-lipoprotein fractions in hyperapobetalipoproteinemia, normolipidemia, and familial hypercholesterolemia. Proc Natl Acad Sci USA 1983;80;6662–6.

178. Nielsen LB. Transfer of low-density lipoprotein into the arterial wall and risk of atherosclerosis. Atherosclerosis 1996;123:1–15.

179. Kwiterowich PO, Coresh HH, Bachorik PS, Derby CA, Pearson TA. Comparison of plasma levels of apolipoproteins B and A-I and other risk factors in men and women with premature coronary artery disease. Am J Cardiol 1992;69:1015–21.

180. Stampfer MJ, Sacks FM, Salvini S, Willett WC, Hennekens CH. A prospective study of cholesterol, apolipoproteins, and the risk of myocardial infarction. N Engl J Med 1991;325:373–81.

181. Schmidt SB, Wasserman AG, Muesing RA, Schlesselman SE, La Rosa JC, Roos AM. Lipoprotein and apolipoprotein levels in angiographically defined coronary atherosclerosis. Am J Cardiol 1985;55:1459–62.

182. Lamarche B, Moorjani S, Lupien PJ, Cantin B, Bernard P-M, Dagenais GR, Després J-P. Apolipoprotein A-I and B levels and the risk of ischemic heart disease during a five-year follow-up of men in the Québec cardiovascular study. Circulation 1996;94:273–78.

183. Lamarche B, Tchernof A, Moorjani S, Cantin B, Dagenais GR, Lupien PJ, Després J-P. Small, dense low-density lipoprotein particles as a predictor of the risk of ischemic heart disease in men. Prospective results from the Québec cardiovascular study. Circulation 1997;95:69–75.

184. Bachorik PS, Lovejoy KL, Carroll MD, Johnson CL. Apolipoprotein B and A-I distributions in the United States, 1988–1991: results of the National Health and Nutrition. Examination survey III (NHANES III). Clin Chem 1997;43:2364–78.

185. Jungner I, Marcovina SM, Walldius G, Holme I, Kolar W, Steiner E. Apolipoprotein B and A-I values in 147576 Swedish males and females, standardized according to the World Health Organization-International Federation of Clinical Chemistry first international reference materials. Clin Chem 1998;44:1641–9.

186. Gordon JG, Rifkind BM. High-density lipoprotein: the clinical implications of recent studies. N Eng J Med 1989;321:1311–6.

187. Heiss G, Johnson NJ, Reiland S, Davis CE, Tyroler HA. The epidemiology of plasma high-density-lipoprotein cholesterol levels: The Lipid Research Clinics Program Prevalence Study, summary. Circulation 1980;62(Suppl IV):IV-116–36.

188. Davis CE, Gordon D, LaRosa J, Wood PDS, Halperin M. Correlations of plasma high-density lipoprotein cholesterol levels with other plasma lipid and lipoprotein concentrations: The Lipids Research Clinics Program Prevalence Study. Circulation 1980; 62(Suppl IV):IV-24–30.

189. Schaefer EJ, Genest Jr JJ, Ordovas JM, Salem DN, Wilson WF. Familial lipoprotein disorders and premature coronary artery disease. Curr Opin Lipidol 1993;4:288–98.

190. Schmitz G, Williamson E. High-density lipoprotein metabolism, reverse cholesterol transport, and membrane protection. Curr Opin Lipidol 1991;2:177–89.

191. Parthasarathy S, Barnett J, Fong LG. High-density lipoprotein inhibits the oxidative modification of low-density lipoprotein. Biochim Biophys Acta 1990;1044:275–83.

192. Bhatnagar D, Durrington PN. Clinical value of apolipoprotein measurement. Ann Clin Biochem 1991;28:427–37.

193. Laker MF, Evans K. Analysis of apolipoproteins. Ann Clin Biochem 1996;33:5–22.

194. Armstrong VW, Cremer P, Eberle E, Manke A, Schulze F, Weiland H et al. The association between serum Lp(a) concentrations and angiographically assessed coronary atherosclerosis: dependence on serum DL levels. Atherosclerosis 1986; 62:249–57.

195. Hopkins PN, Hunt SC, Schreiner PJ, Eckfeld JH, Borecki IB, Ellison CR et al. Lipoprotein(a) interactions with lipid and non-lipid risk factors in patients with early onset coronary artery disease: results from the NHLBI Family Heart Study. Atherosclerosis 1998;141:333–45.

196. Stein JH, Rosenson RS. Lipoprotein Lp(a) excess and coronary heart disease. Arch Intern Med 1997;157:1170–6.

197. Rath M, Niendorf A, Reblin T, Dietel M, Krebber H-J, Beisiegel U. Detection and quantification of lipoprotein(a) in the arterial wall of 107 coronary bypass patients. Arteriosclerosis 1989;9:579–92.

198. Wade DP. Lipoprotein (a). Curr Opin Lipidol 1993;4:244–9.

199. Salonen E-M, Jauhiainen M, Zardi L, Vaheri A, Ehnholm C. Lipoprotein(a) binds to fibronectin and has serum proteinase activity capable of cleaving it. EMBO J 1989;8:4035–40.

200. Myiata M, Biro S, Kaieda H, Tanaka H. Lipoprotein (a) stimulates the proliferation of cultured human arterial smooth muscle cells through two pathways. FEBS Lett 1995;377:493–6.

201. Miles LA, Fless GM, Levin EG, Scanu AM, Plow EF. A potential basis for the thrombotic risks associated with lipoprotein(a). Nature 1989;339:301–3.

202. Hajjar KA, Gavish D, Breslow JL, Nachmann RL. Lipoprotein(a) modulation of endothelial surface fibrinolysis and its potential role in atherosclerosis. Nature 1989;339:303–5.

203. Ranby M. Studies on the kinetics of plasminogen activation by tissue plasminogen activator. Biochim Biophys Acta 1982;704:461–9.
204. Loscalzo J, Weinfeld M, Fless G, Scanu AM. Lipoprotein(a), fibrin-binding and plasminogen activation. Arteriosclerosis 1990;10:240–5.
205. Brown MS, Goldstein JL. Teaching old dogmas new tricks. Nature 1987;330:113–4.
206. Sandholzer C, Saha N, Kark JD, Rees A, Jaross W, Dieplinger H et al. Apo(a) isoforms predict risk for coronary heart disease: a study in six populations. Arterioscler Thromb 1992;12:1214–26.
207. Zenker G, Koltringer P, Bone G, Niederkorn K, Pfeiffer K, Jurgens G. Lipoprotein (a) as a strong indicator for cerebrovascular disease. Stroke 1986;17:942–5.
208. Cambillau M, Simon A, Amar J, Giral Ph, Atger V, Segond P et al. Serum Lp(a) as a discriminant marker of early atherosclerotic plaque at three extracoronary sites in hypercholesterolemic men. Arterioscler Thromb 1992;12:1346–52.
209. Berg K, Dahlen G, Borrenson A-L. Lp(a) phenotypes, other lipoprotein parameters and family history of heart disease in middle-aged males. Clin Genet 1977;16:347–52.
210. Durrington PN, Hunt L, Ishola M, Arrol S, Bhatnagar D. Apolipoproteins (a), A-I and B and parental history in men with early onset ischemic heart disease. Lancet 1988; 1:1070–3.
211. Orth-Gomér K, Mittleman MA, Schenck-Gustafsson K, Wamala SP, Eriksson M, Belkic K et al. Lipoprotein(a) as a determinant of coronary heart disease in young women. Circulation 1997;95:329–34.
212. Bostom AG, Gagnon DR, Cupples LA, Wilson PWF, Jenner JL, Ozdovas JM et al. A prospective investigation of elevated lipoprotein (a) detected by electrophoresis and cardiovascular disease in women. Circulation 1994;90:1688–95.
213. Maher VM, Brown G. Lipoprotein (a) and coronary heart disease. Curr Opin Lipidol 1995;6:229–35.
214. Armstrong VW, Cremer P, Eberle E, Manke A, Schulze F, Wieland H et al. The association between serum Lp(a) concentration and angiographically assessed coronary atherosclerosis: dependence on serum LDL levels. Atherosclerosis 1986;62:249–57.
215. Maher VMG, Brown BG, Marcovina SM, Hillger LA, Zhao Z-Q, Albers JJ. Effects of lowering elevated LDL cholesterol on the cardiovascular risk of lipoprotein (a). JAMA 1995;274:1771–4.

Atherogenesis

Deborah R. Gersony and Valentin Fuster

2

✧ Atherosclerosis is the leading cause of morbidity and mortality in the industrial world. In recent years, our understanding of the pathophysiology of this disease has advanced considerably. Coronary heart disease (CHD) is now thought to be primarily a problem of dysfunctional coronary endothelium rather than a simple accumulation of lipids as was thought previously. This dysfunctional endothelium then leads to inflammation, lipid accumulation, and fibromuscular hyperplasia, the foundation for a coronary atherosclerotic plaque formation.

The most vulnerable of such plaque becomes prone to rupture and subsequent thrombus formation. If this pathological progression is interrupted, for example, by stabilizing the high-risk plaque, acute coronary events such as unstable angina could be avoided. Magnetic resonance imaging (MRI) is fast becoming an important tool in the evaluation of the vulnerable atheromatous plaque. By identifying plaque composition and monitoring its progression, MRI can provide valuable information regarding the probability of an acute cardiac event.

This chapter discusses the vascular biology of coronary risk factors, the pathogenesis of plaque formation and rupture, the role of thrombus formation, and the importance of identifying the lesion that is most vulnerable to disruption. Future directions of atherosclerosis therapy are also reviewed.

PATHOPHYSIOLOGY

Nomenclature of Plaque Progression

The American Heart Association Committee on Vascular Lesions has subdivided the progression of a plaque from a "fatty streak" to a "complicated lesion" into five separate phases.[1,2] Within these phases are distinct morphological types, which are summarized in Figure 2–1.[3]

Phase 1 lesions—those that appear early in the progression to clinically significant atherosclerotic heart disease—are common in the general population under 30 years of age. The first such plaque (type I) is identified by the infiltration of macrophage-derived foam cells. This lesion then matures into a type II lesion or "fatty streak" that infiltrates smooth muscle cells and deposits extracellular lipid. Type III le-

Figure 2–1 ✧ Schematic of staging (phases and lesion morphology of the progression of coronary atherosclerosis according to gross pathological and clinical finding). See text for more details. With permission from V. Fuster (2).

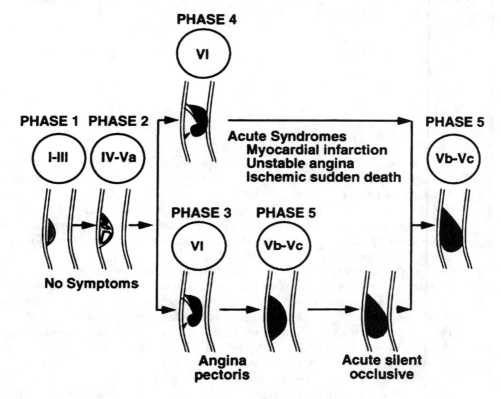

sions consist of smooth muscle cells surrounded by extracellular connective tissue, fibrils, and lipid deposits.

Phase II lesions—the type IV and type Va plaques—may not be significantly stenotic and, therefore, are not reliably identified by cardiac catheterization. Nonetheless, these are the lesions most vulnerable to rupture and the most likely to become culprits in future acute and possibly life-threatening coronary events (Figure 2–2).[1–4] The type IV plaque, also termed "atheroma," consists of a large extracellular intimal lipid core with inflammatory cell infiltration, including macrophages, foam cells, and T-cells. Type Va lesions are similar in composition to type IV lesions; however, these lesions are covered by a thin fibrous cap.

The lesions categorized as Phase 2 can evolve into Phase 3 or Phase 4 lesions, which are both characterized by plaque disruption with overlying thrombus formation (type VI or the "complicated lesion"). This thrombus may be relatively small and non-occlusive (phase 3) or it may occlude the coronary artery (phase 4), which could result in an acute coronary syndrome. Either of these lesion types can progress to

Figure 2–2 ✦ Anatomic changes (plaque disruption and thrombosis) leading to progression of atherosclerotic disease (remodeling) and the acute coronary syndromes. An element of vasoconstriction is usually present. See text for more details. Adapted from Kristensen SD, Raun HB, Falk E. Insights into the pathophysiology of unstable coronary artery disease. *Am J Cardiol* 1997 Sep,4;80(5A):5E–9E.

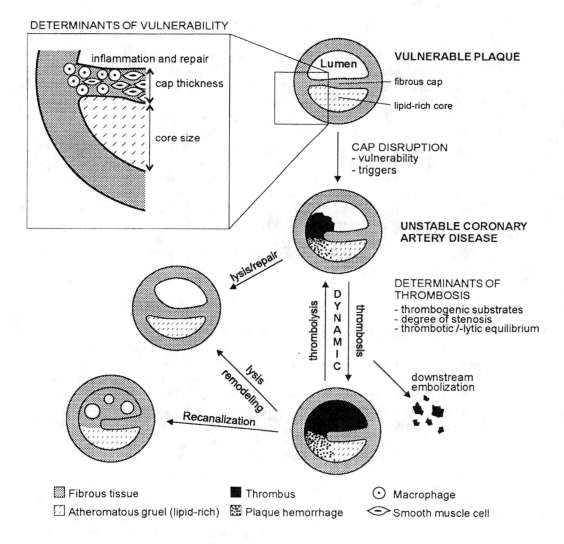

Phase 5 lesions, which organize the mural thrombus by connective tissue and exhibit varying degrees of calcification. Phase 5 lesions may result in a stable angina syndrome or a clinically silent occlusive process. Identifying the "vulnerable plaque," or that lesion which is at the highest risk of rupturing and causing an acute coronary event, is important if we are to prevent significant ischemic heart disease in the future.[5]

Atherosclerotic Risk Factors

Hypercholesterolemia

Lipoproteins are high-molecular-weight complexes that contain both lipid and protein. The role of lipoproteins in normal physiology includes transport of lipids to cells for energy, assistance in normal growth, and storage of energy. Low-density lipoprotein (LDL) plays a particularly important role in atherogenesis because of its effect on the influx and efflux of lipids into the vessel wall.[3] In addition, increased LDL cholesterol (LDL-C) concentrations may promote thrombus formation, which is the final step in most acute coronary events. Another lipoprotein, high-density lipoprotein (HDL), is beginning to be seen as an important factor in protection against atherosclerosis progression. HDL promotes cholesterol efflux from atherosclerotic lesions. In addition, HDL inhibits the oxidation and subsequent accumulation of LDL. (These pathological processes of atherogenesis are reviewed in detail later in this chapter.)

Other types of hyperlipidemia may portend additional risk for CHD. These clinical states include increases in triglyceride-rich lipoproteins, increases in small dense LDLs, and postprandial increases of very-low-density lipoproteins (VLDL) and chylomicrons. Increased lipoprotein (a) [Lp(a)] in plasma, in the presence of high LDL-C levels, is also considered an important risk factor, although the degree of this risk has not yet been established.

Hypertension

Increased systemic blood pressure has been established clinically as a risk factor for atherosclerotic heart disease. Hypertension increases the progression of coronary vascular disease by promoting endothelial dysfunction. High blood pressures attenuate the coronary vessels' response to endothelium-derived vasodilators and increase vascular permeability to macromolecules including LDL. In addition, high blood pressures increase the production of endothelin, which plays an important role in atherogenesis.[3] Leukocyte adherence to the endothelium also seems to be increased when high blood pressure is present. Finally, hypertension has been associated with an increase in smooth muscle cell proliferation and response to growth factors.

Diabetes Mellitus

Insulin resistance in patients with Type 2 diabetes or in patients with poorly controlled Type 1 diabetes leads to hyperinsulinemia. This pathology elevates certain growth factors such as insulin growth factor 1. These growth factors, in the presence of hyperglycemia, promote proliferation of the fibromuscular components of the growing atherosclerotic lesion. Although absolute levels of LDL-C may be normal in patients with diabetes mellitus, LDL function is often abnormal due to glycosylation in the blood. The typical lipid profile in patients with diabetes consists of elevated total triglycerides with low levels of HDL cholesterol (HDL-C). This profile often causes abnormal triglyceride-rich lipoprotein metabolism, which in turn modifies LDL structure. This modification results in smaller, denser LDLs (pattern B, refer to chapter 16), which are known to be markedly atherogenic. In addition, increased levels of Lp(a) are common in patients who have poorly controlled diabetes mellitus.

Obesity and Physical Inactivity

Obesity is a significant risk factor for cardiovascular disease. It is a primary risk factor in young patients, and is associated with established risk factors such as hypertension and hyperlipidemia in other patients. Physical activity favorably alters lipid profiles, lowers adiposity and blood pressure, and increases cardiovascular and pulmonary functional capacities. In addition, physical fitness, a condition that is amenable to being tested in an exercise laboratory, independently reduces the risk of premature CHD.

Family History

It is clear that single gene mutations influence lipid metabolism. Complex polygenic disorders including hypertension, diabetes, and homocysteinemia also portend significant risk for CHD. Interestingly, currently mapped genetic abnormalities only partially account for the risk predicted by a positive family history for premature CHD.

Smoking

Several observational studies have demonstrated that smoking increases atherosclerotic risk by increasing fibrinogen levels in the blood, enhancing platelet reactivity, and increasing whole blood viscosity by inducing secondary polycythemia vera. In addition, the chemical irritants found in tobacco injure the endothelium. Smoking also lowers HDL-C and promotes oxidation of LDL-C. The mechanism of these effects on lipid profile is thought to be the exposure of LDL to the free radicals that are present in cigarette smoke.

Initiation and Decompensation of the Vulnerable Plaque

The early lesions (Phase 1) described previously are common in patients in the first three decades of life and are only microscopically or chemically detectable. The progression of these early minor lesions to clinically significant "complicated plaques" is an area of intense investigation. Several factors combine to create a situation in which atherosclerosis can progress unimpeded in a given coronary artery. One of the primary factors needed for atherogenesis is local endothelial dysfunction or injury.[5]

The endothelium plays an important role in vascular homeostasis. It regulates the permeability of plasma lipoproteins, the adhesion of leukocytes, and the release of prothrombotic and antithrombotic factors, growth factors, and vasoactive substances.[6,7] Endothelial cells are exposed to various mechanical forces, including the blood's hydrostatic forces within the vessel, circumferential stress from vasomotion of the vessel, and, perhaps most importantly, shear stress caused by blood flow within the vessel.[8] A chronic injury pattern is initially low-grade and is detectable in areas of low shear stress and flow reversal, such as branch points in the arterial tree.[9] This chronic endothelial injury is then augmented by confirmed cardiac risk factors such as hyperlipidemia, hypertension, diabetes, and smoking (as discussed previously).[10] Circulating vasoactive amines and immune complexes have also been implicated in the progression of endothelial dysfunction.[5] Eventually, chronic endothelial injury or dysfunction leads to an accumulation of lipids and monocytes at these sites.

Recent data show that atherosclerosis may be initiated and maintained by an inflammatory response to this endothelial injury. Ross and colleagues[11] maintain that the entire process of atherogenesis, at both a molecular and cellular level, is inflammatory in nature. Endothelial dysfunction initiates inflammation by altering normal homeostatic properties. With continued inflammation, increasing numbers of macrophages and lymphocytes migrate from the blood into the lesion. Activation of these cells leads to the release of hydrolytic enzymes, cytokines, chemokines, and growth factors. These inflammatory agents activate smooth muscle cells and cause them to synthesize extracellular matrix.[12] The artery initially responds by remodeling or dilating, until it can no longer compensate adequately. At this point, the luminal area is compromised and coronary blood flow is altered.

A critical step in the progression of clinically significant atherosclerosis is the entry and accumulation of lipids (Figure 2–3), most of which derive from LDL. LDL enters the vessel wall through the injured or dysfunctional endothelium and is oxidized by endothelial cells. After uptake by macrophages in the atherosclerotic lesion, LDL forms lipid peroxides and facilitates the accumulation of cholesterol esters.[13] This initial uptake of LDL by macrophages may be a protective mechanism to prevent the build-up of extracellular lipid. Eventually these macrophages are transformed into foam cells.

HDL may protect against excessive lipid accumulation in the vessel wall by inhibiting the oxidation of LDL, thereby reducing its uptake into macrophages. HDL may also play a protective role by actively removing LDL from the vessel wall and from foam cells. After saturation with lipids and before their death, these macrophages or foam cells can liberate a large number of products, including cholesterol (esterified and oxidized), which can further damage the endothelium and so participate in the evolution of atherosclerotic lesions.

Several factors play a role in the continuing entry and replication of macrophages within the plaque. These factors include endothelial adhesion molecules (i.e., VCAM-1); monocyte chemotactic protein (MCP-1); monocyte colony-stimulating factor (M-CSF); and interleukin-2.[14] The macrophages, which have probably congregated within the plaque in order to limit lipoprotein accumulation, may eventually undergo apoptotic death. While it is not clear whether this process releases matrix metalloproteinases (MMPs), apoptotic death of macrophage does shed membrane microparticles, which exposes phosphatidylserine on the cell surface and confers a potent procoagulant activity. The shed particles account for most of the tissue factor activity present in plaque extract and may be a major contributor to thrombogenesis after plaque disruption.[15]

Figure 2–3 ✧ Schematic of pathogenesis of Phase 1 of progression: chronic endothelial injury and risk factors—influx, accumulation, and the fate of lipoproteins and monocyte-macrophages. ENDOT= endothelial; END ADH MOL = endothelial adhesion molecule; HDL = high-density lipoprotein; LDL = low-density lipoprotein; Lp (a) = lipoprotein (a); MCP-1 = monocyte chemotactic protein-1; M-CSF = monocyte colony-stimulating factor; MM-LDL = minimally modified LDL; NF-kB = necrosis factor kB; OX = oxidized. (Modified with permission from Steinberg D: Oxidative modification of LDL and atherogenesis. Circulation 1997;95:1062–1072.

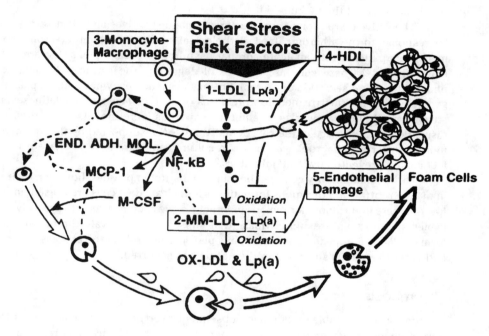

Rupture of the Vulnerable Plaque

Acute thrombosis overlying an atherosclerotic plaque plays a critical role in the pathogenesis of acute coronary syndromes (Figure 2–2).[8] Following either erosion of the endothelial surface or disruption of the cap of a lipid-rich plaque, a thrombus forms on the surface.[16,17] In up to two-thirds of patients in whom unstable angina or another acute coronary syndrome develops, previous angiography revealed only minor coronary lesions. During the acute syndrome, however, these patients develop severe stenosis or complete obstruction.

This finding suggests that plaque rupture of a type IV or V lesion with subsequent acute thrombosis is the mechanism of coronary disease in these patients. This mechanism has been supported by studies that traced the thrombi that have caused myocardial infarctions to cracks or fissures within a plaque.[18] Subsequent work has confirmed that plaque rupture underlies the majority of thrombi responsible for acute coronary syndromes.[19]

Disruption of plaque seems to depend on both active and passive phenomena. The area of the plaque most vulnerable to passive disruption is the area where the fibrous cap is the thinnest and where there is a high concentration of foam cells. This vulnerable area is usually the shoulder region, where the eccentric plaque attaches to the vessel wall.[20,21] Factors that increase the risk of passive rupture include circumferential wall stress or cap "fatigue"; location, size, and consistency of the atheromatous core; and blood-flow characteristics, particularly the impact of flow on the proximal aspect of the plaque.[22,23]

The active disruption of atherosclerotic plaque involves an inflammatory cellular response to the atheroma itself. Pathological examination of atherectomy specimens from patients with an acute coronary syndrome reveal regions that are rich in macrophages.[24] These cells are capable of degrading the extracellular matrix by phagocytosis and secretion of proteolytic enzymes. Such enzymes include plasminogen activators and matrix metalloproteinases (MMPs, collagenases, gelatinases, and stromelysins) and may weaken the fibrous cap, thus increasing its susceptibility to disruption.[25] Knowledge of the role of MMPs has been supported by the finding that monocyte-derived macrophages grown in culture can degrade cap collagen. This effect can by prevented by MMP inhibitors.[26]

Other inflammatory cells can be found in disrupted plaques; however, their role in plaque rupture and thrombus formation is less clear. Mast cells are present in fairly low numbers in the shoulder regions of intact plaques and can secrete proteolytic enzymes such as tryptase and chymase that subsequently activate the proenzymatic form of MMPs. It appears that neutrophils play less of a role in the process of rupture and enter the plaque shortly after disruption has occurred.

Thrombosis

Rupture of the unstable plaque and subsequent overlying thrombosis results in an abrupt change in geometry of the coronary lumen. This change may result in complete occlusion or subocclusion with clinical manifestations of unstable angina or myocardial infarction (Figure 2–4). It is more frequent, however, for the clot to organize into a mural thrombus without clinical symptoms.

Figure 2–4 ✧ Photomicrographs illustrating composition and vulnerability of atherosclerotic plaques. A vulnerable plaque, containing a core of soft atheromatous gruel (devoid of blue-stained collagen) that is separated from the vascular lumen by a thin cap of fibrous tissue. The fibrous cap is infiltrated by foam cells that can be clearly seen at high magnification, indicating ongoing disease activity. Such a thin and macrophage-infiltrated cap is probably weak and vulnerable, and it was indeed disrupted nearby, explaining why erythrocytes can be seen in the gruel just beneath the macrophage-infiltrated cap. With permission from E. Falk et al. (18).

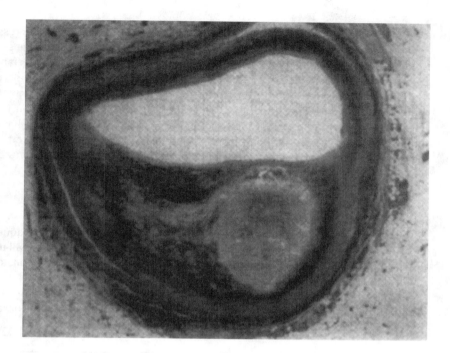

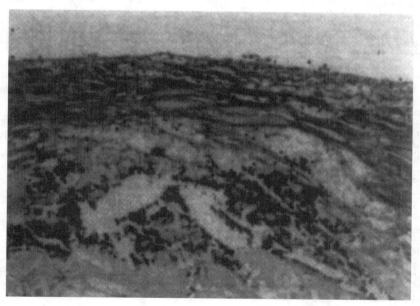

This process of thrombosis and organization may underlie the progression of atherosclerosis. The degree to which the coronary thrombus is obstructive seems to depend on both local and systemic factors (Table 2–1). The most important local factor is plaque composition itself. Lipid-rich content, like that seen in the "vulnerable plaque," tends to be more thrombogenic than the collagen-based substrate of more stable lesions. The amount of tissue factor contained in the lesion has also been found to be an important local factor.[27,28] Several systemic factors have been implicated in promoting coronary thrombosis: plasma cholesterol, cigarette smoking, and perhaps to a lesser degree, infection with such agents as *Chlamydia pneumoniae*.[29]

Local Factors

Several studies have indicated that the thrombogenicity of a vulnerable plaque could be predicted based on its tissue factor content. Tissue factor is a small-molecular-weight glycoprotein that initiates the extrinsic clotting cascade. It is considered a major regulator of coagulation, hemostasis, and thrombosis.

Tissue factor forms a high-affinity complex with coagulation factors VII/VIIa; TF-VIIa complex activates factors IX and X, thereby leading to thrombin generation.[30]

Table 2–1 ◆ Thrombogenic Risk Factors* (1999)
Local Factors
Degree of plaque disruption (i.e., erosion[2], ulcer[1])
Degree of stenosis (i.e., change in geometry)
Tissue substrate (i.e., lipid-rich plaque[1])
Surface of residual thrombus (i.e., recurrence)
Vasoconstriction (i.e., platelets, thrombin)
Systemic Factors
Cholesterol,[2] Lp (a)
Catecholamines (i.e., smoking, stress, cocaine)
Fibrinogen, impaired fibrinolysis (i.e., PAI-1)
Activated platelets and clotting (i.e., Fr VIIa, vWF, thrombin generation—F1+2, or activity—FPA)
Infections (C. Pneum, CMV, Helic Pylori)
*High Risk: Occlus. (ACS); Low Risk: Mural (progression)   V. Fuster et al., Circ 1994;90:2126   AP Burke et al., NEJM 1997;336:1276   CH Hennekens, Circ 1998;97:1095   Rd Rosenberg et al., NEJM 1999;340:1955

The tissue factor antigen is normally present in the arterial adventitia. However, each of the major cell types in plaque (smooth muscle cells, macrophages, and endothelial cells) is capable of tissue factor expression. Specifically inhibiting vascular tissue factor by using recombinant tissue factor pathway inhibitor (r-TFPI) was associated with a significant reduction of acute thrombus formation.[31] This finding implies a possible clinical benefit to the inhibition of the tissue factor pathway in the treatment of CHD.

Evidence suggests that macrophages are the primary source of tissue factor within the lipid core. This observation emphasizes the importance of macrophage cells in both the progression of atherosclerosis as well as the stability and thrombogenicity of these lesions following plaque rupture.

Systemic Factors

Clinical and experimental evidence now suggests that systemic factors play a significant role in the process of focal thrombosis.

One important factor is hypercholesterolemia. Previous studies have reported that lipid-lowering statins, which successfully lower cholesterol to a normal level, reduce the increased blood thrombogenicity observed in the same patients under hyperlipidemic conditions. In addition, the mechanism of action was related more to lipid-lowering activity than to the specific medication used.[32]

Other important systemic factors include

✧   catecholamines, which may be derived from smoking;

✧   stress or cocaine ingestion;

✧   fibrinogen from impaired fibrinolysis or activated platelets;

✧   and infections such as *Chlamydia Pneumoniae*, CMV, and *H. Pylori* (Figure 2–5)[19,28]

Some studies have reported that increased antibody titres predict future adverse events in patients post-myocardial infarction. A possible mechanism may be that infectious agents activate circulating monocytes and white blood cells and create a hypercoagulable state. Elevated levels of C-reactive protein, which have been shown to be predictive of coronary events, may be a marker of this white blood cell activation.[33–36] Tissue factor is a known local contributor to thrombogenesis; however, the finding of a blood-borne pool of tissue factor suggests a systemic role for this glycoprotein as well.

Interestingly, one-third of patients who have acute coronary syndrome have no plaque disruption, only superficial erosions.[37,38] Thus, complicated thrombi in such cases may depend on a hypercoagulable state triggered by the systemic factors mentioned above.

IDENTIFICATION OF THE VULNERABLE PLAQUE

Imaging Studies

The identification of the plaque most likely to become the culprit lesion in an acute coronary syndrome remains a challenge. Coronary angiography has not been able to

Figure 2–5 ◇ C-reactive protein (compared to other risk factors) and risk for myocardial infarction. Based on Physicians Health Study. With permission from PM Ridker (33).

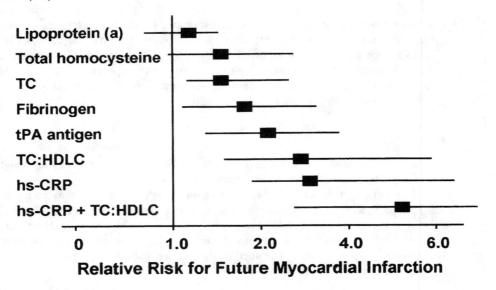

provide detailed information regarding the composition of atherosclerotic plaques in the coronary wall. In addition, the lipid-rich vulnerable plaques may not be apparent through angiography because of remodeling and dilatation of the coronary vessel wall, thereby preserving luminal cross-sectional area. Intravascular ultrasound, electron beam computed tomography, and angioscopy have all advanced our understanding of the pathophysiology of atherosclerosis by providing details about plaque composition and degree of atheromatous disease within coronary arteries. However, the MRI is the most promising non-invasive technique for delineating the degree of atheromatous disease and identifying the vessel most at risk for causing clinical disease.

A recent study conducted at Mount Sinai Medical Center compared coronary plaques with carotid plaques obtained from endarterectomy specimens[39,40] The carotid plaques had minimal inflammatory cell and lipid content but showed more calcification. Rupture of a carotid plaque appears to be precipitated by mechanical factors as in aortic dissection, in which the stenotic lesion is fractured by the force of blood in systole. In contrast, the coronary plaque is softer, with a greater lipid composition. It is less vulnerable to mechanical forces than to its own internal characteristics.

In addition, by using MRI with a peptide that identifies the IIb/IIIa receptor, recent investigations at our institution have reported that carotid plaques form thrombi only in the presence of deep ulcerations independent of whether the plaque contains fat.[41] Because ulcerations of coronary plaques tend to be shallow, another thrombogenic mechanism must be involved. That mechanism may involve macrophage and tissue factor exposure from within the lipid core after plaque disruption.

There have also been recent significant advances in the use of the MRI in animal models of vascular disease. At our institution, real-time visualization of platelet deposition and thrombolysis occurring in vivo has been successfully conducted. Platelet deposition and lysis have been visualized using a gamma camera in a pig model of angioplasty.[42] This technique is now used in patients undergoing angioplasty of the iliofemoral artery with (111)Indium-labeled platelets in order to follow the clot as it grows and then regresses in response to treatment with various antithrombotic agents.

Another animal model involves the sequential imaging by MRI of the aorta in hyperlipidemic, genetically engineered mice.[43] Despite the small caliber of such vessels, high-quality images have been obtained. These imaging techniques may become an important tool in the detection and long-term evaluation of early atherosclerotic heart disease. For example, physicians will be able to non-invasively monitor coronary lesions in detail and evaluate the response to plaque-stabilizing therapy, such as lipid-lowering and anti-thrombotic medication.

PLAQUE STABILIZATION AND ANTITHROMBOTIC THERAPY

Several large prospective studies have demonstrated significant benefit in terms of mortality and number of coronary events in those patients with dyslipidemia treated with statin therapy.[44] In addition, successful lipid-lowering therapy has been shown to provide significant clinical benefit without angiographic evidence of plaque regression. This finding implies that stabilization rather than resolution of an atherosclerotic plaque is the mechanism of benefit in these patients.

One possible explanation of this finding is that lipid-lowering helps transform the vulnerable type IV or Va plaque with its soft lipid-rich core to a more stable, stiffer lesion that is abundant in crystalline cholesterol and fibrous tissue. In addition, oxidized LDL activates macrophages and is a direct endothelial toxin. Finally, reducing the level of circulating LDL decreases the amount of cholesterol entering the plaque and permits increased cholesterol clearance by HDL. Lipid-lowering medication has also been shown to reduce MMP activity within the plaque.

Angiotensin-converting enzyme (ACE) inhibitors have been shown to reduce the incidence of myocardial infarction by 14% to 28% in patients with left ventricular dysfunction. Recent data from the HOPE (Heart Outcomes Prevention Evaluation) trial, however, demonstrate a significant benefit in patients who have normal left ventricular function.[45] This study enrolled approximately 9500 patients with normal ejection fraction to either ACE inhibitor or placebo. During the 4.5 years of follow-up, there was a highly statistically significant reduction in the primary end points of death: myocardial infarction and stroke. The blood pressure reduction in this study was relatively modest. The exact mechanism of this benefit is not yet known; however, it is clear that ACE inhibitors can interfere with endothelial fibrinolysis.[7] This inhibition may decrease the thrombogenicity of the ruptured plaque.

Future directions in the attempt to stabilize vulnerable plaque will focus on the role of inflammation in plaque rupture. Molecular strategies include blocking the sites of attachment for the various adhesion molecules present on the monocytes to prevent passage into the intima. Gene therapy may become an important tool in the stabilization of plaque. Possible approaches might be the over-expression of tissue inhibitors of MMPs and anti-sense strategies to block inflammatory molecules, such as nuclear factor kB.[7]

It has been reported recently that oxidized LDL leads to apoptotic death of monocytes, which is associated with the release of tissue factor and other proteins that increase thrombus formation. HDL may prevent this pathological process.[46] Thus, HDL elevation may become an important method of plaque stabilization.

It seems clear that plaque stabilization, with the aim of preventing plaque disruption, should be the primary goal of therapy. However, if plaque does rupture, anti-thrombotic therapy has proven to be beneficial in terms of prevention of acute coronary events. Both antiplatelet and anticoagulant agents have been demonstrated to be effective in patients with either acute or chronic CHD. Newer approaches to antithrombotic therapy include the potential therapeutic possibilities of inhibiting the tissue factor pathway. The use of low-dose tissue factor pathway inhibitor (rTFPi) in high-risk patients is currently being explored.[19]

SUMMARY

Atherosclerotic heart disease has a major impact on life expectancy and is the most prevalent disease in modern society. The underlying mechanism of acute coronary syndromes is primarily the rupture of a vulnerable plaque and subsequent overlying thrombus formation, which may result in either unstable angina or another acute cardiac event. The identification of these vulnerable lesions is of critical importance in the prevention of significant ischemic heart disease. MRI imaging is evolving into an important tool in this area of predicting which plaques are the most vulnerable.

Plaque stabilization is the primary preventive measure in the treatment of patients with chronic coronary disease. Lipid-lowering therapy is an established approach to such stabilization. ACE-inhibitors may also prove to be beneficial at preventing plaque rupture. Molecular approaches aimed at diminishing the inflammatory response of the endothelium are also promising methods of treatment. The experimental use of tissue factor pathway inhibiting agents is being evaluated currently as an approach to prevent or lessen the degree of plaque thrombosis, which is the final step in most cases of acute cardiac events.

REFERENCES

1. Stary HC, Chandler AB, Dinsmore DE et al. A definition of advanced types of atherosclerotic lesions and a histological classification of atherosclerosis: a report from the Committee on Vascular Lesions of the Council on Arteriosclerosis, American Heart Association. Circulation 1995;92:1355–74.
2. Fuster V, Lewis A. Conner Memorial Lecture. Mechanisms leading to myocardial infarction: insights from studies of vascular biology. Circulation 1994;90:2126–46.
3. Fuster V, Gotto AM, Libby P, Loscalzo J, McGill HC. Matching the intensity of risk factor management with the hazard for coronary disease events. Pathogenesis of coronary disease: the biologic role of risk factors. J Am Coll Cardiol 1996;27:964–76.
4. Fuster V. Human lesion studies. Ann N Y Acad Sci 1997;811:207–25.
5. Ross R. The pathogenesis of atherosclerosis: a perspective for the 1990s. Nature 1993;362:801–9.

6. Rubanyi GM. The role of endothelium in cardiovascular homeostasis and diseases. J Cardiovasc Pharmacol 1993;(Suppl 4):S1–S14.

7. Badimon JJ, Zaman A, Helft G, Fayad Z, Fuster V. Acute coronary syndromes: Pathophysiology and preventive priorities. Thromb Haemost. 1999 Aug;82(2):997–1004.

8. Traub O, Berk BC. Laminar shear stress: mechanisms by which endothelial cells transduce an atheroprotective force. Arterioscler Thromb Vasc Biol 1998;18:801–9.

9. Ku DN, Giddens DP, Zarins CK, Glagov S. Pulsatile flow and atherosclerosis in the human carotid bifurcation: positive correlation between plaque location and low oscillating shear stress. Arteriosclerosis 1985;5:293–301.

10. Fuster V, Badimon L, Badimon JJ, Chesboro JH. The pathogenesis of coronary artery disease and the acute coronary syndromes. N Engl J Med 1992;326:310–8.

11. Ross R. Atherosclerosis—an inflammatory disease. N Engl J Med 1999;340:115–26.

12. Ross R, Masuda J, Raines EW, Gown AM, Katsuda S, Sasahara M, Malden LT, Masuko H, Sato H. Localization of PDGF-B protein in macrophages in all phases of atherogenesis. Science 1990;248:1009–12.

13. Steinberg D. Antioxidative modification of LDL and atherogenesis. Lewis A. Conner Memorial Lecture. Circulation 1997;95:1062–71.

14. Steinberg D. Oxidative modification of LDL and atherogenesis. Circulation 1997;95:1062–72.

15. Mallat Z, Hugel B, Ohan J, Leseche G, Freyssinet J, Tedgui A. Shed membrane microparticles with procoagulant potential in human atherosclerotic plaques: a role for apoptosis in plaque thrombogenicity. Circulation 1999;99:348–53.

16. Davies MJ. Stability and instability: two faces of coronary atherosclerosis. The Paul Dudley White Lecture 1995. Circulation 1996;94:2013–20.

17. Farb A, Burke AP, Malcolm GT, Liang Y, Mannan P, Smialek J, Virmani R. Coronary risk factors and plaque morphology in men with coronary disease who died suddenly. N Engl J Med 1997;336;1276–82.

18. Falk E. Morphological features of unstable atherothrombotic plaques underlying acute coronary syndromes. Am J Cardiol 1989;63:114E–120E.

19. Falk E. Why do plaques rupture? Circulation 1992;86(Suppl):III3–III42.

20. Fuster V, Fayad ZA, Badimon JJ. Acute coronary syndromes: biology. Lancet 1999;353(Suppl 11) 5–9.

21. Davies MJ, Richardson PD, Woolf N, Katz DR, Mann J. Risk of thrombosis in human atherosclerotic plaques: role of extracellular lipid, macrophages, and smooth muscle content. Br Heart J 1993;69:377–81.

22. Fuster V. Mechanisms leading to myocardial infarction: insights from studies of vascular biology. Circulation 1994;90:2126–46.

23. Ambrose JA, Tannenbaum M, Alexpoulos D et al. Angiographic progression of coronary artery disease and the development of myocardial infarction. J Am Coll of Cardiol 1988;12:56–62.

24. Moreno PF, Falk E, Palacios IF, Newell JB, Fuster V, Fallon JT. Macrophage infiltration in acute coronary syndromes. Implications for plaque rupture. Circulation 1994;90:775–78.

25. Libby P. Molecular bases of the acute coronary syndromes. Circulation 1995;91:2844.

26. Falk E, Shah PK, Fuster V. Coronary plaque disruption. Circulation 1995; 92: 657–71.

27. Fernandez-Ortiz A, Badimon J, Falk E et al. Characterization of the relative thrombogenicity of atherosclerotic plaque components: implications for consequences of plaque rupture. J AM Coll Cardiol 1994;23:1562–69.

28. Toschi V, Gallo R, Lettino M et al. Tissue factor modulates the thrombogenicity of human atherosclerotic plaques. Circulation 1997;95:594–9.

29. Libby P, Egan D, Skarlatos S. Roles of infectious agents in atherosclerosis and restenosis: an assessment of the evidence and need for future research. Circulation 1997;96:4095–103.

30. Banner DW, D'Arcy A, Chene C et al. The crystal structure of the complex of blood composition factor VIIIa with soluble tissue factor. Nature 1996;380:41–6.

31. Badimon JJ, Lettino M, Toschi V et al. Local inhibition of tissue factor reduces the

thrombogenicity of disrupted human atherosclerotic plaques: Effects of TFPI on plaque thrombogenicity under flow conditions. Circulation 1999;14:1780–7.

32. Dangas F, Badimon JJ, Smith DA et al. Pravastatin therapy in hyperlipidemia: effects on thrombus formation and the systemic hemostatic profile. J Am Coll Cardiol 1999; 33:1294–304.

33. Ridker PM, Glynn RJ, Hennekens CH. C-reactive protein adds to the predictive value of total and HDL cholesterol in determining risk of first myocardial infarction. Circulation 1998;98:839–44.

34. Ridker PM, Rifai N, Pfeffer MA et al. Inflammation, Pravastatin, and the risk of coronary events after myocardial infarction in patients with average cholesterol levels. Circulation 1998;98:839–44.

35. Koenig W, Sund M, Frohlich M et al. C-Reactive protein, a sensitive marker of inflammation, predicts future risk of coronary heart disease in initially healthy middle-aged men: results from the MONICA (monitoring trends and determinants in cardiovascular disease) Augsburg Cohort study, 1984 to 1992. Circulation 1999;99:237–42.

36. Biasucci LM, Liuzzo G, Grillo RL et al. Elevated levels of C-reactive protein at discharge in patients with unstable angina predict recurrent instability. Circulation 1999;99:55–60.

37. Burke AP, Farb A, Malcom GT et al. Coronary risk factors and plaque morphology in men with coronary disease who died suddenly. N Engl J Med 1997;336:1276–81.

38. Farb A, Burke AP, Tang AL et al. Coronary plaque erosion without rupture into a lipid core: a frequent cause of coronary thrombosis in sudden coronary death. Circulation 1996;93:1354–63.

39. Shinnar M, Fallon JT, Wehrlis S et al. The diagnostic accuracy of ex vivo magnetic resonance imaging for human atherosclerotic plaque characterization. Aterioscler Tromb Vasc Biol 1999;19:2756–61.

40. Fuster V. Mechanisms of arterial thrombosis: foundation for therapy. Am Heart J 1998;135:S361–6.

41. Vallabhajosula S, Fuster V. Atherosclerosis: imaging techniques and the evolving role of nuclear medicine. J Nucl Med 1997;38:1788–96.

42. Gallo R, Padurean A, Badimon JJ et al. In vivo real-time monitoring of arterial thrombus growth with 99mTC-platelets (abstract). Circulation 1994;94:I–269.

43. Shinnar M, Fallon JA, Badimon JJ, Fuster V. Circulation 1996;94:I–345.

44. Fuster V, Badimon JJ. Regression or stabilization of atherosclerosis means regression or stabilization of what we don't see in the arteriogram. Eur Heart J 1995;16:6–12.

45. Yusuf S, Sleight P. Heart outcomes prevention evaluation trial. Clinical trial results. American Heart Association 72nd Scientific Sessions. Nov 1999. Atlanta, Georgia USA

46. Xu HP, Meisel SR, Ong JM et al. Oxidized low-density lipoprotein regulates matrix metalloproteinnase-9 and its tissue inhibitor in human monocyte-derived macrophages. Circulation 1999;99:993–8.

Genetic Markers to Predict Cardiovascular Disease

3

David J. Galton and Andrea Kay

✧   During the past 15 years there have been unprecedented advances in the study of complex genetic diseases, i.e., diseases that are both polygenic and multifactorial, such as cardiovascular and malignant diseases. Since 1982 more than 20 genes coding for proteins involved in plasma lipid transport have been identified, chromosomally localized, and their DNA sequences characterized.[1,2] This has led to a much greater understanding of the genetic basis of coronary heart disease. The genetics of other multifactorial disorders, such as diabetes mellitus and venous thromboembolism, have also been partially clarified in the present decade and have provided a wealth of new genetic markers.

These developments in the field of genetic markers for polygenic disease and other complex biological traits are accompanied by indications for potential or actual misuse. One problem is that in complex diseases such as coronary atherosclerosis, there is often a subset of the affected population that inherits the condition as a simple monogenic trait. This has sometimes led to uncritically transferring the ideas underlying the genetic determinism of rare monogenic disorders, such as familial hypercholesterolemia, thereby oversimplifying genetic determinism for complex multifactorial disease such as ischemic heart disease, diabetes, hypertension, and others. This is inappropriate because complex genetic disease involves the co-inheritance of several genetic variants that often must interact with environmental factors before the disease manifests. The genetic determinants for a phenotype can vary and may interact in different ways; some of the genetic factors can even be protective against the occurrence of the disease. This chapter therefore presents a review and critique of some medical and social issues arising from the clinical use of genetic markers for polygenic disease such as cardiovascular disorders, and highlights some of the basic limitations of the current approach.

BACKGROUND: GENETIC MARKERS

In situations where there is an absence of definitive tests for causative disease mutations, it is useful to be able to identify individuals who are at risk by using disease markers. A disease marker is a characteristic that segregates with a particular disease; it must be identifiable and polymorphic. These markers all arise due to differences in an individual's DNA that may be unrelated to the disease, but are located in the genome within or nearby the disease gene; as will be seen later, it is not always necessary to be able to identify markers at the level of DNA. These markers are used to track monogenic diseases within families, but they can also be used in the population to identify associations between a disease and a specific gene. This is particularly useful in complex genetic disease, where there is a clear-cut hereditary component, i.e., the disease aggregates in families but without the usual Mendelian inheritance ratios defined for monogenic disease, and where environmental factors are often required for the occurrence of the disease (Figure 3–1).

Figure 3–1 ✧ A Venn Diagram Illustrating Gene-Gene and Gene-Environment Interactions Contributing to Multifactorial Disease Such as Premature Coronary Heart Disease

The circles represent different genetic factors, with overlapping regions corresponding to increased genetic susceptibility due to multiple gene effects. The background represents the overall environmental contribution which may either be protective or deleterious. The letters in the figure relate to overall risk of disease:

A   Low risk unless monogenic disorder [e.g., familial hypercholesterolemia]
B   Medium risk
C   Moderate-High risk
D   High genetic susceptibility
E   Disease phenotype

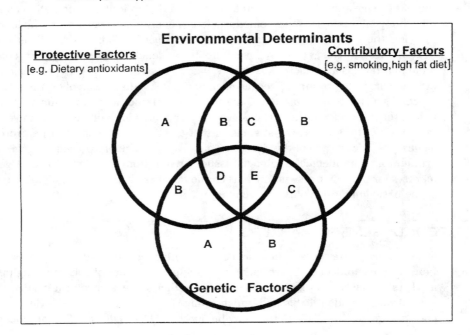

PROTEIN POLYMORPHISMS AND DISEASE ASSOCIATIONS

The earliest associations between illness and genes were those observed between certain diseases and polymorphic proteins detectable in blood. Thus the first major observation of disease association with identifiable, polymorphic markers was the relationship between stomach cancer and blood groups: the A, B, and O polymorphisms. Blood group O and stomach cancer are both more common in the North of England. Aird and his colleagues discovered that the strongest association was in fact with blood group A.[3] Later studies did reveal a weak association between blood group O, duodenal ulcers, and non-secretor status, with a contribution of 2.5% to the total variance.

Another source of polymorphic markers can also be defined in the blood: the Human Leukocyte Antigens (HLA) are highly polymorphic proteins that were identified as the proteins involved in graft rejection. These informative markers were eventually genetically mapped to the HLA locus on chromosome 6, but even before this locus was genetically identified it was possible to demonstrate that certain serologically defined proteins showed strong disease associations.[4] For example, HLA B27 is found in more than 90% of subjects with ankylosing spondylitis. Unfortunately, this observation is of no use in predicting the disease because approximately 10% of the healthy European population also carry HLA B27, whereas only approximately 1% of them will develop ankylosing spondylitis. Another striking example is the almost 100% association of narcolepsy with the HLA DR2 antigen, yet about 15% of the European population possess this particular polymorphism without developing narcolepsy. Clearly such polymorphic variants would be of no use for risk prediction in the population, but they can help in research to elucidate the mechanisms of pathogenesis of the disease and may be used as an adjunct to diagnosis: i.e., if a patient with sacroileitis also possesses the HLA B-27 variant, then the diagnosis of ankylosing spondylitis is much more likely before other manifestations of the disease become apparent.

Other polymorphic proteins that have proven useful adjuncts in diagnosis and that have also elucidated possible pathogenic mechanisms have been identified. The polymorphic protein apolipoprotein E (apo E) provides a good example of this: more than 90% of subjects with Type III hyperlipoproteinemia have the apo E phenotype of E2/E2. This phenotype occurs in 0.2%–1.6% of an unselected healthy population studied in various countries, but only 2% of subjects with E2/E2 will actually develop the dyslipidemia.[5] The genetic basis for this variation, which was originally observed as a polymorphic protein, has now been characterized in human DNA. As with the HLA markers, this polymorphism cannot be used for risk prediction, but can be used as an adjunct to diagnosis. With regard to pathogenic mechanisms, it has been shown that the affinity of the apo E2 peptide for hepatic remnant receptors is less than for apo E3, which in turn is less than for apo E4; and the suggestion is that remnant lipoprotein particles carrying E2/E2 cannot be cleared as effectively from the blood stream as those particles possessing the other apo E variants of E3 or E4.[6] Although more than 95% of E2/E2 homozygotes do not develop Type III hyperlipidemia, an increase in their very-low-density lipoprotein (VLDL) cholesterol content is detectable, probably because of the slower clearance of their apo E2-containing lipoproteins. It is therefore apparent that other factors, either genetic or environmental, must occur for Type III hyperlipidemia to develop.

DNA POLYMORPHISMS AND DISEASE ASSOCIATIONS

The use of recombinant DNA techniques allowed a wealth of DNA markers to be discovered throughout the human genome. This has greatly enlarged the scope of study involving the genetics of disease associations or linkage other than at the HLA locus. The original DNA markers, which made screening the genome for disease associations possible, were initially observed as restriction-fragment-length polymorphisms (RFLPs): i.e., when the same section of the genome was cut with restriction enzymes, it was often possible to distinguish individuals by the different-sized DNA fragments that this process produced. Thus variations in the genome could be identified without the requirement for these variations to be reflected in the structure of proteins. The disadvantage of RFLPs is that they are by nature biallelic: the restriction enzyme will either cut the DNA or it will not. Currently microsatellite markers, a much more polymorphic and therefore informative type of marker, are being used to scan the human genome for disease-related alleles either by linkage or association studies.

The first DNA polymorphisms that have reliably been associated with complex genetic diseases are the variable number of tandem repeats (VNTR) 5' to the insulin gene on chromosome 11 that relate to insulin-dependent diabetes mellitus;[7,8] and a biallelic polymorphism in exon 4 of the apo C-III gene on chromosome 11, where the nucleotide C3175 is transverted to G.[9,10,11,12] Here, the rare allele is associated with dyslipidemia (raised plasma triglyceride and low high-density lipoprotein (HDL) cholesterol).[13,14,15,16] Common genetic variants of lipoprotein lipase that show relationships with dyslipidemia have also been identified.[17,18] Many other DNA polymorphic variants have subsequently been demonstrated to relate to a variety of other disorders including cancer, the dementias, venous thrombosis, and other metabolic diseases. Some of these, with their DNA markers, are listed in Table 3–1.

THE USE OF DNA POLYMORPHISMS AS DISEASE MARKERS

Genetic markers have impacted the study and treatment of complex genetic disease in a number of areas. The discovery of disease-related alleles as listed in Table 3–1 has improved our understanding of the pathogenesis of such disorders and the pathways involved in their development; how the apo E gene variants relate to the dyslipidemias is a good example.

From a clinical perspective, some DNA polymorphisms can be used as adjuncts to diagnosis in the same way that some HLA markers are used in the diagnosis of, for example, ankylosing spondylitis. Thus apo E4 has been proposed as an adjunct to diagnosis in subjects presenting with an early dementia with a provisional diagnosis of Alzheimer's disease. DNA variants can also be used in determining the prognosis of disease. For example, there are more than 230 mutations described for the low-density lipoprotein (LDL) receptor,[19] and the site of these mutations can have very different effects on the phenotype, familial hypercholesterolemia. Thus point mutations in exon 16 or 17 coding for the transmembrane portion of the molecule can have serious

Table 3–1 ✧ Some Genetic Markers for Diagnosis, Prognosis, or Prediction of Multifactorial Disease

Disease	Frequency*	Genetic Markers
METABOLIC		
Type I Diabetes Mellitus	1:500	HLA-DRE^3/$_4$; INS.vntr
Type II Diabetes Mellitus	1%–7%	INS-R; GLU-t; GK; HNF1a; HNF4a
Hypertriglyceridemia	5%–10%	AI-CIII-AIV cluster; LPL
Hypercholesterolemia	1%–5%	LDL-R; apo B; MTP (-493T)
CANCER		
Breast	25,000 per annum	BRCA1; BRCA2; Her2/neu
Colorectal (HNPC)	20,000 deaths per annum	PMS1; PMS2; MLH1; MLH2
NEUROLOGY		
Late-onset Alzheimer's disease	10% of over-65's	Apo E4; APP; S1; S2
Narcolepsy	1:2000	HLA-DR2
Schizophrenia	1:100	Dopamine D2; telomeric X-chromosome
CARDIOVASCULAR		
Premature CHD	1:5 male adults	Apo E and others
Venous thromboembolism	0.1–1%	Factor V Ledien, Prothrombin (G20210A)
Hypertension	15%–20%	ACE; antiotensinogen; renin
RHEUMATOLOGY		
Ankylosing spondylitis	0.5%	HLA-B27

Abbreviations: INS=insulin gene; vntr=variable number tandem repeats; INS-R=insulin receptor; GLU-t=glucose transporter; GK=glucokinase; HNF=hepatic nuclear transcription factor; LDL-R=low-density lipoprotein receptor; MTP=Microsomal triglyceride transfer protein; apoE=apolipoprotein E; ACE=angiotensin-converting enzyme; BRCA=breast cancer gene; p53=tumor-suppressor gene; APP=amyloid precursor protein; LPL=lipoprotein lipase; AI-CIII-AIV=apolipoprotein AI-CIII-AIV complex; PMS1/2 and MLH1=mismatch repair genes; S1/2=presenilin genes; K-ras=an oncogene.

*Frequency refers to either incidence, prevalence, or frequency depending on population studied.

effects on LDL clearance from plasma because the receptor comes adrift from the cell membrane, leading to a severe monogenic form of familial hypercholesterolemia. Other mutations in exons 7–14, for example, that only affect the region of epidermal growth factor homology of the molecule may minimally affect ligand binding of LDL. This leads to a much less severe disease phenotype[20] or even one that requires other genetic variants (e.g., at the apo E locus) for overt hypercholesterolemia to develop as a polygenic disorder (see also chapter 34).

Another use for the identification of the mutations as listed in Table 3–1 is to reveal new therapeutic targets. For example, the discovery that familial hypercholesterolemia is due to mutations of the LDL-receptor has led to the development of a new class of drugs, the statins, to increase the number of defective cell-surface LDL-receptors in patients with heterozygous familial hypercholesterolemia, thereby improving LDL clearance from the bloodstream. This class of drugs has been used successfully to treat familial hypercholesterolemia and can reduce the incidence of long-term complications of coronary atherosclerosis[21,22] (for additional information, refer to chapter 5). Additionally, it may also be possible in the future to stratify patients with a given disorder by their particular genotype and so predict whether they will respond to a pharmacological agent. This will obviate the need for placing patients on long-term drug therapy when it can be predicted from their genotype analysis that they will not respond.

SCREENING THE BLASTOCYST

More controversially, the mutations listed in Table 3–1 could also be used to screen pre-implantation embryos, and if any are found, the embryo could be discarded and another zygote used in its place. The feasibility of pre-implantation genetic diagnosis was first established in the 1980s as a result of pressure from married couples who were at risk of transmitting an X-linked disorder and who had moral objections to abortion. Polymerase chain reaction (PCR) amplification of DNA isolated from one or two cells removed from an 8-to 10-celled embryo after *in vitro* fertilization now permits pre-implantation diagnosis of cystic fibrosis, Tay-Sachs disease, Duchenne muscular dystrophy, and mutations of the APC gene for familial adenomatous polyposis coli.[23,24]

Worldwide, more than 100 babies have been born after pre-implantation genetic diagnosis, with no reported increase in congenital anomalies. The main advantage of pre-implantation diagnosis is that it obviates the need for selective abortion; the main disadvantage is that it requires *in vitro* fertilization, which currently has a success rate of only about 1:5.

The United Kingdom Human Fertilization and Embryology Authority (HFEA) is currently licensing several hospitals to perform such diagnoses for monogenic disease of pre-implantation embryos; of course the ethics of extending such techniques to screen for polygenic disorders to create "designer babies" for healthy married couples must now be critically assessed. It is natural that parents would want, and have the right, to choose the best possible health for their children; pre-implantation screening may be one way of ensuring "optimal" gene transfer to their offspring. One group of advisors on the Ethical Implications of Biotechnology of the European Commission recommended prenatal diagnosis (of which pre-implantation diagnosis is a special case) and stated that "it should always be considered a medical act and be offered on the basis of specific medical indications. The choice of sex or other characteristics for non-medical reasons is an ethically unacceptable indication for pre-natal diagnosis and should be prohibited."

All the conditions listed in Table 3–1 fall into the category of medical conditions and therefore are potential candidates for detection. The technique falls within the original definition of eugenics by F Galton (1822–1911) and is potentially open to all the abuses that characterized this field in the early 20th century. Covertly, it signifies a negative value statement about other members of society who possess the trait that is being screened and rejected for implantation. That is not to say that the use of the technique should be banned, only that extreme care should be taken in its implementation.

CLINICAL PROBLEMS

The basic problem in disease prediction involves distinguishing between legitimate and illegitimate uses of genetic markers to identify—and discriminate against—individuals in the areas of disease control (from conception to adult life), employment, career promotion, and life and health insurance.

Risk Prediction

The use of DNA markers for predicting risks of polygenic disease is always going to suffer from limitations, probably until the entire genome has been mapped and its function ascertained. However, some combinations of genetic markers may be of use for diagnosis or risk prediction of multifactorial disease. But uncertainty will arise from the nature of polygenic disease that (1) involves environmental interactions for expression and (2) involves gene-gene interactions, and can require the assessment of protective genotypes acting against the appearance of the disease phenotype.

Environmental Interactions

The genetic variants underlying multifactorial conditions are not the sole determinants of the disease. For the dyslipidemias, Type II diabetes, or premature atherosclerosis, environmental factors such as food intake, food composition, physical exercise, and obesity may all be involved before the disease fully manifests. For example, the genotype underlying the inherited basis of non-insulin-dependent diabetes mellitus (Type II diabetes mellitus) often requires caloric excess and obesity for the disease to manifest, and when the patient returns to normal body mass index, the disorder of abnormal blood sugars can resolve. Some genetic variants of apo C-III only manifest as a dyslipidemia when the patient consumes excess amounts of alcohol, and when alcohol is restricted the dyslipidemia resolves.[25] The effects of a high cholesterol diet on serum cholesterol levels are influenced by genetic factors, such as apo B and E genotypes.[26] Therefore, risk prediction on the basis of genetics alone is incomplete until the extent and impact of the exposure to environmental factors have been assessed.

Gene-Gene Interactions

The fact that two or more genetic variants are required for expression of the disease phenotype implies that there could be gene-gene interactions. With current methodology these are difficult to demonstrate, but this situation has been observed occasionally: a common genetic variant of the apo A-II gene, detectable as a restriction-fragment-length polymorphism using the enzyme *Msp* I, appears to be associated with higher plasma triglyceride levels when co-inherited with an uncommon variant of the apo A-I–C-III–A-IV gene cluster.[27]

Other good examples of genetic interactions include the observation that some genetic variants appear to protect against the development of the disease. A common mutation in the lipoprotein lipase gene, occurring at a frequency of about 10%–15% in the healthy population, involves a C to G transversion at the codon for serine 447. This mutation converts the serine 447 codon to a stop codon and thereby truncates the protein by two amino acids at the carboxy terminal end.[28] This might be expected to impair the enzyme's function of plasma triglyceride clearance, but several research groups have shown the opposite. Although the kinetic constants (Km and Vmax) of the mutant enzyme appear no different from wild-type, there is greater release of the mutant enzyme from the vascular endothelium compared to the wild-type enzyme. This may account for its enhanced activity *in vivo*. Alternatively, the mutation may affect dimerization of the enzyme for full catalytic activity. The mutation is found more frequently in healthy controls than in subjects with dyslipidaemia[29] or premature coronary atherosclerosis.[30] Therefore this variant appears to be protective for the development of dyslipidemia and coronary artery disease.

Protective mutations have been described in other complex genetic diseases: some HLA variants such as HLA DR 2/DQB1*0602 appear to have a stronger protective role against the development of insulin-dependent diabetes (Type I diabetes mellitus) than the susceptibility genotypes of HLA DR ¾.[31]

Before accurate risk prediction can be achieved in any individual, all the susceptibility and protective genotypes will have to be mapped. This may require an extensive genome search. With the development of the new oligonucleotide array (DNA chip) technology this may become feasible within the next decade, but it is certainly not possible to perform now.

Life & Health Insurance and Genetic Discrimination

The insurance industry has already laid out guidelines for the declaration of genetic tests before the purchase of life insurance, disability income insurance, and critical illness insurance. In the United Kingdom, the purchase of life insurance up to a total of £100,000 (approximately $170,000) that is directly linked to a new mortgage for a private dwelling requires reporting the results of any genetic tests, but these results may not be taken into account by the insurance company.[32] It is implied that for sums greater than £100,000 (approximately $170,000) such genetic tests will be taken into account and the premiums adjusted accordingly.

Most insurance companies work on the basis of equity, insisting that the premium paid must truly reflect the risks of disability of the individual, otherwise people at high risk will purchase a higher-claim policy and will financially profit from premiums paid by lower-risk individuals. Other possible modes of operating are on the basis of either equality, where the inherited risks of disease are not taken into account since the individual should not be held responsible or penalized for the genetic endowment he receives arbitrarily from his parents; or even on the basis of solidarity, where the premiums are reduced for individuals carrying genetic risks for the development of chronic disease and their financial claims are paid out of the premiums of the more fortunate healthy members of society. Both models of equality or solidarity, although appealing to notions of social justice, are unacceptable to the insurance industry, which is in the business of predicting risks to health or life.[33]

Risk discrimination by the insurance industry may become genetic discrimination, especially as new genetic tests for chronic illness appear on the market; and this may profoundly affect the purchase of long-term-care insurance or critical illness cover for individuals found to be genetically susceptible to chronic disease. A somewhat analogous situation is that of Type I diabetics who may find it difficult to obtain travel insurance. Currently a moratorium on genetic testing, effective for two years, has been requested by the United Kingdom Human Genetics Advisory Commission to prevent the disclosure of existing genetic tests to insurance companies until more information is available on the actuarial relevance of such tests. The European Council at Strasbourg, in Article 11 of the document on Human Rights and Biomedicine (1997), stated, "Any form of discrimination against a person on the grounds of his or her genetic heritage is prohibited."[34] Clearly the claims for actuarial fairness by the insurance industry versus the claims for social justice by the European Council will require new forms of legislation to address this problem.

Employment Rights and Genetic Discrimination

Illustrations of the problems involved in distinguishing between the legitimate and illegitimate use of genetic markers have been highlighted by recent experiences in the USA.

At least six American corporations screen employees for sensitivity to toxic substances that they may encounter during their work and deny employment to such allergic individuals. This would appear to be a reasonable policy, but this kind of discrimination has been extended to genetic screening with the result that denial of employment to individuals who carry a single mutant allele for sickle cell anemia has already occurred in the United States, even though these individuals are clinically unaffected.[35] The problem arose out of the demand for sickle cell screening for African Americans of marriageable age. If both partners were discovered to carry the sickle cell trait, they were counseled with regard to their future family. Sickle cell screening laws were enacted in 17 states, often under the sponsorship of African American legislators. In 1972, Congress passed the National Sickle Cell Anemia Control Act, which provided for research, screening, counseling and education. The preamble to this legislation erroneously stated that two million Americans suffered from sickle cell disease. In fact two million were carriers of the harmless sickle cell trait, and fewer than 100,000 had the disease. However, the American Air Force Academy, acting on this erroneous statement, restricted the entry of heterozygous subjects to its Academy; commercial airlines restricted sickle cell carriers to ground employment only, and African Americans found their career promotion to high-quality jobs blocked. The airlines justified this based on the fear that sickling of red cells in heterozygotes would occur at high altitudes (under minor degrees of oxygen deficiency) although there was no clinical evidence for this. Spokespersons for the African American community in the United States indicted the compulsory sickle-cell screening program as a form of racial discrimination and eventually the law was repealed.[36]

The sickle cell screening program began with good intentions (reducing the birth rate of babies with sickle cell disease), but due to misapplication became a means of genetic discrimination.

Employers should have the right to information about the genetic defects of prospective employees, if these defects pose a risk to the lives of others. Mutations of the LDL-receptor, for example, can predispose an individual to early myocardial infarction, and clearly such individuals should not be employed as airline pilots, sailors, or drivers. Similar considerations could apply to the genetic defects of the rhodopsin gene, which leads to some forms of night blindness. The array of new genetic tests that are becoming available will require new legislation to balance employment rights for at-risk individuals with the possible hazards that they may create for themselves or others in the workplace.

THE FUTURE

What applications might be expected for new genetic markers in the future; and what safeguards should be put in place to prevent future gross misapplications?

One can expect the availability of a large array of susceptibility and protective genes to be identified within the next two decades, which will enable clinical scientists to partly predict the risks of developing common disorders such as premature atherosclerosis, hypertension, diabetes mellitus, and Alzheimer's dementia. A good start in this direction has already been made (Table 3–1). Such markers can be used for either direct or indirect eugenic purposes. A direct eugenic method that includes the screening of genetic markers for polygenic disorders in pre-implantation embryos and discarding the ones that possess a large number of disease-related alleles is already in practice—diagnosing monogenic disorders in several infertility clinics throughout the United Kingdom. Such practices could become much more widespread among healthy married couples, especially if any genetic disease was present in their families. It is possible but doubtful whether selective abortion of implanted embryos following ante-natal screening would ever be an acceptable practice (as is done currently for some homozygous monogenic disorders) since the methods for risk prediction of these polygenic disorders are too uncertain at present.

Discrimination against certain people may inadvertently arise from the use of genetic markers for disease prediction by creating a genetic "underclass" and making it more difficult for affected individuals to obtain mortgages, life insurance products, employment, or job promotions. In turn, such social factors may influence an individual's reproductive choice and size of family.

Clearly, a regulatory framework must be derived from reasoned ethical values and must provide guidance for using the new genetic advancements and taking into account the following factors: respect for individual autonomy and privacy; personal reproductive choices uninfluenced by exterior pressures related to genetic discrimination; rights to as normal a family life as possible; and protection of the rights of other family members and members of the rest of society and their safeguard from harm.

Currently there is a multitude of regulatory bodies (however, without statutory powers) including local ethical committees in hospitals, national funding bodies such as the United Kingdom Medical Research Council or Wellcome Trust, various advisory bodies (such as the Human Genetics Advisory Commission, the Advisory Committee on Genetic Modification, the UK Xenotransplantation Interim Regulatory Authority, the United Kingdom Human Fertilization and Embryology Authority, and the European Medicines Evaluation Agency) and the Convention of Human Rights and Biomedicine of the Council of Europe. The difficulty, of course, is finding the correct balance between individual personal freedom and legitimate interference by the various government agencies. Even the most private and intimate of personal actions can legitimately be the subject of state interference if other members of society could be put at risk (e.g., the intention to make it a criminal offense if a man, knowing that he is suffering from AIDS, has sexual intercourse with a woman).

The new laws relating to genetic advances should be made primarily for the benefit of the community. It is the duty of the legislators that no injustice be done, even to only one individual. The legal framework must be equitable and refrain from transgressing the common rights of citizens; it should be flexible as new developments occur and be able to accommodate every particular foreseeable case as new discoveries are made. But legal responses are not easy to formulate in such a rapidly changing field. Indeed, it may be better to react to new situations as precedents, rather than to attempt proactive legislation. ✧

Acknowledgments: *This work was supported by Grant PL 931211 of the Commission of the European Communities (to DJG and AK). With the editors' permission some of this chapter has been emended from material appearing in the Quarterly Journal of Medicine in 1999, volume 92 pages 223–232.*

REFERENCES

1. Dammerman M, Breslow JL. Genetic basis of lipoprotein disorders. Circulation 1995;91:505–12 .
2. Breslow JL. Apolipoprotein genes and atherosclerosis. J Clin Invest 1992;70:377–84.
3. Aird JM, Bentall HH, Roberts JAF. A relationship between cancer of the stomach and the ABO blood groups. Brit Med J 1953; I:799–801.
4. McDevitt HO, Bodmer WF. HLA immune response genes and disease. Lancet 1974;I:1269–75.
5. Mahley RW, Innerarity TL, Rall SC Jr., Weisgraber KH. Lipoproteins of special signifi-

cance in atherosclerosis. Insights provided by studies of type III hyperlipoproteinemia. Ann N Y Acad Sci 1985;454:209–21.

6. Schneider WJ, Kovanen PT, Brown MS, et al. Familial dysbetalipoproteinemia. Abnormal binding of mutant apoprotein E to low-density lipoprotein receptors of human fibroblasts and membranes from liver and adrenal of rats, rabbits, and cows. J Clin Invest 1981;68:1075–85.

7. Hitman GA, Tarn AC, Winter RM, et al. Type 1 (insulin-dependent) diabetes and a highly variable locus close to the insulin gene on chromosome 11. Diabetologia 1985;28:218–22.

8. Raffel LJ, Hitman GA, Toyoda H, Karam JH, Bell GI, Rotter JI. The aggregation of the 5′ insulin gene polymorphism in insulin-dependent (type I) diabetes mellitus families. J Med Genet 1992;29:447–50.

9. Rees A, Shoulders CC, Stocks J, Galton DJ, Baralle FE. DNA polymorphism adjacent to human apoprotein A-1 gene: relation to hypertriglyceridaemia. *Lancet* 1983;1(8322): 444–6.

10. Rees A, Stocks J, Williams LG, et al. DNA polymorphisms in the apolipoprotein C-III and insulin genes and atherosclerosis. Atherosclerosis 1985;58:269–75.

11. Ferns GAA, Stocks J, Ritchie C, Galton DJ. DNA polymorphisms of the genes for apoprotein CIII and insulin in survivors of myocardial infarction. Lancet 1985;ii:300–1.

12. Ferns GAA, Galton DJ. Haplotypes of the human apoprotein A1/C111/AIV gene cluster in coronary atherosclerosis. Hum Genet 1986;73:245–9.

13. Humphries SE, Talmud PJ. Apolipoprotein C111 gene variation and dyslipidaemia. Current Opinion Lipidology 1997;8:154–8.

14. Hayden Mr, Kirk H, Clark C, et al. DNA polymorphisms in and around the Apo-A1-CIII genes and genetic hyperlipidemias. Am J Hum Genet 1987;40:421–30.

15. Dammerman M, Sandkuijl La, Halaas JL, Chung W, Breslow JL. An apolipoprotein CIII haplotype protective against hypertriglyceridemia is specified by promoter and 3′ untranslated region polymorphisms. Proc Natl Acad Sci USA 1993;90:4562–6.

16. Zeng Q, Dammerman M, Takada Y, Matsunaga A, Breslow JL, Sasaki J. An apolipoprotein CIII marker associated with hypertriglyceridemia in Caucasians also confers increased risk in a west Japanese population. Hum Genet 1995;95:371–5.

17. Mailly F, Fisher RM, Nicaud V, et.al. Association between the LPL-D9N mutation in the lipoprotein lipase gene and plasma lipid traits in myocardial infarction survivors from the ECTIM study. Atherosclerosis 1996;22:21–8.

18. Fisher RM, Humphries SE, Talmud PJ. Common variation in the lipoprotein lipase gene: effects on plasma lipids and risk of atherosclerosis. Atherosclerosis 1997;135: 145–159.

19. Hobbs HH, Russell DW, Brown MS, Goldstein JL. The LDL receptor locus in familial hypercholesterolemia: mutational analysis of a membrane protein. Ann Rev Genet 1990;24:133–70.

20. Russell DW, Lehrman MA, Sudhof TC et al. The LDL receptor in familial hypercholesterolemia: use of human mutations to dissect a membrane protein. Cold Spring Harb Symp Quant Biol 1986;51Pt2:811–9.

21. Havel RJ. Analysis of angiographic trial data in women. Drugs 1994;47S2:11–5.

22. Betteridge DJ, Durrington PN, Fairhurst GJ, et al. Comparison of lipid-lowering effects of low-dose fluvastatin and conventional-dose gemfibrozil in patients with primary hypercholesterolemia. Am J Med 1994;96:45S–54S.

23. WDelhanty JDA, Handyside AH, Winston RML. Preimplantation diagnosis. Lancet 1994;343:1569–70.

24. Schulman JD, Edwards RG. Preimplantation diagnosis in disease control, not eugenics. Hum Reprod 1996;11:463–4.

25. Stocks J, Holdsworth G, Galton D. Hypertriglyceridaemia associated with an abnormal triglyceride-rich lipoprotein carrying excess apolipoprotein C-III-2. Lancet 1979;2 (8144):667–71.

26. Gylling H, Kontula K, Koivisto UM, Miettinen HE, Miettinen TA. Influence of apoprotein

E and B gene polymorphisms on LDL levels during increased cholesterol intake. Arterioscl Thromb Vasc Biol 1977;17:38–44.

27. Ferns GAA, Shelley CS, Stocks J, Rees A, Baralle F, Galton DJ. A DNA polymorphism of the apoprotein AII gene in hypertriglyceridaemia. Hum Genet 1986;74:302–306.

28. Stocks J, Thorn JA, Galton DJ. Lipoprotein lipase genotypes for a common premature termination codon mutation detected by PCR-mediated site-directed mutagenesis and restriction digestion. J Lipid Res 1992;33:853–7.

29. Mattu RK, Needham EW, Morgan R et al. DNA variants at the LPL gene locus associate with angiographically defined severity of atherosclerosis and serum lipoprotein levels in a Welsh population. Arterioscler Thromb 1994;14:1090–7.

30. Zhang Q, Cavanna J, Winkelman BR et al. Common genetic variants of lipoprotein lipase that relate to lipid transport in patients with premature coronary artery disease. Clin Genet 1995;48:293–8.

31. Todd JA. Genetic analysis of type I diabetes using whole genome approaches. Proc Nat Acad Sci (USA) 1995;92:8560–5.

32. Genetic Tests. Association of British Insurers document L.627. Dec 1997.

33. Pokorski RJ. Insurance underwriting in the genetic era. Am J Hum Genet 1997;60: 205–16.

34. Convention on human rights and biomedicine. Council of Europe. European Treaty Series 164, Oviedo 1997.

35. Kevles DJ. In the name of eugenics. Boston, MA (USA): Harvard University Press, 1995.

36. Duster T. Backdoor to Eugenics. New York: ST (USA): Keegan Paul, 1991.

Beyond Cholesterol: C-Reactive Protein and Homocysteine as Predictors of Cardiovascular Risk

Paul M. Ridker

✧　　Hyperlipidemia represents a fundamental risk factor for coronary heart disease (CHD), and large-scale randomized trials of lipid reduction demonstrate that lowering cholesterol can reduce coronary risk.[1] However, nearly half of all myocardial infarctions occur in individuals whose records show no evidence of increased low-density-lipoprotein cholesterol (LDL-C). Thus, considerable pathophysiologic and clinical research has focused on the development of novel biomarkers for CHD risk including those that might enable clinicians to better detect patients prone to thrombosis.[2] As shown in Figure 4–1, plasma-based biomarkers that could predict vascular risk include

✧　　concentration markers [such as tissue type plasminogen activator (t-PA) antigen and total plasma homocysteine (tHcy) levels];

✧　　process markers [such as D-dimer or thrombin/anti-thrombin III complex (TAT complex)];

✧　　functional markers (such as activated protein C resistance and clot lysis time);

✧　　platelet markers (including aggregation, size, and volume); and

✧　　inflammatory markers [such as high-sensitivity C-reactive protein (hs-CRP), serum amyloid A (SAA), and interleukin-6 (IL-6)].

Faced with such a broad series of choices, clinicians must seek guidelines to determine if and when to measure a putative novel risk factor. In general, markers that have the greatest clinical utility will be those that

✧　　can easily and reproducibly be measured in simple outpatient clinic settings;

✧　　have been shown in a consistent series of prospective epidemiological studies to predict vascular risk in varied patient groups; and

✧　　significantly add to the ability to predict risk over and above screening for total cholesterol and high-density-lipoprotein cholesterol (HDL-C).[3]

Meeting these criteria has proven difficult for many potential biomarkers (Table 4–1). For example, despite a clear pathophysiologic role in atherothrombosis, screening for lipoprotein(a) [Lp(a)] is of limited utility—standardization of clinical assays is poor and substantial controversy remains concerning appropriate methods to deter-

Figure 4–1 ✧ Potential Biomarkers for the Detection of Arterial Thrombosis

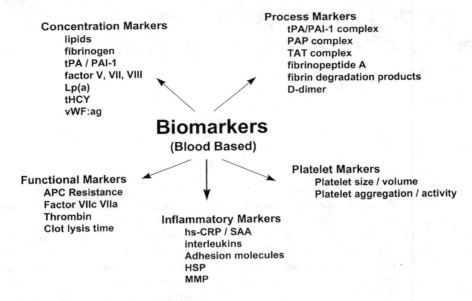

Concentration Markers
lipids
fibrinogen
tPA / PAI-1
factor V, VII, VIII
Lp(a)
tHCY
vWF:ag

Process Markers
tPA/PAI-1 complex
PAP complex
TAT complex
fibrinopeptide A
fibrin degradation products
D-dimer

Biomarkers
(Blood Based)

Functional Markers
APC Resistance
Factor VIIc VIIa
Thrombin
Clot lysis time

Inflammatory Markers
hs-CRP / SAA
interleukins
Adhesion molecules
HSP
MMP

Platelet Markers
Platelet size / volume
Platelet aggregation / activity

mine this unique plasma lipid fraction.[4] Other biomarkers such as those involved in the regulation of endogenous fibrinolysis including *t*-PA and plasminogen activator inhibitor (PAI-1) have been proven to consistently predict vascular risk in epidemiological studies, but have not been proven to have substantial clinical value when added to lipid screening.[5–8]

In this chapter, data describing the clinical utility of the two most promising "novel" plasma based biomarkers for CHD—tHcy and hs-CRP—are presented, as are general recommendations concerning how and when to employ these novel biomarkers.

TOTAL PLASMA HOMOCYSTEINE (THCY)

Homocysteine (Hcy) is a sulphur-containing amino acid derived from the breakdown of dietary methionine. Homozygous homocystinuria, a rare inherited deficiency of cystathione beta-synthase, is associated with markedly increased levels of Hcy and a predilection for premature atherosclerosis and venous thromboembolism.[9] Mechanisms hypothesized to link marked increases of Hcy (plasma concentration of free plus protein-bound forms > 150 µmol/L) to atherothrombotic risk include direct vascular toxicity, smooth muscle proliferation, augmented production of oxidized low-density lipoprotein (LDL), impairment of endothelial-derived relaxing factor, and reduced flow-mediated arterial reactivity.[10]

In contrast to homozygous homocystinuria, mild to moderate elevations of plasma tHcy (levels > 15 µmol/L) are common and present among 5% to 8% of apparently healthy individuals not currently taking folic acid.[11,12] While some cases of

Table 4–1 ✧ Assessment of the Clinical Utility of Novel Markers of Cardiovascular Risk

	Assay Conditions Standardized?	*Prospective Studies Consistent?*	*Additive to Total/HDL Cholesterol?*
Lp(a)	—	±	±
tHcy	+	±	±
t-PA/PAI-1	±	+	—
Fibrinogen	±	+	+
hs-CRP	+	+	+

t-PA = tissue type plasminogen activator antigen.
PAI-1 = plasminogen activator inhibitor.
Lp(a) = lipoprotein(a).
tHCY = total plasma homocysteine.
hs-CRP = high sensitivity C reactive protein.
Adapted from Ridker PM. Evaluating novel cardiovascular risk factors: Can we better predict heart attacks? Ann Intern Med 1999;130:933–7.

moderate hyperhomocysteinemia are related to mutation in the methylene-tetra-hydrofolate reductase (MTHFR) gene, the most common cause of increased tHcy is poor dietary intake of folate, a problem particularly relevant in elderly populations.[11] Recent data indicate that carriers of mutation in the MTHFR gene, while having increase tHcy levels, do not have increased vascular risk.[13]

Retrospective studies consistently demonstrate positive association between tHcy level and vascular disease such that those with levels above 15 µmol/L have adjusted relative risks approximately 40% higher than those with lower levels.[14] However, retrospective studies of this analyte may be confounded as tHcy levels increase following infarction and stroke.[15,16] Prospective studies in which plasma samples are obtained prior to the onset of disease avoid this potential error. As shown in Figure 4–2, recent prospective studies of tHcy as a vascular risk factor have been mixed, with both positive and null studies reported.

For example, in a study of more than 21,000 men followed for 8.7 years in the British United Provident Study, those who died of CHD (n = 229) had significantly higher baseline levels of tHcy compared to age-matched controls, such that the relative risk for those in the highest quartile at baseline was 2.9 (95% CI 2.0–4.1).[17] Similarly, in the Women's Health Study of nearly 40,000 postmenopausal women, those who subsequently developed cardiovascular events had higher baseline levels of tHcy, an observation that persisted in analyses stratified by those taking and not taking folate-containing supplements.[18] In both the Framingham Heart Study[19] and in a prospective follow-up of residents of Jerusalem[20] and Norway,[21] increases in risk (50%–70%) have been reported. A graded positive association between tHcy and subsequent risk has also been found among those referred for coronary angiography.[22]

By contrast, prospective data from the Multiple Risk Factor Intervention Trial (MRFIT),[23] the Atherosclerosis Risk in Communities (ARIC) Study,[24] and a large-scale

Figure 4–2 ◇ Prospective Studies of Total Plasma Homocysteine and the Risk of Coronary Heart Disease among Currently Healthy Men and Women

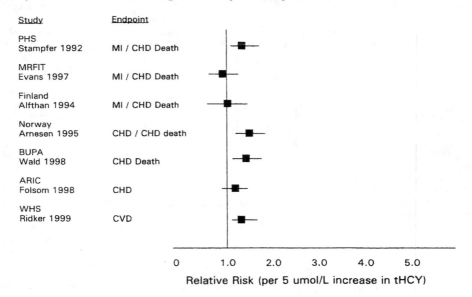

From Ridker PM. Novel risk factors and markers for coronary disease. In: Advances in Internal Medicine Vol 45 (Chapter 13). St. Louis, MO: Mosby, Inc. 2000.

prospective cohort from Finland[25] all failed to find significant differences between baseline levels of tHcy among those who subsequently developed CHD compared to those who did not. Similarly, in two recently reported prospective cohorts from the Netherlands,[26,27] only small risk increases with increased levels of tHcy were observed which, after adjustment for other risk factors, were no longer statistically significant. Adding to this apparent inconsistency, the Physicians' Health Study of 22,000 initially healthy middle-aged men has reported modest positive associations between tHcy and myocardial infarction on short-term follow-up,[28] but these effects were no longer present with longer-term observation[29] and were null for other vascular endpoints including peripheral arterial disease and stroke.[30]

Due to these inconsistent findings, recommendations for tHcy screening are uncertain. However, it is clear that folic acid supplementation in doses between 0.5 and 5.0 mg/day can substantially reduce tHcy levels, perhaps by as much as 25%.[31] Thus, some authorities have advocated folate supplementation as a method for vascular risk reduction. It is important to recognize, however, that no randomized clinical trials have yet demonstrated the efficacy of this approach. Moreover, neither the American Heart Association nor the American College of Cardiology currently advocates tHcy screening in the general population.[32] One reason is that the United States food supply was recently fortified with folic acid in order to reduce the incidence of peri-conceptual neural tube defects.[33] Fortification has already had an effect: mean tHcy concentrations in the United States have dropped nearly 10% and the number of individuals with very low levels of folate is now less than 1%.[31] Thus, even if available prospective studies were consistent, uncertainty would still exist as to whether additional supplementation is needed for cardiovascular risk reduction, or whether general population screening has clinical utility.

Screening for tHcy has been recommended for evaluating premature atherothrombosis. It has also been recommended for use in certain high-risk population subgroups, including those with renal failure and hypothyroidism, conditions that impair methionine metabolism.[32,34,35] For these subgroups, assessment of plasma tHcy, including evaluation of both disulfide Hcy and cysteine-Hcy, can be accomplished with high-pressure liquid chromatography (HPLC) or with recently released immunoassays.[36] Methionine loading has been advocated to uncover additional cases of hyperhomocysteinemia. However, the clinical relevance of this approach is uncertain and may not justify the additional effort needed.

HIGH-SENSITIVITY C-REACTIVE PROTEIN (HS-CRP)

Experimental data and clinical studies indicate that atherothrombosis, in addition to resulting from lipid accumulation, also fundamentally represents a chronic inflammatory process. As such, it is not surprising that biomarkers capable of detecting an enhanced state of inflammatory activity have proven to have predictive value in determining cardiovascular risk. For example, cytokines including IL-6[37,38] and tumor necrosis factor alpha (TNF-alpha)[39] have been shown to have predictive value in determining risk of both first and recurrent myocardial infarction. Further, IL-6 levels and interlukin-1 receptor antagonist appear to be increased among those with unstable angina at high risk for coronary occlusion.[40] Measurement of cytokine levels is unlikely to have clinical utility, however, as plasma half-lives of these molecules are short and there is wide day-to-day variability. In contrast, the downstream result of hepatic stimulation by IL-6 is production of C-reactive protein (CRP), a stable analyte that can easily be measured with newly developed high-sensitivity assays (hs-CRP).[41]

CRP derives its name from its ability to bind the C polysaccharide of *Streptococcus pneumoniae.*[42] Composed of five identical subunits, CRP is produced by the liver in response to a variety of inflammatory stimuli and may play a role in innate immunity. Because levels of CRP rise dramatically with infection or trauma, and because early assays could only detect it during such elevations, CRP first had a clinical role as an "acute phase reactant." With a half-life of approximately 19 h, CRP levels are stable over long periods of time in the absence of any acute inflammatory stimuli, and thus provide a measure of long-term enhanced inflammatory activity.[43,44] Production of CRP is largely controlled by a single gene and its promotor on chromosome 1, which in turn is activated primarily by IL-6, TNF-alpha, and glucocorticoids. Although CRP has been shown to bind avidly to monocytes, to have a role in activating the complement system, and to potentially increase activity of other pro-inflammatory cell lines,[45] its biologic functions remain elusive.

The introduction of high-sensitivity testing for CRP (hs-CRP) has enabled this analyte to be used not only as a marker of acute inflammation, but also to distinguish levels of low-grade inflammation within the normal range. The prognostic value of hs-CRP analysis was first suggested among patients with acute ischemia[46] and unstable angina.[47] Minor increases of hs-CRP predicted in-hospital clinical events over and above those associated with myocardial necrosis as determined by troponin levels. Since that time, clinical evaluations have demonstrated the predictive value of hs-CRP across the full spectrum of the acute coronary syndromes[48–51] as well as among those in the stable phase following myocardial infarction.[52]

In terms of vascular risk prediction, the most promising clinical role for hs-CRP is likely to be in the primary prevention setting, where its addition to lipid screening may improve our ability to determine future risk of myocardial infarction or stroke.[53–56] As shown in Figure 4–3, several large-scale prospective studies report that healthy men and women with increased baseline levels of hs-CRP are at significantly increased risks of future cardiovascular disease. Overall, those with levels in the upper quartile of hs-CRP tend to have risk three to four times higher than those with levels in the lowest baseline quartile.

In several of these studies, including both the Physicians Health Study[53] and the Women's Health Study,[54,55] these effects were independent of other vascular risk fac-

Figure 4–3 ✦ Prospective Studies of C-Reactive Protein and the Risk of Coronary Heart Disease among Currently Healthy Men and Women

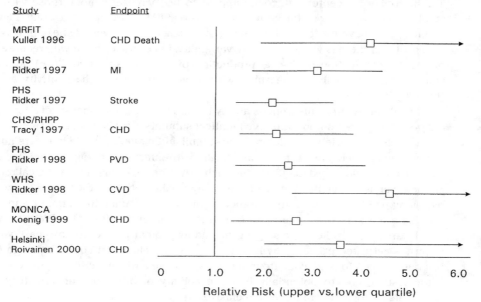

Prospective Studies of hs-CRP as a Risk Factor For Future Cardiovascular Disease in Populations Free of Clinical Disease

Adapted from Ridker PM and Haughie P. Prospective studies of C-reactive protein as a risk factor for cardiovascular disease. J Invest Med 1998;46:391–5.

tors including total cholesterol and HDL-C, older age, cigarette consumption, body mass index, and blood pressure. The consistency of these findings has been remarkable: strong positive associations between hs-CRP and future CHD risk have also been observed in populations of elderly patients enrolled in the Coronary Heart Study and the Rural Health Promotion Project;[57] in high-risk individuals in MRFIT defined by smoking pattern;[58] and in two independent European studies, the MONICA project[59] and the Helsinki Heart Study.[60] Vascular endpoints in most of these prospective studies have included myocardial infarction, stroke, and total CHD, although positive relationships between hs-CRP and peripheral vascular disease[61] and all-cause mortality [37] have also been demonstrated.

Beyond being a univariate predictor of risk, several studies indicate that measurement of hs-CRP may significantly add to the predictive value of total cholesterol and HDL-C screening.[54,56,59] In this regard, the effects of lipid screening and hs-CRP testing appear multiplicative, such that individuals with increases of both cholesterol and hs-CRP have far greater risks of future vascular disease compared to individuals with hyperlipidemia or hs-CRP increases alone.[56] Perhaps of greatest clinical relevance is the observation that hs-CRP screening predicts vascular risk even among individuals with low levels of LDL-C, a group traditionally considered "safe" by guidelines based upon National Cholesterol Education Program algorithms. As shown in Figure 4–4, which profiles postmenopausal women, hs-CRP appears to improve vascular risk prediction at all baseline levels of cholesterol.[55]

Unlike Hcy, there is no specific therapy currently available that reduces hs-CRP levels without interacting with other vascular risk markers. However, while hs-CRP levels are stable over long periods of time,[62] several preventive approaches appear to modulate the effect of inflammation on vascular risk. Both exercise and diet may reduce hs-CRP levels,[63,64] a finding consistent with population-based studies demonstrating increased concentrations of hs-CRP among obese individuals,[64] an effect that likely reflects enhanced IL-6 production from adipocytes.[65] Pharmacologic therapies commonly used to reduce vascular risk may also act through inflammatory targets. In the Physicians Health Study, the magnitude of risk reduction in first coronary events associated with aspirin use was greater among those with increased levels of hs-CRP than among those with lower levels, data that raise the possibility that the anti-inflammatory effects of aspirin may be important in vascular prevention.[53] Specifically, the attributable risk reduction due to aspirin use was nearly 60% among those with hs-CRP levels in the top quartile but was reduced substantially as levels of hs-CRP declined.[53] This observation is supported by a recent study suggesting that low-dose aspirin treatment can reduce levels of both IL-6 and hs-CRP.[66]

Hormone replacement therapy in postmenopausal women also appears to impact hs-CRP levels. In cross-sectional studies,[67,68] women taking estrogen alone or estrogen plus progesterone were found to have higher levels of hs-CRP compared to women not taking these agents, an effect that does not appear to be secondary to hepatic induction. Intervention studies have also reported significant increases in hs-CRP following initiation of hormone replacement therapy.[69] These data are provocative as results from the Heart and Estrogen/Progestin Replacement Study (HERS) trial have suggested that women beginning hormone replacement may experience an

Figure 4–4 ✧ Additive Value of C-Reactive Protein in the Assessment of Coronary Risk: The Women's Health Study

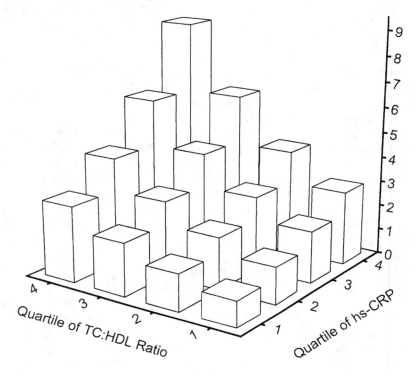

early thrombotic hazard.[70] By contrast, it is not clear whether topical estrogens or selective estrogen receptor modulators have similar effects.

Lipid lowering with hydroxymethylglutaryl Coenzyme A reductase inhibitors has also been reported to lower hs-CRP levels. In particular, in the Cholesterol and Recurrent Events (CvARE) trial of pravastatin, those randomly assigned to lipid reduction had a mean decrease of 40% in hs-CRP levels over a five-year follow-up period that was independent of any pravastatin induced changes in LDL-C.[62] In that trial, the magnitude of risk reduction attributable to pravastatin use was greater among those with increased levels of hs-CRP. Specifically, the association between hs-CRP and subsequent risk of recurrent coronary events was significant among those allocated to placebo therapy (relative risk = 2.1, p < 0.05) but was attenuated and non-significant among those allocated to pravastatin (relative risk = 1.29, p = 0.5).[62] These clinical data confirm experimental studies that indicate statin therapy's stabilizing effect on atherosclerotic plaque, at least in part through anti-inflammatory mechanisms.[71] In particular, animal models have demonstrated that statins reduce collagenase expression, increase collagen content, and reduce macrophage and monocyte accumulation within coronary and aortic atheroma.[72–74]

Table 4–2 ✧ Evaluation of Automated hs-CRP Methods for the Detection of Cardiovascular Risk

Assay	Lower Detection Limit* (mg/dL)	Imprecision (%)	Sensitivity (mg/dL)	FDA Approved**
Dade-Behring BN II	0.001	≤ 7.6	0.030	Yes
Abbott IMx	0.005	≤ 12.0	0.032	No
DPC IMMUNLITE	0.010	≤ 9.8	0.085	No
Beckman IMMAGE	0.1	≤ 9.7	0.226	No

*Zero Calibrator + 3 SD → standard deviation
**FDA approved for risk prediction of cardiovascular disease
Roberts et al., Clin Chem 2000

Adapted from Roberts WL, Sedrick R, Moulton L, Spencer A, Rifai N. Evaluation of four automated high-sensitivity C-reactive protein methods: implications for clinical and epidemiological applications. Clin Chem 2000 (in press).

Although clinical guidelines for hs-CRP testing have not been fully developed, the American Heart Association has considered hs-CRP testing to be a promising new method to improve coronary risk prediction.[75] It is important to recognize, however, that predictive value in large-scale population studies does not guarantee predictive value for individual patients, and thus more research is needed. Further, for clinical application to be successful, highly standardized and reproducible commercial assays for hs-CRP are required. One such assay, performed on an automated nephelometer (BN II system, Dade-Behring), has recently been cleared by the United States Food and Drug Administration for cardiovascular risk assessment largely on its ability to reliably reproduce hs-CRP levels based on previously validated in-house ELISA-based assays.[41] In addition, this high-throughput assay system has been shown to predict cardiovascular events with similar fidelity as compared to research-based assays used in several prior prospective studies.[41] Unfortunately, not all commercial tests for hs-CRP perform equally well. In a recent direct comparison, methods on IMx (Abbott laboratories), IMMULITE (Diagnostic Products Corporation), and IMMAGE (Beckman Coulter) systems demonstrated significantly lower precision than the BN II system. Furthermore, only the IMx assay had sensitivity, i.e., a low detection limit, similar to the BN II, a critical issue for cardiovascular risk prediction.[76] Characteristics of these assay systems are reviewed in Table 4–2.

Table 4–3 provides population-based quintile cutpoints for hs-CRP using the Dade-Behring assay, and a simple system for converting hs-CRP values to a clinical estimate of cardiovascular risk.

Table 4–3 ✧ Population Distribution of hs-CRP in Apparently Healthy American Men and Women

Quintile	Range (mg/dL)	Risk Estimate
1	0.01–0.069	Low
2	0.07–0.11	Mild
3	0.12–0.19	Moderate
4	0.20–0.38	High
5	0.39–1.50	Highest

DIRECT COMPARISONS OF THCY, HS-CRP, AND OTHER VASCULAR RISK FACTORS

To date, at least three prospective cohort studies have simultaneously evaluated baseline levels of both tHcy and hs-CRP, allowing for direct comparisons of these novel markers. In the MRFIT cohort of high-risk individuals, hs-CRP was a strong and statistically significant independent predictor of future vascular risk[58] whereas tHcy was not.[23] By contrast, in the Physicians Health Study of middle-aged men, both tHcy[28] and hs-CRP[53,61] were predictive of risk, although the magnitude of risk prediction associated with hs-CRP was far greater. Further, while both tHcy and hs-CRP had short-term predictive value, only hs-CRP was found to have long-term predictive value.[29]

Finally, prospective data evaluating a large series of lipid and non-lipid risk factors has recently been reported from the Women's Health Study.[55] In that analysis, of 12 putative markers of risk, hs-CRP was the single strongest univariate predictor of future cardiovascular events, with a relative risk for women in the fourth compared to the first quartile of 4.4 (95% confidence interval 2.2–8.9). Importantly, this magnitude of risk prediction was greater than that associated with any lipid parameter measured and substantially greater than that associated with tHcy (univariate relative risk = 2.0, 95% confidence interval = 1.1–3.0) (Figure 4–5). Moreover, in multivariate analysis, the predictive value of hs-CRP persisted and was largely additive to that associated with total cholesterol and HDL-C. In contrast, after adjustment for hs-CRP and lipid levels, there was no residual predictive value associated with increased tHcy levels.[55]

Taken together, these data suggest that general screening programs designed to improve vascular risk prediction may benefit from hs-CRP assessment in addition to standard lipid analysis. In contrast, broad-based evaluation of tHcy as an adjunct to lipid screening is unlikely to have clinical utility, although focused evaluation of tHcy in certain high-risk subgroups such as those with renal failure may be warranted. ✧

Figure 4–5 ✧ Relative Risks of Future Cardiovascular Events

Risk factors associated with baseline levels of: Lp(a) = lipoprotein(a); tHCY = total plasma homocysteine; IL-6 = interleukin-6; TC = total cholesterol; LDLC = LDL cholesterol; sICAM-1 = soluble intercellular adhesion molecule type 1; SAA = serum amyloid A; Apo B-100 = apolipoprotein B-100; TC:HDL = total to HDL cholesterol ratio; hs-CRP = high-sensitivity C-reactive protein.

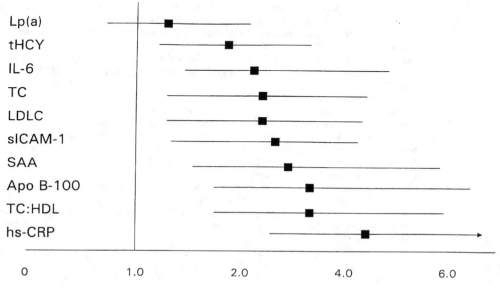

Relative Risk of Future Cardiovascular Events

Adapted from Ridker PM, Hennekens CH, Buring JE, Rifai N. Inflammatory and lipid predictors of cardiovascular disease in women. N Engl J Med 2000; 342:836–43. For consistency, risks are computed for women in the top versus bottom quartile for each marker.

REFERENCES

1. Knopp RH. Drug treatment of lipid disorders. N Engl J Med 1999;341:498–511.
2. Ridker PM. Fibrinolytic and inflammatory markers for arterial occlusion: the evolving epidemiology of thrombosis and hemostasis. Thromb Haemost 1997;78:53–9.
3. Ridker PM. Evaluating novel cardiovascular risk factors: can we better predict heart attacks? Ann Intern Med 1999;130:933–7.
4. Tate JR, Rifai N, Berg K, Couderc R, Dati F, Kostner GM, Sakurabayashi I, Steinmetz A. International Federation of Clinical Chemistry standardization project for the measurement of lipoprotein(a). Phase 1. Evaluation of the analytical performance of lipoprotein(a) assay systems and commercial calibrators. Clinical Chemistry 1998;44:1629–40.
5. Hamsten A, Walldius G, Szamosi A et al. Plasminogen-activator inhibitor in plasma: risk factor for recurrent myocardial infarction. Lancet 1987;2:3–9.
6. Ridker PM, Vaughan DE, Stampfer MJ, Manson JE, Hennekens CH. Endogenous tis-

sue–type plasminogen activator and risk of myocardial infarction. Lancet 1993;341: 1165–8.

7. Thogersen AM, Jansson JH, Boman K, Nilsson TK, Weinehall L, Huhtasaari F, Hallmans G. High-plasminogen-activator inhibitor and tissue plasminogen activator levels in plasma precede a first acute myocardial infarction in both men and women: evidence for the fibrinolytic system as an independent primary risk factor. Circulation 1998;98: 2241–7.

8. Ridker PM, Hennekens CH, Stampfer MJ, Manson JE, Vaughan DE. Prospective study of endogenous tissue plasminogen activator and risk of stroke. Lancet 1994;343:940–3.

9. McCully KS. Vascular pathology of homocysteinemia: implications for the pathogenesis of arteriosclerosis. Am J Pathol 1969;56:111–28.

10. Welch GN, Loscalzo J. Mechanisms of disease: homocysteine and atherothrombosis. N Engl J Med 1998;338:1042–50.

11. Selhub J, Jacques PE, Wilson PW, Rush D, Rosenberg IH. Vitamin status and intake as primary determinants of homocysteinemia in an elderly population. JAMA 1993;270: 2693–8.

12. Rimm EB, Willett WC, Hu FB, Sampson L, Colditz GA, Manson JE, Hennekens C, Stampfer MJ. Folate and vitamin B6 from diet and supplements in relation to risk of coronary heart disease among women. JAMA 1998;279:359–64.

13. Brattstrom L, Wilcken DEL, Ohrvik J, Brudin L. Common methylenetetrahydrofolate reductase gene mutation leads to hyperhomocysteinemia but not to vascular disease. The result of a meta–analysis. Circulation 1998;98:2520–6.

14. Boushey CJ, Beresford SAA, Omenn GS, Motulsky AG. A quantitative assessment of plasma homocysteine as a risk factor for vascular disease: probable benefits of increasing folic acid intakes. JAMA 1995;274:1049–57.

15. Lindgren A, Brattstrom L, Norrving B, Hultberg B, Anderson A, Johansson BB. Plasma homocysteine in the acute and convalescent phases after stroke. Stroke 1995;26: 795–800.

16. Egerton W, Silberberg J, Crooks R, Ray C, Dudman N. Serial measures of plasma homocysteine after acute myocardial infarction. Am J Cardiol 1996;77:759–61.

17. Wald NJ, Watt HC, Law MR, Weir DG, McPartlin J, Scott JM. Homocysteine and ischemic heart disease—results of a prospective study with implications regarding prevention. Arch Intern Med 1998;158:862–7.

18. Ridker PM, Manson JE, Buring JE, Shih J, Matias M, Hennekens CH. Homocysteine and risk of cardiovascualr disease among postmenopausal women. JAMA 1999;281: 1817–21.

19. Bostom AG, Silbershatz H, Rosenberg IH, Selhub J, D'Agostino RB, Wolf PA, Jacques PF, Wilson PWF. Non-fasting plasma total homocysteine levels and all-cause and cardiovascular disease mortality in elderly Framingham men and women. Arch Intern Med 1999;159:1077–80.

20. Kark JD, Selhub J, Adler B, et al. Non-fasting plasma homocysteine level and mortality in middle-aged and elderly men and women in Jeruselem. Ann Int Med 1999;131: 321–30.

21. Arnesen E, Refsum H, Bonaa KH, Ueland PM, Forde OH, Nordrehaug JE. Serum total homocysteine and coronary heart disease. Int J Epidemiol 1995;24:704–9.

22. Nygard O, Nordrehaug JE, Refsum H, Ueland PM, Farstad M, Vollset E. Plasma homocysteine levels and mortality in patients with coronary artery disease. N Engl J Med 1997;337:230–6.

23. Evans RW, Shaten J, Hempel JD, Cutler JA, Kuller LH. Homocysteine and risk of cardiovascular disease in the Multiple Risk Factor Intervention Trial. Arterioscler Thromb Vasc Biol 1997;17:1947–53.

24. Folsom AR, Nieto FJ, McGovern PG, Tsai MY, Malinow MR, Eckfeldt JH, Hess DL, David CE. Prospective study of coronary heart disease incidence in relation to fasting total homocysteine, related genetic polymorphisms, and B vitamins. Circulation 1998;98: 204–10.

25. Alfthan G, Pekkanen J, Juahianen M, Pitkaniemi J, Karvonen M, Tuomilehto J, Salonen JT, Ehnholm C. Relation of serum homocysteine and lipoprotein(a) concentrations to atherosclerotic disease in a prospective Finnish population-based study. Atherosclerosis 1994;106:9–19.

26. Stehouwer CD, Weijenberg MP, van den Berg M et al. Serum homocysteine and risk of coronary heart disease and cerebrovascular disease in elderly men: a 10-year follow-up. Arterioscler Thromb Vasc Biol 1998;18:1895–901.

27. Bots ML, Launer LJ, Lindemans J, et al. Homocysteine and short-term risk of myocardial infarction and stroke in the elderly: the Rotterdam Study. Arch Intern Med 1999;159:38–44.

28. Stampfer MJ, Malinow MR, Willett WC, Newcomer LM, Upson B, Ullmann D, Tishler PV, Hennekens CH. A prospective study of plasma homocyst(e)ine and risk of myocardial infarction in U.S. physicians. JAMA 1992;268:877–81.

29. Chasen-Taber L, Selhub J, Rosenberg IH et al. A prospective study of folate and vitamin B6 and risk of myocardial infarction in US physicians. J Am Coll Nutr 1996;15:136–43.

30. Verhoef P, Hennekens CH, Allen RH, et al. Plasma total homocysteine and risk of angina pectoris with subsequent coronary artery bypass surgery. Am J Cardiol 1997;79:799–801.

31. Jacques PF, Selhub J, Bostom AG, Wilson PWF, Rosenberg IH. The effect of folic acid fortification on plasma folate and total homocysteine concentrations. N Engl J Med 1999;340:1449–554.

32. Malinow MR, Bostom AG, Krauss RM. Homocysteine, diet, and cardiovascular diseases. A statement for healthcare professionals from the Nutrition Committee, American Heart Association. ACC/AHA Scientific Advisory January 5/12, 1999;178–82.

33. Werler MM, Shapiro S, Mitchell AA. Peri-conceptional folic acid exposure and risk of occurrent neural tube defects. JAMA 1993;269:1257–61.

34. Bostom AG, Lathrop L. Hyperhomocysteinemia in end-stage renal disease: prevalence, etiology, and potential relationship to arteriosclerotic outcomes. Kidney Int 1997;52:10–20.

35. Nedrebo BG, Ericsson UB, Nygard O, Refsum H, Ueland PM, Aakvaag A, Aanderud S, Lien EA. Plasma total homocysteine levels in hypothyroid and hyperthyroid patients. Metabolism 1998;47:89–93.

36. Shipchandler MT, Moore EG. Rapid, fully automated measurement of plasma homocyst(e)ine with the Abbott Imx analyzer. Clin Chem 1995;41:991–5.

37. Harris TB, Ferrucci L, Tracy RP et al. Associations of elevated interleukin–6 and C–reactive protein levels with mortality in the elderly. Am J Med 1999;106:506–12.

38. Ridker PM, Rifai N, Stampfer MJ, Hennekens CH. Plasma concentration of interleukin–6 and the risk of future myocardial infarction among apparently healthy men. Circulation 2000 (in press).

39. Ridker PM, Rifai N, Pfeffer M, Sacks F, Lepage S, Braunwald E, for the Cholesterol and Recurrent Events (CARE) Investigators. Elevation of tumor necrosis factor-alpha and increased risk of recurrent coronary events following myocardial infarction. Circulation 2000 (in press).

40. Biasucci LM, Liuzzo G, Fantuzzi G et al. Increasing levels of interleukin (IL)–1Ra and IL–6 during the first two days of hospitalization in unstable angina are associated with increased risk of in-hospital coronary events. Circulation 1999;99:2079–84.

41. Rifai N, Tracy RP, Ridker PM. Clinical efficacy of an automated high-sensitivity C–reactive protein assay. Clin Chem 1999;45:2136–41.

42. Tillot WS, Francis T. Serological reactions in pneumonia with a non-protein somatic fraction of pneumococcus. J Exp Med 1930;52:561–71.

43. Pepys MG. The acute phase response and C-reactive protein. In: Weatherall DJ, Ledingham JGG, Warrell DA (eds.). Oxford Textbook of Medicine, 3rd ed. Oxford, England: Oxford University Press;1995:1527–33.

44. Young B, Gleeson M, Cripps A. C-reactive protein: a critical review. Pathology 1991;23:118–24.

45. Lagrand WK, Visser CA, Hermens WT, Niessen HWM, Verheugt FWA, Wolbink G-J, Hack CE. C-reactive protein as a cardiovascular risk factor: more than an epiphenomenon? Circulation 1999;100:96–102.

46. Liuzzo G, Biasucci LM, Gallimore JR et al. The prognostic value of C-reactive protein and serum amyloid A protein in severe unstable angina. N Engl J Med 1994;331: 417–24.

47. Haverkate F, Thompson SG, Pyke SDM, Gallimore JR, Pepys MB. Production of C-reactive protein and risk of coronary events in stable and unstable angina. Lancet 1997;349:462–6.

48. Morrow D, Rifai N, Antman E, et al. C-reactive protein is a potent predictor of mortality independently and in combination with troponin T in acute coronary syndromes. J Am Coll Cardiol 1998;31:1460–5.

49. Toss H, Lindahl B, Siegbahn A, Wallentin L for the FRISC Study Group. Prognostic influence of fibrinogen and C-reactive protein levels in unstable coronary artery disease. Circulation 1997;96:4204–10.

50. Liuzzo G, Buffon A, Biasucci LM et al. Enhanced inflammatory response to coronary angioplasty in patients with severe unstable angina. Circulation 1998;98:2370–6.

51. Biasucci LM, Liuzzo G, Grillo RL et al. Elevated levels of C-reactive protein at discharge in patients with unstable angina predict recurrent instability. Circulation 1999;99: 855–60.

52. Ridker PM, Rifai N, Pfeffer MA, Sacks FM, Moye LA, Goldman S, Flaker GC, Braunwald E, for the Cholesterol and Recurrent Events (CARE) Investigators. Inflammation, pravastatin, and the risk of coronary events after myocardial infarction in patients with average cholesterol levels. Circulation 1998;98:839–44.

53. Ridker PM, Cushman M, Stampfer MJ, Tracy RP, Hennekens CH. Inflammation, aspirin, and the risk of cardiovascular disease in apparently healthy men. N Engl J Med 1997;336:973–9.

54. Ridker PM, Buring JE, Shih J, Matias M, Hennekens CH. Prospective study of C-reactive protein and the risk of future cardiovascular events among apparently healthy women. Circulation 1998;98:731–3.

55. Ridker PM, Hennekens CH, Buring JE, Rifai N. Inflammatory and lipid predictors of cardiovascular disease in women. N Engl J Med 2000;342:836–43.

56. Ridker PM, Glynn RJ, Hennekens CH. C-reactive protein adds to the predictive value of total and HDL cholesterol in determining risk of first myocardial infarction. Circulation 1998;97:2007–11.

57. Tracy RP, Lemaitre RN, Psaty BM et al. Relationship of C-reactive protein to risk of cardiovascular disease in the elderly. Results from the Cardiovascular Health Study and the Rural Health Promotion Project. Arterioscler Thromb Vasc Biol 1997;17:1121–7.

58. Kuller LH, Tracy RP, Shaten J, Meilahn EN, for the MRFIT Research Group. Relationship of C-reactive protein and coronary heart disease in the MRFIT nested case-control study. Am J Epidmiol 1996;144:537–47.

59. Koenig W, Sund M, Froelich M et al. C-reactive protein, a sensitive marker of inflammation, predicts future risk of coronary heart disease in initially healthy middle-aged men: results from the MONICA (Monitoring trends and determinants in cardiovascular disease) Augsberg Cohort Study, 1984 to 1992. Circulation 1999;99:237–42.

60. Roivainen M, Viik–Kajander M, Palosuo T et al. Infections, inflammation, and the risk of coronary heart disease. Circulation 2000;101:252–7.

61. Ridker PM, Cushman M, Stampfer MJ, Tracy RP, Hennekens CH. Plasma concentration of C-reactive protein and risk of developing peripheral vascular disease. Circulation 1998;97:425–8.

62. Ridker PM, Rifai N, Pfeffer M, Sacks F, Braunwald E. Long-term effects of pravastatin on plasma concentration of C-reactive protein. Circulation 1999;100:230–5.

63. Smith JK, Dykes R, Douglas JE, Krishnaswamy G, Berk S. Long-term exercise and atherogenic activity of blood mononuclear cells in persons at risk of developing ischemic heart disease. JAMA 1999;281:1722–7.

64. Visser M, Bouter LM, McQuillen GM, Wener MH, Harris TB. Elevated C-reactive protein levels in overweight and obese adults. JAMA 1999;282:2131–5.

65. Yudkin JS, Stehouwer CDA, Emeis JJ, Coppack SW. C-reactive protein in healthy subjects: Associations with obesity, insulin resistance, and endothelial dysfunction. A potential role for cytokines originating from adipose tissue? Arterioscler Thromb Vasc Biol 1999;19:972–8.

66. Ikonomidis I, Andreotti F, Economou E, Stefanadis C, Toutouxas P, Nihoyannopoulos P. Increased pro-inflammatory cytokines in patients with chronic stable angina and their reduction by aspirin. Circulation 1999;100:793–8.

67. Cushman M, Meilhan EN, Psaty BM, Kuller LH, Dobs AS, Tracy RP. Hormone replacement therapy, inflammation, and hemostasis in elderly women. Arterioscler Thromb Vasc Biol 1999;19:893–9.

68. Ridker PM, Hennekens CH, Rifai N, Buring JE, Manson JE. Hormone replacement therapy and increased plasma concentration of C-reactive protein. Circulation 1999;100:713–6.

69. Cushman M, Legault C, Barrett-Connor E et al. Effect of postmenopausal hormones on inflammation sensitive proteins: The Postmenopausal Estrogen/Progestin Interventions (PEPI) Study. Circulation 1999;100:717–22.

70. Hulley S, Grady D, Bush T, Furberg C, Herrington D, Riggs B, Vittinghoff E, for the Heart and Estrogen/Progestin Replacement Study (HERS) Research Group. JAMA 1998;280:605–13.

71. Rosenson RS and Tangney CC. Anti-atherothrombotic properties of statins: implications for cardiovascular event reduction. JAMA 1998;279:1643–50.

72. Aikawa M, Rabkin E, Okada Y et al. Lipid lowering by diet reduces matrix metalloprotwinase activity and increases collagen content of rabbit atheroma: a potential mechanism of lesion stabilization. Circulation 1998;97:2433–44.

73. Shiomi M, Ito T, Tsukada T, Yata T, Watanabe Y, Tsujita U, Fukami M, Fukushige J, Hosokawa T, Tamura A. Reduction of serum cholesterol levels alters lesional composition of atherosclerotic plaques: effect of pravastatin sodium on atherosclerosis in mature WHHL rabbits. Arterioscler Thromb Vasc Biol 1995;15:1938–44.

74. Williams JK, Sukhova GK, Herrington DM, Libby P. Pravastatin has cholesterol-lowering independent effects on the artery wall of atherosclerotic monkeys. J Am Coll Cardiol 1998;31:684–91.

75. Greenland P, Abrams J, Aurigemma GP, Bond MG, Criqui MH, Clark LT, Crouse JR, Friedman L, Fuster V, Herrington DM, Kuller LH, Ridker PM, Robverts WC, Stanford W, Stone N, Swan HJ, Taubert KA, Wexler L. Prevention Conference V: beyond secondary prevention: identifying the high-risk patient for primary prevention: non-invasive tests of atherosclerotic burden. Circulation 2000 (in press).

76. Roberts WL, Sedrick R, Moulton L, Spencer A, Rifai N. Evaluation of four automated high-sensitivity C-reactive protein methods: Implications for clinical and epidemiological applications. Clin Chem 2000 (in press).

Overview of the Diagnosis and Treatment of Lipid Disorders

5

Ernst J. Schaefer and Judith R. McNamara

✧   Current guidelines published by the National Cholesterol Education Program (NCEP) Adult Treatment Panel focus on dietary treatment of all adults over age 20 if their serum low-density lipoprotein cholesterol (LDL-C) values are ≥160 mg/dL (4.1 mmol/L), or ≥130 mg/dL (3.4 mmol/L) in the presence of two or more coronary heart disease (CHD) risk factors, or ≥100 mg/dL (2.6 mmol/L) in the presence of CHD.[1,2]
     CHD risk factors include the following:

✧   age ≥45 y (male) and ≥55 y (female) or with premature menopause and no hormonal replacement therapy (female),

✧   family history of premature CHD (<55 y in male first-degree relative, or <65 y in female first-degree relative),

✧   cigarette smoking,

✧   hypertension,

✧   high-density lipoprotein cholesterol (HDL-C) <35 mg/dL (0.91 mmol/L, or

✧   diabetes.

A risk factor is subtracted if the HDL-C value is ≥60 mg/dL (1.6 mmol/L).[1,2]
     After an adequate trial of a diet restricted in total fat (≤30% of calories), saturated fat (<7%), and cholesterol (<200 mg/day), and after ruling out secondary causes of hypercholesterolemia, especially thyroid, renal, and liver disease, persons with LDL-C values ≥190 mg/dL (4.9 mmol/L), or ≥160 mg/dL (4.1 mmol/L) in the presence of two or more CHD risk factors, or ≥130 mg/dL (3.4 mmol/L) in the presence of CHD, are candidates for pharmacologic therapy with agents such as hydroxymethylglutaryl-CoA (HMG CoA) reductase inhibitors, anion exchange resins, niacin, fibric acid derivatives, or a combination of these agents.
     Guidelines for preventing CHD in the entire United States adult population, as well as for children and adolescents, have also been formulated. These guidelines focus on modifying diets so that they include ≤30% fat, <10% saturated fat, and <300 mg cholesterol/day. Diet therapy, and in some cases resins, are prescribed for high-risk children.[3,4] The rationale for these guidelines is that in prospective studies, increased LDL-C concentrations are clearly associated with premature CHD, and low-

ering LDL-C with dietary therapy or a combination of dietary and drug treatment can reduce CHD risk.

LIPOPROTEIN METABOLISM

Plasma cholesterol and triglycerides (TG), along with phospholipids and proteins, are carried on lipoprotein particles. As shown in the overview of lipoprotein metabolism presented in Figure 5–1,[5] dietary fats are packaged by the intestine into large, TG-rich

Figure 5–1 ✧ A Simplified Overview of Lipoprotein Metabolism

Open arrows signify synthetic pathways; thin closed arrows signify transfer pathways; thick closed arrows signify catabolic pathways; dotted arrows signify minor pathways; and solid boxes or symbols signify receptors. Fats absorbed in the intestine are packaged into large TG-rich particles known as chylomicrons (Step 1). These lipoproteins undergo lipolysis (removal of TG) to form chylomicron remnants (Step 4), which are taken up by the liver via an apo E receptor (Step 5). The liver can also secrete TG-rich lipoproteins known as VLDL (Step 2). Following lipolysis, these particles can be converted to LDL (Step 6) or taken up by the liver via an apo E receptor (Step 7). LDL are catabolized mainly by the liver (Step 8) or other tissues (Step 9) via LDL receptors that recognize both apo B-100 and apo E but not apo B-48. If LDL are modified, they can also be taken up by scavenger receptors on macrophages (Step 11). HDL are synthesized by both the liver and the intestine (Step 3). HDL donate apolipoproteins and lipids to chylomicrons & VLDL, and also pick up constituents from these particles as they undergo lipolysis (Steps 4 and 6). HDL pick up free cholesterol from peripheral tissues (Step 10) and macrophages (Step 11) and are catabolized mainly in the liver (Step 12).

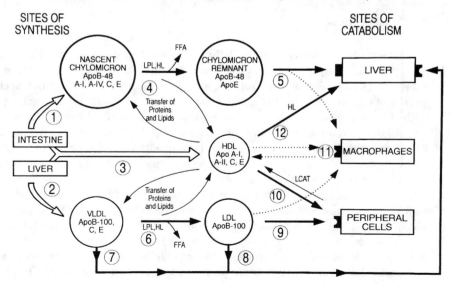

chylomicrons (Step 1), which rapidly lose much of their TG after entry into plasma due to lipolysis (Step 4). Apolipoprotein (apo) B-48 is the important structural protein of chylomicrons and contains the initial 48% of the apo B-100 sequence. During lipolysis, chylomicrons are transformed into chylomicron remnants, which become increasingly apo E- and cholesterol-enriched as TG is removed. These remnants are rapidly taken up by the liver via a receptor-mediated process (Step 5).

The liver synthesizes another form of triglyceride-rich lipoproteins, i.e., very-low-density lipoproteins (VLDL) (Step 2). In fasting subjects, VLDL are the major TG-carrying lipoproteins in serum or plasma. Much of VLDL TG and phospholipids are rapidly removed via lipolysis, forming VLDL remnants, which can be catabolized directly by the liver (Step 7), or can be converted to LDL (Step 6).

If chylomicron and VLDL remnants accumulate in the bloodstream, they are potentially atherogenic.[6,7] An assay has recently been developed to isolate and measure remnant concentration, providing the potential for information on increased CHD risk.[8–13] When present in excessive amounts, chylomicron and VLDL remnants, as well as LDL, can be deposited in the arterial wall, modified, and taken up by macrophages, resulting in atheroclerosis.[12–14] (For additional information on this process, refer to Chapters 1 and 28.)

LDL generally are the major cholesterol-carrying lipoproteins in the serum or plasma and are mainly catabolized in the liver and other tissues by an LDL receptor-mediated process (Steps 8 and 9). Apo B-100 is the major structural protein of both VLDL and LDL.

HDL (whose major protein is apo AI) are synthesized in both the liver and the intestine (Step 3). They can donate protein (E and C apolipoproteins) and lipid (cholesteryl esters and phospholipids) to TG-rich lipoproteins (chylomicrons and VLDL) and pick up lipid (phospholipid and TG) and protein (apos A-I, E, and C) from these lipoproteins (Steps 4 and 6). HDL accept cholesterol from tissues (Step 10) and deliver it to the liver directly (Step 12) or transfer it to other lipoproteins, such as chylomicron or VLDL remnants, which are then taken up by the liver. In the liver, cholesterol can either be excreted directly into bile, converted to bile acids, or re-utilized in lipoprotein production. A decreased HDL-C level is a significant independent CHD risk factor, while an elevated level is protective for CHD. (A more extensive review of lipoprotein metabolism is provided in Chapter 1.)

Another lipoprotein not shown in Figure 5–1 is lipoprotein(a) or Lp(a). This lipoprotein consists of an LDL particle with apo(a) attached to it by a disulfide bond.[15] Apo(a) is a unique glycoprotein with protein domains, known as kringles, that have homology with similar protein domains in plasminogen. Apo(a) contains multiple and variable numbers of kringle 4-like domains and one kringle 5-like domain. Variability in Lp(a) concentration relates to apo(a) molecular weight, number of kringle 4-like domains, and differences in hepatic apo(a) secretion rates.[16–20] Increased concentrations may interfere with fibrinolysis or clot lysis.[21–23] Like LDL, Lp(a) can be deposited directly in the arterial wall, promoting atherosclerosis.[17] Increased Lp(a) concentrations have been associated with premature CHD in most studies.[24–44] Though Lp(a) measurement, based on protein concentration, is difficult, due to variability in the number of kringle repeats and homology with plasminogen, Lp(a) can now be measured, based on cholesterol content [Lp(a)-C], potentially circumventing some of the problems associated with Lp(a) protein standardization.[44,45] For additional information, refer to Chapter 17.

RATIONALE FOR TREATMENT OF LIPID DISORDERS

NCEP guidelines focus on decreasing LDL-C values because LDL-C has clearly been shown to be an independent risk factor for CHD and because CHD risk decreases when LDL-C is lowered by diet, with or without drugs, in patients with increased LDL-C concentrations and/or with CHD. Plasma LDL-C values are increased by diets high in saturated fat and cholesterol mainly because of decreased LDL receptor-mediated catabolism. Animals that consume such diets develop high LDL-C levels and atherosclerosis. Such diets can also increase HDL-C concentrations; this change may be compensatory. Human populations on diets high in saturated fat and cholesterol have more elevated LDL-C concentrations and significantly greater incidence of CHD due to atherosclerosis than populations that maintain diets low in saturated fat and cholesterol.[1–3] In U.S. society, increased LDL-C concentrations as well as decreased HDL-C values are independent risk factors for premature CHD.[1–3,46–50] Women have higher HDL-C values than men and thus have a lower risk of CHD.

Prospective studies indicate that dietary treatment or combined dietary and drug therapy that decreases LDL-C can reduce subsequent CHD morbidity and mortality.[47,48,51–69] Moreover, studies indicate that aggressive lipid modification in CHD patients [i.e., reducing LDL-C concentrations to <100 mg/dL (2.6 mmol/L)] can stabilize existing coronary atherosclerosis, or make it regress.[54,70–81] Small changes in angiographic results appear to reap large benefits in clinical CHD event reduction; this is consistent with the concept of plaque stabilization.[74,75,77] Recent statin trials indicate significant benefit in patients, even those whose LDL-C levels measure in the 130–160 mg/dL (3.4–4.0 mmol/L) range,[68,69] and results from the recently completed Atorvastatin Versus Revascularization Treatment (AVERT) study indicate that aggressively lowering LDL-C levels may reduce the need for angioplasty.[81] Because of these studies, consensus was reached on the use of drugs for lowering LDL-C,[82] but not for lowering TG or raising HDL-C.[83]

In a meta-analysis, but not in most individual studies, increased TG concentration has been shown to be an independent CHD risk factor, especially in women.[49,84] Although increased TG concentrations correlated with decreased HDL-C values, and raising HDL-C concentration with medication reduced CHD risk (and lowered LDL-C) in both the Lipid Research Clinics Trial and the Helsinki Heart Study, no such data were obtained for lowering TG.[47,48,60,61,85,86] In fact, despite a 34% reduction in triglycerides in the Helsinki Heart Study, no benefit in CHD risk reduction could be ascribed to this effect.[61]

In the recently completed Veterans Affairs Cooperative Studies Program High-Density Lipoprotein Cholesterol Intervention Trial (VA-HIT), conducted in men with CHD who had HDL-C <40 mg/dL (1.0 mmol/L), LDL-C <140 mg/dL (3.6 mmol/L), and TG <300 mg/dL (3.4 mmol/L) at baseline, a significant 22% CHD risk reduction was noted with gemfibrozil.[87] This reduction was associated with an 8% rise in HDL-C and a 25% reduction in TG. No benefit was noted in a similar trial in Israel with bezafibrate.[88]

EVALUATION OF THE PATIENT

For screening purposes serum or plasma total cholesterol (TC) and HDL-C concentrations can be measured in the fasting or non-fasting state.[2] EDTA plasma values for TC are approximately 3% lower than serum or heparin plasma values and should be adjusted upward if EDTA is the anticoagulant used. Compact analyzers that screen finger-stick specimens for TC, TG, and HDL-C are available.[89,90]

Lipid values for adults over age 20 have been classified as listed in Table 5–1. According to guidelines issued by the U.S. NCEP Adult Treatment Panel II, patients without CHD who have a desirable TC value of <200 mg/dL (5.2 mmol/L) and an HDL-C value of ≥35 mg/dL (0.9 mmol/L) should have their values checked again within 5 y.[2] In addition, all patients should be educated about recommended diet guidelines (≤30% fat, <10% saturated fat, and <300 mg of cholesterol/day), exercise, and general risk factor reduction. If the patient's TC value registers in the borderline range of 200–239 mg/dL (5.2–6.2 mmol/L), information about other CHD risk factors should be obtained.[2] These risk factors are listed in Table 5–2.

In the absence of CHD (prior myocardial infarction, angina), if a patient's measurements include a TC value in the borderline range, a normal HDL-C value, and less than two CHD risk factors, provide information on diet and CHD risk reduction and check the patient's values again within the next 1–2 y. If the patient has CHD, or has a TC value ≥240 mg/dL (6.2 mmol/L), or has a borderline TC value in the presence of two or more CHD risk factors, or has an HDL-C value <35 mg/dL (0.9 mmol/L), measure a fasting (at least 9 h; preferably 12 h) lipid profile (TC, TG, HDL-C). Laboratories should maintain a coefficient of variation (CV) of ≤3% and a bias of ≤3% for their TC assay as compared to the National Reference System for Cholesterol (NRS/CHOL).[91] TG assays should have precision and bias of ≤5%, compared to the Centers for Disease Control (CDC) reference method;[92] HDL-C assays should have precision of ≤4% at concentrations >42 mg/dL (1.08 mmol/L) and a standard deviation of ≤1.7 mg/dL (0.04 mmol/L) at concentrations <42 mg/dL (1.08

Table 5–1 ✧ Lipid Abnormalities in Adults*

	Desirable	Borderline High Risk for CHD	High Risk for CHD	High Risk for Pancreatitis
Cholesterol	< 200 (5.2)	200–239 (5.2–6.2)	≥ 240 (6.2)	—
LDL Cholesterol	< 130 (3.4)	130–159 (3.4–4.1)	≥ 160 (4.1)	—
HDL Cholesterol	> 60 (1.6)	—	< 35 (0.9)	—
Triglyceride	< 200 (2.3)	200–400 (2.3–4.5)	> 400 (4.5)	> 1000 (11.3)
TC/HDL	< 5.0	5.0–6.0	> 6.0	

*All values in mg/dL; values in parentheses are in mmol/L. Elevated triglycerides have been shown to be a risk factor for pancreatitis (> 1000 mg/dL or 11.3 mmol/L), but have not been clearly shown to be an independent risk factor for CHD.

Table 5–2 ✧ NCEP ATP II Major Risk Factors for CHD in Addition to Elevated LDL Cholesterol*

✧	Male ≥ 45 years, Female ≥ 55 years or with premature menopause without estrogen replacement therapy
✧	Family history of premature CHD (definite myocardial infarction or sudden death before age 55 in a male first-degree relative or before age 65 in a female first-degree relative)
✧	Current cigarette smoking
✧	Hypertension (≥ 140/90 mmHG or taking antihypertensive medication)
✧	HDL cholesterol < 35 mg/dL (0.9 mmol/L)
✧	Diabetes mellitus

*A risk factor should be subtracted if the HDL-C concentration is ≥ 60 mg/dL (1.6 mmol/L).

mmol/L), and bias <5%;[93] and LDL-C assays should have precision and bias ≤4% each.[94]

The formula commonly used to calculate LDL-C is the following:[95]

$$LDL\text{-}C = TC - HDL\text{-}C - TG/5$$

when values are in mg/dL, or TG/2.22 when values are in mmol/L.

This formula cannot be used for values obtained on serum or plasma from non-fasting individuals or those whose TG values are >400 mg/dL (4.5 mmol/L).[95,96] Moreover, there is considerable variability in calculated LDL-C concentrations when TG values are 200–400 mg/dL (2.3–4.5 mmol/L) as compared to values obtained by ultracentrifugation.[96] Our data indicate that about 5% of the population have fasting TG values >400 mg/dL (4.5 mmol/L), and that an additional 14% have calculated LDL-C values that are not placed in the appropriate NCEP categories (as compared to values obtained by ultracentrifugation).[96] In the early 1990s the NCEP Lipoprotein Working Group recommended developing direct methods for measuring LDL-C.[94] Several direct LDL-C assays have now been developed using a variety of methodological principles to isolate chylomicrons, VLDL, and HDL from serum or plasma, leaving LDL behind, followed by measurement of the cholesterol content in LDL by automated enzymatic techniques. (For additional information, refer to Chapter 12.)

An LDL-C concentration of 160 mg/dL (4.1 mmol/L) represents approximately the 75th percentile of middle-aged Americans. Since values are subject to considerable biologic variation (see Chapter 8), it is important to confirm the presence of abnormalities by repeat determinations.[97] Hospitalization or acute illness can also affect lipid values,[98] and therefore lipid determinations should generally be carried out when subjects are in the free-living state. Getting LDL-C and HDL-C measurements at the time of screening may be more cost-effective.

Although an increased TG concentration has not consistently been shown to be an independent risk factor for CHD, TG concentration is inversely associated with a low concentration of HDL-C, which has been shown to be a significant risk factor for CHD. Moreover, markedly increased TG concentrations are associated with pancreatitis.

Common secondary causes of lipid abnormalities are shown in Table 5–3.[1,2] These secondary causes should be screened by measuring TSH, glucose, liver enzymes, and kidney function. Abnormalities should be treated, if possible, prior to initiating drug therapy for lipid disorders. In addition, some forms of dyslipidemia are genetic and therefore can be identified by family studies.

In some studies, low apo AI values and small LDL particle size, as well as elevated apo B concentrations, have been reported to be superior to LDL-C and HDL-C concentrations as markers for CHD.[99–105] However, these have all been case-control studies. In our view, apo AI and apo B concentrations are less affected by dietary modification and the use of beta blockers than are TG, LDL-C, and HDL-C concentrations, and LDL particle size.[30,106] Most CHD patients have modified their diet and are often taking beta-adrenergic blocking agents, and these are confounders in such case-control studies.[31] Supporting this view is our finding that LDL size is not an independent CHD risk factor after controlling for the effects of beta blockers and LDL-C and HDL-C concentrations.[106] Data from the Physicians' Health Study also indicate that LDL size does not provide additional information about CHD risk above and beyond that provided by a standard lipid profile.[107] Moreover, of several prospective studies assessing the utility of apo AI and apo B versus LDL-C and HDL-C concentrations as CHD markers, none has documented that apolipoprotein values added significant additional information about CHD risk.[35,108–113] Adequate standardization for apo AI and apo B is available;[114–117] and gels for the determination of LDL fraction size are also commercially available. It is

Table 5–3 ◇ Secondary Causes of Lipid Abnormalities*	
◇	Obesity
◇	Diet
◇	Lack of Exercise
◇	Cigarette Smoking
◇	Alcohol Intake
◇	Diabetes Mellitus
◇	Hypothyroidism
◇	Obstructive Liver Disease
◇	Renal Insufficiency
◇	Nephrotic Syndrome
◇	Medications (hormones, beta blockers, diuretics)
*Screen by measuring glucose, TSH, creatinine, urinary protein, transaminases, and alkaline phosphatase.	

our view that apo AI, apo B, and LDL size measurements are not likely to have significant additional clinical utility and because of cost considerations cannot be recommended for CHD risk assessment at this time. However, more data from large-scale prospective studies are required before definitive conclusions can be reached.

In contrast, an increased Lp(a) concentration is considered to be a significant independent CHD risk factor. This concept is supported by many case-control studies, prevalence studies, and nine of thirteen prospective studies.[24–44,110,111,117–119] Problems associated with Lp(a) measurement have included lack of assay standardization and considerable heterogeneity within apo(a). However, reference materials have been developed by a committee of the International Federation of Clinical Chemistry (IFCC) to provide assistance to manufacturers for setting calibrator values. When calculated as total particle mass, an Lp(a) value of >40 mg/dL is clearly above the 90th percentile, but many authorities feel that a value >30 mg/dL is a high-risk value. An elevated Lp(a)-C level (>10mg/dL) may be associated with CHD in men.[44] Our data indicate that familial Lp(a) excess (values above the 90th percentile) is a highly heritable disorder found in 15%–20% of kindreds with premature CHD.[32] Niacin administration has been shown to lower Lp(a) concentrations, as well as to reduce CHD morbidity and mortality in unselected men with CHD.[58,60,121] For these reasons, we believe that Lp(a) concentrations should be measured in patients who are candidates for drug therapy for lowering LDL-C, especially those with CHD, as well as individuals with a strong family history of CHD. Patients whose values are increased—with Lp(a) >30 mg/dL or Lp(a)-C >10 mg/dL—should be treated with niacin if they can tolerate it, or in postmenopausal women, with hormonal replacement. Both niacin and hormonal replacement have been shown to reduce CHD risk as well as lower both LDL-C and Lp(a). Therefore, their use in this situation can be justified before use of a statin.

FAMILIAL LIPOPROTEIN DISORDERS

An overview of familial hypercholesterolemic states is provided in Table 5–4. By far the most common of these disorders is familial combined hyperlipidemia, in which affected kindred members may have increased LDL-C alone (above the 90th percentile of age- and gender-adjusted reference ranges), increased TG alone, or increases of both variables. Family studies (which are often difficult) that include sampling of available first-degree relatives (parents, siblings, and offspring) are required to make the diagnosis.[32,122,123] These patients also often have decreased HDL-C values due to enhanced degradation of HDL protein (Step 12 in Figure 5–1).[32] They have also been shown to overproduce VLDL apo B-100, but not TG (Step 2).[124,125] (Approximately 15% of patients with premature CHD have this disorder.[32]) Sporadic or polygenic hypercholesterolemia is also quite common and is observed in approximately 2% of kindreds with premature CHD.[32,121] Treatment consists of diet and, if necessary, HMG CoA reductase inhibitors, niacin, gemfibrozil, or combinations of these medications with anion exchange resins.[126]

A much rarer form of combined increases of TC and TG is known as familial dysbetalipoproteinemia (Type III hyperlipoproteinemia), in which affected subjects have accumulations of chylomicron and VLDL remnants in the fasting state. These patients usually are homozygous for a mutation in the apo E protein (apo E 2/2 pheno-

Table 5–4 ✧ Familial Hypercholesterolemic States

	Familial Combined Hyperlipidemia	Familial Hypercholesterolemia	Familial Dysbetalipoproteinemia
Physical findings:	Arcus senilis	Arcus senilis, tendinous xanthomas	Arcus senilis, tubo-eruptive and planar xanthomas
Associated findings:	Obesity, glucose intolerance, hyperuricemia, HDL deficiency	—	Obesity, glucose intolerance, hyperuricemia
Mode of inheritance:	Autosomal dominant	Autosomal co-dominant	Autosomal recessive
Defect:	Overproduction of hepatic VLDL apo B-100	Defective LDL receptor or defective apo B-100	Defective apo E
Estimated population frequency:	1:50	1:500	1:5000
Estimated frequency in CHD patients:	15%	1–3%	0.5%
CHD risk:	Moderate	High	Low
Treatment:	Diet, niacin, resin, statins, gemfibrozil	Diet, niacin and resin, statins and resin, or triple therapy	Diet, niacin, gemfibrozil, statins

type), or in rare cases have apo E deficiency, resulting in defective hepatic clearance of chylomicron and VLDL remnant particles as well as increased VLDL production (Steps 2, 5, and 6).[127–131] They may also have tubo-eruptive and palmar xanthomas. Diagnosis requires documentation of a VLDL-C/TG ratio >0.3 after measurement of VLDL-C following ultracentrifugation, and documentation of the apo E 2/2 phenotype by isoelectric focusing, or of the genotype by DNA analysis. Treatment consists of diet, niacin, gemfibrozil, or HMG CoA reductase inhibitors. Patients with both familial combined hyperlipidemia and familial dysbetalipoproteinemia often have obesity, glucose intolerance, and hyperuricemia.[129]

Isolated increases of LDL-C are found in patients with a disorder known as familial hypercholesterolemia, often associated with tendinous xanthomas. These patients generally have marked hypercholesterolemia (>350 mg/dL [9.0 mmol/L]) with normal TG values, and have defects at the LDL receptor locus or abnormalities of the apo B protein (apo B-3500 mutation).[122,123,131–133] The major metabolic abnormality in these individuals is an impaired ability to catabolize LDL (Steps 8 and 9).[134] Approximately 0.1% of the population and 1% of the patients with premature CHD have this disorder due to mutations at the LDL receptor locus.[32,122] Apo B mutations, specifically at residue 3500, are even less common. Phenotypically, these patients are similar to familial hypercholesterolemic (FH) patients. Treatment generally consists of diet and a combination of medications (generally HMG CoA reductase inhibitors and resin).[135–137]

Isolated deficiency of HDL-C (below of the 10th percentile of normal) can be genetic in nature, and is then known as familial hypoalphalipoproteinemia. This disorder is found in approximately 4% of patients with premature CHD.[32,138–140] In our own recent studies, patients in families with HDL deficiency and premature CHD had decreases in all lipoproteins containing apo AI (Lp AI, Lp AI/AII) and increases in lipoproteins containing apo B, including those containing both apo B and apo E (LpB:E).[138] Treatment of HDL deficiency consists of diet, weight reduction if indicated, and an exercise program.[83] In these patients, efforts should be made to optimize their LDL-C values according to NCEP guidelines, and the agent of choice would be an HMG CoA reductase inhibitor.

An overview of familial hypertriglyceridemic states is provided in Table 5–5. By far the most common of these disorders is familial hypertriglyceridemia, an autosomal-dominant disorder in which obesity, glucose intolerance, hyperuricemia, and HDL deficiency are often present.[32,122] The disorder is associated with overproduction of hepatic VLDL TG but not VLDL apo B-100 (Step 2).[124,126] Some patients may have defects in VLDL clearance as well (Steps 6 and 7). CHD risk appears to be increased in those kindreds in whom HDL deficiency is also present. Approximately 15% of patients with premature CHD appear to have this disorder.[32] HDL concentrations are low in these subjects because of enhanced degradation (Step 12). Treatment with diet, exercise, abstinence from the use of alcohol and exogenous oral estrogens is recommended. In patients with CHD, lipid values can be optimized by use of HMG CoA reductase inhibitors, niacin, or gemfibrozil.

Severe hypertriglyceridemia, wherein TG values are >1000 mg/dL (11.3 mmol/L), is often observed in middle-aged or elderly individuals who are obese and who have glucose intolerance and hyperuricemia. These subjects usually have familial hypertriglyceridemia or familial combined hyperlipidemia which is exacerbated by other factors, such as obesity, alcohol consumption, and/or diabetes mellitus. These patients generally also exhibit HDL deficiency and may develop lipemia retinalis and eruptive xanthomas. They are at increased risk for developing pancreatitis due to TG deposition in the pancreas and may have paresthesias and emotional lability. In addition, these patients often have delayed chylomicron and VLDL clearance and excess VLDL production (Steps 2, 4, 6, and 7). Treatment consists of the calorie-restricted Step 2 diet of the American Heart Association. In patients with diabetes mellitus, it is crucial to control blood glucose concentrations as much as possible. Medications that are effective in lowering TG to <1000 mg/dL (11.3 mmol/L) in these patients, thereby reducing their risk of pancreatitis, include gemfibrozil, or other fibric acid derivatives, and/or fish-oil capsules (6–10 capsules/day).

Patients who present with severe hypertriglyceridemia in childhood or early adulthood and who are not obese often have a deficiency of the enzyme lipoprotein lipase or its activator protein, apo CII, resulting in markedly impaired removal of TG, which affects chylomicron and VLDL catabolism (Steps 4, 6, and 7). These patients are at increased risk for recurrent pancreatitis, and it is important to restrict their di-

Table 5–5 ✧ Familial Hypertriglyceridemic States

	Familial Hypertriglyceridemia	Severe Hypertriglyceridemia	
		Early Onset	*Adult Onset*
Physical findings:	None	Lipemia retinalis, eruptive xanthomas	Lipemia retinalis, eruptive xanthomas
Associated findings:	Obesity, glucose intolerance, hyperuricemia, HDL deficiency	HDL deficiency, pancreatitis	Obesity, glucose intolerance, hyperuricemia, HDL deficiency, pancreatitis, paresthesias, emotional lability
Mode of inheritance:	Autosomal dominant	Autosomal recessive	Autosomal recessive
Defect:	Overproduction of hepatic VLDL triglyceride	Lipoprotein lipase deficiency, apo C-II deficiency	Overproduction of VLDL triglyceride, delayed catabolism of chylomicrons and VLDL
Estimated population frequency:	1:50	< 1:10,000	1:1000
Estimated frequency in CHD patients:	15%	—	1:500
CHD risk:	Low	—	Low
Treatment:	Diet, niacin, gemfibrozil	Diet	Diet, gemfibrozil, fish oil

etary fat to < 20% of calories. Niacin and/or gemfibrozil are generally ineffective in these patients; however, fish-oil capsules may be helpful in certain patients to keep their TG concentrations below 1000 mg/dL (11.3 mmol/L) and minimize their risk of pancreatitis.

TREATMENT GUIDELINES FOR INCREASED LDL-C

The NCEP Adult Treatment Panel has developed guidelines for the diagnosis and treatment of individuals over age 20 y who have increased TC concentrations associated with increased LDL-C concentrations.[1,2] The NCEP's decision values for LDL-C are given in Table 5–6. Concentrations of LDL-C requiring the initiation of diet and drug therapy, as well as the goals of therapy itself, are dependent upon the presence or absence of CHD or CHD risk factors (see Table 5–6) and the presence of secondary causes of lipid abnormalities (see Table 5–3).

Table 5–6 ✧ NCEP ATP II LDL Cholesterol Decision Values			
	Initiate Drug Therapy	*Initiate Drug Therapy After Diet Therapy*	*Goal of Therapy*
< 2 CHD risk factors	≥ 160 mg/dL (4.1 mmol/L)	≥ 190 mg/dL (4.9 mmol/L)	< 160 mg/dL (4.1 mmol/L)
2 or more CHD risk factors	≥ 130 mg/dL (3.4 mmol/L)	≥ 160 mg/dL (4.1 mmol/L)	< 130 mg/dL (3.4 mmol/L)
CHD	≥ 100 mg/dL (2.6 mmol/L)	≥ 130 mg/dL (3.4 mmol/L)	< 100 mg/dL (2.6 mmol/L)

Dietary Therapy

Dietary therapy is the cornerstone for the treatment of lipid disorders.[2] According to our estimates, 50% of the saturated fat and 70% of the cholesterol in the U.S. diet come from hamburgers, cheeseburgers, meat loaf, butter, whole milk products, cheeses, beef dishes, hot dogs, ham, luncheon meats, pork, doughnuts, cookies, and cakes. Hence, such foods should be restricted. Instead, foods such as poultry (white meat without skin), fish, skimmed milk, non-fat or low-fat yogurt, and low-fat cheeses are recommended. The use of fruits, vegetables, and grains is encouraged.

Oils rich in saturated fat, such as coconut oil, palm oil, and palm kernel oil, should be restricted.[141–145] Oils that can be used include unsaturated vegetable oils containing polyunsaturated and mono-unsaturated fatty acids, such as canola, soybean, olive, and corn oil. However, such oils should only be used in moderation because they are pure fat and very calorie rich.

Excellent dietary pamphlets are available from the American Heart Association and the National Cholesterol Education Program. NCEP guidelines on dietary therapy are given in Table 5–7. The benefits of the NCEP's Step 1 and Step 2 diets (in terms of lowering LDL-C) may not be striking unless patients restrict total fat and calories, increase exercise, and lose excess weight.[40] Patients who are unable to get an adequate response from diet modification after being given pamphlets and counseling can be referred to a registered dietitian for instructions on the Step 2 diet. In most cases, dietary therapy should be tried for at least six months prior to initiating drug therapy.

Drug Therapy

An overview of available lipid-lowering medications is provided in Table 5–8. These medications can be divided into two general classes: those that are effective in decreasing LDL-C by more than 15%, and those that are effective in decreasing TG concentrations by more than 15%. Currently, three classes of agents meet the LDL-lowering criteria: HMG CoA reductase inhibitors (lovastatin, pravastatin, simvastatin, fluvastatin, atorvastatin, and cerivastatin); anion exchange resins (cholestyr-

Table 5–7 ✦ NCEP ATP II Dietary Therapy*			
Nutrient	*Average U.S. Diet*	*Step 1 Diet*	*Step 2 Diet*
Total Fat	36%	≤ 30%	≤ 30%
Saturated Fat	15%	< 10%	< 7%
Polyunsaturated Fat	6%	< 10%	< 10%
Mono-unsaturated Fat	15%	< 15%	< 15%
Cholesterol (mg/d)	400–500	< 300	< 200
Total Calories	To achieve and maintain desired weight		

*% indicates percentage of total calories.

amine and colestipol); and niacin. Of these three types of drugs, patient acceptance and compliance with resins and niacin is often poor, while with HMG CoA reductase inhibitors it is generally excellent. Moreover, long-term safety in adults has now been documented with all three types of agents, and CHD risk reduction has also been reported. Because of efficacy and compliance, HMG CoA reductase inhibitors are now the drugs of choice for LDL-C lowering in all patients. Recent data clearly indicate that these drugs are safe and reduce CHD risk in primary and secondary prevention studies and stroke risk in secondary prevention studies. Furthermore, these drugs are equally effective in men and women, and in young and elderly patients.[64–69,81] These agents reduce LDL-C and CHD risk by approximately 33%. In addition, the AVERT study has shown that aggressive LDL-C lowering reduces the need for angioplasty in patients with stable CHD.[81]

There are currently three classes of agents that decrease TG concentrations by more than 15%: niacin; fibric acid derivatives (gemfibrozil, bezafibrate, ciprofibrate, fenofibrate); and HMG CoA reductase inhibitors. All of these agents generally also lower LDL-C concentrations and increase HDL-C concentrations. Both niacin and gemfibrozil have been shown to lower CHD risk prospectively.[58,60,61,146] The combination of a reductase inhibitor and an anion exchange resin is very effective, as is the combination of resins and niacin. However, the introduction of atorvastatin, which is extremely effective in lowering LDL-C and TG, may obviate the need for combination drug therapy.

It should be noted that in postmenopausal women, estrogen replacement is quite effective in lowering LDL-C and raising HDL-C, but it can also raise TG. If hormonal replacement is undertaken in postmenopausal women who are hypertriglyceridemic, the estrogen patch should be used, since there is little or no lipid effect with this form of therapy. Progesterone must be given along with estrogen in women with an intact uterus. Use of estrogens has been associated with a significant reduction in CHD mortality in postmenopausal women in most studies.[147,148] However, these were observational studies and not randomized placebo-controlled studies. The recently completed HERS trial in women with previously diagnosed CHD found an

Table 5–8 ✧ Lipid Medications

	Resins	Niacin	HMG CoA Reductase Inhibitors*	Fibric Acid Derivatives
Patient acceptance and compliance:	Often poor	Often poor	Generally excellent	Generally excellent
Side effects:	Constipation, bloating, decreased absorption of certain medicines	Flushing, itching, gastritis, hepatotoxicity, hyperuricemia, hyperglycemia	Hepatotoxicity, myositis, GI side effects	Myositis, hepatotoxicity, GI side effects, coumadin interaction
Usual dose:	8–10 g po BID	1 g po BID or TID with food	10, 20, 40, or 80 mg po QD	600 mg po BID-gemfibrozil 200 mg QD-fenofibrate
LDL reduction:	10–20%	10–20%	20–60%	10%
Triglyceride reduction:	**	40%	20%	35%
HDL increase:	5%	15–20%	5–15%	5–20%
CHD risk reduction documented:	Yes 19% 7 y	Yes 20% 5 y	Yes 20–40% 5 y	Yes 34% 5 y
Long-term safety documented:	Yes	Yes	Yes	Yes

*Current HMG CoA reductase inhibitors include lovastatin, pravastatin, simvastatin, fluvastatin, atorvastatin, and cerivastatin.
**May increase triglycerides.

increased risk of thrombosis during the first year, but a reduced CHD risk beyond the first year.[149]

For patients with increases in both LDL-C and TG, the agent of choice is an HMG CoA reductase inhibitor. For patients with hypertriglyceridemia only and normal LDL-C concentrations, there are as yet no clear guidelines in the United States for the use of medication. If the patient's fasting TG concentration exceeds 1000 mg/dL (11.3 mmol/L) while on a restricted diet, medication to reduce the risk of pancreatitis is recommended. However, prior to taking this step, the physician should make sure that these patients are not taking estrogens, thiazides, or beta blockers, are not consuming alcohol, and do not have uncontrolled diabetes mellitus. Use of these agents or of alcohol should be discontinued, and every effort should be made to control their diabetes. Calorie and fat restriction and exercise are important in these patients. The drug of choice for these patients is generally gemfibrozil (600 mg po bid) or another fibric acid derivative, such as bezafibrate or fenofibrate. In the absence of glucose intolerance, niacin can be tried. In patients for whom these agents are not effective, or if additional TG reduction is needed, fish-oil capsules (1 g), at a dose of 3–5 capsules twice daily, are effective in lowering TG.

In patients with moderate hypertriglyceridemia, especially in the presence of HDL-C deficiency, lifestyle changes including weight reduction and an exercise program are very helpful, as are cessation of alcohol and beta blocker use and increased control of diabetes (if present). If patients have established CHD, the use of HMG CoA reductase inhibitors to optimize their LDL-C concentrations should be considered. In CHD patients with HDL-C <40 mg/dL (1.0 mmol/L) and LDL-C <140 mg/dL (3.6 mmol/L), results from the HIT study justify the use of a fibric acid derivative such as gemfibrozil.[87] The goal of therapy in CHD patients is to get their LDL-C concentrations to <100 mg/dL (2.6 mmol/L).

Properties of Lipid-Lowering Drugs

HMG CoA reductase inhibitors inhibit the activity of HMG CoA reductase, the rate-limiting enzyme in cholesterol biosynthesis. In some patients this may enhance LDL catabolism (Steps 8 and 9), and decrease plasma LDL-C by 20%–60%. However, in most patients these inhibitors decrease VLDL and LDL production (Steps 2 and 6). These agents decrease plasma LDL-C by 20%–60%, TG levels by 10%–30%, and moderately increase HDL-C by 5%–10%.[77] The drugs are usually started at 10–20 mg/day and can be increased to a maximal dose of 40–80 mg/day, depending on the individual preparation. At 40 mg/day for lovastatin, pravastatin, simvastatin, fluvastatin, and atorvastatin, LDL-C reductions of approximately 27%, 34%, 38%, 25%, and 50%, respectively, have been reported; reduced CHD risk and improved atheroclerosis have also been reported for these statins.[64–69,81] These drugs are generally well tolerated, but may occasionally increase liver enzymes and creatine kinase (CK) (with myalgia and myositis), and may cause gastrointestinal upset. Large-scale studies using these agents have now been completed. These studies show reductions not only in CHD risk and mortality, but also in risk of stroke in patients with established CHD, and in total mortality as well.[64–69]

Cholestyramine and colestipol are anion exchange resins that bind bile acids, increase conversion of liver cholesterol to bile acids, and up-regulate LDL receptors in liver, increasing LDL catabolism (Step 8 and 9 of Figure 5–1) and decreasing plasma LDL-C by about 20%. Side effects include bloating and constipation, increased TG, and interference with the absorption of digoxin, tetracycline, d-thyroxine, phenylbutazone, and coumadin (these drugs should be given 1h before or 4h after resin). Cholestyramine (4g scoops) or colestipol (5g scoops) can be started at 1 scoop twice per day and gradually increased to 2 scoops twice per day (the scoops are half the price of the packets) or two scoops three times daily. Treatment for constipation may be required. Cholestyramine use has been shown to lower LDL-C by 12% and to reduce CHD risk prospectively by 19% over a 7-y period in middle-aged, asymptomatic, hypercholesterolemic men.[47]

Niacin decreases VLDL (Step 2) and LDL production (Step 6) and raises HDL-C values (by 20%). Niacin should be started at 100 mg orally twice daily with meals and gradually increased to 1g two or three times daily with meals. Side effects include flushing, gastric irritation, and elevation of uric acid, glucose, and liver enzymes in some patients. Niacin should not be used in patients with liver disease, those who have a history of ulcers, or diabetics who are not on insulin. Long-acting niacin, known as niaspan, causes less flushing but more gastrointestinal side effects than regular niacin. One aspirin daily will minimize flushing and can be used initially. Niacin should be discontinued if liver enzymes increase to more than twice the upper normal limit. Niacin has been shown to decrease TC concentrations by 10% and reduce the recurrence of myocardial infarction by 20% over a 5-y period of administration in men with CHD. The use of niacin was also associated with an 11% reduction in all-cause mortality 10y after cessation of niacin. Niacin in combination with clofibrate has been shown to reduce mortality in CHD patients as compared to usual care.[59]

Gemfibrozil and fenofibrate are the only fibrates currently used in the United States. However, another fibric acid derivative, bezafibrate, is available in many countries. Current data indicate that fenofibrate and bezafibrate are as effective as gemfibrozil for TG reduction, and more effective for LDL-C reduction. However, no prospective data from large-scale clinical trials have been reported for the latter two agents. Gemfibrozil is given at an oral dose of 600 mg twice daily and is generally well tolerated. The drug is very effective in lowering TG and VLDL (by 35%) by decreasing production and enhancing breakdown of VLDL (Steps 2 and 6). The drug usually lowers LDL-C by 10% and increases HDL-C by 5%–15%. Rarely, patients may experience gastrointestinal symptoms, muscle cramps (increased CK, 1%), or intermittent indigestion. The drug should not be used in patients with renal insufficiency, and it is also known to potentiate the action of coumadin. The drug may raise LDL-C concentrations in some hypertriglyceridemic patients. Gemfibrozil lowered LDL-C by 9%, increased HDL-C by 10%, and reduced CHD prospectively by 34% over a 5-y period in middle-aged asymptomatic hypercholesterolemic men in the Helsinki Heart Study.[60] In the HIT study, gemfibrozil lowered TG by 31% and increased HDL-C by 6% at one year, and decreased CHD events by 22% and stroke by 25%.[87]

Drug Combinations

HMG CoA reductase inhibitors and resins, as well as niacin and resin in combination, are very effective in lowering LDL-C concentrations. Fibrates and HMG CoA reductase inhibitors can be combined, but may increase the incidence of myositis; therefore, this combination should be used with caution.

GOALS OF THERAPY

NCEP therapeutic goals include reducing LDL-C values to <100 mg/dL (2.6 mmol/L) in CHD patients, to <130 mg/dL (3.4 mmol/L) in patients with two or more CHD risk factors, and to <160 mg/dL (4.1 mmol/L) in all patients. In our view, it is also prudent (in CHD patients) to lower TG to 200 mg/dL (2.25 mmol/L), to lower Lp(a)-C concentrations to <10 mg/dL, to increase HDL-C concentrations to >35 mg/dL (0.9 mmol/L), and to try to lower the TC/HDL-C ratio to <5.0. In patients with severe hypertriglyceridemia and pancreatitis, the goal of therapy is to reduce TG concentrations to <500 mg/dL (3.65 mmol/L).

SUMMARY

This chapter gives laboratory personnel an overview of the diagnosis and treatment of lipoprotein disorders and presents NCEP guidelines for therapy. Current recommended diagnostic tests include screening for serum TC and HDL-C in the fasting or non-fasting state, and serum TC, TG, HDL-C, and calculated LDL-C in the fasting state. Routine measurements of apo AI, apo B, or LDL particle size cannot be recommended because of a lack of prospective data documenting that these assays provide significant additional information about CHD risk prediction. Lp(a) or Lp(a)-C is an important addition to lipoprotein assessment, since it provides significant additional information about CHD risk. We believe that direct measurement of LDL-C, HDL-C, Lp(a)-C, and, perhaps, lipoprotein remnant-C, along with serum TG, will become standard practice in lipoprotein assessment. Moreover, researchers are actively developing methodologies that will simplify analysis for increased precision, accuracy, and throughput. ✧

REFERENCES

1. The Expert Panel. Report of the National Cholesterol Education Program Expert Panel on Detection, Evaluation, and Treatment of High Blood Cholesterol in Adults. Arch Intern Med 1988;148:36–69.
2. Expert Panel. National Cholesterol Education Program. Second report of the expert panel on detection, evaluation, and treatment of high blood cholesterol in adults (Adult Treatment Panel II). Circulation 1994;89:1329–433.
3. Expert Panel. Blood cholesterol levels in children and adolescents. National Institutes of Health Publication No. 91–2732, 1–119. Washington, DC: U.S. Government Printing Office, 1990.
4. Expert Panel. Population strategies for blood cholesterol reduction. National Institutes of Health Publication No. 90–3046, 1–39. Washington, DC: U.S. Government Printing Office, 1991.
5. Schaefer EJ, Levy RI. The pathogenesis and management of lipoprotein disorders. N Engl J Med 1985;312:1300–10.
6. Eisenberg S. Lipoprotein abnormalities in hypertriglyceridemia: significance in atherosclerosis. [Review] Am Heart J 1987;113:555–61.
7. Phillips NR, Waters D, Havel RJ. Plasma lipoproteins and progression of coronary artery disease evaluated by angiography and clinical events. Circulation 1993;88:2762–70.
8. Nakajima K, Saito T, Tamura A, Suzuki M, Nakano T, Adachi M. Cholesterol in remnant-like lipoproteins in human serum using monoclonal anti-apo B-100 and anti-apo A-I immunoaffinity mixed gels. Clin Chim Acta 1993;223:53–71.
9. McNamara JR, Shah PK, Nakajima K, et al. Remnant lipoprotein cholesterol and triglyceride: reference ranges from the Framingham Heart Study. Clin Chem 1998; 44:1224–32.

10. Takeichi S, Yukawa N, Nakajima Y, et al. Association of plasma triglyceride-rich lipoprotein remnants with coronary atherosclerosis in cases of sudden cardiac death. Atherosclerosis 1999;142:309–15.

11. Kugiyama K, Doi H, Takazoe K, et al. Remnant lipoprotein levels in fasting serum predict coronary events in patients with coronary artery disease. Circulation 1999;99:2858–60.

12. Gianturco SH, Bradley WA. Pathophysiology of trigylceride-rich lipoproteins in atherothrombosis: cellular aspects. Clin Cardiol 1999;22(suppl):II7–14.

13. Doi H, Kugiyama K, Ohgushi M, et al. Membrane-active lipids in remnant lipoproteins cause impairment of endothelial-dependent vasorelaxation. Arterioscler Thromb Vasc Biol 1999;19:1918–24.

14. Steinberg D, Parthasarathy S, Carew TE, Khoo JC, Witztum, JL. Beyond cholesterol: modifications of low-density lipoprotein that increase its atherogenicity. New Engl J Med 1989;320:915–24.

15. Xu S. Apolipoprotein(a) binds to low-density lipoprotein at two distant sites in lipoprotein(a). Biochemistry 1998;37:9284–94.

16. Berg K. A new serum type system in man: the Lp system. Acta Pathol Microbiol Scand 1963;59:369–82.

17. McLean JW, Tomlinson JE, Kuang WJ, et al. cDNA sequence of human apolipoprotein (a) is homologous to plasminogen. Nature 1987;330:132–7.

18. Utermann G. The mysteries of lipoprotein(a). Science 1989;246:904–10.

19. Lackner C, Boerwinkle E, Leffert CC, Rahmig T, Hobbs HH. Molecular basis of apolipoprotein(a) isoform heterogeneity as revealed by pulsed-field gel electrophoresis. J Clin Invest 1991;87:2153–61.

20. Boerwinkle E, Leffert CC, Lin J, Lackner C, Chiesa G, Hobbs HH. Apolipoprotein(a) gene accounts for greater than 90% of the variation in plasma lipoprotein(a) concentrations. J Clin Invest 1992;90:52–60.

21. Loscalzo J, Weinfeld M, Fless GM, Scanu AM. Lipoprotein (a), fibrin binding, and plasminogen activation. Arteriosclerosis 1990;10:240–5.

22. Miles LA, Fless GM, Levin EG, Scanu AM, Plow EF. A potential basis of the thrombotic risks associated with lipoprotein (a). Nature 1989;339:301–3.

23. Hajjar KA, Gavish D, Breslow JL, Nachman RL. Lipoprotein (a) modulation of endothelial cell surface fibrinolysis and its potential role in atherosclerosis. Nature 1989;339:303–5.

24. Dahlen GH, Guyton JR, Altar M, Farmer JA, Kautz JA, Gotto AM. Association of levels of lipoprotein (a), plasma lipids, and other lipoproteins with coronary artery disease documented by angiography. Circulation 1986;74:758–65.

25. Armstrong VW, Cremer P, Eberle E, et al. The association between serum Lp(a) concentrations and angiographically assessed coronary atherosclerosis. Atherosclerosis 1986;62:249–57.

26. Zenker G, Költringer P, Bone G, Niederkorn K, Pfeiffer K, Jurgens G. Lipoprotein(a) as a strong indicator for cerebrovascular disease. Stroke 1986;17:942–5.

27. Murai A, Miyahara T, Fujimoto N, Matsudo M, Kameyama M. Lp(a) lipoprotein as a risk factor for coronary heart disease and cerebral infarction. Atherosclerosis 1986; 59:199–204.

28. Hoefler G, Harnoncourt F, Paschke E, Mitrl W, Pfeiffer KH, Kostner GM. Lipoprotein Lp(a): a risk factor for myocardial infarction. Arteriosclerosis 1988;8:398–401.

29. Sandkamp M, Funke H. Schulte H, Koher E, Assman G. Lipoprotein (a) is an independent risk factor for myocardial infarction at a young age. Clin Chem 1990;36:20–3.

30. Genest J Jr, Jenner JL, McNamara JR, et al. Prevalence of lipoprotein (a) [Lp(a)] excess in coronary artery disease Am J Cardiol 1991;67:1039–45.

31. Genest JJ Jr, McNamara JR, Ordovas JM, et al. Lipoprotein cholesterol, apolipoprotein A-I and B and lipoprotein(a) abnormalities in men with premature coronary artery disease. J Am Coll Cardiol 1992;19:792–802.

32. Genest JJ Jr, Martin-Munley SS, McNamara JR, et al. Familial lipoprotein disorders in patients with premature coronary artery disease. Circulation 1992;85:2025–33.

33. Jenner JL, Ordovas JM, Lamon-Fava S, et al. Effects of age, sex, and menopausal status on plasma lipoprotein (a) levels. The Framingham Offspring Study. Circulation 1993;87:1135–41.

34. Rosengren A, Wihelmsen L, Eriksson E, Risberg B, Wedel H. Lipoprotein (a) and coronary heart disease: a prospective case-control study in the general population sample of middle-aged men. Br Med J 1990;301:1248–51.

35. Sigurdsson G, Baldursdottir A, Sigvalderson H, Agnarsson G, Thorgeirsson G, Sigfusson N. Predictive value of apolipoproteins in a prospective survey of coronary artery disease in men. Am J Cardiol 1992;69:1251–4.

36. Jauhiainen M, Koskinen P, Ehnholm C, et al. Lipoprotein (a) and coronary heart disease risk: a nested case-control study of the Helsinki Heart Study participants. Atherosclerosis 1991;89:59–67.

37. Ridker PM, Hennekens CH, Stampfer MJ. A prospective study of lipoprotein (a) and the risk of myocardial infarction. JAMA 1993;270:2195–9.

38. Schaefer EJ, Lamon-Fava S, Jenner JL, et al. Lipoprotein (a) levels and risk of coronary heart disease in men. The Lipid Research Clinics Coronary Primary Prevention Trial. JAMA 1994;271:999–1003.

39. Cremer P, Nagel D, Labrot B, Mann H, Muche R, Elster H, Seidel D. Lipoprotein Lp(a) as predictor of myocardial infarction in comparison to fibrinogen, LDL cholesterol, and other risk factors: results from the prospective Gottingen Risk Incidence and Prevalence Study (GRIPS). Eur J Clin Invest 1994;24:444–53.

40. Cantin B, Moorjani S, Despres J-P, Dagenais GR, Lupien P-J. Lp(a) in ischemic heart disease: the Quebec Cardiovascular Study. [Abstract]. JACC 1994;23:482A.

41. Bostom AG, Gagnon DR, Cupples LA, Wilson PWF, Jenner JL, Ordovas JM, Schaefer EJ, Castelli WP. A prospective investigation of elevated lipoprotein(a) detected by electrophoresis and cardiovascular disease in women. The Framingham Heart Study. Circulation 1994;90:1688–95.

42. Assman G, Schulte H, von Eckardstein A. Hypertriglyceridemia and elevated lipoprotein(a) are risk factors for major coronary events in middle-aged men. Am J Cardiol 1996;77:1179–84.

43. Bostom AG, Cupples LA, Jenner JL, Ordovas JM, Seman LJ, Wilson PWF, Schaefer EJ, Castelli WP. Elevated lipoprotein(a) and coronary heart disease in men aged 55 years and younger. JAMA 1996;276:544–48.

44. Seman LJ, DeLuca C, Jenner JL, et al. Lipoprotein(a)-cholesterol and coronary heart disease in the Framingham Heart Study. Clin Chem 1999;45:1039–46.

45. Seman LJ, Jenner JL, McNamara JR, Schaefer EJ. Quantitation of plasma lipoprotein(a) by cholesterol assay of lectin-bound lipoprotein(a). Clin Chem 1994;40:400–3.

46. Kannel WB, Castelli WP, Gordon T. Cholesterol in the prediction of atherosclerotic disease: new perspectives based on the Framingham Study. Ann Int Med 1979;90:85–91.

47. The Lipid Research Clinics Program. The Lipid Research Clinics Coronary Primary Prevention Trial. I. Reduction in incidence of coronary heart disease. JAMA 1984;251:351–64.

48. The Lipid Research Clinics Program. The Lipid Research Clinics Coronary Primary Prevention Trial. II. The relationship of reduction in incidence of coronary heart disease to cholesterol lowering. JAMA 1984;251:365–74.

49. Anderson KM, Wilson PWF, Odell PM, Kannel WB. An updated coronary risk profile. A statement for health professionals. AHA medical/scientific statement science advisory. Circulation 1991;83:356–62.

50. Stamler J, Wentworth D, Neaton JD. Is the relationship between serum cholesterol and risk of premature death from coronary heart disease continuous and graded? Findings in 356,222 primary screenees of the Multiple Risk Factor Intervention Trial (MRFIT). JAMA 1986;256:2823–8.

51. Dayton S, Pearce ML, Hashimoto S, Dixon WJ, Tomiyasu U. A controlled clinical trial of

a diet high in unsaturated fat in preventing complications of atherosclerosis. Circulation 1969;40(Suppl II):11–63.

52. Hjermann I, Holme I, Byre KV, Leren P. Effect of diet and smoking intervention on the incidence of coronary heart disease. Lancet 1981;2:1303–10.

53. Holme I, Hjermann I, Helgelend A, Leren P. The Oslo Study. Diet and anti-smoking advice: additional results from a 5-y primary prevention trial in middle-aged men. Prev Med 1985;14:279–92.

54. Miettinen M, Karvonen MJ, Turpeiner O, Elosuo R, Paavilainen F. Effect of cholesterol-lowering diet on mortality from coronary heart disease and other causes: a 12-y clinical trial in men and women. Lancet 1972;2(782):835–8.

55. Ornish D, Brown SK, Scherwitz LW, et al. Can lifestyle changes reverse coronary heart disease? Lancet 1990;326:129–33.

56. Leren P. The effect of plasma-cholesterol-lowering diet in male survivors of myocardial infarction. Acta Med Scand 1966;466(Suppl):92–116.

57. de Lorgeril M, Renaud S, Mamelle N, Salen P, Martin JL, Monjaud I, et al. Mediterranean alpha-linolenic acid-rich diet in secondary prevention of coronary heart disease. Lancet 1994;343:1454–9.

58. Canner PL, Berge KG, Wenger NK, et al. Fifteen-year mortality in Coronary Drug Project patients: long-term benefit with niacin. J Am Coll Cardiol 1986;8:1245–55.

59. Carlson LA, Rosenhamer G. Reduction of mortality in the Stockholm Ischemic Heart Disease Study by combined treatment with clofibrate and nicotinic acid. Acta Med Scand 1988;223:405–18.

60. Frick MH, Elo O, Haapa K, et al. Helsinki Heart Study: primary prevention trial with gemfibrozil in middle-aged men with dyslipidemia. N Engl J Med 1987;317:1237–45.

61. Manninen V, Elo O, Frick MH, et al. Lipid alterations and decline in the incidence of coronary heart disease in the Helsinki Heart Study. JAMA 1988;260:641–51.

62. Manninen V, Tenkanen L, Koskinen P, et al. Joint effects of serum triglyceride and LDL cholesterol and HDL cholesterol concentrations on coronary heart disease risk in the Helsinki Heart Study: implication for treatment. Circulation 1992;85:37–45.

63. Scandinavian Simvastatin Survival Study Group. Randomized trial of cholesterol lowering in 4444 patients with coronary heart disease: the Scandinavian Simvastatin Survival Study (4S). Lancet 1994;344:383–9.

64. Pedersen TR, Kjekshus J, Berg K, Olsson AG, Wilhelmsen L, Wiedel H, et al. Cholesterol lowering and the use of healthcare resources: results of the Scandinavian Simvastatin Survival Study. Circulation 1996;93:1796–802.

65. Byington RP, Jukema JA, Salonen JT, Pitt B, Bruschke AV, et al. Reduction in cardiovascular events during pravastatin therapy. Pooled analysis of clinical events of the Pravastatin Atherosclerosis Intervention Program. Circulation 1995;92:2419–25.

66. Shepherd J, Cobbe SM, Ford I, Isles CG, Lorimer AR, MacFarlane PW, McKillop JH, Packard CJ. Prevention of coronary heart disease with pravastatin in men with hypercholesterolemia: West of Scotland Coronary Prevention Study Group. N Engl J Med 1995;333:1301–7.

67. Sacks FM, Pfeffer MA, Moye LA, Rouleau JL, Rutherford JD, Cole TG, et al. The effect of pravastatin on coronary events after myocardial infarction in patients with average cholesterol levels: Cholesterol and Recurrent Events Trial investigators. N Engl J Med 1996;335:1001–9.

68. Downs JR, Clearfield M, Weis S, et al. Primary prevention of acute coronary events with lovastatin in men and women with average cholesterol levels. Results of AFCAPS/TexCAPS. JAMA 1998;279:1615–61.

69. The Long-Term Intervention with Pravastatin in Ischemic Disease (LIPID) Study Group. Prevention of cardiovascular events and death with pravastatin in patients with coronary heart disease and a broad range of initial cholesterol levels. N Engl J Med 1998;339:1349–57.

70. Haskell WL, Alderman EL, Fair JM, Maron DJ, Mackey SF, Superko HR, et al. Effects of intensive multiple risk factor reduction on coronary atherosclerosis and clinical cardiac

events in men and women with coronary artery disease: the Stanford Coronary Risk Intervention Project (SCRIP). Circulation 1994;89:975–90.

71. Blankenhorn DH, Nessim SA, Johnson RL, Sanmarco ME, Azen SP, Cashin-Hemphill L. Beneficial effects of combined colestipol-niacin therapy on coronary atherosclerosis and coronary venous bypass grafts. JAMA 1987;257:3233–40.

72. Blankenhorn DN, Azen SP, Kramsch DM, et al. Coronary angiographic changes with lovastatin therapy: the monitored atherosclerosis regression study (MARS). Ann Intern Med 1993;1119:969–76.

73. Brensike JF, Levy RI, Kelsey SF, et al. Effects of therapy with cholestyramine on progression of coronary atherosclerosis: results of the NHLBI Type II Coronary Intervention Study. Circulation 1984;69:313–24.

74. Brown BG, Zhao XQ, Sacco DE, Albers JJ. Lipid lowering and plaque regression: new insights into prevention of plaque disruption and clinical events in coronary disease. Circulation 1993;87:1781–91.

75. Brown BG, Albers JJ, Fisher LD, et al. Regression of coronary artery disease as a result of intensive lipid-lowering therapy in men with high levels of apolipoprotein B. N Engl J Med 1990;323:1289–98.

76. Buchwald H, Varco RL, Matts JP, Long JM, Fitch LL, Campbell GS. Effect of partial ileal bypass surgery on mortality and morbidity from coronary heart disease in patients with hypercholesterolemia: report of the Program on Surgical Control of the Hyperlipidemias (POSCH). N Engl J Med 1990;323:946–55.

77. Fuster V, Badimon L, Badimon JJ, Chesbro JH. The pathogenesis of coronary artery disease and the acute coronary syndrome. N Engl J Med 1992;326:242–56, 310–18.

78. Kane JP, Malloy MJ, Ports TA, Phillips NR, Diehl JC, Havel RJ. Regression of coronary atherosclerosis during treatment of familial hypercholesterolemia with combined drug regimens. JAMA 1990;264:3007–12.

79. Watts GF, Lewis B, Brunt JNH, et al. Effects on coronary artery disease lipid-lowering diet: a diet plus cholestyramine in the St. Thomas Atherosclerosis Regression Study (STARS). Lancet 1992;339:563–9.

80. Schuler G, Hambrecht R, Schlierf G, et al. Regular exercise and low-fat diet: effects on progression of coronary artery disease. Circulation 1992;86:1–11.

81. Pitt B, Waters D, Brown WV, et al. Aggressive lipid-lowering therapy compared with angioplasty in stable coronary artery disease. Atorvastatin versus Revascularization Treatment Investigators. N Engl J Med 1999;341:70–6.

82. NIH Consensus Conference. Lowering blood cholesterol to prevent heart disease. JAMA 1985;253:2080–6.

83. NIH Consensus Conference. Triglyceride, HDL cholesterol, and coronary heart disease. JAMA 1993;269:505–10.

84. Hokanson JE, Austin MA, Plasma triglyceride level as a risk factor for cardiovascular disease independent of high-density lipoprotein cholesterol level: a meta-analysis of population-based prospective studies. J Cardiovasc Risk 1996;3:213–19.

85. Gordon DJ, Knoke J, Probstfeld JL, Superko R, Tyroler HA. High-density lipoprotein cholesterol and coronary heart disease in hypercholesterolemic men: the Lipid Research Clinics Coronary Primary Prevention Trial. Circulation 1986;74:1217–25.

86. Gordon DJ, Rifkind BM. High-density lipoprotein: the clinical implications of recent studies. N Engl J Med 1989;321:1311–16.

87. Rubins HB, Robins SJ, Collins D, et al. Gemfibrozil for the secondary prevention of coronary heart disease in men with low levels of high-density lipoprotein cholesterol. N Engl J Med 1999;342:410–8.

88. Haim M, Benderly M, Brunner D, et al. Elevated serum triglyceride and long-term mortality in patients with coronary heart disease: the Bezafibrate Infarction Prevention (BIP) Registry. Circulation 1999;100:475–82.

89. Kaufman HW, McNamara JR, Anderson KM, Wilson PWF, Schaefer EJ. How reliably can compact chemistry analyzers measure lipids? JAMA 1990;263:1245–9.

90. Bard RL, Kaminsky LA, Whaley MH, Zajakowski S. Evaluation of lipid profile measure-

ments obtained from the Cholestech L.D.X. analyzer. J Cardiopulm Rehabil 1997;17: 413–8.

91. Laboratory Standardization Panel. Current status of blood cholesterol measurement in clinical laboratories in the United States: a report from the Laboratory Standardization Panel of the National Cholesterol Education Program. Clin Chem 1988;34:193–201.

92. Stein EA, Myers GL, for the National Cholesterol Education Program Working Group on Lipoprotein Measurement. National Cholesterol Education Program recommendations for triglyceride measurement: executive summary. Clin Chem 1995;41: 1421–6.

93. Warnick GR, Wood PD, for the National Cholesterol Education Program Working Group on Lipoprotein Measurement. National Cholesterol Education Program recommendations for measurement of high-density lipoprotein cholesterol: executive summary. Clin Chem 1995;41:1427–33.

94. Bachorik PS, Ross JW, for the National Cholesterol Education Program Working Group on Lipoprotein Measurement. National Cholesterol Education Program recommendations for measurement of low-density lipoprotein cholesterol: executive summary. Clin Chem 1995;41:1414–20.

95. Friedewald WT, Levy RI, Fredrickson DS. Estimation of the concentration of low-density lipoproteins cholesterol without use of the preparative ultracentrifuge. Clin Chem 1972;18:499–502.

96. McNamara JR, Cohn JS, Wilson PWF, Schaefer EJ. Calculated values for low-density lipoprotein cholesterol in the assessement of lipid abnormalities and coronary disease risk. Clin Chem 1990;36:36–42.

97. Cooper GR, Smith SJ, Myers GL, Sampson EJ, Magid E. Estimating and minimizing effects of biologic sources of variation by relative range when measuring the mean of serum lipids and lipoproteins. Clin Chem 1994;40:227–32.

98. Genest JJ, Corbett H, McNamara JR, Schaefer MM, Salem DN, Schaefer EJ. Effect of hospitalization on high-density lipoprotein cholesterol in patients undergoing elective coronary angiography. Amer J Cardiol 1988;61:998–1000.

99. Avogaro P, Bittolo Bon G, Cazzolato G, Quinci GB. Are apolipoproteins better discriminators than lipids for atherosclerosis? Lancet 1979;1:901–3.

100. Sniderman A, Shapiro S, Marpole D, Skinner B, Teng B, Kwiterovich PO Jr. Association of coronary atherosclerosis with hyperapobetalipoproteinemia (increased protein but normal cholesterol levels in human plasma low-density lipoproteins). Proc Natl Acad Sci USA. 1980;77:604–8.

101. Whayne TF, Alaupovic P, Curry MD, Lee ET, Anderson PS, Snecter E. Plasma apolipoprotein B and VLDL-, LDL-, and HDL-cholesterol as risk factors in the development of coronary artery disease in male patients examined by angiography. Atherosclerosis 1981;39:411–24.

102. Kwiterovich PO Jr, Bachorik PS, Smith HH, et al. Hyperapobetalipoproteinaemia in two families with xanthomas and phytosterolaemia. Lancet 1981;1:466–9.

103. Maciejko JJ, Holmes DR, Kottke BA, Zinsmeister AR, Dinh DM, Mao SJT. Apolipoprotein A-I as a marker of angiographically assessed coronary artery disease. N Engl J Med 1983;309:385–9.

104. Austin MA, Breslow JL, Hennekens CH, Buring JE, Willett WC, Krauss RM. Low-density lipoprotein subclass patterns and risk of myocardial infarction. JAMA 1988;260: 1917–21.

105. Graziani MS, Zanolla L, Righetti G, Marchetti C, Mocarelli P, Marcovina SM. Plasma apolipoprotein A-I and B in survivors of myocardial infarction and in a control group. Clin Chem 1998;44:134–40.

106. Campos H, Genest JJ, Blijlevens E, et al. Low-density lipoprotein particle size and coronary artery disease. Arterioscler Thromb 1992;12:187–95.

107. Stampfer MJ, Krauss RM, Ma J, Blanche PJ, Holl LG, Sacks FM, Hennekens CH. A prospective study of triglyceride level, low-density lipoprotein particle diameter, and risk of myocardial infarction. JAMA 1996;276:882–8.

108. Ishikawa T, Fidge N, Thelle DS, Forde DH, Miller NE. The Tromso Heart Study: serum apolipoprotein A-I concentration in relation to future coronary heart disease. Eur J Clin Invest 1978;8:179–82.

109. Salonen JT, Salonen R, Penttila I, et al. Serum fatty acids, apolipoproteins, selenium and vitamin antioxidants and the risk of death from coronary artery disease. Am J Cardiol 1985;56:226–31.

110. Stampfer MJ, Sacks FM, Salvini S, Willett WC, Hennekens CH. A prospective study of cholesterol, apolipoproteins, and the risk of myocardial infarction. N Engl J Med 1991;325:373–81.

111. Coleman MP, Key TJ, Wang DY, et al. A prospective study of obesity, lipids, apolipoproteins, and ischemic heart disease in women. Atherosclerosis 1992;92: 177–85.

112. Wald NJ, Law M, Watt HC, Wu T, Bailey A, Johnson AM, Craig WY, Ledue TB, Haddow JE. Apolipoproteins and ischemic heart disease: implications for screening. Lancet 1994;343:75–79.

113. Lamarche B, Despres JP, Moorjani S, Cantin B, Dagenais GR, Lupien P-J. Prevalence of dyslipidemic phenotypes in ischemic heart disease (prospective results from the Quebec Cardiovascular Study). Am J Cardiol 1995;75:1189–95.

114. Marcovina SM, Albers JJ, Henderson LO, Hannon WH. International Federation of Clinical Chemistry standardization project for measurements of apolipoproteins A-I and B. III. Comparability of apolipoprotein A-I values by use of international reference material. Clin Chem 1993;39:773–81.

115. Marcovina SM, Albers JJ, Kennedy H, Mei JV, Henderson LO, Hannon WH. International Federation of Chemistry standardization project for measurements of apolipoproteins A-I and B. IV. Comparability of apolipoprotein B values by use of international reference material. Clin Chem 1994;40:586–92.

116. Contois JH, McNamara JR, Lammi-Keefe CJ, Wilson PWF, Schaefer EJ. Reference intervals for plasma apolipoprotein A-I as determined with a commercially available immunoturbidometric assay: results from the Framingham Offspring Study. Clin Chem 1996;42:507–14.

117. Contois JH, McNamara JR, Lammi-Keefe CJ, Wilson PWF, Schaefer EJ. Reference intervals for plasma apolipoprotein B as determined with a commercially available immunoturbidometric assay: results from the Framingham Offspring Study. Clin Chem 1996;42:515–23.

118. Alfthan G, Pekkanen J, Juuhiainen M, Pitkaniemi J, Karvonen M, Tuomilehto J, Salonen JT, Ehnholm C. Relation of serum homocysteine and lipoprotein(a) concentrations to atherosclerotic disease in a prospective Finnish population-based study. Atherosclerosis 1994;106:9–19.

119. Schaefer EJ, Lamon-Fava S, Jenner JL, McNamara JR, Ordovas JM, Davis E, Abolafia JM, Lippel K, Levy RI. Lipoprotein(a) levels and risk of coronary heart disease in men. The Lipid Research Clinics Coronary Primary Prevention Trial. JAMA 1994;271: 999–1003.

120. Kronenberg F, Kronenberg MF, Kiechl S, et al. Role of lipoprotein(a) and apolipoprotein(a) phenotype in atherogenesis: prospective results from the Bruneck study. Circulation 1999;100:1154–60.

121. Carlson LA, Hamsten A, Asplund A. Pronounced lowering of serum lipoprotein Lp(a) in hyperlipidemic subjects treated with nicotinic acid. J Intern Med 1989;226:271–6.

122. Goldstein JL, Schrott HG, Hazzard WR, Bierman EL, Motulsky AG. Hyperlipidemia in coronary heart disease. II. Genetic analysis of lipid levels in 176 families and delineation of new inherited disorder, combined hyperlipidemia. J Clin Invest 1973;52: 1544–68.

123. Goldstein JL, Brown MS. Familial hypercholesterolemia. In: Stanbury JB, Wyngaarden JB, et al. (eds). The metabolic basis of inherited disease, 5th ed. New York: McGraw Hill, 1983:672–712.

124. Janus ED, Nicoll AM, Turner PR, Magill P, Lewis B. Kinetic bases of the primary

hyperlipidemias: studies of apolipoprotein B turnover in genetically defined subjects. Eur J Clin Invest 1980;10:161–72.

125. Chait A, Albers JJ, Brunzell JD. Very-low-density lipoprotein overproduction in genetic forms of hypertriglyceridemia. Eur J Clin Invest 1980;10:17–22.

126. Schaefer EJ. Hyperlipoproteinemia. In: Rakel RE (ed). Conn's current therapy. Philadelphia: W. B. Saunders, 1991:515–24.

127. Rall SC Jr, Weisgraber KH, Innerarity TL, Mahley RW. Structural basis for receptor-binding heterogeneity of apolipoprotein E from type III hyperlipoproteinemic subjects. Proc Natl Acad Sci USA 1982;79:4696–700.

128. Schaefer EJ, Gregg RE, Ghiselli G, et al. Familial apolipoprotein E deficiency. J Clin Invest 1986;78:1206–19.

129. Schaefer EJ. Dietary and drug treatment. In: Brewer HB Jr., moderator. Type III hyperlipoproteinemia: diagnosis, molecular defects, pathology and treatment. Ann Int Med 1983;98:623–40.

130. Ordovas JM, Litwack-Klein LE, Schaefer MM, Wilson PWF, Schaefer EJ. Apolipoprotein E isoform phenotyping methodology and population frequency with identification and apo E1 and apo E5 isoforms. J Lipid Res 1987;28:371–80.

131. Fredrickson DS, Levy RI , Lees RS. Fat transport in lipoprotein: an integrated approach to mechanisms and disorders. N Engl J Med 1967;276:34–44, 94–103, 148–56, 215–25, 273–81.

132. Brown MS, Goldstein JL. The LDL receptor concept: clinical and therapeutic implications. In: Stokes J III, Mancini M, eds. Hypercholesterolemia: clinical and therapeutic implications. Atherosclerosis Reviews 1987, Vol 18. New York: Raven Press. 1988: 85–94.

133. Innerarity TL, Weisgraber KH, Arnold KS, et al. Familial defective apolipoprotein B-100: low-density lipoproteins with abnormal receptor binding. Proc Natl Acad Sci 1987;84:6919–25.

134. Langer T, Strober W, Levy RI. The metabolism of low-density lipoprotein in familial type II hyperlipoproteinemia. J Clin Invest 1972;51:1528–36.

135. Kane JP, Malloy MJ, Tun P, et al. Normalization of low-density lipoprotein levels in heterozygous familial hypercholesterolemia with a combined drug regimen. New Engl J Med 1981;304:251–8.

136. Mabuchi H, Sakai T, Sakai Y. Reduction of serum cholesterol in heterozygous patients with familial hypercholesterolemia: additive effects of compactin and cholestyramine. New Engl J Med 1983;308:609–19.

137. Hunninghake DB, Stein FA, Dujorne CA, et al. The efficacy of intensive dietary therapy alone or combined with lovastatin in outpatients with hypercholesterolemia. New Engl J Med 1993;328:1213–19.

138. Genest JJ Jr, Bard JM, Fruchart JC, Ordovas JM, Schaefer EJ. Familial hypoalphalipoproteinemia in premature coronary artery disease. Arterioscler Thromb 1993;13:1728–37.

139. Vergani C, Bettale A. Familial hypoalphalipoproteinemia. Clin Chim Acta 1981; 114:45–52.

140. Third JLHC, Montag J, Flynn M, Freidel J, Laskarzewski P, Glueck CJ. Primary and familial hypoalphalipoproteinemia. Metabolism 1984;33:136–46.

141. Lichtenstein AH, Ausman LM, Carrasco W, et al. Effects of canola, corn, and olive oils on fasting and postprandial plasma lipoproteins in humans as part of a National Cholesterol Education Program Step 2 diet. Arterioscler Thromb 1993;13:1533–42.

142. Schaefer EJ, Lichtenstein AH, Lamon-Fava S, Contois JH, Li Z, Rasmussen H, McNamara JR, Ordovas JM. Efficacy of a National Cholesterol Education Program Step 2 diet in normolipidemic and hyperlipidemic middle-aged and elderly men and women. Arterioscler Thromb Vasc Biol 1995;15:1079–85.

143. Schaefer EJ, Lichtenstein AH, Lamon-Fava S, McNamara JR, Schaefer MM, Rasmussen H, Ordovas JM. Body weight and low-density lipoprotein cholesterol changes after consumption of a low-fat *ad libitum* diet. JAMA 1995;274:1450–55.

144. Schaefer EJ, Lichtenstein AH, Lamon-Fava S, Contois JH, Li Z, Goldin BR, Rasmussen H, McNamara JR, Ordovas JM. Effects of National Cholesterol Education Program Step 2 diets relatively high or relatively low in fish-derived fatty acids on plasma lipoproteins in middle-aged and elderly subjects. Am J Clin Nutr 1996;63:234–41.

145. Krauss RM, Deckelbaum RJ, Ernst N, Fisher E, Howard BV, Knopp RH, et al. Dietary guideline for healthy American adults: a statement for health professionals from the Nutrition Committee, American Heart Association. Circulation 1996;94:1795–1800.

146. Schlant RC, Forman S, Stamler J, Canner PL. The natural history of coronary heart disease: prognostic factors after recovery from myocardial infarction in 2,787 men. The 5-year findings of the Coronary Drug Project. Circulation 1982;66:401–14.

147. Stampfer MJ, Colditz GA, Willett WC, Manson JE, Posner B, Speizer FE, Hennekens CH. Postmenopausal estrogen therapy and cardiovascular disease. N Engl J Med 1991;325:756–62.

148. Kim CJ, Jang HC, Min YK. Effect of hormone replacement therapy on lipoprotein(a) and lipids in post-menopausal women. Arterioscler Thromb 1994;14:275–81.

149. Hulley S, Grady D, Bush T, Furberg C, Herrington D, Riggs B, Vittinghoff E. Randomized trial of estrogen plus progestin for secondary prevention of coronary heart disease in postmenopausal women. Heart and Estrogen/progestin Replacement Study (HERS) Research Group. JAMA 1998;280:605–13.

The System of Cardiovascular Prevention

6

Marek H. Dominiczak and Judith R. McNamara

✧ Cardiovascular prevention is about preventing, or delaying, the development of atherosclerosis and its clinical consequences: coronary heart disease (CHD), stroke, and peripheral vascular disease. The risk of subsequent cardiac events in persons who already suffer from atherosclerotic disease is several times higher than the risk of event in a healthy individual. This risk differential has been the basis for dividing preventive activities into primary prevention (prevention in healthy individuals) and secondary prevention (prevention of subsequent events in persons who suffer from atherosclerotic disease).

The main components of cardiovascular prevention are risk stratification (to determine the probability of an individual experiencing an atherosclerosis-related event), and subsequent management (tailored to the level of risk). Management involves lifestyle modifications and a range of cardioprotective therapies.

The diversity of factors that affect atherosclerosis makes cardiovascular prevention, by definition, multidisciplinary. This chapter illustrates how knowledge about cardiovascular risk factors has been translated into clinical practice, and describes the system of cardiovascular prevention necessary for the effective management of risk. We emphasize the role of clinical laboratories in supporting clinical practice and research in the field. More details on the significance of risk factors other than lipids are given in chapter 4.

APPLICATION OF LIPID HYPOTHESIS TO CLINICAL PRACTICE

Increased serum concentration of total cholesterol (TC) and LDL-cholesterol (LDL-C), and low concentration of HDL-cholesterol (HDL-C), are major cardiovascular risk factors. The significance of an increased triglyceride (TG) concentration is still under discussion, but there is little doubt that it also contributes to the risk. Here, we discuss the key clinical trials that led to the establishment of lipid-lowering treatment as one of mainstays of cardiovascular prevention.

The association between lipids and atherosclerosis was observed at the beginning of this century.[1] The recent article by Steinberg and Gotto recalls research that led to the elucidation of the role of lipids in atherosclerosis and the rationale for the treatment of dyslipidemia.[2] The lipid hypothesis of atherosclerosis, which says that the deposition of LDL in arteries is proportional to its concentration in plasma, was formulated in the 1950s.[1] This complemented the "response to injury hypothesis" developed by Ross, which emphasized cellular, mitogenic, and growth factor responses to endothelial injury. Both hypotheses were subsequently combined into one theory.[3,4,5]

Since then, the concept of atherosclerosis as chronic, low-grade inflammation, probably caused by oxidative processes that generate free radicals and toxic products such as modified LDL or homocysteine, gained acceptance.[6,7] Low-grade inflammation can be monitored by measuring C-reactive protein (CRP) with a sensitive method.[8] Meta-analysis of available studies on CRP suggests that patients who fall in the top one third of CRP concentration levels have a relative risk (RR) of CHD of 1.7 compared to those who fall in the lowest third of the population distribution (see chapter 4). There is presently no conclusive evidence that infections of *Chlamydia pneumoniae*, *Helicobacter pylori*, or periodontal disease play a role as causal factors in atherosclerosis.[9]

The role of lipids in atherogenesis is now supported by extensive evidence that lowering cholesterol concentration in plasma decreases CHD mortality and morbidity.[10] Indeed, recent data show that cholesterol lowering might be equally important in the prevention of stroke.[11–14] Recent meta-analysis of five major clinical trials of treatment with statins (two in primary prevention and three in secondary prevention) suggests a 31% reduction in coronary events and 29% reduction in coronary deaths. For all trials combined, the treatment led to a 21% reduction in the risk of death from any cause and 27% reduction in the risk of cardiovascular death.[15] In pooled secondary prevention trials, the reduction in the risk of death from any cause was 23% ($p<0.001$). However, when the primary prevention trials were analyzed separately, reduction in all-cause mortality did not reach statistical significance (RR reduction 13%, $p=0.18$).

Cholesterol Lowering in Secondary Prevention

Statins are drugs that inhibit hydroxymethylglutaryl-CoA (HMG-CoA) reductase, the rate-limiting enzyme in cholesterol synthesis. The evidence for the clinical benefit of lowering cholesterol with statins is particularly strong in secondary prevention. Clinical trials such as the Scandinavian Simvastatin Survival Study (4S),[12] the Cholesterol and Recurrent Events (CARE),[11] and the Long-Term Intervention with Pravastatin in Ischemic Disease (LIPID)[13] demonstrated a decrease in cardiovascular mortality when cholesterol was lowered. For the first time since the 15-year follow-up results of Coronary Drug Trial in 1986,[16] 4S and LIPID confirmed a decrease in total mortality in the treatment group. In the Coronary Drug Trial, there was an 11% decrease in mortality in the niacin-treated group.[16]

The 4S involved 4444 patients with a history of either myocardial infarction (MI) or angina with a positive exercise test. The age of participants was between 35 and 70 years and 18% were women. Cholesterol levels at entry were between 212 mg/dL and 309 mg/dL (5.5–8.0 mmol/L; average 259 mg/dL, 6.7mmol/L). In the statin-treated group, total mortality decreased by 30%.[12] Importantly, apart from all-cause mortality, several secondary endpoints also indicated clinical benefit, e.g, coronary death decreased by 42% and the incidence of coronary events decreased by 34%.

In the LIPID trial, the participants had a history of MI or unstable angina at entry. There were 9014 patients aged 31 to 75 years with TC levels of 155 mg/dL to 271 mg/dL (4.0–7.0 mmol/L). Fasting TG level was no more than 445 mg/dL (5.0 mmol/L). The primary endpoint was the death from CHD; death from any cause was one of the secondary outcomes. TC in the treatment group decreased by 18% from the initial level of 218 mg/dL (5.6 mmol/L). LDL-C decreased by 25% from 150 mg/dL (3.9 mmol/L) but at the six-years point, the difference in TC between the treatment and placebo group decreased to 13%. TG decreased by 11% from the initial level of 142 mg/dL (1.6 mmol/L). Initial HDL-C level was 36 mg/dL (0.93 mmol/L) and it increased on treatment by 5% in comparison with the placebo group. Total mortality decreased by 24%: the incidence of cardiovascular death in the treatment group was 6.4% and in the placebo group 8.3%. This represents a 24% decrease on treatment (confidence intervals [CI] 12%–95%; p<0.001). In addition, all-cause mortality decreased from 14.1% in the placebo group to 11% in the treatment group, which corresponds to 22% relative reduction (CI 13%–31%; p<0.001). There was also a 29% reduction in the incidence of non-fatal MI and a 19% reduction in the incidence of stroke (p=0.048).[13]

The CARE trial[11] tested the benefits of lipid lowering in patients with a history of myocardial infarction and "normal" cholesterol concentration. TC levels were below 240 mg/dL (6.2 mmol/L) and a mean LDL-C was 139 mg/dL (3.6 mmol/L) . The study population—86% men and 14% women—was treated with pravastatin for five years. Overall, there was a 20% reduction in serum TC and a 24% decrease in the combined CHD deaths and MI. CARE results suggest that the LDL-C concentration below 125 mg/dL (3.2 mmol/L) is not associated with further decrease in risk.

Another study, the Post-Coronary Artery Bypass Graft (CABG), compared two lipid-lowering therapies of different intensity. The trial was conducted in patients with LDL-C levels of 130–175 mg/dL (3.4–4.5 mmol/L). An average 4.3 years' aggressive lowering of cholesterol with statin, and cholestyramine where appropriate, lowered LDL-C to a mean level of 93–99 mg/dL (2.4–2.6 mmol/L) in the intensive treatment group.[17] This was associated with a significant decrease in atherosclerosis progression (in 27% of grafts), compared to a group that received a less intensive cholesterol-lowering regimen (39% of grafts), resulting in LDL-C levels of 132–136 mg/dL (3.4–3.5 mmol/L). In the intensively treated group the percentage of revascularization procedures was 29% lower. Low-dose warfarin did not reduce the progression of atherosclerosis.

While the above data confirm that lowering cholesterol is indeed beneficial, the status of TG as an independent risk factor is still controversial. In the above trials, the average initial TG levels were below 221 mg/dL (2.5 mmol/L) (4S); 156 mg/dL (1.76 mmol/L) (CARE); 156–160 mg/dL (1.76–1.80 mmol/L) (CABG); and 140 mg/dL (1.58 mmol/L) (LIPID). Recent meta-analysis suggest that TG concentrations do affect risk, if only to a moderate extent.[18]

Non-Statin Secondary Prevention Trials

The second major group of lipid-lowering drugs are the derivatives of fibric acid, such as gemfibrozil, bezafibrate, fenofibrate, or ciprofibrate. Fibrates have a limited cholesterol-lowering potential, but they lower TG concentration better than statins, and increase HDL-C to a greater degree. They affect gene expression of several apoproteins by acting through the activation of transcription factors known as peroxisome-proliferator-activated receptors (PPARs), in particular, PPAR-alpha.[19]

Several recent trials addressed the role of fibrates in cardiovascular prevention. The Bezafibrate Infarction Prevention Study (BIP) was a 6.4-year trial in 3122 patients with stable CHD. Initial TC measurements ranged from 180–250 mg/dL (4.65–6.46 mmol/L); TG measured < 300 mg/dL (3.39 mmol/L); and HDL-C < 45 mg/dL (1.15 mmol/L). Bezafibrate lowered TC only by 4% and LDL-C by 5%. However, it lowered TG by a significant 22% and raised HDL-C by 12%. There was no significant reduction in cardiovascular events in the treatment group, although *post-hoc* analysis indicated a 40% risk reduction in a group of patients with TG levels of 200 mg/dL (2.26 mmol/L) and above.[20]

Another trial that used bezafibrate was the Bezafibrate Coronary Atherosclerosis Intervention Trial (BECAIT), an angiographic study in young male survivors of myocardial infarction.[21] Most of these survivors had mild to moderate mixed hyperlipidemia, with mean TG at 216 mg/dL (2.44 mmol/L) and LDL-C at 180 mg/dL (4.66 mmol/L). They were treated with bezafibrate for five years. As a result, serum TC decreased by 14%, TG decreased by 26%, and HDL-C increased by 9%. There was also a 12% decrease in plasma fibrinogen level, and no change in LDL-C concentration. After five years, minimum coronary diameter decreased less in the bezafibrate group, but there were no differences in the rate of progression or regression of angiographic changes. The combination of coronary events and revascularization procedures was lower in the bezafibrate-treated group.

Another fibrate, gemfibrozil, was used in the recent Veterans Affairs Cooperative Studies Program High-Density-Lipoprotein Cholesterol Intervention Trial (VA-HIT), a study with a median follow-up period of 5.1 years.[115] The participants were 2531 men with CHD (mean age 64 years); 25% of participants had diabetes and 57% had hypertension. Mean HDL-C was 32 mg/dL (0.8mmol/L); LDL-C, 111 mg/dL (2.9 mmol/L); TC, 175 mg/dL (4.5 mmol/L); and TG, 160 mg/dL (1.8 mmol/L). At one year after randomization. TG decreased 31%, HDL-C increased 6%, and TC decreased 4%. In contrast to the BIP trial, there was a 22% (CI 7%–35%) reduction in the cardiovascular event rate in the treatment group.

Primary Prevention Trials

The results of secondary prevention trials are now corroborated by primary prevention studies. The West of Scotland Coronary Prevention Study (WOSCOPS) involved only men, aged 45–64 years, with average TC levels of 272 mg/dL (7.0 mmol/L), and an average LDL-C of 192 mg/dL (5.0 mmol/L); the average TG level was 164 mg/dL (1.85 mmol/L). The men were treated with pravastatin for an average of 4.9 years. A 20% decrease in cholesterol, achieved with pravastatin, decreased the risk of myocardial infarction or coronary death 31%. Although this was not the primary endpoint, there was a 22% decrease (p=0.051) in total mortality.[22]

The Air Force/Texas Coronary Atherosclerosis Prevention Study (AFCAPS/TexCAPS) is the recent trial of the use of lovastatin for the prevention of first coronary event, defined as fatal or non-fatal MI, unstable angina, or sudden cardiac death, in

6605 men and women who had no history of clinical CHD.[23] Participants ranged in age from 45 (men) and 55 (women) years to 73 years. Average TC concentration was 221 mg/dL (5.71 mmol/L) and average LDL-C, 150 mg/dL (3.89 mmol/L). Median TG in the treatment group was 141 mg/dL (1.59 mmol/L). Importantly, HDL-C was low: 36 mg/dL (0.94 mmol/L) in men and 40 mg/dL (1.03 mmol/L) in women. After 5.2 years, TC decreased by 18%, LDL-C decreased by 25%, and HDL-C increased by 6%. TC to HDL ratio decreased by 22%. At the end of the study, 42% of treated individuals reached LDL-C level ≤ 110 mg/dL (2.84 mmol/L) and 81% ≤ 130 mg/dL (3.36 mmol/L). Lovastatin reduced the incidence of events by 37% (CI 0.50–0.79; p<0.001).

Angiographic Trials

Clinical studies that used angiographic data as endpoints provide insight into the effects of cholesterol lowering on development of arterial occlusion.

❖ The landmark Cholesterol Lowering of Atherosclerosis Study (CLAS), which involved approximately 200 patients with a history of coronary artery bypass grafting, demonstrated reduced progression of coronary artery stenosis after two years of treatment with nicotinic acid and colestipol.[24]

❖ The Pravastatin Limitation of Atherosclerosis in Coronary Arteries (PLAC1) study demonstrated a 30%–40% decrease in the progression of the lesions over 36 months, and a reduction in the number of events after 12 months of treatment.[25]

❖ The Multicenter Anti-Atheroma Study (MAAS) and Regression Growth Evaluation Statin Study (REGRESS) employed quantitative coronary angiography. MAAS demonstrated less angiographic progression and more frequent regression in the simvastatin-treated group.[26] REGRESS demonstrated an average 0.04-mm decrease in mean segment diameter in the pravastatin-treated group.[27]

❖ Two studies demonstrated a particularly large decrease in clinical events: the Familial Atherosclerosis Treatment Study (FATS), where intensive cholesterol lowering that included lovastatin and colestipol showed as much as 73% reduction,[28] and the St. Thomas Atherosclerosis Regression Study (STARS), which showed an 89% reduction in events in a group treated with diet and cholestyramine.[29]

❖ In the Program on the Surgical Control of the Hyperlipidemias (POSCH), where cholesterol lowering was induced by partial ileal bypass surgery, the incidence of fatal and non-fatal myocardial infarction decreased after 12 years' follow up.[30]

Recent exciting animal data suggest that HDL plays a role in plaque regression; Tangirala et al. observed regression of atherosclerosis after somatic gene transfer of apolipoprotein A-I (apo A-I) in LDL receptor-deficient mice, a mouse model of familial hypercholesterolemia.[31] The lesion surface area decreased over a period of four weeks and there were fewer macrophages and foam cells in the lesions (see chapter

1). The HDL-mediated regression may well include not only cholesterol efflux, but also other metabolic, oxidative, or inflammatory processes.[31,32]

The Atherosclerotic Plaque

Let's now examine how this clinical and anatomical evidence for the benefit of cholesterol lowering fits with our current views on atherogenesis. Arterial wall consists of three layers: the intima, the media, and the adventitia. Normally the artery remains in a state of dynamic relaxation mediated by nitric oxide[33–35] and also by prostacyclin and acetylcholine.[36,37] Vascular endothelium plays a key role in the function of the vascular wall. The endothelium regulates vascular tone, and controls thrombogenesis, leukocyte adhesion, and the breakdown of collagen. It is an active regulator of cell growth and participates in inflammatory phenomena.

Functional damage to the endothelium is an early event in atherogenesis, and the permeability of the arterial wall to LDL may play a role.[38] Endothelial function is affected by a number of substances, such as oxidized LDL.[39,40,41] When the endothelium was removed in cholesterol-fed rabbits, superoxide production increased.[42,43] The degree of impairment of endothelial function correlates with cholesterol level,[44] and the reduction of cholesterol level improves endothelial function.[45,46] During apheresis, for example, endothelial function improves almost instantly with cholesterol lowering and it improves after about two weeks of treatment with statin.[33,47]

Atherosclerotic plaque is a dynamic structure. Cells such as macrophages, smooth muscle cells, T-lymphocytes, fibroblasts, and endothelial cells are key factors in plaque formation. Lipids, particularly LDL, and the extracellular matrix (collagens) also participate in the process.[3,4,5,48] Monocytes and macrophages in the plaque continue to secrete growth factors and display metalloproteinase activity.[49,6] The classification of atherosclerotic lesions proposed by the American Heart Association Committee of Vascular Lesions essentially follows the classification introduced by Stary[50] and recognizes six stages in the development of atherosclerotic plaque[51–53] (see chapter 2 for details).

The majority of coronary events are not due to slowly progressing plaque that occludes the vessel. The lesions responsible for most clinical incidents cause only 35%–65% stenosis. Instead, acute events are precipitated by plaque rupture, which stimulates thrombus formation, and it is the occluding thrombus that causes the majority of myocardial infarctions. Plaque fissuring and rupture are major causes of clinical events,[54,55,6] and plaque that ruptures most often is plaque that has the highest lipid content, reduced collagen and proteoglycan content in the cap, relatively few smooth muscle cells, and more macrophages.[56,57] In advanced lesions, the periphery of the lesion, which is macrophage-rich, is particularly vulnerable to rupture.

Thus there are be two distinct but related processes within what we call atherosclerosis: the "background" of gradual build-up of occlusive atherosclerotic plaque, and superimposed on this, the much faster process of plaque destabilization and disruption, which acutely precipitate ischemic events.[6,58] Figure 6–1 presents a schematic view of the atherosclerotic plaque.

Figure 6–1 ✧ The Atherosclerotic Plaque

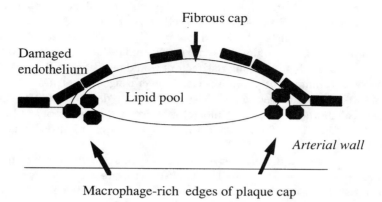

Macrophage-rich edges of plaque cap

Disparity between Degree of Arterial Lumen Occlusion and Clinical Event Rate

Results of the trials described above consistently show early divergence of survival curves between the treatment and placebo groups; this diversion occurs 6–12 months after treatment is initiated. On the other hand, in studies with angiographic endpoints, changes in lumen diameter are, in absolute terms, too minor to account for the improved clinical event rate. Thus, cholesterol lowering appears to have a shorter-term effect that is still different from that of inducing plaque regression. This hypothesis is strengthened by data showing that, in patients treated with diet and lovastatin for 4–6 months, cholesterol lowering by an average of 25% improves ischemic ECG changes such as ST-segment depression[59] and improves endothelial function.[60–62] In experimental animals, reducing cholesterol reduces the number of inflammatory cells in the plaque.[48]

Thus cholesterol lowering appears to affect atherogenesis at all main stages: by improving endothelial function, slowing the progression of arterial occlusion, and, most importantly, stabilizing plaque and decreasing the risk of plaque rupture.

THE CONCEPT OF TOTAL CARDIOVASCULAR RISK

Risk factors represent characteristics of healthy individuals that have been associated with subsequent occurrence of CHD in observational epidemiological studies.[63] Several risk factors continue to contribute to disease progression and to prognosis after CHD has been diagnosed.

Many individuals have more than one cardiovascular risk factor. For instance, in a survey of hypertension, hypercholesterolemia, and smoking based on health insurance registries in nine Canadian provinces, 66% of men and 63% of women had more than one cardiovascular risk factor.[64] These percentages increased to 80% and 89% respectively in the age bracket of 65 to 74 years. Twenty percent of the men and 18% of the women had two risk factors for CHD, and 2% of men and 1% of women evidenced three risk factors.

Several large epidemiological studies, notably the Framingham Study (see below), the Multiple Risk Factor Intervention Trial (MRFIT),[65,66] and the Prospective Cardiovascular Munster (PROCAM) study,[67,68] have demonstrated the multiplicative effect of risk factors on the risk of MI (early studies have been reviewed in [69]). It was thus proposed that managing risk factors would mitigate the risk of MI, and so trials on risk factor intervention were devised. Several significant trials on the effect of multiple risk factor intervention on CHD conducted to date include MRFIT,[65,66] the European Collaborative Trial on Multifactorial Prevention of Coronary Heart Disease,[71] the Oslo Diet-Heart Study,[70] and the Stanford Coronary Risk Intervention Project (SCRIP).[72]

Interestingly, the present evidence for management of risk factors is based almost exclusively on unifactorial trials. No trial to date convincingly demonstrates that multi-risk factor intervention is more effective clinically than intensive lipid lowering, although combining several types of lifestyle modifications, such as implemented in the Oslo Diet-Heart Trial, was indeed beneficial (see below).[70]

The European Collaborative Trial on Multifactorial Prevention of Coronary Heart Disease involved men aged 40–59 years who received dietary and anti-smoking advice, and hypotensive treatment where appropriate. The combined incidence of nonfatal myocardial infarction and CHD death subsequently decreased by 10.2% after six years.[71]

The MRFIT involved men aged 35–57 years whose coronary risk factor score, based on TC concentration, blood pressure, and smoking status, was in the upper 10%–15% of population distribution.[66] Intervention, which occurred over a period of seven years, involved dietary and anti-smoking counseling and antihypertensive treatment. Note that there was only a 2% decrease in cholesterol levels in the intervention group compared to the "usual care" group. No difference in CHD mortality or all-cause mortality occurred. However, there was a 21% decrease in CHD mortality in subgroups of non-hypertensive nonsmokers and normotensive hypercholesterolemic smokers, respectively. After 10.5 years CHD mortality in the "special intervention" group decreased 10.6% decrease.[66]

The Oslo Diet-Heart Trial involved normotensive men, aged 40–49, who had high TC levels (329 mg/dL; 8.5 mmol/L). As many as 79% of the men smoked. Intervention included diet and anti-smoking advice, and at the 8.5–10 years follow-up, combined nonfatal myocardial infarctions and CHD deaths had decreased 42%.[70]

SCRIP was a study with angiographic endpoints involving 300 men and women who had had CHD for four years. The participants were given individualized programs to follow that involved smoking cessation, dietary modification, and counseling about exercise, as well as lipid-lowering treatment where indicated. During the trial, lipid levels decreased LDL-C 22% and TG 20%, and increased HDL-C levels as much as 12%. These results were accompanied by a 4% decrease in body weight (average weight loss of 3.0 kg) and a 20% increase in exercise capacity. Compare this with the usual care group where, for instance, LDL-C changed only by 6 mg/dL (0.16 mmol/L ; 4%) during the trial.

In the intensive treatment group, the changes noted above were accompanied by a 47% decrease in the rate of narrowing of diseased segments of coronary arteries (measured as changes in the minimal diameter of the coronary artery) compared to the usual care group.[72]

Clearly, the effectiveness of intensive multiple risk reduction using combined treatments and lifestyle measures still needs to be studied. The ongoing Antihypertensive and Lipid-Lowering Treatment to Prevent Heart Attack Trial (ALLHAT) of 40,000 men and women aged 55 years or older, which will be followed for six years, will be important to our understanding of multiple risk factor interventions.[73] ALLHAT tests the effects of different hypotensive drugs on a combined endpoint of the incidence of fatal CHD and non-fatal MI in hypertensive patients with atherosclerotic disease or diabetes. The participants are randomized to therapy with a diuretic (chlorthalidone), a calcium channel antagonist (amlodipine), an ACE-inhibitor (lisinopril), and an alpha-adrenergic blocker (doxazosin). Importantly, the study includes an open-label lipid-lowering arm involving patients with LDL-C of 120–189 mg/dL (3.1–4.9 mmol/L; 100–129 mg/dL or 2.59–3.3 mmol/L in the presence of CHD) and TG below 300 mg/dL (3.39 mmol/L).[73]

Risk stratification and recommendations on risk management are reviewed in chapter 7. In spite of the availability of such recommendations, such management is still inadequate. For instance, the recent British Cardiac Society survey of recording of risk factors in medical records of patients with coronary artery disease, Action on Secondary Prevention through Intervention to Reduce Events (ASPIRE), demonstrated that information about cholesterol levels was much less completely recorded than information about blood pressure or smoking status.[74] More than 75% of CHD patients who were reviewed had cholesterol above 200 mg/dL (5.2 mmol/L), and 10%–27% of them were still smoking. The study concluded that there is a considerable potential for intervention using lifestyle measures, rigorous management of blood pressure and cholesterol, and the use of other prophylactic drugs such as aspirin and beta-blockers.

BEHAVIOR MODIFICATION

Diet, exercise, and smoking are behavior patterns, and to change these patterns in the interest of improving one's health requires behavior modification. The diabetes field has much to teach about approaches to behavior change. The Diabetic Control and Complications Trial (DCCT), for instance, which demonstrated that intensive insulin therapy prevents or delays the development of microvascular and neuropathic complications of type 1 diabetes,[75] required prolonged implementation of intensive insulin treatment: behavior changes such as administering insulin more frequently; modifying, quantifying, and regulating dietary intake; and engaging in physical activity.[76] To help patients make these changes, DCCT created a team of trainers and counselors that included nurses, nutritionists, clinical psychologists, psychiatrists, and social work professionals, and this multidisciplinary team-based approach is now being recommended for diabetes care.[77]

The DCCT results suggest that adoption and maintenance of substantial behavioral change is possible, but that it requires a carefully structured approach. At the beginning, attention to assessing patients in terms of candidacy for intensive therapy is important. Assessment includes identifying patients who have contraindications to intensive therapy such as, for instance, personality disorders or severe family or environmental instability. The patient's personal commitment to the therapeutic goal is essential.

After patients are selected, the team and patients negotiate realistic treatment goals and plan the optimal strategy for behavior change. Problem-solving skills are critical for success.[76] Inducing behavioral change always depends to a large extent on the ability of patients to care for themselves and their satisfaction with the plan. The patient's intentions to follow a treatment plan strongly influence whether or not the plan is followed.

Experience from diabetes management suggests that when patients carry out self-care behaviors, they improve glycemic control. Non-adherence to at least part of the regimen, however, is common.[78] Interestingly for cardiovascular protection in complex diabetic regimens, implementing dietary change and exercise is most difficult.[79,80] Not surprisingly, how the patient's regimen fits his/her lifestyle affects adherence to treatment.[80,81]

Maintaining behavioral change after achieving the initial goal is essential, and thus a proper follow-up is necessary.[76] DCCT data suggest that frequent contact between patient and health care providers is beneficial, particularly during the initial period of lifestyle change. Even verbal reinforcement such as telephone contact is significant. One cannot underestimate the importance of the involvement of a multi-specialist team. DCTT found that different team members worked more efficiently with certain patients. Teams capitalize on the various skills and knowledge of many individuals, and optimal application of therapy requires a range of skills and knowledge rarely found in a single individual.

Not all the pressure in inducing the behavior change is on the patient. Communication among the health care team is also essential. The team must adopt a collaborative style of interaction, which may require special training. It is suggested that behavioral interventions be targeted both to patients and their physicians, to improve communication and adherence.[81]

These considerations are important for preventing cardiovascular disease, not only from the standpoint of changes in lifestyle but also in other types of intervention. The discontinuation rates in lipid-lowering trials are high. For instance, in AFCAPS/TexCAPS discontinuation rate was 29% in the treatment group and 37% in the placebo group,[23] and these percentages are likely to be higher in the nontrial environment when the monitoring of therapy is less strict than in clinical studies.

LABORATORY ROLE IN PREVENTION

Lipoprotein testing plays an important role in the assessment of CHD risk,[3,82,83,84] and therefore laboratory support is an essential component of a CHD prevention system.[85] The main task of the lipid laboratory is to provide precise and accurate measurements of lipid and lipoprotein concentrations to clinicians and patients, to assess individual cardiovascular risk and to monitor lipid-lowering therapy.[83,84,86] There are three general tiers of lipoprotein testing complexity, all of which have an important role in identifying individuals at risk: screening, general clinical laboratory assessment, and specialty laboratory lipoprotein testing.

Screening

Lipoprotein screening for CHD risk, the first level of testing, is widely available in the United States, but is less frequently utilized elsewhere. Screening clinics and home testing frequently make it possible to reach segments of a population that may not otherwise have access to medical care, or may not take the time and effort to seek it. Clinics are frequently set up in shopping malls, elderly and subsidized living facilities, recreation facilities, and other public areas. From the individual's perspective, they involve a minimal amount of time, no prior preparation, and little or no cost.

Lipoprotein screening is most frequently performed in the nonfasting state, on blood obtained from finger-sticks, using small compact analyzers or non-instrumented devices. Finger-sticks are convenient and can be applied to a relatively large number of people; however, they can provide increased variability of results.[86–92] Therefore, every effort must be taken to ensure minimal error. As part of that effort, pre-analytical sources of variation must be controlled to the extent possible.[93] (See Chapters 8 and 13 for details.)

The NCEP-ATP II has recommended that lipid profiles outside the desirable range be repeated approximately one to eight weeks after the first profile.[82] No such recommendations have been made for individuals whose results are in the desirable range. If screening results misclassify a person with abnormal values into the desirable category, the excess risk may go undetected for an extended period of time, since such individuals are only advised to have the tests repeated within five years.[82] It is important, therefore, when setting up screening clinics that

✧ the chosen equipment is capable of providing accurate and precise results,

✧ the proper standardization and quality assurance procedures are in place, and

✧ personnel are adequately trained to perform the testing and correctly interpret the results.

The TC assay is the test most frequently performed in lipid screening clinics and is currently the only one available for home testing. Screening HDL-C measurements has also been recommended by the NCEP-ATP II because they represent an independent risk factor for CHD: HDL-C is inversely associated with CHD and cannot be deduced from a TC value. Its measurement is currently offered at many screening clinics and physician offices in the United States. Measurement of LDL-C may eventually replace that of TC but is not applicable in current screening equipment.[94–96] Screening clinics are also encouraged to provide guidance on dietary and physical activity habits and on risk factor reduction.

Individuals assessed in screening clinics have generally not fasted. TC can be measured with good accuracy in the nonfasting state, since the increase in TG-rich lipoprotein cholesterol is generally offset by decreased LDL-C and HDL-C.[86] To date, LDL-C measurements have not generally been available on screening equipment, but probably will be in the future. HDL-C measurement is frequently available on screening analyzers and patients can be screened for HDL-C in the nonfasting state, with the understanding that values may be slightly lower than those obtained in the fasting state.[86]

After an average meal, HDL-C (and LDL-C) will decrease by approximately 3%–5% in most individuals. These decreases are generally not of sufficient magnitude to negate their screening value, but those who interpret results need to be aware of this fact, and should query patients regarding the magnitude of, and the time since, their last meal. After a meal with a very high fat content (1g/kg body weight), at six hours postprandially, HDL-C and LDL-C can drop by as much as 9%–10%, and apo A-I and apo B values can decrease by approximately 6%, but this magnitude of change would not be common.[86]

TG should not be measured unless the individual has fasted for 12–14 hours, since the magnitude and variability of the postprandial TG change is sufficient to preclude any extrapolation back to fasting values. For this reason, TG are not commonly measured at screening facilities.

While screening provides only a cursory survey of lipoprotein status, if properly conducted it can alert individuals at risk that they need follow-up care—information that they might otherwise not obtain.

Assessment of Lipoprotein Status in a General Clinical Laboratory

Most clinical laboratories, whether hospital-based or independent, are equipped to measure TC, HDL-C, TG, and, in many cases, apo A-I and apo B. Typically, LDL-C values are calculated using the formula of Friedewald et al.[97] The formula provides an adequate estimation of VLDL-C and LDL-C, provided that patients are truly fasting and provided that TG < 400 mg/dL (4.7 mmol/L), and preferably < 250 mg/dL (2.9 mmol/L).

Currently, at the recommendation of the NCEP Working Group on Lipoprotein Measurement,[98] new methods to measure LDL-C directly, without ultracentrifugation, have become available. These assays give clinical laboratories the capability of assessing LDL-C in hypertriglyceridemic and nonfasting samples.[94–96] (See also Chapter 12.)

It is essential that laboratories develop and monitor assay precision and, for it is important that values obtained in one laboratory, or at one point in time, be comparable to those obtained in another place, at another time. Therefore, clinical laboratories and manufacturers of analytical systems for clinical laboratories should use precision and accuracy guidelines[98–100] and available standardization programs to ensure that results are accurate.[101]

One such standardization option is the Cholesterol Reference Method Laboratory Network, coordinated by the Centers for Disease Control and Prevention (CDC) in Atlanta, which performs fresh sample comparisons between field methods and the Abell-Kendall reference method for cholesterol for both manufacturers and individual laboratories[102] (see also Chapters 9 and 36). Other standardization and proficiency testing opportunities are also available for evaluating lipid, lipoprotein, and apolipoprotein assays.

From a practical perspective, it is important for general clinical laboratories to be able provide meaningful results on a large number of samples, for both diagnostic and therapeutic purposes. Clinical laboratories cannot and should not be expected to perform all of the specialty tests that are ultimately possible. Lipoprotein tests that are not ordered routinely, or those that require exceptional expertise or costly equipment to perform, are better left to the lipoprotein specialty laboratory. But the tests that the clinical laboratory does offer must provide accurate and reproducible results.

Lipoprotein Specialty Laboratory Assessment

The lipoprotein specialty laboratory is the ultimate resource in the lipoprotein testing field. Samples with unusual profiles or from patients who have rare diseases may require testing procedures that are not available in the average clinical laboratory. Typically, the lipoprotein specialty laboratories are research laboratories, frequently in an academic setting. Even these laboratories will have particular specialty procedures in use, depending on their research needs and interests. Most lipoprotein specialty laboratories perform ultracentrifugation to obtain reference method lipoprotein determinations important to clinical laboratories and private physicians seeking more comprehensive lipid profiles on dyslipidemic.[103]

As with the screening and clinical laboratory settings, it is extremely important for a lipoprotein specialty laboratory to monitor the precision and accuracy of the tests it performs. Precision can be readily evaluated within the laboratory. Accuracy evaluations are more difficult, since no clearly defined reference points exist for many of the specialty assays. In many cases the normal ranges for these tests must be determined within the laboratory, after analyses have been completed in large normal populations. These ranges may or may not be transferable to similar tests performed in other research laboratories, unless some effort has been made to coordinate the test procedures.

For example, prior to the efforts of the International Federation for Clinical Chemistry and Laboratory Medicine (IFCC) to standardize apo A-I and apo B assays,[104–106] there was frequently little or no relationship between values for these tests from one laboratory to another. Each laboratory produced and purified its own antibodies, with different binding characteristics, and each used its own methodology, with varying limitations. The IFCC Committee on Apolipoproteins, working with the CDC, developed a set of standard reference materials to be used by manufacturers for assay calibration. This allowed different assay methodologies to be calibrated on the same basis, so that results among laboratories could be compared[107,108] (see also Chapter 14), and so that individual patients could have apo A-I and apo B levels meaningfully interpreted as part of the CHD risk evaluation. The end result of this process has been the transfer of what were once research assays to the clinical laboratories, for wider utilization.

Lipoprotein specialty laboratories serve four major functions, all of which ultimately help individual patients through better preventive, diagnostic, and therapeutic interventions. First, they perform sophisticated test procedures on patients already identified as having an abnormal lipoprotein status. The patient samples may be forwarded from screening clinics, physician's offices, or clinical laboratories, or they may originate in specialty referral clinics, such as lipid, cardiology, diabetic, and endocrinology clinics. In this instance, the testing performed helps the patient directly by providing the physician with test results to assist in diagnosis and/or specialized treatment.

Secondly, such laboratories participate in epidemiological studies. These studies provide the database from which normal and high-risk values can be identified and analyzed. The Framingham Heart Study,[109] the U. S. National Health and Nutrition Examination Survey,[110] the Seven Countries Study,[111] and the very large Swedish population study[112] are just a few examples of large epidemiological studies that have had a major impact on the basic understanding of CHD risk factors.

Thirdly, lipoprotein specialty labs participate in clinical intervention trials to evaluate potential new therapies. Also included in this category are the safety and efficacy studies of new medications and dietary intervention trials. The studies may be performed in populations at risk but without diagnosed disease for primary prevention, such as the Lipid Research Clinics Primary Prevention Trial,[113,114] the WOSCOPS,[22] and the AFCAPS/TexCAPS,[23] or in specific disease populations for secondary intervention purposes, such as the 4S Study,[12] the CARE Trial,[11] and VA-HIT,[115] described above.

Finally, lipoprotein specialty laboratories conduct basic research. Although removed (in an immediate sense) from the individual patient, basic research is perhaps one of the most important aspects of investigation, as the research testing of today will lead to the epidemiological and intervention studies of tomorrow, and eventually to preventive, diagnostic, and therapeutic interventions for individuals. The lipid specialty laboratory also provides training and development, and validation of new assays applicable to the assessment of cardiovascular risk. While there has been a drop in mortality of almost 50% due to CHD in the past 30 years in the U. S., according to the National Center for Health Statistics CHD remains the leading cause of death and kills almost twice as many people as all causes of cancer combined (see also chapter 7).

SPECIALTY OUTPATIENT CLINICS

The optimal way to develop cardiovascular disease prevention programs, both for primary and secondary prevention, is to modify all existing risk factors. Concepts for managing patients at risk have been developed in parallel by specialists in hypertension, cardiology, lipid, and nutrition. Risk management by any single specialty has flaws. Lack of a coordinated approach could be one of the reasons for poor effectiveness of risk factor management, as illustrated by the ASPIRE Study described above.[74]

Effective cardiovascular prevention requires multiple skills that can only be obtained through a team approach.[116] Examples of coordinated approaches in other areas of medical care include provision of nutritional services[117] and, as described above, the treatment of diabetes.

Figure 6–2 illustrates the organization of the cardiovascular disease prevention system currently operating in one of the authors' hospitals. It is based in two specialty outpatient clinics. The Lipid Clinic is run by a lipid specialist who is a physician. The biochemistry laboratory offers on-site TC and TG measurements, thereby providing immediate results; this reinforces medical and dietetic advice. These results are later confirmed using conventional clinical laboratory methods.

Figure 6–2 ✧ The Lipid and Cardiovascular Risk Factor Specialist Clinic System

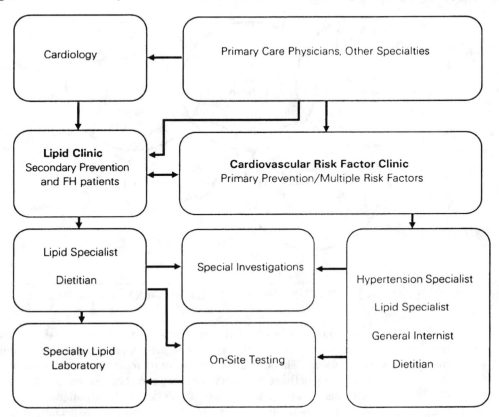

The dietetic service is another part of the clinic. At the first visit, patients receive a dietary score, which is then monitored at subsequent visits. In addition, the Lipid Clinic specializes in intensive management of lipid disorders in patients with CHD and in individuals with familial lipoprotein disorders. In 1999 the clinic was transformed into a comprehensive secondary prevention clinic run jointly with the cardiology department.

Patients who require multi-specialist treatment are referred to the Cardiovascular Risk Factor Clinic, which involves a larger team comprised of internists, hypertension and lipid specialists, dietitians, and nurse specialists. The Cardiovascular Risk Factor Clinic specializes in primary prevention in individuals who have multiple risk factors.

These clinics have direct access to a range of procedures (ECG, exercise testing, cardiac and carotid ultrasound, cardiac imaging, 24-h blood pressure monitoring, etc.). The multidisciplinary approach reduces the number of patient visits required for a comprehensive assessment of risk, and for a multifactorial approach to risk reduction.

Figure 6–3 ✧ The Components of a Comprehensive Cardiovascular Event Prevention Program

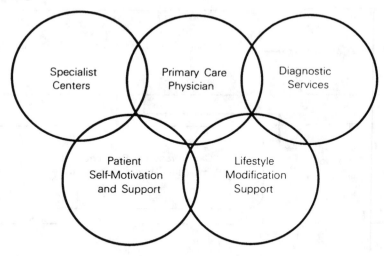

RISK FACTOR MANAGEMENT IN PRIMARY CARE AND SPECIALTY CENTERS

Broad realization of the medical effectiveness of lowering cholesterol has increased the numbers of patients undergoing therapy, consequently potentially overwhelming the specialty clinic system. The increased number of patients necessitates devolving the management of many of these patients to primary care. Shared-care arrangements involving specialty clinics and primary care physicians[77] allow patients who have complicated health requirements to be treated and monitored in specialty centers, whereas patients who have less complicated needs for management can be treated in the primary care setting using recommended regimens.[116] An arrangement that allows close communication, training, and information exchange is essential.

In the majority of patients, effective cardiovascular prevention requires modifying lifestyles and effectively collaborating with health care professionals.[116] The importance and difficulties in implementing non-pharmacological interventions, such as smoking cessation, diet, and exercise, are often underestimated.[118] Intensive lifestyle change requires individualized advice, appropriate monitoring, and close follow-up and support. These measures include plans for cardiac rehabilitation and exercise, help with smoking cessation, and advice about diet and weight reduction. The components of such a program are shown in Figure 6–3.

SPECIALIST TRAINING IN PREVENTION OF CARDIOVASCULAR DISEASE

Most cardiology training programs do not include specialists in lipid disorders or risk factor management on their staff.[116,119] Traditionally, prevention of cardiovascular disease has been biased towards lifestyle and public health measures. In the last 10 to

Figure 6–4 ✧ Suggested Components of a Training Program in Cardiovascular Event Prevention

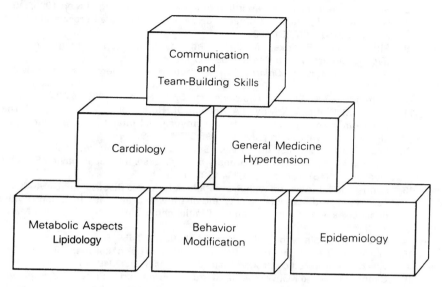

15 years, however, prevention has developed into a field that requires multi-disciplinary expertise in both medical therapy and lifestyle modification.

The suggested components of training for a specialist in cardiovascular disease prevention are illustrated in Figure 6–4. The specialist must develop sufficient understanding of all relevant sub-specialties to efficiently and safely manage multi-risk patients. In addition, part of the training needs to address lifestyle and behavior modification as well as strategies for communication among a variety of specialists and primary care providers.

Training programs need to address the epidemiology of risk factors, as well as case management.[120] Metabolic aspects of lipid metabolism and hypertension must also be addressed. These issues have been raised in the cardiology community.[116,119] Now might well be the time for prevention of cardiovascular disease to become a recognized entity in medical training programs. ✧

REFERENCES

1. Stamler J. Established major coronary risk factors. In: Marmot M, Elliot P, (eds.). Coronary heart disease epidemiology: from etiology to public health. Oxford: Oxford Medical Publications, 1992:35–66.
2. Steinberg D, Gotto AM. Preventing coronary artery disease by lowering cholesterol levels. Fifty years from bench to bedside. JAMA 1999;282:2043–50.
3. Ross R, Glomset J. The pathogenesis of atherosclerosis, Part 1. N Engl J Med 1976; 295:369–77.
4. Ross R, Glomset J. The pathogenesis of atherosclerosis: part 2. N Engl J Med 1976; 295:420–28.

5. Ross R. The pathogenesis of atherosclerosis: a perspective for the 1990s. Nature 1993;362:801–13.

6. Ross R. Atherosclerosis—an inflammatory disease. N Engl J Med 1999;340:115–26.

7. Diaz MN, Frei B, Vita JA, Keaney Jr JF. Antioxidants and atherosclerotic heart disease. N Engl J Med 1997;337:408–16.

8. Rifai N, Tracy RP, Ridker PM. Clinical efficacy of an automated high-sensitivity C-reactive protein assay. Clin Chem 1999;45:2136–41.

9. Shor A, Phillips JI. *Chlamydia pneumoniae* and atherosclerosis. JAMA 1999;282:2071–3.

10. Dominiczak MH. Lipids: the story so far. Br J Cardiology 1997;4:425–9.

11. Sacks FM, Pfeffer MA, Moye LA, Rouleau JL, Rutherford JD, Cole TG et al. The effect of pravastatin on coronary events after myocardial infarction in patients with average cholesterol levels. N Engl J Med 1996;335:1001–9.

12. Scandinavian Simvastatin Survival Study Group. Randomized trial of cholesterol lowering in 4444 patients with coronary heart disease: the Scandinavian Simvastatin Survival Study (4S). Lancet 1994;334:1383–9.

13. Long-Term Intervention with Pravastatin in Ischemic Disease (LIPID) Study Group. Prevention of cardiovascular events and death with pravastatin in patients with coronary heart disease and a broad range of initial cholesterol levels. N Engl J Med 1998;339:1349–57.

14. Oliver MF. Cholesterol and strokes. BMJ 2000;320:459–60.

15. LaRosa JC, He J, Vupputuri S. Effect of statins on risk of coronary disease. A meta-analysis of randomized controlled trials. JAMA 1999;282:2340–6.

16. Canner PL, Berge KG, Wenger J, Stamler J, Friedman L, Prineas RJ, Friedewald W. Fifteen-year mortality in coronary drug project patients: long-term benefit with niacin. J Am Coll Cardiol 1986:8:1245–55.

17. The Post Coronary Artery Bypass Graft Trial Investigators. The effect of aggressive lowering of low-density-lipoprotein cholesterol levels and low-dose anticoagulation on obstructive changes in saphenous-vein coronary-artery-bypass grafts. N Engl J Med 1997;336:153–62.

18. Hokanson JE, Austin MA. Plasma triglyceride level is a risk factor for cardiovascular disease independent of high-density-lipoprotein cholesterol level: a meta-analysis of population-based prospective studies. J Cardiovasc Risk 1996;3:213–19.

19. Torra IP, Gervois P, Staels B. Peroxisome-proliferator-activated receptor alpha in metabolic disease, inflammation, atherosclerosis, and aging. Curr Opin Lipidol 1999;10:151–9.

20. Verheugt FWA. Hotline sessions at the 20th European Congress of Cardiology. Eur Heart J 1999;20:7–10.

21. Ericsson C-G, Hamsten A, Nilsson J, Grip L, Svane B, de Faire U. Angiographic assessment of effects of bezafibrate on progression of coronary disease in young male post-infarction patients. Lancet 1996;347:849–53.

22. Shepherd J, Cobbe SM, Ford I, Isles CG, Lorimer AR, Macfarlane PW et al. Prevention of coronary heart disease with pravastatin in men with hypercholesterolemia. N Engl J Med 1995;333:1301–7.

23. Downs JR, Clearfield M, Weis S, Whitney E, Shapiro DR, Beere BA et al. Primary prevention of acute coronary events with lovastatin in men and women with average cholesterol levels: Results of AFCAPS/TexCAPS (Air Force/Texas Coronary Atherosclerosis Prevention Study). JAMA 1998;279:1615–22.

24. Blankenhorn DH, Nessim SA, Johnson RL, Sanmarco ME, Azen SP, Cashin-Hemphill L. Beneficial effects of combined colestipol-niacin therapy on coronary atherosclerosis and coronary venous bypass grafts. JAMA 1987;257:3233–40.

25. Pitt B, Mancini GBJ, Ellis SG, Rosman RS, Park J-S, McGovern M et al., for the PLAC1 Investigators. Pravastatin limitation of atherosclerosis in the coronary arteries (PLAC1): reduction in atherosclerosis progression and clinical events. J Am Coll Cardiol 1995; 26:1133–9.

26. MAAS Investigators. Effect of simvastatin on coronary atheroma: the Multicenter Anti-Atheroma Study (MAAS). Lancet 1994;344:633–8.

27. Jukema JW, Bruschke AVG, van Boven AJ, Reiber JHC, Bal ET, Zwinderman AH et al. Effects of lipid lowering by pravastatin on progression and regression of coronary artery disease in symptomatic men with normal to moderately elevated serum cholesterol levels. The Regression Growth Evaluation Statin Study (REGRESS). Circulation 1995;91:2528–40.

28. Brown G, Albers JJ, Fisher LD, Schaefer SM, Lin JT, Kaplan C et al. Regression of coronary artery disease as a result of intensive lipid-lowering therapy in men with high levels of apolipoprotein B. N Engl J Med 1990;323:1289–98.

29. Watts GF, Lewis B, Brunt JNH, Lewis ES, Coltart Dj, Smith LDR et al. Effects on coronary artery disease of lipid-lowering diet, or diet plus cholestyramine, in the St. Thomas Atherosclerosis Regression Study (STARS). Lancet 1992;339:563–9.

30. Buchwald H, Vargo RL, Matts JP, Long JM, Fitch LL, Campbell GS et al. Effect of partial ileal bypass surgery on mortality and morbidity from coronary heart disease in patients with hypercholesterolemia. N Engl J Med 1990;323:946–55.

31. Tangirala RK, Tsukamoto K, Chun SH, Usher D, Puré D, Rader DJ. Regression of atherosclerosis induced by liver-directed gene transfer of apolipoprotein A-I in mice. Circulation 1999;100:1816–22.

32. Dansky HM, Fisher EA. High-density lipoprotein and plaque regression. The good cholesterol gets even better. Circulation 1999;100:1762–3.

33. Selwyn AP, Kinlay S, Libby P, Ganz P. Atherogenic lipids, vascular dysfunction, and clinical signs of ischemic heart disease. Circulation 1997;95:5–7.

34. Burnett Jr JC. Coronary endothelial function in health and disease. Drugs 1997;53(Suppl 1):20–29.

35. Glasser SP, Selwyn AP, Ganz P. Atherosclerosis: risk factors and the vascular endothelium. Am Heart J 1996;131:379–84.

36. Rossi V, Breviario F, Ghezzi P Dejana E, Mantovani A. Prostacyclin synthesis induced in vascular cells by interleukin-1. Science 1985;229:174–6.

37. Furchgott RF, Zawadzki JV. The obligatory role of endothelial cells in the relaxation of arterial smooth muscle by acetylcholine. Nature 1980;288:373–6.

38. Nielsen LB. Transfer of low-density lipoprotein into the arterial wall and risk of atherosclerosis. [Review]. Atherosclerosis 1996;123:1–15.

39. Chin JH, Azhan S, Hoffman BB. Inactivation of endothelial-derived relaxing factor by oxidized lipoproteins. J Clin Invest 1992;89:10–18.

40. Chen LH, Mehta P, Mehta JL. Oxidized LDL decreases L-arginine uptake and nitric oxide protein expression in human platelets. Relevance of the effect of oxidized LDL on platelet function. Circulation 1996;93:1740–6.

41. Anderson TJ, Meredith IT, Charbonneau F, Yeung AC, Frei B, Selwyn AP, Ganz P. Endothelium-dependent coronary vasomotion relates to the susceptibility of LDL to oxidation in humans. Circulation 1995;93:1647–50.

42. Ohara Y, Pederson TE, Harrison DG. Hypercholesterolemia increases endothelial superoxide production. J Clin Invest 1993;91:2546–51.

43. Harrison DG. Endothelial function and oxidative stress. Clin Cardiol 1997;20(Suppl II):II11–II17.

44. Steinberg HO, Bayazeed B, Hook G, Johnson A, Cronin J, Baron AD. Endothelial dysfunction is associated with cholesterol levels in the high normal range in humans. Circulation 1997;96:3287–93.

45. Vogel RA, Corretti MC, Plotnick GD. Changes in flow-mediated brachial artery vasoactivity with lowering of desirable cholesterol levels in healthy middle-aged men. Am J Cardiol 1996;77:37–40.

46. Vogel RA, Corretti MC, Plotnick GD. The mechanism of improvement in endothelial function by pravastatin: direct effect of, through cholesterol lowering. J Am Coll Cardiol 1998;31:60A.

47. Vogel RA. Cholesterol lowering and endothelial function. Am J Med 1999;107:479–87.

48. Libby P. Molecular bases of the acute coronary syndromes. Circulation 1995;91: 2844–50.

49. Galis ZS, Sukhova GK, Lark MW, Libby P. Increased expression of matrix metallo-proteinases and matrix-degrading activity in vulnerable regions of human atherosclerotic plaques. J Clin Invest 1994;94:2493–503.

50. Stary HC. Evolution and progression of atherosclerotic lesions in coronary arteries of children and young adults. Arteriosclerosis 1989;9(suppl 1):I-19–1–32.

51. Stary HC, Blankenhorn DH, Chandler AB, Glagov S, Insull W Jr, Richardson M et al. A definition of the intima of human arteries and of its atherosclerosis-prone regions: a report from the Committee on Vascular Lesions of the Council on Arteriosclerosis, American Heart Association. Circulation 1992;85:391–405.

52. Stary HC, Chandler AB, Glagov S, Guyton JR, Insull W Jr, Rosenfeld ME et al. A definition of initial, fatty streak, and intermediate lesions of atherosclerosis: a report from the Committee on Vascular Lesions of the Council on Arteriosclerosis, American Heart Association. Circulation 1994;89:2462–78.

53. Stary HC, Chandler AB, Dinsmore RE, Fuster V, Glagov S, Insull W Jr et al. A definition of advanced types of atherosclerotic lesions and a histological classification of atherosclerosis: a report from the Committee on Vascular Lesions of the Council on Arteriosclerosis, American Heart Association. Arterioscler Thromb Vasc Biol 1995;15: 1512–31.

54. Fuster V. Elucidation of the role of plaque instability and rupture in acute coronary events. Am J Cardiol 1995;76:24C–33C.

55. Hackett D, Davies G, Maseri A. Pre-existing coronary stenoses in patients with first myocardial infarction are not necessarily severe. Eur Heart J 1988;9:1317–23.

56. Davies MJ, Thomas AC. Plaque fissuring: the cause of acute myocardial infarction, sudden ischemic death, and crescendo angina. Br Heart J 1985;53:363–73.

57. Davies MJ. A macro and micro view of coronary vascular insult in ischemic heart disease. Circulation 1990;82(Suppl II):II-38–46.

58. Dominiczak MH. Atherosclerosis. In: Colaco C (ed.). The glycation hypothesis of atherosclerosis. Georgetown: Landes Bioscience, 1997:1–27.

59. Andrews TC, Raby K, Barry J, Naimi CL, Allred E, Ganz P, Selwyn AP. Effect of cholesterol reduction on myocardial ischemia in patients with coronary disease. Circulation 1997; 95:324–8.

60. Tamai O, Matsuoka H, Itabe H, Wada Y, Kohno K, Imaizumi T. Single LDL apheresis improves endothelium-dependent vasodilation in hypercholesterolemic humans. Circulation 1997;95:76–82.

61. Treasure CB, Klein JL, Weintraub WS, Talley JD, Stillabower ME, Kosinski AS et al. Beneficial effects of cholesterol-lowering therapy on the coronary endothelium in patients with coronary artery disease. N Engl J Med 1995;332:481–7.

62. Leung WH, Lau CP, Wong CK. Beneficial effects of cholesterol-lowering therapy on coronary endothelium-dependent relaxation in hypercholesterolemic patients. Lancet 1993;341:1496–500.

63. Pyorala K, De Backer G, Graham I, Poole-Wilson P, Wood D, on behalf of the Task Force. Prevention of coronary heart disease in clinical practice: recommendations of the Task Force of the European Society of Cardiology, European Atherosclerosis Society and European Society of Hypertension. Eur Heart J 1994;15:1300–31.

64. MacDonald S, Joffres MR, Stachenko S, Horlick L, Fodor G, Canadian Health Surveys Research Group. Multiple cardiovascular risk factors in Canadian adults. Can Med Assoc J 1992;142(Suppl):48–56.

65. Multiple Risk Factor Intervention Trial Research Group. Multiple Risk Factor Intervention Trial: risk factor changes and mortality results. JAMA 1982;248:1465–77.

66. Multiple Risk Factor Intervention Trial Research Group. Mortality rates after 10 years for participants of the Multiple Risk Factor Intervention Trial: findings related to the *a priori* hypotheses of the trial. Circulation 1990;82:1616–28.

67. Assmann G, Schulte H. Relation of high-density lipoprotein cholesterol and triglycer-

ides to incidence of atherosclerotic coronary artery disease: the PROCAM experience. Am J Cardiol 1992;70:733–7.

68. Assmann G, Schulte H. Modeling the Helsinki Heart Study by means of risk equations obtained from the PROCAM Study and the Framingham Heart Study. Drugs 1990;40(Suppl 1):13–18.

69. Dominiczak MH, Packard CJ, Shepherd J. Hyperlipidemia, its risks and treatment. In: Lorimer AR, Shepherd J (eds.). Preventive cardiology. Oxford: Blackwell, 1991:54–86.

70. Hjerrman I, Velve-Byre DV, Holme I, Leren P. Effect of diet and smoking intervention on the incidence of coronary heart disease: report from the Oslo Study Group of a randomized trial of healthy men. Lancet 1981;ii:1303–10.

71. WHO (World Health Organization Collaborative Study Group). European collaborative trial of multifactorial prevention of coronary heart disease: final report on the six-year results. Lancet 1986;I:869–72.

72. Haskell WL, Alderman EL, Fair JM, Maron DJ, Mackey SF, Superko R et al. Effects of intensive multiple risk factor reduction on coronary atherosclerosis and clinical cardiac events in men and women with coronary artery disease. The Stanford Coronary Risk Intervention Project (SCRIP). Circulation 1994;89:975–90.

73. Davis BR, Cutler JA, Gordon DJ, Furberg CD, Wright JT, Cushman WC et al. Rationale and design for the Antihypertensive and Lipid-Lowering Treatment to Prevent Heart Attack Trial (ALLHAT). Am J Hypertens 1996;9:342–60.

74. ASPIRE Steering Group. A British Cardiac Society survey of the potential for the secondary prevention of coronary heart disease: ASPIRE (Action on Secondary Prevention through Intervention to Reduce Events). Heart 1996;75:334–42.

75. DCCT Research Group. The effect of intensive treatment of diabetes on the development and progression of long-term complications of insulin-dependent diabetes mellitus. N Engl J Med 1993;329:977–86.

76. Lorenz RA, Bubb J, Davis D, Jacobson A, Jannasch K, Kramer J. Changing behavior: practical lessons from the Diabetes Control and Complications Trial. Diabetes Care 1996;19:648–52.

77. Scottish Intercollegiate Guidelines Network (SIGN). Report on good practice in the care of children and young people with diabetes. Edinburgh: SIGN, 1996:1–10.

78. Golin CE, DiMatteo MR, Gelberg L. The role of patient participation in the doctor visit: implications for adherence to diabetes care. Diabetes Care 1996;19:1153–64.

79. Goodall T. Self-management of diabetes mellitus; a critical review. Health Psychol 1991; 10:1–8.

80. Anderson L. Health care communication and selected psychological adherence in diabetes management. Diabetes Care 1990;13:66–67.

81. Hulka B, Cassel J, Kupper L, Burdette J. Communication, compliance, and concordance between physicians and patients with prescribed medications. Am J Public Health 1976;66:847–53.

82. The Expert Panel. Summary of the second report of the National Cholesterol Education Program (NCEP) on detection, evaluation, and treatment of high blood cholesterol in adults (Adult Treatment Panel II). JAMA 1993;269:3015–23.

83. The Bezafibrate Infarction Prevention (BIP) Study Group, Israel. Lipids and lipoproteins in symptomatic coronary heart disease: distribution, intercorrelations, and significance for risk classification in 6700 men and 1500 women. Circulation 1992;86:839–48.

84. American College of Physicians. Guidelines for using serum cholesterol, high-density-lipoprotein cholesterol, and triglyceride levels as screening tests for preventing coronary heart disease in adults. Ann Intern Med 1996;124:515–17.

85. Pearson TA, Fuster V. Matching the intensity of risk factor management with the hazard for coronary disease events: executive summary. 27th Bethesda Conference, September 14–15, 1995. J Am Coll Cardiol 1996;5:957–63.

86. Cohn JS, McNamara JR, Cohn SD, Ordovas JM, Schaefer EJ. Postprandial plasma lipoprotein changes in human subjects of different ages. J Lipid Res 1988;29:469–79.

87. Cohn JS, McNamara JR, Schaefer EJ. Lipoprotein cholesterol concentrations in the

plasma of human subjects as measured in the fed and fasted states. Clin Chem 1988;34:2456–59.

88. Warnick GR, Leary ET, Ammirati EB, Allen MP. Cholesterol in finger-stick capillary specimens can be equivalent to conventional venous measurements. Arch Path Lab Med 1994;118:1110–14.

89. Koch TR, Mehta U, Lee H, Aziz K, Temel S, Donlon JA, Sherwin R. Bias and precision of cholesterol analysis by physicians office analyzers. Clin Chem 1987;33:2262–7.

90. Warnick GR. Measurement of cholesterol, triglycerides, and HDL using compact analysis systems. Clin Lab Med 1989;9:73–88.

91. Kaufman HW, McNamara JR, Anderson KM, Wilson PWF, Schaefer EJ. How reliably can compact chemistry analyzers measure lipids? JAMA 1990;263:1245–9.

92. McNamara JR, Warnick GR, Leary ET, Wittels E, Nelson FE, Pearl MF, Schaefer EJ. A multi-center evaluation of a patient-administered test for blood cholesterol measurement. Prev Med 1996;25:583–92.

93. Cooper GR, Myers GL, Smith SJ, Schlant RC. Blood lipid measurements: variations and practical utility. JAMA 1992;267:1652–60.

94. McNamara JR, Cole TG, Contois JH, Ferguson CA, Ordovas JM, Schaefer EJ. Immunoseparation method for measuring low-density lipoprotein cholesterol directly from serum evaluated. Clin Chem 1995;41:232–40.

95. Jialal I, Hirany SV, Devaraj S, Sherwood TA. Comparison of an immunoseparation method for direct measurement of LDL cholesterol with beta-quantification (ultracentrifugation). Am J Clin Path 1995;104:76–81.

96. Pisani T, Gebski CP, Leary ET, Warnick GR, Ollington JF. Accurate direct determination of low-density-lipoprotein cholesterol using an immunoseparation reagent and enzymatic cholesterol assay. Arch Pathol Lab Med 1995;119:1127–35.

97. Friedewald WT, Levy RI, Fredrickson DS. Estimation of the concentration of low-density-lipoprotein cholesterol in plasma, without use of the preparative ultracentrifuge. Clin Chem 1972;18:499–502.

98. Bachorik PS, Ross JW. National Cholesterol Education Program recommendations for measurement of low-density-lipoprotein cholesterol: executive summary. Clin Chem 1995;41:1414–20.

99. Stein EA, Myers GL. National Cholesterol Education Program recommendations for triglyceride measurement: executive summary. Clin Chem 1995;41;1421–6.

100. Warnick GR, Wood PD. National Cholesterol Education Program recommendations for measurement of high-density-lipoprotein cholesterol: executive summary. Clin Chem 1995;41:1427–33.

101. McNamara JR, Leary ET, Ceriotti F, Boersma-Cobbaert CM, Cole TG, Hassemer DJ et al. Status of lipid and lipoprotein standardization. Clin Chem 1997;43:1306–10.

102. Abell LL, Levy BB, Brodie BB, Kendall FE. Simplified methods for the estimation of total cholesterol in serum and demonstration of its specificity. J Biol Chem 1953;195:357–66.

103. Manual of laboratory operations, Lipid Research Clinics Program. Lipid and lipoprotein analysis. Washington, DC: NIH, U.S. Dept. of Health and Human Services, 1982.

104. Albers JJ, Marcovina SM. Standardization of apolipoprotein B and A-I measurements. Clin Chem 1989;35:1357–61.

105. Marcovina SM, Albers JJ, Henderson LO, Hannon WH. International Federation of Clinical Chemistry standardization project for measurements of apolipoproteins A-I and B. III. Comparability of apolipoprotein A-I values by use of international reference material. Clin Chem 1993;39:773–81.

106. Marcovina SM, Albers JJ, Henderson LO, Hannon WH. International Federation of Clinical Chemistry standardization project for measurements of apolipoproteins A-I and B. IV. Comparability of apolipoprotein A-I values by use of international reference material. Clin Chem 1994;40:586–92.

107. Contois JH, McNamara JR, Lammi-Keefe CJ, Wilson PWF, Schaefer EJ. Reference intervals for plasma apolipoprotein A-I as determined with a commercially available

immunoturbidometric assay: results from the Framingham Offspring Study. Clin Chem 1996;42:507–14.

108. Contois JH, McNamara JR, Lammi-Keefe CJ, Wilson PWF, Massor T, Schaefer EJ. Reference intervals for plasma apolipoprotein B as determined with a commercially available immunoturbidometric assay: results from the Framingham Offspring Study. Clin Chem 1996;42:515–23.

109. Wilson PWF, Garrison RJ, Abbott RD, Castelli WP. Factors associated with lipoprotein cholesterol levels: the Framingham Study. Arteriosclerosis 1983;3:273–81.

110. Sempos C, Fulwood R, Haines C, Carroll M, Anda R, Williamson DF et al. The prevalence of high blood cholesterol levels among adults in the United States. JAMA 1989;262:45–52.

111. Keys A (ed.). Coronary heart disease in seven countries. Circulation 1970;41(Suppl I): 1–198.

112. Jungner I, Marcovina SM, Walldius G, Holme I, Kolar W, Steiner E. Apolipoprotein B and A-I values in 147576 Swedish males and females, standardized according to the World Health Organization-International Federation of Clinical Chemistry First International Reference Materials. Clin Chem 1998;44:1641–9.

113. The Lipid Research Clinics Program. The Lipid Research Clinics Coronary Primary Prevention Trial. I. Reduction in incidence of coronary heart disease. JAMA 1984;251: 351–64.

114. The Lipid Research Clinics Program. The Lipid Research Clinics Coronary Primary Prevention Trial. II. The relationship of reduction in incidence of coronary heart disease to cholesterol lowering. JAMA 1984;251:365–74.

115. Rubins HB, Robins SJ, Collins D, Fye CL, Anderson JW, Elam MB et al. Gemfibrozil for the secondary prevention of coronary heart disease in men with low levels of high-density-lipoprotein cholesterol. N Eng J Med 1999;341:410–8.

116. McBride PE, Houston Miller N, Smith SC. Task Force 8. Organization of preventive cardiology service. J Am Coll Cardiol 1996;27:964–1047.

117. Committee on Clinical Practice Issues in Health and Disease. The role and identity of physician nutrition specialists in medical school-affiliated hospitals. Am J Clin Nutr 1995;61:264–8.

118. Simon HB. Patient-directed, nonprescription approaches to cardiovascular disease. Arch Intern Med 1994;154:2283–93.

119. Gunnar RM, Williams RG. Future personnel needs for cardiovascular health care. Excerpt from conference program of the 25th Bethesda Conference, November 15–16, 1993. J Am Coll Cardiol 1994;24:280–81.

120. Swan HJC. Gersh BJ, Graboys TB, Ullyot DJ. Task force 7. Evaluation and management of risk factors for the individual patient (case management). J Am Coll Cardiol 1996; 27:964–1047.

Review of International Guidelines for the Diagnosis and Treatment of Lipid Disorders

7

Marek H. Dominiczak

✧ The practice of lowering plasma lipid levels to decrease the risk of cardiovascular events is now established in clinical practice. The evidence from clinical trials shows a substantial benefit to this approach, particularly in secondary prevention,[1-5] where lipid lowering has become one of the cardioprotective therapies.

The key issues in today's prevention of cardiovascular disease are risk assessment in an individual, and optimization of lifestyle-related interventions and drug treatment. Current guidelines translate available evidence into clinical practice. This chapter summarizes the components of cardiovascular risk assessment and discusses the key clinical guidelines related to cardiovascular disease prevention in adults that are available from international and national bodies. The information in this chapter complements that in Chapters 5 and 6.

CHD PREVENTION STRATEGIES: PRIMARY AND SECONDARY

The concept of coronary heart disease (CHD) prevention includes the population strategy, the goal of which is to decrease the severity of CHD risk factors by modifying the lifestyle of the general population. It involves, for instance, anti-smoking campaigns, food pricing policies, etc. Complementary to the population strategy is the high-risk strategy, which targets intervention to individuals known to be at increased risk of a cardiac event.[6]

Within these two strategies, primary prevention describes activities in apparently healthy persons free of CHD. Secondary prevention means preventing subsequent events in persons with established atherosclerotic disease (see chapter 6). Secondary prevention requires more aggressive management of risk factors because the risk of subsequent events in persons with CHD is three to four times higher than that of the first event. In clinical trials involving subjects with existing CHD, the incidence of events varied from 11.68% in the Cholesterol and Recurrent Event (CARE) trial[2] to 23.6% in the Scandinavian Simvastatin Survival Study (4S).[1] In contrast, in primary prevention trials the incidence of CHD was much lower, ranging from 4.52% in the Air Force/Texas Coronary Atherosclerosis Prevention Study (AFCAPS/TexCAPS)[5] to 6.39% in the West of Scotland Coronary Prevention Study (WOSCOPS).[4]

Pathophysiologically, primary and secondary prevention focus on different stages of the same disease. Current evidence supports including persons with stroke and peripheral vascular disease into the secondary prevention category.[7]

RISK FACTORS FOR CARDIOVASCULAR DISEASE

Risk factors for CHD are taken into account in widely used risk assessment algorithms: gender, age, smoking status, total cholesterol (TC) or low-density-lipoprotein cholesterol (LDL-C), high-density-lipoprotein cholesterol (HDL-C), and diabetes. Some algorithms, such as that derived from the Framingham Heart Study, include ECG-determined left ventricular hypertrophy.[8]

Although genetic factors play an important role in determining risk, genetic analysis is presently limited to few disorders, particularly LDL-R gene mutations (Chapters 3, 29, and 34). Such testing is usually performed in research institutions. In the future, genetic testing will likely become much more common;[9] today, family history of premature CHD is still the marker used in clinical practice.

Other recognized CHD risk factors include a diet high in saturated fat, obesity, physical inactivity, psychosocial factors, insulin resistance, and high lipoprotein (a) (Lp[a]) concentration. The "newer," currently studied, factors include homocysteine, thrombogenic factors, and markers of low-grade inflammation. Prospective studies involving measurements of fibrinogen, high-sensitivity C-reactive protein (hs-CRP), and antifibrinolytic markers have been completed.[10] Future risk assessment will, without doubt, include factors such as genetic polymorphisms and mutations, markers of endothelial function, further markers of low-grade inflammation, and markers of LDL oxidation.[11,12] Ridker listed the following characteristics that need to be established for a new risk marker before its measurement could be introduced into clinical practice:[10]

❖ methodological consensus (sensitivity, specificity, method standardization)

❖ prospective epidemiological studies to ascertain relationship of a factor with risk

❖ assessment of predictability of risk over and above established markers of CHD risk

Figure 7–1 shows the main determinants of cardiovascular risk. It illustrates that cardiac status itself is an important factor in determining a probability of future CHD event. It follows that a comprehensive approach to CHD risk management must include lifestyle changes together with treatment of dyslipidemia, and the control of glycemia and blood pressure. In addition, persons who already suffer from cardiovascular disease need specific cardioprotective treatment aimed at combating ischemia and improving ventricular function.

Age and Gender

The effects of age and gender on CHD risk are substantial. Age is an independent risk factor for CHD, and becomes a dominant risk factor in older individuals. The key effect of age is best illustrated by comparing the one-year risk of CHD between the ages of 22 and 62 years, which differs by the factor 500 (see ATP II guidelines below).

Figure 7–1　◇　Determinants of Cardiovascular Risk

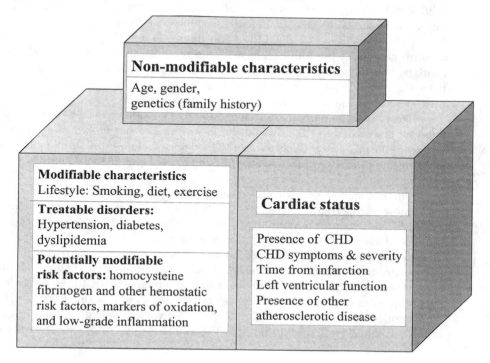

Present studies suggest that, at least in secondary prevention, the benefit of lowering cholesterol is independent of age. In the 4S there was no difference in treatment benefit in patients aged below and above 60 years.[1] Similarly, the pooled analysis of the Pravastatin Atherosclerosis Intervention Program suggested that risk reduction, if anything, was greater in patients older than 65 years.[13] In primary prevention, the AFCAPS/TexCAPS study, which recruited participants aged 43–73 years, showed lipid-lowering benefits in both men and in women, and in older individuals.[5] The recent meta-analysis of major clinical studies further confirmed the benefit of lipid lowering in older persons.[14]

Most data demonstrate that CHD risk is two to three times higher in men than in women, but in this case the risk differential decreases with age. In AFCAPS/TexCAPS, the mortality among women was almost 2.5 times lower than that of men (2% vs. 4.97%)[5], but the mortality in the secondary prevention trials was comparable between men and women.[14]

There are other important differences in the natural history of CHD in women as compared to men. TC/HDL-C ratio is a better predictor of CHD in women than TC alone.[15] Estrogen use in post-menopausal women was associated with a 50% risk reduction in CHD.[16] In 1998, however, the Heart and Estrogen/Progestin Replacement Study (HERS) demonstrated that in post-menopausal women with CHD, the average

4.1 years of treatment with conjugated equine estrogens plus medroxyprogesterone acetate did not reduce the incidence of CHD. Also, there was an increased rate of thromboembolic events and an increase in gallbladder disease.[17]

Clinical manifestations of CHD occur approximately 10 years later in women than in men,[18–21] while the occurrence of myocardial infarction (MI) and sudden death lags by 20 years compared to men. However, women who present with MI have twice the risk of reinfarction compared to those who originally present with angina. Also, symptoms and prognosis after MI are worse in women.[21]

The Framingham Heart Study suggested that a random glucose level is an independent predictor of CHD in non-diabetic women but not in men.[22] Women who smoke are 3.6 times more likely to have MI than non-smokers[23] but the combination of smoking and the use of oral contraceptives results in up to 20 times increased risk of CHD.

There is much less epidemiological data available for women than for men. Recent lipid-lowering trials suggest the equal benefit of treatment between genders. The evidence for the benefit of statin treatment in women with CHD is also clear. However, because of the small number of recorded events, the evidence for the benefit of treatment in women without CHD is weaker. Meta-analysis of major statin trials mentioned above failed to show a significant benefit for women in primary prevention, in terms of cardiovascular endpoints. While there was an encouraging trend, the evidence in this subgroup relies on a total of 20 coronary events observed in a single study.[5] This is compounded by the fact that AFCAPS/TexCAPS involved individuals with relatively low HDL-C concentration, and, therefore, the results may not be applicable to the population at large.

Diabetes

Diabetic patients are at two to three times higher risk of CHD than non-diabetics,[24,25] but only about half of the observed excess of CHD risk in persons with diabetes and impaired glucose tolerance (IGT) can be explained by the rise in conventional risk factors.

Individuals with diabetes often present with dyslipidemia characterized by increased triglycerides (TG) and intermediate-density-lipoprotein cholesterol (IDL) and decreased HDL-C.[26] The protective effect of female gender is not observed in diabetics. Of particular importance is the high coronary mortality in patients with diabetic nephropathy.[27] Atherosclerotic plaques in diabetics are similar to those in non-diabetics. Diabetic macroangiopathy is often regarded as equivalent to atherosclerosis, but it is historically interesting that this condition was originally described as a non-atherosclerotic disease of large vessels.[28]

Diabetes involves a widespread modification of structural and functional proteins, including apoproteins, by glucose.[29] Such modifications lead to the formation of protein cross-links known as advanced glycosylation end-products (AGE), which may play a role in the formation of atherosclerotic plaque.[30,31] Also, the Framingham Offspring Study showed that the fasting insulin concentration correlates with levels of hypercoagulability markers (von Willebrand Factor [vWF] antigen, and factor VII antigen) and antifibrinolytic markers (plasminogen activator inhibitor-1 [PAI-1]-antigen, and tissue-type plasminogen activator [tTPA]-antigen).[32]

The elegant study by Haffner et al. demonstrated that mortality of non-diabetic individuals with CHD is similar to that of diabetic patients free of CHD.[33] With regard to lipid-lowering, this observation provides a very strong argument for treating patients with diabetes similarly to those who remain in the secondary prevention category. Such an approach has now been adopted in several clinical practice guidelines.

Previously, the treatment of diabetes focused almost exclusively on the maintenance of glycemic control to prevent ketoacidosis and to prevent or delay the development of microvascular complications. The Diabetic Control and Complications Trial (DCCT), a landmark trial of diabetes, provided proof for the effectiveness of such an approach to delay microvascular complications, but the data on CHD events in this trial were inconclusive due to the relatively young age of participants.[34] Only recently has the focus in management of diabetic patients shifted towards prevention of macrovascular atherosclerotic disease.

The recently completed United Kingdom Diabetes Prospective Study (UKPDS) provided more data on the effect of treatment on CHD events in diabetic patients. UKPDS was a randomized controlled trial that compared the effects of intensive blood glucose control (achieved with either sulphonylurea derivatives or insulin) with conventional treatment, on the risk of microvascular and macrovascular complications of diabetes.[35] The participants were 3867 newly diagnosed type 2 patients, aged 54 years (median) with fasting plasma glucose (FPG) above 108 mg/dL (6 mmol/L). Their mean cholesterol level was 209 mg/dL (5.4mmol/L); LDL-C 135 mg/dL (3.5 mmol/L); and HDL-C 41 mg/dL (1.07 mmol/L). Endpoints of the study included any diabetes-related endpoint, diabetes-related death, and all-cause mortality.

During the trial, hemoglobin A1c decreased by 11% (from 7.9% to 7.0%) in the intensive treatment group compared to the conventional treatment group. This reduction was smaller than in the DCCT, where a reduction of 20% was achieved. In the UKPDS, there was a lower risk (p=0.029) for any diabetes endpoint in the intensive treatment group (diabetes-related endpoints were sudden death, death from hyperglycemia or hypoglycemia, fatal or non-fatal MI, angina, heart failure, stroke, renal failure, amputation, vitreous hemorrhage, retinopathy requiring photocoagulation, blindness in one eye, or cataract extraction). The intensive group had a 25% reduction in the microvascular endpoints (p=0.0099) compared to individuals undergoing conventional treatment. The reduction in risk of MI was 12%. The relative risk (RR) of MI in the intensive treatment group was 0.84 (confidence limits 0.71–1.00; p=0.052). The incidence of stroke was not affected.

Another clinical trial, the Diabetes Atherosclerosis Intervention Study (DAIS), in which non-insulin-dependent diabetes mellitus patients with CHD are being treated with fenofibrate, should provide further data in this patient group.[36]

Hypertension

Hypertension is a metabolically related disease associated with abnormalities of carbohydrate metabolism, and in particular with insulin resistance.[37] Hypertension is an important risk factor for CHD. In the UK, approximately 25% of hypertensive patients have a history of angina.[38] In several studies, dyslipidemia was associated with hypertension.[39] Endothelial dysfunction induced by LDL, or oxidized LDL, may well be a link.

Similarly to plasma TC, the relationship of diastolic blood pressure (DBP) to CHD risk is continuous and graded. However, in contrast to the large effect on the incidence of stroke, the benefit of treating hypertension in terms of coronary events is limited.[40,41] A decrease in DBP of 5–6 mm Hg with treatment is associated with a 40% reduction in risk of stroke.[42] Hypertension is also a more important risk factor in women.[43–45]

Smoking

Smoking is an independent risk factor for CHD.[46–49] The relative risk for heavy smokers is 5.5 for CHD death and 5.5 for non-fatal MI.[49] Risk associated with smoking is greatest if there are also other additional risk factors.

In a survey of MI survivors, smokers were approximately 10 years younger than non-smokers, were more frequently men, and more frequently had a family history of MI. The 30-day mortality was lower in smokers (6% vs. 15.7%), but ceased to be significantly different after adjustment for age. Smokers with MI had fewer other risk factors than non-smokers, which may indicate that coronary obstruction in smokers may be more thrombotic and less atherosclerotic in nature.[50] Thus smoking precipitates CHD at an earlier age.[51–53]

Diet

In primary prevention trials that used low-saturated-fat, low-cholesterol diets, there was only a limited benefit with regard to cardiovascular mortality.[54,55] On the other hand, several secondary prevention trials did yield a significant benefit.

A vegetarian diet in the Leiden Intervention Trial decreased CHD progression.[56] The St. Thomas' Atherosclerosis Regression Study (STARS), which involved a low-fat, low-cholesterol diet, resulted in a decrease in CHD progression in the diet-treated patients.[57] In the Lifestyle Heart Trial, a one-year trial involving 28 patients treated with very-low-cholesterol diet (less than 5 mg cholesterol per day), there was a significant regression in stenosis in the treated group.[58] A 29% reduction in total mortality was observed in the Diet and Reinfarction Trial (DART), in which patients with a history of MI reduced the consumption of saturated fat and increased polyunsaturated fat, fiber, and in particular, fatty fish intake.[59]

More recent dietary studies such as the DART trial,[59] the Lyon Trial,[60] and the Indian Study[61] focused not only on the fat and cholesterol content of diet, but also on the general diets consumed by populations with low incidence of CHD such as Asian-vegetarian or Mediterranean. The decrease in the relative risk of combined cardiac deaths and non-fatal MI was 16% in the DART, 41% in the Indian Study, and 73% in the Lyon study. The overall risk of death decreased by 29%, 45%, and 70% respectively. These results suggest that the reducing total and saturated fat levels should be supplemented by maintaining the intake of omega-6 fatty acids, increasing the consumption of oleic acid and omega-3 fatty acids, increasing the intake of natural antioxidants and micro-elements, and also by maintaining intake of vegetable proteins.[54]

Obesity

The prevalence of obesity (body mass index [BMI] not less than 30 kg/m[2]) in the U. S. population increased between 1991 and 1998, from 12% to 17.9%.[62] Obesity carries a wide range of health risks. National Health and Nutrition Examination Survey III data show a graded increase in hypertension, type 2 diabetes, osteoarthritis, and gallbladder disease with the increasing severity of obesity.[63] Although persons with BMI of 25 kg/m2 or more were more likely to have hypercholesterolemia than those with lower BMI, there was no association between TC level and the grade of obesity.[63]

In the prospective Munster Heart Trial (PROCAM), an epidemiological study of people at work, which between 1979 and 1991 recruited 23,616 persons, BMI did not emerge as an independent risk factor: the risk was mediated through other risk factors. However, LDL-C rose from the mean of 98 mg/dL (2.5 mmol/L) in men and 105 mg/dL (2.7 mmol/L) in women aged 16–25 years whose BMI = 20 kg/m[2], to 156 mg/dL (4.3 mmol/L) in men and 167 mg/dL (4.3 mmol/L) in women aged 56–65 years whose BMI exceeded 30 kg/m[2]. As BMI decreased, HDL-C decreased. In men, TG increased with increasing BMI. Also, obesity increased FBG concentration and systolic blood pressure (SBP) with age.[64,65]

A two-year treatment program for obesity with a gastrointestinal lipase inhibitor showed an initial average weight loss of 8.76 kg, 35% of which was regained over two years, and decreased LDL-C only modestly (131 to 121 mg/dL; 3.38 to 3.14 mmol/L). However, there was a significant decrease in fasting serum insulin levels in the treated group.[63,66]

Exercise

Inactive lifestyle is a major contributor to obesity.[67,68] There are associations between lipids and lipoprotein concentrations, exercise, and CHD mortality and morbidity.[69–71] Obesity, smoking, and excess fat intake are less prevalent in physically active individuals.[72–75]

Interestingly, low energy expenditure may be more important in the development of obesity than overeating.[76] In exercise programs, a combination of frequency, duration, and intensity is important. Unfortunately, the dropout rate from supervised exercise classes is high. Apart from cardiovascular benefit, individuals who exercise regularly report an improved mood and a sense of well-being.[77] Practically speaking, lifestyle changes that involve everyday physical activity are as effective in improving cardio-respiratory fitness as structured exercise programs.[78]

Interactions among Risk Factors

The main thrust of cardiovascular event prevention actions is to decrease the severity of risk factors. In addition, the Multiple Risk Factor Intervention Trial (MRFIT) results provide a powerful argument for population interventions aimed at maintaining low

Figure 7–2 ◇ The Metabolic Interrelationships between Cardiovascular Risk
Factors

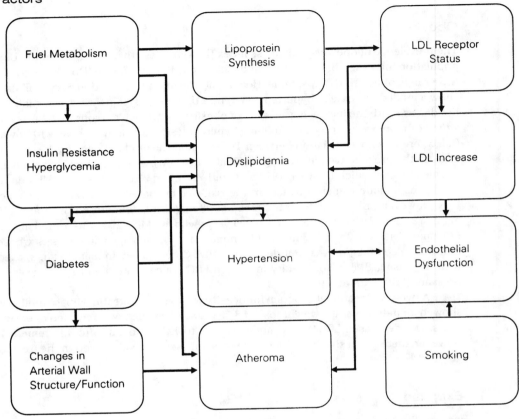

cardiovascular risk status throughout life. MRFIT showed that persons who maintain
low levels of the three main risk factors—TC below 200 mg/dL (5.17 mmol/L); blood
pressure below 120/80 mm Hg; and non-smoking—carry a low mortality risk (RR 0.60
in women and 0.42 in men) and increased longevity.[79]

CHD risk factors have a mutiplicative effect and therefore persons who have
one, two, or three risk factors in moderate severity could be at an overall higher risk
than an individual with a severe single risk factor. Metabolic interrelationships between cardiovascular risk factors are illustrated in Figure 7–2.

Clinical Trial Environment vs. Clinical Practice

It is well recognized that the realities of clinical practice differ from those of the clinical trial environment. An important factor in the implementation of therapies is patient compliance.

Even in the clinical trial setting, there is a substantial difference in how lipid-lowering occurs. In the 4S study, TC decreased 26%,[1] whereas in the Long-Term Intervention with Pravastatin in Ischemic Disease (LIPID), it decreased by 18% at the most, and only by 13% in the sixth year of the study.[3] These differences would be difficult to explain as the just the efficacious result of statin preparations. Compliance in some of the mainline studies was relatively poor, with up to 30% of patients dropping out before a trial was completed. Other studies suggest that the effectiveness of lipid-lowering treatment in the clinical practice environment is much less than in the clinical trial setting.[80]

Another important consideration is frequency of patient monitoring, for instance, the standard annual review of diabetic patients in Diabetic Clinics, which may not be compatible with optimal introduction of lipid-lowering and hypertensive treatment.

THE DEVELOPMENT OF GUIDELINES FOR CARDIOVASCULAR EVENT PREVENTION

Approximately 10 years ago the views on cardiovascular prevention started to move from a single risk factor approach to comprehensive cardioprotective management. In 1996, the Bethesda Conference endorsed the principle of matching intensity of risk factor management with the risk of coronary events, and stressed the importance of the management of cardiovascular risk factors as a part of broader care.[81] However, one must remember that our perception of benefits of multi-risk factor management is still to a large extent based on evidence extrapolated from studies of single risk factor(s), such as dyslipidemia or hypertension.

Current clinical guidelines for cardiovascular risk management integrate the practice of cardiovascular prevention across medical disciplines. Several recent guidelines adopted the multi-specialist approach,[82–84] in which one document deals with multidisciplinary management of risk factors. In secondary prevention, the management of dyslipidemia has been integrated with other cardioprotective therapies such as beta-blockers, angiotensin-converting enzyme (ACE) inhibitors, anti-platelet therapy, and anti-coagulant treatment.

Clinical guidelines can only fulfill their role if they are accepted widely by the medical community. To ensure such acceptance, they must be prepared not only by the academic experts but by multi-disciplinary teams of health care providers that include all stakeholders.[85,86] For instance, the Sixth Report of the Joint National Committee on Prevention, Detection, Evaluation, and Treatment of High Blood Pressure (JNC VI) was prepared with participation from 38 professional societies and from seven U. S. federal agencies.[85]

The most recent recommendations of the European Task Force on the Prevention of Coronary Heart Disease in Clinical Practice included representation from the European Society of Cardiology, European Atherosclerosis Society, European Society of Hypertension, International Society of Behavioural Medicine, European Society of General Practice/Family Medicine, and the European Heart Network.[82] The Joint British Recommendations on Prevention of Coronary Heart Disease in Clinical Practice[83] were published in 1998 by the British Cardiac Society, the British Hyperlipidaemia Association, and the British Hypertension Society and were endorsed by the British Diabetic Association. The joint American College of Cardiologists (ACC) and American Heart Association (AHA) guidelines on the management of MI were developed by cardiologists with participation of representatives from various medical speciality groups other than cardiology.[84]

The development of guidelines involves collecting available evidence through formal literature review, and subsequently weighing the strength of data for or against a particular treatment or procedure. It also includes estimates of expected health outcomes.[84] Sophisticated consultative mechanisms are put in place during guideline preparation to achieve consensus and to ensure a systematic approach to evidence. For instance in the U. K., the Scottish Intercollegiate Guidelines Network (SIGN) formulated recommendations on a wide range of medical and surgical treatments, primarily for the implementation in the National Health Service in Scotland. SIGN recently published a structured template for guideline development,[86] which agrees with the recommendations of the U. S. Institute of Medicine[87] (Figure 7–3).

By definition, international recommendations are meant for a broad audience and, as happens in Europe, may address populations with differing prevalence of atherosclerotic disease, different economies, and health care systems. Such international guidelines are developed on the assumption that they will be subsequently adjusted for local circumstances. The "derived" local guidelines take into account local prevalence of CHD, lifestyle patterns, health care resources, diagnostic facilities, and the availability of drugs. They also relate the recommendations to the prevailing practices and resources for cardiovascular prevention in the particular area and the attitudes of the medical community, among other factors. Such local guidelines are particularly useful in emerging programs.

The goal of local recommendations is to facilitate practical implementation and acceptance of the international/national guidelines. Such guidelines should be treated as interim, revised as circumstances change, and interpreted together with national/international documents. The essence of "field" guidelines should be their simplicity. For instance, in the Greater Glasgow Health Board area, the guidelines are provided on two pages in A5 format and distributed, with lipid results, by hospital laboratories.

Finally, it must be emphasized that all guidelines are intended to assist health care providers in clinical decision making, but not to substitute for a clinical judgment.[86,87] They define practices that meet the needs of most patients in most circumstances. As stressed in the preamble to the ACC/AHA guidelines on the management of MI, "the ultimate judgment regarding care of a particular patient must be made by the physician and patient in the light of circumstances specific to that patient."[84]

Weighting of Evidence

The evidence supporting new medical procedures comes from randomized controlled trials, case control studies, retrospective analyses, cohort studies, cross-sectional population studies, and clinical interventions, together with meta-analysis. During clinical guideline development, such evidence is systematically evaluated to produce practice guidelines. It is now a standard practice that recommendations contain a

Figure 7–3 ✧ Scottish Intercollegiate Guidelines Network (SIGN) Guideline Development Process

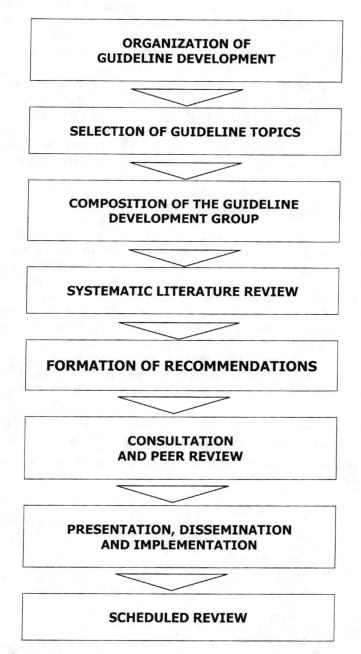

Reproduced with permission from reference 86.

weighting of quoted evidence. For instance, JNC VI adopted the Last and Abramson classification of evidence base, with a classification symbol appended to the number of the reference article when quoted in the guideline text[88] (Table 7–1).

The Scottish SIGN adopted an evidence-weighting system based on that of the U. S. Agency for Health Care Policy and Research,[89] which combines grading of recommendations with the classification of evidence level. A similar system has been accepted for the AHA/ACC guidelines on the management of MI.[84]

The readability of guidelines is a key issue. Often, full guideline text is accompanied by summary documents and/or concise summary leaflets. One of the editorially most elegant is the JNC VI report, which combines clear presentation of key supporting data with well-laid-out classification tables and a clear summary of available drugs. The report includes the weighing of evidence (see above), and there is no excess of pathophysiologic information that is easily available from other sources.

INDIVIDUAL RECOMMENDATIONS

Selected international and national recommendations are described below to give the reader a broad view of approaches adopted by different expert groups, and to demonstrate converging views on cardiovascular prevention worldwide. The section starts with a short summary of National Cholesterol Education Program Adult Treatment Panel II (NCEP-ATP II) recommendations (these have been treated more extensively elsewhere[6] and are also described in chapter 5). ATP II recommendations are followed by the discussion of AHA, ACC, and American College of Physicians (ACP) statements that incorporated ATP II views into comprehensive risk management programs. To illustrate a disease-specific multidisciplinary guideline, two sets of recommendations are described: AHA/ACC guidelines on the management of MI, and the JNC VI report, which remains a U. S. standard for the management of hypertension.

Table 7–1 ✧ Classification of Evidence Base for Guideline Development

Sixth Report of the Joint National Committee on Prevention, Detection, Evaluation, and Treatment of High Blood Pressure (JNC VI; ref 85).

Category	Definition/synonym
Meta-analysis	analysis of compendium of experimental studies
Randomized controlled study	experimental study
Retrospective analysis	case control study
Prospective follow up	cohort study (includes historical studies)
Cross-sectional population study	prevalence study
Previous review or position statements	
Clinical interventions (non-randomized)	

The second part of this section covers guidelines that incorporate the assessment of absolute CHD risk and that employ a variety of risk assessment charts. The described guidelines of this type are current European recommendations, recommendations recently published in Britain, and guidelines developed in New Zealand, which remain one of the clearest recommendations available to date.

GUIDELINES THAT INCORPORATE RISK ASSESSMENT BASED ON THE SEVERITY OF DYSLIPIDEMIA AND THE PRESENCE OF OTHER RISK FACTORS

Recommendations of the National Cholesterol Education Program Adult Treatment Panel II ((NCEP-ATP II)

First recommendations of the ATP (ATP I) were published in 1987 and these of the second panel (ATP II) in 1994.[90] These are now a standard for the U. S. and have achieved worldwide recognition. NCEP, through other panels, addressed not only patient-related practices, but also dealt extensively with laboratory support for the diagnosis and management of lipid disorders.[91–93] The present ATP II guidelines were prepared before the results of large statin trials were known, and are now somewhat dated. Revised guidelines are due to appear in 2001.[94]

The main concept adopted by ATP II is the adjustment of the intensity of preventive measures to the number of CHD risk factors in an individual, and intensifying these measures further in persons with atherosclerotic disease. However, apart from TC and LDL-C, these recommendations do not grade the severity of risk factors. Risk factors used by ATP II are listed in Table 7–2. Note that although obesity and physical inactivity are not included as "primary" risk factors, their modification is recommended because of a secondary effect on the "main" risk factors.

ATP II recognizes three levels of TC or LDL-C: desirable, borderline, and high (Table 7–3). TG concentration is classed as desirable, borderline, high, and very high because of the risk of pancreatitis at very high TG level. HDL-C is classed as low, normal, and high, the latter being regarded as a negative risk factor. In its recommendations on lipid lowering, ATP II proposes several cut-off points for the initiation of lipid-lowering treatment and sets specific goals for treatment in terms of plasma lipids.

Diet (or indeed a change in eating behavior) is the first measure taken to decrease LDL-C. In primary prevention, six months of dietary treatment are suggested before drug therapy is considered. This involves first the AHA step I diet (30% or less fat, 10% or less saturated fat, 300 mg or less cholesterol per day) for the first three months and then the step II diet. In secondary prevention, the dietary treatment begins with AHA Step II diet (total fat content 30% or less, saturated fat less than 7%, and cholesterol less than 200 mg /day).

Initiation of drug treatment is tailored to the risk level defined as a number of risk factors (less than two, and two or more). Also, treatment levels are set higher in men below 35 years of age and in pre-menopausal women who have no other risk factors. Therefore, initiation of treatment is recommended at different LDL-C levels, depending on risk factor status: from above 220 mg/dL (5.7 mmol/L) in young men or in pre-menopausal women free of other risk factors, to above 100 mg/dL (2.6 mmol/L) in

Table 7–2 ✧ NCEP Second Adult Treatment Panel (ATP II) Modifiable and Non-Modifiable Cardiovascular Risk Factors

Key independent CHD risk factors	Modifiable risk factors
Male sex	
Age (men ≥ 45 years, women ≥ 55 years)	
Family history of premature CHD;	
(men < 55 years , women < 65 years)	
Current smoking	Current smoking
Hypertension	Hypertension
Diabetes mellitus	Diabetes mellitus
High LDL-C	High LDL-C
Low HDL-C (< 35 mg/dl; 0.9 mmol/l)	Low HDL-C
Presence of CHD or other atherosclerotic disease	
Negative risk factor (protective factor)	**Negative risk factor** (protective factor)
High HDL-C (≥ 60 mg/dL; 1.6 mmol/L)	High HDL-C
	Physical inactivity
	Obesity

patients with CHD and in persons with multiple risk factors or diabetes (the need for aggressive treatment of dyslipidemia in diabetics has been confirmed by the ADA statement[95]).

Rather than using the TC/HDL-C ratio, ATP II focuses separately on LDL-C and HDL-C management. The argument is that these are independent risk factors, and as such should be treated separately. Apart from measures to lower LDL-C, the recommendations suggest the possible use of drug treatment in patients with isolated low HDL-C, if such persons are at high CHD risk because of family history of CHD.[96]

Lipid Testing

ATP II recommends non-fasting TC and HDL-C as a screening test. When screening test results are abnormal, fasting analysis that includes TC, LDL-C, TG, and HDL-C is recommended.

Table 7–3 (A and B) ✧ NCEP Second Adult Treatment Panel (ATP II) Interpretation of Serum Lipid Concentrations.

A. Interpretation of LDL-cholesterol and triglyceride concentrations.

LDL-cholesterol mg/dL (mmol/L)	Triglyceride mg/dL (mmol/L)	Interpretation
< 100 (2.6)		desirable (secondary prevention)
< 130 (3.4)	< 200 (2.3)	desirable (primary prevention)
130–159 (3.4–4.1)	200–400 (2.26–4.51)	borderline
≥160 (4.1)	> 400–1000 (4.5–11.2)	high
	>1000 (11.2)	very high

B. Interpretation of HDL-cholesterol concentration.

HDL-C mg/dL (mmol/L)	Interpretation
< 35 (0.9)	Low
35–60 (0.9–1.6)	Normal
> 60 (1.6)	high; "negative" risk factor

Assessment of ATP II

The ATP II guidelines have been recently assessed in view of the new data that became available since their publication.[97] The changes suggested in view of recent data include initiation of drug therapy in secondary prevention without the need for initial trial of lifestyle measures. Also, current trials do not support the use of hormone replacement therapy (HRT) as the primary treatment to normalize lipid levels.[17] The list of lipid-lowering drugs in the ATP II is now outdated. The up-to-date list can be found in a recent review.[98]

Recommendations of the American College of Physicians (ACP) on Lipid Screening

In 1996, the ACP addressed the issue of cholesterol screening.[99] They suggested screening is appropriate but not mandatory in men aged 35–65 years and women aged 45–65 years. This excludes situations where other risk factors are present or where there is a suspicion of inherited dyslipidemia. On the other hand, screening is not recommended for men younger than 35 years and women younger than 45 years of age. Also, according to ACP, there was insufficient evidence to make a pronouncement on screening in persons aged 65–75 years, and screening is not recommended for persons older than 75 years.

These guidelines confirm that the measurement of HDL-C helps to stratify CHD risk, but they fall short of recommending its use for general screening because of insufficient evidence about the effect on management. Some aspects of this statement have been recently challenged and it was argued that the results of the most recent studies show that the effect of statins is independent of sex and age.[14]

GUIDELINES THAT INCORPORATE COMPREHENSIVE MANAGEMENT OF RISK IN PRIMARY PREVENTION, AND CARDIOPROTECTION IN INDIVIDUALS WITH ATHEROSCLEROTIC DISEASE

The AHA Consensus Panel Statement on Primary Prevention of Cardiovascular Diseases

This 1997 AHA statement took into account results of recent large lipid-lowering trials and emphasized the need for comprehensive risk factor management.[100] The goals for prevention include

✧   complete cessation of smoking;

✧   blood pressure control, with a goal of 140/90 mm Hg or below;

✧   management of LDL-C concentration according to ATP II goals, with secondary goals including HDL-C > 35 mg/dL (0.9 mmol/L) and TG < 200 mg/dL (2.26 mmol/L);

✧   dietary recommendations include promoting the AHA step 1 diet for all persons;

✧   increased physical activity, with a goal of 20 minutes of exercise three to four times per week;

✧   weight reduction, with a goal of BMI 21–25 kg/m²; and

✧   consideration of HRT in post-menopausal women on an individualized basis.

AHA Consensus Panel Statement on Preventing Heart Attack and Death in Patients with Coronary Disease

This statement also adopted the ATP II risk factors and algorithm for lipid testing.[101] The statement was endorsed by ACC and goes beyond lipids and lifestyle measures. Its recommendations include a range of cardioprotective treatments in addition to lipid lowering. The document also emphasizes the need for a team approach in patients who have CHD and other vascular diseases. Such team should include physicians, nurses, and dieticians. The main recommendations included

✧   cessation of smoking (identical to primary prevention);

✧   lipid lowering (more aggressive drug treatment with an LDL-C goal of < 100 mg/dL [2.6 mmol/L]), and the AHA step 2 diet for all patients;

✧   rehabilitation and increased physical activity;

✧   cardioprotective treatments such as anti-platelet agents (aspirin) or anti-coagu-

Table 7–4 ✧ American Heart Association (AHA) Lipid-Lowering Goals for the Primary and Secondary Prevention of Cardiovascular Disease

Patient category	LDL cut-off point for initiation of drug treatment mg/dl (mmol/L)	Primary treatment goal (LDL-C) mg/dL (mmol/L)	Secondary treatment goals mg/dL (mmol/L)
Men < 35 years, pre-menopausal women; (both with < 2 CHD risk factors)	220* (5.7)	< 160 (4.1)	TG < 200 (2.3), HDL > 35 (0.9)
Men ≥ 45 years, and post-menopausal women with < 2 CHD risk factors	190 (4.9)	< 160 (4.1)	TG < 200 (2.3), HDL > 35 (0.9)
Men ≥ 45 years , and post-menopausal women with = 2 CHD risk factors	130 (3.4) 100* (2.6)	< 130 (3.4)	TG < 200 (2.3) HDL > 35 (0.9)
All patients with CHD		< 100 (2.6)	TG < 200 (2.3) HDL > 35 (0.9)
All type 2 diabetic patients (ADA statement; ref 95)	130 (3.4)	< 100 (2.6)	TG < 200 (2.3) HDL > 35 (0.9)
*Use clinical judgment			

lation, ACE-inhibitors post-MI and long-term in patients with left ventricular dysfunction, beta blockers post-MI, and consideration of HRT in post-menopausal women; and

✧   treatment of hypertension with a goal of blood pressure ≤ 140/90 mm Hg.

The AHA (ATP II) lipoprotein treatment goals for primary and secondary prevention are summarized in Table 7–4.

DISEASE-RELATED GUIDELINES: THE MANAGEMENT OF MYOCARDIAL INFARCTION AND HYPERTENSION

The ACC/AHA Task Force Practice Guidelines for the Management of Patients with Acute Myocardial Infarction

These guidelines provide a detailed approach to the management of MI and include emergency diagnosis and management, hospital management, preparation for discharge, and long-term management.[84] They incorporate secondary prevention lipid lowering into long-term therapy.[84]

With regard to dyslipidemias, the guidelines follow ATP II recommendations. The cut-off point for drug therapy is LDL-C concentration > 130 mg/dL (3.4 mmol/L) despite diet, and the goal of reducing LDL-C to < 100 mg/dL (2.6 mmol/L). The main recommendations as to cardioprotective treatment post-MI are that after acute MI, the patient should continue to receive aspirin;[102] all but low-risk patients and those with clear contraindications should receive beta-blockers.[103,104] ACE inhibitor should be prescribed as appropriate in the acute stage and long-term in patients with left ventricular dysfunction. Selected post-MI patients, i.e., those who are unable to take aspirin, should be anticoagulated. Post-menopausal, post-MI women should be carefully counseled about the potential benefits of HRT and offered this option of they desire it.

These guidelines also provide detailed recommendations on the introduction of lifestyle changes such as the Houston-Miller and Taylor[105] stepped approach to smoking cessation and the recommendations as to cardiac rehabilitation and return to prior levels of activity.

With regard to the use of HRT, both the AHA statement on secondary prevention and the ACC/AHA recommendations on the treatment of MI were published before the results of the HERS study were known.[17]

The Sixth Report of the Joint National Committee on Prevention, Detection, Evaluation, and Treatment of High Blood Pressure (JNC VI)

JNC VI includes the physiological rationale, clinical evidence, and practical recommendations for the diagnosis and treatment of hypertension.[85] The scope of JNC VI ranges from the description of relevant public health issues, through staging of hypertension, to an account of available drugs. The management of high blood pressure is based on principles similar to these applied to hypercholesterolemia, i.e., the intensity of management should depend on the severity of hypertension, and on the presence of other CHD risk factors. The severity of hypertension also determines the required time lag between diagnosis and the institution of drug treatment (Table 7–5). Special treatment groups, which require particularly intensive management, are identified. These are persons with target organ damage nephropathy, retinopathy, left ventricular hypertrophy, or with present diabetes and cardiovascular disease, such as stroke, transient ischemic attacks, and peripheral vascular disease.

GUIDELINES THAT INCORPORATE THE ASSESSMENT OF ABSOLUTE CARDIOVASCULAR RISK

Presentation of clinical trial results in terms of relative risk (RR) may be misleading, because it does not take into account the prevalence of a given condition in a population. For instance, if the prevalence is 0.5% and the RR associated with a particular risk factor is 1.5 (an impressive 50% risk increase) then the presence of such risk factor would increase the absolute chance of a person having the condition from 1:200 to 1:133. On the other hand, if the prevalence is, say 10%, the same RR would mean that a

Table 7–5 ✧ The Sixth Report of the Joint National Committee on Prevention, Detection, Evaluation, and Treatment of High Blood Pressure (JNC VI)

RISK STRATIFICATION AND TREATMENT*			
Blood Pressure Stages (mm Hg)	*Risk Group A (no risk factors; no TOD/CCD)†*	*Risk Group B (at least 1 risk factor, not including diabetes; no TOD/CCD)*	*Risk Group C (TOD/CCD and/or diabetes, with or without other risk factors)*
High-normal (130–139/85–89)	Lifestyle Modification	Lifestyle Modification	Drug therapy§
Stage 1 (140–159/90–99)	Lifestyle Modification (up to 12 months)	Lifestyle Modification‡ (up to 6 months)	Drug therapy
Stages 2 and 3 (≥ 160/≥ 100)	Drug therapy	Drug therapy	Drug therapy

For example, a patient with diabetes and a blood pressure of 142/94 mmHg, plus left ventricular hypertrophy, should be classified as having stage 1 hypertension with target organ disease (left ventricular hypertrophy) and with another major risk factor (diabetes). This patient would be categorized as **Stage 1**, **Risk Group C**, and recommended for immediate initiation of pharmacologic treatment.
* Lifestyle modification should be adjunctive therapy for all patients recommended for pharmacologic therapy.
† TOD/CCD indicates target organ disease/clinical cardiovascular disease.
‡ For patients with multiple risk factors, clinicians should consider drugs as initial therapy plus lifestyle modifications.
§ For those with heart failure, renal insufficiency, or diabetes.
Source: National Heart, Lung and Blood Institute.
NIH Publication 98–4080. Reproduced from Ref. 85

chance of event would increase, at a much higher level, from 1:10 to approximately 1:7. The recommendations on risk management developed in New Zealand and in Europe base their risk assessment on the concept of absolute risk. This approach has also been adopted in the new British recommendations.

Recommendations of the Second Joint Task Force of the Joint European Societies on Coronary Prevention

The first recommendations of the European Task Force of the European Society of Cardiology, European Atherosclerosis Society, and the European Society of Hypertension were published in 1994.[106] The participation of professional bodies was widened during the preparation of the updated recommendations in 1998.[82]

These recommendations combine lipid-lowering treatment, management of blood pressure, and aspects of diabetes management relevant to CHD prevention. The risk is calculated as the probability of an event per year, referring to a 10-year timeframe and assessed with the aid of a risk chart. The definition of high risk is a risk of non-fatal event or coronary death exceeding 20% (1:5) over 10 years, or exceeding 20% when projected to age 60 years (the latter statement is somewhat vague). Such risk level also justifies the treatment with lipid-lowering drugs, if dietary management proves inadequate.

Risk assessment is based on the Framingham algorithm. The risk assessment includes gender, age, cholesterol level, smoking status, and systolic blood pressure (SBP). The two major risk factors, which are omitted, are the family history of CHD and the HDL-C level. The assessment is based on an average HDL-C concentration of 39 mg/dL (1 mmol/L) for men and 43 mg/dL (1.1 mmol/L) for women. Persons with diabetes, familial hyperlipidemia, and a family history of premature CHD are assumed to be at higher risk than that predicted by the risk table. Persons with familial hyperlipidemia, diabetes, family history of premature cardiovascular disease, HDL-C concentration < 40 mg/dL (1.0 mmol/L) in men and < 43 mg/dL (1.1 mmol/L) in women, and TG concentration > 180 mg/dL (2 mmol/L), are at higher risk than that indicated by the risk chart.

The risk chart table classifies individuals into the following risk categories: low risk if the 10-year chance of event is under 5%, mild risk at 5%–10%, moderate risk at 10%–20%, high risk at 20%–40%, and very high risk over 40%. There are separate risk charts for men and women with diabetes mellitus. The treatment goals include the following:

✧ Cessation of smoking, choices for healthy foods, physical activity, and maintenance of ideal body weight. The recommendations on smoking cessation suggest nicotine replacement therapies when appropriate. The recommendations about aerobic exercise are for 20–30 minutes four to five times each week. Weight loss is recommended in patients whose BMI is above 25 kg/m,[2] or who have waist circumference above 93 cm (men) or 79 cm (women). Diet in the European recommendations is described as "healthy food choices" and includes

✧ reducing total fat intake to 30% or less of total energy intake;

✧ replacing saturated with monounsaturated and polyunsaturated fats;

✧ increasing fruit, vegetables, and cereal intake;

✧ reducing total calorie intake when weight loss is required; and

✧ limiting salt and alcohol use in hypertensive patients.

✧ Blood pressure target is below 140/90 mm Hg.

✧ TC target is < 190 mg/dL (5mmol/L), and LDL-C < 115 mg/dL (3.0 mmol/L).

✧ Other cardioprotective measures in secondary prevention are similar to ACC/AHA recommendations mentioned above.

The substantial part of the European recommendations relates to blood pressure management. Here, similarly to the treatment of hyperlipidemia, the treatment depends on the absolute risk level and on the severity of blood pressure increase. The details of JNC VI risk stratification are given in Table 7–5 and the comparison of European and British recommendations on the management of hypertension is shown in Table 7–6.

European recommendations also include goals for glycemic control in diabetes: a FBG between 91 and 120 mg/dL (5.1–6.5 mmol/L). The goal for postprandial glucose is 136–160 mg/dL (7.6–9 mmol/L) and for hemoglobin A1c concentration, 6.2–7.5%.

Table 7-6 ◇ For details of JNC VI recommendations on risk stratification and treatment see Table 7-1

JNCVI	JNC VI SBP (mm Hg)		JNC VI DBP (mm Hg)	JNC VI Management	Joint British Recommendations: management	European Recommendations SBP (mm Hg)		European Recommendations DBP (mm Hg)	European Recommendations: management
Optimal	< 120	and	< 80		General target < 140/85				
Normal	< 130	and	< 85						
High-normal	130–139	or	85–89	Manage in context of risk & TOD/CCD					
Hypertension									
Stage 1*	140–159	or	90–99	Manage in context of risk & TOD/CCD	Manage in context of risk and TOD	140–179	and/or	90–99	Manage in context of risk & TOD
Stage 2*	160–179	or	100–109	Drug therapy	Lifestyle and drug therapy if sustained				
Stage 3*	≥ 180	or	≥ 110	Drug therapy	Confirm within 1–2 weeks. Lifestyle and drug therapy if sustained.	≥ 180		≥ 100	Lifestyle and drug therapy
Reference no	85		85	85	83	82		82	82

TOD: Target organ damage
CCD: cardiovascular disease
Comparison of JNC VI, Joint British Recommendations, and Second European Task Force Recommendations on the Management of Hypertension

These reflect the necessary balance between the benefits of tight glycemic control and the risks of hyperglycemia. The goals could be adjusted in individual patients: because it is safer to decrease blood glucose in type 2 diabetes, the achieved level of glucose could be lower than recommended. On the other hand, the goals for the elderly and patients who have difficulties in recognizing hypoglycemia should be set higher.

The European guidelines prioritize the coronary event prevention as follows:

✧   persons with established CHD and other atherosclerotic disease

✧   healthy individuals at high risk of developing CHD, close relatives of patients with early onset CHD or other atherosclerotic disease, and other individuals who are at particularly high risk

✧   other individuals met in connection with ordinary clinical practice

Setting such priorities is somewhat controversial, as it implies rationing care. The danger is that it may be construed as decreasing the importance of the prevention in subgroups at lower risk. From the health economy point of view, the high-risk population yields a greater absolute number of people benefiting from treatment. Formulating the above as priorities (or a level of concern) for patients rather than health care providers would probably be more acceptable. Nevertheless, prioritization could be helpful at early stages of the development of cardiovascular prevention systems, in situations where it may be impossible to address all related issue at the same time.

Lipid Testing

European guidelines recommend no general screening. Screening of close relatives is indicated in people with a family history of premature heart disease (men younger than 55 years, women younger than 65 years) and also if familial hypercholesterolemia or other inherited dyslipidemia is diagnosed. The initial recommended measurement is TC, with TC, HDL-C, and TG measured whenever the absolute risk increases beyond 20%. Monitoring of therapy should be by the measurement of TC or LDL-C.

New Zealand 1996 National Heart Foundation Clinical Guidelines for the Assessment and Management of Dyslipidemia

The absolute risk assessment was introduced as a part of the New Zealand recommendations as early as 1993. Revised recommendations were published in 1996[107] and the latest update in March 2000.[108] They are also based on the Framingham risk algorithm.[8]

New Zealand guidelines consider the risk of cardiovascular event rather than just CHD event: this includes CHD death, non-fatal MI, new angina, stroke, and transient ischemic attacks. Risk factors included in the algorithm are age, gender, blood pressure, dyslipidemia (TC/HDL-C ratio), diabetes, and impaired glucose tolerance (IGT). Family history, physical inactivity, obesity, left ventricular hypertrophy (LVH), fibrinogen, and Lp(a) are not included. However, it is assumed that the family history of early cardiovascular disease is associated with RR of a cardiovascular event

1.3–3.0, and physical inactivity with RR 1.5–2.0 compared to individuals without these risk factors.

Risk is graded as very high if the probability of event exceeds 20% over five years, high if the risk is 15%–20%, moderate at 10%–15%, and mild if the chance of event over five years is below 10%. Categories of patients who automatically remain at risk above 20% are patients with cardiovascular disease, with previous angioplasty or coronary artery bypass graft, with genetic lipid disorders, and diabetic persons with established diabetic nephropathy (albuminuria > 300 mg/day).

The goals of therapy are to get TC below 193 mg/dL (5 mmol/L); LDL-C below 116 mg/dL (3 mmol/L); and HDL-C above 39 mg/dL (1 mmol/L). The suggested goal for TG is < 180 mg/dL (2 mmol/L). Alternatively the goal is 20%–25% reduction in TC (or smaller reduction with an increase in HDL-C). The TC/HDL-C ratio should be < 4.5. Persons who have undergone coronary artery bypass grafting (CABG) are excepted from all exclusions if their TC is above 399 mg/dL (4.5 mmol/l).

Regarding drug treatment, these guidelines recommend intervening with antihypertensive drugs and aspirin at the risk level of 10% over five years, and the use of statins when the risk level exceeds 20% in five years. The 1996 recommendations suggest that HRT should not be considered as an alternative to lipid lowering. The latest update of the guidelines contains the assessment of the likely benefit of treatment.[108]

Lipid Testing

Everyone should have TC measured by early adulthood, but the measurement in children is only indicated on suspicion of lipid genetic disease. Two tests are required to establish baseline. The TC/HDL ratio is regarded as a better prognostic indicator than TC or HDL-C alone.[109]

The Joint British Recommendations on Prevention of Coronary Disease in Clinical Practice (JBR)

These recently published guidelines also emphasize comprehensive assessment of cardiovascular risk.[83] Similarly to the ATP II and Second European Task Force Recommendations, JBR risk calculation is based on the Framingham function. The Joint British guidelines also include the "order of priority" for preventive actions similar to European recommendations, and these include

✧ patients with established CHD as the first priority,

✧ patients with other major atherosclerotic disease,

✧ individuals at high risk who have hypertension, dyslipidemia, diabetes, or a family history of premature CHD.

Coronary risk prediction chart produced by JBR is a set of risk curves that delineate the CHD risk (i.e., the combined risk of nonfatal MI and CHD death) of less than 15% over the next ten years, 15%–30%, and above 30%. There are separate charts for men and women. Each gender is then subdivided into smokers and non-smokers and separate charts are provided for diabetics. It is then approximated that the family history of premature CHD (men under 55 years and women under 65 years) increases the risk by a factor of 1.5.

Software that contains risk assessment algorithms is available as an alternative to risk charts. The most recent version of the risk table with updated layout was published in March 2000.[110] The recommended treatment initiation levels for lipid lowering treatment are as follows:

✧ Individuals with a total risk of 30% over the next ten years should all be treated.

✧ Following this, the guidelines suggest expansion of the opportunistic screening and risk factor intervention down to the overall risk level of 15% over 10 years. The exceptions are persons with severe hypertension (SBP >160 mm Hg and DBP >100 mm Hg), those with familial hypercholesterolemia and other inherited lipid disorders, and patients who have diabetes with associated target organ damage and those with renal dysfunction.

✧ Lipid-lowering therapy is required for patients with MI and TC > 232 mg/dL (6mmol/L).

✧ The treatment target is TC < 193 mg/dL (5 mmol/L) and LDL-C < 116 mg/dL (3 mmol/L).

In primary prevention, the operating principle is tailoring the intensity of lifestyle changes and therapy to the absolute risk of CHD. In secondary prevention the recommended upper age limit for initiating lipid-lowering medication is 75 years, and for primary prevention 69 years (69 years was the upper age limit of WOSCOPS participants[4]). Hypertensive agents have beneficial effects up to the age of 80 years. It is recommended that no hypertensive or lipid-lowering treatment should be stopped at any particular age.

Lifestyle Modifications

The dietary goal for the British recommendations is a total dietary intake of fats less than 35% of the total caloric intake. The intake of saturated fats should be no more than a third of total fat intake, and the intake of cholesterol < 300 mg per day. This should be accompanied by an increase in use of monounsaturated and polyunsaturated fats and fresh fruit and vegetables. Alcohol consumption should be less than 21 units per week for men and less than 14 units for women. In weight-reducing diets, the decreased intake of saturated fats should not be replaced by polyunsaturates. Physical activity guidelines rely on recommendations of the British Associations for Cardiac Rehabilitation.[111–113]

Hypertension

The JBR document features an extensive section devoted to the treatment of hypertension. The treatment of hypertension is divided into three categories and the classification adopted by JBR reflects stages 1–3 of JNC VI:

❖   Severe hypertension with DBP > 110mm H; requires treatment within one to two weeks.

❖   Moderate hypertension with DBP 100–109 mm Hg; in primary prevention, three to six months of observation are required before starting treatment.

❖   Mild hypertension with DBP between 90–99 mm Hg; similarly to lipid lowering, drug treatment is tailored to the level of absolute risk. The CHD risk of 15% over a 10-year period is taken as a cut-off point for treatment.

The target for blood pressure is < 140/85 mm Hg. The approach to patients with target organ damage and to those with other risk factors is more aggressive. All patients with CHD and SBP above 149 mm Hg and DBP above 84 mm Hg should be on anti-hypertensive treatment.

Patients with peripheral vascular disease and history of stroke should, in terms of risk factor reduction, be treated exactly like those with CHD. The target for blood pressure control in diabetes is SBP < 130 mm Hg and DBP < 80 mm Hg. Table 7–6 compares the key aspects of hypertension management as recommended by JNC VI, JBR, and the European Task Force.

Lipid Testing

Screening is required for patients who have early CHD (MI before 55 years in men, before 65 years in women); in those with CHD and cholesterol > 193 mg/dL (5 mmol/L); and also in all patients with TC levels = 309 mg/dL (8 mmol/L). The JBR recommend measuring TC and HDL-C within 24 hours of MI, to avoid the subsequent decrease in LDL-C and HDL-C.[114] For screening purposes, the JBR suggest a non-fasting TC level and non-fasting HDL-C. This should be followed by a fasting lipid profile in patients with pronounced dyslipidemia. In patients without hypertriglyceridemia, the measurement of non-fasting TC is recommended.

The Sheffield Table

The Sheffield Risk and Treatment Table, for estimation of CHD risk in primary prevention, has been developed in Britain. Here the concept was to estimate the absolute risk on the basis of gender, the presence of hypertension (SBP > 160 mm Hg), diabetes, smoking status, and ECG-diagnosed left ventricular hypertrophy, and relate this to the level of TC (or in its most recent form a TC/HDL ratio) associated with a particular risk threshold. The Framingham risk algorithm was used. Versions of the table that include TC levels are based on average HDL-C of 44 mg/dL (1.15 mmol/L) for men and 54 mg/dL (1.40 mmol/L) for women.

Three versions of the table are available. The original 1995 table estimates TC levels associated with 1.5 % per year risk of coronary death, which approximates 4.5% risk of combined fatal and non-fatal coronary events.[115] The later 1996 version, and the 2000 update, are based on the risk of combined fatal and nonfatal CHD events. The 1996 version estimates 3% annual risk of CHD event in relation to TC level.[116] The 2000 version relates the risk to TC/HDL-C ratio rather than to TC, and includes a 10-year risk of event of 15% and 30%.[117]

Sheffield tables attempt to show that the risk associated with high concentrations of TC, or with low ratios of TC/HDL-C in primary prevention, in many instances remains below the absolute risk threshold that would justify drug treatment. The authors suggest that there are situations when lipid measurements can be ignored in the assessment of risk. For instance, according to the latest version, men younger than 42 years and women younger than 40 years with no other risk factors never reach the TC/HDL-C ratio associated with a 1.5% annual risk of event. The same is true for women younger than 48 years. The authors suggest that the only indication for lipid measurement in these instances is a suspicion of familial hypercholesterolemia.

When individuals with multiple risk factors are taken on account, one might see a situation like the following: e.g., a 60-year-old, non-smoking, diabetic woman with hypertension who has no target organ damage will have a 10-year risk of 15% at the TC/HDL-C ratio of 3.7 (e.g., TC of 173 mg/dL [4.48 mmol/L] and HDL of 46 mg/dL [1.2 mmol/L]) and a risk of 30% will be reached only at the TC/HDL-C ratio 6.7 (e.g., TC of 309 mg/dL [8 mmol/L] and HDL-C of 46 mg/dL [1.2 mmol/L]).

Sheffield tables have been much criticized for setting the lipid cut-off point for intervention too high, particularly in women. Even more contentious is the concept that there are instances when lipid levels can be ignored as determinants of CHD risk.

However, even if one disagrees with the authors' views on importance of lipid factors in the CHD risk assessment, in view of the recent data from the AFCAPS/TexCAPS showing the low incidence of cardiovascular events in women with no history of CHD,[5] one cannot dismiss the idea that the present cut-off points for therapy in women with dyslipidemia as the only risk factor may be set too low.

The PROCAM Risk Algorithm

The prospective Munster Heart Study (PROCAM) recruited more than 30,000 individuals at work in Northern Germany between 1978 and 1996. A CHD risk algorithm has been generated from PROCAM data based on an eight-year follow-up of middle-aged men.[11] The risk is categorized as low, moderate, and high, stratification based on both the number and the severity of risk factors.

For instance, the presence of one risk factor of moderate degree, such as a plasma TC of 200–300 mg/dL (5.2–7.8 mmol/L), is regarded as a small increase in risk. On the other hand, the presence of two severe risk factors, such as TC > 300 mg/dL (7.8 mmol/L) and smoking 20 cigarettes per day, indicates high risk. Moderate risk is defined as the presence of one risk factor of severe degree, e.g., smoking 20 cigarettes per day, or two risk factors of moderate degree, e.g., TC of 200–300 mg/dL (5.2–7.8 mmol/L) and HDL-C < 40 mg/dL (1 mmol/L). The software containing this algorithm is available.

Similarly to other guidelines, category of risk determines the intensity of lipid-lowering treatment, and the targets for lowering cholesterol increase with increased risk. For the low-risk group, the target for LDL-C reduction is 160 mg/dL (4 mmol/L); for the moderate risk group, 135 mg/dL (3.5 mmol/L); and for the high-risk group, less than 100 mg/dL (2.6 mmol/L). The recommended desirable TG concentration is as low as 150 mg/dL (1.7 mmol/L).[11]

OTHER RELEVANT GUIDELINES

Other guidelines relevant to cardiovascular event prevention are the new criteria for the diagnosis of diabetes from the American Diabetes Association[118] and the recent proposal for the new criteria diabetes diagnosis for the World Health Organization (WHO).[119] The issues associated with dyslipidemia in children, which are beyond the scope of this chapter, have been addressed by the NCEP Children's Panel (see chapter 5) and The British Hyperlipidaemia Association jointly with British Paediatric Association.[120,121]

The most recent monospecialist guidelines on hypertension are those of the 1999 WHO/International Society of Hypertension Guidelines for the Management of Hypertension.[122] The British Hypertension Society guidelines for hypertension management 1999[123] link hypertension treatment to comprehensive cardiovascular event prevention and cardioprotection.

COMPARISON OF DIFFERENT GUIDELINES

None of the current recommendations is based on the assessment of the presence and severity of all key CHD risk factors. ATP II guidelines are based on the greatest number of risk factors but, apart from recommending less aggressive therapy in pre-menopausal women, they do not differentiate between gender in terms of dyslipidemia management. Also, they do not grade the severity of non-lipid risk factors. The drawback of European risk tables is that they are based on arbitrarily assigned "mean" HDL-C level. The PROCAM algorithm includes both family history and TG level in the assessment of risk, but applies to middle-aged men only.

The risk level that justifies drug treatment differs from a 15% to a 30% probability of event over 10 years, depending on the specific recommendation-making body. The JBR propose a compromise and institute treatment at the 30% risk level over 10 years, and subsequently widen it to include persons at the 15% risk over 10 years. The 30% risk level approximates the cardiovascular event risk of 20% over five years in the New Zealand Guidelines.[83,107] The Sheffield Tables are based on 1.5% (or 3%) mortality risk per year. Importantly, all these considerations do exclude persons with diabetes, familial lipid disorders, and severe hypertension, where there is universal agreement on treating them as high risk category.

Durrington et al. compared the performance of the Framingham equation, ATP II, European recommendations, and Sheffield tables in determining the number of persons requiring drug treatment from the population attending the specialist lipid clinic.[80] At the risk level of 15% over five years (30% over 10 years), Sheffield tables identified a much smaller proportion of patients than did the Framingham equation. With regard to the number of patients predicted to be at 20% risk over 10 years, there was a broad agreement between the Framingham equation and European risk chart. ATP II guidelines identified a much greater proportion of patients as requiring treatment, particularly among women.

SUMMARY

Substantial evidence now shows the benefit of CHD risk factor reduction by changing lifestyle factors and by treatment with cardioprotective drugs. This evidence, based largely on the results of large epidemiological studies, has been translated into clinical guidelines. The two essential concepts applied to current guidelines are the comprehensive management of all CHD risk factors, and tailoring the intensity of management to the level of risk.

The practice guidelines are an essential tool for clinicians that facilitate implementation of state-of-the-art cardiovascular prevention. However, due to complex interrelationships between risk factors, no single guideline takes into account all aspects of cardiovascular event risk. Thus, the essential role of a physician is to translate the guideline content into advice to an individual person, and to exercise clinical judgment in the process. The guidelines provide overall direction for clinical decisions, but by no means are they its substitute.　　　　　　　　　　　　　　　◇

Acknowledgments: The author acknowledges the excellent secretarial assistance of Ms. Anne Cooney and Ms. Jacky Gardiner. The preparation of this chapter was partly supported by Research into Aging.

REFERENCES

1. Scandinavian Simvastatin Survival Study Group. Randomized trial of cholesterol lowering in 4444 patients with coronary heart disease: the Scandinavian Simvastatin Survival Study (4S). Lancet 1994;334:1383–9.
2. Sacks FM, Pfeffer MA, Moye LA, Rouleau JL, Rutherford JD, Cole TG et al. The effect of pravastatin on coronary events after myocardial infarction in patients with average cholesterol levels. N Engl J Med 1996;335:1001–9.
3. Long-term intervention with pravastatin in ischemic disease (LIPID) study group. Prevention of cardiovascular events and death with pravastatin in patients with coronary heart disease and a broad range of initial cholesterol levels. N Engl J Med 1998;339: 1349–57.
4. Brown G, Albers JJ, Fisher LD, Schaefer SM, Lin JT, Kaplan C et al. Regression of coronary artery disease as a result of intensive lipid-lowering therapy in men with high levels of apolipoprotein B. N Engl J Med 1990;323:1289–98.
5. Downs JR, Clearfield M, Weis S, Whitney E, Shapiro DR, Beere BA et al. Primary prevention of acute coronary events with lovastatin in men and women with average cholesterol levels: Results of AFCAPS/TexCAPS (Air Force/Texas Coronary Atherosclerosis Prevention Study). JAMA 1998;279:1615–22.
6. Rifkind BM (ed.). Lowering cholesterol in high-risk individuals and populations. Fundamental & Clinical Cardiology Series 24. New York: Marcel Dekker, 1995:1–372.
7. Qizilbash N. Are risk factors for stroke and coronary disease the same? Curr Opin Lipidol 1998;9:325–8.
8. Wolf PA, D'Agostino RB, Belanger AJ, Kannel WB. Probability of stroke: a risk profile from the Framingham Study. Stroke 1991;22:312–8.
9. Funke H, Assmann G. Strategies for the assessment of genetic coronary artery disease risk. Curr Opin Lipidol 1999;10:285–91.
10. Ridker PM. Evaluating novel cardiovascular risk factors: can we better predict heart attacks? Ann Intern Med 1999;130:933–7.
11. Assmann G, Cullen P, Jossa F, Lewis B, Mancini M, for the International Task Force for the Prevention of Coronary Heart Disease. Coronary heart disease: reducing the risk;

the scientific background to primary and secondary prevention of coronary heart disease. A worldwide view. Arterioscler Thromb Vasc Biol 1999;19:1819–24.

12. Diaz MN, Frei B, Vita JA, Keaney JF. Mechanisms of disease: anti-oxidants and atherosclerotic heart disease. N Engl J Med 1997;337:408–16.

13. Byington RP, Jukema JW, Salonen JT, Pitt B, Bruschke AV, Hoen H et al. Reduction in cardiovascular events during pravastatin therapy. Pooled analysis of clinical events of the pravastatin atherosclerosis intervention program. Circulation 1995;92:2419–25.

14. LaRosa JC, He J, Vupputuri S. Effect of statins on risk of coronary disease. A meta-analysis of randomized controlled trials. JAMA 1999;282:2340–6.

15. Hong MK, Romm PA, Reagan K, Green CE, Rackley CE. Usefulness of the total cholesterol to high-density-lipoprotein cholesterol ratio in predicting angiographic coronary artery disease in women. Am J Cardiol 1991;68:1646–50.

16. Stampfer MJ, Colditz GA. Estrogen replacement therapy and coronary heart disease: a quantitative assessment of the epidemiologic evidence. Prev Med 1991;20:47–63.

17. Hulley S, Grady D, Bush T, Furberg C, Herrington D, Riggs B, Vittinghoff E. Randomized trial of estrogen plus progestin for secondary prevention of coronary heart disease in postmenopausal women. JAMA 1998;280:605–13.

18. Kannel WB, Feinleib M. Natural history of angina pectoris in the Framingham Study. Am J Cardiol 1972;29:154–63.

19. Stokes J III, Kannel WB, Wolf PA, Cupples LA, D'Agostino RB. The relative importance of selected risk factors for various manifestations of cardiovascular disease among women and men from 35–64 years: 30 years of follow-up in the Framingham Study. Circulation1987;75:(suppl V):V65–V73.

20. Lerner DJ, Kannel WB. Patterns of coronary heart disease morbidity and mortality in the sexes: a 26-year follow-up of the Framingham population. Am Heart J 1986;111:383–90.

21. Fetters JK, Peterson ED, Shaw LJ, Newby LK, Califf RM. Sex-specific differences in coronary artery disease risk factors, evaluation, and treatment: have they been adequately evaluated? Am Heart J 1996;131:796–813.

22. Wilson PW, Cupples LA, Kannel WB. Is hyperglycemia associated with cardiovascular disease? The Framingham study. Am Heart J 1991;121:586–90.

23. American Heart Association. Heart and stroke facts: 1995 statistical supplement. Dallas: American Heart Association, 1994:10.

24. Kannel WB, McGee DL. Diabetes and cardiovascular disease: the Framingham Study. JAMA 1979;241:2035–38.

25. Krolewski AS, Kosinski EJ, Warram JH, Leland OS, Busick EJ, Asmal AC et al. Magnitude and determinants of coronary artery disease in juvenile-onset insulin-dependent diabetes mellitus. Am J Cardiol 1987;14:55–60.

26. Steiner G. The dyslipoproteinemias of diabetes. Atherosclerosis 1994;110(Suppl); S27–S33.

27. Manske CL. Coronary artery disease in diabetic patients with nephropathy. Am J Hypertens 1993;6:367S–374S.

28. Andresen JL, Rasmussen LM, Ledet T. Diabetic macro-angiopathy and atherosclerosis. Diabetes 1996;45(Suppl.3):S91–S94.

29. Lyons TJ. Glycation and oxidation: a role in the pathogenesis of atherosclerosis. Am J Cardiol 1993;71:26B–31B.

30. Dominiczak MH. The significance of the products of the Maillard (browning) reaction in diabetes. Diabetic Med 1991;8:505–16.

31. Chappey O, Dosquet C, Wautier M-P, Wautier J-L. Advanced glycation end products, oxidant stress, and vascular lesions. Eur J Clin Unvest 1997;27:97–108.

32. Meigs JB, Mittleman MA, Nathan DM, Tofler GH, Singer DE, Murphy-Sheehy PM et al. Hyperinsulinemia, hyperglycemia, and impaired hemostasis. The Framingham Offspring Study. JAMA 2000;283:221–28.

33. Haffner SM, Lehto S, Rönnemaa T, Pyörälä K, Laakso M. Mortality from coronary heart disease in subjects with type 2 diabetes and in non-diabetic subjects with and without prior myocardial infarction. New Engl J Med 1998;339:229–34.

34. DCCT Research Group. The effect of intensive treatment of diabetes on the development and progression of long-term complications of insulin-dependent diabetes mellitus. N Engl J Med 1993;329:977–86.

35. U. K. Prospective Diabetes Study (UKPDS) Group. Intensive blood glucose control with sulphonylureas or insulin compared with conventional treatment and risk of complications in patients with type 2 diabetes (UKPDS 33). Lancet 1998;352:837–53.

36. Steiner G, for the DAIS Project Group. The Diabetes Atherosclerosis Intervention Study (DAIS): a study conducted in cooperation with the World Health Organization. Diabetologia 1996;39:1655–61.

37. National High Blood Pressure Education Program Working Group. National High Blood Pressure Education Program working group report on hypertension in diabetes. Hypertension 1994;23:145–58.

38. Office of Population Censuses and Surveys, Social Survey Division. Health Survey for England 1993. London: HMSO, 1995.

39. Goode GK, Miller JP, Heagerty AM. Hyperlipidemia, hypertension, and coronary heart disease. Lancet 1995;345:362–64.

40. Collins R, Peto R, Cutler JA et al. Blood pressure, stroke, and coronary heart disease. Part 1. Prolonged differences in blood pressure: prospective observational studies corrected for the regression dilution bias. Lancet 1990;335:765–774.

41. Collins R, Peto R, Cutler JA et al. Blood pressure, stroke, and coronary heart disease. Part 2. Short-term reductions in blood pressure: overview of randomized drug trials in their epidemiological context. Lancet 1990;335:827–838.

42. Lithell H. Hypertension and hyperlipidemia. A review. Am J Hypertens 1993;6:303S–308S.

43. Kitler ME. Differences in men and women in coronary heart disease, systemic hypertension, and their treatment. Am J Cardiol 1992;70:1077–80.

44. Medical Research Working Party. MRC trial of mild hypertension: principal results. Br Med J 1985;291:197–204.

45. Hypertension Detection and Follow-up Program Cooperative Group. Five-year findings of the hypertension detection and follow up program. II. Mortality by race, sex, and age. JAMA 1979;242:2572–77.

46. Kannel WB. Update on the role of cigarette smoking in coronary artery disease. Am Heart J 1981;101:319–28.

47. Ramsdale DR, Faragher EB, Bray CL, Bennett DH, Ward C, Beton DC. Smoking and coronary artery disease assessed by routine coronary angiography. Brit Med J 1985; 290:197–200.

48. Nyboe J, Jensen G, Appleyard M, Schnohr P. Smoking and the risk of first acute myocardial infarction. Am Heart J 1991;122:438–47.

49. Pisani T, Gebski CP, Leary ET, Warnick GR, Ollington JF. Accurate direct determination of low-density-lipoprotein cholesterol using an immunoseparation reagent and enzymatic cholesterol assay. Arch Pathol Lab Med 1995;119:1127–35.

50. Gottlieb S, Boyko V, Zahger D, Balkin J, Hod H, Pelled B et al. Smoking and prognosis after acute myocardial infarction in the thrombolytic era (Israeli Thrombolytic National Survey). J Am Coll Cardiol 1996;1506–13.

51. Mueller HS, Cohen LS, Braunwald E et al. for the TIMI investigators. Predictors of early morbidity and mortality after thrombolytic therapy of acute myocardial infarction: analyses of patient subgroups in the Thrombolysis in Myocardial Infarction (TIMI) trial, Phase II. Circulation 1992;85:1254–64.

52. Barbash Gi, Reiner J, White HD et al. for the GUSTO-I investigators. Evaluation of paradoxic beneficial effects of smoking in patients receiving thrombolytic therapy for acute myocardial infarction: mechanism of "smoker's paradox" from the GUSTO-I trial, with angiographic insights. J Am Coll Cardiol 1995;26:1222–29.

53. Kuller L, Meilahn E, Ockene JK. Smoking and coronary heart disease. In: Conner W, Bristow D (eds.). Coronary heart disease. Philadelphia: JB Lippincott,1985:65.

54. de Lorgeril M, Salen P, Monjaud I, Delaye J. The "diet heart" hypothesis in secondary prevention of coronary heart disease. Eur Heart J 1997;18:13–18.

55. Corr LA, Olivier MF. The low-fat/low-cholesterol diet is ineffective. Eur Heart J 1997; 18:18–22.
56. Arntzenius AC, Kromhout D, Barth JD et al. Diet, lipoproteins, and the progression of coronary atherosclerosis: The Leiden Intervention Trial. New Engl J Med 1985; 312:805–11
57. Watts GF, Lewis B, Brunt JNH, Lewis ES, Coltart Dj, Smith LDR et al. Effects on coronary artery disease of lipid-lowering diet or diet plus cholestyramine in the St. Thomas Atherosclerosis Regression Study (STARS). Lancet 1992;339:563–69.
58. Ornish D, Brown SE, Scherwitz LW et al. Can lifestyle changes reverse coronary heart disease? Lancet 1990;336:129–33.
59. Burr MK, Fehily AM, Gilbert JF et al. Effects of changes in fat, fish, and fiber intakes on death and myocardial infarctions: diet and reinfarction trial (DART). Lancet 1989;2:757–61.
60. deLorgeril M, Renaud S Mamelle N et al. Mediterranean alpha-linolenic acid-rich diet in secondary prevention of coronary heart disease. Lancet 1994;343:1454–59.
61. Singh RB, Rastogi SS, Verma R et al. Randomized controlled trial of cardioprotective diet in patients with acute myocardial infarction: results of one-year follow-up. Brit Med J 1992;304:1015–19.
62. Mokdad AH, Serdula MK, Dietz WH, Bowman BA, Marks JS, Koplan JP. The spread of obesity: epidemic in the United States, 1991–1998. JAMA 1999;282:1519–22.
63. Must A, Spadano J, Coakley EH, Field AE, Colditz G, Dietz WH. The disease burden associated with overweight and obesity. JAMA 1999;282:1523–9.
64. Schulte H, Cullen P, Assmann G. Obesity, mortality, and cardiovascular disease in the Munster Heart Study (PROCAM). Atherosclerosis 1999;144:199–209.
65. Dominiczak MH. Hyperlipidemia and cardiovascular disease. Curr Opinion Lipidol 2000;11:(in press).
66. Williamson DF. Pharmacotherapy for obesity. JAMA 1999;281:278–9.
67. Kuczmarski RJ, Flegal KM, Campbell SM, Johnson CL. Increasing prevalence of overweight among U. S. adults: the National Health and Nutrition Examination Surveys 1960 to 1991. JAMA 1994;272:205–11.
68. Prentice AM, Jebb SA. Obesity in Britain: gluttony or sloth? Brit Med J 1995;311: 437–439.
69. Paffenbarger RS, Hyde RT, Wing AL, Steinmetz CH. A natural history of athleticism and cardiovascular health. JAMA 1984;252:491–95.
70. Leon AS, Connett J, Jacobs DR, Rauramaa R. Leisure time physical activity levels and risk of coronary heart disease and death: The Multiple Risk Factor Intervention Trial. JAMA 1987;258:2388–95.
71. Ekelund LG, Haskell WL, Johnson JL, Whaley FS, Criqui MH, Sheps DS. Physical fitness as predictor of cardiovascular mortality in asymptomatic North American men: The Lipid Research Clinic Mortality Follow-Up Study. New Engl J Med 1988;319:1379–84.
72. The Lipid Research Clinics Program. The Lipid Research Clinics Coronary Primary Prevention Trial II. The relationship of reduction in incidence of coronary heart disease to cholesterol lowering. JAMA 1984;251:365–74.
73. McBride PE, Houston Miller N, Smith SC. Task Force 8. Organization of preventive cardiology service. J Am Coll Cardiol 1996;27:964–1047.
74. Blair SN, Jacobs DR, Powell KE. Relationships between exercise or physical activity and other health behaviors. Public Health Rep 1985;100:172–180.
75. Escobedo LG, Marcus SE, Holzman D, Giovino GA. Sports participation, age and smoking initiation, and the risk of smoking among U. S. high school students. JAMA 1993;269:1391–95.
76. Eriksson J, Taimela S, Koivisto VA. Exercise and the metabolic syndrome. Diabetologia 1997;40:125–35.
77. Shephard RJ, Ballady GJ. Exercise as cardiovascular therapy. Circulation 1999;99:963–72.
78. Dunn AL, Marcus BH, Kampert JB, Gracia EM, Kohl HW, Blair SN. Comparison of life-

style and structured interventions to increase physical activity and cardio-respiratory fitness. A randomized trial. JAMA 1999;281:327–34.

79. Stamler J, Stamler R, Neaton JD, Wentworth D, Daviglus ML, Garside D et al. Low risk-factor profile and long-term cardiovascular and noncardiovascular mortality and life expectancy. Findings for five large cohorts of young adults and middle-aged men and women. JAMA 1999;282:2012–8.

80. Durrington PN, Prais H, Bhatnagar D, France M, Crowley V, Khan J, Morgan J. Indications for cholesterol-lowering medication: comparison of risk assessment-methods. Lancet 1999;353:278–81.

81. Fuster V, Pearson TA. 27th Bethesda Conference: Matching the intensity of risk factor management with the hazard for coronary disease events. J Am Cardiol 1996;27: 957–1047.

82. Wood D, De Backer G, Faergeman O, Graham I, Mancia G, Pyörälä K on behalf of the Task Force. Prevention of coronary heart disease in clinical practice. Recommendations of the Second Joint Task Force of European and other Societies on Coronary Prevention. Eur Heart J 1998;19:1434–503.

83. British Cardiac Society, British Hyperlipidaemia Association, British Hypertension Society, endorsed by the British Diabetic Association. Joint British recommendations on prevention of coronary heart disease in clinical practice. Heart 1998;80: S1–S29.

84. Ryan TJ, Anderson JL, Antman EM, Braniff BA, Brooks NH, Califf RM et al. ACC/AHA guidelines for the management of patients with acute myocardial infarction: a report of the American College of Cardiology/American Heart Association Task Force on Practice Guidelines (Committee on Management of Acute Myocardial Infarction). J Am Coll Cardiol 1996;28:1328–428.

85. The Joint National Committee on Prevention, Detection, Evaluation, and Treatment of High Blood Pressure. The Sixth Report of the Joint National Committee on Prevention, Detection, Evaluation, and Treatment of High Blood Pressure (JNC VI). Arch Intern Med 1997;157:2413–46.

86. Scottish Intercollegiate Guidelines Network. SIGN guidelines. An introduction to SIGN methodology for the development of evidence-based clinical guidelines. SIGN 1999; 39:1–34.

87. Field MJ, Lohr KN (eds.). Institute of Medicine Committee to Advise the Public Health Service on Clinical Practice Guidelines. Clinical practice guidelines: directions for a new program. Washington DC: National Academy Press,1990.

88. Last JM, Abramson JH (eds.). A dictionary of epidemiology, third edition. New York, NY: Oxford University Press, 1995.

89. U. S. Department of Health and Human Services. Agency for Health Care Policy and Research. Acute pain management: operative or medical procedures and trauma. Rockville (MD): The Agency; 1993. Clinical Practice Guideline No. 1. AHCPR Publication No. 92–0023:107.

90. National Cholesterol Education Program. Second report of the Expert Panel on Detection, Evaluation, and Treatment of High Blood Cholesterol in Adults (Adult Treatment Panel II). Circulation 1994;89:1329–63.

91. Bachorik PS, Ross JW. National Cholesterol Education Program recommendations for measurement of low-density-lipoprotein cholesterol: executive summary. Clin Chem 1995;41:1414–20.

92. Stein EA, Myers GL. National Cholesterol Education Program recommendations for triglyceride measurement: executive summary. Clin Chem 1995;41;1421–6.

93. Warnick GR, Wood PD. National Cholesterol Education Program recommendations for measurement of high-density-lipoprotein cholesterol: executive summary. Clin Chem 1995;41:1427–33.

94. Lenfant C. Conquering cardiovascular disease: progress and promise. JAMA 1999; 282:2068–70.

95. American Diabetes Association. Management of dyslipidemia in adults with diabetes (position statement). Diabetes Care 1999;22:S56–S59.

96. Gordon DJ, Rifkind BM. High-density lipoproteins: the clinical implications of recent studies. N Engl J Med 1989;321:1311–16.
97. Ansell BJ, Watson KE, Fogelman AM. An evidence-based assessment of NCEP adult treatment panel II guidelines. JAMA 1999;282:2051–7.
98. Knopp RH. Drug treatment of lipid disorders. N Engl J Med 1999;341:498–511.
99. American College of Physicians. Clinical Guidelines, Part 1. Guidelines for using serum cholesterol, high-density-lipoprotein cholesterol, and triglyceride levels as screening tests for preventing coronary heart disease in adults. Ann Intern Med 1996;124:515–7.
100. Grundy SM, Balady GJ, Criqui MH, Fletcher GF, Greenland P, Hiratzka LF et al. Guide to primary prevention of cardiovascular diseases: a statement for healthcare professionals from the Task Force on risk reduction. Circulation 1997;95:2329–31.
101. Smith SC, Blair SN, Criqui MH, Fletcher GF, Fuster V, Gersh BJ et al. Preventing heart attack and death in patients with coronary disease. Circulation 1995;92:2–4.
102. Juul-Moller S, Edvardsson N, Jahmatz B, Rosen A, Sorensen S, Omblus R. Double-blind trial of aspirin in primary prevention of myocardial infarction in patients with stable chronic angina pectoris: the Swedish Angina Pectoris Aspirin Trial (SAPAT) Group. Lancet 1992;340:1421–5.
103. The beta-blocker heart attack trial: Beta-Blocker Heart Attack Study Group. JAMA 1981;246:2073–4.
104. Hjalmarson A, Elmfeldt D, Herlitz J et al. Effect on mortality of metoprolol in acute myocardial infarction: a double-blind randomized trial. Lancet 1981;2:823–7.
105. Houston-Miller N, Taylor CB. Lifestyle management for patients with coronary heart disease. Champaigne, IL: Human Kinetics,1995.
106. Pyörälä K, De Backer G, Graham I, Poole-Wilson P, Wood D on behalf of the Task Force. Prevention of coronary heart disease in clinical practice. Recommendations of the Task Force of the European Society of Cardiology, European Atherosclerosis Society, and European Society of Hypertension. Eur Heart J 1998;19:1300–31.
107. Dyslipidemia Advisory Group on behalf of the scientific committee of the National Heart Foundation of New Zealand. 1996 National Heart Foundation clinical guidelines for the assessment and management of dyslipidemia. NZ Med J 1996;109:224–32.
108. Jackson R. Updated New Zealand cardiovascular disease risk-benefit prediction guide. BMJ 2000;320:709–10.
109. Kinosian B, Glick H, Garland G. Cholesterol and coronary heart disease: predicting risk by levels and ratio. Ann Intern Med 1994;121:641–7.
110. British Cardiac Society, British Hyperlipidaemia Association, British Hypertension Society, British Diabetic Society. Joint British Recommendations on prevention of coronary heart disease in clinical practice: summary. BMJ 2000;320:705–708.
111. Coats A, McGee H, Stokes H et al. (eds.). British Association of Cardiac Rehabilitation. Guidelines for cardiac rehabilitation. Oxford: Blackwell Science, 1995.
112. Horgan J, Bethell H, Carson P et al. Working part report on cardiac rehabilitation. Br Heart J 1992;67:412–8.
113. Task force of the working group on cardiac rehabilitation of the European Society of Cardiology. Long-term comprehensive care of cardiac patients. Eur Heart J 1992;13:1–45.
114. Mbewu AD, Durrington PN, Bulleid S et al. The immediate effect of streptokinase on serum lipoprotein (a) concentration and the effect of myocardial infarction on serum lipoprotein (a), apolipoprotein A-I and B, lipids, and C-reactive protein. Atherosclerosis 1993;103:65–71.
115. Haq IU, Jackson PR, Yeo WW, Ramsay LE. Sheffield risk and treatment table for cholesterol-lowering for primary prevention of coronary heart disease. Lancet 1995;346:1467–71.
116. Ramsay LE, Haq IV, Jackson PR et al. Targeting lipid-lowering drug therapy for primary prevention of coronary disease: an updated Sheffield table. Lancet 1996;348:387–8.
117. Wallis EJ, Ramsay LE, Ul Haq I, Ghahramani P, Jackson PR, Rowland-Yeo K, Yeo WW. Coronary and cardiovascular risk estimation for primary prevention: validation of a

new Sheffield table in the 1995 Scottish health survey population. BMJ 2000;320: 671–5.

118.   The Expert Committee on the diagnosis and classification of diabetes mellitus. Report of the Expert Committee on the diagnosis and classification of diabetes mellitus. Diabetes Care 1997;20:1183–97.

119.   Alberti KGMM, Zimmett P, for the WHO Consultation. Definition, diagnosis, and classification of diabetes mellitus and its complications. Part 1: Diagnosis and clarification of diabetes mellitus. Provisional report of a WHO consultation. Diabet Med 1998;15: 539–53.

120.   Wray R, Neil A, Rees A. Hyperlipidemia in childhood: a screening strategy. U. K. recommendations. In: Neil A. Rees A, Taylor C (eds.). Hyperlipidemia in childhood. London: London Royal College of Physicians, 1996:99–105.

121.   Expert Panel. Blood cholesterol levels in children and adolescents. National Institutes of Health Publication No. 91–2732. Washington, DC: U.S. Government Printing Office, 1990: 1–119.

122.   1999 World Health Organization—International Society of Hypertension. Guidelines for the management of hypertension. J Hypertension 1999;17:151–83.

123.   Ramsay LE, Williams B, Johnston GD, MacGregor GA, Poston L, Potter JF et al. British Hypertension Society guidelines for hypertension management 1999: summary. BMJ 1999;319:630–5.

Preanalytical Variation in Lipid, Lipoprotein, and Apolipoprotein Testing

8

Nader Rifai, D. Robert Dufour, and Gerald R. Cooper

✧ Accurate measurement of serum lipids is dependent on controlling both analytical and preanalytical factors. Preanalytical variation in subjects results from

✧ differences in lifestyle,

✧ altered lipid metabolism due to disease,

✧ the source of the specimen, and

✧ the conditions of sample collection.

Variation can arise from biological, behavioral, and clinical factors, as well as from variability in specimen collection and handling (see Figure 8–1). This chapter discusses the factors that contribute to preanalytical variations and addresses the importance of standardizing patient preparation for lipid testing.

BIOLOGICAL VARIATIONS

Intra-Individual Variation

As in most laboratory tests, intra-individual variation in lipid values is generally smaller than person-to-person or inter-individual variation. An assessment of biological components of variation of total cholesterol (TC), high-density lipoprotein cholesterol (HDL-C), and apolipoproteins (apo) A-I and B showed an index of individuality much less than 0.6.[1] (The index of individuality is calculated by dividing the intra-individual coefficient of variation [CV_B] by the inter-individual coefficient of variation [CV_P]). This finding indicates that the use of conventional population-based reference intervals in an interpretation is of little value and may be misleading.[2] Population-based reference ranges are not useful unless the index of individuality is greater than 1.4.[3] Therefore, experts derived health-based cut-points for the classification of hyperlipoproteinemia from large population studies.

With recent improvements in analytical performance of lipid assays, it has become easier to define the day-to-day variations in lipid concentrations. Knowledge of such variations is important in that it gives both laboratorians and clinicians a framework for comparing results to evaluate the efficacy of therapy. With improvement in methods, a major fraction of the variation in lipid measurements may be due to bio-

Figure 8–1 ✧ Components of Preanalytical Variation

BIOLOGICAL

Intra-individual   Gender
Age   Race

BEHAVIORAL

Diet   Alcohol Intake
Obesity   Caffeine Intake
Cigarette Smoking   Exercise
          Stress

CLINICAL

Disease-Induced*

Endocrine & Metabolic   *Renal*
  Hypothyroidism   Nephrotic Syndrome
  Hypopituitarism   Chronic Renal Failure
  Diabetes Mellitus
  Acute Intermittent Porphyria   *Hepatic*
  Pregnancy   Congenital Biliary Atresia

Storage Disease   *Acute & Transient*
  Gaucher Disease   Burns
  Glycogen Storage Disease   Infections
  Tay-Sachs Disease   Myocardial Infarction

              Others
          Anorexia Nervosa
          Systemic Lupus Erythematosus

Drug-Induced*

Antihypertensives   *Immunosuppressives*   *Sex Steroids*
  Thiazides   Cyclosporine   Estrogen
  Chlorothalidone   Tacrolimus   Progestin
  Beta-blockers   Prednisolone

SAMPLE COLLECTION & HANDLING

Fasting Status   Hemoconcentration
Anticoagulants & Preservatives   Specimen Storage
Capillary vs. Venous

*Limited list

logical variability rather than analytical variability. One recent study attributed from 69% [for low-density lipoprotein cholesterol (LDL-C)] to 96% [for very-low-density lipoprotein cholesterol (VLDL-C) and triglyceride (TG)] of total variance to biological variation.[4] Biological variation is similar in adults and children.[5]

Intra-individual variation (CV_I) is due to a combination of biological variation (CV_B), which includes

❖ collection variables (discussed below),

❖ diurnal variation, and

❖ other inherent changes in the person, as well as

❖ analytical imprecision (CV_A), which is dependent on the method and instrumentation used.[6]

The total variability can be expressed mathematically as

$$CV_I = \left[\frac{CV_A^2}{(NR) \times (NS)} + \frac{CV_B^2}{(NS)} \right]^{1/2}$$

Where NS is the number of specimens and NR is the number of replicate laboratory determinations per specimen.[7] Cooper et al. have proposed that to reliably classify the risk of coronary heart disease (CHD), the total intra-individual variation for TC should be less than 5%.[7,8] If the total variation is more than 5%, then it will be necessary to obtain more than one sample to reduce the variation to the acceptable 5% level. Both analytical and biological variation must be reduced to allow estimates of risk of atherosclerosis to be made on the fewest number of specimens possible.

Table 8–1 shows the total individual variation obtained by varying the number of samples and the analytical variation, and by decreasing the biological variation from the average TC CV_B of 6.1%[7] through rigorous patient preparation. Although the table indicates the need to use at least two specimens to reach this goal, which is also the recommendation of the National Cholesterol Education Program (NCEP),[9] single specimens may suffice for classification of patients whose TC values are far from the cut-points. In a recent study, using single samples resulted in accurately classifying risk category for patients with TC concentrations below 185 mg/dL (4.79 mmol/L), between 215 and 225 mg/dL (5.57–5.83 mmol/L), or over 255 mg/dL (6.60 mmol/L) when using a method with analytical variation of 1.3%.[10] Because of greater measurement imprecision ($CV_A = 4.4\%$), LDL-C values could be correctly classified as to risk category with a single specimen for concentrations below 116 mg/dL (3.00 mmol/L) or above 174 mg/dL (4.51 mmol/L).[10] The new NCEP guidelines use a cutoff of 100 mg/dL (2.60 mmol/L) for clinical decision making in subjects with CHD. A single determination for this lower LDL-C value would no longer be reliable. Thus, two samples will continue to be needed for LDL-C, except for patients with the highest results. When CV_A is below 2%, there is virtually no effect of repeat analysis of the same specimen on total variation.

Table 8–1 ✧ Effect of Multiple Specimens on Total Individual Variation (CV$_I$%) of TC (200 mg/dL or 5.17 mmol/L)

Samples per person=K	$CV_A = 5\%$		$CV_A = 3\%$		$CV_A = 2\%$		$CV_A = 1\%$	
	n = 1	n = 2	n = 1	n = 2	n = 1	n = 2	n = 1	n = 2
CV_B 6.5%, Number of Replicate Measurements to Reach CV$_I$ 5%								
1	7.9	7.1	6.8	6.4	6.4	6.3	6.2	6.1
2	5.6	5.0	4.8	4.6	4.5	4.4	4.4	4.3
3	4.6	4.1	3.9	3.7	3.7	3.6	3.6	3.6
4	3.9	3.5	3.4	3.2	3.2	3.1	3.1	3.1
CV_B 5%, Number of Replicate measurements to Reach CV$_I$ 5%								
1	7.1	6.1	5.8	5.4	5.4	5.2	5.1	5.0
2	5.0	4.3	4.1	3.8	3.8	3.7	3.6	3.6
3	4.1	3.5	3.4	3.1	3.1	3.0	2.9	2.9
4	3.5	3.1	2.9	2.7	2.7	2.6	2.5	2.5

CV$_A$ = Analytical coefficient of variation
CV$_B$ = Biological coefficient of variation
The thick line indicates the number of specimens required to meet the NCEP guideline of <5% total variability in cholesterol measurement. If biological variation is at the average value of 6.5%, this goal can be achieved with duplicate samples if the analytical CV is <2%, but requires 3 or 4 specimens if analytical variation is greater. If biological variation were only 5%, which may be achieved with careful patient preparation, duplicate measurements on a single specimen would be close to the guideline with a single specimen for methods with analytical CV<2%.

A simple method for estimating the degree of biological variability in an individual is to use the relative range (RR), defined as :

$$\text{Relative range} = \frac{\text{Difference between highest and lowest result}}{\text{Average result}}$$

Cooper et al. have suggested that the CV$_I$ for an individual should be below the average population CV$_B$ and have calculated values of RR that satisfy this goal (Table 8–2).[7] In many individuals, CV$_B$ is much greater than average. Maximum individual variation (CV%) may range as much as 10%–15% for TC, LDL-C, HDL-C, apo A-I and apo B, but up to 50% for Lp(a) and up to 75% for TG.[11,12] Longitudinal data from the Framingham Heart Study suggest that patients with increased CV$_B$ are at increased risk of cardiovascular disease.[13] If the individual's RR is below the cutoff values listed in Table 8–2, the average cholesterol can be used to estimate risk of CHD. If the RR is above the cutoff value, additional samples should be analyzed before a decision on risk is made.

The minimum time between repeated measurements needed to determine maximum variability has not been conclusively determined. While the NCEP recommends

Table 8–2 ✧ Maximum Allowable Relative Range (RR) to Conclude that Intra-Individual Variation is Below Average Population Biological Variation at NCEP Target Values for Analyte Variation

n	Maximum RR			
	Total Cholesterol (CV_B 6.1%, CV_A 3.0%)	*HDL Cholesterol* (CV_B 7.4%, CV_A 6.0%)	*LDL Cholesterol* (CV_B 9.5%, CV_A 4.0%)	*Triglyceride* (CV_B 22.6%, CV_A 5.0%)
2	0.19	0.27	0.29	0.67
3	0.23	0.32	0.35	0.82
4	0.25	0.35	0.38	0.90
5	0.26	0.37	0.40	0.94

RR (Relative Range) = difference between highest and lowest results divided by mean of observed values; CV_A = analytical variation; CV_B = biological variation; n = number of samples analyzed from an individual subject.

at least one week between serial measurements, recent studies have suggested that a period of two weeks provides a more reliable measure of variability.[14]

Serum TC is the most stable lipid analyte; day-to-day biological variation averages 6.1%,[6,7] although some individuals may vary by up to 11%.[8] Time of day has little effect on TC concentration, as within-day variation is generally less than 3%.[8,15] TC tends to be higher in winter than in summer by an average of 2.5%.[11,16] In women, TC concentrations may fluctuate during the menstrual cycle, averaging 10%–20% lower in the late luteal and menstrual phases.[17,18] For the average woman, TC concentrations increase by about 14 mg/dL (0.36 mmol/L) around ovulation and fall to a nadir during menstruation.[19]

TG concentrations show marked intra-individual variation. Even excluding the known marked postprandial fluctuation, fasting TG concentrations differ by an average of 23% over one or more months, and in some persons may fluctuate as much as 40% around the mean value.[6,8] During the day, TG concentrations typically rise from a nadir at 3 AM to reach peak values in mid-afternoon, then progressively fall throughout the evening; average diurnal variation is approximately 30%.[20] Because of this marked random variation, it is difficult to assess seasonal, menstrual, and other types of rhythmic fluctuations of TG.

HDL-C concentrations show an average intra-individual variation of 7% over one month to a year, but seldom differ by more than 12%. Seasonal variation in HDL-C is slightly less than that of TC and LDL-C.[16]

Whether LDL-C concentration is measured directly or derived from measurements of TC, HDL-C, and TG, biological variability is similar at an average of 9.5%.[6,21] As with TC, LDL-C concentration is approximately 2.5% higher in winter than in summer,[8,16] and in women is lower in the late luteal phase and during menstruation.[18,19]

A recent study has demonstrated that the CV_B of TC, TG, HDL-C and calculated LDL-C is the same in specimens collected by fingerstick or venipuncture.[22]

Data from apolipoprotein measurements show similar variability. Apo A-I biological variation averages 7%–8%; there are apparently no changes during the menstrual cycle.[8,23] The intra-individual variation for both HDL-C and apo A-I is greater in smokers than in non-smokers.[24] Apo A-I concentrations tend to be highest in the evening and fall to a nadir at 6 AM.[25] It is not clear whether these differences are governed by sleep-wake or light-dark cycles.

Apo B has an average within-day biological variation of 6.5%, with a day-to-day variation of 8%–10%.[23] Lipoprotein(a) [Lp(a)] shows an average biological variation of 8.6%.[26] There is no significant diurnal variation in apo B or Lp(a) concentrations.[25,27] Lp(a) increases during the luteal phase in a minority of women; in most, it is unaffected by the menstrual cycle.[28]

Effects of Age, Gender, and Race on the Lipoprotein Profile

Numerous demographic factors within the population are correlated with differences in lipid and lipoprotein concentrations. In newborns, TC, TG, and most lipoprotein and apolipoprotein concentrations rise rapidly from the low values in cord blood to 80% of adult values by four days of age.[29] Lp(a) rises more slowly, continuing to increase gradually through at least the first six months of life.[30,31] In children, lipid concentrations of both boys and girls remain stable until just before puberty, when a transient fall in TC, TG, HDL-C, and LDL-C occurs.[29] At puberty, lipid values begin to diverge; in boys, TC decreases slightly, due to a significant fall in HDL-C (and apo A-I).[32,33] After puberty, HDL-C and apo A-I continue to decline through the early 20s, then remain stable, at least until age 55 y.[33,34] In girls, HDL-C and apo A-I increase gradually from menarche to the time of menopause.[32,35] Lp(a) is similar in men and women of all ages, although it is slightly higher in young and adolescent girls.[36]

In black children, HDL-C, apo A-I, Lp(a), and VLDL-C concentrations are noticeably higher than those of white children by about age 9, while LDL-C and apo B concentrations are lower.[37,38] In adulthood, these sex- and race-related differences persist.[39] A recent report has demonstrated that in fact gender- and race-related differences are already present at birth and suggested that these variations are influenced by genetic factors.[40]

Little data exist on other minority groups in the population. In two studies, no differences were found in most lipid measurements between Hispanic and non-Hispanic whites.[41,42] In contrast, Lp(a) is significantly lower in Hispanic whites, intermediate in Asians and non-Hispanic whites, and highest in blacks.[43–45] Similar plasma TC and TG changes were observed with respect to age and sex in the Lipid Research Clinics prevalence study of 60,502 participants in a survey of 11 separate and well-defined North American populations.[46]

In all individuals, TC concentrations gradually increase with age, although the magnitude of increase is not as great in more recent studies as it was 20 or more years ago.[47] In the Second National Health and Nutrition Examination Survey, mean TC concentration increased from approximately 180 mg/dL (4.66 mmol/L) at age 20 to approximately 230 mg/dL (5.96 mmol/L) in men and 250 mg/dL (6.48 mmol/L) in women by age 65.[48] This increase is due primarily to increasing LDL-C concentration and is accompanied by an increase in apo B values. In the Framingham Heart Study, TC increased biannually by an average of 3.7% in men and 6.6% in women.[13] In women, there is a 14% increase in TC and a 19% increase in LDL-C in the five years surrounding menopause; TG and HDL-C are unaffected.[49] The TG concentration also increases with age.[32,50] Lp(a) appears to rise slightly with age, and increases an average of 25% in women after menopause.[51,52]

BEHAVIORAL VARIATIONS

The major behavioral factors that affect the lipid, lipoprotein, and apolipoprotein serum concentrations include

❖   diet,

❖   obesity,

❖   cigarette smoking,

❖   alcohol and caffeine intake,

❖   exercise, and

❖   stress.

Since these lifestyle elements are controllable, it is imperative that subjects maintain their usual behavior for several days before blood specimens for lipid testing are obtained.

Diet

The effect of diet on lipid and lipoprotein concentrations is well established. The extent of this effect, however, varies among individuals. It has been shown that an increase in dietary intake of cholesterol can cause serum TC concentration to rise more than 5% in only 30% of the studied population.[8] Various fatty acids appear to have different effects on the lipoprotein profile and CHD risk.[53] In general, diets rich in mono- and polyunsaturated fatty acids cause serum TC, LDL-C, apo B, and TG to decrease, while diets rich in saturated fat, mainly palmitic acid, cause serum TC and LDL-C to increase.[54–56] However, stearic acid, which is also a saturated fatty acid, does not appear to increase LDL-C.[55] Progression of CHD over 39 months measured by angiography was strongly related to intakes of long-chain saturates, especially 18:0, and trans-unsaturates such as t-18:1, apparently independent of plasma TC concentration.[57]

Omega-3 fatty acids, from fish oil, have been shown to consistently decrease TG and VLDL in both normal and hypertriglyceridemic subjects, possibly by inhibiting the hepatic synthesis of VLDL-apo B and VLDL-TG.[58] In contrast, the documented effects of fish oil on TC, LDL-C, and HDL-C have been inconsistent.

The Cholesterol-Lowering Atherosclerosis Study observed that when total and saturated fat intakes are reduced, protein and carbohydrate are preferred substitutes for fat calories rather than mono- or polyunsaturated fats.[59] Furthermore, the reduction in fat intake was reflected in a significant decrease in TC concentrations.[59]

The effect of dietary intake of fiber on serum lipids remains controversial.[60] However, water-soluble fibers were shown to reduce TC.[61,62]

Vegetarians are known to have a healthier lipid profile than non-vegetarians. The Lifestyle Heart Trial studying the effect of comprehensive lifestyle changes (low fat, vegetarian diet, cessation of smoking, stress management training, and moderate exercise) observed regression of severe coronary atherosclerosis by angiography after only one year.[63] One study has demonstrated that LDL-C is 37% lower and HDL-C is 12% higher in strict vegetarians than in non-vegetarians.[64] In one study, Lp(a) was 35% lower in strict vegetarians than in non-vegetarians.[65]

Changes in eating habits have been shown to significantly alter lipid and lipoprotein profiles within a relatively short period of time. When the low-fat and high-fiber diet of a group of Tarahumara Indians was substituted with an "affluent" diet for a period of five weeks, increases in TC and LDL-C (up to 39%) and TG concentrations (19%) as well as body weight (7%) were observed.[66]

Because diet modification can affect lipid concentrations, subjects should maintain customary dietary intake and eating habits before blood samples are collected for lipid and lipoprotein studies. When subjects have changed their dietary habits significantly, the NCEP guidelines suggest a waiting period of 3–6 months before performing any lipid testing.[9]

Obesity

Obesity has become a major problem in the United States, mainly because of reduced physical activity and increased carbohydrate intake. Longitudinal studies, such as the Framingham Heart Study, have shown that obesity is associated with increased risk of CHD.[67,68] It is important to note that adult obesity and its cardiovascular consequences appear to originate during childhood.[69,70] The mechanisms linking overweight to cardiovascular risk are not clearly defined. However, insulin resistance appears to be strongly related to obesity.[71] Obese individuals have higher TG, TC, and LDL-C and lower HDL-C compared to non-obese controls.[8] After weight loss, an obese individual will experience a decrease in TG of about 40%, a decrease in TC and LDL-C of about 10%, and an increase in HDL-C of about 10%.[72] In a study of identical twins, obesity was independently associated with TC, LDL-C, HDL-C, and TG, as well as systolic and diastolic blood pressure and glucose tolerance.[73]

Current evidence suggests that body fat distribution has a stronger association with various morbidities, such as hyperlipidemia, hypertension, diabetes, and CHD, than just body weight, in both adults and children.[75–77] The intra-abdominal fat accumulation (waist-to-hip ratio) in obese women was associated with higher TG and VLDL-C and lower HDL-C, independent of total obesity.[78] Visceral abdominal fat measured independently by computed tomography is the most relevant positive obesity factor for TC, TG, and apo B-containing lipoproteins, and negative for HDL-C.[79]

Repeated weight gain and loss in obese individuals would precipitate significant variations in serum lipid and lipoprotein concentrations. Therefore, subjects should avoid any alterations in lifestyle that can cause weight changes at the time when blood specimens are collected.

Cigarette Smoking

Cigarette smoking is an established independent risk factor for CHD. A recent report describing the relationship between exposure to cigarette smoking and progression of atherosclerosis showed that those who currently smoke cigarettes experience a 50% increase in progression of atherosclerosis, compared to a 25% increase in those who smoked in the past, and a 20% increase in those who were exposed to environmental tobacco smoke.[80] An examination of 18 epidemiological studies further supported the modest association between CHD risk and passive smoking.[81] The impact of smoking on atherosclerosis appears to be greater in subjects with diabetes and hypertension.[80] Smoking-associated physiological changes that probably contribute to the high risk of heart disease include increased clotting factors and carboxyhemoglobin concentrations, increased blood viscosity, and altered lipoprotein profile.[82] The strong association of smoking with white blood cell count, hematocrit, and heart rate suggests that smoking-induced risk is more associated with occlusive thrombosis than with atherosclerosis.[83] In addition, oxidized LDL produced after exposure to cigarette smoke was shown to cause the accumulation of cholesteryl ester in macrophages *in vitro*.[84] Therefore, oxidized LDL could also contribute to foam cell formation and atherosclerosis in smokers.

Compared to non-smokers, cigarette smokers have significantly higher serum TG, VLDL-C, and LDL-C, and lower apo A-I and HDL-C (mainly the HDL_3-C fraction).[85,86] Smokers also have 38% higher Lp(a) than non-smokers.[87] Furthermore, the relationship between smoking and HDL-C was shown to be dose-dependent in both men and women;[88] therefore, the extent of smoking will affect the degree of alteration in the lipoprotein profile. Passive smoking through multiple components of secondhand smoke affects platelet activity, accelerates atherosclerotic lesions, increases ischemic tissue damage,[89] and decreases HDL-C.[90]

Subjects should not change their smoking pattern at the time when blood specimens are collected.

Alcohol Intake

Several epidemiological studies have demonstrated a relationship between alcohol consumption, lipoprotein profile changes, and cardiovascular mortality.[91] Alcohol-induced alterations in the lipoprotein pattern depend on the amount of alcohol consumed, individual susceptibility, genetic variables, and dietary factors. Therefore, these changes differ among moderate and heavy drinkers. Moderate alcohol drinkers (1.2 oz/day; 34 g/day) have increased concentrations of HDL-C, apo A-I, and apo A-II compared to non-drinkers.[92,93] Another study has shown that moderate alcohol intake increases total HDL-C, HDL_2-C, and HDL_3-C; increases TC, LDL-C, and VLDL-C; and decreases the risk of myocardial infarction.[79] In premenopausal women, moderate daily alcohol consumption has resulted in a 10% increase in HDL-C, an 8% decrease in LDL-C, and unchanged Lp(a) concentrations.[95] In men, alcohol intake significantly reduced Lp(a) in several studies,[96,97] but not in others.[98] Furthermore, ethanol withdrawal was associated with a rapid increase in Lp(a) levels.[99] However, moderate alcohol consumption in patients with primary hypertriglyceridemia usually causes a profound increase in TG.[100] With increased alcohol intake, LDL-C and HDL_2-C are reduced and TG is increased.[93] In chronic alcoholic men with normal liver function and structure, TG is usually in the normal range, HDL-C is increased, and LDL-C is decreased.[93]

Alcohol appears to influence Lp(a) concentration differently than it influences other lipids. Lp(a) concentrations decrease by about 33% initially, then return to baseline after six weeks of alcohol intake.[101] In African-American males, a dose-dependent inverse relationship between alcohol consumption and Lp(a) concentration has recently been reported.[102]

Alcohol consumption has been shown to have a U-shaped relationship to heart disease.[8] However, increased alcohol consumption is not only associated with increased mortality due to CHD but also mortality from other causes including cirrhosis and cancers of mouth, esophagus, pharynx, and liver.[103] Although several mechanisms have been suggested, including increased levels of HDL,[76] inhibition of platelet aggregation,[104] antioxidant capacity,[105] antithrombogenesis,[106] and reduction of psychosocial stress, the actual mechanism of the link between moderate alcohol consumption and lowered CHD risk is uncertain at present. Furthermore, the molecular basis of the alcohol-induced lipid changes remains unclear.

Subjects should maintain their usual pattern of alcohol intake prior to blood specimen collection.

Caffeine Intake

Several epidemiological studies have investigated the link between coffee consumption, cardiovascular morbidity, and altered lipid concentrations. These correlations have been inconsistent and have been largely dismissed as being due to confounding variables. Intake of coffee in Norway has been associated with a trend toward an atherogenic diet and unhealthy lifestyle.[107] Recently it was suggested that the inconsistency in these findings may result from the coffee-brewing methods used. The strongest evidence for a direct association between coffee consumption and increased TC and LDL-C values comes from Scandinavia, where coffee is normally brewed by boiling.[108] Consumption of filtered coffee was reported to have a substantially lesser effect on cholesterol values than consumption of coffee brewed by boiling. The serum concentrations of apo A-I, apo A-II, apo B, HDL-C, and VLDL-C appear to be unaffected by consumption of coffee, even when brewed by boiling.[109] However, in another study, boiled Scandinavian-style coffee was found to contain more lipid material than drip-filtered coffee, and this was reported to raise serum LDL-C and VLDL-C concentrations.[110] The diterpenes, cafestol, and kahweol present in the unfiltered coffee may be responsible for increasing TC, TG, and alanine transaminase.[111]

Replacing regular coffee with decaffeinated coffee did not alter TG, TC, or HDL-C in healthy men and women.[112] Coffee as consumed by U.S. women apparently causes no increased risk of subsequent CHD.[113] However, a randomized clinical trial found that consumption of filtered regular coffee led to a statistically significant increase in the plasma concentration of TC, which was due to increases in both LDL-C and HDL-C concentrations.[114]

Subjects should maintain their usual daily intake of caffeine during the days prior to lipid testing, but abstain from drinking coffee and cream 12 h prior to collecting blood specimens.

Exercise

Several epidemiological investigations have reported an association between a sedentary lifestyle and an increased risk of developing the clinical manifestations of CHD.[115] A lower level of physical fitness is associated with higher serum concentrations of LDL-C and TG and higher risk of death from cardiovascular disease.[116] Exercise exerts a preventive effect on the progression of coronary atherosclerosis, possibly by altering the lipoprotein profile. In hyperlipidemic subjects, additional favorable alteration in the lipoprotein profile was seen when physical exercise accompanied dietary treatment.[117,118]

Strenuous exercise decreases serum TG, LDL-C, and apo B, and increases HDL-C (mainly the HDL$_2$-C fraction) and apo A-I.[8,119] Furthermore, the extent of these changes may be dependent on the intensity and type of exercise training program.[119] Acute exercise causes a significant rise in HDL-C, which is due to an increase in HDL$_3$-C.[120] Moderate and regular physical exercise also appears to favorably affect serum lipids. Adults who walk 2.5 h to 4 h each week have lower TC and higher HDL-C than those who do not walk regularly.[121] In previously sedentary women who walked briskly an average of 155 min each week for one year, TC decreased by 6.5% and HDL-C increased by 27%.[122] While normal levels of physical activity do not alter Lp(a) levels,[123] intense physical training may cause a 10%–15% increase in Lp(a).[124]

Subjects should maintain their usual level of exercise on days before lipid testing, but avoid any strenuous exercise 24 h prior to blood specimen collection.[8]

Stress

A high level of stress, as well as a Type A personality, has been linked to increased risk of CHD. Furthermore, several studies have demonstrated an increase in TC concentration during stressful situations,[125] which is possibly due to dietary changes that accompany stress.[126] The stressors employed in these trials were diverse and included both chronic stressors and acute challenges posed in the laboratory. Some evidence suggests that stress affects the lipid concentrations of males and females differently.[127] In addition, elective hospitalization was shown to decrease HDL-C and apo A-I by approximately 10%.[102] Following coronary artery bypass grafting, Lp(a) falls by almost 50% by three days after surgery.[129]

The exact mechanism of the interplay of stress with CHD and lipid changes remains unclear. Therefore, it is not advisable to perform lipid testing for cardiac risk assessment in a stressful period such as during academic examinations or hospitalization, even for elective procedures.

To minimize the effect of acute stress on lipid testing, subjects who report to the laboratory should be encouraged to relax for at least 5 min prior to blood sample collection.

CLINICAL VARIATIONS

An individual's lipoprotein profile is markedly altered in acute infectious and metabolic diseases. In addition, drug-induced hyperlipidemia has been reported in several patient populations. To obtain the subject's usual lipid and lipoprotein concentrations, testing should preferably be performed in the absence of any secondary dyslipoproteinemia. Otherwise, the disorder or the medication causing the disruption in lipid values should be noted on the patient's analytical report.

Disease-Induced Secondary Lipid Alterations

Several endocrine, metabolic, renal, hepatic, and storage diseases precipitate secondary hyper- or hypolipidemia. Hypothyroidism and diabetes mellitus are perhaps the most common disorders to cause secondary hyperlipidemia. Serum TC and LDL-C are increased in 30% of patients with hypothyroidism because of increased production and decreased removal of LDL.[130] Lp(a) and HDL-C are also increased in hypothyroidism, but fall with thyroid hormone replacement.[131] Variable degrees of hypertriglyceridemia are observed in patients with type 1 and type 2 diabetes mellitus.[8,132] The CARDIA Study found that higher concentrations of insulin are associated positively with unfavorable values of TC and LDL-C, TG, apo B, and blood pressure, and negatively with HDL-C, HDL_2-C, HDL_3-C, and apo A-I.[133] Insulin treatment of non-insulin-dependent diabetics usually results in a significant change toward normalization of TG, HDL-C, and LDL-C concentrations.[134] Lp(a) appears to be increased in both type 1 and type 2 patients.[135] Evidence suggests that a direct correlation might exist between diabetic control and Lp(a) concentrations,[135,136] although there was no correlation between levels and degree of control of diabetes in another study.[137] The lack of induction of the lipoprotein lipase by insulin is thought to be responsible for the hyperlipidemic status in the diabetic population.[138]

Patients with nephrotic syndrome or chronic renal failure who are undergoing hemodialysis have significantly higher serum TC and LDL-C, TG, apo B, and Lp(a), and lower concentrations of apo A-I compared to controls.[139–141] Furthermore, increases in Lp(a) concentrations were documented in patients with pronounced proteinuria of various origins.[142] The exact nature of these abnormalities remains uncertain. However, it has been recently suggested that lipid alterations in patients with nephrotic syndrome are attributable to reversible increases in VLDL production.[143] In one study, increased Lp(a) was found only in patients with the smallest size apo(a) forms [144] [see chapter 17 for additional information on Lp(a)]. Following renal transplantation, Lp(a) levels decrease, although the decrease was smaller in patients treated with azathioprine than in those treated with other immunosuppressive agents.[145] Obstructive biliary tract disease causes the production of the abnormal lipoprotein "lipoprotein X." Since this cholesterol-rich particle is poorly removed from circulation, TC concentrations in these patients are markedly increased (over 1000 mg/dL [25.90 mmol/L]).[146]

Cancer, in general, tends to lower TC and HDL-C.[147] The most profound decrease is usually noted in patients with hematological malignancies.[147,148] These changes may be the reflection of active cell proliferation. In addition, long-term survivors of cancer have persistently low HDL-C and apo A-I, despite resolution of their underlying disease.[148,149]

Acute myocardial infarction is associated with variable decreases in TC, LDL-C, apo A-I, and apo B, and with an increase in Lp(a).[150,151] The extent of the decrease is usually dependent on the original lipid values. For example, TC would change little when the original concentration is below 200 mg/dL (5.17 mmol/L). Lipid concentrations remain stable within 24 h after the infarction and then decrease gradually to a lower plateau at which they remain for 6–8 weeks.[8] Changes in serum lipids similar to those encountered after a myocardial infarction were reported after a stroke.[152]

Blood specimens should be obtained within 24 h after a myocardial or stroke or 3 months following the infarct in order to reflect accurately the person's usual lipid values.

Infections and inflammations cause TG and Lp(a) to increase and TC and HDL-C to decrease, independently of the infectious agent, the cause of the illness, and the clinical condition of the patient.[153–155] Various forms of dyslipoproteinemia are produced by numerous other disorders, such as acute intermittent porphyria, glycogen storage disease, Gaucher disease, Tay-Sachs disease, rheumatoid arthritis, anorexia nervosa, and systemic lupus erythematosus. The treatment of the primary disorder (except inherited disorders) will usually normalize the lipoprotein profile. Therefore, serum lipid assessment should only be conducted after a complete recovery from illness.

Recently, assays for the direct determination of LDL-C and HDL-C have been introduced. These homogeneous methods offer improved reproducibility and reduced susceptibility to interference from increased TG and can be performed online (for additional information on these assays, refer to chapters 11 and 12). Although the principles of these assays differ, they are largely based on the use of modified enzymes or specific detergents to disperse lipoprotein complexes. Therefore, changes in the composition of lipoproteins could cause variability in their performance. Although these assays were shown to work well in the general population, their performance in specific patient populations such as those with diabetes, renal, hepatic, or storage disease, and hypothyroidism has not been closely examined. For example, in our laboratory, we found that the LDL-C assay from Daüchi gave results that are approximately 20% lower than those estimated by the Friedewald calculation in patients with growth hormone deficiency, and the HDL-C assay from Roche Diagnostics gave results that are 80% to 90% lower than those determined by the dextran sulfate precipitation method or the homogeneous HDL-C assay from Daüchi in subjects with gestational diabetes. In another study, also using the Daüchi method, homogeneous HDL-C results were 20% lower than with the reference method in patients with cirrhosis, and 7.5% lower in patients with nephrotic syndrome.[156] Bilirubin also causes a negative interference with some direct HDL-C methods, while reference methods are minimally affected.[156,157] Laboratorians should be very careful in interpreting the results of the homogeneous assays in these specific patient groups.

Drug-Induced Secondary Lipid Alterations

Medications that alter lipoprotein metabolism and serum concentrations include diuretics, some beta-blockers, sex steroids, glucocorticoids, and cyclosporine, among others. Thiazides and chlorothalidone, the most commonly used diuretics in the treatment of mild essential hypertension, cause increases in serum TC (12%), LDL-C (20%), TG (7%), and apo B (20%) concentrations, and decreases in HDL-C (16%) and apo A-I (6%) concentrations compared to controls.[158] Other diuretics are also known to disrupt the lipoprotein profile.[159] In addition, propranolol, a non-cardioselective beta-blocker that is also used in the treatment of hypertension, significantly increases serum TG and decreases HDL-C (mainly the HDL_2-C fraction).[160] Up to 50% of children receiving asparaginase for the treatment of acute lymphoblastic leukemia exhibit gross increase in TG concentrations [over 5,000 mg/dL (5.65 mmol/L)].[148] These increases subside after the treatment is discontinued.

Various investigators have reported conflicting findings concerning the effect of oral contraceptives on the lipid and lipoprotein concentrations. This discrepancy can be largely attributed to the variations in the hormonal content of the medications used in these studies, mainly differences in the estrogen to progestin ratio.[161,162] Oral contraceptives with a high progestin content increase serum TC and LDL-C and decrease HDL-C.[163] The opposite can be expected in women taking oral contraceptives with a high estrogen content and in postmenopausal women receiving an estrogen supplement.[164] Estrogen treatment, both in women and in men suffering from prostatic carcinoma, appears to decrease Lp(a) concentration by as much as 50%.[165] A similar decrease is observed with tamoxifen.[166]

Immunosuppressive agents are also reported to alter lipid metabolism. Prednisolone increases serum TC, LDL-C, HDL-C, VLDL-C, TG, apo A-I, and apo B, possibly by increasing lipoprotein production.[167] Cyclosporine markedly increases TC, LDL-C, and apo B, and decreases Lp(a).[168,169] However, hypertriglyceridemia is the most profound lipid change after prednisolone and azathioprine therapy, and hypercholesterolemia is the more common finding after cyclosporine therapy in transplant patients.[170] In contrast, tacrolimus (previously known as FK 506) appears to decrease TC concentration.[171] The actual mechanisms for the distinct effect of the two immunosuppressive agents, tacrolimus and cyclosporine, on lipoprotein metabolism are currently unknown.

Because of the effect of various pharmacological agents on lipoprotein metabolism, medications should be suspended, if possible, for several days or weeks, depending on the drug and its effects, before lipid studies are conducted. Otherwise, any medication that is known to alter lipid values should be noted on the laboratory report.

Pregnancy

Physiologic and endocrine systems are greatly affected during pregnancy, altering the concentration of several biochemical parameters. Serum TC, LDL-C, TG, apo A-I, apo A-II, apo B, and Lp(a) increase significantly during pregnancy, mainly in the second and third trimesters.[8,172–174] The concentrations of these analytes usually return to normal within 10 weeks postpartum, unless the woman is breast feeding.[175] The increased mobilization of lipids probably reflects the rise in maternal metabolic demand as a result of pregnancy. Therefore, the assessment of the lipoprotein profile during pregnancy does not reflect the usual pattern of the subject.

Lipid studies should be performed at least 3 months postpartum or 3 months following cessation of lactation.

VARIATION DUE TO SPECIMEN COLLECTION AND HANDLING

Fasting versus Non-Fasting

The effect of food ingestion on lipid measurements has long been established. A controlled dietary study showed that ingestion of a typical fat-containing meal significantly increased TG; this increase persisted for at least 9 h.[15] VLDL-C also increases, while LDL-C falls significantly; both changes persist for at least 9 h. The increased VLDL-C and decreased LDL-C are greater for values calculated by the Friedewald equation than for those obtained by ultracentrifugation. The changes, however, are significant regardless of the methodology used. For calculated LDL-C, the differences seen are the result of not only falsely increased VLDL-C, but also of changes in lipoprotein composition. Postprandially, precipitation methods show a slight but significant decrease in HDL-C, while ultracentrifugation methods show a slight increase in HDL-C; the cause of this discrepancy is not yet known. Some homogeneous HDL-C and LDL-C assays differ from reference methods in non-fasting specimens. For example, the N-geneous HDL-C method from Daüchi shows a 3% decrease in post-prandial specimens.[176,177] The N-geneous LDL-C assay showed no difference from reference methods in non-fasting specimens except in a small percentage of specimens where marked differences between fasting and non-fasting values were observed.[178] With more prolonged fasting, profound changes occur in lipid concentrations. TC and TG increase an average of 25% after one week of fasting, falling to baseline after three weeks. Refeeding causes a 13% fall in TC but an 86% increase in TG.[179]

The second report of the NCEP Adult Treatment Panel recommends that initial screening for lipid disorders should include both TC and HDL-C. These measurements may be performed using non-fasting samples.[9] As a result, it is important for the laboratory to verify that the method used for HDL-C is not affected in the non-fasting state. TC, Lp(a), apo A-I, and apo A-II are unchanged after food ingestion.[15,180] Some investigators have reported an increase in apo B after meals,[25] while others report no change; the latter finding is consistent with constancy of the sum of VLDL-C and LDL-C in the postprandial state.[15,180] Therefore, except for measurements of TC, Lp(a), apo A-I, and apo A-II, lipid measurements should be carried out only after a fast of at least 12 h.

Anticoagulants and Preservatives

The type of specimen collected is an important consideration in interpreting lipid values. Most laboratories use serum or EDTA plasma. At 4 °C, TC and TG concentrations are stable for at least four days in either serum or plasma.[8] EDTA has a theoretical advantage in that metal-ion induced oxidation and enzymatic cleavage of lipoproteins is retarded, but this does not appear to be an issue in the routine laboratory. Current NCEP cut-points are based on serum sample values. Because of its osmotic effect,

EDTA causes a method-dependent artifactual fall in most lipid and lipoprotein concentrations, but a paradoxical rise in HDL-C.[181] In the past, most reports stated that this reduces TC by 3%;[8] however, a recent study reports that the average difference between plasma and serum using tubes with disodium EDTA is now 4.7%, because the EDTA concentration has been made 50% higher in blood collection tubes.[182] Since EDTA concentration is dependent on volume of blood added, the actual decrease in TC in underfilled tubes may be as much as 10%.[183] It would be prudent to insist on fully filled evacuated tubes to minimize the effect of differing anticoagulant concentration.

Use of other anticoagulants such as oxalate and citrate is associated with even greater osmotic fluid shifts.[8] Fluoride, for example, causes fluid shift and has an inhibitory effect on some enzymatic measurements of TC.[183] These anticoagulants are not recommended for use in lipid measurements. Heparin does not produce fluid shifts and appears to be an acceptable alternative for TC measurement;[184] however, heparin activates lipoprotein lipase both *in vitro* and *in vivo*.[185] TG concentration falls gradually in specimens containing heparin, including "serum" specimens from patients who are receiving therapeutic doses of heparin.[186] Most serum separator tubes do not appear to affect the results of lipid measurements.[183]

Capillary vs. Venous Blood

The source of specimen appears to have some effect on TC concentration, which may be important in remote-site screening programs. Several studies have reported that TC is higher in capillary blood plasma than in venous serum, the average bias being approximately 3%.[187] Since heparin was utilized, this effect is not due to shifts in fluid from the anticoagulant. Other studies have reported no difference[188] or lower[189] concentrations of TC in capillary blood. It is unclear whether these conflicting results are due to variations in the site of collection, the puncture technique, the postprandial state, or other variables. Further research is necessary to clarify this issue, because different measurement techniques may be a source of inaccurate classification of patients' risk factors.[190] Use of a standardized protocol for collecting capillary samples can produce results that agree closely with venous plasma.[191]

Hemoconcentration

Hemoconcentration from posture or other causes increases the relative concentration of proteins and protein-bound substances, which would produce a predictable change in all lipid and apolipoprotein measurements. A patient who stands for 5 min will experience an apparent increase in lipid concentration of 9%, and a further increase to 16% after 15 min.[192] This can be minimized by having a patient remain seated for at least 15 min before venipuncture.[8,192,193]

Use of a tourniquet can also cause significant hemoconcentration. After 1 min there is no significant change in TC or protein concentration; however, after 2 min the apparent TC concentration increases up to 5%, and after 5 min apparent increases of 10%–15% can occur.[8] If a tourniquet remains for 15 min during phlebotomy, lipid measurements increase by 20%–40%.[194]

Posture changes have also become associated with changes in plasma noradrenaline concentrations, and apparent sympathetic activity, which may also indirectly alter lipid concentration.[195]

Specimen Storage

Specimens for most lipid testing are stable at 0°–4°C for up to 4 days, with HDL-C and LDL-C being less stable. Serum specimens show some spontaneous hydrolysis of phospholipids and TG, which is inhibited in EDTA plasma.[8] For longer storage of lipids, specimen stability is better at −70°C than at −20°C, since serum does not fully freeze until about −40°C. Apo B can decrease slightly when frozen,[196] but other lipid components appear stable when frozen for up to 6 months.[183] The effects of storage on measured lipoprotein cholesterol values may differ between historical methods and newer homogeneous assays. For example, storage of specimens caused no decrease in measured HDL-C [178] and LDL-C [177] using the N-geneous methods (Daüchi); stability was significantly greater compared to ultracentrifugation for LDL-C or precipitation methods for HDL-C.

Distribution of lipids among lipoproteins can change during storage at 4°C or −20°C; ultracentrifugation should be performed as soon as possible after collection.[197] Alterations in apo B and apo(a) measurements after storage are method-dependent; if specimens are to be stored for long periods, the laboratory must verify that its method is not affected by specimen storage. Repeated freezing and thawing should be avoided, as it can affect results of lipid measurements after as few as two cycles.[198] This is a particular concern for specimens stored at −20°C, as most frost-free freezers regularly increase temperatures to melt accumulated frost, which may result in specimen thawing; specimens for lipid testing should not be stored in frost-free freezers.

RECOMMENDATIONS FOR MINIMIZING PREANALYTICAL VARIATION

Highlights from the NCEP Laboratory Standardization Panel recommendations for minimizing the effect of preanalytical factors on lipid and lipoprotein testing are presented in Figure 8–2.[199] No specific recommendations were made by the Panel concerning apolipoprotein testing. However, steps similar to those described should be taken to help minimize preanalytical sources of variation in apolipoprotein measurements.

SUMMARY

Lipid measurement results are affected by many biological, behavioral, and clinical factors, and by variability in sample collection and handling. Failure to control for these variables can lead to misclassification of patient risk. Therefore, standardizing preanalytical sources of variation to the fullest extent possible will improve the accuracy and utility of lipid testing in assessing the risk of CHD. ✧

Figure 8–2 ✧ Recommendations for Minimizing Preanalytical Variation

1. A subject's lipid and lipoprotein profile should only be measured when the individual is in a steady metabolic state.

2. Subjects should maintain their usual diet and weight for at least two weeks prior to the measurement of their lipids or lipoproteins.

3. Multiple measurements should be performed within two months, at least one week apart, before making a medical decision about further action.

4. Subjects should not perform vigorous physical activity during the 24 hours prior to testing.

5. Fasting or non-fasting specimens can be used for TC testing. However, a 12-h fasting specimen is required for TG and recommended for lipoproteins.

6. The subject should be seated for at least five minutes before specimen collection.

7. The tourniquet should not be kept on more than one minute during venipuncture.

8. TC, TG, and HDL-C concentrations can be determined in either serum or plasma. When EDTA is used as the anticoagulant, plasma should be immediately cooled to 2°–4°C to prevent changes in composition, and values should be multiplied by 1.03.

9. For TC testing, serum can be transported either at 4°C or frozen. Storage of specimens at −20°C is adequate for TC measurement. However, specimens must be stored frozen at −70°C or lower for TG and lipoprotein/apolipoprotein testing.

10. All blood specimens should be considered potentially infectious and handled accordingly.

REFERENCES

1. Pagani F, Panteghini M. Significance of various parameters derived from biological variability for lipid and lipoprotein analyses. Clin Biochem 1993;26:415–20.
2. Harris EK. Statistical aspects of reference values in clinical pathology. Prog Clin Pathol 1981;8:45–66.

3. Ford RP. Essential data derived from biological variation for establishment and use of lipid analysis. Ann Clin Biochem 1989;26:281-5.

4. Mogadam M, Ahmed SW, Mensch AH, Godwin ID. Within-person fluctuations of serum cholesterol and lipoproteins. Arch Intern Med 1990;150:1645-8.

5. Kafonek SD, Derby CA, Bachorik PS. Biological variability of lipoproteins and apolipoproteins in patients referred to a lipid clinic. Clin Chem 1992;38:864-872.

6. Smith SJ, Cooper GR, Myers GL, Sampson EJ. Biological variability in concentrations of serum lipids: sources of variation among results from published studies and composite predicted values. Clin Chem 1993;39:1012-22.

7. Cooper GR, Smith SJ, Myers GL, Sampson EJ, Magid E. Estimating and minimizing effects of biologic sources of variation by relative range when measuring the mean of serum lipids and lipoproteins. Clin Chem 1994;40:227-32.

8. Cooper GR, Myers GL, Smith SJ, Sampson EJ. Standardization of lipid, lipoprotein, and apolipoprotein measurements. Clin Chem 1988;34:B95-B105.

9. Summary of the second report of the National Cholesterol Education Program (NCEP) Expert Panel on Detection, Evaluation and Treatment of High Blood Cholesterol in Adults (Adult Treatment Panel II). JAMA 1993;269:3015-23.

10. Bookstein L, Gidding SS, Donovan M, Smith FA. Day-to-day variability of serum cholesterol, triglyceride, and high-density-lipoprotein cholesterol levels: impact on the assessment of risk according to the National Cholesterol Education Program guidelines. Arch Intern Med 1990;150:1653-7.

11. Warnick GR, Albers JJ. Physiological and analytical variation in cholesterol and triglyceride. Lipids 1976;11:203-8.

12. Marcovina SM, Gaur VP, Albers JJ. Biological variability of cholesterol, triglyceride, low- and high-density lipoprotein cholesterol, lipoprotein(a), and apolipoproteins A-I and B. Clin Chem 1994;40:574-8.

13. Kreger BE, Odell PM, D'Agostino RB, Wilson PF. Long-term intraindividual cholesterol variability: natural course and adverse impact on morbidity and mortality—the Framingham Study. Am Heart J 1994;127:1607-14.

14. Choudhury N, Wall PM, Truswell AS. Effect of time between measurements on within-subject variability for total cholesterol and high-density lipoprotein cholesterol in women. Clin Chem 1994;40:710-5.

15. Cohn JS, McNamara JR, Schaefer EJ. Lipoprotein cholesterol concentrations in the plasma of human subjects as measured in the fed and fasted states. Clin Chem 1988;34:2456-9.

16. Gordon DJ, Trost DC, Hyde J et al. Seasonal cholesterol cycles: the Lipid Research Clinics Coronary Primary Prevention Trial placebo group. Circulation 1987;76:1224-31.

17. Kim HJ, Kalkhoff RK. Changes in lipoprotein composition during the menstrual cycle. Metabolism 1979;28:663-8.

18. Lussier-Cacan S, Xhignesse M, DesmarA-Is JL et al. Cyclic fluctuations in human serum lipid and apolipoprotein levels during the normal menstrual cycle: comparison with changes occurring during oral contraceptive therapy. Metabolism 1991;40:849-54.

19. Tangney C, Brownie C, Wu SM. Impact of menstrual periodicity on serum lipid levels and estimates of dietary intakes. J Am Coll Nutr 1991;10:107-13.

20. Terstrat J, Hessel LW, Seepers J, Van Gent CM. The influence of meal frequency on diurnal lipid, glucose and cortisol levels in normal subjects. Eur J Clin Invest 1978;8:61-6.

21. Schectman G, Patsches M, Sasse EA. Variability in cholesterol measurements: comparison of calculated and direct LDL cholesterol determinations. Clin Chem 1996; 42:7 32-7.

22. Kafonek SD, Donovan L, Lovejoy KL, Bachorik PS. Biological variation of lipids and lipoproteins in fingerstick blood. Clin Chem 1996;42:2002-7.

23. Fraser CG. Biological variation in clinical chemistry. An update: collected data, 1988-1991. Arch Path Lab Med 1992;116:916-23.

24. Haarbo J, Christiansen C. Treatment-induced cyclic variations in serum lipids, lipoproteins, and apolipoproteins after two years of combined hormone replacement therapy: exaggerated cyclic variations in smokers. Obstet Gynecol 1992;80:639–44.

25. Matuchansky C, Fabre J, Guillard O, Morechar-Beauchant M, Reinberg A. Effects of cyclic (nocturnal) total parenteral nutrition and continuous enteral nutrition on circadian rhythms of blood lipids, lipoproteins, and apolipoproteins in humans. Am J Clin Nutr 1985;41:727–34.

26. Panteghini M, Pagani F. Preanalytical, analytical and biological sources of variation of lipoprotein(a). Eur J Clin Chem Clin Biochem 1993;31:23–8.

27. Chandler WL, Loo SC. Lipoprotein (a) does not show circadian variations. Thromb Haemost 1990;63:151.

28. Tonolo G, Ciccarese M, Brizzi P, Milia S, Dessole S, Puddu L, Secchi G, MA-Ioli M. Cyclical variation of plasma lipids, apolipoproteins, and lipoprotein(a) during menstrual cycle of normal women. Am J Physiol 1995;269:E1101–5.

29. Strobl W, Widhalm K. The natural history of serum lipids and apolipoproteins during childhood. In: Widhalm K, NA-Ito HK (eds.). Detection and treatment of lipid and lipoprotein disorders of childhood. New York: Alan R. Liss, 1985:101–21.

30. Rifai N, Heiss G, Doetsch K. Lipoprotein(a) at birth, in blacks and whites. Atherosclerosis 1992;92:123–9.

31. Van Biervliet JP, Labeur C, Michiels G, Usher DC, Rosseneu M. Lipoprotein(a) profiles and evolution in newborns. Atherosclerosis 1991;86:173–81.

32. Siest, G, Henny J, Schiele F, Young DB (eds.). Interpretation of clinical laboratory tests. Foster City, CA: Biomedical Publications, 1985.

33. Berenson GS, Srinivasan SR, Cresanta JL, Foster TA, Webber LS. Dynamic changes of serum lipoproteins in children during adolescence and sexual maturation. Am J Epidemiol 1981;113:157–70.

34. Twisk JW, Kemper HC, Mellenbergh GJ. Longitudinal development of lipoprotein levels in males and females aged 12–28 years: the Amsterdam Growth and Health Study. Int J Epidemiol 1995;24:69–77.

35. Steinmetz J, ChoukA-Ife A, Visvikis S, Henny J, Siest G. Biological factors affecting concentration of serum LpA-I lipoprotein particles in serum, and determination of reference ranges. Clin Chem 1990;36:677–80.

36. Jenner JL, Ordovas JM, Lamon-Fava S et al. Effects of age, sex, and menopausal status on plasma lipoprotein(a) levels: the Framingham Offspring Study. Circulation 1993;87:1135–41.

37. Srinivasan SR, Freedman DS, Webber LS, Berenson GS. Black-white differences in cholesterol levels of serum high-density lipoprotein subclasses among children: the Bogalusa Heart Study. Circulation 1987;76:272–9.

38. Srinivasan SR, Dahlen GH, Jarpa RA, Webber LS, Berenson GS. Racial (black-white) differences in serum lipoprotein(a) distribution and its relation to parental myocardial infarction in children: the Bogalusa Heart Study. Circulation 1991;84:160–7.

39. Tyroler HA, Heiss G, Schonfeld G et al. Apolipoprotein A-I, A-II, and C-II in black and white residents of Evans county. Circulation 1980;62:249–54.

40. Loughrey CM, Rimm E, Heiss G, Rifai N. Race and gender differences in cord blood lipoproteins. Atherosclerosis 2000;148:57–65.

41. Webber LS, Harsha DW, Phillips GT, Srinivasan SR, Simpson JW, Berenson GS. Cardiovascular risk factors in Hispanic, white, and black children: the Brooks County and Bogalusa Heart studies. Am J Epidemiol 1991;133:704–14.

42. Fulton-Kehoe DL, Eckel RH, Shetterly SM, Hamman RF. Determinants of total high-density-lipoprotein cholesterol and high-density-lipoprotein-subfraction levels among Hispanic and non-Hispanic white persons with normal glucose tolerance: the San Luis Valley Diabetes Study. J Clin Epidemiol 1992;45:1191–200.

43. Haffner SM, Gruber KK, Morales PA, et al. Lipoprotein(a) concentrations in Mexican Americans and non-Hispanic whites: the San Antonio Heart Study. Am J Epidemiol 1992;136:1060–8.

44. Cobbaert C, Kesteloot H. Serum lipoprotein(a) levels in racially different populations. Am J Epidemiol 1992;136:441–9.
45. Marcovina SM, Albers JJ, Jacobs DR Jr et al. Lipoprotein(a) concentrations and apolipoprotein(a) phenotypes in Caucasians and African-Americans: the CARDIA study. Arterioscler Thromb 1993;13:1037–45.
46. Lipid Research Clinics Population Studies Data Book. Volume 1. The Prevalence Study. Aggregate distributions of lipids, lipoproteins and selected variables in 11 North American Populations. (NIH publication No. 80–1527). Bethesda, MD: Public Health Service, National Institutes of Health, July 1980.
47. Johnson CL, Rifkind BM, Sempos CT et al. Declining serum total cholesterol levels among U.S. adults. JAMA 1993;269:3002–8.
48. National Center for Health Statistics, National Heart, Lung, and Blood Institute Collaborative Lipid Group. Trends in serum cholesterol levels among U.S. adults aged 20 to 74 years: data from the National Health and Nutrition Examination Surveys, 1960 to 1980. JAMA 1987;257:937–42.
49. Fukami K, Koike K, Hirota K, Yoshikawa H, Miyake A. Perimenopausal changes in serum lipids and lipoproteins: a 7-year longitudinal study. Maturitas 1995;22:193–7.
50. Cowan LD, Wilcosky T, Criqui MH et al. Demographic behavioral, biochemical, and dietary correlates of plasma triglyceride. Arteriosclerosis 1985;5;466–80.
51. Slunga L, Asplund K, Johnson O, Dahlen GH. Lipoprotein (a) in a randomly selected 25- to 64-year-old population: the Northern Sweden Monica Study. J Clin Epidemiol 1993; 46:617–24.
52. Kim CJ, Ryu WS, Kwak JW, Park CT, Ryoo UH. Changes in Lp(a) lipoprotein and lipid levels after cessation of female sex hormone production and estrogen replacement therapy. Arch Intern Med 1996;156:500–4.
53. Lichenstein AH, Ausman LM, Jalbert SM, Schaefer EJ. Effects of different forms of dietary hydrogenated fats on serum lipoprotein cholesterol levels. N Engl J Med 1999; 340:1933–9.
54. Kloer HU. Diet and coronary heart disease. Postgrad Med J 1989;65:S13–21.
55. Grundy SM, Denke MA. Dietary influences on serum lipids and lipoproteins. J Lipid Res 1990;31:1149–72.
56. Kris-Etherton PM, for the Nutrition Committee. Monounsaturated fatty acids and risk of cardiovascular disease. Circulation 1999;100:1253–8.
57. Watts GF, Jackson P, Burke V, Lewis B. Dietary fatty acids and progression of coronary artery disease in men. Am J Clin Nutr 1996;64:202–9.
58. Harris WS, Connor WE, Illingworth DR, Rothrock DW, Foster DM. Effects of fish oil on VLDL triglyceride kinetics in humans. J Lipid Res 1990;31:1549–58.
59. Blankenhorn DH, Johnson RL, Mack WJ, El Zein HA, VA-Illas LI. The influence of diet on the appearance of new lesions in human coronary arteries. JAMA 1990;263: 1646–52.
60. Ripsin CM, Keenan JM, Jacobs DR et al. Oat products and lipid lowering: a meta-analysis. JAMA 1992;267:3317–25.
61. Kris-Atherton DM, Krommel D, Russell ME et al. The effects of diet on plasma lipids, lipoproteins and coronary heart disease. J Am Diet Assoc 1988;88:1373–400.
62. Cooper GR, Myers GL, Smith SJ, Sehlant RC. Dietary oat fiber sources and blood lipids. JAMA 1992;268:986.
63. Ornish D, Brown SE, Scherwitz LW et al. Can lifestyle changes reverse coronary heart disease? Lancet 1990;336:129–33.
64. Sacks FM, Ornish D, Rosner B et al. Plasma lipoprotein levels in vegetarians. JAMA 1985;524:1337–41.
65. Li D, Ball M, Bartlett M, Sinclair A. Lipoprotein(a), essential fatty acid status and lipoprotein lipids in female Australian vegetarians. Clin Sci 1999;97:175–81.
66. McMurray MP, Cerqueira MT, Connor SL, Connor WE. Changes in lipid and lipoprotein levels and body weight in Tarahumara Indians after consumption of an affluent diet. N Engl J Med 1991;325:1704–8.

67. Rexrode KM, Manson JE, Hennekens CH. Obesity and cardiovascular disease. Curr Opin Cardiol 1996;11:490–5.
68. Kannel WB, D'Agostino RB, Cobb JL. Effect of weight on cardiovasclar disease. Am J Clin Nutr 1996;63(Suppl 1):419S–22S.
69. Dietz WH. Health consequences of obesity in youth: childhood predictors of adult disease. Pediatrics 1998;101:518–25.
70. Sinaiko AR, Donahue RP, Jacobs DR, Prineas RJ. Relation of weight and rate of increase in weight during childhood and adolescence to body size, blood pressure, fasting insulin, and lipids in young adults. The Minneapolis Children's Blood Pressure Study. Circulation 1999;99:1471–6.
71. Ferrannini E, Natali A, Bel P, Cavallo-Perin, Lalic N, Mingrone G. Insulin resistance and hypersecretion in obesity. J Clin Invest 1997;100:1166–73.
72. Wolf RN, Grundy SM. Influence of weight reduction on plasma lipoproteins in obese patients. Arteriosclerosis 1983;3:160–9.
73. Newman B, Selby JV, Quesenberry Jr. et al. Nongenetic influences of obesity on other cardiovascular disease risk factors: an analysis of identical twins. Am J Public Health 1990;80:675–8.
74. Kaplan NM. Obesity: location matters. Heart Dis Stroke 1992;1:148–50.
75. Daniels SR, Morrison JA, Sprecher DL, Khoury P, Kimball TR. Association of body fat distribution and cardiovascular risk factors in children and adolescents. Circulation 1999;99:541–45.
76. Schwartz MW, Brunzell JD. Regulation of body adiposity and the problem of obesity. Aterioscler Thromb Vasc Biol 1997;17:233–8.
77. Siervogel RM, Wisemandle W, Maynard LM et al. Serial changes in body composition throughout adulthood and their relationships to changes in lipid and lipoprotein levels. Aterioscler Thromb Vasc Biol 1998;18:1759–64.
78. Despres JP, Moorjani S, Lupien PJ et al. Regional distribution of body fat, plasma lipoproteins, and cardiovascular disease. Arteriosclerosis 1990:10:497–511.
79. Zamboni M, Armellini F, Cominacini L et al. Obesity and regional body-fat distribution in men: separate and joint relationships to glucose tolerance and plasma lipoprotein. Am J Clin Nutr 1994;60:682–7.
80. Howard G, Wagenknecht LE, Burke GL et al. Cigarette smoking and progression of atherosclerosis. The Atherosclerosis Risk in Communities study. JAMA 1998;279:119–24.
81. He J, Vupputuri S, Allen K, Prerost MR, Hughes J, Whelton PK. Passive smoking and the risk of coronary heart disease—a meta-analysis of epidemiologic studies. N Engl J Med 1999;340:920–6.
82. McGill HC Jr. Potential mechanisms for the augmentation of atherosclerosis and atherosclerotic disease by cigarette smoking. Prev Med 1979;8:390–403.
83. Knoke JD, Hunninghake DB, Heiss G. Physiological markers of smoking and their relation to coronary heart disease. Arteriosclerosis 1987;7:477–82.
84. Yokode M, Kita T, Arai M, et al. Cholesteryl ester accumulation in macrophages incubated with low-density lipoprotein pretreated with cigarette smoke extract. Proc Natl Acad Sci USA 1988;85:2344–8.
85. Craig WY, Palomaki GE, Haddow JE. Cigarette smoking and serum lipid and lipoprotein levels: an analysis of published data. Br Med J 1989;298:784–8.
86. CrA-Ig WY, Palomaki GE, Johnson M, Haddow JE. Cigarette smoking-associated changes in blood lipid and lipoprotein levels in the 8- to 19-year-old age group: a meta-analysis. Pediatrics 1990;85:155–8.
87. Weiss SR, Bachorik PS, Becker LC, Moy TF, Becker DM. Lipoprotein(A) and coronary heart disease risk factors in a racially mixed population: the Johns Hopkins Sibling Study. Ethn Dis 1998;8:60–72.
88. Willet W, Hennekens CH, Castelli W et al. Effects of cigarette smoking on fasting: triglyceride, total cholesterol, and HDL cholesterol in women. Am Heart J 1983;105:417–21.

89. Glantz SA, Parmley WW. Passive smoking and heart disease. Mechanisms and risk. JAMA 1995;273:1047–53.

90. Neufeld EJ, Meietus-Snyder M, Bieser A, Baker A, Newberger JW. Passive smoking is associated with reduced HDL-cholesterol levels in children with high-risk lipid profiles. [Abstract]. Circulation 1994;90:I–102.

91. Steinberg D, Pearson TA, Kuller LH. Alcohol and atherosclerosis. Ann Intern Med 1991; 114:967–76.

92. Haskell WL, Camargo C, Williams PT et al. The effect of cessation and resumption of moderate alcohol intake on serum high-density-lipoprotein subfractions: a controlled study. N Engl J Med 1984;310:805–10.

93. Taskinen MR, Nikkila EA, Valimaki M et al. Alcohol-induced changes in serum lipoproteins and in their metabolism. Am Heart J 1987;113:458–64.

94. Gaziano JM, Buring JE, Breslow JL et al. Moderate alcohol intake, increased levels of high-density lipoprotein and its subfractions, and decreased risk of myocardial infarction. N Engl J Med 1993;329:1829–34.

95. Clevidence BA, Reichman ME, Judd JT et al. Effects of alcohol consumption on lipoproteins of premenopausal women. A controlled diet study. Arterioscler Throm Vasc Biol 1995;15:179–84.

96. Paassilta M, Kervinen K, Rantala AO et al. Social alcohol consumption and low Lp(a) lipoprotein concentrations in middle-aged Finnish men: population-based study. BMJ 1998;316:594–5.

97. Sharpe PC, Young IS, Evans AE. Effect of moderate alcohol consumption on Lp(a) lipoprotein concentrations. Reduction is supported by other studies. BMJ 1998;316:1675.

98. Simmons LA, Friedlander Y, McCallum J, Simmons J. Risk factors for coronary heart disease in the prospective Dubbo study of Australian elderly. Atherosclerosis 1995;117:107–118.

99. Kervinen K, Savolainen MJ, Kesaniemi YA. A rapid increase in lipoprotein (a) levels after ethanol withdrawal in alcoholic men. Life Sci 1991;48:2183–2188.

100. Wilson DE, Schneibman PH, Brewster AC, Arky RA. The enhancement of alimentary lipemia by ethanol in man. J Lab Clin Med 1970;75:264–74.

101. Valimaki M, Laitinen K, Ylikahrit R et al. The effect of moderate alcohol intake on serum apolipoprotein A-I-containing lipoproteins and lipoprotein(a). Metabolism 1991; 40:1168–72.

102. Fontana P, Mooser V, Bovet P, Shamlaye C et al. Dose-dependent inverse relationship between alcohol consumption and serum Lp(a) levels in black African males. Aterioscler Thromb Vasc Biol 1999;19:1075–82.

103. Thun MJ, Peto R, Lopez AD et al. Alcohol consumption and mortality among middle-aged and elderly U.S. adults. N Engl J Med 1997;337:1705–14.

104. Renaud S, de Lorgeril M. Wine, alcohol, platelets, and the French paradox for coronary heart disease. Lancet 1991;338:464–8.

105. Fuhrman B, Lavy A, Aviram M. Consumption of red wine with meals reduces the susceptibility of human plasma and low-density lipoprotein to lipid peroxidation Am J Clin Nutr 1995;61:549–54.

106. Demrow HS, Slane PR, Folts JD. Administration of wine and grape juice inhibits *in vivo* platelet activity and thrombosis in stenosed canine coronary arteries. Circulation 1995;91;1182–8.

107. Solvoll K, Selmer R, Loken EB, Foss OP, Trygg K. Coffee, dietary habits, and serum cholesterol among men and women 35–49 years of age. Am J Epidemiol 1989;129: 1277–88.

108. Thelle DS, Arnesen E, Forde OH. The Tromso Heart Study: does coffee raise serum cholesterol? N Engl J Med 1983;308:1454–7.

109. Bak AAA, Grobbee DE. The effect on serum cholesterol levels of coffee brewed by filtering or boiling. N Engl J Med 1989;321:1423–7.

110. Zock PL, Katan MB, Merkus MP, Van Dusseldorp M, Harryvan JL. Effect of a lipid-rich fraction from boiled coffee on serum cholesterol. Lancet 1990;335:1235–37.

111. Urgert R, Schulz GM, Katan MB. Effects of cafestol and kahweol from coffee grounds on serum lipids and serum liver enzymes in humans. Am J Clin Nutr 1995;61:149–54.

112. Van Dusseldorp M, Katan MB, Demacker PNM. Effect of decaffeinated versus regular coffee on serum lipoproteins: a 12-week double-blind trial. Am J Epidemiol 1990;132: 33–40.

113. Willett WC, Stampfer MJ, Manson JE et al. Coffee consumption and coronary heart disease in women. JAMA 1996;275:458–62.

114. Fried RE, Levine DM, Kwiterovich PO et al. The effect of filtered-coffee consumption on plasma lipid levels: results of a randomized clinical trial. JAMA 1992;267:811–5.

115. Berlin JA, Colitz GA. A meta-analysis of physical activity in the prevention of coronary heart disease. Am J Epidemiol 1990;132:612–28.

116. Ekelund LG, Haskell WL, Johnson JL et al. Physical fitness as a prediction of cardio-vascular mortality in asymptomatic North American men. N Engl J Med 1988;319: 1379–84.

117. Wood PD, Stefanick ML, Williams PT, Haskell WL. The effects of plasma lipoproteins on a prudent weight-reducing diet, with or without exercise, in overweight men and women. N Engl J Med 1991;325:461–6.

118. Lampman RM, Santinga JT, Hodge MF, Block WD, Flora JD, Bassett DR. Comparative effects of physical training and diet in normalizing serum lipids in men with type IV hyperlipoproteinemia. Circulation 1977;55:652–9.

119. Dufaux B, Assmann G, Hollmann W. Plasma lipoproteins and physical activity: a review. Int J Sports Med 1982;3:123–36.

120. Swank AM, Robertson RJ, Deitrich RW, Bates M. The effect of acute exercise on high-density-lipoprotein cholesterol and the subfractions in females. Atherosclerosis 1987; 63:187–92.

121. Tucker LA, Friedman GM. Walking and serum cholesterol in adults. Am J Public Health 1990;80:1111–3.

122. Hardman AE, Hudson A, Jones PRM, Norgan NG. Brisk walking and plasma high-density lipoprotein cholesterol concentration in previously sedentary women. Br Med J 1989; 299:1204–5.

123. Kostka T, Lacour JR, Berthouze SE, Bonnefoy M. Relationship of physical activity and fitness to lipid and lipoprotein (a) in elderly subjects. Med Sci Sports Exerc 1999;31:1183–9.

124. Mackinnon LT, Hubinger LM. Effects of exercise on lipoprotein(a). Sports Med 1999;28: 11–24.

125. McCann BS, Warnick GR, Knopp RH. Changes in plasma lipids and dietary intake accompanying shifts in perceived workload and stress. Psychosomatic Med 1990;52: 97–108.

126. Dimsdale JE, Herd JA. Variability of plasma lipids in response to emotional arousal. Psychosom Med 1982;44:413–30.

127. Stoney CM, Matthews KA, McDonald RH, Johnson CA. Sex differences in lipid, lipoprotein, cardiovascular, and neuroendocrine responses to acute stress. Psychophysiology 1988;25:645–56.

128. Genest JJ, McNamara JR, Ordovas JM et al. Effect of elective hospitalization on plasma lipoprotein cholesterol and apolipoproteins A-I, B, and Lp(a). Am J Cardiol 1990;65:677–9.

129. Cobbaert C, Louisa A, Struijk L, Demeyere R, Meyns B. Lipoprotein(a) changes during and after coronary artery bypass grafting: an epiphenomenon? Ann Clin Biochem 1998;35:75–9.

130. Walton KW, Scott PJ, Dykes PW, Dawids JWL. The significance of alteration in serum lipids in thyroid dysfunction. II. Alteration of the metabolism and turnover of ^{131}I-low density lipoprotein in hypothyroidism and thyrotoxicosis. Clin Sci 1965;29:217–38.

131. Martinez-Triguero ML, Hernandez-Mijares A, Nguyen TT et al. Effect of thyroid hormone replacement on lipoprotein(a), lipids, and apolipoproteins in subjects with hypothyroidism. Mayo Clin Proc 1998;73:837–41.

132. Betteridge DJ. Lipids, diabetes, and vascular disease: the time to act. Diabetic Med 1989;6:195–218.

133. Manolio TA, Savage PJ, Burke GL et al. Association of fasting insulin with blood pressure and lipids in young adults. Arteriosclerosis 1990;10:430–6.

134. Hughes TA, Clements RS, Fairlough PK, Bell DSH, Segrest JP. Effects of insulin therapy on lipoproteins in non-insulin-dependent diabetes mellitus. Atherosclerosis 1987;67:105–14.

135. Ruotolo G, Zoppo A, Parlavecchia M, Giberti B, Micossi P. Apolipoprotein(a) levels in type 1 and type 2 diabetes mellitus. Acta Diabetol 1991;28:158–61.

136. Haffner SM, Tuttle KR, Rainwater DL. Decrease of Lp(a) with improved metabolic control in subjects with insulin-dependent diabetes mellitus. Diabetes Care 1991;14:302–7.

137. Perez A, Carreras G, Caixas A et al. Plasma lipoprotein(a) levels are not influenced by glycemic control in type 1 diabetes. Diabetes Care 1998;21:1517–20.

138. Pollare T, Vessby B, Lithell H. Lipoprotein lipase activity in skeletal muscle is related to insulin sensitivity. Arterioscler Thromb 1991;11:1192–203.

139. Wheeler DC, Varghese Z, Moorhead JF. Hyperlipidemia in nephrotic syndrome. Am J Nephrol 1989;9(Suppl 1):78–84.

140. Rifai N, King ME, Sica D. Effects of long-term hemodialysis on lipid, lipoprotein, and apolipoprotein levels of black patients with chronic renal failure. Ann Clin Biochem 1988;25:242–5.

141. Murphy BG, McNamee, Duly E et al. Increased serum apolipoprotein(a) in patients with chronic renal failure treated with continuous ambulatory peritoneal dialysis. Atherosclerosis 1992;93:53–5.

142. Karadi I. Romics L, Palos G et al. Lp(a) lipoprotein concentration in serum of patients with heavy proteinuria of different origin. Clin Chem 1989;35:2121–3.

143. Joven J, Villabona C, Vilella E et al. Abnormalities of lipoprotein metabolism in patients with the nephrotic syndrome. N Engl J Med 1990;323:579–84.

144. Sechi LA, Zingaro L, Catena C, Perin A, De Marchi S, Bartoli E. Lipoprotein(a) and apolipoprotein(a) isoforms and proteinuria in patients with moderate renal failure. Kidney Int 1999;56:1049–57.

145. Kerschdorfer L, Konig P, Neyer U et al. Lipoprotein(a) plasma concentrations after renal transplantation: a prospective evaluation after four years of follow-up. Atherosclerosis 1999;144:381–91.

146. Levy RI. Cholesterol, lipoproteins, apolipoproteins, and heart disease: present status and future prospects. Clin Chem 1981;27:653–62.

147. Dessi A, Batetta B, Spano O et al. Clinical remission is associated with restoration of normal high-density-lipoprotein cholesterol levels in children with malignancies. Clin Sci 1995;89:505–10.

148. Parsons SK, Skapek SX, Neufeld EJ et al. Asparaginase-associated lipid abnormalities in children with acute lymphoblastic leukemia. Blood 1997;89:1886–95.

149. Talvensaari KK, Laning M, Tapanainen P et al. Long-term survivors of childhood cancer have an increased risk of manifesting the metabolic syndrome. J Clin Endo Met 1996;81:505–10.

150. Gore JM, Goldberg RJ, Matsumoto AS et al. Validity of serum total cholesterol level obtained within 24 hours of acute myocardial infarction. Am J Cardiol 1984;54:722–5.

151. Shephard MDS, Hester J, Walmsley RN, White GH. Variation in plasma apolipoprotein A-I and B concentrations following myocardial infarction. Ann Clin Biochem 1990;27:9–14.

152. Mendez I, Hachinski V, Wolfe B. Serum lipids after stroke. Neurology 1987:37:507–11.

153. Rantapaa-Dahlqvist S, Wallberg-Jonsson S, Dahlen G. Lipoprotein (a), lipids, and lipoproteins in patients with rheumatoid arthritis. Ann Rheum Dis 1991;50:366–8.

154. Alvarez C, Ramos A. Lipids, lipoprotein and apolipoproteins in serum during infection. Clin Chem 1986;32:142–5.

155. Maeda S, Abe A, Makino K, Noma A, Kawade M. Transient changes of serum lipoprotein(a) as an acute phase reactant. Clin Chem 1989;89:145–50.

156. Simo JM, Castellano I, Ferre N, Joven J, Campos J. Evaluation of a homogeneous assay for high-density-lipoprotein cholesterol: limitations in patients with cardiovascular, renal, and hepatic disorders. Clin Chem 1998;44:1233–41.

157. Nauck M; Marz W; Jarausch J et al. Multi-center evaluation of a homogeneous assay for HDL-cholesterol without sample pretreatment. Clin Chem 1997;43:1622–9.

158. McKenney JM, Wright JT, Goodman RP et al. The effect of low dose of hydrochlorothiazide on blood pressure, serum potassium, and lipoproteins. Pharmacotherapy 1986;6:179–84.

159. Krone W, Nagele H. Effects of antihypertensives on plasma lipids and lipoprotein metabolism. Am Heart J 1988;116:1729–34.

160. Woodcock BG, Rietbrock N. Beta-blocker-induced changes in the cholesterol:high-density lipoprotein cholesterol ratio and risk of coronary heart disease. Klin Wochenschr 1984;62:843–9.

161. Goldsland IF, Crook D, Simpson R, Proudler T, Felton C. The effects of different formulations of oral contraceptive agents on lipid and carbohydrate metabolism. N Engl J Med 1990;323:1375–81.

162. Wahl P, Walder C, Knopp R et al. Effects of estrogen/progestin potency on lipid/lipoprotein cholesterol. N Engl J Med 1983;308:862–7.

163. Bush TL, Fried LP, Barrett-Conner E. Cholesterol, lipoproteins, and coronary heart disease in women. Clin Chem 1988;34:B60–B70.

164. Miller VT, Muesing RA, LaRosa JC et al. Effects of conjugated estrogen with and without three different progestogens on lipoproteins, high-density lipoprotein subfractions and apolipoprotein A-I. Obstet Gynecol 1991;77:235–40.

165. Henriksson P, Angelin B, Berglund L. Hormonal regulation of serum Lp(a) levels. Opposite effects after estrogen treatment and orchidectomy in males with prostatic carcinoma. J Clin Invest 1992;89:1166–71.

166. Decensi A, Robertson C, Ballardini B et al. Effect of tamoxifen on lipoprotein(a) and insulin-like growth factor-I (IGF-I) in healthy women. Eur J Cancer 1999;35:596–600.

167. Ilowite NT, Samuel P, Ginzler E, Jacobson MS. Dyslipoproteinemia in pediatric systemic lupus erythematosus. Arthritis and Rheumatism 1988;31:859–63.

168. Ballantyne CM, Podet EJ, Patsch WP et al. Effects of cyclosporine therapy on plasma lipoprotein levels. JAMA 1989;262:53–6.

169. Farmer JA, Ballantyne CM, Franzier OH et al. Lipoprotein(a) and apolipoprotein changes after cardiac transplantation. J AM Coll Cardiol 1991;18:926–30.

170. Markell MS, Friedman EA. Hyperlipidemia after organ transplantation. Am J Med 1989; 87(suppl 5N):61–67.

171. Van Thiel DH, Iqbal M, Jaln I, Todo S, Starzl TE. Gastrointestinal and metabolic problems associated with immunosuppression with either CsA or FK 506 in liver transplantation. Transplant Proc 1990;22(Suppl 1):37–40.

172. Reichel R, Widhalm K. Lipids and lipoproteins during pregnancy. In: Widhalm K, Naito HK (eds.). Recent aspects of diagnosis and treatment of lipoprotein disorders. New York: Alan R. Liss, 1988:125–133.

173. Rifai N, Pham Q, McMurray RG. Serum lipid and apolipoprotein changes in normal pregnancy. Clin Chem 1989;35:1066.

174. Panteghini M, Pagani F. Serum concentrations of lipoprotein(a) during normal pregnancy and postpartum. Clin Chem 1991;37:2009–10.

175. Knopp RH, Walden CE, Wahl PW et al. Effect of postpartum lactation on lipoprotein lipids and apoproteins. J Clin Endocrinol Metab 1985;60:542–7.

176. Hubbard RS, Hirany SV, Devaraj S, Martin L, Parupia J, Jialal I. Evaluation of a rapid homogeneous method for direct measurement of high-density-lipoprotein cholesterol. Am J Clin Pathol 1998;110:495–502.

177. Rifai N, Iannotti E, De Angelis K, Law T. Analytical and clinical performance of a homogeneous enzymatic LDL-cholesterol assay compared with the ultracentrifugation-dextran sulfate-Mg2+ method. Clin Chem 1998;44:1242–50.

178. Harris N, Galpchian V, Thomas J, Iannotti E, Law T, Rifai N. Three generations of

high-density-lipoprotein cholesterol assays compared with ultracentrifugation/dextran sulfate-Mg2+ method. Clin Chem 1997;43:816–23.

179. Thampy KG. Hypercholesterolemia of prolonged fasting and cholesterol-lowering of refeeding in lean human subjects. Scand J Clin Lab Invest 1995;55:351–7.

180. Rifai N, Merrill JR, Holly RG. Postprandial effect of a high-fat meal on plasma lipid, lipoprotein cholesterol, and apolipoprotein measurements. Ann Clin Biochem 1990;27: 489–93.

181. Beheshti I, Wessels LM, Eckfeldt JH. EDTA plasma vs. serum differences in cholesterol, high-density-lipoprotein cholesterol, and triglyceride as measured by several methods. Clin Chem 1994;40:2088–92.

182. Cloey T, Bachorik PS, Becker D et al. Reevaluation of serum-plasma differences in total cholesterol concentration. JAMA 1990;263:2788–9.

183. Naito HK. Problems associated with lipid and lipoprotein analyses. In: Widhalm K, Naito HK (eds.). Detection and treatment of lipid and lipoprotein disorders of childhood. New York: Alan R. Liss, 1985:19–60.

184. Lum G, Gambino R. A comparison of serum versus heparinized plasma for routine chemistry tests. Am J Clin Pathol 1974;61:108–13.

185. Ferlito S, Ricceri M, Ossino AM. Acute lipidemic effect of calcium heparin in normolipemic and hyperlipemic subjects. Int Angiol 1989;8:140–4.

186. Horton G, Cole TG, Gibson DW, Kessler G. Decreased stability of triglycerides and increased free glycerol in serum from heparin-treated patients. Clin Chem 1988;34: 1847–9.

187. Greenland P, Bowley NL, Meiklejohn B, Doane KL, Sparks CE. Blood cholesterol concentration: fingerstick plasma vs. venous serum sampling. Clin Chem 1990;36:628–30.

188. Ishikawa TT, Morrison J, Fallat R, Parsons D, Glueck CJ. Comparison of capillary and venous blood sampling for quantitation of plasma cholesterol. J Lab Clin Med 1974;84:281–6.

189. Kupke IR, Zeugner S, Gottschalk A, Kather B. Differences in lipid and lipoprotein concentrations of capillary and venous blood samples. Clin Chim Acta 1979;97:279–83.

190. Naughton MJ, Luepker RU, Strickland D. The accuracy of portable cholesterol analyzers in public screening programs. JAMA 1990;283:1213–7.

191. Warnick GR, Leary ET, Ammirati EB, Allen MP. Cholesterol in fingerstick capillary specimens can be equivalent to conventional venous measurement. Arch Pathol Lab Med 1994;118:1110–14.

192. Tan MH, Wilmshurst EG, Gleason RE, Soldner JS. Effect of posture on serum lipids. N Engl J Med 1973;289:416–19.

193. Miller M, Bachorik PS, Cloey TA. Normal variation of plasma lipoproteins: postural effects on plasma concentrations of lipids, lipoproteins, and apolipoproteins. Clin Chem 1992;38:569–74.

194. Page IH, Moinuddin M. The effect of venous occlusion on serum cholesterol and total protein concentration: a warning. Circulation 1962;25:651–2.

195. Howes LC, Krum H, Louis WJ. Plasma cholesterol levels are dependent on sympathetic activity. J Hypertension 1987;5(Supp):S361–3.

196. Brown SA, Epps DF, Dunn JK et al. Effect of blood collection and processing on radioimmunoassay results for apolipoprotein B in plasma. Clin Chem 1990;36:1662–6.

197. Evans K, Mitcheson J, Laker MF. Effect of storage at 4°C and −20°C on lipid, lipoprotein, and apolipoprotein concentrations. Clin Chem 1995;41:392–6.

198. Sgoutas DS, Tuten T. Effect of freezing and thawing of serum on the immunoassay of lipoprotein(a). Clin Chem 1992;28:1873–7.

199. National Cholesterol Education Program. Recommendations for improving cholesterol measurement: a report from the Laboratory Standardization Panel of the National Cholesterol Education Program. (NIH Publication No. 90–2964). Bethesda, MD: National Institutes of Health, 1990:28–9.

Measurement of Cholesterol Concentration

Joseph D. Artiss and Bennie Zak

♦   In 1988, the National Cholesterol Education Program's (NCEP) Expert Panel on the Detection, Evaluation, and Treatment of High Blood Cholesterol in Adults released guidelines for the treatment of adults who have high blood serum total cholesterol (TC) concentrations.[1] Subsequently, the NCEP released guidelines for children and adolescents.[2,3] The first of these reports succinctly outlined the then-current knowledge about the direct relationship between increased concentrations of serum TC and coronary heart disease. Further, it emphasized that TC is a major component of a very complex pathophysiological process. The pediatric report confirmed that there is a reasonably close relationship between juvenile and adult TC levels. That is, children with elevated levels of TC tend to grow into adults with elevated levels of TC. Furthermore, the atherogenic processes leading to vascular disease in adults do, in fact, begin at a relatively young age. These reports also established standardized cut-off concentrations for blood serum TC (Table 9–1).

Both of these reports recommended that treatment decisions should be based on low-density lipoprotein cholesterol (LDL-C) values. (Please refer to Chapter 5 for further details on the two NCEP reports.) To calculate LDL-C using the Friedewald calculation, one must establish accurate values for serum TC, triglyceride (TG), and high-density lipoprotein cholesterol (HDL-C), as all three are utilized for the estimation of an LDL-C value. Although the Friedewald approach is still very common, direct methods for measuring serum LDL-C have become commercially available and are applicable to most clinical laboratories. (Please refer to Chapter 12 for additional information on the measurement of LDL-C.)

Concurrent with the report from the Adult Treatment Panel, the Laboratory Standardization Panel of the NCEP released its report on the status of the measurement of serum TC in the United States.[4] This report was unique in that, for the first time, guidelines for the accuracy and precision of serum TC determinations were established. As of 1992, laboratories have been expected to consistently attain TC concentrations within 3% of the "true value" as defined by the reference method, a total imprecision (CV) of ≤ 3%, and a total error within 9%. These comparatively tight standards were established in order to minimize the possibility of inappropriately reporting a TC value that was two cut-off levels higher or lower. For example, if the total imprecision stood at 10%, a specimen in the range of 200 mg/dL (5.17 mmol/L) could be reported as > 240

Table 9–1 ✧ Standardized Cut-Off Concentrations for Blood Serum TC		
	Adults	*Children Ages 2–19 Years*
Desirable	<200 mg/dL (5.17 mmol/L)	<170 mg/dL (4.39 mmol/L)
Borderline	200–239 mg/dL (5.17–6.19 mmol/L)	170–199 mg/dL (4.39–5.14 mmol/L)
High	≥240 mg/dL (6.20 mmol/L)	≥200 mg/dL (5.17 mmol/L)

mg/dL (6.20 mmol/L). Conversely, a high TC level could be reported as acceptable (mean ± 2SD). Each possibility has its own undesirable ramifications.

The NCEP reports were part of a well-planned and well-executed program to decrease serum TC concentrations in the general population of the United States. At the time of the report, by the definitions set forth by the NCEP, a full 40% of adults in the United States had unacceptably high levels of serum TC. For the first time, the determination of TC had become the subject of a great deal of interest not only in the medical community, but also in the popular press and general population.

In this chapter we will briefly describe the reference system for TC; however, these methods are neither applicable nor transferable to most clinical laboratories. Since the first report from the standardization panel, most manufacturers of TC reagents have aligned their products with the recommended guidelines for accuracy and precision. This has occurred through not only their own efforts but also those of the NCEP member organizations. In this chapter we also discuss considerations for the evaluation and implementation of commercially available reagents by specialty and general clinical chemistry laboratories.

METHODS

Definitive Method

The underlying concept for a definitive method is that its levels of bias and imprecision are of a magnitude compatible with the method's stated purpose. That is, the mean value of the definitive method is considered to be the "true value."[5] For a method to be considered definitive, it must have been subjected to an extensive investigation and evaluation for sources of inaccuracy, including non-specificity.[6] The definitive method for TC is an isotope dilution–mass spectrometric method, developed by the National Institute of Standards and Technology (NIST).[7] As definitive methods are generally very labor intensive, expensive, and require highly specialized instrumentation, they are not recommended for use in clinical laboratories.

Reference Method

A reference method is one that has been thoroughly investigated and that exactly and clearly describes the necessary conditions and procedures for the accurate measurement of a substance. Furthermore, the accuracy and precision of the method are such that the method may be used for assessing other methods and assigning values to reference materials.[5]

The currently accepted reference method for TC is a Centers for Disease Control and Prevention (CDC) modification[8,9] of the Abell modification[10] of the earlier method of Sperry and Brand.[11] The substance of this method rests in the hydrolysis of cholesterol esters prior to purification by organic solvent extraction and reaction of the purified cholesterol with a Liebermann-Burchard reagent.[12,13] The purity and freedom (from interfering substances) of the extract obtained with this method has been established by counter-current extraction. However, the reference method has been demonstrated to yield results that are, on average, 1.6% higher than the definitive method.[14,15]

Although the reference method is intended to be technically and financially less demanding relative to the definitive method, it is still beyond the capabilities of all but a few clinical laboratories. The reference method for TC, as performed by the Lipids Section of the CDC, is no exception to this rule. A more detailed protocol than the one described below is available from the CDC.[16]

Materials

Reagents, all are ACS reagent grade and include absolute ethanol, glacial acetic acid, potassium hydroxide, acetic anhydride, and sulfuric acid. Certified hexanes (boiling range 68°–70°C or less) are also required, as well as reagent grade water (specific resistance $\geq$ 10 megohm/cm, specific conductivity $\geq$ 0.1 microhm/cm), Drierite™ indicating desiccant, and silica gel (for drying) 6–16 mesh. Standards are prepared from cholesterol SRM 911b, obtained from the NIST.

Reagents

Aqueous Potassium Hydroxide (33%). Add 165g of dry potassium hydroxide to about 400mL of reagent-grade water. Dissolve. Upon cooling to room temperature, transfer the solution to a graduated cylinder and make up to 500 mL with reagent grade water. Store in a Pyrex™, Teflon™, or polyethylene bottle with a lined screw cap. Prepare fresh monthly or whenever appreciable amounts of K_2CO_3 precipitate appear.

Alcoholic KOH (approximately 0.36 mol/L). Prepare immediately prior to use by transferring 6.0 ± 0.1 mL of 33% KOH (for each 10 mL of reagent) to a graduated cylinder and make up to 10 mL with absolute ethanol. Store, stoppered, in a glass or Teflon Erlenmeyer flask.

Liebermann–Burchard Reagent. Add 200 mL of acetic anhydride to a 1-L glass stoppered Erlenmeyer flask and cool to 5°C in the freezing compartment of a refrigerator. Constantly mix the acetic anhydride, as you steadily add 10mL of sulfuric acid. Swirl gently and add 100mL of acetic acid, then place the mixture in a 25°C water bath.

The reagent should show no discoloration and should have an absorbance ≤ 0.003 at 620 nm.

Primary Standard Solution (stock standard). Dry cholesterol SRM 911b overnight at 55°C in an open bottle in a vacuum oven with a 250-mL evaporating dish full of silica gel. Allow the oven to drop to room temperature (approximately 4 h) while still under vacuum. Then allow the pressure to slowly increase to atmospheric. Immediately remove, cap, and store the bottle in a desiccator containing dry silica gel.

Cholesterol Standard Solution. Warm ethanol to 55°C in a glass-stoppered Erlenmeyer flask. Transfer 2.0000 ± 0.0002 g of recently dried cholesterol into a 200-mL volumetric flask and dissolve with warm alcohol. Once the cholesterol is fully dissolved, allow the solution to cool to 25°C and dilute to the mark with ethanol that has been equilibrated to 25°C.

Working Standards

Dilute 5.0 mL of standard cholesterol solution to 200 mL with ethanol (0.25 g/L) to be used for HDL-C standard. Dilute 5.0, 10.0, 20.0, 30.0, and 40.0 mL to 100 mL with ethanol (0.50, 1.0, 2.0, 3.0, and 4.0 g/L). Label five screw-capped 20 × 150 mm test tubes for each set of standards and transfer about 20 mL of each working standard into each tube and cap tightly. Store in a desiccator, containing a 1 cm layer of ethanol, in a refrigerator at 4°C.

Preparation of Extracts

Transfer 2.0 mL of standards and samples into clean, dry, labeled vials with caps. Standards and samples are equilibrated for approximately 15 min in a 25°C ± 1°C water bath. Deliver 0.5 mL of each standard, control, and sample into labeled tubes to which 5 mL of alcoholic KOH has been added. Cap the tubes, vortex, mix, and incubate at 50°C ± 2°C for 60 ± 5 min. Place all tubes in a 25°C water bath, add 5 mL of water, and equilibrate for 10 min. Add 10 mL of hexanes to each tube, cap firmly, and mix for 15 min in a mechanical shaker. Allow 5 min for phase separation. Transfer 2.0 mL of the organic phase to test tubes and deliver it with 3.0 mL of hexane into labeled, clean, dry racked test tubes. Evaporate all tubes to dryness in a vacuum oven maintained at 55°C.

Color Development

Transfer freshly-prepared Liebermann-Burchard (L-B) reagent to a two- or three-necked Teflon-stoppered Pyrex flask that has one neck connected to a drying tube containing Drierite™ cotton, and fine mesh protecting the flask inlet. Add 3.25 mL of L-B reagent to each of the dried extracts from above at 20-sec intervals with vortex mixing, and place each tube in a 25°C ± 1°C water bath. Following a 30-min incubation, read each tube in sequence against a water blank at 620 nm. The concentrations of the unknowns are determined from the line of regression calculated from the standards run in duplicate. The correlation coefficient of the line of regression should be between 0.9998 and 1.0000. The CDC uses a number of criteria to define an acceptable standard curve; the authors refer the reader to the more detailed description for a complete listing of these criteria.[16]

Enzymic Methods

Enzyme-based reagents for the determination of TC (Figure 9–1) have largely supplanted the older (strong acid) chemical approaches for routine laboratory measurements. The change to enzymic methods is due mainly to the better specificity afforded by the enzymes, their applicability to automation, and the elimination of some of the hazardous materials used in the older methods. However, as is often the case, the new enzymic methods frequently have problems with interferences that may not have been experienced with the older methods that involved extraction (purification) of the cholesterol prior to the reaction with color-forming reagents. Several articles[4,17,18] have discussed the measurement of TC, but have made only passing mention of interferences. There have also been reports of interference studies carried out on several chemistry analyzers,[19,20,21] as well as a related review on glucose measurement[22] that includes interference effects that may be applicable due to similar indicator reactions. There was only one review on TC measurements throughout the 90s,[23] and prior to that article, there had not been a review in over a decade.[24,25]

Space does not permit a thorough review of enzymic methods and all potential interferences. However, a brief description and various approaches for evaluating the common substances that may interfere with enzymic TC procedures follows.

Enzyme Specificity

The specificity of the enzymes used in TC determinations—or for that matter, any other analytical procedure—may be considered suspect by some. One argument that is almost certainly valid is that the enzymes cannot be characterized to the same degree as other reagent chemicals. Furthermore, it is doubtful that in the foreseeable future we will be able to characterize enzymes to this degree. However, it may be that, unlike the wet chemical procedures, enzyme preparations are much more forgiving and therefore do not require the same degree of characterization. The reason these systems seem so robust is not at all clear. It may be simply because the enzymes be-

Figure 9–1 ✧ Enzyme-Based Reactions

$$Cholesterol\ Esters\ + H_2O \xrightarrow{\text{Cholesterol Esterase}} Cholesterol + Fatty\ Acids$$

$$Cholesterol + O_2 \xrightarrow{\text{Cholesterol Oxidase}} \Delta^4\text{-Cholesten-3-one} + H_2O_2$$

$$2H_2O_2 + Phenolic\ + 4-Aminoantipyrine \xrightarrow{\text{Peroxidase}} Chromogen\ + 4H_2O$$

have as catalysts and therefore do not participate directly in the analytical process. Alternatively, perhaps we have learned how to characterize and control their behavior for any given system. The use of recombinant sources for enzymes may facilitate more uniformity among preparations.

Cholesterol Esterase

At one time, the completeness (or perhaps, specificity) of enzymic hydrolysis of cholesterol esters was considered to be a problem with totally enzymic procedures.[26] Even when the enzyme cocktail, which often included nonspecific lipases or proteases, hydrolyzed all of the serum cholesterol esters, discrepancies often appeared when synthetic or short-chain fatty acid esters (e.g., acetate) of cholesterol were used to "spike" control or calibrator materials. However, this is no longer a major problem.[27,28,29,30]

The significant difference between earlier reagents and newer ones is the incorporation of esterase(s) of microbial rather than mammalian origin. Although kit manufacturers often protect their proprietary information, it would appear that the preferred enzyme comes from the microbe whose genus is *Pseudomonas*[31,32] and that the species is probably *fluorescens*. The Roche Diagnostics claim of at least 99.5% hydrolysis seems to have been verified.[26,27] Bateson et al.,[28] in comparing enzymic to chemical hydrolysis using an esterase from the above-mentioned genus and species, reported the efficiency of the enzyme(s) to be in excess of 99%. Therefore, it seems reasonable to conclude that the current generation of esterases provides quite an acceptable degree of hydrolysis. Unlike other enzymes in the typical TC reagent, specificity of the esterase is undesirable.

Although surfactants do not participate directly in the hydrolytic reaction, and therefore do not have to be identified on the package insert, they are a critical component of the reagent. In the absence of the appropriate surfactant the esterase reaction, if it occurs at all, will be very slow and unlikely to reach completion. Various sources of esterases respond differently not only to different surfactants but also to the concentration of those surfactants.

Cholesterol Oxidase

Like the esterases, it is not always easy to identify the microbial source of the oxidases. However, Deeg and Ziegenhorn[26] have reported the use of an enzyme from a *Streptomyces* species as being ideal for Roche Diagnostics' kinetic TC procedure. Likewise they utilize an enzyme from *Nocardia erythropolis* for endpoint measurements.[27] Bateson et al.[28] utilized an oxidase from a *Cellulomonas* genus; in this case it is not the authors but rather the enzyme producer who does not wish to exactly identify the specific species of microbe used to obtain the enzyme.

Almost certainly none of the above-mentioned sources of enzyme is totally specific to a 3,5-beta hydroxysterol such as cholesterol, but it might be concluded that this lack of specificity is not particularly important. We say this in light of the fact that all other reactive steroidal compounds that occur naturally in human blood are present in concentrations of at least several orders of magnitude less than cholesterol.

Therefore, even if there were 100% cross-reactivity, the effects would normally not be appreciable.

Although cholesterol oxidase is quite specific to free cholesterol, the authors have found that, on occasion, impurities in the phenolic chemical used in the color reaction will inhibit the oxidase. It is unlikely that readers will encounter this problem unless they are preparing their own reagent.

Measurement

In order to complete the enzymic measurement of TC, one final step is necessary: the detection and measurement of the product of the cholesterol oxidase reaction as a means of quantifying the amount of cholesterol present. Three general approaches have been used to quantify the products of the cholesterol oxidase reaction. Each is discussed in the sections that follow.

Electrochemical Measurement of Oxygen Consumed

Methods have been described[31,32] and made commercially available for measuring oxygen consumption (by electrode), in a manner similar to that used for some glucose oxidase methods. Noma and Nakayama[32] reported that bilirubin and ascorbic acid, at 10 mg/dL (171 μmol/L and 568 μmol/L, respectively), did not affect either the amount or the rate of oxygen consumption. Oxygen consumption methods are not easily automated and generally require a substantial amount of cholesterol oxidase. Thus, these methods have not become widely used.

Ultraviolet Spectrophotometric Measurement of Δ^4-Cholesten-3-one

An early approach to quantitating the cholesterol dehydrogenase reaction involved measuring the cholestenone produced during the dehydrogenase reaction. Flegg[29] measured the absorption of this compound at 240 nm, and the absorption of the 2,4-dinitrophenylhydrazone derivative at 390 nm. The procedure is time consuming and difficult to perform and is probably useful only in research applications; even there, it seems to have little utility when compared to the next approach to be discussed. Interference studies have not been reported, and it is quite unlikely that all other ultraviolet-absorbing species would be absent. Additionally, it almost certainly would not be able to achieve the analytical sensitivity of the peroxidase-coupled reaction.

Measurement of Hydrogen Peroxide Produced by the Cholesterol Oxidase Reaction

The most common method of quantitating the cholesterol oxidase reaction is to measure the hydrogen peroxide produced. The measurement of hydrogen peroxide has been accomplished by use of several different approaches. Allain et al.[30] reported the first totally enzymic method of determining serum TC by measuring hydrogen peroxide. This method was based on the Trinder reaction previously used for the determination of glucose.[33] The hydrogen peroxide produced in the cholesterol oxidase reaction was used to oxidatively couple two chromogenic substrates by catalysis with horseradish peroxidase (EC 1.11.1.7). The original procedure used the chromogenic compounds phenol and 4-aminoantipyrine (4AAP). The product of the reaction is presumed to be a quinoneimine dye that can be measured photometrically at a wavelength of about 500 nm. Compounds other than 4AAP and phenol represent variations of the same analytical theme. Their ease of use and ready applicability to automation have made numerous variations of this procedure very popular.

The peroxidase used in most clinical assays is, typically, derived from horseradish. Although new microbial sources that almost certainly exhibit different specificities are available, they are not in common use. The catalytic properties of peroxidase are very nonspecific; therefore, interferences are most common with this step in the reaction sequence.

The list of substances that may interfere with the peroxidase-catalyzed measurements have been reported to include the following:

✧ ascorbic acid,[32,33]

✧ bilirubin,[32,33,34,35,36,37]

✧ triglycerides,[32,35]

✧ hemolysis,[33] and

✧ possibly unknown substances.[38]

It is difficult to put absolute estimates on the degree of interference that may be exhibited. The magnitude of this difficulty is relatively obvious when one considers the numerous types of reagent formulations and instrument configurations that are available for use.

Evaluation of Interfering Substances

As mentioned above, space does not permit an in-depth discussion of all possible interfering substances and their effects on all possible combinations of instruments and reagents. In fact, this has never been done, and probably will never be done, due to the sheer magnitude of the task. Hence, we limit our discussion to the most common interfering substances—ascorbate, bilirubin(s), lipids, and hemolysis—and various approaches to assessing their effects on any given measurement system.

Ascorbic Acid

Ascorbic acid is well known for its properties as a reducing agent. These properties allow it to interfere in peroxidase-catalyzed reactions by competing with the intended chromogen substrates for generated peroxide. Thus, if sufficiently high levels of ascorbate are present in a sample, the measured TC value will be spuriously low.[39] The interference caused by ascorbate must be considered to be insidious as it is invisible to the person making the measurement. Furthermore, it is somewhat difficult to assess experimentally, as in solution it is subject to air oxidation; thus, experiments must be carefully planned and quickly carried out or the interfering substance will have disappeared prior to initiating the measurement process.

This same phenomenon is probably what prevents ascorbate from being a bigger problem than it is. That is, by the time the sample reaches the laboratory and eventually the instrument, any ascorbate present may have already been oxidized.

Although it is a common practice to include ascorbate oxidase in reagents used for the determination of uric acid, we are not aware of the need for it in wet-chemistry reagent systems for cholesterol. This may not be the case with point-of-care testing. We need also to be cautious with the current trend toward the use of self-prescribed and often high doses of various "anti-oxidants." We know of no studies of potential interference from vitamin A and E supplements.

Bilirubin

From an academic perspective, the mechanism of interference by bilirubin in peroxidase-coupled reactions is quite interesting in its complexity. As with ascorbate, bilirubin competes with the intended chromogenic substrates for peroxide. In addition, both the native and oxidized bilirubin contribute their spectral characteristics to the blank and/or final measurement.[40] To further complicate the issue, what we commonly refer to as "bilirubin" is, in fact, a family of species of which some are water soluble while others are not, and some are protein bound while others are not. Furthermore, those that are water soluble may be either mono- or di-conjugated. Thus, spiking a sample or standard with something from a bottle labeled "Bilirubin from bovine gall bladder" may not be an appropriate approach for evaluating its effects on enzymic reactions.

In an effort to circumvent this issue, we have begun to use serial dilutions of pools of icteric samples with pools of clear serum. Although this approach is not as neat and straightforward in appearance as simply dissolving some yellow/orange powder in a bit of base and then spiking samples with it, we believe that the results will better reflect reality. The premise underlying this approach is that there is no interference at low concentrations of the bilirubin, and that as the concentration of the bilirubin increases, a point will be reached where errors will begin to occur. By plotting the measured TC concentration versus the sample dilution factor, the point at which interference occurs should present itself as a deviation from linearity. Repeating the experiment several times with different pools should give the investigator more useful information as to the effects of the interfering substance. Note that the effects of bilirubin may vary among reagents and instruments.

The enzymatic cholesterol reagent potassium ferrocyanide (described later in this chapter) has been reported to eliminate bilirubin interference by acting as an electron transfer agent that demonstrates preferential specificity to the intended chromogen system.[41]

Lipids

The interference caused by the turbidity and volume displacement of hypertriglyceridemia is of particular concern with lipid measurements. Traditional approaches for clearing a specimen, such as ultracentrifugation or solvent extraction/precipitation, simply will not work in this case because some of the species of interest will be removed in the clearing process.

In the past, investigators,[20,21] including ourselves,[42] have used total parenteral nutrition solutions such as Intralipid™ to spike clear specimens in order to evaluate the effects of the turbidity caused by elevated levels of TG. Although we knew that this artificial turbidity did not behave in exactly the same manner as serum TG, we believed that it was a reasonable approach in that it was probably a worst-case scenario for liquid reagents. In comparing instruments of traditional wet-chemistry and dry-film technologies, Cobbaert and Tricarico have reported that this is, in fact, a best-case scenario for the non-liquid systems.[43] We also presume that the use of the relatively water-insoluble synthetic materials exacerbates the volume displacement error that hypertriglyceridemia is known to cause. For these reasons, we have adopted an approach similar to the one mentioned above for bilirubin: that is, serially diluting pools of clear sera with turbid ones and plotting the measured TC against the sample dilution factor.

The results of such experiments are valid for only one given reagent system on one given instrument. Reagents for the measurement of lipids typically contain surfactants that partially clear turbid specimens. This clearing process is not likely to be immediate, so that small differences in the timing sequence and the blank measurement, for example, will significantly affect the final concentration.[32]

The volume error caused by hypertriglyceridemia probably does not significantly impact the measurement of either TC or HDL-C separately. However, if a separation technique is used to prepare the HDL-C fraction and a ratio of TC and HDL-C fractions is calculated, the volume displacement error may have a very significant impact. As TG-rich lipoproteins are removed in the preparation of the HDL-C fraction, the sample volume will change, relative to what was pipetted. In order to correct the error one must use either a direct HDL-C method or corrective mathematics similar to the corrections made for pseudohyponatremia.

Hemolysis

Hemoglobin, with its pseudo-peroxidase-like activity, should have little effect on a peroxidase-coupled reaction sequence. However, the inherent color of the hemoglobin will be a problem if the instrument is not capable of blanking it out of the measurement. For the most part, this does not cause a problem with the current equipment.

Although when we see a hemolyzed sample we tend to immediately think of hemoglobin, we must consider those cellular components that we cannot see that are spilled at the same time as the hemoglobin. Erythrocytes, as do lymphocytes, contain a relatively high concentration of catalase, which will compete for the generated peroxide with peroxidase. Liquid reagent systems usually contain enough peroxidase to overcome the interference. However, this may not be the case with all thin-film technologies. As "spiking" samples with (partially) purified hemoglobin would not include these cellular components, we recommend that the effects of hemolysis be evaluated in a manner similar to bilirubin and triglycerides.

STANDARDIZATION, CALIBRATION, AND CONTROL

We must first define the terms, "standard," "calibrator," and "control," as they are often interchanged, and in lipid measurements the distinctions become very important.

✧   A **standard** material is a pure material that can be accurately measured and prepared to some predetermined concentration.

✧   A **calibrator**, on the other hand, is a material (typically provided by a manufacturer) with an assigned concentration to be used for some specific application. This assigned concentration may not always reflect the true concentration of the analyte of interest.

✧   A **control** material typically is processed serum of human or bovine source. The analyte concentration is usually presented as a range, and this, coupled with the fact that the material has been processed, makes it unsuitable for assessing the accuracy of an assay. This does not mean that the material is not suitable for the day-to-day assessment and monitoring of imprecision.

As reference ranges for TC have evolved, from population distributions (i.e., concentrations found in 95% of the population) to "optimal" target values with specific cutoff points above which intervention is recommended, extraordinary attention has been focused on the accuracy with which the laboratory measurement of TC must be performed. The initial goal put forward by the NCEP in 1988 was that levels of bias and imprecision for routine TC measurement should not exceed ± 5%. By 1992, these levels were to be no greater than ± 3% for bias and imprecision, and the NCEP suggested that all TC concentrations should be traceable to the Abell-Kendall reference method. The decrease in bias and imprecision from 5% to 3% leads to a concomitant decrease in total allowable error from 15% to 9%.

The standardization of lipid assays in general is not an easy process. The lipids are unlike other water-soluble analytes (e.g., sodium, glucose, etc.). Thus, by converting to enzymic reagents we have created a situation in which the reagents are dissolved in one phase and the analyte of interest is contained in a second phase (i.e., the lipoprotein particles that contain the lipids are not in aqueous solution). This is best exemplified by the chylous sample that, upon sitting in the refrigerator overnight, forms an obvious biphasic system.

With this concept in mind it becomes easier to appreciate that standardization becomes a somewhat complicated process. We might pose the rhetorical question, "How do we dissolve our pure standard in a matrix that will mimic human serum?". The answer may be disturbing to the purist: It has not been done. However, this is not important for all enzymic assays. The manual method that we describe below seems to respond well to the certified reference material NBS SRM 911b dissolved in an organic solvent matrix. It should not be construed that this is necessarily the case with the same method on an automated system, as the wetting properties of the solvents may affect the instrument's pipetting system.

To avoid these problems, manufacturers tend to provide calibrators for their systems. Typically, the value on the label is not the "true" but rather the "assigned" concentration of the analyte. The manufacturer has, in its facility, measured the concentrations of species of interest numerous times and presumably compared them to fresh serum results, as will be described below. If this is the case, one should not assume that the assigned value is transferable from one instrument to another, nor even to a different model from the same manufacturer. Furthermore, one should be able to obtain documentation from manufacturers that they and their calibrator materials are indeed certified by the CDC Cholesterol Reference Method Laboratory Network for the particular application of interest.

The CDC Cholesterol Reference Method Laboratory Network has been established in order to allow both manufacturers and individual laboratories access to results from the established reference method for TC. A list of these laboratories is presented in Chapter 36. By sharing split samples with one of the network laboratories, laboratorians can establish the validity of their calibration.

A typical approach involves contacting one of the network laboratories and arranging for the delivery of the appropriate samples. Prior to the arrival of the fresh serum samples from the network laboratory (or *vice versa*, depending on the arrangements that are made), laboratorians would calibrate their instrument according to the manufacturer's directions. Once the fresh split samples are run and the results compared to those of the network laboratory, the calibration can be adjusted, if need be, and then the samples re-assayed to confirm the adjusted calibration.

Because there is a cost involved with this service, a laboratory may not wish to do this regularly; however, it is a relatively convenient approach for resolving any concerns about calibration. Remember that this approach has been adopted by many of the equipment/reagent manufacturers, and that appropriate documentation to confirm the accuracy of their calibration material should be available.

Although it is good practice for clinical laboratories to subscribe to at least one proficiency-testing program, the results of many programs must be interpreted with caution. Programs that use fresh frozen serum pools as the control material are rare; most control programs utilize processed serum. It cannot be over-emphasized that processed materials may or may not behave in a manner identical to serum with any given instrument/reagent system. Therefore, these programs are best suited for assessing imprecision and not accuracy.

Several companies sell materials that are traceable to the CDC reference method for standardization purposes (refer to Chapter 36 for details). The College of American Pathologists (CAP) also provides survey materials that are traceable to the CDC reference method as well as materials to test for linearity. Linearity checks are a sensitive technique to observe analytical problems before they have profound effects on accuracy.[44] Once again, it is important to note that the user may experience problems using these materials to establish accuracy if the system being standardized is sensitive to matrix effects (refer to Chapter 35 for additional information).

Even when a particular method, or a particular combination of method and instrument, is traceable to the CDC or NIST and has acceptable imprecision and inaccuracy, it is quite a different matter to say that the system in one's own laboratory meets the required limits if any modifications have been made to the reagent or instrument settings. The SRM911b and the CAP survey materials demonstrate marked matrix effects with some methods. As with all calibration and control materials, great care must be exercised in extrapolating the values provided by the manufacturer to another situation unless all conditions are identical to those used by the manufacturer.

ENZYMIC METHOD

Materials

The following materials can be obtained from Genzyme Corporation (Cambridge, MA):

✧   cholesterol esterase (CHE), from *Pseudomonas sp.*, sterol-ester acylhydrolase (EC 3.1.1.13);

✧   cholesterol oxidase (COX), from *Cellulomonas sp.*, cholesterol: oxygen oxido-reductase (EC 1.1.3.6);

✧   lipase, from *Chromobacterium viscosum*, triacylglycerol acylhydrolase (EC 3.1.13); and

✧   peroxidase (HRP), from horseradish (donor: hydrogen-peroxide oxidoreductase) (EC 1.11.1.7).

Triton X-100™, α-cyclodextrin (α-CD), magnesium acetate, and 4-aminoantipyrine may be obtained from Sigma Chemical Co. (St. Louis, MO).

Potassium ferrocyanide (reagent grade) may be obtained from Spectrum Chemical Manufacturing Co. (Redondo Beach, CA).

The sodium salt of 2-hydroxy-3,5-dichlorobenzenesulfonic acid (may also be listed as 3,5-dichloro-2-hydroxybenzenesulfonic acid) (HDCBS) may be obtained from Research Organics, Inc. (Cleveland, OH). (There are other sources.)

Cholesterol (SRM911b) may be obtained from NIST, the U.S. Department of Commerce (Gaithersburg, MD).

Reagents

The TC reagent is prepared in TRIS-HCl buffer (50 mmol/L, pH 7.6) to contain, per liter,

✧   0.5 g of Triton X-100™,

✧   1.0 mmol of 4AAP,

✧   2.0 mmol of HDCBS,

✧   4.1 mmol of α-cyclodextrin,

✧   50 μmol of potassium ferrocyanide,

✧   400 U* of CHE,

✧   800 U* of COX,

✧   294 U* (guaiacol) of HRP, and

✧   200 kU* of lipase.

*Units are as defined by the specified supplier.

Cholesterol standards are prepared with SRM911b cholesterol that has been dried under vacuum over silica gel at 55°C for at least 12 h.[45] The appropriate amount of this material is dissolved in 2-methoxyethanol containing 200 g/L Triton X-100.

Specimen Collection and Storage

A detailed description of specimen collection is given in Chapter 8. Blood is generally drawn from the patient's antecubital vein or other convenient arm vein.[46] Concentrations of TC in finger-stick samples of whole blood have been found to be comparable with venous plasma, providing that the initial drop of blood that contains tissue fluid is discarded and excessive "milking" of the finger is minimized to prevent hemolysis.[47,48]

TC concentrations in serum or plasma have been shown to be stable when subjected to various storage conditions. Although it is standard practice to separate serum from the blood clot by centrifugation within 1 h, a delay in this procedure for up to 48 h produced no significant change in measured TC.[49] However, when blood was collected, allowed to clot, centrifuged, and stored at 6°–7°C in the same serum separator tube for 7 d, a slight increase (1.8%) was observed.[50]

After using a secondary serum standard in the long-term Lipid Research Clinics Program, no evidence to suggest that cholesterol in pooled serum deteriorates when stored at −20°C was uncovered.[51] Cholesterol was also shown to be stable in either frozen or lyophilized forms of pooled serum during nearly 5 y of storage at −20°C.[52]

When plasma is to be used for TC analysis, anticoagulant-treated blood should be centrifuged as soon as possible to prevent hemolysis of red blood cells. No change in TC was noted upon storage of heparinized plasma for 4 d at 25°C.[53] The patient need not be fasting if the sample is to be used for measuring only TC.[54]

Procedure

Pipette 1.0 mL of reagent into the appropriate test tubes, then add and mix 3 μL of sample, standard or control. Allow the reaction mixture to incubate for 12 minutes at 37°C. The absorbance is measured at 510 nm against a reagent blank.

Performance

The data collected with the manual procedure suggests that the within-run reproducibility of this reagent system should be less than 1.5% and that the between-run reproducibility should be less than 3%.[55] The reagent is linear to about 900 mg/dL (23 mmol/L) cholesterol. Interference studies conducted at the concentrations recommended by the National Committee for Clinical Laboratory Standards (NCCLS) illustrate minimal interference from ascorbate,[55] hemolysis,[55] and lipemia.[56] Bilirubin at a level of 20 mg/dL (342 μmol/L) will cause a negative interference of about 6% with this procedure.[55] NCCLS recommends evaluation of ascorbate at concentrations up to 30 mg/dL (1.7 mmol/L). Although this is well above concentrations that are most frequently encountered, extremely increased concentrations of ascorbate will almost certainly interfere.[39]

REFERENCE RANGES

Within the last decade, the reference ranges for serum TC filled the better part of two pages of most clinical chemistry textbooks. There were different ranges for age (one per half-decade) and sex. To simplify treatment decisions, the NCEP has recommended the use of two cut-off values for TC. Adult serum concentrations below 200 mg/dL (5.17 mmol/L) are considered desirable; concentrations between 200 and 239 mg/dL (5.17–6.19 mmol/L) are considered borderline; and concentrations of 240 mg/dL (6.20 mmol/L) and above are considered high. Thus, the clinician's decision as to whether follow-up studies are necessary is based solely upon two numbers: 200 and 240 mg/dL (5.17 and 6.20 mmol/L). Decisions concerning treatment are based upon patients' medical histories and their LDL-C concentrations. (For additional information, please refer to Chapter 5.)

Earlier in this chapter we discussed transferability (or the lack of it) of the Abell-Kendall method to the routine laboratories in which the method might be attempted. The fact that more complex procedures such as Abell-Kendall are designated as "accurate" does not guarantee accuracy in any or all cases. The time and care required to perform the tests, as well as to make up a reagent whose matrix is so critical to the quality of the measurement, are beyond the scope of many laboratories. The procedure proposed here does not suffer from the same problems as the Abell-Kendall method, in that it is easily carried out in any laboratory and offers certain features that are not available in the field methods it closely resembles. A critical aspect of its reagent matrix is that severely hypertriglyceridemic specimens are more amenable to measurement, owing to the lipolysis that occurs simultaneously with the sequence of enzyme reactions leading to the measured color. In addition, the fatty acids split off by both the esterase and the lipase are trapped as the transparent guests of the host molecule, α-cyclodextrin. Consequently, interference by turbidity of the sample is avoided, for both the sample and the sample blank.   ✧

REFERENCES

1. Report of the National Cholesterol Education Program Expert Panel on the Detection, Evaluation, and Treatment of High Blood Cholesterol in Adults. Arch Intern Med 1988;148:36–68.
2. National Cholesterol Education Program (NCEP). Highlights of the report of the Expert Panel on Blood Cholesterol Levels in Children and Adolescents. Pediatrics 1992;89: 495–501.
3. National Cholesterol Education Program. Report of the Expert Panel on Blood Cholesterol Levels in Children and Adolescents. Pediatrics 1992;89:525–76.
4. Current status of blood cholesterol measurement in clinical laboratories in the United States: a report from the Laboratory Standardization Panel of the National Cholesterol Education Program. Clin Chem 1988;34:193–201.
5. Development of definitive methods for the National Reference System for the Clinical Laboratory, NRSCL1-A. Villanova, PA: National Committee for Clinical Laboratory Standards, 1991.
6. Dorsey DB. How does the National Reference System for the clinical laboratory standardize results? Pathologist 1984;May:307.
7. Cohen A, Hertz HS, Mandel J et al. Total serum cholesterol by isotope dilution/mass spectrometry: a candidate definitive method. Clin Chem 1980;26:854–60.

8. Duncan IW, Mather A, Cooper GR. The procedure for the proposed cholesterol reference method. Atlanta, GA: Centers for Disease Control, 1982.

9. Cooper GR, Smith SJ, Duncan IW, et al. Interlaboratory testing of the transferability of a candidate reference method for total cholesterol in serum. Clin Chem 1986;32: 921–9.

10. Abell LL, Levy BB, Brodie BB, Kendall FE. Simplified methods for the estimation of total cholesterol in serum and demonstration of its specificity. J Biol Chem 1951;195:357–66.

11. Sperry WM, Brand FC. The colorimetric determination of cholesterol. J Biol Chem 1943;150:315–24.

12. Liebermann C. Ueber des Oxychinoterpen. Ber Dtsch Chem Ges 1885;18:1803–9.

13. Burchard H. Beitrage Zur Kenntnis des Cholesterins. Chem Zentralbl 1890;61:25–7.

14. Ellerbe P, Myers GL, Cooper GR et al. A comparison of results for cholesterol in human serum obtained by the reference method and by the definitive method of the national reference system for cholesterol. Clin Chem 1990;36:370–5.

15. Bernert JT, Akins JR, Cooper GR et al. Factors influencing the accuracy of the National Reference System total cholesterol reference method. Clin Chem 1991; 37:2053–61.

16. Etheridge SF, Waynack, PP. The cholesterol reference method. Centers for Disease Control and Prevention, 1994:1–24.

17. Naito HK. Reliability of lipid, lipoprotein, and apolipoprotein measurements. Clin Chem 1988;34(suppl):B84–94.

18. Cooper GR, Myers GL, Smith SJ, Sampson EJ. Standardization of lipid, lipoprotein, and apolipoprotein measurements. Clin Chem 1988; 34(suppl):B95–105.

19. Joseph JC, Konishi R, Peterson D. Interference studies on four chemistry analyzers [Abstract]. Clin Chem 1984;30:949–50.

20. Glick MR, Ryder KW, Jackson SA. Graphical comparisons of interferences in clinical chemistry instrumentation. Clin Chem 1986;32:470–5.

21. Glick MR, Ryder, KW. Analytical systems ranked by freedom from interferences. Clin Chem 1987;33:1453–8.

22. Burrin JM, Price CP. Measurement of blood glucose [Review]. Ann Clin Biochem 1985; 22:327–42.

23. Zak B, Artiss JD. Some observations on cholesterol measurement in the clinical laboratory [Review]. Microchem J 1990;41:251–70.

24. Zak B. Cholesterol methodologies: a review. Clin Chem 1977;23:1201–14.

25. Witte DL, Brown LF, Feld RD. Enzymatic analysis of serum cholesterol and triglycerides: a brief review. Lab Med 1978;9:39–44.

26. Deeg R, Ziegenhorn J. Kinetic enzymatic method for automated determination of total cholesterol in serum. Clin Chem 1983;29:1798–802.

27. Siedel J, Rollinger W, Röschlau P, Ziegenhorn J. Total cholesterol, endpoint and kinetic method. In: Bergmeyer HU, Bergmeyer J, Graßl, M, eds. Methods of enzymatic analysis, 3rd ed. Weinheim: VCH Verlagsgesellschaft GmbH, 1985:139–48.

28. Bateson J, Artiss JD, Zak B. Sensitive enzymic methods for HDL and HDL subclass cholesterol measurement. Clin Chem 1988;34:1230.

29. Flegg HM. An investigation of the determination of serum cholesterol by an enzymatic method. Ann Clin Biochem 1973;10:79–84.

30. Allain CC, Poon LS, Chan CSG, Richmond W, Fu PC. Enzymatic determination of total serum cholesterol. Clin Chem 1974;20:470–5.

31. Trinder P. Determination of glucose in blood using glucose oxidase with an alternative oxygen acceptor. Ann Clin Biochem 1969;6:24–7.

32. Pesce MA, Bodourian SH. Interference with the enzymic measurement of cholesterol in serum by use of five reagent kits. Clin Chem 1977;23:757–60.

33. Garber CC, Feldbruegge D. Evaluation of the performance of the automated enzymatic cholesterol method on the SMAC [Abstract]. Clin Chem 1978;24:1020.

34. Pesce MA, Bodourian SH. Enzymic measurement of cholesterol in serum with the Centrifichem centrifugal analyzer. Clin Chem 1977;23:280–2.

35. Fingerhut B. Enzymic serum cholesterol measurement with a basic autoanalyzer and the DuPont ACA method. Clin Chem 1978;24:1624–7.

36. Witte DL, Brown LF, Feld RD. Effects of bilirubin on detection of hydrogen peroxide by use of peroxidase. Clin Chem 1978;24:1778–82.

37. McGowan MW, Artiss JD, Zak B. Spectrophotometric study on minimizing bilirubin interference in an enzyme reagent-mediated cholesterol reaction. Microchem J 1982;27:564–73.

38. James DR, Price CP. Interference in colorimetric reactions for measuring hydrogen peroxide. Ann Clin Biochem 1984;21:398–404.

39. Peddicord CH, Barnes WA. Ascorbic acid interferogram for cholesterol in the Demand and TDx. Clin Chem 1988;34:773–4.

40. Perlstein MT, Thibert RJ, Zak B. Bilirubin and hemoglobin interference in direct colorimetric cholesterol reactions using enzyme reagents. Microchem J 1977;22:403–19.

41. Fossati P, Prencipe L, Berti G. Use of 3,5-dicholo-2-hydroxybenzenesulfonic acid/4-aminophenazone chromogenic system in direct enzymic assay of uric acid in serum and urine. Clin Chem 1980;26:227–231.

42. Sharma A, Artiss JD, Strandbergh DR, Zak B. The turbid specimen as an analytical medium: hemoglobin determination as a model. Clin Chim Acta 1985;147:7–14.

43. Cobbaert C, Tricarico A. Different effect of Intralipid™ and triacylglycerol-rich lipoproteins on the Kodak Ektachem serum cholesterol determination. Eur J Clin Chem Clin Biochem 1993;31:107–9.

44. Kroll MH, Emancipator K. A theoretical evaluation of linearity. Clin Chem 1993;39:405–13.

45. Deacon AC, Dawson JG. Enzymic assay for total cholesterol involving chemical or enzymic hydrolysis: a comparison of methods. Clin Chem 1979;25:976–84.

46. Bachorik PS, Albers JJ, Ellefson RD, Kane JP, Wood, PD. Collection of blood samples for lipoprotein analysis. Clin Chem 1982;28:1375–8.

47. Alzofon J, Tilton KA, Haley NJ. Enzymatic determination of cholesterol in plasma obtained by fingerstick. Clin Chem 1985;31:168.

48. Kaplan SA, Yuceoglu AM, Strauss J. Chemical microanalysis: analysis of capillary and venous blood. Pediatrics 1959;24:270.

49. Ono T, Kitaguchi K, Takehara M, Shiiba M, Hayami K. Serum constituents analyses: effect of duration and temperature of storage of clotted blood. Clin Chem 1981;27:35–8.

50. Haider T, Per Foss O. The analytical variation and mean difference of serum lipid values in duplicate samples subjected to different times of storage. Scand J Clin Lab Invest 1983;43:439–43.

51. Hainline A, Karon JM, Winn CL, Gill JB. Accuracy and comparability of long-term measurements of cholesterol. Clin Chem 1986;32:611–15.

52. Kuchmak M, Taylor L, Olansky AS. Suitability of frozen and lyophilized reference sera for cholesterol and triglyceride determinations. Clin Chim Acta 1982;120:261–71.

53. Keller VH. Errors, resulting from storage, in the determination of eleven parameters in heparinized whole blood and plasma. Z Klin Chem Klin Biochem 1975;6:217–24.

54. Manual of laboratory operations for the Lipid Research Clinics Program. In: Hainline A, Karon J, Lippel K, eds. Lipid and lipoprotein analysis, 2nd ed. Bethesda MD: National Heart, Lung, and Blood Institute, National Institutes of Health, 1982:5.

55. Bateson JE, Artiss, JD, Zak B. The development of an enzymic reference equivalent method for total cholesterol. Clin Chem 1989;35:1071–2.

56. Bateson JE, Artiss JD, Zak B. Cholesterol measurement in grossly lipemic specimens. Clin Chem 1989;35:1072.

Measurement of Triglyceride Concentration

10

Thomas G. Cole, Sigrid G. Klotzsch, and Judith R. McNamara

✧ In 1983, the National Institutes of Health Consensus Development Conference on Treatment of Hypertriglyceridemia released recommendations for evaluating triglyceridemic status.[1] These recommendations (with slight modifications)[2] were then adopted by the National Cholesterol Education Program (NCEP) Expert Panel on Detection, Evaluation, and Treatment of High Blood Cholesterol in Adults[3] (Table 10–1). According to those recommendations, fasting serum triglyceride (TG) concentrations below 200 mg/dL (2.3 mmol/L) are considered desirable; concentrations between 200 and 400 mg/dL (2.3 and 4.5 mmol/L) are borderline high; and fasting concentrations above 400 mg/dL (4.5 mmol/L) are considered elevated.[3]

CLINICAL SIGNIFICANCE

Both borderline and elevated concentrations require attention in the presence of other coronary heart disease (CHD) risk factors. Extremely elevated levels require attention, unrelated to CHD risk, as TG concentrations above 1000 mg/dL (11.3 mmol/L) can cause abdominal pain and may be life-threatening due to chylomicron-induced pancreatitis.[4] Fasting TG concentrations are also indicators of postprandial response. Even within the desirable range, the magnitude of postprandial response is positively associated with fasting TG concentration, as well as with fat and total caloric intake.[5] Alcohol intake also increases serum TG concentration and abstinence for 24 h is recommended before blood is drawn for a lipid profile. (TG distributions of North American males and females are presented in the appendix to this book.)

Estrogen replacement in postmenopausal women is associated with a significant increase in TG, the magnitude of which is generally positively associated with pre-estrogen TG levels. This is one of the rare instances where increases in TG are accompanied by increases in high-density lipoprotein cholesterol (HDL-C) and apolipoprotein A-I (apo A-I).[6] Hormone replacement has been associated with decreased CHD risk in most, but not all, studies.[7–13]

The relationship between TG concentration and risk of CHD has not been firmly established. Most studies find increased TG concentrations to be positively correlated with increased risk for CHD in univariate analyses, but when other CHD risk factors, such as reduced concentrations of HDL-C, are included in multivariate models, TG often loses its significance.[14–16] However, there is a growing consensus that TG, or

Table 10–1 ✧ Recommended Cutpoints for Evaluation of Fasting Triglyceridemic Status

Classification	mg/dL	mmol/L
Normal	TG < 200	TG < 2.3
Borderline High	TG 200–400	TG 2.3–4.5
Hypertriglyceridemic	TG > 400	TG > 4.5
High Risk for Pancreatitis	TG > 1000	TG > 11.3

a subset of triglyceride-rich lipoproteins (TRL), may be directly involved in CHD risk.[16–20]

TRIGLYCERIDE METABOLISM

TG are water-insoluble lipids, consisting of three fatty acids linked to one glycerol molecule. They represent a concentrated source of metabolic energy, contributing 9 kcal/g, as opposed to 4 kcal/g for protein or carbohydrate. TG are transported in the blood as core constituents of all lipoproteins, but the greatest concentration of these molecules is carried in the TG-rich chylomicrons and very-low-density lipoproteins (VLDL). Although these two species of TG-rich lipoproteins are frequently combined into the single category TRL, they are synthesized in two separate metabolic pathways.

A major source of circulating TG is dietary fat, which is hydrolyzed in the gut into free fatty acids and mono- and diglycerides for transportation through the intestinal villi. After absorption by the enterocyte, they are resynthesized into new TG, assembled into chylomicrons, and secreted into the lymph. Chylomicrons ultimately enter the blood compartment, where lipoprotein lipase rapidly hydrolyzes most of the TG in the capillary bed to glycerol and free fatty acids. The glycerol and fatty acids are then stored in adipose tissue or are used for energy by other tissues. A peak concentration of chylomicron-associated TG occurs within 3h–6h after ingestion of a fat-rich meal; however, the absorption rate of fats is highly variable, depending on the individual and the dietary composition of the fat.[5] Chylomicrons that have been partially hydrolyzed in the circulation are termed chylomicron remnants. Relative to chylomicrons, they are relatively cholesterol- and protein-enriched and are taken up by the liver through a receptor-mediated process in which apolipoprotein (apo) E and/or apo B-48 on the chylomicron remnant surface binds to the apo E receptor, LDL receptor, or LDL receptor-related protein (LRP).[21–23] This entire absorptive process is termed the exogenous lipoprotein metabolic pathway (see Chapter 5, Figure 5–1).

Appreciable amounts of circulating TG are also transported in VLDL, which are synthesized in the liver from constituents derived from the receptor-mediated uptake of chylomicron remnants, as well as from de novo synthesized components. Following synthesis and secretion into the blood stream, they are hydrolyzed by lipoprotein lipase into VLDL remnants, in much the same way that chylomicrons are hydrolyzed. Some VLDL remnants are taken up directly by the liver and catabolized, while others continue in the hydrolysis cascade through intermediate-density lipoproteins (IDL), to become low-density lipoproteins (LDL).[24-29] Synthesis and catabolism of lipoproteins originating in the liver are part of the endogenous lipoprotein metabolic pathway.

The rates of VLDL synthesis and hydrolysis are regulated by many factors, including substrate availability, hormonal status, hydrolytic enzyme activity, and co-factor activity of specific apolipoproteins. While increased levels of circulating LDL have clearly been shown to be atherogenic, there is also a growing body of evidence to support the hypothesis that TRL, or perhaps, specific subspecies of TRL, i.e., remnants, are also atherogenic.[30-36] Isolating remnants for assessment of risk, however, has been extremely difficult, since there is much overlap in compositional constituents and particle size. However, a method to separate TRL remnants from nascent TRL has been developed.[37,38] If separation of TRL subspecies can provide better evaluation of TG-associated CHD risk, in a manner similar to the separation of LDL and HDL, perhaps more sensitive risk analysis may be gained. [33,35,36] (For additional information on TRL remnants, refer to Chapter 28.)

TRIGLYCERIDE MEASUREMENT

TG are measured in the clinical laboratory for three major purposes: to establish triglyceridemic status, to assess risk of CHD, and to calculate LDL-C concentration through use of the Friedewald equation[39] when LDL-C cannot be determined directly:

$$\text{LDL-C (mg/dL)} = \text{Total Cholesterol} - TG/5 - \text{HDL-C}$$

For results in mmol/L, use TG/2.22.

Using the Friedewald equation to approximate LDL-C concentration makes three assumptions: that all TRL are actually VLDL (i.e., no chylomicrons are present); that all serum TG are contained in VLDL, with none in any other lipoproteins; and that the relative proportion of cholesterol in VLDL is constant at 20% of VLDL mass. These assumptions, which are only partially true, are increasing unreliable when TG concentrations exceed 250 mg/dL (2.8 mmol/L), or when individuals are not fasting, and are completely unreliable at TG concentrations above 400 mg/dL (4.5 mmol/L) and in individuals who have Type III hyperlipoproteinemia.[40,41] In addition, the Friedewald equation requires the measurement of three analytes, each with individual and independent contributions of both analytical and biological variability.

The recent introduction of methodologies for measuring LDL-C directly reduces the need to use the Friedewald calculation, since the methods are less affected by increased TG concentrations and do not depend on mathematical assumptions. (For additional information on the limitations of calculations, and on direct methods for measuring LDL-C, refer to Chapter 12.)

Methods for determining TG concentration involve the enzymatic measurement of total serum glycerol after hydrolysis of TG into glycerol and free fatty acids. Since glycerol is formed through normal metabolic processes, and is not specific to TG, and since each glycerol molecule is calculated to represent a triglyceride molecule, TG concentrations will be overestimated if endogenous unesterified glycerol is not subtracted through the use of a glycerol blank. Even then, it will be slightly overestimated by the presence of endogenous mono- and diglycerides, which will also be measured as TG. In normal individuals, endogenous glycerol represents the equivalent of 5–20 mg/dL (0.06–0.22 mmol/L) TG, which is a tolerable amount of error. In certain situations, however, endogenous, non-TG-associated glycerol concentrations may be much higher, confounding TG measurement. Such situations can include diabetes mellitus, emotional stress, intravenous administration of drugs or nutrients containing glycerol, and contamination of blood collection devices or blood samples by glycerol. In addition, prolonged storage of whole blood under non-refrigerated conditions can cause increased concentrations of free glycerol liberated from erythrocyte membrane phospholipids. Although reagents and methods are currently available to eliminate the interference of glycerol, only about 5% of all American clinical laboratories blank TG measurements for endogenous glycerol.

REVIEW OF EXISTING METHODOLOGIES

Almost all clinical laboratories use enzymatic methods for the analysis of TG concentration. Though these methods vary, three basic steps are common to all (Figure 10–1).[42,43]

The first step uses lipases that are optimized for the hydrolysis of TG to glycerol and fatty acids. Earlier formulations were not always optimized to hydrolyze the TG commonly found in the circulation, i.e., those containing fatty acids of 16 or more carbon atoms. However, manufacturers are now aware of the importance of complete hydrolysis. Although phospholipids are not hydrolyzed by current lipase mixtures, mono- and diglycerides are hydrolyzed and contribute to the amount of glycerol quantified and calculated as TG. Since mono- and diglycerides represent only about 3% of the total plasma neutral glyceride concentration, and since a portion of the mono- and diglycerides arises from *in vivo* and *in vitro* hydrolysis of TG, they are included as part of the TG measurement and do not contribute a significant source of error. All enzymatic methods then quantify the amount of glycerol present after hydrolysis.

The conversion step commonly uses an enzyme, such as glycerol kinase, to phosphorylate glycerol for further enzymatic reactions, or may generate an intermediate which can be used directly for the quantification of TG.

Figure 10–1 ✧ Generalized Scheme of Enzymatic TG Analyses

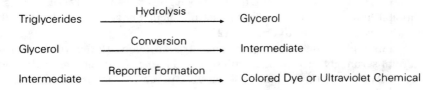

The final step leads to the formation of either a colored dye (commonly quinoneimine or formazin) or an ultraviolet light-absorbing chemical whose concentration can be measured spectrophotometrically (appearance or disappearance of NADH) and which can then be related to the concentration of TG in the specimen.

The calibration of TG analyses is confounded by the lack of validated definitive and reference methods. A "reference" chromotropic acid method, as used by the Centers for Disease Control and Prevention (CDC), is considered the accuracy base for TG. Calibrators should be traceable to this method. Glycerol solutions, although suitable as standards, should not be used alone for calibration, because the hydrolysis step of the analytical process is not evaluated. Since TG are a heterogeneous mixture of glycerides with various fatty acid moieties, the choice of analytical standard becomes critical. The CDC uses a standard composed of triolein and tripalmitin (2:1, w/w), as this ratio approximates the distribution of fatty acids in lipoprotein-associated TG; however, serum values are reported as triolein equivalents. Due to the difference in molecular weights, a disparity of approximately 10% occurs when values are reported as tripalmitin equivalents. Truly unambiguous values would result if the Systeme International d'Unites units (mmol/L) were adopted, as recommended by the International Federation of Clinical Chemistry; however, such a change does not appear to be close at hand for the United States.

Because all enzymatic methods measure TG based on the quantity of glycerol in a specimen, the endogenous glycerol will cause TG concentration to be overestimated if the endogenous glycerol is not taken into consideration. Two methods for the elimination of this interference have been devised. The first, the "external blanking" method, requires using two assay reagent solutions: one containing all components necessary for the measurement of TG and endogenous glycerol, and one that is similar but lacks the lipase enzymes and therefore measures only the endogenous glycerol. In practice, a specimen is run twice, once with each reagent, and the difference in values represents the true TG concentration. The major advantage of this method is that it can be used with most analytical systems; one need only set up a separate test for each reagent solution. In addition, if the system is arranged so that each test provides a value before calculation of the true TG concentration, the concentration of the endogenous glycerol will be known (in some situations, this may have medical significance). A disadvantage is that this method requires the duplicate analysis of a specimen using two complete sets of reagents, cuvettes, and other consumable supplies, thereby increasing the cost and time of analysis.

An alternative method, the "internal blanking" method, uses a single reagent that is split into two components: the first contains all enzymes necessary to consume the endogenous glycerol without generating a measurable light-absorbing compound or subtracting the resulting absorbance as blank; the second contains lipase and any other chemicals necessary to measure TG. In practice, the specimen reacts with the first component of the reagent until all the endogenous glycerol is removed. At this point a baseline reading is taken, the second component of the reagent is added, and the complete reaction, including the hydrolysis of TG, is carried to completion. The value obtained from the second reaction represents the true or net TG concentration. In contrast to external blanking, this method requires that only a single test on the analyzer be devoted to the analysis; therefore the process is economical, since each analysis requires only a single, but divided, reagent, and a single cuvette, and labor is reduced. However, this method requires a versatile instrument capable of performing two-reagent analysis. In addition, the time required for analysis is prolonged due to the sequential reactions occurring in a single cuvette, and the actual value of the endogenous glycerol is not available. The measurement of free glycerol concentration may be desirable in some situations, such as when a patient has a high level of endogenous lipoprotein lipase activity in response to heparin therapy.[44]

Much discussion has been devoted to the issue of why and when to glycerol-blank TG measurements.[45] Ideally, if economical and convenient methods were available, a glycerol blank should be included in every TG measurement. In reality, such is not the case, and therefore, glycerol blanking is not utilized in most clinical laboratories. Complicating the decision is the fact that excessively high concentrations of endogenous glycerol are a problem in only a very small percentage of specimens;[46] however, in these situations an inappropriate medically significant decision may be made. Therefore, if all specimens are not glycerol blanked, decisions must be made as to which specimens are to be blanked. Unfortunately, lack of communication between the laboratory and the ordering physician often precludes proper decision-making, and any system that depended upon it probably would be in error a large part of the time. To reduce the potential for errors:

1. Clinical laboratories should use only systems and reagents with glycerol blanking capabilities and should have the reagent available at all times to be used as appropriate.

2. All hospital in-patient specimens should be glycerol-blanked due to the higher incidence of endogenous glycerol in this population.

3. Specimens from hospital outpatients or from other sources generally need not be glycerol-blanked, unless specimens are from patients who may be expected to have increased concentrations of glycerol, such as patients from clinics that treat diabetes or other endocrine disorders.

4. All specimens must be kept refrigerated until analyzed. Improper storage or transport of specimens may increase free glycerol. At room temperature, lipases may continue to hydrolyze TG. In addition, unrefrigerated whole blood may have high concentrations of free glycerol from hydrolysis of erythrocyte phospholipid.

5. Any specimen with TG concentration > 200 mg/dL (2.3 mmol/L) should be glycerol-blanked using a "reflex" ordering system.

6. Any suspicious specimen, such as one that has a high TG concentration but is not turbid, should also be glycerol-blanked.

Grossly lipemic specimens are often associated with other potential sources of error. One error is caused by the "clearing effect" of the lipase as it hydrolyzes TG. In systems that use a serum blank rather than a reagent blank, light scattering due to large-sized, TG-rich lipoproteins causes an artificially high baseline absorbance measurement. As the analysis progresses, turbidity is reduced as the lipase hydrolyzes TG and reduces the size of lipoproteins. The overall effect is a slight underestimation of total TG concentration in an up-reaction (NADH appearance), or an overestimation in a down-reaction (NADH disappearance). Reagent-blanked systems are not affected by this phenomenon. Several methods have been devised to minimize the error. For example, including proper detergents in the reagent mixture will eliminate the problem in some, but not all, cases.[47] Fortunately, since the magnitude of the error is only a few percent and occurs only in specimens with increased TG concentrations, the level of error is usually acceptable.

In addition, grossly lipemic specimens, particularly those with a high chylomicron content, may become heterogeneous as chylomicrons float to the top of the sample cup in an analyzer. Therefore, grossly lipemic specimens should be mixed thoroughly prior to analysis and the analysis must be carried out with minimal delay. The large amounts of fatty acids liberated by the hydrolysis of TG, particularly in lipemic specimens, can interfere in the analysis due to turbidity and the inactivation of some lipases by product inhibition. This situation can be avoided by including (in the reaction buffer) a chemical reservoir for the liberated fatty acids. Generally, bovine serum albumin or α-cyclodextrin is used for this purpose.[47]

As for all analytes, TG concentration should be measured as soon as possible after blood is drawn. In certain specimens containing a high value level of lipase activity, such as those obtained from heparinized patients, TG will become hydrolyzed upon standing.[43,44] Over time, the glycerol blank concentration in these specimens will increase while the true TG concentration will decrease; however, apparent total TG concentration will remain stable. This process is temperature-dependent and persists at 4°C, but is minimized if the specimen is frozen at –20°C.

REFERENCE, DEFINITIVE, AND RECOMMENDED METHODS

At this time, no true definitive or reference method has been established for measuring TG. The National Institute of Standards and Technology (NIST) has published two candidate definitive methods for the measurement of TG.[48] Both methods are based on isotope dilution/mass spectrometry using $^{13}C_3$-triolein. One method measures only true TG and the other measures total glycerides (tri-, di-, and monoglycerides as well as free glycerol).

The chemical method that the CDC uses as its "in-house reference method" has been accepted by The National Committee for Clinical Laboratory Standards as the interim reference method for the U.S. National Reference System. The CDC uses this method to maintain the accuracy base for the CDC-NHLBI (National Heart, Lung, and Blood Institute) Lipid Standardization Program, which requires precision consistent with a coefficient of variation of 5% and accuracy within 5% of the target values set by the CDC on frozen serum specimens. The method involves silicic acid-methylene chloride extraction, alkaline hydrolysis, and color formation with chromotropic acid.[49–52] Due to several technical factors, including the difficulty of transferring the method between laboratories, the CDC is investigating modifications of the method, as well as alternative candidate methods. The Cholesterol Reference Method Laboratory Network (CRMLN) is currently evaluating a combination of the CDC extraction and hydrolysis steps with enzymatic detection of glycerol to produce a "designated comparison method" for the purpose of evaluating current and future TG assays.

Given the lack of true definitive and reference methods for the analysis of TG, it is difficult to recommend any particular method over another, beyond the recommendation of using a method that incorporates a form of glycerol blanking.

RECOMMENDED NOMENCLATURE

Due to the chemical heterogeneity of the analyte commonly termed "triglycerides" on laboratory reports, there is often confusion as to what is actually being measured by the clinical laboratory. The confusion becomes readily evident during attempts to standardize the measurement of "TG" to an acceptable accuracy base, particularly through the CDC's Lipid Standardization Program. The enzymatic quantitation of TG by most clinical laboratories includes the measurement of mono- and diglycerides and endogenous glycerol, in addition to TG. As described above, the use of a glycerol blanking reagent removes glycerol, but still includes the measurement of monoglycerides and diglycerides. Complicating the situation further is that the chemical reference method used by the CDC to establish the accuracy base removes various amounts of monoglycerides and diglycerides along with endogenous glycerol.

To minimize the confusion caused by nonstandard nomenclature, the CRMLN has recommended use of the following terminology with regard to the measurement of TG

◇ **Total Glycerides.** This term describes the enzymatic measurement of triglycerides, diglycerides, monoglycerides, and endogenous free-glycerol, which is the most common type of measurement currently made in clinical laboratories for triglycerides. This term replaces the commonly used terms "triglycerides" and "total triglycerides" and is consistent with the terminology as used by NIST.[48]

◇ **Triglycerides.** This term describes the enzymatic measurement of triglycerides, diglycerides, and monoglycerides and is currently performed in only a few clinical laboratories. This term replaces other commonly used terms, such as "net triglycerides," "glycerol-blanked triglycerides," "glycerol-corrected triglycerides," and "true triglycerides."

◇ **CDC-Reference Triglycerides.** This term describes the chemical measurement of triglycerides and small amounts of diglycerides and monoglycerides by the chromotropic acid reference method at the CDC.

To avoid confusion and to provide consistency with other chapters in this book, the recommended nomenclature will not be used in this chapter, but will be incorporated into future revisions.

INTERFERING SUBSTANCES AND CAUTIONS

The sources of potential interfering substances in the analysis of TG have been reviewed in depth,[42] and such reviews should be consulted for more detailed information. The limits of acceptable analytical performance in the presence of ascorbic acid, bilirubin, hemolysis, and gross lipemia need to be evaluated for each system.[53] In many situations, the inclusion of a serum blank may eliminate the effects of the interfering substances.

Glycerol

As discussed above, endogenous glycerol causes an overestimation of all enzymatic TG measurements. Methods are available to eliminate this interference and should be used whenever the inclusion of the endogenous glycerol concentration may lead to errors in medical judgment. However, when blanking is instituted, it is important to avoid conditions that would cause *in vitro* hydrolysis prior to analysis, since this would result in a falsely underestimated TG concentration.

Ascorbic Acid

As an antioxidant, ascorbic acid can interfere with oxidation/reduction reactions. Specimens from patients ingesting megadoses of Vitamin C may have improper analysis of TG and other analytes. Concentrations of ascorbic acid up to 20 mg/dL (1135 µmol/L) may be acceptable for most systems.

Bilirubin

Both chemical and spectral interference can be a serious problem with high concentrations of bilirubin in colorimetric methods. Concentrations of bilirubin up to 20 mg/dL (340 µmol/L) may be acceptable for most systems.

Hemolysis

Slight to moderate hemolysis may cause no interference, but gross hemolysis is unacceptable. The effects of hemoglobin interference will vary, depending on the oxidative state of the hemoglobin, the type of reaction being performed, and the type of spectrophotometric system in use. In addition, the lysis of erythrocytes results in the dilution of lipid constituents.

Carryover

Carryover among reagents exists in all random-access analyzers and has been described for many instruments.[54–57] Carryover errors can alter results by 10%–15% in the first sample that follows a series of tests with another reagent. Reagents that are particularly prone to exhibit carryover problems into TG reagents include total protein and iron, due to their concentrations of oxidizing/reducing substances affecting the Trinder sequence of reactions. If direct bilirubin is measured after TG, errors occur due to the carryover of surfactants.

To avoid interference, the manufacturer's programmed test sequence or module use must be followed to take advantage of the software-controlled wash cycles. The manufacturers of all clinical chemistry instruments test carryover interference. For random sampling, some interference is not avoidable, and the software is often programmed to add an extra rinse, for example, if TG is followed by a request for total protein (to avoid redox reactions). Trinder reagents are sometimes formulated with phosphates (to eliminate alkaline phosphatase) and may affect a subsequent phosphorus measurement. High surfactant concentration can affect direct bilirubin. The degree of interference with iron measurements depends on the presence of potassium ferrocyanide.

Other Interferences

Analytical errors in TG, as well as in other analytes, can also be caused by increased TG concentration due to plasma displacement, as described by McGowan et al.[58] An important example is the artifact of pseudohypo values for electrolytes in the presence of severe hypertriglyceridemia.

The complete hydrolysis of all fatty acid esters by lipase affects the reaction time, which in turn depends on the presence and characteristics of surfactants, the pH, the ionic strength, and most of all, the source of the enzyme. The difference among various enzyme preparations becomes evident if the reaction kinetics of bovine and human calibrators are investigated. Absorbence readings taken at defined time intervals may not reflect complete hydrolysis of all specimens.

Most of the currently marketed TG reagents meet CDC criteria, provided that the systems are correctly calibrated. Ideally, the calibrator's assigned value should be the same as or close to the result that is obtained with the reference (CDC) method. If this is not the case, a calibrator "set-point" masks a matrix effect (Chapter 35). The presence of a large y-intercept in the linear regression relationship when two methods are compared can signal the presence of a matrix effect in one of the methods.

SUMMARY

Although TG concentration is a less powerful indicator of cardiovascular risk than is cholesterol concentration in most circumstances, evolving evidence suggests that certain TG-rich lipoproteins and their remnant particles may be very important in the development of heart disease. With the availability of a definitive method for TG and the incorporation of a designated reference method into the Cholesterol Reference Method Laboratory Network program, manufacturers can calibrate TG assays with improved accuracy.   ✧

REFERENCES

1. Consensus Development Conference. Treatment of hypertriglyceridemia. JAMA 1984; 251:1196–1200.
2. National Cholesterol Education Program. Summary of the second report of the National Cholesterol Education Program Expert Panel on Detection, Evaluation, and Treatment of High Blood Cholesterol in Adults. (Adult Treatment Panel II). JAMA 1993;269: 3015–23.
3. National Cholesterol Education Program. Report of the National Cholesterol Education

Program Expert Panel on Detection, Evaluation, and Treatment of High Blood Cholesterol in Adults. Arch Intern Med 1988;148:36–69.

4. Goldstein JL, Hobbs HH, Brown MS. Familial hypercholesterolemia. In: Scriver CR, Beaudet AL, Sly WS, Valle D, eds. Metabolic and molecular bases of inherited diseases, 7th ed. New York: McGraw-Hill, 1995:1981–2030.

5. Cohn JS, McNamara JR, Cohn SD, Ordovas JM, Schaefer EJ. Postprandial plasma lipoprotein changes in human subjects of different ages. J Lipid Res 1988;29:469–79.

6. Granfone A, Campos H, McNamara JR, et al. Effects of estrogen replacement on plasma lipoproteins and apolipoproteins in postmenopausal, dyslipidemic women. Metabolism 1992;41:1193–98.

7. Stampfer MJ, Colditz GA. Estrogen replacement therapy and coronary heart disease: a quantitative assessment of the epidemiologic evidence. Prev Med 1991;20:47–63.

8. McLaughlin VV, Hoff JA, Rich S. Relation between hormone replacement therapy in women and coronary artery disease estimated by electron beam tomography. Am Heart J 1997;134:1115–9.

9. Koh KK, Bui MN, Mincemoyer R, Cannon RO 3rd. Effects of hormone therapy on inflammatory cell adhesion molecules in postmenopausal healthy women. Am J Cardiol 1997;80:1505–7.

10. Frolich M, Schunkert H, Hense HW, et al. Effects of hormone replacement therapies on fibrinogen and plasma viscosity in postmenopausal women. Br J Haematol 1998;100:577–81.

11. Sorenson KE, Dorup I, Hermann AP, Mosekilde L. Combined hormone replacement therapy does not protect women against the age-related decline in endothelium-dependent vasomotor function. Circulation 1998;97:1234–8.

12. Hulley S, Grady D, Bush T, et al. Randomized trial of estrogen plus progestin for secondary prevention of coronary heart disease in postmenopausal women. Heart and Estrogen/progestin Replacement Study (HERS) Research Group. JAMA 1998;280:605–13.

13. Dubuisson JT, Wagenknecht LE, D'Agostino RB Jr et al. Association of hormone replacement therapy and carotid wall thickness in women with and without diabetes. Diabetes Care 1998;21:1790–6.

14. Austin MA. Plasma triglyceride and coronary heart disease. Arterioscler Thromb 1991;11:2–14.

15. Castelli WP. The triglyceride issue: a view from Framingham. Am Heart J 1986;112:432–7.

16. Hokanson JE, Austin MA. Plasma triglyceride level as a risk factor for cardiovascular disease independent of high-density lipoprotein cholesterol level: a meta-analysis of population-based prospective studies. J Cardiovasc Risk 1996;1996:312–19.

17. Miller M, Seidler A, Moalemi A, Pearson TA. Normal triglyceride levels and coronary artery disease events: the Baltimore Coronary Observational Long-Term Study. J Am Coll Cardiol 1998;31:1252–7.

18. Gotto AM Jr. Triglyceride as a risk factor for coronary artery disease. Am J Cardiol 1998;82:22Q–25Q.

19. Durrington PN. Triglycerides are more important in atherosclerosis than epidemiology has suggested. Atherosclerosis 1998;141 Suppl 1:S57–62.

20. Sprecher DL. Triglycerides as a risk factor for coronary artery disease. Am J Cardiol 1998;82:49U–56U.

21. Borensztajn J, Getz GS, Kotlar TJ. Uptake of chylomicron remnants by the liver: further evidence for the modulating role of phospholipids. J Lipid Res 1988;29:1087–96.

22. Brasaemle DL, Cornely-Moss K, Bensadoun A. Hepatic lipase treatment of chylomicron remnants increases exposure of apolipoprotein E. J Lipid Res 1993;34:455–65.

23. Hussain MM, Innerarity TL, Brecht WJ, Mahley RW. Chylomicron metabolism in normal, cholesterol-fed, and Watanabe heritable hyperlipidemic rabbits. J Biol Chem 1995;270:8578–87.

24. Phair RD, Hammond MG, Bowden JA, et al. A preliminary model for human lipoprotein metabolism in hyperlipoproteinemia. Fed Proc 1975;34:2263–70.

25. Packard CJ, Munro A, Lorimer AR, Gotto AM, Shepherd J. Metabolism of apolipoprotein B in large triglyceride-rich very low density lipoproteins of normal and hypertriglyceridemic subjects. J Clin Invest 1983;74:2178–92.

26. Beltz WF, Kesaniemi YA, Howard BV, Grundy SM. Development of an integrated model for analysis of the kinetics of apolipoprotein B in plasma very-low-density lipoproteins, intermediate-density lipoproteins, and low-density lipoproteins. J Clin Invest 1985;76: 575–85.

27. Fisher WR, Zech LA, Kilgore LL, Stacpoole PW. Metabolic pathways of apolipoprotein B in heterozygous familial hypercholesterolemia: studies with a [3H]leucine tracer. J Lipid Res 1991;32:1823–36.

28. Millar JS, Lichtenstein AH, Cuchel M, et al. Impact of age on the metabolism of VLDL, IDL, and LDL apolipoprotein B-100. J Lipid Research 1995;36:1155–67.9.

29. Welty FK, Lichtenstein AH, Barrett PHR, et al. Decreased production and increased catabolism of apolipoprotein B-100 in apolipoprotein B-67/B-100 heterozygotes. Arterioscler Thromb Vasc Biol 1997;17:881–8.

30. Kane JP, Chen G, Hamilton RL, et al. Remnants of lipoproteins of intestinal and hepatic origin in familial dysbetalipoproteinemia. Arteriosclerosis 1983;3:47–56.

31. Karpe F, Steiner G, Uffelman K, Olivecrona T, Hamsten A. Postprandial lipoproteins and progression of coronary atherosclerosis. Atherosclerosis 1994;106:83–97.

32. Ooi TC, Ooi DS. The atherogenic significance of an elevated plasma triglyceride level. Crit Rev Clin Lab Sci 1998;35:489–516.

33. Takeichi S, Yukawa N, Nakajima Y, et al. Association of plasma triglyceride-rich lipoprotein remnants with coronary atherosclerosis in cases of sudden cardiac death. Atherosclerosis 1999;142:309–15.

34. Packard CJ. Understanding coronary heart disease as a consequence of defective regulation of apolipoprotein B metabolism. Curr Opin Lipidol 1999;10:237–44.

35. Kugiyama K, Doi H, Takazoe K, et al. Remnant lipoprotein levels in fasting serum predict coronary events in patients with coronary artery disease. Circulation 1999;99: 2858–60.

36. Doi H, Kugiyama K, Ohgushi M, et al. Membrane active lipids in remnant lipoproteins cause impairment of endothelial-dependent vasorelaxation. Arterioscler Thromb Vasc Biol 1999;19:1918–24.

37. Campos E, Nakajima K, Tanaka A, Havel RJ. Properties of an apolipoprotein E-enriched fraction of triglyceride-rich lipoproteins isolated from human blood plasma with a monoclonal antibody to apolipoprotein B-100. J Lipid Res 1992;33:369–80.

38. Nakajima K, Saito T, Tamura A, et al. Cholesterol in remnant-like lipoproteins in human serum using monoclonal anti apo B-100 and anti apo A-I immunoaffinity mixed gels. Clin Chim Acta 1993;223:53–71.

39. Friedewald WT, Levy RI, Frederickson DS. Estimation of the concentration of low-density lipoprotein cholesterol in plasma, without use of the preparative ultracentrifuge. Clin Chem 1972;18:499–502.

40. Warnick GR, Knopp RH, Fitzpatrick V, Branson L. Estimating low-density lipoprotein cholesterol by the Friedewald equation is adequate for classifying patients on the basis of nationally recommended cutpoints. Clin Chem 1990;36:15–19.

41. McNamara JR, Cohn JS, Wilson PWF, Schaefer EJ. Calculated values for low-density lipoprotein cholesterol in the assessment of lipid abnormalities and coronary disease risk. Clin Chem 1990;36:36–42.

42. Klotzsch SG, McNamara JR. Triglyceride measurements: a review of methods and interferences. Clin Chem 1990;36:1605–13.

43. Naito HK, David JA. Laboratory considerations: determination of cholesterol, triglycerides, phospholipids and other lipids in blood and tissues. In: Story JB, ed. Lipid research methodology. New York: Alan R. Liss, 1984:31.

44. Hortin GL, Cole TG, Gibson DW, Kessler G. Decreased stability of triglycerides and increased free glycerol in serum for heparin-treated patients. Clin Chem 1988;34: 1847–9.

45. Cole TG, Glycerol blanking in triglyceride assays: is it necessary? Clin Chem 1990; 36:1267–8.

46. Jessen RH, Dass CJ, Eckfeldt JH. Do enzymatic analyses of serum triglycerides really need blanks of free glycerol? Clin Chem 1990;36:1372–5.

47. Artiss JD, Strandbergh DR, Zak B. Elimination of glycerol interference in a colorimetric enzymic triglyceride assay. Clin Chim Acta 1989;182:109–16.

48. Ellerbe P, Sniegoski LT, Welch MJ. Isotope dilution mass spectrometry as a candidate definitive method for determining total glycerides and triglycerides in serum. Clin Chem 1995;41:397–404.

49. Carlson LA, Wadstrom LB. Determination of glycerides in blood serum. Clin Chim Acta 1959;4:197–205.

50. Carlson LA. Determination of serum triglycerides. J Athero Res 1963;3:334–6.

51. Van Handel E. Zilversmit DB, Micromethod for the direct determination of triglycerides. J Lab Clin Med 1957;50:152–7.

52. Lofland Jr HB. A semiautomated procedure for the determination of triglycerides in serum. Anal Biochem 1964;9:393–400.

53. Glick JR, Ryder KW. Interferographs. User's guide to interferences in clinical chemistry instruments. Indianapolis: Science Enterprises, Inc., 1987.

54. Haeckel R. Carryover effects from reagent to reagent. J Clin Chem Clin Biochem 1985;23:255–6.

55. Bailey IR, McVittie JD. Gaseous diffusion as a source of carryover. Clin Chem 1986; 32:5(L).

56. DellAnna L, Morosini L, Franceschin A, Bortolussi A. Carryover in the TRAF technology: really impossible? Clin Chem 1986;32:7(L).

57. Dixon K. A theoretical study of carryover in selective access analyzers. Ann Clin Biochem 1990;27:139–42.

58. McGowan MW, Artiss JD, Zak B. Description of analytical problems arising from elevated serum solids. Anal Biochem 1984;142:239–51.

Measurement of High-Density-Lipoprotein Cholesterol

11

Matthias Nauck, Donald Wiebe, and G. Russell Warnick

✧ High-density-lipoprotein cholesterol (HDL-C) is an integral part of the lipoprotein profile—cholesterol (TC), triglycerides (TG), HDL-C, and low-density-lipoprotein cholesterol (LDL-C)—used to assess an individual's risk for developing coronary heart disease (CHD). Epidemiological studies have demonstrated the inverse relationship between HDL-C and CHD, such that individuals with low values of HDL-C tend to have increased incidence of CHD. At the other extreme, individuals with high concentrations of HDL-C, as in familial hyperalpha-lipoproteinemia, seldom present with CHD symptoms. The fact that pre-menopausal females tend to have higher HDL-C and less CHD compared to males and post-menopausal women supports the protective role of HDL-C. As a consequence, there has been substantial interest in HDL-C measurements to assess potential risk for CHD, and most clinical laboratories routinely perform HDL-C analysis.

CLINICAL SIGNIFICANCE OF HDL-C CONCENTRATIONS

Recommendations of the National Cholesterol Education Program (NCEP) Adult Treatment Panel II (ATP II), released in 1993, recognized HDL-C as an independent risk factor for CHD and enhanced its importance by recommending measurement of HDL-C together with TC during the initial screen.[1] An HDL-C concentration of < 35 mg/dL (0.91 mmol/L) is considered high risk for CHD, while HDL-C ≥ 60 mg/dL (1.55 mmol/L) is considered protective. Similar cut-off values were recommended by the European Atherosclerosis Society.[2] Thus, reliably classifying patients under current guidelines requires dependable methods for measuring HDL-C.

Physicians generally treat patients who have lipid patterns associated with increased risk of developing CHD. Occasionally, patients will have normal concentrations of TC (< 200 mg/dL; 5.18 mmol/L) but low HDL-C (< 35 mg/dL; 0.91 mmol/L). As HDL-C values increase above 35 mg/dL (0.91 mmol/L), which is associated with decreasing CHD risk, TC to HDL-C ratios also tend to decrease, a relationship that is sometimes used to estimate CHD risk. However, the ratio has no physiological significance and NCEP guidelines suggest the physician make decisions based on the individual TC or LDL-C to HDL-C values rather than on the ratios.

Among therapeutic approaches available for increasing HDL-C, exercise, cessation of smoking, and weight loss are perhaps the most effective. More often, patients

221

at risk present with increased TC or LDL-C concentrations and the intervention programs are primarily oriented toward lowering cholesterol by diet and, if necessary, drug therapy. Some of the common cholesterol-lowering drugs, such as niacin, fibrates, and the newer statins, tend to increase HDL-C (see Chapter 5 for additional information).[3] Thus, HDL-C is an important component of the lipoprotein profile and accurate measurements are necessary to diagnose and monitor therapy appropriately.

ANALYTICAL PERFORMANCE GOALS FOR HDL-C MEASUREMENT

Regardless of which method a laboratory selects to measure HDL-C on patient specimens, the procedure should be capable of achieving acceptable analytical performance. Analytical performance goals for precision, accuracy, and total error in HDL-C measurement have been developed by the Lipoprotein Working Group of the NCEP (see Table 11–1).[4] Most of the methods, such as precipitation techniques, common in the clinical laboratory can provide acceptable results when performed with careful technique and an accurate and reproducible cholesterol assay. The newer fully automated homogeneous HDL-C procedures give superior precision compared with the manual precipitation assays and are more likely to meet current analytical performance goals, at least for precision and total error.

Precision can be assessed by replicate analysis of commercial controls or frozen serum pools. Currently the only reliable approach for ensuring the accuracy of a routine HDL-C assay is a comparison study on actual patient specimens with an accepted Reference Method, which can be accomplished through the Cholesterol Reference Method Laboratory Network (CRMLN) using the Reference Method or the Designated Comparison Method (DCM) (see Chapter 36 for more detail). Reference materials for HDL-C that behave as patient materials (no matrix effects) for the transfer of accuracy from laboratory to laboratory have not been available through the usual commercial sources (see Chapter 35).

Table 11–1 ✧ NCEP HDL-C Analytical Goals
1998 GOALS
Precision, HDL-C ≥ 42 mg/dL (1.09 mmol/L): CV ≤ 4% HDL-C < 42 mg/dL: SD ≤ 1.7 mg/dL (0.044 mmol/L)
Accuracy,* bias ≤ ±5%
Total Allowable Error, ≤ 13%
* Bias compared to CDC three-step Reference Method

POPULATION FREQUENCY DISTRIBUTION FOR HDL-C

Population distributions for HDL-C from the Lipid Research Clinics (LRC) program[5] prevalence study (using the heparin/$MnCl_2$ precipitation procedure and Technicon AutoAnalyzer cholesterol method) are presented in the Appendix. Keep in mind that the LRC HDL-C method at the time of this study specified the use of 0.046 mol/L $MnCl_2$ and heparin with EDTA plasma specimens. If the study were repeated today, the method would use a higher concentration of $MnCl_2$ (0.092 mol/L) and have slightly lower HDL-C values.

HDL DEFINITION

High-density lipoprotein (HDL), the smallest in size of the lipoproteins, includes a complex family of lipoprotein particles (refer to chapter 15). These particles exist in a constant state of dynamic flux as they interact with other HDL particles, low-density lipoprotein (LDL), and very-low-density-lipoprotein (VLDL) particles.

HDL has the highest proportion of protein relative to lipid compared to other lipoproteins (HDL is > 50% protein). Its major proteins are designated apolipoproteins AI (apo A-I) and A-II, with small amounts of the C apolipoproteins (C-I, C-II, and C-III), E, A-IV, and D. HDL's principal lipid components are the phospholipids, with lesser amounts of cholesterol esters, unesterified cholesterol, and TG (see Table 11–2). Since cholesterol esters are hydrolyzed to unesterified or free cholesterol in most analytical procedures, the esterified portion is usually quantified as unesterified cholesterol.

Classically, HDL-C refers to the fraction of TC (both free cholesterol and cholesterol esters) associated with HDL as defined by ultracentrifugation (hydrated density). In common practice, these fractions, separated by chemical precipitation or electrophoretic (mobility) properties are also referred to as HDL. Therefore, HDL is defined by the operation used to isolate the lipoprotein and includes a family of similar particles that vary in size and composition.

Table 11–2 ✧ Lipid Composition of HDL Particles

Lipid	% of Total Lipid
Phospholipids	50
Cholesterol esters	30
Cholesterol (unesterified)	10
Triglycerides	10

REVIEW OF EXISTING METHODS

Ultracentrifugation

Lipoproteins can be readily separated on the basis of their differing hydrated densities using ultracentrifugation techniques. The proportion of lipid, especially TG, associated with the proteins in a particular lipoprotein adds to the buoyancy of the total complex, allowing the major classes to be separated by either equilibrium or rate methods.

In the literature, the nomenclature assigned to lipoproteins is based on their relative densities. Therefore, VLDL by definition includes particles with density < 1.006 kg/L, the background density of serum. LDL particles range in density from 1.006–1.063 kg/L; HDL, from 1.063–1.210 kg/L. (For additional information on the separation of lipoproteins by ultracentrifugation, refer to Chapter 32.) These classes are approximately comparable to electrophoretic fractions designated pre-beta, beta, and alpha lipoproteins, respectively.

Specimen density is adjusted with salts, such as NaBr or KBr , and then ultracentrifugation is used to fractionate the lipoproteins.[6] Figure 11–1 illustrates the 1.063 kg/L separation of VLDL and LDL (top fraction) from HDL (bottom fraction).

The reliability of lipoprotein quantitations following separation by ultracentrifugation techniques depends on both the performance of the analytical method, such as cholesterol analysis, and the skills of the technologist performing recovery and transfer of the lipoprotein fractions from the ultracentrifuge tube. Further adjustment of the 1.063 kg/L bottom fraction to a density of 1.210 kg/L, followed by ultracentrifugation, can be used to isolate the HDL from other serum proteins. However, for quantitative analysis, HDL is usually considered to be simply the fraction of density >1.063 kg/L.

Ultracentrifugation has long been considered the ultimate comparison method for the isolation and quantitation of lipoproteins. Unfortunately, ultracentrifugation cannot meet the stringent requirements needed for a reference method. Achieving complete and reproducible recovery is difficult, even for experienced technologists,

Figure 11–1 ✧ Ultracentrifugation at 1.063 kg/L

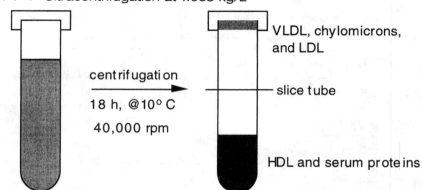

and fractions may be cross-contaminated. In addition, fractions isolated by ultracentrifugation are heterogeneous, containing other functional particles. For example, the HDL fraction with density between 1.063 and 1.210 kg/L may contain considerable amounts of Lp(a).

Electrophoresis

Historically, lipoproteins were also isolated using electrophoretic techniques and the lipoproteins, visualized with lipophilic dyes, were named on the basis of mobility by comparison to mobilities of common serum proteins. Thus, lipoprotein classes were commonly referred to as alpha, pre-beta, and beta lipoproteins (see Figure 11–2). Lipoproteins can be separated using a variety of electrophoretic media, such as paper, agarose gel, cellulose acetate, and polyacrylamide with numerous buffers.[7] Lipid stains, such as Oil Red O, Fat Red 7B, or Sudan Black, have been used to detect lipoproteins after electrophoresis. Alpha lipoproteins, which exhibit mobility comparable to alpha-proteins, are approximately comparable to the HDL class.

Electrophoresis has proven primarily useful for qualitative analysis of lipoproteins and has not been considered appropriate for quantitation. The lipophilic dyes

Figure 11–2 ✧ Separation by Electrophoretic Systems

The left panel illustrates the typical pattern observed for serum proteins, with immunoglobulins at the origin in the gamma region and albumin migrating past the alpha region. The middle and right panels demonstrate differences observed for lipoproteins separated on cellulose acetate or agarose media compared to polyacrylamide. Polyacrylamide separates the lipoproteins on the basis of size.

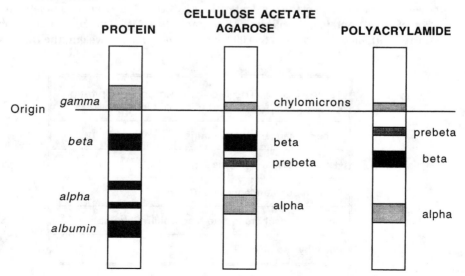

are not specific for a class of lipid, such as cholesterol, TG, or phospholipids, and as result cannot be used to accurately quantitate lipoproteins. Performing quantitative precipitation with phosphotungstic acid after agarose gel electrophoresis allows lipoprotein cholesterol to be reliably quantified, but the process is of limited usefulness in samples containing lipoproteins of atypical composition.[8] Staining electrophoretic plates with specific enzyme reagents, such as cholesterol esterase and oxidase for cholesterol coupled with a peroxidase indicator, is an interesting approach.[9] More promising is the use of the enzyme cholesterol dehydrogenase instead of cholesterol oxidase, allowing the use of the dye nitroblue tetrazolium chloride (NBT), which is insoluble after reduction. Automated electrophoretic systems using this approach may be suitable for the accurate quantitation of HDL-C and other lipoproteins.[10,11] For additional information on electrophoresis of lipoproteins, refer to Chapter 30.

Precipitation

Selective chemical precipitation techniques were reported by Burstein and Samaille in 1960 as a rapid method of measuring cholesterol associated with the lipoproteins.[12] Selective precipitation of lipoproteins can occur by mixing polyanions and divalent cations or other chemicals with the serum/plasma specimens to precipitate VLDL and LDL that are sedimented by low-speed centrifugation.[13-15] Cholesterol in the supernate is quantitated by a conventional enzymic or other assay. Table 11–3 lists several of the common reagents available for selective isolation of lipoproteins.[16-20]

Each of the chemical precipitation methods has several modifications or variations that reportedly improve the selectivity or performance of the system. For example, heparin-manganese chloride methods are reported with 1.0 and 2.0 mol/L $MnCl_2$, where the lower concentration is the preferred reagent with serum and the latter with EDTA plasma. The higher concentration with plasma is required to compensate for the chelation of some of the divalent cations by EDTA and avoid incomplete precipitation of apo-B-containing lipoproteins. Dextran sulfate-$MgCl_2$ precipitation has been reported with materials of both 500,000 and 50,000 molecular weight; the HDL-C values

Table 11–3 ✧ The Most Common Precipitation Procedures for the Isolation of Lipoproteins
Heparin-Manganese Chloride[16]
Heparin-Calcium Chloride[17]
Dextran Sulfate-Magnesium Chloride[18]
Sodium Phosphotungstate-Magnesium Chloride[19]
Polyethylene glycol[20]

are significantly lower with the first reagent. The sodium phosphotungstate procedures have been used with or without $MgCl_2$, adjusted for pH and at several concentrations. Similarly, a variety of polyethylene glycol concentrations and pH conditions have been reported for HDL-C analysis.

Until a few years ago, quantitation of HDL-C in routine laboratories was performed almost exclusively using one of the precipitation techniques. The high demand for routine quantitation of HDL-C generated by its role as a CHD risk factor and its use in the estimation of LDL-C by the Friedewald calculation required a relatively simple procedure that could be partially automated using equipment readily available in the clinical laboratories. Precipitation resulted in a supernate that could be analyzed for cholesterol by the highly automated analyzers prevalent in clinical laboratories. Other methods used in the research laboratory required specialized equipment and were generally too cumbersome and technically demanding for the clinical laboratory. Therefore, compared to either ultracentrifugation or electrophoresis methods, HDL-C was more easily quantitated by the relatively simple and inexpensive selective precipitation techniques. In very recent years a new generation of fully automated methods for HDL-C, designated homogeneous assays, became commercially available and are steadily replacing the precipitation procedures in many laboratories, mainly due to the desire to avoid any manual sample pre-treatment.

Selection of the most suitable HDL reagent for a given laboratory is not a simple decision. Inordinate effort would be required to perform an in-depth evaluation of each method that would assess all possible performance characteristics and optimize procedures to ensure that the cholesterol in the supernate accurately represents the patient's HDL-C. Most laboratories rely on commercial reagents; prior to the advent of homogeneous methods, most laboratories used procedures involving either dextran sulfate[18] or sodium phosphotungstate (PTA).[19] The phosphotungstate reagent is advantageous in that the chemical is inexpensive and readily available. However, some consider the reagent unstable under extended storage, and separations may be sensitive to technique.[16] A method using dextran sulfate of 50,000 dalton was developed as a Selected Method for Clinical Chemistry[18] and became the most common of the pre-treatment methods prior to the introduction of homogeneous methods. This method is also the precursor to the DCM described subsequently.

CDC Reference Method

There is no validated Definitive Method for HDL-C. The accepted reference method has not been fully validated, as is the case for the cholesterol Reference Method. Instead, the accepted accuracy target is a procedure used at the Centers for Disease Control and Prevention (CDC) to assign HDL-C target values for human-based serum pools.[21] This procedure can be considered the best current target for accuracy because most of the major epidemiologic/population studies have used CDC pools as the reference target for analyses. Since the accepted NCEP cut-points for HDL-C are derived from such population studies, appropriate patient classification is dependent on obtaining routine results that are in agreement with the CDC method. Therefore, the CDC HDL-C method is considered appropriate for calibrating and checking the accuracy of routine methods.

There are three key components to the CDC HDL-C method, outlined below and illustrated in Figure 11–3.

1. Ultracentrifuge at density 1.006 kg/L to isolate HDL and LDL from chylomicrons and VLDL.[21] Selective precipitation procedures for HDL may be falsely elevated when increased triglyceride-rich lipoproteins (chylomicrons and VLDL) prevent their sedimentation. Therefore, ultracentrifugation eliminates these lipoproteins as potential interferences.

2. Perform selective precipitation of LDL with heparin/$MnCl_2$. CDC uses the same precipitation reagent as that used for the Lipid Research Clinics studies.

    a. *Reagents:* Pharmaceutical-grade heparin [(40,000 units/mL); Lipo-Hepin, Riker Laboratories, Minneapolis, MN] and reagent-grade $MnCl_2.4H_2O$ (available from several chemical suppliers) are used for the HDL procedure.
    b. *Solutions:* Working heparin solution (5,000 units/mL). Mix 1.0 mL heparin with 7.0 mL saline (0.15 mol/L NaCl). The solution is stable for at least 1 mo when stored at 4°C. A 1.0 mol/L $MnCl_2$ solution is prepared by dissolving 197.91 g of the tetrahydrate in water and bringing to volume in a 1.0-L volumetric flask.
    c. *Precipitation:* Add 80 µL heparin solution and 100 µL $MnCl_2$ to 2.0 mL of 1.006 bottom fraction in an ice bucket, mixing thoroughly after each addition. Let stand for 30 min in the ice bucket and centrifuge for 30 min at 1500 g and at 4°C. Recover supernates by pipetting for subsequent cholesterol analysis.

3. Analyze cholesterol in the HDL supernate by the CDC reference method, a modified Abell-Kendall assay. The Abell-Kendall reference method for TC is the accepted accuracy target for any cholesterol tests in specific lipoproteins, including HDL-C. (For additional information on the cholesterol assay refer to chapter 9.) To increase the sensitivity of the analysis in the lower HDL-C range requires twice the amount of HDL supernate required for analysis of TC.

Designated Comparison Method (DCM)

Few laboratories have an ultracentrifuge available to perform the CDC Reference Method for HDL-C. In addition, ultracentrifugation requires a sample volume greater than 5.0 mL, which exceeds the amount laboratories generally receive for a total lipid panel. Therefore, the CRMNL developed a modified dextran sulfate procedure as the DCM to provide results approximately equivalent to those of the CDC reference method on a more practical specimen volume. The reagent concentration was decreased slightly to make the separation consistent with that of the CDC Reference Method. The DCM is available through the CRMLN laboratories for comparison analysis of methods by outside laboratories and diagnostic manufacturers evaluating their accuracy.[22] (For additional information on CRMLN, refer to Chapter 36).

Figure 11–3 ✧ CDC HDL-C Reference Method

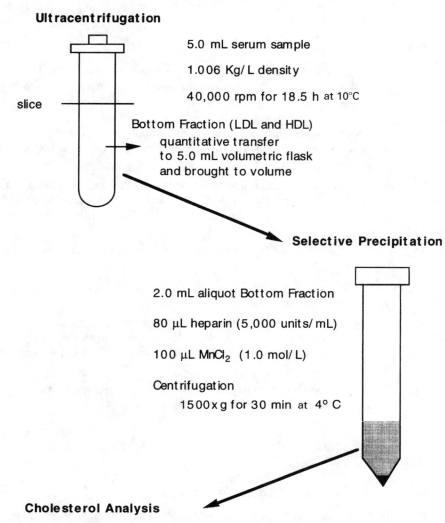

Ultracentrifugation

5.0 mL serum sample

1.006 Kg/L density

40,000 rpm for 18.5 h at 10°C

slice

Bottom Fraction (LDL and HDL)
quantitative transfer
to 5.0 mL volumetric flask
and brought to volume

Selective Precipitation

2.0 mL aliquot Bottom Fraction

80 μL heparin (5,000 units/mL)

100 μL MnCl$_2$ (1.0 mol/L)

Centrifugation
1500xg for 30 min at 4° C

Cholesterol Analysis

Modified Abell-Kendall procedure for cholesterol
optimized for the low range of HDL-C values

Solutions

✧ Stock dextran sulfate solution is prepared with 2.0 g dextran sulfate (Dextralip 50, Cat #70-5800, available from Genzyme) and 50 mg NaN$_3$ (sodium azide) in 100 mL deionized water. Store at 2°–8°C.

✧ Prepare stock 0.7 mol/L magnesium chloride with dry 14.22 g MgCl$_2$ hexa-hydrated salt and 50 mg NaN$_3$ in 100 mL deionized water. Store at 2°–8°C.

✧ Prepare combined working solution by mixing equal volumes of the two stock solutions to obtain a solution of 10 g/L dextran sulfate and 0.35 mol/L MgCl₂.

Precipitation Sequence

1. Equilibrate specimens and reagents to room temperature. It is recommended that HDL separation be performed on the same day the specimen is collected; otherwise, the sample off the cells may be stored up to 48 h at 4°C or frozen at −70°C. (Frozen samples at −15°C are probably acceptable.)

    Note: The method states the samples should be collected from individuals who have fasted 12 h–14 h. Also, samples must have TG < 200 mg/dL (2.26 mmol/L).

2. Transfer an accurate and reproducible volume of specimen (either plasma or serum) to a 4.5-mL tube. Pipette 1000 μL of well-mixed sample and add 100 μL of the combined reagent into the tube. Cap the tube with parafilm and vortex for 5 sec.

3. Incubate the tubes for 10 min starting from the time the last tube in the rack is vortexed.

4. Centrifuge the tubes at the highest speed for 32 min in a Beckman TJ-3 refrigerated centrifuge (or equivalent) set at 10°C.

5. Transfer clear supernates, without disturbing the pellet, to a suitably labeled tube. Place cloudy supernates on a low-speed centrifuge with 0.22 μm filters (Millipore Corp., Bedford, MA, catalog #AP20 29325). If supernate is not clear, do not assay.

6. Assay the supernates by enzymic or Abell-Kendall method on the same day as precipitated, or freeze at −20°C.

NEWER HDL-C METHODS

Second-Generation HDL-C Assays

Cholesterol analysis can be performed with automated chemistry analyzers, but the HDL precipitation step requires pipetting, mixing, and centrifuging, steps that are usually performed manually and are somewhat difficult to automate. These labor-intensive and time-consuming steps include the volume transfer of both the patient specimen and precipitation reagent before mixing, and the transfer of the HDL supernate after centrifugation for cholesterol analysis. If the procedure is not performed properly, significant error can be introduced into the HDL-C result. Efforts have been made to streamline the pre-treatment steps and improve the efficiency of the quantitation with robotic pipetting stations, but this has generally only been practical in laboratories with a very high workload. The following sections describe attempts by manufacturers to provide laboratories with more user-friendly methods for performing HDL-C analysis.

One alternative commercial approach involves a plastic device (Spin-Pro) that contains pre-measured precipitation reagent.[23] The user simply adds an unmeasured volume of serum or plasma in the top of the plastic tube and centrifuges the device. During centrifugation, a measured portion of the sample mixes with the precipitation reagent and the resultant precipitate sediments. After centrifugation, the supernate rises into the central well and the device can be placed in the sample tray of a chemistry analyzer for direct sampling. This device streamlines and standardizes the HDL separation.

A second commercial method involves the use of dextran sulfate linked to encapsulated iron beads. This allows for the separation of the complexed lipoproteins (VLDL and LDL) from the HDL-containing supernate with a magnet rather than a centrifuge, an advantage especially for smaller laboratories.[24,25] Magnets can also be placed directly in the sample tray slots, streamlining separation in conjunction with automated chemistry analyses. The specificity of separation was carefully investigated by using lipoprotein electrophoresis and apolipoprotein measurements of the supernatant and the precipitate, which did not show any contamination.[24] Correlation coefficients with two different comparison methods in two independent studies were 0.96 and 0.98, and the slopes were 0.94 and 1.00, respectively. The average biases were negative (-0.7 mg/dL; -0.02 mmol/L compared with dextran sulfate precipitation), but positive compared with the phosphotungstic acid/MgCl2 procedure ($+3.8$ mg/dl; 0.1 mmol/L)[24,25]. Samples with TG concentrations above 1000 mg/dL (11.3 mmol/L) should be assayed both undiluted and after dilution with 0.9% saline. However, spiking experiments with VLDL showed that at TG concentrations above 500 mg/dL (5.65 mmol/L) HDL-C results were falsely decreased. Hemoglobin increased the observed HDL-C concentrations; increased concentrations of free fatty acids did not interfere. For physican office laboratories and other point-of-care sites, compact analyzers have been developed with integrated HDL separation schemes that use whole blood and eliminate the need for pre-treatment steps.[26,27] (See Chapter 13.)

Third-Generation (Homogeneous) HDL-C Assays

The newer commercial methods for HDL-C analysis, all developed in Japan, can be fully automated, eliminating the tedious manual steps of the precipitation assays (see Figure 11–4). In fact, the only sample handling required may be as simple as placing a bar-coded specimen on the automated analyzer and allowing the system to do the rest of the work. These recently released methods can be readily adapted to the modern highly automated analyzers in clinical laboratories and provide cost savings; even through the reagents are more expensive, this is generally offset by decreased labor costs. Another advantage of these newer methods is the improved precision gained from automated pipetting by the analyzer, which may help laboratories achieve NCEP analytical performance goals. During the past few years, clinical laboratories have rapidly adopted these methods based on their capability for full automation and consequent cost savings. Thus, these new third-generation HDL-C assays will likely have a significant impact on the performance of HDL-C analysis by clinical laboratories.

Figure 11–4 ✧ Third-Generation (Homogeneous) HDL-C Assays. These New HDL-cholesterol Assays all Share One Common Trait: The Use of Detergents, Surfactants, or Antibodies to Modify the Surface of Chylomicrons, VLDL, and LDL. The Altered Lipoproteins Have Reduced Activity Towards Cholesterol Oxidase and Esterase. Thus, the Primary Substrate for These Enzymes Is HDL and Its Cholesterol Contents Is Readily Quantitated

---

PEG HDL-C (Kyowa Medix/Roche Diagnostics)

1. CM, VLDL, and LDL + α-cyclodextrin + $MgCl_2$ $\longrightarrow$
   soluble complexes of CM, VLDL, and LDL

2. HDL + PEG modified CE and CO $\longrightarrow$
   Cholestenone + H_2O_2

3. H_2O_2 + 4AAP/peroxidase $\longrightarrow$ Color

SP HDL-C (Daiichi/Genzyme)

1. CM, VLDL, and LDL + synthetic polymers $\longrightarrow$
   soluble complexes of CM, VLDL, and LDL

2. HDL + selective detergent + CE and CO $\longrightarrow$
   Cholestenone + H_2O_2

3. H_2O_2 + 4AAP/peroxidase $\longrightarrow$ Color

Immunologic HDL-C (International Reagent Corp)

1. CM, VLDL, and LDL + antibodies to apoB/C-III + detergents
   $\longrightarrow$ insoluble complexes of CM, VLDL, and LDL

2. HDL + CE and CO $\longrightarrow$ Cholestenone + H_2O_2

3. H_2O_2 + 4AAP/peroxidase $\longrightarrow$ Color

4. Guanidine HCl to stop enzymatic reaction and solubilize Lps from 1.

2nd Immunologic HDL-C (Wako/Sigma)

1. CM, VLDL, and LDL + antibodies to apoB $\longrightarrow$
   soluble complexes of CM, VLDL, and LDL

2. HDL + CE and CO $\longrightarrow$ Cholestenone + H_2O_2

3. H_2O_2 + 4AAP/peroxidase $\longrightarrow$ Color

Figure 11–4 ✧ (Continued)

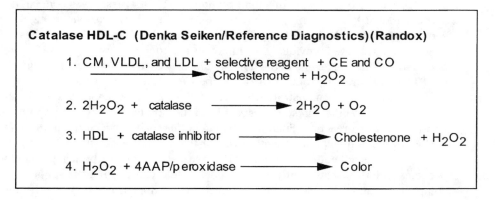

Catalase HDL-C (Denka Seiken/Reference Diagnostics)(Randox)

1. CM, VLDL, and LDL + selective reagent + CE and CO $\longrightarrow$ Cholestenone + H_2O_2

2. $2H_2O_2$ + catalase $\longrightarrow$ $2H_2O + O_2$

3. HDL + catalase inhibitor $\longrightarrow$ Cholestenone + H_2O_2

4. H_2O_2 + 4AAP/peroxidase $\longrightarrow$ Color

HDL-C Determination Using Polyethylene-Glycol-Modified Enzymes

A method reported by Kyowa Medix in 1995 and distributed by Roche Diagnostics (formerly Boehringer Mannheim) uses sulfated α-cyclodextrin, $MgCl_2$, polyethylene-glycol (PEG)-modified cholesterol esterase, and oxidase to obtain specificity to cholesterol in HDL.[28] Sulfated α-cyclodextrin, in the presence of 2 mol/L $MgCl_2$, reduced the activity of the modified enzymes with both VLDL and chylomicrons. The α-cyclodextrin-lipoprotein interactions resulted in soluble complexes that do not react and do not interfere with the absorbance readings of the enzyme cholesterol reagents. In addition, the authors found the 6,000-dalton form of PEG to be the most efficient in maintaining functional activity towards cholesterol and cholesterol esters with intact HDL. However, this PEG simultaneously inhibited the interaction of these enzymes with the other complexed lipoproteins, especially LDL.

Several evaluations of this assay have been published. In most studies, the precision of this assay was very good with total CVs below 3.1 %. The detection limit of the PEG HDL-C assay was about 3 mg/dL (0.08 mmol/L) and the test was linear up to at least 150 mg/dL (3.89 mmol/L) HDL-C.

An early report from Okamoto et al.[29] used gel chromatography to separate lipoproteins according to their size. These authors showed that the homogeneous assay using PEG-modified enzymes includes the measurement of apo-E-containing HDL particles; this population was precipitated by the PTA procedure and, therefore, not measured as HDL-C. Consequently, the HDL-C results were about 10% higher using the homogeneous method in comparison to the PTA procedure. Because the apo-E-containing HDL particles belong to the HDL population, they recommended using the homogeneous assay to determine HDL-C concentrations. This finding was confirmed by Okazaki et al.[30] when they compared this homogeneous method with a high-performance liquid chromatography (HPLC) procedure. They found a very good agreement between these two methods (PEG=1.026HPLC − 0.75 mg/dL (0.02 mmol/L); r=0.998); whereas, a combined PTA dextran sulfate/$MgCl_2$ method showed a negative bias towards the HPLC procedure (PTA=0.84HPLC + 10.2 mg/dL (0.26 mmol/L); r=0.987). In a study performed in Taiwan, the homogeneous PEG HDL-C assay was compared with a conventional PTA precipitation procedure. Both methods correlated highly with each other in normo- (r=0.987) and hypertriglyceridemic (r=0.953) samples. However, as demonstrated previously, a y-intercept of about 5–7 mg/dL (0.13–0.2 mmol/L) occurred, so that the results of the homogeneous assay were significantly higher than the PTA procedure. The total error ranged between 12% and 28%.[31]

These studies demonstrate that this particular homogeneous assay yielded an HDL fraction that differs in some respect from the HDL found in the supernate of the PTA precipitation reaction. Such a systematic difference between the homogeneous PEG assay and a precipitation method, or for that matter between any two precipitation methods, is not entirely surprising. HDL represents a polydispersed population of particles differing significantly in physicochemical characteristics, apolipoprotein composition, and pathobiochemical significance. On the basis of their apo E content, two populations of HDL particles can be distinguished: those without apo E, and those with apo E. The latter amounts to approximately 10% of the total HDL-C and is not measured by the PTA assay,[32] in contrast to the homogeneous PEG assay.[29] Other precipitation methods have been reported to include the apo-E-containing HDL fraction. How the various HDL subfractions behave in other homogeneous methods has not yet been established.

The homogeneous PEG HDL-C assay showed excellent agreement with both the CDC-Reference Method (RM) for HDL-C (PEG = 1.068RM − 1.7 mg/dL (0.04 mmol/L), r=0.993, mean bias: 2.2%) and the DCM for HDL-C (PEG = 1.037DCM + 0.4 mg/dL (0.01 mmol/L), r =0.996, mean bias: 4.5 %). The latter comparisons were performed only in samples with total TG below 200 mg/dL (2.26 mmol/L).[33]

In a multi-center study performed in six laboratories in Europe, comparisons with a PTA precipitation method from Roche Diagnostics (formerly Boehringer Mannheim) gave results with correlation coefficients from 0.96 to 0.99 but slopes that ranged from 0.95 to 1.08. In this study, a preliminary HDL-C concentration of the calibrator, given by the manufacturer, was used. Overall, the results of the homogeneous HDL-C assay showed a systematic error of 3% compared to the CDC Reference Method and the PTA procedure. However, as a result of the reference standardization and the pre-marketing evaluation, a calibrator reassignment was recommended and the manufacturer adjusted the calibrator by the suggested 3% to reduce the bias.[33,34] In an optimal setting, the total error of this assay should be less than or equal to 7.5%, which is below the 13% error recommended by the NCEP.

An earlier comparison of the homogeneous PEG HDL-C assay with the combined ultracentrifugation/dextran sulfate method revealed a slope of 0.87 with a negligible y-intercept that resulted in a (negative) total error of 15% to 21%.[24] This large bias was not reproduced with the assay distributed by Roche Diagnostics using a different calibrator.

However, in additional comparisons, the promising results of the multi-center study and the reference standardization could not be reproduced when performed with the first commercial reagents introduced to the market. The correlation coefficients were high (r=0.987), and the slope also was 12% too high; whereas, the y-intercept was only 1.0 mg/dL (0.03 mmol/L).[25] At the clinical decision cut-off points of 35 and 60 mg/dL (091 and 1.55 mmol/L), total errors of 16.2% and 14.5% were observed. However, subsequent calibrator lots yielded results as expected from the reference standardization (y=0.994x + 2.1 mg/dL (0.05 mmol/L), r=0.997).[35,36] Similar agreement was observed by other investigators.[37]

The challenges in appropriately assigning target values for calibrators are obvious from these studies. The discrepant behavior of the homogeneous PEG assay and the PTA procedure with regard to apo-E-containing HDL may at least in part account for the bias found between the two methods. The concentration of the calibrator for the PEG assay now appears to be usually correct, which is supported by a U.S. proficiency survey.[14,15,19,38,39] However, users should be aware of this issue and carefully verify the accuracy of each new calibrator lot, which can be accomplished by a comparison study with one of the CRMNL laboratories.

In 1998, the PEG reagent was significantly modified by replacing the former lyophilized second reagent with a liquid formula. In addition, concentrations of enzymes were modified and the dye was replaced. A multi-center study with this new liquid assay resulted in performance characteristics similar to the older lyophilized version.[40] Both homogeneous PEG assays correlated highly with each other in seven different laboratories (r=0.989) and gave a mean deviation of 0.2 mg/dL (0.005 mmol/L). Comparison with the DCM showed a good correspondence (PEG= 0.968DCM + 2.49 mg/dL (0.06 mmol/L), r=0.996) and resulted in a total error at the HDL-C decision points of 35 and 60 mg/dL (0.91 and 1.55 mmol/L) of 7.3% and 3.4%, respectively. These data fully agree with the predicted deviations.[33]

Triglyceride concentrations up to about 1000 mg/dL (11.3 mmol/L) do not interfere with the homogeneous PEG HDL assay. It is important to note that TG interference does not differ in dependence on the predominance of chylomicrons or VLDL. It was shown with the liquid version that hypertriglyceridemic samples should be diluted with 0.9% saline so that the TG concentration in the diluted sample was below 1800 mg/dL (20.34 mmol/L) in order to obtain reliable HDL-C determinations. LDL-C concentrations of 300–400 mg/dL (7.77–10.36 mmol/L) did not show a significant bias; LDL-C concentrations above 600 mg/dL (15.54 mmol/L) falsely elevated the PEG HDL-C assay. Hemoglobin up to concentrations of 10,000 mg/L did not interfere, whereas in more hemolytic samples, a slight negative bias was observed with the PEG HDL-C assay. Bilirubin concentrations above 10 mg/dL (0.17 mmol/L) yielded discrepant results when the homogeneous PEG assay was compared with the precipitation procedures, but it is likely that the interference in this homogeneous assay was less pronounced. No interference was observed in sera with elevated free fatty acids. In some samples with paraproteinemia, discrepant results were observed when compared to the PTA procedure. Heparinized plasma can be used with no problem, but the results with EDTA plasma should be multiplied by 1.06. Interferences caused by hemoglobin and bilirubin are much less pronounced in this homogeneous assay as compared to conventional precipitation procedures.

Other Pitfalls

In sera of patients with manifest Type III hyperlipoproteinemia, falsely high results by the homogeneous PEG HDL-C assay were observed. This leads to the assumption that the cholesterol content of some remnant particles was included with the HDL-C.[41] A very recent report focused on the accuracy of readings in mice.[42] In mice with normal cholesterol and TG concentrations, the PTA precipitation and the PEG assay showed a good agreement. If these mice (C57BL/6) became hyperlipidemic by eating a high-fat and high-cholesterol diet, they accumulated cholesterol-rich remnant particles. Under such conditions the homogeneous PEG assay overestimated the HDL-C by 72%. In apo-E-deficient mice, where remnant lipoproteins accumulate, the overestimation was 228%. This discordance depended on the degree of hyperlipidemia, because the apo-E-deficient mice showed much higher VLDL-C plus LDL-C concentrations. Therefore, the PEG assay should be used in animal models and in specimens containing high amounts of remnant-like particles only with great caution, because HDL-C overestimation of the PEG assay must be taken into consideration.

It is currently not known if the homogeneous PEG assay is able to determine HDL-C concentrations reliably from patients with liver diseases. Because the interference caused by bilirubin is rather low, serum with atypical lipoprotein composition might give different results with this homogeneous HDL-C assay.

HDL-C Determination Using Synthetic Polymers (SP)

A homogeneous assay developed by Daiichi and distributed by Genzyme Diagnostics incubates the specimen with a reagent that forms stable complexes with all apo-B-containing lipoproteins. Unlike previous HDL precipitation methods, these complexed-lipoprotein particles remain soluble in the reaction mixture. However, HDL remain nearly free of the complexing agents. In the second step, the selective detergent, enzymic reagents, cholesterol oxidase, and esterase are added. These enzymes only react with the HDL particles, whereas the apo-B-containing lipoproteins remain stable in their complexed form. Very recently, the occurrence of the complexes and the selectivity of these processes were shown by Kondo et al. using electron microscopy.[43]

Like the PEG HDL-C assay, the homogeneous SP HDL-C assay was distributed during the first years as a lyophilized reagent. Evaluations performed during this period showed a poor specificity to HDL-C.[23,25,31,44] Even very low VLDL-C and LDL-C concentrations resulted in falsely elevated HDL-C measurements by this SP assay. On the other hand, the recovery was only about 70% when HDL isolated by ultracentrifugation was added to specimens in spiking experiments.

The results of the regression lines of the method comparisons with a combined ultracentrifugation and dextran sulfate precipitation procedure (UC/DS) were discrepant in samples with TG both below and above 400 mg/dL (4.52 mmol/L) [TG < 400 mg/dL (4.52 mmol/L): SP=0.96UC/DS + 0.8 mg/dL (0.02 mmol/L); TG ≥ 400 mg/dL (4.52 mmol/L): SP =0.85UC/DS + 10.8 mg/dL (0.28 mmol/L)] in spite of a high correlation coefficient of 0.96 in both comparisons.[23] In another evaluation, compared to a PTA precipitation procedure, the regression lines showed the opposite behavior: In samples with TG < 400 mg/dL (4.52 mmol/L) the slope of the regression line was significantly below 1.00 [SP=0.84PTA + 10.5 mg/dL (0.27 mmol/L), r=0.986]; whereas, in samples with TG > 400 mg/dL (4.52 mmol/L), the regression fitted much better [SP = 0.96PTA + 7.6 mg/dL (0.20 mmol/L); r=0.864].[31] However, in both subsets the y-intercept of the regression lines were significantly higher than zero. The total errors of the SP assay were below 13%, with the exception of a set of samples with TG concentrations > 400 mg/dL (4.52 mmol/L) or low HDL-C concentrations.[23,25,31,44] From this point of view the assay met the current NCEP criteria for HDL-C determination. The drawbacks of these evaluations were that the accuracy was never determined using the CDC Reference Method or DCM as the accuracy base for HDL-C. However, according to the lack of specificity, this earlier-generation assay could not be recommended for the use in a clinical chemical laboratory,[25,31] especially in hypertriglyceridemic samples[23] or in patients with liver cirrhosis.[44]

In the meantime, the assay has been significantly improved and is now available as a liquid reagent. A new detergent directly hydrolyzes the HDL particles, whereas, in the lyophilized version, polyanion-polymer interactions were used to sequester non-HDL and the HDL were disrupted by a general detergent.

The comparison of the improved SP HDL-C assay with the CDC Reference Method [SP=1.020RM + 0.2 mg/dL (0.01 mmol/L); r=0.985] and the DCM [SP=1.015DCM + 1 mg/dl (0.03 mmol/L); r=0.993] showed mean biases of 1.5% and 3.3%, respectively. The total errors at the HDL-C decision points of 35 and 60 mg/dL (0.91 and 1.55 mmol/L) were 5.1% and 5.3%, respectively. These easily meet current NCEP requirements.[45]

Two independent comparisons with the PTA procedure yielded comparable results with excellent correlation coefficients of about 0.99 and a mean bias of about 3 mg/dL (0.08 mmol/L).[36,45] The CV of repeated measurements (between run and total CV) of the new liquid version was, in both publications, below 2.1%. The detection limit was between 0.3 and 4 mg/dL (0.01 and 0.1 mmol/L); the assay was at least linear up to 120 mg/dL (3.1 mmol/L), which is clinically sufficient. Spiking experiments with isolated VLDL and LDL revealed no interference up to 700 mg/dL (18.13 mmol/L) LDL-C and 1900 mg/dL (21.47 mmol/L) VLDL-TG. Spiking experiments with bilirubin up to 30 mg/dL (0.51 mmol/L), free hemoglobin up to 6000 mg/L, ascorbic acid up to 50 mg/dL (2.84 mmol/L), and gamma globulin levels up to 10,000 mg/L did not show an interference of more than 5%. Using the SP HDL-C method sera with high concentrations of IgG or IgM paraproteins produced similar results after dilution with 0.9% saline. In contrast to the lyophilized version, the liquid SP HDL-C assay did not show any interference in samples with elevated concentrations of free fatty acids.[25] Comparison of samples of 10 subjects drawn in the fasting or postprandial state revealed mean HDL-C concentrations of 44.65 and 43.95 mg/dL (1.16 and 1.14 mmol/L), respectively,[45] suggesting fasting is not required for reliable results.

Other Pitfalls

In the study from Escolà-Gil, which evaluated the accuracy of homogeneous HDL-C methods in mice, the SP assay was also included.[42] The mice developed hyperlipidemia with accumulation of remnant-like particles, which was induced by high-fat feeding or due to apo-E-knock-out animals. In apo-E-deficient animals with high concentrations of remnant particles, the SP assay overestimated the HDL-C by 101%. In contrast to the PEG assay, no data are currently available in humans with manifest Type III hyperlipoproteinemia. Surprisingly, no difference was observed using EDTA plasma instead of serum, despite the fact that EDTA has an osmotic effect and causes a dilution of about 3% to 6.0%.[46,47] On the other hand, in heparinized plasma a small but statistically significant difference was observed.

The evaluation by Simó et al.[44] concluded that the set point of the calibrator was incorrect. In addition, the concordance of the SP HDL-C assay with a PEG precipitation method depended on the patients selected for the comparison. The best results were obtained in healthy controls and elderly people; the scatter increased in patients with myocardial infarction, nephrotic syndrome, and liver cirrhosis. However, this study was performed with the old lyophilized reagent and there are no data available about the current liquid formula with respect to such patient groups.

Immunological Separation for the Determination of HDL-C

In 1996 the first report of a homogeneous HDL-C assay (designated IRC) was published by International Reagent Corp., Kobe Japan. This report described the separation of HDL by blocking apo-B-containing lipoproteins with detergents and antibodies directed against apo B and apo C-III.[48] This first assay required four successive reagent additions. In the first step 4 μL of sample were incubated with 60 μL PEG of 4000 dalton for 1.5 min to complex chylomicrons, VLDL, and LDL. In the second step, 100 μL of antibodies specific for apo B and apo C-III were added to produce aggregates of chylomicrons, VLDL, and LDL. After an additional incubation of 3.5 min, 130 μL of enzymatic cholesterol reagent was added, containing cholesterol esterase (EC 3.1.1.13), cholesterol oxidase (EC 1.1.3.6), peroxidase (EC 1.11.1.7), and 4-aminoantipyrine as dye. The enzymes were allowed to react with the cholesterol of the non-complexed lipoproteins for 5 min. Subsequently, 200 μL of guanidine hydrochloride were added and incubated with the reaction mixture for 5 min to stop the enzymatic reactions and to solubilize the aggregates of chylomicrons, VLDL, and LDL, formed in step one and two, that would otherwise interfere with the subsequent reading of the absorption. The absorbance of the product formed by the cholesterol oxidase/peroxidase reaction was measured bichromatically after a time interval of 5 min at 600 (signal) and 700 (noise) nm.

Total imprecision of this assay ranged between 2.4% and 8.4%, comparable with the precipitation procedure. The detection limit of 3 mg/dL (0.08 mmol/L) and a linearity up to 150 mg/dL (3.89 mmol/L) were adequate. The homogeneous assay was in good agreement with a conventional PTA precipitation procedure [IRC=0.987PTA + 1.72 mg/dL (0.04 mmol/L); r=0.970]. LDL-C and VLDL-C up to 400 mg/dL (10.36 mmol/L) and 80 mg/dL (2.07 mmol/L) [corresponding to 400 mg/dL (4.52 mmol/L) TG] did not interfere substantially with the HDL-C measurements. However, increasing LDL-C up to 650 mg/dL (16.84 mmol/L) and VLDL-C up to 250 mg/dL (6.48 mmol/L) [corresponding to > 1100 mg/dL (12.43 mmol/L) TG] falsely elevated the HDL-C measurements by about 50%. Intralipid® up to 2500 mg/dL (28.25 mmol/L) did not influence the HDL-C determinations; hemoglobin significantly increased, and bilirubin lowered, the results of the HDL-C assay. In spite of the fact that this assay showed reasonable performance characteristics, it was not introduced to the market because of the limited number of analyzers that are able to use four different reagents for one test.

In 1998 Wako (distributed by Sigma Diagnostics) introduced another homogeneous HDL assay using antibodies to separate HDL from apo-B-containing lipoproteins.[25,37,49] Antibodies to human apo B react with non-HDL particles, i.e., chylomicrons, VLDL, and LDL (reagent 1). These complexes do not react with the enzymes involved in the subsequent enzymatic cholesterol measurement, whereas the cholesterol content of the HDL particles is measured (reagent 2). The precision of the assay is very high (total CV $\leq$ 1.8%). The assay was linear up to at least 100 mg/dL (2.59 mmol/L) and was not subject to interference by LDL-C and VLDL-TG up to 600 and 900 mg/dL (15.54 and 10.17 mmol/L) respectively. In contrast to the previous IRC assay, these interferences were significantly reduced, because the antibody concentrations of the Wako assay were sufficient to complex all non-HDL particles. The PTA precipitation method, performed with and without ultracentrifugation to remove VLDL, showed a good correlation to this immunoseparation-based homogeneous method. However, the slope of the regression line was significantly greater than 1.00 and had a positive y-intercept, resulting in significantly increased HDL-C results [41.4 vs. 33.6 mg/dL (1.07 vs. 0.87 mmol/L)]. According to the high systematic error, the total error was 22.3% and 15.6% at the clinical decision point for HDL-C at 35 and 60 mg/dL (0.91 and 1.55 mmol/L). These data indicate that the set point of the calibrator was not optimal at the time the study was performed. In samples with relatively high deviations between the methods, the Wako assay tended to overestimate HDL-C in samples with elevated concentrations of free fatty acids.

Hemoglobin up to 2000 mg/L did not interfere with this homogeneous HDL-C assay. In summary, the Wako assay produces precise HDL-C measurements, but should be improved in regard to calibration. In addition, the assay is very specific for HDL-C and the accuracy is not limited by cross-reactivity to LDL and VLDL. In this aspect and due to the use of only two reagents, the Wako assay represents a significant improvement over the IRC assay.

Catalase Reagent Method (CAT)

Another homogeneous reagent, developed by Denka Seiken Co. (Niigata, Japan), was presented in abstract and poster by the US distributor, Reference Diagnostics (Bedford, MA) at the 1998 annual meeting of American Association for Clinical Chemistry.[50] (A reagent with apparently identical characteristics is also distributed by Randox.) This method reportedly uses a selective reagent with cholesterol esterase and oxidase to generate peroxidase from the cholesterol in lipoproteins other than HDL. The initial non-HDL derived peroxidase is scavenged by catalase. A second reagent includes an inhibitor to the catalase and reacts with the HDL-C through a coupled peroxidase sequence to give specific color. Precision consistent with CVs of 2.3% was reported. The method was linear from 9 to 147mg/dL (0.23 to 3.81 mmol/L) and observed insignificant interference from TG below 1700 mg/dL (19.21 mmol/L), bilirubin to 25 mg/dL (0.43 mmol/L), ascorbic acid to 50 mg/dL (2.85 mmol/L), and hemoglobin to 5000 mg/L. The relationship by linear regression to the PEG method was as follows: CAT = 1.09PEG -4.9 mg/dL (-0.127 mmol/L) with r = 0.966.

Standardization of HDL-C Measurements

Standardization of TC measurements has been improved by the activities of the CRMLN, which was organized by CDC to make reference methods readily available for direct comparison on fresh patient specimens. Recently, the Network has established a similar program for standardizing HDL-C measurement using the DCM described above. The CRMLN laboratories will be available to manufacturers and clinical laboratories to verify the accuracy of their HDL-C methods. A detailed protocol for conducting a comparison study is available through the Network program. (See Chapter 36 for additional information on the Network Laboratories.)

In addition to participating in the CDC Network program, diagnostic manufacturers and individual laboratories may wish to perform supplementary validation. The following set of universal evaluation and performance considerations is presented to enable a laboratory to validate an HDL-C procedure. These evaluation steps are primarily appropriate for HDL-C separation by pre-treatment precipitation procedures. Nevertheless some aspects will be appropriate for the new homogeneous HDL-C assays that require standardization and a reliable set point for the calibrator. Therefore, point 4 of the following list should be carefully performed and checked repeatedly, before and after the introduction of any homogeneous HDL-C method in a clinical chemistry laboratory.

1. Optimize the cholesterol method.
   a. Linearity from 0–120 mg/dL (0–3.11 mmol/L).
   b. Reproducibility with 1SD = 2 mg/dL (0.05 mmol/L) or less.

2. Establish reproducible specimen and reagent transfers using precise pipettes. Methods may be automated using programmable dispensing apparatus. For example, the Beckman Accu-Prep or Micromedic systems are capable of high precision. High-volume laboratories may automate this process to the extent of achieving a "walk-away" system.

3. Establish specific conditions for specimen processing.
   a. Length of time for mixing (vortexing).
   b. Time and temperature for incubation.
   c. Time, temperature, and force of centrifugation.

4. Compare HDL-C results on fresh patient specimen with a reliable laboratory using accurate methods.
   a. The CRMLN sponsored by CDC is available for such comparisons (phone 770-488-4126 for additional information).
   b. Patient specimens should be distributed throughout the usual assay range of 20–100 mg/dL (0.52–2.59 mmol/L).
   c. Analyze specimens stored or shipped under similar conditions at about the same time to minimize confounding effects of specimen deterioration.

The following experiments can be performed to assess the specificity and separation characteristics of precipitation-based HDL-C procedures:

1. Lipoprotein electrophoresis of the supernates and resolubilized precipitates indicates the specificity of the separation. The HDL precipitates should be first washed with saline/precipitation reagent solution and then dissolved with 0.6 mol/L NaCl prior to electrophoresis. The supernate should have an HDL or al-

pha band only and no beta or pre-beta band, and the precipitate should have no HDL band. The sensitivity of this technique depends upon the characteristics of the stain used with the particular electrophoresis method.

2. Analysis of both the supernates and solubilized precipitates for apo AI and apo B can assess the possible inadequate separation of lipoproteins; for example, apo B in the supernate would suggest the presence of non-HDL contamination. High levels of apo AI in the precipitate suggest precipitation of HDL.

3. Select several patient specimens with varying amounts of TG to compare the performance of the HDL-C assay at low and increased concentrations of TG. Some HDL-C methods experience incomplete sedimentation and supernatant turbidity when TG exceed 400–500 mg/dL (4.52–5.65 mmol/L). Specimens with chylomicrons can give erroneous values, often yielding cloudy supernates and overestimated HDL. Such specimens should be re-precipitated after dilution or the supernates filtered to obtain reliable results.

SUMMARY

HDL-C analysis has been routine for almost 20 years, and yet there is still a need to improve analytical performance to ensure that HDL-C results meet clinical requirements. The analytical goals for accuracy and precision developed by the NCEP provide a performance target for clinical laboratories. The CDC-CRMLN program, which has been effective in standardizing TC, provides a similar service for HDL-C. This will facilitate improvements in accuracy.

Development and widespread availability of HDL-C reference materials that behave as patient specimens (no matrix effects) for use in comparing other HDL-C assays to the consensus reference procedure would make the standardization process more efficient. Manufacturers should be encouraged to take advantage of the opportunity to validate and standardize their methods, as this will improve performance in many laboratories.

The importance of accurate HDL-C measurements was emphasized by Robert Levy, MD, past director of the National Heart Lung and Blood Institute, who made the following statement concerning HDL-C performance requirements in *Clinical Chemistry*[51] almost two decades ago:

> One has to be able to measure accurately in the range below 50 mg/dL (1.30 mmol/L) a difference of less than 5 mg/dL (0.13 mmol/L) if the HDL determination is to be used to define an individual's risk.

The newer generation HDL-C assays will help laboratories achieve this lofty performance standard. The new fully automated procedures will likely provide better precision in HDL-C measurements, which in turn will lead to better comparison studies to resolve biases that may exist between different approaches. Development of better HDL-C reference materials that can be used to transfer accuracy among methods is a critical component that would facilitate this process. ✧

REFERENCES

1. The Expert Panel. Summary of the second report of the National Cholesterol Education Program (NCEP) expert panel on detection, evaluation, and treatment of high blood cholesterol in adults (Adult Treatment Panel II). JAMA 1993;269:3015–23.
2. Prevention of coronary heart disease: scientific background and new clinical guidelines. Recommendations of the European Atherosclerosis Society prepared by the International Task Force for Prevention of coronary heart disease. Nutr Metab Cardiovasc Dis 1992;2:113–56.
3. Fuster V, Badimon L, Badimon J, Chesebro J. The pathogenesis of coronary artery disease and the acute coronary syndromes. N Eng J Med 1992;326:242–50.
4. Warnick GR, Wood PD. National Cholesterol Education Program recommendations for measurement of high-density-lipoprotein cholesterol: executive summary. The National Cholesterol Education Program Working Group on Lipoprotein Measurement. Clin Chem 1995;41:1427–33.
5. The Lipid Research Clinics population studies data book. Vol 1: The prevalence study. (NIH Publication No. 80–1527). Bethesda, MD: National Institute of Health, 1980.
6. Lindgren F, Jensen LC, Hatch FT. The isolation and quantitative analysis of serum lipoproteins. In: Nelson GF (ed.), Blood lipids and lipoproteins: quantitation, composition, and metabolism. Wiley Intersience, 1972:181–274.
7. Lewis LA and Oppelt JJ (eds.). CRC handbook of electrophoresis. Vol. 1. Boca Raton: CRC Press, 1980.
8. Neubeck W, Wieland H, Habenicht A, Müller P, Baggio G, Seidel D. Improved assessment of plasma lipoprotein patterns. III. Direct measurement of lipoproteins after gel-electrophoresis. Clin Chem 1977;23:1296–1300.
9. Conlon D, Blankstein L, Pasakarins P, Steinberg C, D'Amelio J. Quantitative determination of high-density-lipoprotein cholesterol by agarose gel electrophoresis. Clin Chem 1979;25:1965–9.
10. Nauck M, Graziani M, Jarausch J, Bruton D, Cobbaert C, Cole TG, et al. A new liquid homogeneous assay for HDL cholesterol determination evaluated in seven laboratories in Europe and the United States. Clin Chem Lab Med 1999;37:1067–76.
11. Contois J, Gillmor R, Moore R, Contois L, Macer J, Wu A. Quantitative determination of cholesterol in lipoprotein fractions by electrophoresis. Clin Chim Acta. 1999;282:1–14.
12. Burstein M, Samaille J. Sur un dosage rapide du cholesterol lie aux a- et aux b-lipoproteins du serum. Clin Chim Acta 1960;5:609.
13. Levin SJ. High-density-lipoprotein cholesterol: review of methods. American Society of Clinical Pathologists. Core Chemistry No. PTS 89-2 (PTS-36) 5/2, 1989.
14. Warnick GR, Cheung MC, Albers JJ. Comparison of current methods for high-density-lipoprotein cholesterol quantitation. Clin Chem 1979;25:596–604.
15. Demacker PN, Vos-Janssen HE, Hijmans AG, van't Laar A, Jansen AP. Measurement of high-density-lipoprotein cholesterol in serum: comparison of six isolation methods combined with enzymic cholesterol analysis. Clin Chem 1980;26:1780–86.
16. Warnick G, Albers JJ. A comprehensive evaluation of the heparin-manganese precipitation procedure for estimating high-density-lipoprotein cholesterol. J Lipid Res 1978;19:65–76.
17. Srinivasan S, Radhakrishnamurthy B, Berenson G. Studies on the interaction of heparin with serum lipoproteins in the presence of Ca2+, Mg2+, and Mn2+. Arch Biochem Biophys 1975;170:334–40.
18. Warnick G, Benderson J, Albers JJ. Dextran sulfate-Mg2+ precipitation procedure for quantitation of high-density-lipoprotein cholesterol. Clin Chem 1982;28:1379–88.
19. Lopes-Virella MF, Stone P, Ellis S, Colwell JA. Cholesterol determination in high-density-lipoproteins separated by three different methods. Clin Chem 1977;23:882–84.
20. Briggs C, Anderson D, Johnson P, Deegan T. Evaluation of the polyethylene glycol precipitation method for the estimation of high-density-lipoprotein cholesterol. Ann Clin Biochem 1981;18:177–81.

21. Hainline A, Karon J, Lippel K, eds. Manual of laboratory operations. In: Lipid Research Clinics Program, Lipid and lipoprotein analysis, 2nd ed. Bethesda, MD: U.S. Dept. Health and Human Services, 1982.

22. Kimberly M, Leary E, Cole T, Waymack P. Selection, validation, standardization, and performance of a designated comparison method for HDL-cholesterol for use in the cholesterol reference method laboratory network. Clin Chem 1999;45:1803–12.

23. Harris N, Galpachian V, Thomas J, Iannotti E, Law T, Rifai N. Three generations of high-density-lipoprotein cholesterol assays compared with ultracentrifugation/dextran sulfate-Mg2+ method. Clin Chem 1997;43:816–23.

24. Harris N, Galpchian V, Rifai N. Three routine methods for measuring high-density-lipoprotein cholesterol compared with the Reference Method. Clin Chem 1996;42:738–43.

25. Nauck M, März W, Wieland H. New immunoseparation based homogeneous assay for HDL-cholesterol compared with three homogeneous and two heterogeneous methods for HDL-cholesterol. Clin Chem 1998;44:1443–51.

26. Beranek J, Carlson C, Roberts P, Feld R. Evaluation of the Cholestech LDX lipid analyzer for cholesterol, triglyceride, and HDL cholesterol (HDL-C) using whole blood. Clin Chem 1994;40:S1104.

27. Bodewll J, Roberts K. An evaluation of three lots of Reflotron HDL-cholesterol. Clin Chem 1992;38:S1062.

28. Sugiuchi H, Uji Y, Okabe H, Irie T, Uekama K, Kayahara N, et al. Direct measurement of high-density-lipoprotein cholesterol in serum with polyethylene-glycol-modified enzymes and sulfated alpha-cyclodextrin. Clin Chem 1995;41:717–23.

29. Okamoto Y, Tanaka S, Nakano H. Direct measurement of HDL cholesterol preferable to precipitation method. Clin Chem 1995;41:1784.

30. Okazaki M, Sasamoto K, Muramatsu T, Hosaki S. Evaluation of precipitation and direct methods for HDL-cholesterol assay by HPLC . Clin Chem 1997;43:1885-90.

31. Huang YC, Kao JT, Tsai KS. Evaluation of two homogeneous methods for measuring high-density-lipoprotein cholesterol. Clin Chem 1997;43:1048–55.

32. Okamoto Y, Tsujii H, Haga Y, Tanaka S, Nakano H. Determination of apolipoprotein E in high-density-lipoprotein fraction by immunofixation method and turbidimetric immunoassay after precipitation. J Atheroscler Thromb 1994;1:23–29.

33. Cobbaert C, Zwang L, Ceriotti F, Modenese A, Cremer P, Herrmann W, et al. Reference standardization and triglyceride interference of a new homogenous HDL-cholesterol assay compared with a former chemical precipitation assay. Clin Chem 1998;44:779–89.

34. Nauck M, März W, Jarausch J, Cobbaert C, Sägers A, Bernard D, et al. Multi-center evaluation of a homogeneous assay for HDL-cholesterol without sample pre-treatment. Clin Chem 1997;43:1622–29.

35. Arranz-Pena M, Tasende-Mata J, Martin-Gil F. Comparison of two homogeneous assays with a precipitation method and an ultracentrifugation method for the measurement of HDL-cholesterol. Clin Chem 1998;44:2499–505.

36. Nauck M, Neumann I, März W, Wieland H. A new liquid homogeneous assay for the determination of HDL cholesterol. A comparison to precipitation with phosphotungstic acid/MgCl2 and a lyophilized homogenous assay. Clin Chem Lab Med 1999;37:537–43.

37. de Keijzer M, Elbers D, Baadenhuijsen H, Demacker PNM. Evaluation of five different high-density-lipoprotein cholesterol assays: the most precise are not the most accurate. Ann Clin Biochem 1999;36:168–75.

38. Rifai N, Cole TG, Ianotti E, Law T, Macke M, Miller R, et al. Assessment of inter-laboratory performance in external proficiency testing programs with a direct HDL-cholesterol assay. Clin Chem 1998;44:1452-58.

39. Warnick GR, Albers JJ, Leary ET. HDL cholesterol: results of inter-laboratory proficiency tests. Clin Chem 1980;26:169–70.

40. Nauck M, Graziani M, Jarausch J, Bruton D, Cobbaert C, Cole TG, et al. A new liquid homogeneous assay for HDL cholesterol determination evaluated in seven laboratories in Europe and the United States. Clin Chem Lab Med 1999;37:(in press).

41. Lackner K, Schmitz G. Beta-VLDL of patients with type III hyperlipoproteinemia interferes with homogeneous determination of HDL-cholesterol based on polyethylene glycol-modified enzymes. Clin Chem 1998;44:2546–8.

42. Escola-Gil J, Jorba O, Julve-Gil J, Gonzalez-Sastre F, Ordonez-Llanos J, Blanco-Vaca F. Pitfalls of direct HDL-cholesterol measurements in mouse models of hyperlipidemia and atherosclerosis. Clin Chem 1999;45:1567-9.

43. Kondo A, Muranaka Y, Ohta I, Kanno T. Dynamic reaction in a homogeneous HDL-cholesterol assay visualized by Electron Microscopy. Clin Chem 1999;45:1974–80.

44. Simo J, Castellano I, Ferre N, Joven J, Camps J. Evaluation of a homogeneous assay for high-density-lipoprotein cholesterol: limitations in patients with cardiovascular, renal, and hepatic disorders. Clin Chem 1998;44:1233–41.

45. Halloran P, Roetering H, Pisani T, van den Berg B, Cobbaert C. Reference standardization and analytical performance of a liquid homogeneous high-density-lipoprotein cholesterol method compared with chemical precipitation method. Arch Path Lab Med 1999; 123:317–26.

46. Cloey T, Bachorik PS, Becker D, Finney C, Lowry D, Sigmund W. Re-evaluation of serum-plasma differences in total cholesterol concentration. JAMA 1992;267:234–5.

47. Behesti I, Wessels LM, Eckfeldt JH. EDTA-plasma vs. serum differences in cholesterol, high-density-lipoprotein cholesterol, and triglyceride as measured by several methods. Clin Chem 1994;40:2088–92.

48. Nauck M, März W, Haas B, Wieland H. Homogeneous assay for direct determination of high-density lipoprotein cholesterol evaluated. Clin Chem 1996;42:424–29.

49. Lin M, Hoke C, Ettinger B. Evaluation of homogeneous high-density-lipoprotein cholesterol assay on a BM/Hitachi 747-200 analyzer. Clin Chem 1998;44:1050–2.

50. Lawlor J, Pelczar D, Sane R, Siek G. Performance characteristis of the RDI homogeneous HDL cholesterol assay. Clin Chem 1998;44:A79.

51. Levy R. Cholesetrol, lipoproteins, apoproteins, and heart disease: present status and future prospects. Clin Chem 1981;27:653–62.

Measurement of Low-Density-Lipoprotein Cholesterol

12

Paul S. Bachorik

✧ In serum or plasma from normal fasting individuals, cholesterol is associated with three major classes of lipoproteins: very-low-density lipoprotein (VLDL, $d <$ 1.006 kg/L); low-density lipoprotein (LDL, d 1.019–1.063 kg/L); and high-density lipoprotein (HDL, d 1.063–1.21 kg/L). About two-thirds of this cholesterol is associated with LDL and most of the remainder is carried by the other two lipoproteins. A small amount of cholesterol (2–4 mg/dL [0.50–1.0 mmol/L], on average) is also found in intermediate-density lipoprotein (IDL, d 1.006–1.019 kg/L) and Lp(a) (d 1.045–1.080 kg/L), although the concentrations of both of these lipoproteins can be considerably higher in certain individuals. In addition, patients with Type III hyperlipoproteinemia manifest an unusual lipoprotein called beta-VLDL, or "floating beta" lipoprotein, which is not present in normal individuals.[1]

LDL is formed in the circulation as the end product of VLDL catabolism. During this process, VLDL-triglycerides are hydrolyzed, and apolipoproteins other than apolipoprotein B (apo B) are removed. Intermediates in this process include VLDL remnants, part of which are removed by the liver, and IDL, which arise from the further catabolism of VLDL remnants. IDL is ultimately converted to LDL.

LDL is a spherical molecule consisting of a hydrophobic core of cholesteryl esters and triglycerides (TG) surrounded by an amphipathic coat composed of phospholipids, unesterified cholesterol, and apo B-100. Each LDL molecule contains one mole of apo B-100. Small amounts of apo C-III (0.34–1.90 molecules) and apo E (0.08–0.74 molecules)[2] are also present on LDL. The lipids, as a percentage of the total mass of the LDL particle, consist of about 38% cholesterol ester, 22% phospholipid (principally phosphatidyl choline and sphingomyelin), 11% TG, and 8% unesterified cholesterol.[3] Protein makes up about 21% of the lipoprotein mass, and of this, 95% or more is apo B.

LDL cholesterol (LDL-C) plays a causal role in the development of atherosclerosis. In 1988, the National Cholesterol Education Program Adult Treatment Panel (NCEP-ATP) developed recommendations for the diagnosis and treatment of patients with hypercholesterolemia.[4] These recommendations define hypercholesterolemia and use LDL-C as the primary criterion for treatment. The treatment recommendations are based on the patient's LDL-C concentration and also take into account a number of other risk factors. The ATP recommendations were updated in 1993.[5] The revised guidelines still use LDL-C concentration and risk factor profile as the primary

Table 12–1 ✧ NCEP Guidelines for Adults and Classification for Children and Adolescents[1]

Revised NCEP Guidelines for Adults: Initiation of Therapy		
	Initial Concentration	*Goal of Therapy*
Without 2 or more CHD risk factors	LDL-C ≥ 160 mg/dL(4.14 mmol/L)	LDL-C < 160 mg/dL(4.14 mmol/L)
With 2 or more CHD risk factors	LDL-C ≥ 130 mg/dL(3.36 mmol/L)	LDL-C < 130 mg/dL(3.36 mmol/L)
Revised NCEP Guidelines for Adults: Initiation of Drug Therapy after Diet Therapy		
	Initial Concentration	*Goal of Therapy*
Without 2 or more CHD risk factors	LDL-C ≥ 190 mg/dL(4.92 mmol/L)	LDL-C < 160 mg/dL(4.14 mmol/L)
With 2 or more CHD risk factors	LDL-C ≥ 160 mg/dL(4.14 mmol/L)	LDL-C < 130 mg/dL(3.36 mmol/L)
With CHD	LDL-C ≥ 130 mg/dL(3.36 mmol/L)	LDL-C < 100 mg/dL(2.59 mmol/L)
NCEP Classification for Children and Adolescents		
Desirable: LDL-C < 110 mg/dL (2.85 mmol/L)		
Borderline: LDL-C 110–129 mg/dL (2.85–.34 mmol/L)		
High: LDL-C >130 mg/dL (3.36 mmol/L		

[1]See Chapter 5 for list of risk factors.

treatment criteria, but additional emphasis was placed on the measurement of HDL-cholesterol (HDL-C) (see Chapter 11). The NCEP has also issued recommendations for the classification of cholesterol levels in children and adolescents;[6] these are given in Table 12–1. For additional information on the NCEP guidelines, refer to chapter 5.

METHODOLOGY

General

Measurement of LDL-C requires *separating* LDL particles in serum from other lipoproteins, followed by *measuring* cholesterol in the LDL fraction. LDL can be separated from VLDL and HDL based on physical characteristics such as density, size, charge, or apolipoprotein composition. Some of the approaches that have been used are described briefly here.

Because of their lipid content, lipoproteins densities are lower than those of the other serum proteins, and the lipoproteins can be separated from them, and from each other, using the ultracentrifuge. Methods for lipoprotein separation with the analytical ultracentrifuge were developed in the 1950s[7–9] and are used today in some research laboratories. In this technique, the lipoproteins are separated according to their rates of flotation under defined conditions of density, temperature, and ultracentrifugal force. After lipoprotein migration, the changes in optical refraction during centrifugation are measured. The result is expressed as the total mass of lipoproteins, but this number does not provide information about their lipid or protein compositions. Analytical ultracentrifugation is useful for certain kinds of physical chemical studies and is the basis for the original definition of the lipoproteins in terms of their flotation rates and densities. Because of the complexity of the method, however, it is not suitable for use in the routine clinical laboratory or even in most research laboratories.

Sequential ultracentrifugation was developed by Havel, Eder, and Bragdon[10] in 1955. In this technique, the sample is ultracentrifuged at an appropriate density (e.g., d 1.006 kg/L for VLDL), and the floating layer is collected. The infranatant is then adjusted to the next density (e.g., d 1.019 kg/L), ultracentrifuged again, and the lipoproteins that float at the new density, in this case IDL, are recovered. The process is repeated until all lipoprotein fractions of interest have been isolated.[10,11] Lipoproteins can be isolated within any desired density interval and in sufficient quantities to allow for multiple chemical analyses. Sequential ultracentrifugation continues to be used today for preparing lipoproteins in quantities sufficient for studies in cells and for other purposes. It is also used for clinical purposes in certain circumstances (see discussion below).

Equilibrium density gradient ultracentrifugation evolved from sequential ultracentrifugation.[12–22] In this approach, the sample is placed onto a density gradient that is generally constructed using solutions of a dense salt, such as KBr. A smooth density gradient can be constructed with the aid of a gradient maker. Alternatively, a series of solutions of different density can be layered onto each other to produce a gradient that is discontinuous initially, but that becomes smooth during ultracentrifugation. When ultracentrifuged, each lipoprotein migrates to its isopycnic (equilibrium) density, and the separated lipoproteins are collected for analysis. Depending on the density gradient used, this method can be used either to separate the major classes of lipoproteins from each other, or to separate each lipoprotein class into several subfractions whose densities and sizes differ slightly. Once collected, the lipoproteins or their subfractions can then be quantitated by measuring their cholesterol (or other compositional component) content. The technique is labor intensive and its throughput is limited compared to the more commonly used methods (see discussion below). For this reason, its use is confined primarily to the research laboratory, although a commercial lipoprotein analytical service is available that uses a procedure based on density gradient ultracentrifugation (VAP Atherotech, Inc., Birmingham, AL). For additional information about ultracentrifugation refer to Chapter 32.

Other methods for separating LDL-C include gel filtration and other types of chromatography, electrophoresis, and precipitation or binding with appropriate reagents.

Gel Filtration Methods

The gel filtration methods include agarose column chromatography,[23] high-performance gel filtration chromatography,[24,25] and fast-flow gel filtration.[26] Affinity chromatography using heparin, dextran sulfate, or antibodies to apo B, linked to Sepharose gels, has also been used to isolate LDL. Some chromatographic methods can exhibit considerable biases compared to ultracentrifugation for LDL and HDL.[25] For additional information, refer to Chapter 33.

Electrophoretic Methods

Electrophoretic methods separate lipoproteins according to their charge and size. They are primarily used for qualitatively assessing the presence of beta-VLDL, which is characteristic of Type III hyperlipoproteinemia (see discussion below). Electrophoretic methods are available from commercial sources as kits containing pre-formed agarose gels, buffer, and stain. A small quantity of the sample, typically 1–2 µL, is applied to the gel and electrophoresis is conducted at pH 8.6. The separated lipoproteins are made visible using lipophilic stains such as Oil Red O or Sudan Black B or with enzymatic cholesterol reagents. Because the lipoproteins contain essentially all the circulating lipids, the use of lipid stains precludes the need to separate the lipoproteins from the other plasma proteins. Figure 12–1 illustrates the migration of LDL and other lipoproteins using agarose gel electrophoresis.

Although attempts have been made to quantitate the separated lipoproteins by densitometry or by measuring lipoprotein cholesterol enzymatically in the separated fractions, these methods have not been widely accepted for this purpose for several reasons. First, the apo-B-containing lipoproteins cannot be completely resolved from each other. For example, in paper or agarose gel, IDL can run as a smear overlapping LDL and VLDL; Lp(a) generally migrates with or near VLDL; and beta-VLDL, when present, co-migrates with LDL. Second, electrophoretic methods can be imprecise because of lot-to-lot and gel-to-gel variations in the gels themselves. Third, depending on their lipid composition, the intensity of staining per mole of lipoprotein differs among the lipoproteins. An extreme example of this occurs with samples from patients with biliary cirrhosis, who have high concentrations of unesterified cholesterol. Because unesterified cholesterol is not well visualized with lipophilic stains, electropherograms from such patients can appear normal despite the presence of cholesterol in concentrations above 1,000 mg/dL (25.9 mmol/L).[27] For additional information on electrophoretic separations, refer to Chapter 30.

Selective Chemical Precipitation

Various methods for selective chemical precipitation have been reported.[28–34] In these methods, LDL-C is calculated as the difference between total cholesterol (TC) and that which remains soluble after precipitating LDL. Such methods can be reasonably accurate in samples with low TG concentrations, but can be quite inaccurate in samples with high TG concentrations.[28,29,33–37] In general, precipitation methods have been most successfully applied to remove the apo-B-containing lipoproteins from HDL rather than to separate apo-B-containing lipoproteins from each other, because they can also precipitate some of the remnants and IDL present in many samples with high TG concentrations.

Finally, using immunochemical techniques, LDL can be separated from the

Figure 12–1 ✧ Representation of agarose electropherogram of normal plasma (A) and plasma from patient with Type III hyperlipoproteinemia (B). Left to right: patterns observed in unfractionated plasma; ultracentrifugal top fraction (d < 1.006 kg/L); and ultracentrifugal bottom fraction (d > 1.006 kg/L). When present, β-VLDL ("floating beta lipoprotein") appears in the ultracentrifugal top fraction as a band with the mobility of LDL. Note also that when Lp(a) is present in sufficiently high concentration (~ 30 mg/dL) it is observed in the ultracentrifugal bottom fraction as a band with mobility similar to VLDL. Lp(a) is not shown in this diagram.

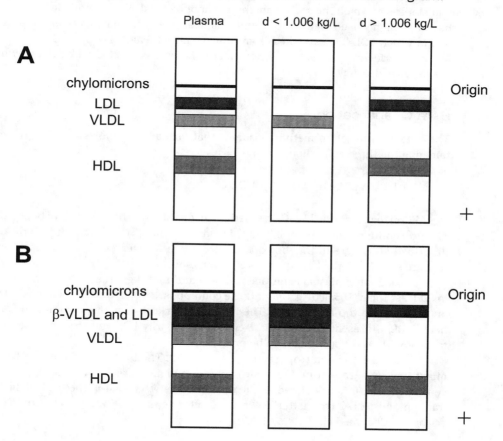

other lipoproteins using specific antibodies to particular apolipoproteins found in HDL and in the other apo-B-containing lipoproteins. This approach is the basis for a method described later in this chapter.

COMMON METHODS FOR LDL-C MEASUREMENT

The following discussion describes the most commonly used methods for LDL-C measurement, as well as relatively new methods for direct LDL-C measurement.

Clinical LDL-C measurements, and those in most large-scale clinical and epidemiological studies, particularly those from which the relationships between LDL-C concentration and risk for coronary heart disease (CHD) were established, were made using one of two methods.[38] The first method combines ultracentrifugation and polyanion precipitation and is generally referred to as "beta quantification." Because the method is somewhat involved, it is not generally used for routine clinical measurements. Rather, beta quantification is primarily used in the initial diagnosis of hyperlipoproteinemia to rule out Type III hyperlipoproteinemia, and in certain circumstances in which the second method cannot be used. The second, and by far the most commonly used method for routine clinical purposes and large-scale studies, is one in which LDL-C is estimated from primary measurements of TC, TG, and HDL-C using the Friedewald equation.[39] Both methods have been studied extensively and are described below.

Beta Quantification

The beta quantification method assumes that virtually all cholesterol (TC) is contained in the three major lipoprotein classes:

(a) TC = VLDL-C + LDL-C + HDL-C

In addition to measuring LDL-C, the method also evaluates the presence of beta-VLDL. The procedure requires several kinds of measurements (TC, TG, and HDL-C) that are described elsewhere in this book. This discussion focuses on those manipulations that are specific to the beta quantification method.

An aliquot of plasma is ultracentrifuged at d 1.006 kg/L (i.e., at its own density) for at least 18h at 105,000 Xg. Under these conditions, the VLDL accumulates as a floating layer at the top of the tube. The floating layer also contains chylomicrons and beta-VLDL, if present. The infranate contains primarily LDL and HDL, but also contains any IDL and Lp(a) that may be present.

The VLDL fraction (top fraction) is removed. The bottom fraction is collected quantitatively, reconstituted to known volume, and measured for its cholesterol concentration. LDL-C is calculated as the difference between that in the d 1.006 bottom fraction and HDL-C (the latter determined after separation by precipitation as described in Chapter 11):

(b) LDL-C = [d 1.006 kg/L bottom-C] − HDL-C

Because the TG-rich lipoproteins are removed from the sample, neither high TG concentrations nor chylomicrons nor beta-VLDL affect the measurement of LDL-C in the d 1.006 kg/L bottom C.

VLDL-C is calculated as the difference between TC and that in the ultracentrifugal bottom fraction:

(c) VLDL-C = TC − [d 1.006 kg/L bottom-C]

VLDL-C is not generally quantitated directly in the d 1.006 kg/L supernate because it can be difficult to recover the top fraction quantitatively, particularly in samples with high TG concentrations.

What is referred to as "LDL-C" actually contains the contributions of intermediate-density lipoprotein cholesterol (IDL-C) and lipoprotein(a) cholesterol (Lp[a]-C) also. Since IDL and Lp(a) are both thought to be atherogenic,[40–43] the "LDL-C" measurement actually represents the amount of cholesterol being transported in potentially atherogenic particles. In normal individuals, IDL concentrations contribute only about 2 mg/dL (0.05 mmol/L) to the LDL-C measurement, but IDL-C concentrations may be considerably higher in certain patients with high TG concentrations in whom IDL may be overproduced or not cleared normally. On average, Lp(a) also contributes only about 3–4 mg/dL (0.08–0.1 mmol/L) to the measured LDL-C.[38] Lp(a) concentrations, however, are largely genetically determined and are independent of the concentrations of the other plasma lipoproteins. Therefore, the contribution of Lp(a)-C to the measurement cannot be readily evaluated without actually measuring Lp(a). It has been estimated that Lp(a) would contribute about 7% to the LDL-C measurement in a patient with a measured LDL-C concentration of 130 mg/dL (3.37 mmol/L) and an Lp(a) concentration of 30 mg/dL (expressed as total Lp[a] mass).[38]

A more accurate estimation of the concentration of LDL-C itself (LDL-C$_{corr}$) could be made by adjusting the observed LDL-C (LDL-C$_{obs}$) value for the contribution of Lp(a). This can be done using the following relationship:[43,44]

(d) $\text{LDL-C}_{corr} = \text{LDL-C}_{obs} - [0.3 \times \text{Lp(a) mass}]$

where LDL-C$_{obs}$ is the measured LDL-C concentration and the factor 0.3 x Lp(a) mass represents the average sterol content of Lp(a).

It should be kept in mind, however, that the risk cut-offs relating LDL-C levels to cardiovascular disease[4,5] include the contributions of both IDL-C and Lp(a)-C. It is likely that correcting the measured LDL-C value for the contribution of either IDL or Lp(a) would decrease the sensitivity of the LDL-C measurement as a risk indicator because it would not include all of the potentially atherogenic lipoproteins. Furthermore, patients who are at risk for CHD can, as a group, be expected to have higher concentrations of both IDL-C and Lp(a)-C. Adjusting the LDL-C measurements in this group would be expected to invalidate, to some extent, the current risk-based cut-offs for LDL-C. After considering these factors, the NCEP Working Group on Lipoprotein Measurement recommended that LDL-C measurements not be corrected for the contribution of Lp(a)-C.[38]

Type III hyperlipoproteinemia, a rare genetic disorder, is characterized in part by the presence of beta-VLDL, an unusual lipoprotein that when present is found in the ultracentrifugal top fraction, but migrates electrophoretically with LDL (beta lipoprotein) rather than VLDL (pre-beta lipoprotein)[1] (see Figure 12–1). When present, beta-VLDL can be observed electrophoretically as a beta-migrating band in the ultracentrifugal top fraction, and for this reason has been called "floating beta" lipoprotein. Because it is richer in cholesterol than normal VLDL, it increases the amount of cholesterol in the VLDL fraction. Thus, the ratio of cholesterol to TG in the VLDL-containing fraction is higher in Type III hyperlipoproteinemia than in normal individuals or patients with other lipoprotein disorders. The beta quantification method includes two assessments for the presence of beta-VLDL, one quantitative and the other qualitative.

The quantitative indicator is to determine the ratio of VLDL-C to plasma TG. This assumes that most of the plasma TG is carried on VLDL. This ratio is < 0.3 in normal individuals or those with other forms of hyperlipoproteinemia. Because beta-VLDL is enriched in cholesterol compared to normal VLDL, the Type III pattern is indicated when the ratio exceeds 0.3. It is not unusual for the VLDL-C:plasma TG ratio to be 0.4 or higher in Type III patients.

The qualitative indicator is the observation of beta-VLDL in the ultracentrifugal top fraction when examined electrophoretically. The procedure is performed as follows. Aliquots of unfractionated plasma, and the two ultracentrifugal fractions, are subjected to agarose gel electrophoresis at pH 8.6. In this evaluation, focus is on the top fraction. The unfractionated plasma and the ultracentrifugal bottom fraction serve to help mark the position of the LDL band, i.e., each sample serves as its own control.

VLDL migrates with pre-beta mobility and is observed in the ultracentrifugal top fraction as in Figure 12–1. LDL and HDL have beta and alpha mobility, respectively, and are found in the bottom fraction. When present, beta VLDL is also observed in the top fraction, but as a band with LDL mobility. The observation of a VLDL-C:plasma TG ratio > 0.3 and beta-VLDL in the ultracentrifugal top fraction defines the Type III pattern. This pattern tends to persist even in treated Type III patients. The interpretation of the electrophoretic pattern, however, requires skill and can be equivocal in some samples.

LDL-C Estimation Using the Friedewald Equation

This method also assumes that TC is distributed among the three major lipoprotein classes. Using measurements of TC, TG, and HDL-C, the empirical equation of Friedewald et al.[39] is used to calculate LDL-C as follows:

(e) LDL-C = TC − HDL-C − TG/5

where the factor TG/5 is an estimate of VLDL-C when contractions are expressed in mg/dL or TG/2.22 when they are expressed in mmol/L. As with beta quantification, "LDL-C" estimated in this way also contains the contributions of IDL-C and Lp(a)-C.

The Friedewald equation gives LDL-C values within about 2 mg/dL (0.05 mmol/L) of those determined by beta quantification when the samples have TG values up to about 200 mg/dL (2.26 mmol/L), and in practice the equation can be used with samples having TG concentrations up to 400 mg/dL (4.52 mmol/L).

The equation cannot be used in certain cases. It cannot be used in samples with TG > 400 mg/dL (4.52 mmol/L) or in samples with significant amounts of chylomicrons, as occurs in non-fasting samples. The TG:cholesterol ratio of normal VLDL is about 5:1. In samples with high TG or significant chylomicrons, however, the VLDL fraction can contain more TG than normal VLDL, and the factor plasma TG/5, when cholesterol is expressed in mg/dL or TG/2.22 when expressed in mmol/L, will not give a sufficiently accurate estimate of cholesterol associated with this lipoprotein fraction. For example, the TG:cholesterol ratio of chylomicrons can be 15:1 or higher. Thus, the factor TG/5 simply does not apply, and use of the Friedewald equation in such cases will over-estimate the amount of cholesterol associated with the VLDL fraction. This produces an underestimate of LDL-C, and in some instances can obscure the presence of increased LDL-C.

The error is in the opposite direction if the equation is applied to the Type III patient. In this case, the TG:cholesterol ratio of the VLDL fraction will be 3:1 or lower due to the presence of beta-VLDL, which is richer in cholesterol than normal VLDL. Use of the Friedewald formula in this case underestimates the amount of cholesterol in the VLDL fraction and therefore overestimates LDL-C. Thus, a Type III patient can be misdiagnosed as having a high LDL-C concentration (Type II hyperlipoproteinemia), and since the two disorders are managed differently, such a misdiagnosis can lead to inappropriate treatment. It is for this reason that beta quantification is used in the initial evaluation of Type III hyperlipoproteinemia, and thereafter whenever an accurate LDL-C measurement is needed.

These considerations normally do not preclude the use of the Friedewald equation for most clinical or research purposes. First, chylomicrons are not normally present in plasma from fasting patients, and when present in significant amounts are visible as a floating layer when plasma is allowed to stand in the refrigerator overnight. Second, samples with TG exceeding 400 mg/dL (4.52 mmol/L) are generally turbid, although the author has occasionally observed a clear sample with a TG concentration in the 400–500 mg/dL (4.52–5.65 mmol/L) range. Third, the 99th percentile for TG is under 300 mg/dL (3.39 mmol/L), even in women taking estrogens.[45] Finally, the prevalence of Type III hyperlipoproteinemia is about 1–2 per thousand in the general population.[46] Thus, the Friedewald equation generally can be used with most individuals, and most samples for which it is not appropriate can be detected simply by observing whether the sample is turbid or contains significant amounts of chylomicrons after standing in the refrigerator overnight. Such samples would then be referred for analysis by beta quantification, if necessary.

DIRECT METHODS FOR LDL-C MEASUREMENT

General

Efforts have been made to develop methods capable of measuring LDL-C directly, rather than calculating it from several primary measurements. A fairly simple direct LDL-C method, developed by Genzyme Corporation, is available as a kit from several distributors. This method uses polyclonal antibodies to apo AI, and apo E attached to latex beads, to remove lipoproteins other than LDL in a manual pre-treatment step. LDL-C is then measured directly in the resulting supernatant. This is a promising approach, but the currently limited information available on its performance is somewhat inconsistent.

For example, Leary et al.[47] presented data indicating that the direct method tended to run 7%–10% high compared with beta quantification, but displayed a fairly high correlation with the beta quantification method ($r = 0.96$). On the other hand,

Devaraj et al.[48] reported no significant difference in LDL-C values of samples from 249 patients when measured with the direct method compared to beta quantification, but the correlation between the two methods was only about 0.89. This is fairly low for two methods that should be measuring the same thing in the same samples. Harris et al.[49] found average biases of about −6% in samples from 96 fasting patients, and +14% in 42 samples from non-fasting, hypertriglyceridemic patients, when compared with beta quantification. Bias was related to both TG and LDL-C concentration, and the correlation between the two methods was only 0.86 when the two groups were combined, although it was a little better (0.93) in samples from fasting patients. However, McNamara et al.[50] also found very little bias between the two methods in samples from 115 patients, and reported a very good correlation ($r = 0.97$) between the direct LDL method and beta quantification. The reproducibility (i.e., co-efficient of analytical variation) of the direct LDL method was found to be in the same range as for conventional LDL-C measurements,[49–51] despite the fact that it requires less sample handling and only a single cholesterol measurement, and it appeared to offer no clear advantage over the conventional methods in terms of precision.[51]

This particular method has several intriguing characteristics that deserve further study. First, some workers found no significant difference in LDL-C concentrations in samples from fasting or non-fasting patients.[50] Since it is known that following a fat-containing meal LDL-C undergoes actual compositional changes that transiently lower LDL-C values,[52–54] it is not clear why this was not observed with this direct method. It might be noted that other researchers using this method did observe a postprandial decrease of about 5%,[48] about as expected.

Second, the method cannot be used in frozen samples, since freezing has been found to *reduce* the measured LDL-C values by up to 25%.[48–50] The loss of LDL-C increases with storage time.[50] Again, it is not clear why this should occur. Indeed, assuming complete removal of lipoproteins containing apo A-I and apo E in fresh samples, one might expect that if freezing had any effect at all, it would be to change the immunochemical properties of those lipoproteins containing apo A-I and apo E such that they might not be completely removed. This should *increase* rather than decrease measured LDL-C values. The observed decrease in LDL-C values implies that some of the LDL itself may become bound after freezing. Such large decreases have not been observed when applying the conventional methods to frozen specimens, however, and it is not apparent why losses of this magnitude occur using antibodies that are specific for apo A-I and apo E, since neither apolipoprotein is found in LDL.

Finally, apparently neither immunochemical nor chemical precipitation methods for LDL-C can be used in lyophilized samples either, as evidenced by the 20% negative biases observed for these methods among laboratories participating in the College of American Pathologists Chemistry Proficiency Surveys[55] (Table 12–2). The large losses observed with the direct method in both frozen and lyophilized samples makes the method unsuitable for long-term clinical or epidemiological studies because they preclude the assessment of analytical bias or long-term analytical trends. They also complicate quality control monitoring of routine clinical measurements, because frozen or lyophilized serum pools cannot be used for this purpose. Further study is needed to develop reagents that overcome these difficulties.

A newer direct method for LDL-C capable of full automation was recently devised

Table 12–2 ✧ Accuracy and Precision of LDL-C Measurements[1]

Pool	CDC Confirming value[2](mg/dL)	Mean[3]	Mean Bias[4]	CV[5]
Friedewald equation				
LP-01	126.9	127.0	0.1%	5.7%
LP-02	159.2	181.4	13.9%	5.7%
LP-06	151.3	143.2	−5.4%	6.5%
LP-07	172.2	172.3	0.6%	5.6%
Precipitation methods				
LP-01	126.9	101.6	−19.9%	25.3%
LP-02	159.2	132.4	−16.8%	22.7%
LP-06	151.3	123.3	−18.5%	28.9%
LP-07	172.2	143.5	−20.0%	21.8%

[1]Data from CAP Clinical Chemistry Surveys. Northfield, IL: College of American Pathologists, 1999.
[2]CDC-confirming values were calculated by CAP from CDC-confirming values for TC, TG, and HDL-C using the equation (mg/dL): LDL-C = TC − HDL-C − (TG/5). To convert to mmol/L, multiply by 0.0259.
[3]Results from 2945 to 2989 participating laboratories (Friedewald method), or 69 to 77 participating laboratories (precipitation methods).
[4]Bias with respect to CDC-confirming values.
[5]CV, coefficient of variation, calculated as (SD/mean) x 100. CV refers to among-laboratory analytical variation.

by Sugiuchi et al.[56] This method uses a non-ionic detergent, polyoxyethylene-polyoxy-propylene block co-polymer (POE-POP), in combination with α-cyclodextrin, dextran sulfate, and Mg^{+2} to block chylomicrons, VLDL, and HDL such that the cholesterol in these lipoproteins does not react with the enzymatic cholesterol reagent used to measure LDL-C. These interactions take place without precipitating the lipoproteins, allowing LDL-C to be measured directly in serum or plasma using an automated analyzer without the need for off-line pre-treatment. The method was also found to allow the reaction of IDL-C, and the authors presented evidence that Lp(a)-C also reacts.[56] It therefore seems to detect the potentially atherogenic particles that are included in LDL-C measurements made with the beta quantification and Friedewald methods. The authors reported correlations of = 0.98 between the direct method and beta quantification, and the method did not appear to be affected by high concentrations of TG.[56]

Rifai et al.[57] evaluated another commercially available fully automated direct method (Equal Diagnostics, Exton, PA) using serum, heparin-plasma, and EDTA plasma. They reported that LDL-C concentrations measured in serum or heparin-plasma were not significantly different. As expected, the values in EDTA plasma averaged about 3% lower than in serum, due to the osmotic effect of EDTA, which dilutes non-diffusable plasma constituents slightly. The direct method was fairly highly correlated with the beta quantification method (r = 0.95). It exhibited an average negative bias of 4.5% in 199 patient specimens analyzed over a one-month period. The among-day imprecision of the method was reflected in coefficients of analytical variation of < 4%. The authors reported no significant bias related to TG concentrations up to 1132 mg/dL (12.78 mmol/L), or in response to the addition of TG-rich lipoprotein in concentrations up to about 1078 mg/dL (12.18mmol/L). The lack of interference by endogenous or added TG-rich lipoproteins suggests that the blocking reagents were very effective in preventing the reaction of cholesterol in chylomicrons and VLDL. In addition, there were no significant changes in LDL-C values after periods of storage for up to one month at 4°C, −20°C, or −80°C.[57]

Interestingly, Rifai et al.[57] also reported no significant change in LDL-C in postprandial specimens taken several hours after a meal containing 31 g fat. Again, the basis for this observation is not clear because LDL-C generally decreases in response to a fat-containing meal. The authors speculated that a portion of VLDL remnants may have been included in the LDL-C measurement and compensated for the lower level of postprandial LDL-C.[57]

Nauck et al.[58] recently evaluated another direct LDL-C method, a commercial version of the method developed by Sugiuchi et al. (Roche Diagnostics, Indianapolis, IN). They similarly reported a high correlation between the direct LDL-C method and beta quantification (r = 0.97) in 355 fresh serum specimens. The method showed a negative bias of 6 mg/dL (0.155 mmol/L; about 4.4 percent) in samples with TG concentrations below 400 mg/dL (4.52 mmol/L), and the bias was independent of LDL-C concentration. There was no significant TG-related bias up to TG concentrations of 600 mg/dL (6.78 mmol/L), but the method was affected by higher concentrations of TG-rich lipoproteins and reached about 10% in specimens with TG > 1,000 mg/dL (11.3 mmol/L). The authors reported CVs of 3% or less for the direct method. The findings with this direct method were similar to those of Rifai et al.[57] However, unlike that study, these investigators did find a postprandial decrease of 6.2% in LDL-C.[58] Apparently, this direct LDL-C method was capable of detecting the physiological decrease in LDL-C that occurs in response to fat-feeding.

Originally, it was expected that if LDL-C could be measured directly, the measurements would be made more quickly, and would be more precise because the process would involve only a single measurement. In general, however, neither of these expectations has been realized. First, the development of excellent methods for measuring HDL-C directly in unfractionated serum or plasma obviated the need for the preliminary removal of apoB-containing lipoproteins, and allowed HDL-C to be measured simultaneously with TC and TG. LDL-C can then be calculated immediately. Second, improvements in TC, TG, and HDL-C methods and instrumentation have made these measurements more precise, and there has proven to be no meaningful difference between the precision of direct LDL-C methods and the Friedewald method.

Overall, however, the newer, detergent-based direct methods simplify the measurement of LDL-C, and based on the limited information currently available, they seem capable of providing accurate and precise measurements. It is therefore worthwhile to consider their potential in the context of patient care. For diagnostic purposes and in many cases for follow-up also, LDL-C measurement alone is not sufficient; TG and HDL-C must also be considered.[4,5] One exception, of course, would be when monitoring treatment in patients whose only lipoprotein abnormality is an elevated LDL-C, a condition that is much less common than combined elevations of LDL-C and TG, or elevated TG and low HDL-C. At first glance, it might appear that since TG and HDL-C must be measured anyway and LDL-C can be readily calculated with the Friedewald equation, the direct methods would have limited use. However, the Friedewald equation requires the measurement of TC also. It becomes less accurate at higher TG concentrations and cannot be used at all in specimens with TG exceeding 400 mg/dL. Direct LDL-C methods, on the other hand, would obviate the need for the TC measurement altogether, and they appear not to be affected very much over the range of TG concentration usually encountered in patients with hypertriglyceridemia. The direct LDL-C methods can therefore be more broadly applied than the Friedewald method. The direct methods are still quite new, however; they must be validated further and must be more widely evaluated under field conditions before they can replace conventional Friedewald measurements. Nonetheless, they promise to be quite useful additions to clinical lipoprotein methodology.

REFERENCE METHOD FOR LDL CHOLESTEROL DETERMINATION

Since LDL does not have a unique chemical structure, it has not been possible to develop a true reference method for LDL-C measurement. For this reason, "accuracy" must be defined functionally, i.e., in terms of the methods used for the measurement.[38] The method that CDC uses for this purpose is based on beta quantification, but differs from that described above in two ways. First, in order to eliminate interference with the HDL-C measurement in samples with high TG (see discussion of HDL measurement in Chapter 11), the HDL-containing fraction is prepared by precipitating the IDL, LDL, and Lp(a) from the ultracentrifugal bottom fraction rather than from unfractionated serum. Second, cholesterol in both the ultracentrifugal bottom fraction and HDL fraction is measured with the CDC reference method for cholesterol.[59] LDL-C is then calculated as indicated in equation b, above. The method is performed under highly controlled conditions and provides a basis for judging the accuracy of LDL-C measurements.

NCEP Recommendations for LDL-C Measurement

The NCEP Working Group on Lipoprotein Measurement published recommendations for reliable LDL-C measurements. These recommendations cover a variety of issues related to LDL-C measurement, and the interested reader is referred to the Working Group's full report[38] and to the Executive Summary for LDL-C measurement, which has been published separately.[60] Some of the issues considered by the Working Group were discussed above. Following is a summary of some of the main points of the recommendations.

✧ The Working Group *did not* recommend that any particular method be used to measure LDL-C. Rather, the recommendation was for the user to understand exactly which lipoproteins are included in the LDL-C measurement, and that the method be capable of giving results equivalent to those used to establish the epidemiological database from which the relationship between LDL-C concentration and risk for CHD was established.

✧ Because it was necessary to define accuracy in functional terms, the Working Group recommended using the ultracentrifugation-polyanion precipitation (i.e., beta quantification) method, modified to incorporate the use of reference methods for TC and HDL-C, to afford a single setpoint from which to judge accuracy. The reference method should include both IDL and Lp(a) in the LDL-measurement, and the HDL-C method should provide values equivalent to those obtained with the heparin-$MnCl_2$ method (see discussion of HDL measurement in Chapter 11).

✧ Since plasma values can be lower than serum values, depending on the anti-coagulant used, accuracy should be based on serum-equivalent values. EDTA plasma values are converted to serum-equivalent values by multiplying the LDL-C value by the factor 1.03.

✧ Blood samples should be drawn after a 12-h fasting period. A 9-h fasting period, as recommended by the ATP II,[5] can be used, but will underestimate LDL-C 2%–4%, on average.

✧ Lipid and lipoprotein concentrations are subject to postural changes due primarily to the redistribution of water between the vascular and extravascular space as an individual changes from the standing to sitting or supine positions. TC and lipoprotein-C concentrations decrease about 5% when a standing person sits, and about 10% when a person moves from the standing to supine position.[61] The change for TG is almost twice as great.[61] If possible, blood sampling should be standardized to the sitting position, after allowing the patient to sit quietly for at least 5 min. If it is necessary to use the supine position, the patient should be sampled in the same position on each occasion in order to minimize this source of within-individual physiological variation.

✧ Serum or plasma should be removed from cells within 3 h of venipuncture. Specimens can be stored at 4°C for up to 3 days, at −20°C for up to several weeks in a non-self-defrosting freezer, and at −70°C for longer periods.

✧ Lipoprotein concentrations are not constant; they normally fluctuate about some mean value during the normal course of day-to-day activity, even when the patient is in a steady state, i.e., in good health, of stable weight, and observing usual patterns of diet and exercise. When the patient is treated with diet or lipid-lowering medications, lipid levels decrease (i.e., the patient's physiological state changes) until a new steady state is attained, after which normal physiological fluctuation resumes. Based on the results of a number of studies, the co-efficient of normal physiological variation is assumed to be 8.2%. Assuming a maximum total analytical error of 12% (see next bullet, below), when determining the patient's usual average LDL-C concentration, measurements should be made in two or three serial samples and the measurements averaged. The difference between *sequential* individual measurements in the series should not exceed 25%. If they do, the patient's physiological state may have changed or a laboratory error may have occurred; hence, an additional sample should be considered.

❖ With respect to the laboratory measurements themselves, the recommendation for acceptable LDL-C measurements is set in terms of total analytical error, rather than specifying separate criteria for accuracy and precision. The total error specification accounts for *both* accuracy and imprecision at the same time, rather than considering them separately. The recommendation is that LDL-C be measured with an average total error not exceeding 12%. In order to frame this guideline in more familiar terms, the Working Group noted that the total error criterion could be met in a laboratory that operated within a bias limit of ± 4%, and with an imprecision, reflected by coefficient of variation, no greater than 4%. For example, if the bias exceeds 4%, the CV must be smaller by an amount that restricts the total error to no more than 12%, and vice versa. A fairly accurate estimate of total error can be obtained using the following equation:

(f) TE = % bias + 1.96 x % CV

where TE is total error and bias is the average laboratory bias.

The usefulness of the current risk tables relating lipid and lipoprotein concentrations to risk for CHD depends in part on how accurately the measurements are made. The ultimate purpose of establishing standard conditions for patient handling and uniform criteria for reliable measurements is that the same values would be obtained regardless of where or how the measurements are made. Table 12–2 illustrates the results obtained in several serum pools provided in the CAP Chemistry Proficiency Surveys.[55]

The data in the table reflect the results from over 2900 participating laboratories using the Friedewald equation to calculate LDL-C values, compared to CDC-confirming values in the same pools using the Friedewald and CDC reference methods to measure TC, TG, and HDL-C. The results indicate average biases ranging from 0% to 14%, and an *among-laboratory* CV of about 6%, for overall total errors of 12%–25%. This NCEP recommendation was exceeded in two of the four pools, and the biases were quite variable among pools. It should be remembered, however, that

❖ the NCEP recommendation for total error was directed at measurements within laboratories, not among laboratories;

❖ a variety of different methods and variations of methods are used in different laboratories for TC, TG, and HDL-C measurement; and

❖ the CAP surveys use lyophilized serum pools, which are not ideal for HDL-C measurement.

Table 12–2 also indicates results for approximately 70 laboratories that used precipitation methods. These methods exhibited negative biases of about 20%, and the among-laboratory variation was extreme. Such inaccuracy and imprecision, if it actually reflects the performance of these methods, would render them useless for clinical purposes. Again it is likely, however, that much of the apparent inaccuracy and imprecision resulted from the use of lyophilized serum pools that are simply not suitable for analysis with these methods.

SUMMARY

LDL-C measurement is important for the diagnosis and treatment of hyperlipidemia, and for these purposes the ability to standardize LDL-C methods is essential. While a number of different methods are available, beta quantification and LDL-C estimation by the Friedewald equation have been most widely used and investigated. These remain the best characterized and most common methods presently in use. In both methods, the measured LDL-C values include the contributions of the other atherogenic apo-B-containing lipoproteins. Newer direct LDL-C methods have been developed and need to be more extensively evaluated. They may eventually replace TC measurements made for the purpose of estimating LDL, and promise to be particularly useful for measuring LDL-C in most patients with hypertriglyceridema.

As new methods are developed, it remains necessary to define exactly which lipoproteins they measure and to what extent atherogenic lipoproteins other than LDL are also detected. It is also necessary to assess how new methods compare with those used to generate the risk cutoffs for LDL-C. New LDL-C methods should satisfy the criteria for reliable LDL-C measurement; and they must be capable of being monitoring over the long term for quality-control purposes. ❖

REFERENCES

1. Mahley RW, Rall SC. Type III hyperlipoproteinemia (dysbetalipoproteinemia): the role of apolipoprotein E in normal and abnormal lipoprotein metabolism. In Scriver CR, Beaudet AL, Sly WS, Valle D (eds.). The metabolic and molecular basis of inherited disease, Vol. II, 7th ed. New York: McGraw Hill, 1995:1953–80.
2. Lee DM, Alaupovic P. Apolipoproteins B, C-III, and E in two major subpopulations of low-density lipoproteins. Biochim Biophys Acta 1986;879:126–33.
3. Chapman J. Comparative analysis of mammalian plasma lipoproteins. Methods in Enzymology 1986;128:70–143.
4. The Expert Panel. Report of the National Cholesterol Education Program Expert Panel on Detection, Evaluation, and Treatment of High Blood Cholesterol in Adults. Arch Intern Med 1988;148:36–69.
5. The Expert Panel. Summary of the second report of the National Cholesterol Education Panel (NCEP) Expert Panel on Detection, Evaluation, and Treatment of High Blood Cholesterol in Adults (Adult Treatment Panel II). JAMA 1993;269:3015–23.
6. NCEP Expert Panel on Blood Cholesterol Levels in Children and Adolescents. National Cholesterol Education Program (NCEP): Highlights of the report of the Expert Panel on Blood Cholesterol Levels in Children and Adolescents. Pediatrics 1992;89:495–501.
7. Lindgren FT, Elliott HA, Gofman JW. The ultracentrifugal characterization and isolation of human blood lipids and lipoproteins, with applications to the study of atherosclerosis. J Phys & Colloid Chem 1951;55:80.
8. Lewis LA, Green AA, Page IH. Ultracentrifuge lipoprotein pattern of serum of normal, hypertensive, and hypothyroid animals. Am J Physiol 1952;171:391.
9. de Lalla OF, Gofman JW. Ultracentrifugal analysis of serum lipoproteins. Methods of Biochemical Analysis 1954;1:459–78.
10. Havel RJ, Eder HA, Bragdon JH. The distribution and chemical composition of ultracentrifugally separated lipoproteins in human serum. J Clin Invest 1955;34:1345–53.
11. Schumaker VN, Puppione DL. Sequential flotation ultracentrifugation. Methods in Enzymology 1986;128:155–70.
12. Lindgren FT, Nichols AV, Upham FT et al. Subfractionation of the S_f 20–10^5 lipoproteins in a swinging bucket rotor. J Phys Chem 1962;66:2007–11.

13. Lossow WJ, Lindgren FT, Murchio JC et al. Particle size and protein content of six fractions of the S_f >20 plasma lipoproteins isolated by density gradient centrifugation. J Lipid Res 1969;10:68–76.

14. Hinton RH, Kowalski AJ, Mallinson A. Choice of conditions for the gradient flotation of serum lipoproteins in swing-out rotors. Clin Chim Acta 1973;44:267–70.

15. Redgrave TG, Roberts DCK, West CE. Separation of plasma lipoproteins by density-gradient ultracentrifugation. Anal Biochem 1975;65:42–49.

16. Foreman JR, Karlin JB, Edelstein C et al. Fractionation of human serum lipoproteins by single-spin gradient ultracentrifugation: quantification of apolipoproteins B and A-I and lipid components. J Lipid Res 1977;18:759–67.

17. Nilsson J, Mannickarottu V, Edelstein C et al. An improved detection system applied to the study of serum lipoproteins after single-step density gradient ultracentrifugation. Anal Biochem 1981;110:342–48.

18. Belcher JD, Egan JO, Bridgmen G, Baker R, Flack J. A micro-enzymatic method to measure cholesterol and triglyceride in lipoprotein subfractions separated by density gradient ultracentrifugation from 200 microliters of plasma or serum. J Lipid Res 1991; 32:359–70.

19. Chung BH, Wilkinson T, Geer JC et al. Preparative and quantitative isolation of plasma lipoproteins: rapid, single discontinuous density gradient ultracentrifugation in a vertical rotor. J Lipid Res 1980;21:284–91.

20. Cone JT, Segrest JP, Chung BH et al. Computerized rapid high resolution quantitative analysis of plasma lipoproteins based upon single vertical spin centrifugation. J Lipid Res 1982;23:923–35.

21. Campos E, McConathy WJ. Distribution of lipids and apolipoproteins in human plasma by vertical spin ultracentrifugation. Arch Biochem Biophys 1986;249:455–63.

22. Chung BH, Segrest JP, Ray MJ et al. Single vertical spin density gradient ultracentrifugation. Methods in Enzymology 1986;128:181–209.

23. Rudel LL, Lee JA, Morris MD et al. Characterization of plasma lipoproteins separated and purified by agarose-column chromatography. Biochem J 1974;139:89–95.

24. Williams MC, Stenoien CG, Kushwaha RS. Rapid method for measuring plasma low-density-lipoprotein turnover using high-performance gel exclusion chromatography. J Chromatogr 1986;375:233–43.

25. Krause BR, Shork NH, Kieft KA, Smith MP, Maciejko JJ. High correlation but lack of agreement between direct high-performance gel chromatography analysis and conventional indirect methods for determining lipoprotein cholesterol. Clin Chem 1996;42: 1996–2001.

26. März W, Siekmeier R, Scharnagl H, Seiffert UB, Gross W. Fast lipoprotein chromatography: new method of analysis for plasma lipoproteins. Clin Chem 1993;39:2276–81.

27. Levy RI. Cholesterol, lipoproteins, apoproteins, and heart disease; present status and future prospects. Clin Chem 1981;27:653–62.

28. Weiland H, Seidel D. A simple specific method for precipitation of low-density lipoproteins. J Lipid Res 1983;24:904–9.

29. Kersher L, Schiefer S, Draeger B, Maier J, Ziegenhorn J. Precipitation methods for the determination of LDL cholesterol. Clin Biochem 1985;18:118–225.

30. Maier J, Draeger B, Wehmeyer G, Gloger M, Ziegenhorn J. Method for the quantitation of serum low-density lipoprotein cholesterol (LDL-CH) [Abstract]. Clin Chem 1983; 29:1173.

31. Assmann G, Jabs H-U, Kohnert U, Nolte W, Schriewer H. LDL-cholesterol determination in blood serum following precipitation of LDL with polyvinyl sulfate. Clin Chim Acta 1984;140:77–83.

32. Moss MA, Wong CSY, Tan MH et al. Determination of low-density lipoprotein cholesterol (LDL-C) in serum by Biomerieux cholesterol-phospholipids polyanion precipitation method and comparison with preparative ultracentrifugation. [Abstract]. Clin Chem 1986;32:1096–7.

33. Mainard F, Madec Y. Are "precipitated LDL" really low-density lipoproteins? Clin Chim Acta 1987;162:141–6.

34. Shaikh M, Miller NE. Evaluation of a commercial reagent for precipitating human serum low-density lipoprotein. Clin Chim Acta 1985;152:213–17.

35. Demacker PN, Hijmans AG, Brenninkmeijer BJ et al. Five methods for determining low-density-lipoprotein cholesterol compared. Clin Chem 1984;30:1797–1800.

36. Assmann G, Jabs HU, Nolte W, Schriewer H. Precipitation of LDL with sulphopoly-anions: a comparison of two methods for LDL cholesterol determination. J Clin Chem Clin Biochem 1984;22:781–5.

37. Mulder K, van Leeuwen C, Schouten JA et al. An evaluation of three commercial methods for the determination of LDL-cholesterol. Clin Chim Acta 1984;143:29–35.

38. National Cholesterol Education Program Working Group on Lipoprotein Measurement. Recommendations on lipoprotein measurement (NIH Publication No. 95–3044). Bethesda, MD: National Institutes of Health, September 1995.

39. Friedewald WT, Levy RI, Fredrickson DS. Estimation of the concentration of low-density-lipoprotein cholesterol in plasma without use of the ultracentrifuge. Clin Chem 1972;18:449–502.

40. Austin MA. Plasma triglyceride as a risk factor for coronary heart disease: the epidemiological evidence and beyond. Amer J Epi 1989;129:249–59.

41. Simons LA, Dwyer T, Simons J et al. Chylomicrons and chylomicron remnants in coronary artery disease: a case-control study. Atherosclerosis 1987;65:181–9.

42. Krauss RM, Williams PT, Brensike J et al. Intermediate-density lipoproteins and progression of coronary artery disease in hypercholesterolaemic men. Lancet 1987;11:62–66.

43. Sandkamp M, Funke H, Schulte H, Kohler E, Assmann G. Lipoprotein(a) is an independent risk factor for myocardial infarction at a young age. Clin Chem 1990;36:20–23.

44. Jurgens G, Koltringer P. Lipoprotein (a) in ischemic cerebrovascular disease: a new approach to the assessment of risk for stroke. Neurology 1987;37:513–15.

45. The Lipid Research Clinics Population Studies Data Book. Volume I, The Prevalence Study (NIH Publication No. 80–1527). Bethesda, MD: National Institutes of Health, July 1980.

46. LaRosa JC, Chambless LE, Criqui MH et al. Patterns of dyslipoproteinemia in selected North American populations: The Lipid Research Clinics Program Prevalence Study. Circulation 1986;73(I):12–29.

47. Leary ET, Tjersland G, Warnick GR. Evaluation of the Genzyme immunoseparation reagent for direct quantitation of LDL cholesterol. [Abstract]. Clin Chem 1993;39:1124.

48. Devaraj S, Hirany SV, Sherwood TA, Jialal I. Comparison of an immunoprecipitation method for direct measurement of LDL-cholesterol with beta quantification. [Abstract]. Clin Chem 1995;41:S141.

49. Harris N, Neufeld EJ, Newburger JW, Tich B, Baker A, Ginsburg GS, Rimm E, Rifai N. Analytical performance and clinical utility of a direct LDL-cholesterol assay in a hyperlipidemic pediatric population. Clin Chem 1996;42:1182–8.

50. McNamara JR, Cole TG, Contois JH, Furguson CA, Ordovas JM, Schaefer EJ. Immunoseparation method for measuring low-density-lipoprotein cholesterol directly from serum evaluated. Clin Chem 1995;41:232–40.

51. Schectman G, Patsches M, Sasse EA. Variability in cholesterol measurements: comparison of calculated and direct LDL-cholesterol determinations. Clin Chem 1996;42:732–7.

52. Cohn JS, McNamara JR, Cohn SD, Ordovas JM, Schaefer EJ. Postprandial plasma lipoprotein changes in human subjects of different ages. J Lipid Res 1988;29:469–79.

53. Cohn JS, McNamara JR, Schaefer EJ. Lipoprotein cholesterol concentrations in the plasma of human subjects measured in the fed and fasted states. Clin Chem 1988;34:2556–9.

54. Wilder LB, Bachorik PS, Finney CA, Moy TF, Becker DM. The effect of fasting status on the determination of low-density and high-density lipoprotein cholesterol. Am J Med 1995;99:374–7.

55. College of American Pathologists Clinical Chemistry Proficiency Surveys. Northfield, IL: College of American Pathologists, 1999.

56. Sugiuchi H, Irie T, Uji Y, Ueno T, Chaen T, Uekama K, Okabe H. Homogeneous assay for measuring low-density-lipoprotein cholesterol in serum with tri-block copolymer and α-cyclodextrin sulfate. Clin Chem 1998;44:522–31.

57. Rifai N, Iannotti E, DeAngelis K, Law T. Analytical and clinical performance of a homogeneous enzymatic LDL-cholesterol assay compared with the ultracentrifugation-dextran sulfate-Mg^{2+} method. Clin Chem 1998;44:1242–50.

58. Nauck M, Graziani MS, Bruton D, Cobbaert C, Cole TG, Lefevre F, Riesen W, Bachorik PS, Rifai N. Analytical and clinical performance of a detergent-based homogeneous LDL cholesterol assay: A multi-center evaluation. Clin Chem 2000 (in press).

59. Ellerbe P, Myers GL, Cooper GR et al. A comparison of results for cholesterol in human serum by the reference method and by the definitive method of the National Reference System for Cholesterol. Clin Chem 1990;36:370–5.

60. Bachorik PS, Ross JW, for the National Cholesterol Education Program Working Group on Lipoprotein Measurement. Guidelines on the measurement of low-density-lipoprotein cholesterol: executive summary. Clin Chem 1995;44:1414–20.

61. Miller MM, Bachorik PS, Cloey TC. Normal variation of plasma lipoproteins: postural effects on plasma lipid, lipoprotein, and apolipoprotein concentrations. Clin Chem 1992;38:569–74.

Lipid and Lipoprotein Analysis with Desktop Analyzers

13

Paul S. Bachorik

✧   Cholesterol is transported by plasma lipoproteins, primarily low-density lipo-proteins (LDL), which account for about two-thirds, and high-density lipoproteins (HDL), which carry about 20%–25%, of the circulating cholesterol in humans. An increased concentration of LDL cholesterol (LDL-C) is a well-established risk factor for the development of premature coronary heart disease (CHD),[1] and lowering plasma LDL-C concentrations reduces the risk of CHD.[2–7] (Conversely, a low concentration of HDL cholesterol (HDL-C) is independently associated with increased risk of CHD.[8–10]) Total cholesterol (TC) is an effective surrogate measure of LDL-C in adults, and TC measurement has assumed increasing importance in identifying patients with high LDL-C concentrations. Various kinds of screening operations and follow-up analyses measure TC to evaluate the progress of patients being treated for hypercholesterol-emia.

The National Cholesterol Education Program Adult Treatment Panel (NCEP-ATP) has updated[11] its original[12] recommendations concerning the diagnosis and treatment of hypercholesterolemia in adults. The original recommendations focused primarily on TC and LDL-C, while the updated report places increased emphasis on HDL-C by recognizing a high HDL-C concentration as a protective factor and recommending the measurement of HDL-C whenever TC is measured.

Technical developments over the past 20 years have increased the speed and accuracy of clinical measurements of lipids and lipoproteins and, to some extent, have moved the performance of these measurements from the laboratory to the physician's office and to other non-traditional settings. The first of these developments was the introduction into the laboratory of completely enzyme-based reagents for cholesterol and triglyceride (TG) measurement.[13–16] Enzymic methods are now almost universally used. The second development was the adaptation of this methodology to small, portable analyzers, commonly called point-of-care or desktop analyzers. These analyzers were originally designed to be used in the physician's office, but they have also been widely used for TC screening in non-medical settings,[17–20] and are capable of measuring TC, TG, and HDL-C. In this chapter we discuss the use of desktop analyzers for lipid and lipoprotein measurements.

PRINCIPLES OF OPERATION

Total Cholesterol

Virtually all desktop analytical systems that are currently available are based on the same kinds of enzymatic methods used in laboratory settings. For TC measurement, they employ a single, combined reagent mixture that contains all of the necessary enzymes, buffers, and other cofactors required for the test. An aliquot of serum or plasma, usually 10–30 μL, is mixed with the combined reagent and allowed to incubate under controlled conditions for a short period, generally about 3–8 min, during which a colored reaction product forms. The intensity of the color is related to the cholesterol concentration. The results are read from a digital display on the instrument and a paper printout. The chemical reactions involved are as follows:

(a) $\text{Cholesteryl Esters} + H_2O \xrightarrow{\text{Cholesteryl Esterase}} \text{Cholesterol} + \text{Fatty Acid}$

(b) $\text{Cholesterol} + O_2 \xrightarrow{\text{Cholesterol Oxidase}} \text{Cholestanone} + H_2O_2$

(c) $H_2O_2 + \text{Dye} \xrightarrow{\text{Peroxidase}} \text{Colored Dye Product}$

Cholesteryl esters are hydrolyzed and then cholesterol is oxidized to produce cholestanone and hydrogen peroxide. The amount of hydrogen peroxide produced is proportional to the amount of cholesterol in the sample, and is measured through a peroxidase-catalyzed reaction in which a colored dye product is formed.

Triglycerides

TG are similarly measured through a series of enzyme reactions.

(d) $\text{Triglyceride} + H_2O \xrightarrow{\text{Bacterial Lipase}} \text{Fatty Acid} + \text{Glycerol}$

(e) $\text{Glycerol} + \text{ATP} \xrightarrow{\text{Glycerokinase}} \text{Glycerophosphate} + \text{ADP}$

The glycerophosphate formed is most commonly measured using glycerophosphate oxidase:

(f) $\text{Glycerophosphate} + O_2 \xrightarrow{\text{Glycerophosphate Oxidase}} \text{Dihydroxyacetone} + H_2O_2$

In this case, the H_2O_2 produced is proportional to the TG concentration and is usually measured as in reaction (c) above.

   In general, all of the reactions occur once the sample has been placed into the instrument. The instrument controls the time and conditions of the incubation, reads the color intensity, converts the readings to units of concentration, and displays the results. The entire analysis can be accomplished in 10 minutes or less.

HDL Cholesterol

Desktop analyzer methods have also become available for HDL-C measurement.[21-23] These tests rely on the removal of the lipoproteins containing apolipoprotein B (apo B): very-low-density lipoproteins (VLDL), intermediate-density lipoproteins (IDL, LDL, and lipoprotein[a] [Lp(a)]). This is generally done by precipitation with a polyanion in the presence of a divalent cation, under conditions in which HDL remains soluble. Precipitants such as sodium phosphotungstate or dextran sulfate-Mg^{++} have been used. The cholesterol content of the HDL-containing fraction is then measured as described above, but with test strips or cassettes for which the cholesterol measurements have been optimized for use in the HDL-C concentration range. With some desktop analyzers, the apo-B-containing lipoproteins must be precipitated from the sample before the HDL supernate is placed into the analyzer, while in others both the precipitation and cholesterol measurement steps are performed by the test strip.

LDL Cholesterol

For analyzers that measure TC, TG, and HDL-C, LDL-C can be calculated using the empirical relationship of Friedewald et al.:[24]

$$LDL\text{-}C = TC - HDL\text{-}C - TG/5$$

where the factor TG/5 is an estimate of VLDL-C concentrations when given in mg/dL. (The factor TG/2.22 is used when concentrations are expressed in mmol/L.) Within the past several years, direct methods for LDL-C have been developed for the laboratory. These methods use a detergent in combination with several other reactants to block chylomicrons, VLDL, and HDL without precipitating them, and allow LDL-C to be measured directly in serum or plasma. Direct LDL-C methods have not yet been adapted for dry chemistry use or for use in desktop analyzers.

INSTRUMENTS

The desktop instruments differ in their simplicity and ease of use. Most of these instruments are based on dry reagent chemistry. Here we discuss the principles of operation of several of the more commonly used analyzers.

One of the first instruments developed was the Reflotron (Boehringer-Mannheim Corporation, now Roche Diagnostics, Indianapolis, IN). This is one of the so-called portable whole-blood analyzers, capable of making TC and TG measurements using serum, plasma, or whole blood. The sample (30 µL) is applied to the sample application zone of a test strip. The sample moves downward into an absorbent pad through a glass fiber mesh that removes the red cells. The cell-free sample then moves into the reagent-containing zone, an area of the strip that has been impregnated with the enzymes and other reagents needed for the test. The reagents dissolve in the sample, allowing the reaction to proceed.

Once the sample is applied, the strip is inserted into the instrument. The reaction proceeds for about three minutes, during which time the color develops. At the end of this period, the color intensity is measured by reflectance photometry. A light beam is directed at the sample and the amount of light reflected is inversely related to the TC or TG concentration in the sample. The reflectance is converted to units of concentration and the results are displayed either in mg/dL or in mmol/L. The strip is then removed and the next test can be performed. The instrument is capable of analyzing one sample at a time.

The identity of the test, conditions for analysis, and the calibration curve are coded on a magnetic tape on the back of the strip, and this information is read by the instrument when the strip is inserted. This configuration makes the test very simple to use, because the operator need only verify the operation of the optics of the instrument and then perform the tests. Because of its simplicity, the Reflotron has been widely used for large-scale TC screening operations in various field settings.[17–20,25]

Reflotron test strips are also available for HDL-C. For HDL-C, EDTA plasma (not whole blood; 30 μL) is applied to the strip. The sample then moves through a layer impregnated with dextran sulfate (M_r 50,000) and magnesium acetate, which precipitates the apo-B-containing lipoproteins. The HDL-containing fraction then moves to the reagent zone, where HDL-C is measured. The Reflotron, which is no longer manufactured, was replaced by a smaller ProAct instrument and subsequently by the AccuChek device using similar chemistry strips.

The Johnson & Johnson Vitros DT60, and an updated version, the DT60-II (Johnson & Johnson Clinical Diagnostics, now part of Ortho Clinical diagnostics, Rochester, NY), is another example of a portable dry chemistry analyzer. With this instrument, however, the configuration of the test is different. The DT60 is something of a cross between a sequential analyzer and a batch analyzer. Reagents for the test are contained on a test slide in which the reagents are impregnated into a pad immediately below the sample application zone. The slide is also printed with a bar code that identifies the test and test conditions.

The slide is first inserted into the instrument, after which the sample (10 μL) is injected onto the slide through a port in the top of the instrument using a small, battery-powered, motorized pipette. After the sample has been applied, the slide moves automatically to an incubation chamber, where color develops. The reflectance of the sample is then measured and converted to units of concentration, and the results are printed on a paper tape. The entire analysis takes about eight minutes. The incubation chamber, however, can accommodate a number of slides, so that samples can be continuously fed into the instrument. Once in operation, the results are printed about every 30 seconds. Separate test slides are used for TC, TG, and HDL-C.

The HDL-C assay requires the preliminary manual removal of apo-B-containing lipoproteins. The method uses dextran sulfate (M_r 50,000) and $MgSO_4$ as the precipitating reagent, and the reagent is provided with the HDL test kit.

The DT60 differs from the Reflotron in several other respects. First, it is not a whole-blood analyzer; blood cells must be removed before the sample is analyzed. Second, the instrument is calibrated by the user at intervals of about 30 days using lyophilized reference sera provided by the manufacturer. Several levels of reference sera are used, and the calibration curves are calculated and stored by the instrument.

Since the introduction of these instruments, the dry chemistry technology has been developed further to allow several tests to be performed simultaneously on a single sample. This is accomplished by providing a channel through which the cell-free blood filtrate moves from the filter toward the reagent zones. The channel is split to allow portions of the sample to move to different test reagent zones. Using such an arrangement, the Cholestech LDX (Cholestech Corporation, Hayward, CA), another portable analyzer, can simultaneously measure TC, TG, and HDL-C. This instrument has been optimized for use with whole blood. The test parameters are contained in a magnetic strip on the test cassette and are used when the cassette is inserted into the instrument. Serum or plasma can also be used, although the results are slightly less accurate than those obtained with whole blood.[23,26] The instrument completes all three measurements in about four minutes and is capable of analyzing one specimen at a time. The volume of sample applied must exceed 35 µL, but need not be measured accurately since the test cassette automatically meters the appropriate volumes of sample to the reagent zones.

The Abbott VISION (Abbott Laboratories, North Chicago, IL) is an example of a wet-chemistry, batch-type, whole-blood analyzer. The VISION analyzer uses different principles of analysis. First, the liquid reagent mixture is contained in a small plastic cassette. A sample of whole blood is injected into the cassette with the aid of a pipette. The cassette is then placed into the instrument, where it is centrifuged to sediment red cells. After centrifugation, the position of the cassette is automatically changed such that an accurately measured volume of the plasma spills into the chamber containing the reagent. After an appropriate period, the absorbance of the mixture is measured and the absorbance readings are converted to units of concentration and displayed on a printed tape. The instrument can accommodate up to 10 cassettes at one time, and the entire analysis takes about 10 minutes. Test cassettes are available for measuring TC, TG, and HDL-C, but for HDL the apo-B-containing lipoproteins must first be separated by a conventional pretreatment step before loading the supernate into the HDL test cassette.

Because the instrument incorporates a centrifuge, it is physically larger than the other analyzers. It is therefore less mobile and more suitable for use in a fixed location.

Type of Sample Used

These analyzers can be used with either venous or capillary samples, although in mass-screening settings, capillary samples are usually used. In general, the results obtained with the two kinds of samples are similar but not identical. In some studies, the values in capillary samples appear to be lower than those in venous samples; in other studies, the opposite was observed.[23,27–29] On average, the differences between venous and capillary samples are fairly minor, on the order of a few percentage points. However, the values in capillary samples from individual patients can occasionally vary considerably from those in venous samples collected at the same time.[17] The reasons for these differences have not been investigated in any detail, but possibilities may include, among others, the temperature of the patient's finger, differential rates of posture-related concentration changes on capillary and venous samples, and the ease with which blood flows from the finger puncture.

Table 13-1 ✦ Coefficients of Biological Variation for Lipids and Lipoproteins in Venous and Capillary Specimens[1,2]

Specimen	Median $CV_b{}^3$ (%)			
	TC	TG	HDL-C	LDL-C
Venous	5.6	15.8	6.5	7.5
Capillary	5.2	14.7	7.2	5.4

[1]Data from Kafonek et al.[23]
[2]Paired venous serum and heparinized capillary blood specimens were drawn from each of 83 normal fasting (12 h) adults once each month for 3 months. The study population was sampled over a 7-month period. Capillary blood was analyzed immediately and venous serum about 60 min later after the blood had clotted and the serum recovered. All analyses were performed on the Cholestech desktop analyzer using test cassettes that allowed the simultaneous analysis of TC, TG, and HDL-C. LDL-C was calculated with the Friedewald[24] equation. Analytical and biological components of within-individual variance and the median coefficients of biological variation were calculated as describe in Kafonek et al.[23]
[3]CV_b, coefficient of biological variation.

The overall coefficients of normal biological variation (CV_b) for TC, TG, HDL-C, and LDL-C are about the same in capillary and venous blood[23] (Table 13–1), but differences observed in an individual on a given occasion will depend on the magnitude and direction of the concentration changes in the serial and capillary venous specimens. These are generally parallel, but this may not hold on a particular occasion and can produce a fairly large difference between the measurements in a particular venous-capillary sample pair.

Serum plasma differences are another consideration. Certain anticoagulants exert an osmotic effect, resulting in the movement of water from the cells to the plasma. This dilutes the plasma lipoproteins; the degree of dilution depends on the osmotic activity of the anticoagulant used.[30] This difference was estimated to be about 3%,[31] and, according to the NCEP-ATP guidelines,[12] multiplication of plasma values by the factor 1.03 is recommended when evaluating patients. It must be kept in mind, however, that the term "plasma" used in this context refers specifically to EDTA plasma. Some agents, such as citrate, exert much larger osmotic effects, and lipids and lipoproteins should not be measured in samples that contain such anticoagulants. Heparin, on the other hand, exerts no detectable osmotic effect in concentrations used for blood collection, and TC values in heparinized plasma are indistinguishable from those in serum.[32] Capillary blood samples are generally collected into heparinized capillary tubes, and measurements in capillary blood need not be converted to serum values. Nonetheless, it is well to bear in mind possible differences between serum and plasma, since the NCEP-ATP guidelines are based on serum.[11,12]

Note that the factor 1.03 was determined at a time when blood-drawing tubes containing EDTA were supplied with sufficient EDTA to produce an anticoagulant concentration of 1 mg/mL.[31] Tubes supplied currently, however, contain 1.5 mg/mL EDTA, and the resulting hema-dilution is a little greater, at about 4.5%.[32]

RELIABILITY OF LIPID AND LIPOPROTEIN CHOLESTEROL MEASUREMENTS

The NCEP Lipid Standardization Panel (LSP) established guidelines for acceptable TC measurement in the United States (Table 13–2).[33] These guidelines specify minimum standards for accuracy in terms of percent of bias and percent of coefficient of variation (CV), and are consistent with a total analytical error of 8.9, or approximately 9%.

The NCEP Working Group on Lipoprotein Measurement subsequently developed additional guidelines for reliable TG, HDL-C, and LDL-C measurements[34] (Table 13–3). The recommendations for lipoprotein and TG measurement were cast in terms of total error in order to account for both bias and imprecision at the same time; thus, the larger the method bias, the more precise the methods must be to satisfy the recommendations for total error.

The NCEP recommendations do not distinguish between analyses performed in the laboratory and those performed in non-laboratory settings, nor do they establish separate guidelines for desktop analyzers. This is because the medical impact of the measurements on the patient is generally the same regardless of how or where the measurements are made.

A number of investigators have evaluated the reliability of lipid and lipoprotein measurements with desktop analyzers. On average, desktop analyzers give fairly accurate measurements, but the measurements are somewhat more variable than those obtained with laboratory-based methods.[22,23,26] The use of desktop instruments with capillary blood specimens may contribute to this variability. In one study, the distribution of the differences between measurements of finger-stick samples with the Reflotron analyzer and standardized laboratory measurements of venous samples taken at the same time was about twice as wide as that for venous samples analyzed with both methods.[17] Such discrepancies have been noted for non-lipid analytes as well.[35] The reasons for the differences are not clear. They may derive in part from physiological differences between venous and capillary samples or from the mechanics of obtaining capillary specimens.

One type of desktop analyzer provided more reliable results when operated by trained laboratory technologists than by operators lacking formal laboratory training.[36] Desktop analyzers operated under field conditions in which the instruments must be transported frequently and may be operated in climates of varying temperature and humidity generally provide more variable results than instruments operated at a fixed location.

Table 13-2 ✧ NCEP Guidelines for Accuracy and Precision of Cholesterol Measurements	
Bias[1,2]	≤ 3 %
Coefficient of analytical variation (CV_a^2)	< 3 %

[1]With respect to CDC reference method.
[2]These limits for bias and imprecision are consistent with a total error of < 9%.

Table 13-3 ✧ NCEP Recommendations for Reliable Triglyceride, HDL-C, and LDL-C Measurement[1]

Analyte	Total Error	Consistent with[2,3]
Triglyceride	≤ 15 %	bias ≤ 5 % CV_a ≤ 5 %
HDL-C	≤ 13 %	bias ≤ 5 % CV_a ≤ 4 %[4]
LDL-C	≤ 12 %	bias ≤ 4 % CV_a ≤ 4 %

[1]Data taken from NCEP Recommendations on Lipoprotein Measurement.[34]
[2]The primary recommendations are cast in terms of total error. The bias and CV_a shown for each analyte is one example that will satisfy the criterion for that analyte.
[3]CV_a, coefficient of analytical variation.
[4]CV_a shown applies at HDL-C concentrations = 42 mg/dL (1.09 mmol/L). At lower concentrations, use SD ≤ 1.7 mg/dL (0.044 mmol/L).

Even when venous samples are used, there can be substantial differences between measurements made with desktop and laboratory-based systems in individual specimens. This is illustrated in Table 13–4. The data were collected in the author's laboratory in split-sample comparisons conducted over one-year periods with each of two different desktop analyzers, the DT60 and the LDX. The comparison measurements were made on a Hitachi 704 or 717 analyzer, using methods standardized to the Reference Methods at the Centers for Disease Control and Prevention (CDC).

The DT60 displayed small but significant negative biases of 1.9% for TC and 2.5% for TG with respect to the comparison methods. There was no significant bias for HDL-C. However, 35% percent of the HDL-C values, and 25% of the TG values, differed by more than 10% from those derived from laboratory measurements, and 7%–10% of these measurements differed from the laboratory measurements by more than 20%. For TC and TG, the magnitude of the differences was not concentration dependent. The differences for HDL-C tended to increase at higher concentrations ($p = 0.001$).

The results of a similar comparison of the LDX revealed positive average biases of about 7% and 9% for TC and HDL-C, and a negative bias of about 6% for TG. In addition, 40%–60% of the measurements differed from the comparison values by more than 10%, and about a quarter of the TG and HDL-C measurements differed by more than 20%.

Bias and imprecision of measurements with desktop analyzers can be of concern when dealing with individual patients, particularly those whose lipid and lipoprotein concentrations are not already known, and particularly when the error might not be suspected. In such cases the patient might be misclassified or inappropriately treated.

The higher variability of desktop analyzers can also be observed in several ways. Table 13–5 summarizes data from the author's laboratory and indicates the variation in TC, TG, HDL-C, and LDL-C values as reflected by measurements in quality control pools using laboratory methods, the DT60 analyzer, and the LDX analyzer. The

Table 13-4 ✧ Comparison of Cholesterol, Triglyceride, and HDL-Cholesterol Values Measured with Desktop Analyzers and Standard Laboratory Methods

Analyte	Analyzer	n	Desktop Analyzer mean (mg/dL)[3]	Laboratory[1] mean (mg/dL)	Paired difference (%)	p	Percentage of samples with differences exceeding[2] 10%	20%
TC	DT60	203	210.0	206.1	−1.7	< 0.001	6	1
TG		200	157.1	154.0	−2.5	< 0.001	25	7
HDL-C		206	42.5	42.6	1.8	ns[4]	35	10
	Cholestech LDX							
TC		101	236.0	220.2	8.6	< 0.001	39	15
TG		89	191.8	203.2	−7.1	0.020	53	26
HDL-C		88	47.6	43.5	12.0	< 0.001	60	25

[1]Analyses performed with a Hitachi 704 analyzer during the DT60 comparison, and a Hitachi 717 analyzer during the LDX comparison. Both analyzers were standardized through the CDC-NHLBI Lipid and Lipoprotein Standardization Program.
[2]Refers to the absolute values of the differences between methods.
[3]To convert to mmol/L, divide TC or HDL-C by 38.7 and TG by 88.5.
[4]ns, not significant.

control pools used with the two desktop systems were those supplied by the respective manufacturers. In most cases the CVs obtained with the desktop analyzers were somewhat higher than those obtained from laboratory-based measurements. Reports of studies using other desktop analyzers also indicate greater analytical variation for these instruments.[21–23,27]

Table 13–6 illustrates the results of TC, TG, and HDL-C analyses performed in survey pools distributed by the College of American Pathologists for two desktop analyzers, the Abbott Vision and the DT60-II. For comparison, data for the same survey pools for several common laboratory-based analyzers are shown in Table 13–7.

For TC, the among-laboratory CVs of the two desktop analyzers were similar to those for laboratory-based measurements. Among-laboratory CVs of 1.8%–3.8% were obtained for TC by the laboratory-based systems (Table 13–7) versus 1.8%–4.2% for the desktop analyzers (Table 13–6).

In general, the mean biases of the desktop analyzers for TC were only slightly greater than those for the laboratory-based systems (Table 13–8). The Abbott VISION analyzer had a bias of 2.8% for TC compared to the CDC-confirming values for the survey pools, and the DT60-II had about a 1% bias. In comparison, the laboratory-based systems had biases of 0.5%–1.8% for TC.

Table 13-5 ✧ Precision of Lipid and Lipoprotein Measurements Made in the Laboratory and with Desktop Analyzers[1]

Analyte	Analysis	Pool[2]	CDC Reference Value[3](mg/dL)[4]	Mean(mg/dL)	CV_a [5](%)
TC	Lab	SL2I080	177.2	176.8	1.8
		SL2I132	167.5	163.9	1.6
		SL3I080	251.1	251.8	1.7
		SL3I132	234.6	232.9	1.6
	DT60	03	—	158.2	3.5
		04	—	245.8	4.2
	LDX	A	—	179.0	2.9
		B	—	174.0	2.4
		C	—	267.6	2.4
		D	—	270.8	2.1
TG	Lab	SL2I080	98.6	94.7	2.7
		SL2I132	82.9	84.7	3.3
		SL3I080	215.3	215.4	2.0
		SL3I132	205.1	208.4	2.2
	DT60	03	—	132.9	1.5
		04	—	262.5	8.9
	LDX	A	—	38.4	4.2
		B	—	37.5	5.1
		C	—	69.4	4.7
		D	—	76.4	3.0
HDL-C	Lab	LR02	37	36.2	4.7
		SL4I132	52.7	53.0	2.8
	DT60	03	—	29.4	7.8
		04	—	41.9	6.9
	LDX	A	—	38.4	4.2
		B	—	37.5	5.1
		C	—	69.4	4.7
		D	—	74.6	3.0

[1]Data from the author's laboratory.
[2]Serum pools used with the laboratory methods were obtained from Solomon Park Laboratories, (Kirkland, WA), except for pool LR02, which was obtained from Pacific Biometrics, Seattle, WA. Pools used with the desktop analyzers were provided by the respective manufacturers.
[3]Reference values were determined by CDC, except for pool LR02, for which the reference value was provided by Pacific Biometrics.
[4]To convert to mmol/L, divide TC or HDL-C by 38.7 and TG by 88.5.
[5]CVa, coefficient of analytical variation.

Table 13-6 ◇ Performance for Lipid Measurements with Two Desktop Analyzer Systems[1]

Analyte	Pool	CDC-confirming value (mg/dL)[2]	Abbott Vision		Johnson & Johnson Vitros DTII	
			Mean (mg/dL)[2]	Among-Laboratory CV (%)	Mean (mg/dL)	Among-Laboratory CV (%)
TC[3,4]	LP-01	189	199	2.0	191	2.2
	LP-02	245	255	1.8	243	2.6
	LP-03	231	240	1.6	229	2.5
	LP-04	161	164	2.0	158	2.6
	LP-05	177	152	2.6	175	2.2
	LP-06	226	227	3.6	227	4.2
	LP-07	256	260	3.8	255	2.9
	LP-08	175	178	3.3	174	2.6
	LP-09	157	156	3.2	154	3.2
	LP-10	202	204	3.4	200	2.8
HDL-C[5,6]	LP-01	46.8	—	—	43.2	10.4
	LP-02	66.3	—	—	62.0	9.6
	LP-03	32.2	—	—	29.5	10.2
	LP-04	35.3	—	—	33.5	11.9
	LP-05	42.8	—	—	39.8	10.3
	LP-06	39.5	—	—	35.4	6.6
	LP-07	66.3	—	—	61.7	5.4
	LP-08	39.0	—	—	35.1	5.5
	LP-09	32.9	—	—	29.7	6.7
	LP-10	47.2	—	—	44.0	7.4
TG[3,4,6]	LP-01	80	—	—	88.5	5.3
	LP-02	97	—	—	114	5.8
	LP-03	127	—	—	148	6.3
	LP-04	95	—	—	119	7.0
	LP-05	85	—	—	98	6.2
	LP-06	176	—	—	226	2.7
	LP-07	86	—	—	96	4.6
	LP-08	71	—	—	82.3	4.7
	LP-09	84.1	—	—	113	5.3
	LP-10	72	—	—	84	4.4

[1] Data from 1999 CAP Chemistry Survey Sets CA and CB, College of American Pathologists, Chicago, IL.
[2] To convert to mmol/L, divide TC or HDL-C by 38.7 and TG by 88.5.
[3] Data for TC and TG have been rounded to nearest 1 mg/dL.
[4] Results were reported from 10–23 participants for TC and from 10–13 participants for TG.
[5] Results for HDL-C were reported from 11–13 participants.
[6] No results were reported for the Abbot Vision.

Table 13-7 ✧ Performance for Total Cholesterol (TC), HDL-cholesterol (HDL-C), and Triglyceride (TG) Measurements with Three Laboratory-Based Systems[1]

Analyte	Pool	CDC-Confirming Value (mg/dL)[3]	AbbottSpectrum		Vitros950		Hitachi911	
			Mean[2] (mg/dL)	Among-Laboratory CV (%)	Mean[2] (mg/dL)	Among-Laboratory CV (%)	Mean[2] (mg/dL)	Among-Laboratory CV (%)
TC	LP-01	189	188	3.5	188	2.6	190	2.1
	LP-02	245	248	3.5	244	2.7	246	2.0
	LP-03	231	234	3.0	227	2.7	232	2.1
	LP-04	161	163	3.2	156	2.9	161	2.2
	LP-05	177	179	3.2	172	2.8	177	2.0
	LP-06	226	225	3.5	221	2.7	226	2.0
	LP-07	256	258	3.2	254	2.7	255	1.8
	LP-08	172	177	3.4	172	2.7	174	2.0
	LP-09	157	157	3.8	153	3.0	156	1.9
	LP10	202	204	3.0	196	2.8	200	1.9
HDL-C	LP-01	46.8	42.2	8.2	42.6	5.4	48.1	3.4
	LP-02	66.3	60.9	7.3	61.9	5.5	64.2	3.2
	LP-03	32.2	30.7	6.8	29.3	6.0	33.4	3.7
	LP-04	35.3	33.1	8.0	32.6	5.5	36.2	3.5
	LP-05	42.8	39.1	9.7	38.9	5.3	43.2	3.3
	LP-06	39.5	37.2	6.4	37.4	6.4	39.9	3.1
	LP-07	66.3	61.2	5.4	63.9	5.3	67.1	3.6
	LP-08	39.0	37.0	4.3	37.6	6.0	42.2	3.4
	LP-09	32.9	31.1	6.3	32.1	6.4	35.6	3.6
	LP-10	47.2	45.3	6.2	45.9	6.1	50.6	3.1
TG	LP-01	80	87	6.0	95	3.0	84	3.7
	LP-02	97	109	6.1	117	2.8	105	3.3
	LP-03	127	141	5.4	146	2.8	133	3.1
	LP-04	95	109	5.7	121	3.0	103	3.1
	LP-05	85	92	5.3	102	3.0	90	3.2
	LP-06	176	195	4.5	211	2.7	188	2.7
	LP-07	86	94	4.6	100	2.9	92	3.9
	LP-08	71	81	6.0	89	3.1	79	3.8
	LP-09	84	101	5.2	115	3.0	98	3.5
	LP-10	72	81	5.8	90	3.1	80	3.7

[1]Data from 1999 CAP Chemistry Survey Sets CA and CB, College of American Pathologists, Chicago, IL.
[2]Data for TC and TG have been rounded to nearest 1 mg/dL.
[3]To convert to mmol/L, divide TC or HDL-C by 38.7 and TG by 88.5.

Table 13-8 ◇ Bias of TC, TG, and HDL-C Measurements with Various Analytical Systems[1]

	Pool	CDC confirming Value[2] (mg/dL)	Abbott Vision[2] (mg/dL)	Bias (%)	Johnson & Johnson DT60II[2] (mg/dL)	Bias (%)	Abbott Spectrum[2] (mg/dL)	Bias (%)	Vitros 950[2] (mg/dL)	Bias (%)	Hitachi 911[2] (mg/dL)	Bias (%)
TC	LP-01	189	199	5.2%	191	1.0%	188	-0.5%	188	-0.5%	190	1.0%
	LP-02	245	255	4.0%	243	-.9%	247	-0.8%	244	-0.4%	246	0.4%
	LP-03	231	240	3.9%	229	-.9%	234	1.3%	227	-1.7%	232	0.4%
	LP-04	161	164	1.3%	158	-1.9%	163	1.2%	156	-3.1%	161	0.0%
	LP-05	177	152	-8.6%	175	-1.2%	179	1.1%	172	-2.8%	177	-0.0%
	LP-06	226	227	0.4%	227	0.4%	225	-0.4	221	-1.2	226	-0.4
	LP-07	256	260	1.6%	255	-0.4%	258	0.8	254	-0.8	255	-0.4
	LP-08	175	178	1.7%	174	-0.6%	177	1.1	172	-1.7	174	-0.6
	LP-09	157	156	-.6%	154	-1.9%	157	0.0	153	-2.5	156	-0.6
	LP-10	202	204	1.0%	200	-1.0%	204	1.0	196	-3.0	200	-1.0
	mean absolute bias[3]			2.8 %		1.0%		0.8%		1.8%		0.5%

Table 13-8 ◇ Continued

	Pool	CDC confirming Value[2] (mg/dL)	Abbott Vision[2] (mg/dL)	Bias (%)	Johnson & Johnson DT60II[2] (mg/dL)	Bias (%)	Abbott Spectrum[2] (mg/dL)	Bias (%)	Vitros 950[2] (mg/dL)	Bias (%)	Hitachi 911[2] (mg/dL)	Bias (%)
HDL-C[4]	LP-01	46.8	—	—	43.2	−7.7%	42.2	−9.8%	42.6	−9.0%	48.1	2.7%
	LP-02	66.3	—	—	62.0	−6.5%	60.9	−8.1%	61.9	−6.4%	64.2	−3.2%
	LP-03	32.2	—	—	29.5	−8.4%	30.7	−4.7%	29.3	−9.0%	33.4	3.7%
	LP-04	35.3	—	—	33.5	−5.1%	33.1	−6.2%	32.6	−7.6%	36.2	2.5%
	LP-05	42.8	—	—	39.8	−7.0%	39.1	−8.6%	38.9	−9.1%	43.2	0.9%
	LP-06	39.5	—	—	35.4	−10.4	37.2	−5.8	37.4	−5.3	39.9	1.0
	LP-07	66.3	—	—	61.7	−6.9	61.2	−7.7	63.9	−3.6	67.1	1.2
	LP-08	39.0	—	—	35.1	−10.0	37.0	−5.1	37.6	−3.6	42.2	8.2
	LP-09	32.9	—	—	29.7	−9.7	31.1	−5.5	32.1	−2.4	35.6	8.2
	LP-10	47.2	—	—	44.0	−6.8	45.3	−4.1	45.9	−2.8	50.6	7.2
	mean absolute bias[3]					7.9%		6.6%		5.9%		3.9%

TG[4]										
LP-01	80	—	89	13.3%	87	8.8%	95	18.8%	84	5.0%
LP-02	97	—	114	17.5%	109	12.4%	117	20.6%	105	8.2%
LP-03	127	—	148	16.5%	141	11.0%	146	15.0%	133	4.7%
LP-04	95	—	119	25.3%	109	14.7%	121	27.3%	103	8.4%
LP-05	85	—	98	15.3%	92	8.2%	102	20.0%	90	5.9%
LP-06	176	—	226	28.4	195	10.8	211	19.9	188	6.8
LP-07	86	—	96	11.6	94	9.3	100	16.3	92	7.0
LP-08	71	—	82	15.5	81	14.1	89	25.4	79	11.3
LP-09	84	—	113	34.5	101	20.2	115	36.9	98	16.7
LP-10	72	—	84	16.7	81	12.5	90	25.0	80	11.1
mean absolute bias[3]				19.5%		12.2%		22.5%		8.5%

[1] Data from 1999 CAP Chemistry Survey Sets C1, C2, C6, C7A, and B, College of American Pathologists, Chicago, IL.
[2] Data for TC and TG have been rounded to nearest 1 mg/dL.
[3] Mean of the absolute values of the bias for each system.
[4] No results were reported for the Abbott Vision.

For TG, among-laboratory CVs of 2.7%–6.3% were obtained for DT60-II (Table 13–6), compared to 2.7%–3.7% for two of the three laboratory analyzers (Table 13–7). The third laboratory system gave CVs of 4.5%–6.1% (Table 13–7), similar to the DT60-II. No data were reported for the Abbott Vision. The biases for TG were about two-fold greater for the desktop analyzer than for two of the laboratory-based systems and about the same as for the third (Table 13–8). The CDC-confirming values are equivalent to blanked values, while none of the systems shown in Table 13–8 was corrected for TG blanks. Inspection of the TG blanks for the survey pools (not shown), however, indicates that the biases for both the laboratory-based systems and the DT60-II would have been reduced by correcting for the TG blanks.

HDL-C measurements had among-laboratory CVs of 3.1%–6.4% with two of the laboratory-based systems, and 4.3%–9.7% for the third (Table 13–7). This compares with CVs of 5.4%–11.9% for the DT60-II. Again, no data were reported for the Abbott Vision (Table 13–6).

The biases with the DT60-II were about the same as those with two of the three laboratory-based systems in the table (Table 13–8). Substantive "matrix effects" can occur with HDL-C measurement in lyophilized pools, however, and these data may underestimate the reliability of HDL-C measurements with both the laboratory-based systems and the DT60-II.

One of the difficulties encountered when attempting to evaluate the performance of desktop analyzers is the paucity of available information of the kind shown in Tables 13–6 and 13–8. The data in these tables were collected from about 10–20 participants, compared to as many as several hundred participants for the laboratory instruments in Tables 13–7 and 13–8. In addition, some of the instruments, such as the Reflotron and LDX, are not represented at all, making it difficult to generalize about the reliability of desktop analyzers.

From the available information, desktop analyzers generally tend to exhibit fairly small biases with respect to CDC reference methods, on average. They do tend to be somewhat less precise than laboratory based systems, however. As a consequence, the values obtained with desktop analyzers can differ substantially from those with conventional laboratory methods in individual patients. For this reason, it is important to establish a quality control system for each desktop analyzer.

Establishing an adequate quality control system requires the availability of quality control sera in sufficient quantity for use of single lots of control pools over long periods, at least six months to one year. Analysis over the long term allows the user to establish control limits for accuracy and imprecision, and monitor analytical trends over time. Ideally, the reference values for such pools should be traceable to CDC reference methods, and the bias of the reference values with respect to CDC reference methods should be stated by the manufacturer. It can be difficult to procure control pools in sufficient quantity to allow adequate monitoring, however, because the lots of control pools furnished for use with a particular desktop analyzer can change frequently. In addition, instead of a reference value, control pools may be provided with an "acceptable operating range" for each analyte. Table 13–9 illustrates the "acceptable ranges" for two control pools provided for use with one particular desktop analyzer. In this case, the meaning of "acceptable range" was not specified, nor was it clear how the acceptable ranges were determined. Assuming that the midpoint of the range is the manufac-

Table 13-9 ✧ Coefficients of Analytical Variation Calculated from "Acceptable Ranges" Provided for Control Sera

	Pool	Manufacturer's acceptable range[1](mg/dL)	Midpoint[2] (mg/dL)	Calculated CV_a [3](%)
TC	1	146–206	176	5.7
	2	219–307	263	5.6
TG	1	129–179	154	5.4
	2	212–312	262	6.4
HDL-C	1	30–47	38.5	7.4
	2	56–88	72	7.4

[1]As provided in the package insert.
[2]Calculated as (lower limit + upper limit) ÷ 2.
[3]Calculated as $\dfrac{[(\text{midpoint} - \text{lower limit}) \div 3]}{(\text{midpoint})}$
To convert to mmol/L, divide TC or HDL-C by 38.7 and TG by 88.5.

turer's reference value, however, and that the range represents the 99% limits for the mean, it can be calculated that the ranges shown in Table 13–9 correspond to CV_as of 5.6% and 5.7% for TC; 5.4% and 6.4% for TG; and 7.4% for HDL-C.

The CV_as would be greater if the ranges represent 95% limits. The proximity of the means to reference values was not indicated and "acceptable bias," therefore, could not be determined. The calculated CV_as exceed current NCEP guidelines for precision, and depending on the bias, "acceptable performance" might exceed NCEP guidelines for total error as well. For purposes of quality control, it would be more useful for manufacturers to indicate for each control pool:

✧ the mean value for each analyte;

✧ the bias of the value with respect to the reference value; and

✧ the maximum CV_a to be expected for the desktop analyzer.

Desktop analyzers are actually capable of greater precision than indicated from the "acceptable" CV_as in Table 13–9, at least for TC and HDL-C. The example in the table is intended to illustrate the point that the manufacturers' stated acceptable ranges should not be adopted uncritically. Rather, a truly adequate quality control system based on long-term use of single lots of control sera should be established for each instrument. This should be supplemented with a formal split-sample comparison program in which some of the same specimens analyzed with the desktop analyzer are also measured with well-controlled laboratory methods. Such a program can expose problems that may not be evident from the analysis of the control pools (see "Recommendations," below).

RECOMMENDATIONS

The use of desktop analyzers for TC measurement has been discussed in detail in the literature.[31,36,37] The following sections represent, for the most part, a summary of the recommendations emanating from these discussions, and they can also be usefully applied to the measurement of TG and HDL-C.

Use an Accurate System.

Select an instrument-reagent system for which the manufacturer has documented how the measurements were standardized and for which the measurements are traceable to the CDC reference values. This will help to ensure that at least on average, the instrument is capable of providing accurate values.

Use a Precise Instrument.

Select a system that is precise; that is, repeat measurements made in the same sample should be reproducible. Within individual clinical laboratories, CVs of 2% or less can generally be obtained for TC and TG, and 3% or less for HDL-C. With desktop analyzers, however, CVs are generally a little higher for TC, in the range of 3%–5%, and can be several-fold higher for TG and HDL-C.

Use Properly Trained Operators.

Measurements should be made by trained operators. Ideally, the operator should be a trained medical technician who is familiar with clinical chemical measurements and quality control procedures. Before using the measurements for clinical purposes, the operator should be trained in the proper procedures for patient preparation, instrument operation, and regularly scheduled instrument maintenance according to the manufacturer's recommended procedures. Maintenance should be documented and records kept current.

Use a Quality Control System.

Establish a formal quality control system using quality control pools that are available in sufficient quantities to be analyzed for a minimum of six months. Quality control pools should cover the clinically significant range. Two levels of controls should be used. Recommended concentrations are as follows:

TC: 180–200 mg/dL (4.66–5.18 mmol/L) and 240–270 mg/dL (6.22–6.99 mmol/L)
TG: 125–150 mg/dL (1.41–1.69 mmol/L) and 200–250 mg/dL (2.26–2.82 mmol/L)
HDL-C: 35 mg/dL (0.90 mmol/L) and 60 mg/dL (1.55 mmol/L).

When first setting up the analytical system, these materials should be analyzed in duplicate on five to ten different days during a two-week period, and appropriate quality control limits should be established for each. If assistance in calculating these limits is needed, a qualified local laboratory should be consulted.

New quality control pools should be introduced before the current pools are exhausted and should similarly be analyzed to establish control limits for those pools before the original pools are discontinued. Quality control records should be maintained and kept current.

In the laboratory, the results for patient samples are not used when the quality control measurements are outside control limits; instead, the analyses are repeated. Such a procedure is not feasible with desktop analysis because the results may have been reported before it was known that they were "out of control." For this reason, it is recommended that quality control pools be analyzed at the beginning of the day to establish that the analyses are adequate, and again after every 20 samples (or every few hours if fewer than 20 samples are analyzed) to document that the instrument continues to function properly. If quality control values are unacceptable, subsequent measurements should not be accepted, and appropriate corrective measures should be taken.

Setting up an adequate quality control system for desktop analyzers can be difficult. The main constraint is the difficulty of obtaining sufficient quantities of control materials to allow single lots to be used for extended periods. Test kits may be supplied with quantities sufficient only for that kit, and different lots of control materials may be supplied with subsequent kits. While manufacturers define the acceptable operating ranges of the control, these ranges can be considerably wider than can be routinely obtained with the particular instrument being used. This can make it difficult to determine when the system is behaving abnormally. If possible, it is best to purchase a sufficient quantity of test kits for a six-month period and specify that all the control materials for the kits be from the same lots of control materials. Furthermore, it is essential to set up a formal system of split-sample analysis with a qualified, preferably CDC-standardized, laboratory.

Use a System of Split-Sample Analysis.

Measurements in quality control pools can be influenced by factors arising from the way the pools are prepared, and the pools may not accurately reflect the reliability of measurements in freshly drawn patient specimens. It is *not advisable* to rely solely on such pools for quality control. Rather, the accuracy of the results should be monitored by comparing values generated by the desktop analyzer to those in a qualified laboratory that is either CDC standardized or whose methods are ultimately traceable to reference values. The comparison can be done in about 10% of the samples by submitting aliquots of those samples to the laboratory. The comparative results should be examined and frequent instances of large differences should be investigated. When desktop analyzer measurements are made in capillary specimens obtained by finger stick, it is preferable that the split-sample comparison be performed in concurrently collected venous serum, since it may not be feasible to use split capillary specimens for laboratory-based measurements. The author prefers to use at least 100 split-sample measurements spaced evenly throughout the year. The data obtained provide a reasonable indication of the long-term accuracy and precision of the measurements.

Follow Proper Patient Preparation Procedures.

Blood collection should be performed in a standard way to minimize changes that can lead to inaccurate measurements. For further details on patient preparation and specimen collection and handling, refer to Chapter 8.

SUMMARY

Desktop analyzers tend to give a fairly accurate average value in a group of fresh specimens, but the measurements can be less precise than laboratory-based analyses. These instruments can be useful for lipid screening or for following the progress of a patient being treated for hyperlipidemia once the lipoprotein abnormality has been diagnosed using the appropriate medical procedures and lipoprotein measurements. TC concentrations can be measured in samples from non-fasting patients, if necessary. HDL-C measured in non-fasting samples can be expected to be lower than in fasting samples by a few percentage points. TG should not be measured in non-fasting samples. The analyses can be performed in either venous or capillary samples, but if capillary samples are used, it is well to be aware that in individual cases values may differ substantially from venous values. Desktop analyzers should be operated by properly trained personnel, and their performance should be monitored vigorously. Finally, the individuals charged with interpreting the results should become familiar with the limitations of the technology.   ✧

Acknowledgements: *The author wishes to thank Kathleen Lovejoy for assisting with the assembly and analysis of split-sample and quality control data.*

REFERENCES

1. Castelli WP, Garrison RJ, Wilson PWF et al. Incidence of coronary heart disease and lipoprotein levels: the Framingham Study. JAMA 1986;256:2835–8.
2. Lipid Research Clinics Program. The Lipid Research Clinics Coronary Primary Prevention Trial results. I. Reduction in incidence of coronary heart disease. JAMA 1984; 251:351–64.
3. Lipid Research Clinics Program. The Lipid Research Clinics Coronary Primary Prevention Trial results. II. The relation of reduction in incidence of coronary heart disease to cholesterol lowering. JAMA 1984;251:365–74.
4. Stamler J, Wentworth D, Neaton JD, for the MRFIT Research Group. Is the relationship between cholesterol and risk of premature death from coronary heart disease continuous and graded? Findings in 356,222 primary screenees of the Multiple Risk Factor Intervention Trial (MRFIT). JAMA 1986;256:2823–8.
5. Blankenhorn DH, Nessim SA, Johnson RL et al. Beneficial effects of combined colestipol-niacin therapy on coronary atherosclerosis and coronary venous bypass grafts. JAMA 1987;257:3233–40.
6. Frick MH, Elo O, Haapa et al. Helsinki Heart Study: primary prevention trial with gemfibrozil in middle-aged men with dyslipidemia. N Engl J Med 1987;317:1237–45.
7. Brensike EJ, Levy RJ, Kelsey SF et al. Effects of therapy with cholestyramine on progression of coronary arteriosclerosis: results of the NHLBI Type II Coronary Intervention Study. Circulation 1984;69:313–24.
8. Gordon T, Castelli WP, Hjortland MC, Kannel WB, Dawber TR. High-density lipoprotein

as a protective factor against coronary heart disease: the Framingham Study. Am J Med 1977;62:707–14.

9. Castelli WP, Doyle JT, Gordon T et al. HDL cholesterol and other lipids in coronary heart disease: the cooperative lipoprotein phenotyping study. Circulation 1972;55:767–72.

10. Miller NE, Forde OH, Thelle DS, Mjos OD. The Tromso Heart Study. High-density lipoprotein and coronary heart disease: a prospective case-control study. Lancet 1977;1: 965–7.

11. Summary of the Second Report of the National Cholesterol Education Program (NCEP) Expert Panel on Detection, Evaluation, and Treatment of High Blood Cholesterol in Adults (Adult Treatment Panel II). JAMA 1993;269:3015–23.

12. Report of the National Cholesterol Education Program Expert Panel on Detection Evaluation and Treatment of High Blood Cholesterol in Adults. Arch Intern Med 1988;148: 6–69.

13. Allain CC, Poon LS, Chan CSG, Richmond W, Fu PC. Enzymatic determination of total serum cholesterol. Clin Chem 1974;20:470–6.

14. Demaker PNM, Boerma GJM, Baadenhuijsen H et al. Evaluation of accuracy of 20 different test kits for the enzymatic determination of cholesterol. Clin Chem 1983;29: 1916–22.

15. Bucolo G, David H. Quantitative determination of serum triglycerides by the use of enzymes. Clin Chem 1973;19:476–82.

16. Bachorik PS, Levy RI, Rifkind BM. Lipids and dyslipoproteinemia. In: Henry JB, ed. Clinical diagnosis and management by laboratory methods, 18th ed. Philadelphia: WB Saunders, 1991:188–214.

17. Bachorik PS, Rock R, Cloey T et al. Cholesterol screening: comparative evaluation of on-site and laboratory-based measurements. Clin Chem 1990;36:255–60.

18. Sedor FA, Holleman CM, Heyden S, Schneider KA. Reflotron cholesterol measurement evaluated as a screening technique. Clin Chem 1988;34:2542–4.

19. Bachorik PS, Bradford RH, Cole T et al. Accuracy and precision of analyses for total cholesterol as measured with the Reflotron cholesterol method. Clin Chem 1989; 35:1734–9.

20. von Schenck H, Treichl L, Tilling B, Olsson AG. Laboratory and field evaluation of three desktop instruments for assay of cholesterol and triglyceride. Clin Chem 1987;33: 1230–2.

21. Ng RH, Sparks KM, Statland BE. Direct measurement of high-density lipoprotein cholesterol by the Reflotron Assay with no manual precipitation step. Clin Chem 1991; 37:435–7.

22. Warnick GR, Boerma GJM, Assmann G, Endler AT, Gerique G, Gotto AM et al. Multicenter evaluation of Reflotron direct dry-chemistry assay of high-density lipoprotein cholesterol in venous and finger-stick specimens. Clin Chem 1993;39:271–7.

23. Kafonek SD, Donovan L, Lovejoy KL, Bachorik PS. Biological variation of lipids and lipoproteins in finger-stick blood. Clin Chem 1996;42:2002–7.

24. Friedewald WT, Levy RI, Fredrickson DS. Estimation of the concentration of low-density lipoprotein cholesterol in plasma without use of the preparative ultracentrifuge. Clin Chem 1972;18:499–502.

25. Koch TR, Mehtu U, Lee H et al. Bias and precision of cholesterol analysis by physicians' office analyzers. Clin Chem 1987;33:2262–7.

26. Rogers EJ, Misner L, Ockene IS, Nicolosi RJ. Evaluation of seven cholestech LDX analyzers for total cholesterol determinations. Clin Chem 1993;39:860–4.

27. Kupke IR, Zeugner S, Gottschalk A, Kather B. Differences in lipid and lipoprotein concentrations of capillary and venous blood samples. Clin Chim Acta 1979;97:279–83.

28. Kaplan SA, Yuceoglu AM, Strauss J. Chemical microanalysis: analysis of capillary and venous blood. Pediatrics 1959;24:270–4.

29. Greenland P, Bowley NL, Melklejohn B, Doane KL, Sparks CE. Blood cholesterol concentration: finger-stick plasma vs. venous serum sampling. Clin Chem 1990;36:628–30.

30. Bachorik PS. Collection of blood samples for lipoprotein analysis. Clin Chem 1982; 28:1375–8.

31. Laboratory Methods Committee, Lipid Research Clinics Program. Cholesterol and triglyceride concentrations in serum plasma pairs. Clin Chem 1977;26:60–3.

32. Cloey T, Bachorik PS, Becker D, Finney C, Lowry D, Sigmund W. Re-evaluation of serum-plasma differences in total cholesterol concentration. JAMA 1990;263:2788–9.

33. Laboratory Standardization Panel. Recommendations for improving cholesterol measurement: a report from the Laboratory Standardization Panel of the National Cholesterol Education Program, NIH Publication No. 90–2964. Executive Summary, NIH Publication No. 90–2964A. Bethesda, MD: NIH, 1990.

34. National Cholesterol Education Program Recommendations on Lipoprotein Measurement. From the Working Group on Lipoprotein Measurement, NIH Publication No. 95–3044. Bethesda, MD: NHLBI, Sept. 1995.

35. Smith SM, Davis-Street JE, Fontenot TB, Lane HW. Assessment of a portable clinical blood analyzer during space flight. Clin Chem 1997;43:1056–65.

36. Belsey R, Vandenbark M, Goitein RK, Baer DM. Evaluation of a laboratory system intended for use in physicians' offices. II. Reliability of results produced by health care workers without formal or professional laboratory training. JAMA 1987;258:357–63.

37. Recommendations regarding public screening for measuring blood cholesterol: a summary of a National Heart, Lung, and Blood Institute workshop. NIH Publication No. 89–3045. Bethesda, MD: NIH, 1989.

Measurement and Clinical Significance of Apolipoproteins A-1 and B

14

Deepak Bhatnagar and Paul N. Durrington

❖   Apolipoproteins (apo) A-I and B are both integral parts of lipoprotein particles that play an important role in cholesterol transport. Apo B plays an essential role in the delivery of cholesterol to the tissues. Apo A-I has a role in the removal of excess cholesterol from the tissues and is the main apolipoprotein in the interstitial space. Both apo B and apo A-I have a role in the diagnosis and monitoring of disease and in the assessment of coronary risk, but further studies are needed to refine their clinical use.

APOLIPOPROTEIN A-I

Background

The principal apolipoproteins of high-density lipoproteins (HDL) are the A apolipoproteins, so called because HDL was formerly called alpha lipoprotein.[1] In humans, the two major A apolipoproteins are A-I and A-II. Apo A-I is the most abundant. Indeed, it is present in plasma in health at mass concentrations, which generally exceed those of apo B. In the tissue fluid, A-I is the apolipoprotein present at the greatest concentration.[2]

Apo A-I and apo A-II originate in both the gut and the liver, from where they are secreted as phospholipid-rich discs called nascent HDL.[3] The gene for apo A-I is located on chromosome 11, where it occurs in close proximity to the genes for apo C-III and apo A-IV.[4] In common with many of the other apolipoprotein genes, it consists of four exons with three intervening introns. The exons code for a 267 amino acid precursor known as preproapo A. The pre-peptide at the N-terminal end of this molecule is 18 amino acids long and is cleaved co-translationally, leaving the proapo A-I, which is the form secreted.[5] The six amino acid N-terminal propeptide is then removed in the circulation by a specific calcium-dependent protease. This results in the mature 243 amino acid apo A-I.[6] The residence time of proapo A-I in the circulation is approximately 4.5 h, whereas the half-life of mature A-I is about five to six days. Proapo A-I comprises 4% of the total fasting serum apo A-I, but increases transiently after meals.

Most of the C-terminal 200 amino acids of the mature apo A-I are coded for by the fourth exon, which is the largest.[7] In this part of the molecule are six repeated sequences each of 22 amino acids, each ending with proline. In between the prolines is an alpha-helical structure with polar and non-polar faces. This confers upon the A-I molecule powerful detergent properties, the non-polar groups being directed towards the hydrophobic core lipids and the polar groups interfacing with water molecules outside.[8] Most of the apo A-I is present in plasma and extra vascular tissue fluid in HDL. There is, however, a small percentage of apo A-I that is not present in lipoproteins and that is generally referred to as pre-beta HDL, which accurately describes its electrophoretic mobility but wrongly describes its hydrated density, which is greater than that of HDL.[9] Use of the term "free apo A-I" to describe this fraction is also misleading because it contains phospholipid. A discoidal form, called pre-beta-2 HDL, exists in addition to the spherical form of alpha or mature HDL.[10] Recent evidence suggests that pre-beta HDL may be released from larger HDL particles as they circulate through peripheral tissues by the actions of lipoprotein lipase.[11] Studies of epitope mapping[12] indicate that the conformation of apo A-I differs in the various species of HDL (Figure 14–1). *In vitro* evidence suggests it is both an acceptor of cholesterol and a promoter of cholesterol efflux. Besides its structural role, apo A-I is the major activator of the enzyme lecithin:cholesterol acyltransferase (LCAT).[13]

Apo A-I has six polymorphic isoforms designated 1–6, of which 4 and 5 are the most common. In addition, there are genetic mutations of apo A-I referred to as apo A-I$_{Tangier}$, apo A-I$_{Milano}$, apo A-I$_{Marburg}$, and so on (see discussion below). Apo A-I is unusual among the apolipoproteins in that carbohydrate is absent as a component of its mature form.

Figure 14–1 ✧ The Conformation of Apolipoprotein A-I Differs in the Three Main HDL Subspecies

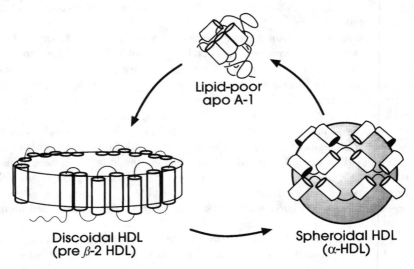

Lipid-poor
apo A-1

Discoidal HDL
(pre β-2 HDL)

Spheroidal HDL
(α-HDL)

Clinical Relevance of Apo A-I Measurement

Apo A-I measurements are of most use in characterizing patients with genetic disorders that lead to low HDL-cholesterol (HDL-C) concentrations. Several disorders of HDL are associated with low apo A-I levels, but only some patients with these disorders will have mutations of apo A-I. The benefits of determining coronary heart disease (CHD) risk through apo A-I assays rather than with HDL-C measurements is unclear. There are few prospective studies of apo A-I in CHD prediction, and in some of them HDL-C was found to be superior to apo A-I.[14–17] Furthermore, until recently issues of standardization of assays were unresolved. Moreover, data from genetic studies of HDL deficiency syndromes, many of which are not associated with CHD, are at odds with data from case-control studies where low apo A-I is often a marker of CHD risk.

Familial Low HDL Concentration

Familial low HDL appears to be quite common and is often associated with increased plasma triglyceride (TG) levels. HDL-C levels below the 10th percentile are often associated with an increased risk of CHD.[18] In the United States, the 10th percentile in men aged 20–69 years was 33 mg/dL (0.8 mmol/L) and in women aged 25–55 years, 39 mg/dL (1.0 mmol/L).[19] No specific defects have been described in these patients, but it is thought that they have an increased turnover of apo A-I and other HDL proteins.[20] Apo A-I measurements are rarely required in these patients unless there is a strong suspicion of apo A-I deficiency disorders.

Familial Apo A-I Deficiency

There have been several reports of patients with apo A-I deficiency, all of whom are characterized by particularly low HDL-C levels.[21] The low apo A-I arises from mutations that result in incomplete forms of apo A-I. These deficiency syndromes are inherited as an autosomal-dominant trait and the associated phenotypes vary greatly. Not all patients develop CHD. Some have corneal clouding and others have planar xanthomata. Some patients with apo A-I deficiency syndromes also have a deficiency of apo C-III or of C-III and apo A-IV. Plasma lipid levels also show variation in phenotype. Mild hypertriglyceridemia is commonly present, but most patients do not have high plasma cholesterol concentrations.

Apo A-I Variants

In contrast to deficiency syndromes, many apo A-I variants have been reported in the literature. However, not all patients with these variants have low HDL-C levels.[22] Often these have been discovered on isoelectric focusing of apo A-I. Some like A-I$_{Milano}$ are associated with longevity.[23]

Tangier Disease

This is a rare autosomal-recessive disorder characterized by low plasma total cholesterol and HDL-C levels and accumulation of cholesteryl esters in many tissues, particularly the reticuloendothelial system.[24] A typical presentation is the presence of hyperplastic yellowish-orange tonsils. In homozygotes, plasma apo A-I levels are usually 1%–3% of normal; in heterozygotes, apo A-I levels are half that of normal. The exact biochemical defect is not known, but the accumulation of cholesteryl ester and low HDL levels suggest a problem with cellular cholesterol storage and processing.[25]

Familial Lecithin:Cholesterol Acyltransferase (LCAT) Deficiency

This is due to a deficiency of the enzyme LCAT.[26] Both alpha and beta LCAT activities are decreased. Plasma apo A-I levels are decreased to 15%–30% of normal and HDL-C concentrations to 10% of normal. Most patients develop corneal opacities and anemia. Proteinuria and renal failure develop over time.

Fish-Eye Disease

Fish-eye disease is also characterized by LCAT deficiency, but it is mainly alpha LCAT activity that is decreased.[27] As in familial LCAT deficiency, patients typically have corneal opacities, but proteinuria and renal failure do not develop. Apo A-I levels are reduced to 15%–30% of normal and HDL-C levels are 10% of normal.

Hyperalphalipoproteinemia

Hyperalphalipoproteinemia occurs in some families in whom HDL-C levels are consistently greater than the highest decile for the population.[28] The genetics of the condition are not clear, but it is important to exclude secondary causes for an increase in HDL-C. Apo A-I levels are increased in parallel to HDL-C levels.

Familial Cholesteryl Ester Transfer Protein (CETP) Deficiency

CETP is a glycoprotein that transfers cholesteryl ester out of HDL to TG-rich lipoproteins with a reciprocal exchange of TG into HDL.[29] Families with CETP deficiency have been described recently.[30] Homozygotes have HDL-C levels that are markedly elevated with a doubling of the apo A-I concentration. Heterozygotes may have normal or high HDL-C, but apo A-I levels are increased. The small number of homozygotes discovered seem to be protected from CHD, but converse data linking CHD and high CETP levels are more convincing.[31]

Apo A-I and Coronary Risk

Many studies have confirmed the ability of HDL-C levels to predict coronary risk.[32–35] It therefore would seem logical that apo A-I levels should behave in a similar fashion, but it is generally thought that they offer little advantage over HDL-C levels. However, apo A-I assays have the theoretical advantage of better precision than HDL-C assays, which employ chemical precipitation. Issues relating to standardization and antibody specificity have been addressed only recently, and prospective studies are needed to show firm benefit over the less expensive HDL-C assays currently in use.

Most case-control studies show an inverse relationship between apo A-I and CHD, similar to that seen with HDL-C. Of the four prospective studies to date,[14–17] one study, in which HDL-C was not measured, showed apo A-I to be a discriminator between subjects with and without CHD. Of the other three studies, two did not find that apo A-I contributed more than HDL-C, and the fourth found that apo A-I added to the value of apo B in predicting CHD.

APOLIPOPROTEIN B

Background

Apo B is central to the lipoprotein transport system. It is essential for the secretion of TG-rich lipoproteins both from the liver and gut. (For further details see Chapters 1 and 5.) A single molecule of apo B is present in each chylomicron, very-low-density lipoprotein (VLDL), or low-density lipoprotein (LDL) particle from the time of its assembly, its secretion, its metabolic transformation within the circulation, and ultimately to its catabolism.[36] Apo B does not exchange between lipoprotein particles. It is for this reason that it has been possible, by labeling apo B with isotopes, to study the metabolic fate of apo-B-containing lipoproteins.[37] A similar approach, such as labeling apo A-I, can give only a limited insight into HDL metabolism.

Apo B is the most abundant protein in LDL. It acquired its name because it was formerly known as beta lipoprotein. Its serum concentration in Northern European and American populations ranges from 50–180 mg/dL.[38] More than 90% of this is in LDL and the rest in VLDL (Table 14–1).[39] In conditions associated with a raised serum concentration of LDL-C, serum apo B is generally also raised, even when increased LDL-C concentrations are not accompanied by hypercholesterolemia (hyperapobetalipoproteinemia; see below). It has long been realized that many of the hyperlipoproteinemias leading to premature atherosclerosis are those in which serum apo B levels are high. In 1974, Fredrickson, commenting about apo B, wrote: "Its resistance to characterization, its seeming essentiality for glyceride transport, and perhaps the added suspicion that it has something to do with atherogenesis have all transformed apo B into one of the central mysteries of lipoprotein physiology."[40]

Since that time, evidence has progressively accumulated for a close association between serum apo B and premature coronary atheroma.[41] Until recently, the structure and properties of the apo B molecule remained a mystery because its enormous size, insolubility even when only partially delipidated, and tendency to aggregate make it resistant to many biochemical techniques. Now, as a result of advances in immunochemistry, in the study of specific proteolytic fragments, and molecular genetic techniques, fascinating details of its biochemistry have emerged.

The apo B gene is situated on chromosome 2.[42] Its messenger RNA (mRNA) contains 14,121 nucleotides and is thus the largest mRNA known. It codes for a 4563 amino acid protein, the N-terminal 27 amino acids of which are cleaved, resulting in a 4536 amino acid native apo B-100.[43] The 27 residue terminal portion is hydrophobic

Table 14–1 ✧ Apolipoprotein B Concentrations in LDL from Patients with Hyperlipidaemia

The great majority of apolipoprotein B in serum is present in LDL unless hypertriglyceridemia is extreme.

WHO Phenotype		Normal	IIa	IIb	IV	V
N		18	15	5	6	4
Serum						
Apolipoprotein B	mg/dL	92 ± 21	223 ± 47	289 ± 149	231 ± 104	130 ± 16
Cholesterol	mmol/L	4.7 ± 0.9	8.8 ± 1.2	8.3 ± 0.8	7.4 ± 1.1	14.3 ± 6.3
	mg/dL	182 ± 35	340 ± 46	321 ± 31	286 ± 43	552 ± 243
Triglyceride	mmol/L	0.9 ± 0.2	1.5 ± 0.3	3.7 ± 1.2	5.6 ± 3.1	28.7 ± 15.9
	mg/dL	80 ± 18	133 ± 27	327 ± 106	496 ± 274	2540 ± 1407
LDL						
Apolipoprotein B	mg/dL	80 ± 18	206 ± 49	235 ± 125	160 ± 73	65 ± 10
% total serum apolipoprotein B		93 ± 9	93 ± 9	91 ± 1	81 ± 9	52 ± 8

Adapted from Reference 39. Durrington et al Clin Chim Acta 1978;78:151–160 (with permission).

and large enough to span a biological membrane. Thus, the apo B gene may be important in the membrane transport and anchoring of the apo B during the synthesis and secretion of the apo-B-containing lipoproteins.[44] Apo B is synthesized in the smooth endoplasmic reticulum. TG may be stored before becoming bound to the apo B and appearing in the Golgi complex.[45] The binding of TG to apo B is facilitated by microsomal TG transfer protein (MTP).[46] The inheritance of defective MTP is the basis of abetalipoproteinemia (see discussion below). Carbohydrate is acquired in the Golgi complex before secretion of the nascent VLDL. N-linked oligosaccharides comprise some 8%–10% of the mass of apo B.

The primary sequence of apo B-100 is unlike that of other apolipoproteins such as the apo A and apo C. It is a much larger molecule. Estimates of its molecular weight from the amino acids present place it around 500,000 daltons which, allowing for the presence of carbohydrate, would suggest an actual mass as high as 550,000 daltons.[47] Therefore, from our knowledge of the protein content of LDL, there can be only one molecule of apo B-100 per molecule of LDL. Typically, apolipoproteins consist largely of alpha helices and beta structure. They bind to lipid through amphipathic sequences in the classical detergent style. Apo B is different. It is very much more hydrophobic. Long hydrophobic sequences interspersed with hydrophilic ones characterize much of its structure, which is only 43% alpha helix, with the rest comprising about equally beta sheet, beta turn, and random structures. About 11 hydrophobic regions are thus strung out along the apo B molecule, and these probably bury themselves in the TG and cholesteryl esters of the lipoprotein core, leaving the more hydrophilic intervening sections at the surface or within the outer phospholipid, free cholesterol, and apo-C-containing regions of the lipoprotein particle. There are several points in the apo B structure where disulfide bonds could either form internally or with another protein such as the apolipoprotein (a) of Lp(a) (see Chapter 17).

Despite its enormous size, apo B, like apo E, has only one receptor-binding site per molecule. It is in a region about one-quarter of the way from the C-terminal of the apo B molecule, which is rich in basic amino acids, homologous with the receptor-binding site of the apo E.[48] It is assumed that during the removal of the lipid core from VLDL in its conversion to LDL, conformational changes occur in the apo B that allow the receptor site to bind to the LDL receptor. Perhaps during the conversion of VLDL to LDL some of the hydrophobic regions of apo B become less deeply embedded in the diminishing lipid core and the surface parts of the molecule crowd closer together and project out further, allowing the receptor-binding site to become more prominently exposed and to assume its most active shape. The removal of VLDL from the circulation via the LDL receptor is thus prevented until it has shed its TG load. Studies on particle surface charge in LDL subspecies indicate that there are differences in confromation of apo B between LDL subspecies. This suggests that small dense LDL may bind less than other LDL species to the LDL receptor, thereby prolonging their stay in the plasma.[49]

In humans, apo B-48 is the apo B produced by the gut but not by the liver.[50] It is estimated to have about 48% of the molecular weight of apo B (hence its name). It does not bind to lipoprotein receptors. Both apo B-100 and apo B-48 appear to arise from an identical gene (Figure 14–2). Apolipoprotein B-48 consists of the N-terminal 2152 amino acids of apo B-100.[51] Examination of the genome shows that it terminates in about the middle of the largest exon, meaning that transcription of the message is unlikely to be broken at this point. However, in the RNAs from gut and liver, codon 2153 is different.[52] In that codon, cytosine is present in hepatic mRNA, whereas uracil is present in intestinal mRNA. This makes the codon read CAA in the liver, which translates as glutamine, and UAA in the gut, which is an order to terminate translation. The intestine proves to possess a highly specific enzyme that changes the cytosine (perhaps by deamination) in codon 2153 of apo B mRNA.[53] The effect of the two types of apo B produced in the liver and gut is of fundamental importance to lipoprotein metabolism. Because the receptor-binding site of apo B-100 is in the C-terminal half not present in apo B-48, the TG-rich lipoproteins from the gut are dependent on apo E for their clearance from the circulation. Mutations of the apo B gene also occur that lead to the premature termination of its translation truncating the apo B molecule[54] and causing an unexplained decrease in the production of apo B from the unmutated gene and to dominant inheritance of hypobetalipoproteinemia (discussed below).

It is also becoming clear that apo B-100 is highly polymorphic. This has been demonstrated by molecular biology techniques, and by individual variation in the binding affinities of apo-B-containing lipoproteins to monoclonal antibodies directed at different parts of the apo B molecule.[55] The present interest in that area of research focuses on which of these polymorphisms influence the metabolism of apo-B-containing lipoproteins sufficiently to have a clinically significant impact on their serum con-

Figure 14–2 ✧ Structure and Organization of the Apolipoprotein Gene

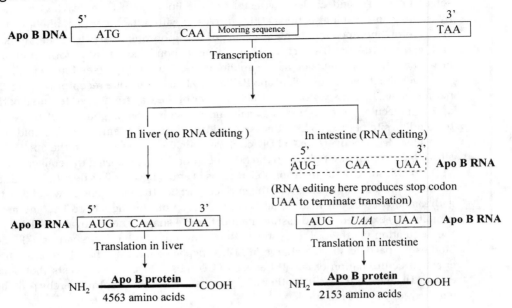

centration and their involvement in atherogenesis. There are also mutations of apo B, the most extensively studied of which has been the apo B-3500 mutation, which affects binding to the LDL receptor [familial defective apo B (FDB)].[56]

The hypothesis that macrophage uptake of LDL is important in atherogenesis has further heightened the interest in apo B, because of evidence that it is the apo B moiety which allows the rapid uptake of LDL crossing the arterial endothelium by macrophages to form foam cells.[57] Macrophages do not possess a particularly active physiological LDL receptor, and macrophage uptake of unmodified LDL cannot account for the generation of foam cells. Modification of LDL, can, however, greatly increase the rate at which it is bound and internalized by macrophages via receptors that are quite distinct from the physiological LDL receptor.[58]

The modification of LDL permitting this rapid uptake, which has attracted much attention, is oxidation.[59] This is because it is plausible that lipid-peroxidation could occur *in vivo*. Macrophage receptors that allow the uptake of oxidized LDL do so by binding to apo B that has been damaged by the breakdown products of the LDL lipids that are peroxidized, particularly the unsaturated fatty acyl groups in the Sn-2 position of phosphatidylcholine.[60] Aldehydes are produced by the schism following the introduction of oxygen-free radicals at sites of double bonds. These aldehydes form adducts with the lysine groups of apo B, leading to its fragmentation.[61] LDL then loses its capacity to bind to the LDL receptor, but binds to the macrophage receptors. (For additional information on this topic, refer to Chapters 20 and 21.)

The most extensively studied of these has been the acetyl-LDL receptor (so-named because the modification of LDL, which led to its discovery, was acetylation) or scavenger receptor.[62] However, there are undoubtedly other classes of receptors that can be involved, and have been termed oxidized LDL receptors.

Glycation is another modification of LDL, which accelerates macrophage uptake.[63] This process involves the addition of glucose to lysine residue on apo B. This may in itself make the LDL more susceptible to fragmentation by products of lipid peroxidation, which may themselves be formed as a consequence of free radical generation during glycation.[64] It is not clear whether glycation might lead directly to foam cell generation by the same mechanism as oxidative modification. Glycated apo B comprises some 4% of the total circulating apo B in non-diabetic people and about twice that amount in diabetic patients with reasonable glycemic control.[65] In normolipidemic non-diabetic people, typical serum levels of glycated apo B are 2–6 mg/dL. Because of the high concentration of LDL in, for example, heterozygous familial hypercholesterolemia, the concentration of glycated apo B may be similar to that in diabetes even though the percentage glycated is not increased.[66] In contrast, oxidatively modified LDL is present only at substantially lower concentrations. It is difficult to be confidant that such levels are present *in vivo* and are not generated during subsequent processing of the blood sample. Because oxidized LDL is antigenic, its generation may be detected by measuring titres of antibodies to modified LDL, and this may prove to be a more reliable method of detecting individuals' increased oxidized LDL production. The usefulness of titres of antibodies to various modifications of LDL in predicting the extent of oxidation is currently undergoing evaluation. Malondialdehyde modification has been most extensively studied thus far.[67]

Clinical Relevance of Apo B

A large body of experimental evidence implicates apo-B-containing plasma lipoproteins in the causation of atherosclerosis. In contrast, epidemiological data relating plasma apo B concentrations to coronary risk are not so numerous. Some of the reasons for this discrepancy probably arise from difficulties in standardizing assays for plasma apo B measurement, but may also be due to a failure of assays to recognize the heterogeneity of apo B which is present in atherogenic particles such as intermediate-density lipoproteins (IDL) and small, dense LDL, and also in the relatively less atherogenic LDL-I and LDL-II subfractions. For additional information on LDL subclasses, refer to chapter 16.

In the last few years, progress has been made in standardizing apo B assays, and data on reference ranges based on population studies and case control studies is now becoming available. At present, the main utility of plasma apo B determination lies in the diagnosis of certain primary disorders of lipoprotein metabolism and as a research tool in the investigation of lipoprotein metabolism. Its role in the assessment of coronary risk remains unclear and needs to be investigated further.

Abetalipoproteinemia

Abetalipoproteinemia is an autosomal-recessive disorder due to a deficiency of apo B in the intestine and the liver.[68] As a consequence, dietary fat is malabsorbed and accumulates in the intestine. The apo B deficiency also characteristically results in acanthocytosis, retinitis pigmentosa, and ataxia due to spinocerebellar degeneration. The latter two conditions respond at least partially to supplementation of vitamins A and E, suggesting that a deficiency of fat-soluble vitamins may be the cause of the neurological features.

Apo B mRNA in the liver is increased. Hepatic steatosis also occurs, although this indicates that the defect does not lie in the gene, but in the assembly and secretion of TG-rich lipoproteins, both by the gut and liver. Recent evidence indicates that abetalipoproteinemia may be due to a defect in the microsomal lipid transfer protein.[69]

Biochemically, patients with abetalipoproteinemia have markedly decreased serum cholesterol and TG, and a firm diagnosis is made on clinical grounds, characteristic changes in gut mucosa, and absent plasma apo B.

Hypobetalipoproteinemia

Hypobetalipoproteinemia is usually an autosomal-dominant disorder, that, like abetalipoproteinemia, also results in low plasma apo B concentrations, but not usually as low as in abetalipoproteinemia unless the patient is a homozygote.[70] Several features distinguish the two disorders. In hypobetalipoproteinemia, a defect in the apo B gene produces a truncated apo B that is unable to associate with lipids. In heterozygotes, plasma apo B concentrations are no more than 25%–50% of normal concentrations. The homozygous state produces a clinical phenotype that is indistinguishable from abetalipoproteinemia. Both heterozygotes and homozygotes can be identified by measuring plasma apo B levels, but it is possible that certain mutations may lead to truncated forms of apo B that are not detected by conventional apo B assays. Family studies are often helpful in establishing the diagnosis of hypobetalipoproteinemia, since, unlike abetalipoproteinemia, the affected relatives are frequently found.

Hyperapobetalipoproteinemia (HABL)

HABL is a condition in which LDL-cholesterol (LDL-C) levels are within the accepted reference range but plasma apo B and LDL apo B concentrations are increased.[71] Patients with HABL generally have mild to moderate hypertriglyceridemia[72] or delayed postprandial TG clearance,[73] and an increased risk of developing CHD.[74] These features of HABL are not dissimilar to those of familial combined hyperlipidemia in which, by definition, serum total cholesterol and LDL-C are also increased. Thus, the measurement of apo B becomes essential if the two conditions are to be differentiated. The prevalence of HABL has not been firmly established. The true frequency of the condition will only be known when both serum total cholesterol and LDL-C measurements and apo B assays are carried out simultaneously in laboratories. Genest et al. found the prevalence of HABL to be around 30% in patients with premature CHD and 5% in the relatives of these probands.[75] In a case-control study, 19.8% of patients with CHD had HABL, compared to 8.4% in controls without CHD.[76]

Apo B and Coronary Risk

In case-control studies in patients with CHD, plasma apo B concentrations have been found to be more discriminating than other plasma lipids and lipoproteins.[77–80] In some of these studies, it is very likely that apo B would have been an even better predictor of ischemic heart disease (IHD) if the effect of myocardial ischemia and use of beta-blockers, both of which can lower apo B and apo A-I levels, had been taken into account.[81] Many prospective studies also confirm the utility of plasma apo B levels in determining coronary risk, although the extent to which plasma apo B concentrations were better than serum lipids in predicting risk varied.[82–85] This is perhaps due to the differing entry criteria and populations in these studies. These data would suggest that the case for measuring plasma apo B is strong, but the reality is that there is a complex biological (and hence statistical) interaction between the various biochemical parameters that predict CHD risk. Plasma apo B measurements perhaps have an inherent advantage over LDL-C levels that are often calculated, and the results have to rely on the patient truly fasting.

Increasing recognition of the heterogeneity of LDL also introduces difficulties in distinguishing which LDL subfraction is associated with CHD risk.[86] While it is known that small, dense LDL and enrichment of LDL with cholesteryl ester are more atherogenic,[87] there is no easy way of identifying these abnormalities in routine laboratories. Since every particle of VLDL secreted from the liver has one molecule of apo B, plasma apo B concentrations provide not only a measure of risk associated with VLDL, IDL, and LDL, but also a measure of LDL particle number. Many of the primary and secondary coronary prevention studies and angiographic regression studies of cholesterol-lowering confirm the need to have a direct measure of a decrease in LDL particle number. This may explain why in some studies apo B does not compare well with total cholesterol or LDL-C as a measure of CHD risk.

So how should a laboratory use plasma apo B assays? Today, many laboratories are reluctant to introduce the test, mainly due to the cost of analysis, and until recently the difficulties in standardization also made the assay unsuitable for routine patient screening. The value of plasma apo B lies in the diagnosis of disorders of lipoprotein metabolism and in the estimation of CHD risk and response to lipid-lowering therapy in most patients other than those with obviously increased serum cholesterol levels. In particular, plasma apo B can provide a measure of risk in patients with hypertriglyceridemia, who may or may not have low HDL-C values.[88] Hypertriglyceridemia has been shown to be associated with CHD in several studies, but its heterogeneity makes it difficult to use serum TG as a marker of CHD with any confidence.[89–91] Apo B measurements can further refine the assessment of CHD risk in patients with hypertriglyceridemia, as increased apo B in this situation indicates the presence of small, dense LDL. At present, LDL subfractions measurements are mainly carried out either by electrophoresis or by ultracentrifugation, neither of which can be automated. (For additional information, refer to Chapter 16)

Another group of patients for whom apo B measurements can be of value are those with impaired glucose tolerance and type 2 diabetes mellitus. In both of these conditions, coronary morbidity is markedly increased and often patients have hypertriglyceridemia and low HDL-C along with serum cholesterol values that are not dissimilar to the non-diabetic general population.[92] There are several studies that now show a relationship between apo B and insulin levels. In a recent prospective study, where serum insulin was shown to be an independent risk factor for IHD, the odds ratio was greatest for those with the highest plasma apo B levels.[93] The Insulin Resistance and Atherosclerosis Study also found that men with glucose intolerance who had increased apo B and TG also had increased serum insulin levels.[94] Similar observations were made in a nested case-control study.[80]

Many laboratories are now able to use molecular biology techniques in the diagnosis of disease. Several studies have suggested that genetic variation at the apo B gene locus can predict atherosclerosis through increasing serum cholesterol concentrations or altering dietary responsiveness to fat.[95] These effects only explain a small proportion of the variation in serum cholesterol and are therefore of limited use.[96] The variation of the apo B gene also does not help in the diagnosis of conditions such as HABL or familial combined hyperlipidemia, in which there is an overproduction of apo B. There is perhaps a role for genetic studies in identifying patients with familial defective apo B. This mutation in the ligand for the LDL receptor can present with a clinical phenotype similar to that of heterozygous familial hypercholesterolemia.[56]

ANALYTICAL ASPECTS OF APOLIPOPROTEIN MEASUREMENT

The analysis of apo B and apo A-I is carried out by immunochemical techniques. In the early years of apolipoprotein investigations, electroimmunoassay (EIA), radial immunodiffusion (RID), and radioimmunoassay (RIA) were widely used. However, the former two methods were difficult to automate for the measurement of large numbers of samples and consumed large amounts of antisera. RIA, on the other hand, has a greater sensitivity and is more precise than either EIA or RID.[97] It also overcomes the need for large amounts of specific antisera and avoids matrix problems observed with EIA and RID. Automation of RIA remains relatively difficult and has the inherent disadvantages of the use of radioactivity and short reagent half-lives.

Advances in the production of monospecific and monoclonal antibodies and the development of enzymic labels led to the development of enzyme-linked immunosorbent assays (ELISA) and better nephelometric and turbidimetric assays.[98] A great advantage of these assays, particularly the latter two, was the potential for automation and thus the capability to assay large numbers of samples. Immunonephelometry requires dedicated instrumentation and often achieves better precision than immunoturbidimetric assay, but both methods require large amounts of specific antisera and are prone to matrix effects. Apolipoprotein analysis by ELISA is highly sensitive and moderately precise, but requires the use of large dilutions. Automated and electronic dispensers have improved the precision of pipetting of both small and large volumes of liquid, but automation of ELISA techniques is not fully achievable in routine clinical laboratories.

Recently, a particle-concentration fluorescence immunoassay (PCFIA) technique has been applied to the determination of apo B.[99] Another method has adapted a time-resolved immunofluorometric assay for apo B measurement in cerebrospinal fluid.[100] Both these methods use fluorescent labels, are extremely sensitive, and their potential for automation makes the measurement of small amounts of apolipoprotein in large numbers a reality.

In most routine laboratories the choice of assay method for apolipoprotein measurement is immunonephelometry or immunoturbidimetry. Both are amenable to automation and can handle large numbers of samples. The need for sample manipulation is minimal, and with modern instruments precision is quite acceptable. The results are generally accurate and assays now can be calibrated against internationally acceptable reference materials for both apo A-I and B.[101, 102] Both nephelometric and turbidimetric assays can suffer from interference due to lipemia.[103] There is also the possibility of unstable immune complex formation, and in apo A-I assays the variation in HDL size may produce variable results.[104] Some of the inherent disadvantages of nephelometry and turbidimetry can be partially overcome by adding reagents to increase the reaction rate, which also aids the formation of more stable immune complexes.[105]

The pros and cons of analytical methods notwithstanding, until recently the main issue was perhaps the standardization of apolipoprotein measurements. Lack of standardization was, and to some extent still is, one of the major causes of analytical variation between laboratories.[106] The standardization issue was addressed in 1994 with the adoption of international reference materials endorsed by the World Health Organization for both apo A-I and B. (For further information, see Chapters 35 and 36.) The standardization problems arise from the close association between the lipid moiety and apolipoproteins and the influence this has on immunoreactivity of apolipoproteins. Antibodies raised against whole lipoproteins do not necessarily react against delipidated apolipoproteins. Moreover, antibodies to synthetic apolipoprotein peptides do not always react with apolipoproteins associated with lipids in lipoproteins. Essentially, masking of apo B in TG-rich lipoproteins is a potential problem, but most assays seem unaffected. The assay of apo B is greatly helped because each molecule of apo B is in a discrete, separate particle. On the other hand, more than one apo A-I molecule can be associated with a single HDL particle. Storage and preanalytical factors can release apo A-I molecules from HDL particles that have multiple apo A-I molecules associated with them; in an assay sensitive to particle number, these additional molecules will lead to inaccuracy. It is important to note that early well-validated apo A-I assays using rocket electrophoresis employed urea disruption or disruption by heating to release all the apo A-I loosely associated with the HDL particles. This step is now generally omitted.

Issues involving the conformation of apolipoproteins in the native lipoproteins are even more relevant than the technical aspects of antibody-antigen reactions. At present it is unclear whether particular epitopes are associated with disease or with coronary risk. It is not certain whether these considerations were taken into account when the International Federation of Clinical Chemistry (IFCC) was preparing candidate reference materials in association with commercial manufacturers.[107]

Apo B and apo A-I present different problems in the development of primary standards and reference methods. With apo B, a particular challenge has been the production of stable lyophilized reference material.[108] Apo B tends to self-associate, producing aggregates. The way around this has been to produce a primary standard based on ultracentrifugally separated LDL of density between 1.030 and 1.050 kg/L. Based on this standard, a secondary standard consisting of a liquid reference material has been produced. The above procedure succeeded in producing a standard material, but when this was analyzed by different methods, marked variation between assay methods was found. Immunoturbidimetric and immunonephelometric assays produced higher apo B values than ELISA and RIA.

The purification of apo A-I to produce a stable lyophilized standard has been much less problematic compared to obtaining apo B reference material. There are difficulties, however, in obtaining suitable antisera for plasma apo A-I measurements.[109] Because of the close association of apo A-I with lipids, many of the protein's immunoreactive sites remain hidden. It is, therefore, desirable that assays for apo A-I include a step in which the immunoreactive sites are exposed via pre-treatment with detergents such as Tween 20 or Triton X-100 and chelating or denaturing agents such as guanidine and urea.

Direct assays recently have been introduced for the easier determination of LDL-C. However, this does not necessarily overcome the main problem of the inability of LDL-C to fully reflect the atherogenic risk associated with the apo B component within the LDL particle. The LDL assays are relatively new and in some situations may be affected by serum TG greater than 400 mg/dL (4.5 mmol/L).[110] Experience with these methods is limited. It is unclear whether they provide a true estimate of LDL-C in all disease states, especially in patients with renal disease or diabetes mellitus. (For additional information, refer to Chapter 12.) An assay that measures apo B by immunonephelometry in LDL separated by a direct LDL assay (immunoseparation) has recently been described.[111]

Direct HDL methods that avoid the need for precipitating apo-B-containing lipoproteins also have been introduced. Again, there have been few comparisons with apo A-I assays, and their performance in different disease states remains untested. (Refer to Chapter 11 for additional information.)

Several preanalytical aspects need to be taken into account when interpreting the results of apolipoprotein measurement.[112] As with serum lipid determination, apolipoproteins are influenced by biological variation and other intra-individual factors. These are summarized in Table 14–2. (For additional information, refer to Chapter 8.)

Utility of Assays for Apo B-48

With a resurgence of interest in the relationship between postprandial lipemia and atherogenesis there has been an effort to develop assays for apo B-48 for the investigation of lipoproteins of intestinal origin. Antibodies that recognize apo B-100 often do not detect apo B-48 in TG-rich lipoproteins. One way to determine apo B-48 is by separating it from apo B-100 by SDS-PAGE gel electrophoresis and measuring apo B-48 by densitometric scanning.[113] The method is imprecise and not amenable to routine use. Recently, an antibody has been raised to the C-terminal end of apo B-48[114] which forms the basis of an ELISA technique that can be used to estimate apo B-48 in TG-rich lipoproteins.[115] A recently described assay for determination of remnant-like particles in human serum that uses immunoprecipitation of apo B-100

Table 14–2 ✧ Preanalytical Factors Affecting Plasma apo B and apo A-I Levels

	Effect on plasma apo B	*Effect on plasma apo A-I*
Diurnal variation	About 5%. Peaks at mid-day and midnight	About 4%. Peaks in late evening
Seasonal variation	Not known	Not known
Gender	Males > females	Females > males
Age	Increases with age	Probably unaffected; some reports indicate fall with age
Menstrual cycle	Lower values or no change	Lower values or no change
Pregnancy	Increases by 60%	Increase by 30%, sustained until delivery
Diet	Acute change: no effect Chronic change: fall	Acute change: no effect Chronic change: increase
Exercise	Not known	Not known
Alcohol	Not known	Higher values
Smoking	Not known	Lower values
Coffee	Probable increase by 15%	No change
Posture	5% fall	9% fall
Venous occlusion	5% increase	5% increase
Storage at -70°C	7% decrease*	No effect*
Storage at 4°C	5% increase*	No effect or increase*
*method dependent		

and apo A-I seems to provide an indirect measure of chylomicron-remnant particles containing apo B-48.[116]

REFERENCE RANGES AND CUTOFF POINTS

Many of the larger epidemiological studies carried out in the past did not measure plasma apolipoproteins. Therefore, few data or reference intervals exist for either apo B or Apo A-I. Laker and Evans have recently summarized reference data for both apo B and apo A-I on studies that included more than 100 subjects,[117] shown in Tables 14–3 and 14–4. The variability in the data is no doubt due to differences in standardization and is method-related. Reference ranges for apo B and apo A-I are now available on Finnish population[118] the Framingham Offspring Study,[119,120] a Swedish population,[121] a French Candian population,[122] and the National Health and Nutrition Examination

Table 14–3 ✧ Reference Data for Apolipoprotein A–I from Studies Including at Least 100 Normolipidemic Subjects

Technique	Subjects (age, years)	Sample	Reference data (g/L)
Radial immunodiffusion	263 M (20–65) 257 F (20–65)	EDTA plasma	1.19 (mean) 1.32 (mean)*
Radial immunodiffusion	95 M (40–49) 104 F (40–49)	Serum	0.91–1.83 0.91–1.83
Radial immunodiffusion	128 NA	EDTA plasma	1.18 (mean)
Radial immunodiffusion	1355 adults (3–18)	Serum	1.02–2.02
Radioimmunoassay	4858 adults (18–30)	EDTA plasma	Effects of gender, ethnic group and age compared
Immunoturbidimetry	I93 adults	Serum	1.10–2.10 (M) 1.24–2.40 (F)
Immunoturbidimetry	I35 adults	EDTA plasma	0.89–1.98
Immunoturbidimetry	1202 adults (9–24)	Serum	1.04–1.96
Immunoturbidimetry	1145 (mean age 53)	Serum	1.45 (SD 0.28)
Radial immunodiffusion and Rate immunonephelometery	11432 adults	Serum	Effects of age, gender and ethnic group compared**
Immunoturbidimetery	147576 adults	Serum	1.31 ± 0.35 (M)*** 1.22 ± 0.36 (F)
Immunonephelometery	1755 M 1764 F	EDTA PLASMA	1.38±0.20**** 1.53±0.24

M = Male; F = female; NA = normolipidemic adults.
Adapted from Reference 117. Laker and Evans Ann Clin Biochem 1996;33:5–22 (with permission)
*Higher mean values found in women receiving hormone preparations (mean 1.41 g/L) compared with those receiving no therapy (mean 1.29 g/L).
**Reference 123
***Reference 121
****Reference 122

Survey III from the United States.[123] All these studies provide reference data for apo B and apo A-I based on WHO-IFCC standardized immunoturbidimetric assays that are commercially available. Despite the similarity of methods and standardization in both surveys, the advice on cutoff values for assigning coronary risk is slightly different (see Table 14–5). This is largely because the apo A-I values below the 10th percentile and apo B values above the 75th percentile, which are thought to indicate increased

Table 14–4. ✧ Reference Data for Apolipoprotein B from Studies Including at Least 100 Normolipidemic Subjects

Technique	Subjects (age, years)	Sample	Reference data (g/L)
Radial immunodiffusion	1355 subjects (3–18)	Serum	0.50–1.38
Enzymeimmunoassay	146 adults	Plasma	0.90 (mean)
Radioimmunoassay	349 adults (20–65)	EDTA plasma	0.41–1.21
Radioimmunoassay	128 adults (16–60)	Plasma	0.27–1.46
Radioimmunoassay	107 adults (15–75)	Serum	0.91 (mean)* 0.59–1.23 (3rd to 97th percentile)
Radioimmunoassay	4858 adults (18–30)	EDTA plasma	Effects of gender, ethnic group and age compared*
Immunoturbidimetry	193 adults	Serum	0.63–1.38
Immunoturbidimetry	135 adults	EDTA plasma	0.30–0.95
Immunoturbidimetry	1188 adults (9–24)	Serum	0.43–1.35
Immunoturbidimetry	1145 (mean age 53)	Serum	0.91 (SD 0.2)
Radial immunodiffusion and Rate immunonephelometery	11483 adults		Effects of age, gender and ethnic group compared**
Immunoturbidimetery	147576 adults	Serum	1.36 ± 0.22 (M)*** 1.51 ± 0.24 (F)
Immunonephelometery	1755 M 1764 F	EDTA plasma	1.03 ± 0.27**** 0.99 ± 0.27

M = Male; F = Female
Adapted from Reference 117. Laker and Evans Ann Clin Biochem 1996;33:5–22 (with permission).
*Reference 39
**Reference 123
***Reference 121
****Reference 122

coronary risk, differ between the two studies. The cutoff points suggested by the Framingham group for apo B have been decided on the basis of comparability with the 75th percentile for LDL-C for the Framingham population.

The effect of gender was apparent in reference ranges for both apo B and apo A-I, with women having lower apo B and higher apo A-I. The effect of age was mainly

Table 14-5

Cutoff points	Men		Women		Remarks
	*Framingham population**	*Finnish population***	*Framingham population*	*Finnish population*	
Apo A-I	1.07	1.09	1.22	1.25	10th percentile
Apo B*	< 1.18	< 1.41	< 1.11	< 1.29	75th percentile. Desired value
	1.18–1.33	1.41–1.59	1.18–1.30	1.29–1.55	75–90th percentile Increased risk
	> 1.33	> 1.59	> 1.30	> 1.55	90th percentile High risk

All values are in g/L
The Framingham group suggest a single cutoff point of 1.20 g/L
* Reference 119 and 120
** Reference 118

apparent for apo B, with increases in concentrations with age. The influence of age on apo A-I is complex and variable. Some studies show a fall in plasma apo A-I levels in men but not in women, and others have generally found no effect. Postmenopausal women tend to have lower plasma apo A-I levels. ✧

REFERENCES

1. Schaefer EJ, Eisenberg S, Levy RI. Lipoprotein apoprotein metabolism. J Lipid Res 1978;19:667–87.
2. Sloop CH, Roheim PS. Interstitial fluid lipoproteins. J Lipid Res 1987;28:225–37.
3. Assman G, von Eckardstein A, Funke H. Mutations in apolipoprotein genes and HDL metabolism. In: Rosseneu M (ed.). Structure and function of apolipoproteins. Boca Raton: CRC Press 1992:85–122.
4. Cheung P, Kno FT, Law ML et al. Localization of the structural gene for human apolipoprotein A-I on the long arm of human chromosome 11. Proc Natl Acad Sci USA 1984;81:508–11.
5. Scanu AM. Proapolipoprotein-converting enzymes and high-density lipoprotein early events in biogenesis. Am Heart J 1987;113:527–32.
6. Edelstein C, Scanu AM. Extracellular post-translational proteolytic processing of apolipoproteins. In: Scanu AM, Spector A (eds.). Biochemistry of plasma lipoproteins. New York: Marcel Dekker 1986:53.
7. Karathanasis SK, Zannis VI, Breslow JL. Isolation and characterization of the human apolipoprotein A-I gene. Proc Natl Acad Sci USA 1983;80:6147–51.
8. Segrest JP, Jones MK, De Loof CG et al. The amphipathic helix in the exchangable apolipoproteins: a review of secondary structure and function. J Lipid Res 1992;33:141–66.
9. Castro GR, Fielding CJ. Early incorporation of cell-derived cholesterol into pre-beta migrating high-density lipoprotein. Biochemistry 1988;27:25–29.
10. Fielding CJ, Fielding PE. Molecular physiology of reverse cholesterol transport. J Lipid Res 1995;36:211–28.

11. Neary R, Bhatnagar D, Durrington PN, Ishola M, Arrol S, Mackness MI. An investigation of the role of lecithin:cholesterol acyl transferase and triglyceride-rich lipoproteins in the metabolism of pre-beta high-density lipoproteins. Atherosclerosis 1991;85:34–48.

12. Fielding PE, Kawano M, Catapano AL, et al. Unique epitope of apolipoprotein A-I expressed in pre-beta-1 high-density lipoprotein and its role in the catalyzed efflux of cellular cholesterol. Biochemistry 1994;33:6981–5.

13. Chen C-H, Albers JJ. Interspecies activation of lecithin:cholesterol acyl transferase by apolipoprotein A-I isolated from the plasmas of humans, horses, sheep, goats and rabbits. Biochim Biophys Acta 1983;753:40–46.

14. Cremer P, Elster H, Labrot B et al. Incidence rates of fatal and non-fatal myocardial infarction in relation to the lipoprotein profile: first prospective results from the Gottingen Risk Incidence and Prevalence Study (GRIPS). Klin Wochenschrift 1988;66(suppl 11):42–49.

15. Ishikawa T, Fidge N, Thelle DS et al. The Tromso Heart Study: serum apolipoprotein A-I concentration in relation to future coronary heart disease. Eur J Clin Invest 1978;8:179–82.

16. Salonen JT, Salonen R, Pentilla I et al. Serum fatty acids, apolipoproteins, selenium and vitamin antioxidants and risk of death from coronary artery disease. Am J Cardiol 1985;56:226–31.

17. Wald NJ, Law M, Watt HC, et al. Apolipoproteins and ischemic heart disease: implications for screening. Lancet 1994;343:75–79.

18. Heiss G, Johnson NJ, Reiland S et al. The epidemiology of plasma high-density lipoprotein cholesterol levels. The Lipid Clinics Research Program Prevalence Study Summary. Circulation 1980;62(suppl iv):116–36.

19. Rifkind BM, Segal P. Lipid Clinics Research Program reference values for hyperlipidemia. JAMA 1983;250:1869–72.

20. Schaefer EJ, Zech LA, Jenkins LL et al. Human apolipoprotein A-I and A-II metabolism. J Lipid Res 1982;23:850–62.

21. Ng DS, Vezina C, Wolever T, Kukis A et al. Apolipoprotein A-I deficiency: biochemical and metabolic characteristics. Arterioscler Thromb Vascl Biol 1995;15:2157–64.

22. Rader DJ, Ikewaki K. Unraveling high-density lipoprotein-apolipoprotein metabolism in human mutants and animal models. Curr Opin Lipidol 1996;7:117–23.

23. Franceschini G, Sirtori CR, Capruso A et al. A-I milano apoprotein: decreased HDL cholesterol levels with significant lipoprotein modifications and without clinical atherosclerosis in an Italian family. J Clin Invest 1980;66:892–900.

24. Assman G, von Eckardstein A, Brewer HB. Familial HDL deficiency: Tangier disease. In: Scriver C, Beaudet A, Sly W, Valle D. The metabolic and molecular bases of inherited disease. New York: McGraw-Hill, 1995:2053–72.

25. Francis GA, Knopp RH, Oram JF. Defective removal of cellular cholesterol and phospholipids by apolipoprotein A-I in Tangier disease. J Clin Invest 1995;96:78–87.

26. Norum KR. Familial lecithin:cholesterol acyltransferase deficiency. In: Miller NE, Miller GJ (eds.). Clinical and metabolic aspects of high-density lipoproteins. Amsterdam: Elsevier, 1984:297–432.

27. Carlson LA. Fish-Eye Disease. A new familial condition with massive corneal opacities and dyslipoproteinemia. Eur J Clin Invest 1981;12:41–53.

28. Glueck CJ, Fallat RW, Millett F et al. Familial hyperalphalipoproteinemia: studies on 18 kindreds. Metabolism 1975;24:1243–65.

29. Fielding CJ, Havel RJ. Cholesteryl ester transfer protein: friend or foe? [Editorial; Comment]. J Clin Invest 1996;97:2687–8.

30. Koizumi J, Mabuchi H, Yoshimura A et al. Deficiency of serum cholesteryl-ester transfer activity in patients with familial hyperalphalipoproteinemia. Atherosclerosis 1985;58:175–86.

31. Anonymous. Cholesteryl ester transfer protein. Lancet 1991;338:666–7.

32. Gordon T, Castelli WP, Hjortland MC, Kannel WB, Dawber TR. High-density lipoprotein as a protective factor against coronary heart disease: The Framingham Study. Am J Med 1977:62:707–14.

33. Kannel WB, Neaton JO, Wentworth O, Thomas HE, Stamler J, Hulley SB, Kjelsberg MO, for the MRFIT Research Group. Overall and coronary heart disease mortality rates in relation to major risk factors in 325,348 men screened for the MRFIT Multiple Risk Factor Intervention Trial. Am Heart J 1986;112:82–36.

34. Gordon DJ, Knoke J, Probstfield JL, Superko R, Tyroler HA, for the LRC Program. High-density lipoprotein cholesterol and coronary heart disease in hypercholesterolemic men: The Lipid Research Clinics Coronary Primary Prevention Trial. Circulation 1986;74:1217–25.

35. Manninen V, Tenkanen L, Koskinen P, Huttunen JK, Manttari M, Heinonen OP, Frick MH. Joint effects of serum triglyceride and LDL cholesterol and HDL cholesterol concentrations on coronary heart disease risk in The Helsinki Heart Study: implications for treatment. Circulation 1992;85:37–45.

36. Berman M, Eisenberg S, Hall M et al. Metabolism of apo B and apo C apoproteins in man: kinetic studies in normal and hyperlipoproteinemic subjects. J Lipid Res 1978;19:38–56.

37. Gaw A, Demant T. Apolipoprotein B metabolism in primary and secondary hyperlipidaemias. Curr Opin Lipidol 1996;7:149–57.

38. Rosseneu M, Vercaerist R, Steinberg KK et al. Some considerations of methodology and standardization of apolipoprotein B immunoassays. Clin Chem 1983;29:427–33.

39. Durrington PN, Bolton CH, Hartog M. Serum and lipoprotein apolipoprotein B levels in normal subjects and patients with hyperlipoproteinaemia. Clin Chim Acta 1978;82:151–60.

40. Fredrickson DS. Plasma lipoproteins and apolipoproteins. The Harvey Lectures 1972–3, Series 68. London: Academic Press, 1974:185.

41. Durrington PN, Ishola M, Hunt L, Arrol S, Bhatnagar D. Apolipoproteins (a), A-I and B and parental history in men with early onset ischemic heart disease. Lancet 1988;I:1070–73.

42. Chan L, VanTunien P, Ledbetter DH et al. The human apo B-100 gene: a highly polymorphic gene that maps to the short arm of chromosome 2. Biochem Biophys Res Commun 1985;133:248–55.

43. Brewer HB, Higuchi K, Hospattankar A et al. Recent advances in the structure and biosynthesis of apolipoproteins B-100 and B48. In: Suckling KE, Groot PHE. Hyperlipidaemia and atherosclerosis. London: Academic Press, 1988:33–44.

44. Yang C-Y, Pownall HJ. Structure and function of apolipoprotein B. In: Rosseneu M (ed.). Structure and function of apolipoproteins. Boca Raton: CRC Press, 1992:63–84.

45. Young SG. Recent progress in understanding apolipoprotein B. Circulation 1990;82:1574–94.

46. Pease RJ, Leiper JM. Regulation of hepatic apolipoprotein-B-containing lipoprotein secretion. Curr Opin Lipidol 1996;7:132–8.

47. Knott TJ, Pease RJ, Powell LM et al. Complete protein sequence and identification of structural domains of human apolipoprotein B. Nature 1986;323:734–8.

48. Beisiegel U. Apolipoproteins as ligands for lipoprotein receptors. In: Rosseneu M (ed.). Structure and function of apolipoproteins. Boca Raton: CRC Press, 1992:269–94.

49. Lundkatz S, Klaplaud PM, Phillips MC et al. Apolipoprotein B-100 conformation and particle surface charge in human LDL subspecies: Implication for LDL receptor interaction. Biochemistry 1998;37:12867–12874.

50. Scott J, Wallis SC, Pease RJ et al. Apolipoprotein B: a novel mechanism for deriving two proteins from one gene. In: Suckling KE, Groot PHE. Hyperlipidaemia and atherosclerosis. London: Academic Press, 1988:347–64.

51. Chen S-H, Yang C-H, Chem P-F et al. The complete cDNA and amino acid sequence of human apolipoprotein B-100. J Biol Chem 1986;261:12918–21.

52. Powell LM, Wallis SC, Pease RJ et al. A novel form of tissue-specific RNA processing produces apolipoprotein B-48 in intestines. Cell 1987;50:831–40.

53. Chan L, Seeburg PH. RNA editing. Scientific American Science and Medicine 1995;2:68–77.

54. Collins DR, Knott TJ, Pease RJ et al. Truncated variants of apolipoprotein B cause hypobetalipoproteinemia. Nucleic Acid Res 1988;16:8361–75.

55. Pease RJ, Milne RW, Jessup WK et al. Use of bacterial expression cloning to localize the epitopes for a series of monoclonal antibodies against apolipoprotein B-100. J Biol Chem 1990;265:553–68.

56. Myant NB. Familial defective apolipoprotein B-100: a review, including some comparisons with familial hypercholesterolemia. Atherosclerosis 1993;104:1–19.

57. Durrington PN. Lipoproteins and their metabolism. In: Durrington PN. Hyperlipidaemia: diagnosis and management. Oxford: Butterworth-Heinneman, 1995:25–71.

58. Henriksen T, Mahoney EM, Steinberg D. Enhanced macrophage degradation of low-density lipoprotein previously incubated with cultured endothelial cells: recognition by the receptor for acetylated low-density lipoproteins. Proc Natl Acad Sci USA 1981;78:6499–503.

59. Esterbauer H, Gebicki J, Puhl H, Jurgens G. The role of lipid peroxidation and antioxidants in oxidative modification of LDL. Free Radical Biol Med 1992;13:341–90.

60. Streinbecher UP, Lougheed M, Kwan W-C, Dirks M. Recognition of oxidized low-density lipoprotein by the scavenger receptor of macrophages results from derivatization of apolipoprotein B by products of fatty acid peroxidation. J Biol Chem 1989;264:15216–23.

61. Esterbauer H, Wag G, Puhl H. Lipid peroxidation and its role in atherosclerosis. Br Med Bull 1993;49:566–76.

62. Witzum JL, Steinberg D. Role of oxidized low-density lipoprotein in atherogenesis. J Clin Invest 1991;88:1785–92.

63. Witzum JL, Mahoney EM, Branks MJ et al. Nonenzymatic glycosylation of low-density lipoprotein alters its biologic activity. Diabetes 1982;31:283–91.

64. Hunt JV, Smith CCT, Wolff SP. Autoxidative glycosylation and possible involvement of peroxides and free radicals in LDL modification by glucose. Diabetes 1990;39:1420–24.

65. Tames FJ, Mackness MI, Arrol S et al. Non-enzymatic glycation of apolipoprotein B in the sera of diabetic and non-diabetic subjects. Atherosclerosis 1992;93:227–44.

66. Durrington PN. Familial hypercholesterolemia. In: Durrington PN. Hyperlipidemia: diagnosis and management. Oxford: Butterworth-Heinneman, 1995:108–39.

67. Parums DV, Brown DL, Mitchinson MJ. Serum antibodies to oxidized low-density lipoproteins and ceroid in chronic periaortitis. Arch Pathol Lab Med 1990;114:383–7.

68. Kane JP, Havel RJ. Disorders of the biogenesis and secretion of lipoproteins containing the B apolipoproteins. In: Scriver C, Beaudet A, Sly W, Valle D (eds.). The metabolic and molecular bases of inherited disease. New York: McGraw-Hill, 1995:1860–66.

69. Wetterau JR, Aggerbeck LP, Bouma M-E et al. Absence of microsomal triglyceride transfer protein in individuals with abetalipoproteinaemia. Science 1992;258:999–1001.

70. Kane JP, Havel RJ. Disorders of the biogenesis and secretion of lipoproteins containing the B apolipoproteins. In: Scriver C, Beaudet A, Sly W, Valle D (eds.). The metabolic and molecular bases of inherited disease. New York: McGraw-Hill, 1995:1866–71.

71. Durrington PN, Bolton CH, Hartog M. Serum and lipoprotein apolipoprotein B levels in normal subjects and patients with hyperlipoproteinemia. Clin Chim Acta 1978;82:151–60.

72. Teng B, Thompson GR, Sniderman AD et al. Composition and distribution of low-density lipoprotein fractions in hyperapobetalipoproteinemia, normolipidemia and familial hypercholesterolemia. Proc Natl Acad Sci USA 1983;80:6662–6.

73. Bhatnagar D, Durrington PN, Arrol S. Postprandial plasma lipoprotein responses to a mixed meal in subjects with hyperapobetalipoproteinemia. Clin Biochem 1992;25:341–43.

74. Sniderman AD, Shapiro S, Marpole D et al. Association of coronary atherosclerosis with hyperapobetalipoproteinemia (increased protein, but normal cholesterol levels in human plasma low-density lipoproteins). Proc Natl Acad Sci USA 1980;77:604–8.

75. Genest J, Marlin-Munley SS, McNamara JR et al. Familial lipoprotein disorders in patients with premature coronary artery disease. Circulation 1992;85:2025–33.

76. Kwiterovich PO Jr, Coresh J, Bachorik, PS. Prevalence of hyperapobetalipoproteinemia and other lipoprotein phenotypes in men (aged $<<$ 50 years) and women ($<<$ 60 years) with coronary artery disease. Am J Cardiol 1993;71:631–9.

77. Durrington PN, Hunt L, Ishola M, Kane J, Stephens WP. Serum apolipoproteins A-I and B in middle-aged men with and without previous myocardial infarction. Br Heart J 1986;56:206–12.

78. Kwiterovich PO Jr, Coresh 3, Smith HH et al. Comparison of the plasma levels of apolipoprotein B and AI, and other risk factors in men and women with premature coronary artery disease. Am J Cardiol 1992;69:1015–21.

79. Tornvall P, Bavenholm P, Landou C, de Faire U, Hamsten A. Relation of plasma levels and composition of apolipoprotein-B-containing lipoproteins to angiographically defined coronary artery disease in young patients with myocardial infarction. Circulation 1993;88:2180–89.

80. Lamarche B, Tchernof A, Mauriege P et al. Fasting insulin and apolipoprotein B levels and low-density-lipoprotein particle size as risk factors for ischemic heart disease JAMA 1998;279:1955–1961.

81. Genest J, McNamara JR, Ordovas JM et al. Effect of elective hospitalization on plasma lipoprotein cholesterol and apolipoproteins A-I, B, and Lp(a). Am J Cardiol 1990;65:677–9.

82. Stampfer MJ, Sacks FM, Salvini S et al. A prospective study of cholesterol, apolipoproteins, and the risk of myocardial infarction. N Engl J Med 1991;325:373–81.

83. Cremer P, Nagel D, Labrot B et al. Lipoprotein Lp(a) as a predictor of myocardial infarction in comparison to fibrinogen, LDL cholesterol, and other risk factors: results from the Gottingen Risk Incidence and Prevalence Study (GRIPS). Eur J Clin Invest 1994;24:444–53.

84. Coleman MP, Key TJ, Wang DY et al. A prospective study of obesity, lipids, apolipoproteins, and ischemic heart disease in women. Atherosclerosis 1992;92:177–85.

85. Sigurdsson G, Baldursdottir A, Sigvaldason H et al. Predictive value of apolipoproteins in a prospective survey of coronary artery disease in men. Am J Cardiol 1992;69:1251–4.

86. Griffin BA. Low-density lipoprotein heterogeneity. Ballieres Clin Endocrinol Metab 1995;9:687–704.

87. Austin MA, Breslow JL, Hennekens CH et al. Low-density lipoprotein subclass patterns and risk of myocardial infarction. JAMA 1988;260:1917–21.

88. Sniderman AD, Cianlone K. Measurement of apoproteins: time to improve the diagnosis and treatment of atherogenic dyslipidemias. Clin Chem 1996;42:489–91.

89. Austin MA. Plasma triglyceride and coronary heart disease. Arterioscler Thromb 1990;11:1–14.

90. Sniderman AD. To (measure apo)B or not to (measure apo)B: a critique of modern medical decision-making. Clinical Chemistry 1997;43:1310–1314.

91. Griffin BA, Freeman DJ, Tait GW, Thomson J, Caslake MJ, Packard CJ, Shepherd J. Role of plasma triglyceride in the regulation of plasma low-density lipoprotein (LDL) subfractions: relative contribution of small, dense LDL to coronary heart disease risk. Atherosclerosis 1994;106:241–253.

92. Durrington PN. Secondary hyperlipidaemia. Br Med Bull 1990;46:1005–24.

93. Despres J-P, Lamarche B, Mauriege P et al. Hyperinsulinemia as a risk factor for ischemic heart disease. N Engl J Med 1996;334:952–7.

94. Laws A, Hoen HM, Selby JV et al. Differences in insulin suppression of free fatty acid levles by gender and glucose tolerance status: relation to plasma triglycerides and apolipoprotein B concentrations. Arteriosclerosis Thrombosis and Vascular Biology 1997;17:64–71.

95. Talmud PJ, Boerwinkle E, Xu CF, Tikkanen MJ, Pietinen P, Huttunen JK, Humphries S. Dietary intake and gene variation influence the response of plasma lipids to dietary intervention. Genet Epidem 1992;9:249–60.

96. Durrington PN. Genetics of lipoprotein disorders and coronary atheroma. In:

Durrington PN. Hyperlipidemia: diagnosis and management. Oxford: Butterworth-Heinneman, 1995:361–84.

97. Durrington PN, Whicher JT, Warren C et al. A comparison of methods for the immunoassay of serum apolipoprotein B in man. Clin Chim Acta 1976;71:95–108.

98. Albers JJ, Marcovina SM. Apolipoprotein measurements. In: Kreisberg RA, Segrest JA (eds.). Plasma lipoproteins and coronary artery disease. Boston: Blackwell Scientific Publications, 1992:265–88.

99. Hallaway BJ, Rastogi A, Kottke BA. Apolipoprotein B quantified by particle-concentration fluorescence immunoassay. Clin Chem 1992;38:2387–91.

100. Osman I, Gaillard O, Meillet D et al. A sensitive time-resolved immunofluorometric assay for the measurement of apolipoprotein B in cerebrospinal fluid: application to multiple sclerosis and other neurological diseases. Eur J Clin Chem Biochem 1995;33: 53–58.

101. Marcovina SM, Albers JJ, Henderson LO, Hannon WH. International Federation of Clinical Chemistry standardization project for measurements of apolipoproteins A-I and B. III. Comparability of apolipoprotein A-I values by use of international reference material. Clin Chem 1993;39:773–8.

102. Marcovina SM, Albers JJ, Kennedy H, Mei JV, Henderson LO, Hannon WH. International Federation of Clinical Chemistry standardization project for measurements of apolipoproteins A-I and B. IV. Comparability of apolipoprotein B values by use of international reference material. Clin Chem 1994;40:586–92.

103. DaCol P, Kostner G. Immunoquantification of total apolipoprotein B in serum by nephelometry: influence of lipase treatment and detergents. Clin Chem 1983;29: 1045–50.

104. Levinson SS. Problems with the measurement of apolipoproteins A-I and A-II. Ann Clin Lab Sci 1990;20:307–18.

105. Kricka LJ. Principles of immunochemical techniques. In: Burtis CA, Ashwood ER (eds.). Tietz textbook of clinical chemistry. Philadelphia: WB Saunders, 1994:297.

106. Bhatnagar D, Durrington PN. Clinical value of apolipoprotein measurements. Ann Clin Biochem 1991;28:427–37.

107. Albers JJ, Marcovina SM. Standardization of apolipoprotein B and A-I measurements. Clin Chem 1989;35:1357–61.

108. Marcovina SM, Adolphson JL, Parlavecchia M, Albers JJ. Effects of lyophilization of apolipoproteins A-I and B. Clin Chem 1990;36:366–9.

109. Marcovina SM, Curtiss LK, Milne R, Albers JJ. Selection and characterization of monoclonal antibodies for measuring plasma levels of apolipoprotein A-I and B. J Aut Chem 1990;12:195–98.

110. Cole TG. The role of immunochemistry in the direct measurement of low-density lipoprotein cholesterol. J Clin Ligand Assay 1996;19:168–71.

111. Vrga L, Contacos C, Li SCH, Sullivan DR. Comparison of methods for measurement of apolipoprotein B and cholesterol in low-density lipoproteins. Clin Chem 1997;43: 390–93.

112. Evans K, Laker MF. Intra-individual factors affecting lipid, lipoprotein and apolipoprotein measurement: a review. Ann Clin Biochem 1995;32:261–80.

113. Bergeron N, Kotite L, Havel RJ. Simultaneous quantification of apolipoproteins B-100, B-48, and E separated by SDS-PAGE. Meth Enzym 1996;263:82–94.

114. Peel AS, Zampelas A, Williams CM, Gould B. A novel antiserum specific to apolipoprotein B-48: application in the investigation of postprandial lipemia in humans. Clin Sci 1993;85:521–4.

115. Lovegrove JA, Isherwood SG, Jackson KG et al. Quantitation of apolipoprotein B-48 in triacylglycerol-rich lipoproteins by specific enzyme-linked immunosorbent assay. Biochim Biophys Acta 1996;1301:221–9.

116. Nakajima K, Okazaki M, Tanaka A et al. Separation and determination of remnant-like particles in human serum using monoclonal antibodies to apo B-100 and apo A-I. J Clin Ligand Assay 1996;19:177–83.

117. Laker MF, Evans K. Analysis of apolipoproteins. Ann Clin Biochem 1996;33:5–22.

118. Leino A, Impivaara O, Kaitsaari M, Jarvisalo J. Serum concentrations of apolipoprotein A-I, apolipoprotein B, and lipoprotein (a) in a population sample. Clin Chem 1995;41: 1633–6.

119. Contois JH, McNamara JR, Lammi-Keefe CJ, Wilson PW, Massov T, Schaefer EJ. Reference intervals for plasma apolipoprotein B determined with a standardized commercial immunoturbidimetric assay: results from The Framingham Offspring Study. Clin Chem 1996;42:515–23.

120. Contois J, McNamara JR, Lammi-Keefe C, Wilson PW, Massov T, Schaefer EJ. Reference intervals for plasma apolipoprotein A-1 determined with a standardized commercial immunoturbidimetric assay: results from The Framingham Offspring Study. Clin Chem 1996;42:507–14.

121. Jungner I, Marcovina SM, Wallddius G, Holme I, Kolar W, Steiner E. Apolipoprotein B and A-1 values in 147576 Swedish males and females, standardized according to the World Health Organization-International Federation of Clinical Chemistry First International Reference materials. Clin Chem 1998;44:1641–9.

122. Connelley PW, Poapst M. Davignon J et al. Reference values of plasma apolipoproteins A-1 and B, and association with non-lipid risk factors in the populations of two Canadian provinces: Quebec and Saskatchewan. Canadian Heart Health Surveys Research Group. Can J Cardiol 1999;15:409–18.

123. Bachorik, Paul S, Lovejoy, Kathleen L, Carroll, Margaret D et al. Apolipoprotein B and A-1 distributions in the United States, 1988–1991: results of the National Health and Nutrition Examination Survey III (NHANES III). Clin Chem 1998;43:2364–78.

Measurement and Clinical Significance of High-Density Lipoprotein Subclasses

15

G. Russell Warnick and Marian C. Cheung

CLINICAL SIGNIFICANCE

The inverse relationship between high-density-lipoprotein cholesterol (HDL-C) values and risk of coronary heart disease (CHD) is well established in epidemiological studies.[1–7] A consensus panel sponsored by the National Institutes of Health (NIH) and the Adult Treatment Panel of the National Cholesterol Education Program (NCEP) endorsed the protective role of high-density lipoprotein (HDL) and recommended its measurement in making treatment decisions.[8–11] Chapter 11 provides detailed information about the clinical value of HDL-C and recommendations for its measurement.

In fact, the predictive association between HDL and CHD risk is much more complicated because HDL is a heterogeneous mixture of lipoprotein particles differing in size, density, charge, lipid and apolipoprotein composition, and function. In 1954, DeLalla, Elliot, and Gofman,[12] pioneers in establishing the effects of the lipoprotein levels on CHD risk, first reported the heterogeneous nature of HDL based on observations using the analytical ultracentrifuge. DeLalla and colleagues observed two major subclasses, designated as HDL2 and HDL3, as well as a relatively minor subclass designated as HDL1. They also reported substantial gender differences, with females having significantly higher HDL2 values than males, but relatively similar HDL3 values. In 1966, the same researchers reported results from a prospective study indicating that subjects with CHD had lower HDL2 values but similar HDL3 values relative to subjects without CHD.[13]

These early reports on the association between CHD risk and HDL and its subclasses were largely ignored for many years but have been confirmed by more recent studies using a variety of measurement techniques and study designs on different populations.[14–22] For example, in a study employing coronary angiography, Miller and colleagues[14] demonstrated that the extent of atherosclerosis is associated with decreased HDL2-C rather than HDL3-C values. Ballantyne et al.[15] reported that HDL2-C but not HDL3-C was reduced in survivors of myocardial infarction relative to control subjects. Recent case-control and angiographic studies found that the inverse relationship of CHD with HDL primarily involves certain size subclasses within HDL2 and HDL3.[21–23] Also, the presence of CHD was more strongly associated with abnormalities in HDL particle size than with low HDL-C level.[21,23] These studies suggest that the measurement of HDL size subclasses might improve the prediction of risk for CHD.

HDL is in fact more heterogeneous than implied by studies that examined major HDL subclasses obtained by ultracentrifugation or gradient gel electrophoresis. The diameter of HDL particles ranges in size between 7 nm and 15 nm (when examined by electron microscopy and non-denaturing gradient polyacrylamide gel electrophoresis).[24–26] Isoelectric focusing and chromatofocusing, high-resolution techniques that achieve separations based on particle charge, reportedly resolved HDL3 into as many as 12 separate peaks[27] and HDL2 into at least 3,[28,29] suggesting that the conventional HDL2 and HDL3 fractions are also heterogeneous with respect to charge. One of the newer gradient gel electrophoresis methods, which separates lipoproteins by particle size, obtains 10 bands in the HDL2 class and 4 in the HDL3 class.[26] When HDL are fractionated by density, charge, or size, the resulting subclasses contain varying combinations of apolipoproteins.[24,25,29,30] The major distinction between particles involves those that contain apolipoprotein (apo) AI without apo AII, and those that contain apo AI with apo AII.[31–34] In addition, there are minor particles with only apo AII and combinations with other HDL proteins such as apo E (See Chapter 27 for more details on apo-defined HDL particles.) A particle within the HDL range containing only apo E has been reported.[35]

These studies emphasize the considerable particle heterogeneity within the major HDL subclasses. Depending on the properties exploited in achieving separations, different subspecies of HDL particles may be obtained, and particles with varying function may be included within the separated subclasses. Therefore, the apparent associations between CHD risk and the major HDL subclasses may vary by separation method. Nevertheless, quantification of HDL subclasses does potentially improve assessment of CHD risk, although the choice of method and fraction is somewhat uncertain. The implications of HDL subclasses are perhaps in some respects analogous to those of total cholesterol (TC), whose value as a predictor of CHD risk can be improved by quantifying the major lipoproteins, the risk-positive low-density-lipoprotein cholesterol (LDL-C), and the risk-negative HDL-C.

Measurement of HDL subclasses has been a useful research tool in studies of lipoprotein metabolism, pathophysiology, and association with CHD risk. One must recognize that the variety of methods used in published clinical applications may use the same nomenclature to refer to subclasses that in fact comprise different populations of particles. HDL is still generally separated into the two major subclasses, HDL2 and HDL3, with hydrated densities originally considered to be 1.063–1.125 kg/L and 1.125–1.210 kg/L, respectively.[12,36] Inter-individual differences in HDL values are largely due to the larger and lighter HDL2; the smaller, more dense HDL3 fraction is relatively more consistent within and among individuals.[10]

The HDL2 and HDL3 fractions appear to be metabolically interrelated.[37] Patsch et al.[38] demonstrated that particles in the HDL3 range are converted into HDL2-like particles during lipolysis of very-low-density lipoprotein (VLDL) by lipoprotein lipase. Patsch and colleagues hypothesized that HDL3 assimilates surface components, cholesterol, and phospholipids derived from lipolysis of triglyceride-rich VLDL particles, and that it is thereby converted to the larger and lipid-enriched HDL2. The lipid enrichment of HDL3 may also result from transfers from cell membranes as the particles transit the circulation. The transfers of phospholipid among lipoproteins, and between cells and lipoproteins, are believed to be facilitated by a plasma phospholipid transfer protein.[39–42] A parallel process in the conversion of HDL3 to HDL2 is the action of lecithin cholesterol acyltransferase (LCAT), which esterifies the surface free cholesterol, and then transfers it to the core. In the process of cholesterol removal from cells, designated as reverse cholesterol transport,[43] the esterified cholesterol can be transferred to very-low-density and low-density lipoproteins (VLDL, LDL) for removal by the liver,[44] or the HDL particles can be removed by specific receptor-mediated processes.[45] The transfer of esterified cholesterol between lipoproteins is mediated by a cholesteryl ester transfer protein (CETP).[44,46,47] When CETP transfers esterified cholesterol from HDL to VLDL and LDL, a reverse transfer of triglyceride from the lower-density lipoproteins to HDL occurs. The triglycerides in HDL are then hydrolyzed by hepatic lipase that can also hydrolyze surface phospholipid thereby converting the larger, more buoyant HDL2 to smaller, denser HDL3. The interconversion of HDL2 and HDL3 subclasses has long been considered reversible. However, two recent kinetic studies suggest that this may not be the case.[48,49] Instead, small HDL particles are converted in a unidirectional manner to medium or large HDL. Thus, the relationships among HDL subclasses are highly complex and have yet to be fully elucidated.

Factors that influence plasma HDL-C concentration often have differential effects on the two major subclasses. For example, increased HDL values in women are primarily due to increased HDL2.[50] Post-menopausal estrogen replacement therapy and estrogen-dominant oral contraceptives increase HDL2 values.[51] Exercise increases HDL2 and may also promote a slight decrease in the HDL3.[52] Thus, female gender, estrogen use, and exercise are all associated with increased HDL2 and thereby with decreased risk of CHD. Alcohol intake is known to increase HDL values, and moderate intake is associated with a decreased risk of CHD.[53,54] One might expect that this benefit is mediated by increasing the HDL2 fraction, but in fact Haskell et al.[55] found that, among moderate drinkers, HDL3 concentrations decreased with abstention from alcohol and increased upon resumption of drinking; there was no significant effect on the reputedly anti-atherogenic HDL2 fraction. Haffner et al.[56] also reported that HDL3, rather than HDL2, was increased by alcohol consumption and decreased by smoking. These latter studies emphasize the complexities of the HDL subclass associations with metabolic factors and CHD risk.

OVERVIEW OF METHODS

Methods for separation of HDL subclasses are summarized in Table 15–1 and discussed in the following sections.

Ultracentrifugation Methods

The HDL subclasses were first identified by using analytical ultracentrifugation and observing their flotation rates through Schlieren patterns.[12] Since analytical ultracentrifugation is technically demanding and requires very expensive, specialized equipment, it is rarely used today, even in specialty laboratories. Although updated methods have been reported,[57] analytical ultracentrifugation is generally reserved for research and is not considered practical for use in large-scale studies.

Table 15–1 ✧ Methods for Separation of HDL Subclasses	
Property	*Method*

Density	Analytical ultracentrifugation
	Sequential density ultracentrifugation
	Density gradient ultracentrifugation:
	   Swinging bucket rotors
	   Vertical rotors
	   Zonal rotors

Size	Gradient gel electrophoresis Chromatographic procedures

Charge and Size	Chemical precipitation:
	   Heparin-Mn^{2+} and 15 kDa dextran sulfate
	   Dextran sulfate (50 kDa) and Mg^{2+}
	   Polyethylene glycol
	   Polyethylene glycol and 15 kDa dextran sulfate

Apolipoprotein composition	Immunoaffinity fractionation Enzyme-linked immunosorbent assay Differential electroimmunoassay

Sequential Density Ultracentrifugation

Sequential density ultracentrifugation is more common and is considered the traditional standard for accuracy in HDL subclass quantitation.[12,36] Total HDL can be isolated by flotation within the 1.063–1.21 kg/L density interval after prior separation by flotation of VLDL and LDL at density 1.063 kg/L. Specimens are adjusted to the indicated density by adding a salt such as KBr, and then subjected to ultracentrifugation at forces upwards of 100,000 Xg, during which lighter particles float to the top and heavier particles sink to the bottom. The fractions are recovered by careful pipetting, often in conjunction with tube slicing to separate the top and bottom fractions. The bottom fraction is adjusted to the next sequential density to cause flotation of the heavier particles. An advantage of sequential flotation methods is the ability to recover fractions on a preparative scale for physical or chemical analysis. The range of densities conferred by the heterogeneity in the proportions of lipid to protein makes density separation appropriate. The variety of ultracentrifuges and rotors available today affords considerable versatility. Conventional floor models and convenient tabletop models suitable for micro-scale fractionation can accommodate large volumes and many samples.

Sequential density ultracentrifugation does have its disadvantages, however, including the fact that only one fraction is isolated in each centrifugation step, thus requiring a sequential centrifugation step for each fraction. The labile lipoproteins may be altered by the harsh conditions, high salt, and high gravity, with accompanying loss of loosely bound apolipoproteins or deterioration during the course of a multi-step ultracentrifugal procedure.[58,59] In addition, the recovered HDL is likely to be contaminated with apo-B-containing lipoproteins in the low end of the density range. For example, the density range of lipoprotein(a) [Lp(a)] overlaps that of HDL. Sequential density ultracentrifugation is tedious and very time-consuming, and the specialized equipment and proficiency required may not be available in many laboratories.

A more convenient variation of sequential density ultracentrifugation for quantitation of the HDL2/HDL3 subclasses involves a single fractionation of serum, usually performed at density 1.125 kg/L.[60,61] Cholesterol recovered in the bottom fraction is taken as a measure of HDL3. Total HDL-C can be determined by a conventional precipitation method and the HDL2-C is calculated by difference (Total HDL-C − HDL3-C.) An alternative procedure involves density adjustment and centrifugation of the HDL supernate obtained by a precipitation method.[62–65] A more recent evaluation suggests that separation at a density of 1.100 kg/L gives more specific fractionation in a single centrifugation.[66]

As indicated previously, the major HDL subclasses, HDL2 and HDL3, were originally separated at a density of 1.125 kg/L.[12,36] In 1972, Kostner and Alaupovic[67] recommended that the optimal density for separation of the two major subclasses was 1.100 kg/L. In a landmark study reported by Anderson et al.[68] in 1977, sequential density separation was used in combination with density gradient ultracentrifugation to subdivide the HDL2 particles into two subclasses, HDL2b (d = 1.063–1.100 kg/L) and HDL2a (d = 1.100–1.125 kg/L). Using this method, the lightest subclass—HDL2b—was clearly separated from HDL2a and HDL3, while the HDL2a subclass showed appreciable overlap with HDL3, suggesting that fractionation at a density of 1.125 kg/L cross-contaminates the HDL2a and HDL3. These researchers decided to seek three major density subfractions because they had observed three major bands using an early version of gradient gel electrophoresis. This observation supports recent recommendations for a major fractionation at 1.100 kg/L.[66,67] There has been no general consensus on the choice of density, but there is considerable evidence that the lower density cutpoint is more specific.

Density Gradient Ultracentrifugation

Density gradient ultracentrifugation methods have been used to separate the major lipoprotein classes, including HDL, in a single spin,[69,70] which for some purposes has an advantage over sequential methods. The major HDL subclasses, and even some of the minor subclasses, can also be separated under appropriate conditions. Density gradient fractionation methods have been described for fixed-angle, vertical, swinging-bucket, and zonal rotors. Separations may be made in continuous (smooth) gradients, or, more commonly, in discontinuous (stepwise) gradients. Bands can then be recovered based on rate of flotation (non-equilibrium) or after fractions reach their equilibrium densities. Fractions may be recovered by pipetting from the top of the tube or by puncturing the tube and collecting the effluent from the bottom in appropriate fractions. The isolated fractions are available for analysis and are usually quantified in terms of the cholesterol content and sometimes the amounts of other lipids and apolipoproteins or total protein. Since the density gradient methods give reasonably good resolution in a single centrifugation, they are less likely to alter the lipoproteins. Depending on the conditions of ultracentrifugation, the fractions may not be completely separated and may be contaminated with other plasma proteins. The number of specimens that can be processed at one time is determined by the capacity of the rotor, but is usually lower than with the sequential density techniques. Meticulous technique is required to achieve the reproducibility required for analytical purposes. Gradient ultracentrifugation is usually used in research-oriented laboratories for small-scale studies.

Three density gradient procedures for isolating HDL subclasses are described here as examples of the technique. A representative approach for processing several specimens simultaneously employs a swinging-bucket rotor.[71–74] Specimens are adjusted to appropriate density and are often pre-stained with a lipophilic dye. They are then introduced into a stepwise gradient established with the tube in the vertical position. The tubes are placed into hinged buckets that allow the tubes to swing out to the horizontal during centrifugation, minimizing disruption of the gradient and affording good separation of the lipoproteins as they migrate along the length of the tube. Following centrifugation, typically for 20–30h, the tubes return to the vertical and fractions are recovered for analysis.

A variation of this approach using a vertical rotor has been refined by Segrest et al.[25,75,76] into a complete analytical system called the vertical autoprofiler (VAP). Specimens are similarly introduced into a gradient, but tubes are placed into cavities (in the vertical rotor) that hold the tubes upright and at right angles to the gravitational force at speed. Rather than the tubes swinging out, the gradient reorients so that separation occurs more rapidly along the shorter side-to-side distance. As the rotor slows, the gradient shifts back to the length of the tube. Fractions may be recovered by puncturing the bottom of the tube. In the VAP procedure, the effluent drawn from the bottom of the tube is continuously analyzed for cholesterol using a continuous-flow chemistry analyzer. The effluent can be split, with a portion going to a fraction collector or used for continuous, simultaneous analysis of other constituents. The cholesterol profile of the effluent is deconvoluted by computerized analysis with quantification of major lipoproteins and minor subclasses including HDL2 and HDL3.

The vertical rotor method has the advantage of giving a complete lipoprotein profile in a single spin, yet it does suffer the general disadvantages of sequential density ultracentrifugation. An additional problem is that some lipoprotein material may adhere to the sides of the tube and not be recovered.

Another gradient method that has value for large-scale preparative isolations but that has also been used as a standard for quantification involves zonal ultracentrifugation.[77–81] To separate HDL subclasses, a sample is introduced into a spinning single-cavity rotor containing a three-step gradient. After centrifugation for 24 h, fractions are recovered from the slowly spinning rotor for analysis. This large-scale method has better resolving power than other density gradient methods, with three fractions in the HDL2 range and five in the HDL3 range.[78] The major fractions are designated as HDL2, HDL3L, and HDL3D. Since this method accommodates only one specimen per run, it is generally reserved for detailed studies of compositional changes in metabolism and lipoprotein characterization. The highly specialized equipment and expertise required are available in only a few centers. (For more details of ultracentrifugation methods, see Chapter 32.)

Electrophoretic Methods

Electrophoretic methods using a homogeneous gel separate particles on the basis of their charge and size; mobility is enhanced by charge and inhibited by size. With a gradient gel, the separation is based on size: particles migrate until their size restricts further penetration into the gradient.[24] Gradient 4–30% polyacrylamide gel electrophoresis (GGE) has been used to study HDL particle size profiles in normal human plasma.[24,82–84] The HDL particles can be detected directly from plasma using lipid staining or immunoblotting with anti apo A-I after electrophoresis[26,85]. A protein stain can be used with the ≤ 1.21 kg/L density fraction isolated by ultracentrifugation[24] or the apo-defined HDL particles isolated by immunoaffinity chromatography.[23,31] With the < 1.21 kg/L fraction, Blanche et al.[24] observed five HDL subclasses, designated (HDL2b)gge (9.7–12nm); (HDL2a)gge (8.8–9.7nm); (HDL3a)gge (8.2–8.8nm); (HDL3b)gge (7.8–8.2nm); and (HDL3c)gge (7.2–7.8nm). The (HDL2b)gge particles correspond to the HDL2b component obtained by gradient ultracentrifugation with a mean hydrated density of 1.090 kg/L. The (HDL3a)gge and (HDL3b)gge particles correspond to HDL3L, with a mean hydrated density of 1.140 kg/L, and to HDL3D, with a mean hydrated density of 1.160 kg/L, identified by rate zonal ultracentrifugation.[78] The (HDL2a)gge and (HDL3c)gge particles are minor particles that are observed less frequently in normal subjects. In healthy, normolipidemic individuals, most of the HDL particles containing apoA-I without A-II are located in the (HDL2b)gge and (HDL3a)gge subclasses, while HDL particles containing both apoA-I and A-II are found predominantly in the (HDL2a+3a+3b)gge intervals.[86]

More recently, using plasma, Li et al.[26] have reported 14 peaks obtained with a modified GGE method in 4–30% gels: 7 peaks corresponding to the HDL2b range, 3 peaks corresponding to HDL2a, and 4 peaks corresponding to HDL3. They reported apolipoprotein composition of the subclasses and comparisons with other separation methods. Williams et al.[87] also compared separations by GGE to those by analytical ultracentrifugation and a precipitation method. They found that correlations of HDL subclasses with concentrations of other lipoprotein variables were generally as strong for GGE as for analytical ultracentrifugation measurements of HDL particles. However, plasma HDL3-C concentration was unrelated to (HDL3b)gge level, which is associated with CHD risk. In the past decade, GGE has been used to characterize HDL subclasses in studies of genetics,[88–90] diabetes,[91] CHD,[21,23] renal disease,[92] Tangier disease,[93] hypolipidemic therapy,[94] hormones,[95,96] alchohol,[95] diet,[97,98] and exercise.[95,99] These studies collectively demonstrated that relative enrichment of small, dense HDL3 in the 7.0–8.2nm size range, and reduction of large HDL2b particles, are associated with high CHD risk. Furthermore, diet, drugs, hormones, alcohol, and exercise have differential effects on the various HDL size subclasses within the conventional HDL2 and HDL3. These differential effects cannot be identified from measurements of HDL2 and HDL3 cholesterol alone.

The protocols for producing[100] and performing[24,100] 4–30% gradient polyacrylamide gel have been published in detail, and pre-formed gels are also available commercially (Alamo Gels, Inc., San Antonio, TX). GGE is a relatively rapid and reproducible method for determining HDL subclasses that are in reasonably good agreement with those obtained by ultracentrifugation methods. However, because quantification is based on staining, either by lipophilic dyes or protein stains, or by immunochemical techniques, results may not agree with ultracentrifugal quantitations based on cholesterol content. The particles may be only partially resolved if electrophoresis is not carried to equilibrium, and are available in very limited quantities for characterization. Nevertheless, since it can be easily performed in most research laboratories, GGE will continue to have considerable use as an analytical tool for the detailed study of HDL size subclass profiles in physiological and pathophysiological states, and for monitoring HDL changes in intervention studies.

Other electrophoretic methods used to separate HDL subclasses include agaraose gel electrophoresis and isotachophoresis. In agaraose gel electrophoresis, the majority of plasma HDL migrates with alpha-electrophoretic mobility, and can be easily detected by lipid staining. Between 2% and 10% of plasma HDL, however, migrate with pre-beta mobility. Because of its small quantity and low lipid content, pre-beta HDL usually can only be detected by immunochemical techniques.[101,102] These small, lipid-poor HDL particles have been identified as initial acceptors of cell cholesterol in the reverse cholesterol transport pathway.[103] At present, the clinical significance of plasma pre-beta HDL level is not known. Using isotachophoresis, Nowicka et al.[104] obtained three major HDL subclasses with fast, intermediate, and slow mobility and determined the interactions of the particles with macrophages. The fast-migrating particles, rich in apo AI, correspond to HDL3a and HDL3b; the intermediate to particles with sizes between HDL2a and HDL3b; and the slow, the predominant class, to HDL2b, HDL3a, and HDL3c. (See Chapter 30 for more details on isotachophoresis.)

Chromatographic and Other Methods

Various chromatographic methods also separate HDL subclasses based on particle size.[105,106] A gel permeation column in high-performance liquid chromatography (HPLC) with quantification of eluate fractions by enzymic cholesterol assay gave separations that corresponded reasonably well to those obtained by sequential density ultracentrifugation.[105] Resolution of two HDL2 and three HDL3 fractions, approximating those observed with GGE, was obtained with a Superose 6B column in fast-protein liquid chromatography.[106] Newer gel permeation columns are reported to be more rugged (see Chapter 33). NMR spectroscopy quantifies 5 HDL subclasses from serum without the need for a separation step (see Chapter 31).

Precipitation Methods

The most common methods for routine separation of the total HDL class involve chemical precipitation of VLDL and LDL with quantification of HDL as cholesterol remaining in the supernate (see Chapter 11). The precipitation techniques are convenient. They are amenable to processing large numbers of specimens without expensive or specialized equipment; hence, it is not surprising that precipitation methods were adapted for quantification of the major HDL subclasses. Selective precipitation exploits differences in size and charge properties of the lipoproteins. Since the HDL subclasses demonstrate relatively smaller differences in these properties than the major lipoproteins, their separation by precipitation is more tenuous. Nevertheless, with careful standardization and attention to technique, the precipitation methods have advantages, especially for large population studies.

One early method[107] involved the addition of heparin-Mn^{2+} for removal of VLDL/LDL, followed by addition to the HDL supernate of 15,000 dalton dextran sulfate to precipitate HDL2-C. Cholesterol was assayed in the supernates and HDL2 calculated by subtracting HDL3-C from total HDL-C. The optimum dextran sulfate concentration was determined in comparisons with ultracentrifugation at a density of 1.125 kg/L. In pooled sera, the amount of dextran sulfate required to achieve separation by precipitation equivalent to the ultracentrifugal fractionation varied over a twofold range. At the concentration of dextran sulfate considered to be optimal for patient specimens, precipitation results correlated reasonably well with ultracentrifugation. The authors concluded that the precipitation method is best suited for large-scale trials, and recommended optimizing concentrations for the conditions of a particular study.

Subsequent evaluations of the method have confirmed that this method does give convenient and reasonably accurate quantification of the HDL2/HDL3 subclasses, but that it is neither highly specific nor rugged.[109–112] Most researchers have endorsed the recommendation that the method be used for large-scale trials and not for routine evaluation of patients. One report cited interference from blood-clotting proteins and the need for substantially different dextran sulfate concentrations for serum than for EDTA plasma.[113] A particular disadvantage of this method is that the manganese cation interferes with the common enzymic cholesterol assays; for this reason, the use of heparin and manganese for precipitation has diminished with increased use of the enzymic assays in both routine and research laboratories.

A similar precipitation procedure[114,115] uses dextran sulfate (50 kDa) and Mg^{2+} to separate total HDL first and then HDL3 in sequence. The first version precipitated HDL2 from the HDL supernate, whereas a subsequent modification,[116] considered more convenient and equally accurate, precipitated VLDL, LDL, and HDL2 together from a second plasma aliquot. Evaluators of the first version observed results in good agreement with zonal ultracentrifugation[80] and concluded that the convenient precipitation method is well suited for population studies. Since this method uses the dextran sulfate reagent, which is compatible with enzymic cholesterol assays and is increasingly common for routine HDL separations, the dextran sulfate technique is described in more detail later in this chapter.

HDL subclasses have also been separated in a dual precipitation procedure using polyethylene glycol (PEG) 6000 to remove VLDL and LDL from serum, followed by addition of 15 kDa dextran sulfate to precipitate HDL2 from the first supernate.[117] One evaluator observed agreement with ultracentrifugation,[118] although a subsequent evaluator urged caution in using the method for routine characterization of patients.[119] Another method used PEG for both steps, the first precipitating VLDL and LDL and the second precipitating VLDL, LDL, and HDL2 from a second aliquot of serum.[120–122] A comparison between these two types of PEG methods revealed substantial disagreement.[123] Use of PEG for HDL separations is common in Europe and Australia but not in the United States. As a precipitant, PEG is much less effective than the polyanions (heparin and dextran sulfate), and the hundredfold higher concentrations required create highly viscous solutions that are difficult to pipette in a way that achieves reproducibility. The inexpensive, single constituent reagent is an advantage, but there are batch-to-batch differences that must be considered in formulating a consistent reagent solution.

Particle Assays

HDL particles can also be separated based on their particular apolipoprotein constituents.[34,124] The major classes contain either apo AI alone or apo AI and apo AII together.[31–34] These classes of particles have been fractionated by immunoaffinity techniques using antibodies specific for the apolipoproteins. Antibodies to apo AII bind the latter particles, after which those particles with apo AI only can be bound by antibody to apo AI. The two types of particles have also been quantified by enzyme-linked immunosorbent assay (ELISA) in a sandwich format.[125] Antibody to apo AII coated on microtiter plates binds those particles that contain apo A-II. A second enzyme-labeled antibody to apo A-I quantifies the particles containing both apo A-I and A-II in terms of the apo AI content. Total apo AI is quantified by a conventional ELISA and the apo-AI-only species is calculated by difference.

A differential electroimmunoassay has also been reported.[126] Specimens are electrophoresed through a gel containing a high concentration of antibody to apo AII and a normal concentration of antibody to apo AI. Particles with both apolipoproteins are precipitated in a small "rocket" near the origin, leaving those particles with apo AI only to migrate into the gel. The conventional rockets formed are then quantified compared to a standard. The apo A-I in particles containing both apo A-I and A-II are calculated by difference. These techniques are described in greater detail in Chapter 27.

Convenient Precipitation Method for Large-Scale Studies

This method is a variation of the dextran sulfate method for the quantification of total HDL-C, as described in Chapter 11.[114,115] HDL-C is quantified by measuring cholesterol in the first supernate after precipitation of VLDL and LDL. HDL3 is measured in a second supernate from a second aliquot of serum after precipitation of HDL2, LDL, and VLDL. HDL2 is calculated as the difference in cholesterol between the two supernates. Use of the method for characterization of CHD risk in patients in the routine laboratory is not recommended, but the procedure is considered suitable for research investigations.[80]

Solutions

The dextran sulfate is of 50,000 dalton (Dextralip 50 from Genzyme Corp., Boston, MA). Reagent-grade magnesium chloride and sodium azide are available from several sources.

TOTAL HDL REAGENT (DS1) PREPARATION

✧   Weigh out 1.0 g dextran sulfate, 10.16 g $MgCl_2 \cdot 6H_2O$, and 50 mg NaN_3.

✧   Dissolve, mix well in deionized water, and bring the total volume to 100 mL. It is not advisable to adjust pH, as fluctuations in ionic strength resulting from pH adjustment seem to contribute to more variability than the slight batch-to-batch differences in pH.

✧   The final working reagent contains 10 mg/mL dextran sulfate, 0.5 mol/L $MgCl_2$, and 0.05% NaN_3.

HDL3 REAGENT (DS2) PREPARATION

✧   Weigh out 1.91 g dextran sulfate, 39.74 g $MgCl_2 \cdot 6H_2O$, and 50 mg NaN_3.

✧   Dissolve, mix well in deionized water, and bring the volume to 100 mL.

✧   The final working reagent contains 19.1 mg/mL dextran sulfate, 1.95 mol/L $MgCl_2$, and 0.05% NaN_3.

Two or more quality control pools are included in the precipitation steps and in the cholesterol analysis together with patient specimens. Additional pool(s) with low cholesterol in the HDL/HDL3 range can be included in the analysis step only.

Precipitation Sequence

1.   Allow specimens to equilibrate to room temperature and mix thoroughly before pipetting.

2.   Pipette 0.5 mL of specimen or control into appropriately labeled tubes. Pipette one aliquot for total HDL (DS1) and one for HDL3 (DS2) determination. Sample volumes can be adjusted provided reagent volumes are adjusted accordingly.

3.   Add 50 μL of the appropriate reagent (DS1 or DS2) to each tube and vortex for 5 sec.

4.   Allow tubes to stand at room temperature for 5–30 min.

5.   Centrifuge for 5 min. at 12,000 Xg. Alternatively, centrifuge at 1500 Xg for 30 min. or some intermediate combination of g and minutes.

6.   Visually examine each supernate for turbidity. If supernate is clear, transfer the supernate—carefully, so as not to disturb the pellet—to a storage vial or sample cup.

     Note: Incomplete sedimentation of apo-B-containing lipoproteins is indicated by the presence of cloudy or turbid supernates in hypertriglyceridemic specimens. Cloudy supernates may be cleared by ultrafiltration with a 0.22 μm filter or by repeating the precipitation procedure with the original specimen diluted 1:1 with saline. Alternatively, the dilution can be made subsequently on turbid supernates. Simply mix equal volumes of the turbid supernate with an equal volume of saline solution containing precipitation reagent at the same concentration as the original specimen.

7.   Perform the cholesterol analysis on clear supernates.

     Note: The cholesterol assay should be optimized for good performance in the low HDL/HDL3 cholesterol concentration range. Analysis of the total HDL and HDL3 supernates consecutively for each specimen may decrease analytical variation and improve precision in the calculation of HDL2-C (HDL2-C = Total HDL-C – HDL3-C).

8.   Correct cholesterol results in the supernates for reagent dilution by multiplying by the factor 1.1. If a turbid supernate was diluted with saline, further multiply the result by the dilution factor (e.g., $\times$ 2).

9.   Calculate the HDL2-C value as: HDL2-C = Total HDL-C – HDL3-C

Since the separation of HDL subclasses is relatively sensitive to reaction conditions and technique, the method should be validated for individual laboratory conditions. Comparison may be made to ultracentrifugation or to an experienced laboratory. Standardization of conditions and technique is essential to achieving reproducible results.

SUMMARY

HDL is highly heterogeneous, consisting of particles with a range of size, density, charge, lipid and protein composition, and with a variety of different functions. While a measure of total HDL is predictive of CHD risk, HDL subclasses may be more or less protective than total HDL. Quantification of specific subclasses is useful in research applications and may provide a better indication of CHD risk, just as measurement of the major lipoproteins, HDL and LDL, better assesses overall risk than TC alone. Drawbacks are that the available separation methods are technically difficult and tedious (e.g., ultracentrifugation); require specialized equipment and skills (e.g., GGE and column chromatography); or are highly sensitive to reaction conditions (e.g., precipitation). Therefore, the measurement of the subclasses is still somewhat tenuous and their predictive value requires additional studies. With further refinements in methods and validation in research and clinical investigations, measurement of certain HDL subspecies may eventually improve the prediction of CHD risk.   ✧

REFERENCES

1.   Miller GJ, Miller NE. Plasma high-density-lipoprotein concentration and development of ischemic heart disease. Lancet 1975;i:16–9.
2.   Rhoads GG, Gulbrandsen CL, Kagan A. Serum lipoproteins and coronary heart disease in a population study of Hawaii Japanese men. N Engl J Med 1976;294:293–8.
3.   Gordon T, Castelli WP, Hjortland MC, et al. High-density lipoprotein as a protective factor against coronary heart disease: The Framingham Study. Am J Med 1977;62;707–14.
4.   Kannel WB, Castell WP, Gordon T. Cholesterol in the prediction of atherosclerotic disease: new perspectives based on The Framingham Study. Ann Intern Med 1979;90:85–91.
5.   Miller NE, Thelle DS, Forde OH, et al. The Tromso Heart Study. High-density lipoprotein and coronary heart-disease: a prospective case-control study. Lancet 1977;1:965–8.
6.   Abbott RD, Wilson PWF, Kannel WB, et al. High-density lipoprotein cholesterol, total cholesterol screening, and myocardial infarction. The Framingham Study. Arteriosclerosis 1988;8:209–11.
7.   Jacobs DR Jr., Mebane IL, Bangdiwala SI, et al. High-density lipoprotein cholesterol as

a predictor of cardiovascular disease mortality in men and women: the follow-up study of the Lipid Research Clinics prevalence study. Am J Epidemiology 1990;131:32–47.

8. NIH Consensus Development Conference. Triglyceride, high-density lipoprotein, and coronary heart disease. Consensus statement. Bethesda, MD: National Institutes of Health, Feb. 26–28, 1992.

9. National Cholesterol Education Program. Report of the Expert Panel on Detection, Evaluation, and Treatment of High Blood Cholesterol in Adults. Arch Intern Med 1988;148:36–69.

10. The Expert Panel. Summary of the Second Report of the National Cholesterol Education Program (NCEP) Expert Panel on Detection, Evaluation and Treatment of High Blood Cholesterol in Adults (Adult Treatment Panel II). JAMA 1993;269(23);3015–23.

11. National Cholesterol Education Program. Second report of the Expert Panel on Detection, Evaluation, and Treatment of High Blood Cholesterol in Adults (NIH Publication No. 93–3095). Bethesda, MD: National Institutes of Health, 1993.

12. DeLalla OF, Elliot HA, Gofman JW. Ultracentrifugal studies of high-density serum lipoproteins in clinically healthy adults. Am J Physiol 1954;179:333–7.

13. Gofman JW, Young W, Tandy R. Ischemic heart disease, atherosclerosis, and longevity. Circulation 1966;34:679–97.

14. Miller NE, Hammett F, Saltissi S, et al. Relation of angiographically defined coronary artery disease to plasma lipoprotein subfractions and apolipoproteins. Br Med J 1981;282:1741–4.

15. Ballantyne FC, Clark RS, Simpson HS, et al. High-density and low-density lipoprotein subfractions in survivors of myocardial infarction and in control subjects. Metabolism 1982;31:433–9.

16. Nichols AV. Human serum lipoproteins and their interrelationships. Adv Biol Med Phys 1967;11:109–58.

17. Anderson DW, Nichols AV, Pan SS, Lindgren FT. High density lipoprotein distribution: resolution and determination of three major components in a normal population sample. Atherosclerosis 1978;29:161–79.

18. Glueck CJ, Fallat RW, Millett F et al. Familial hyperalphalipoproteinemia. Arch Intern Med 1975;135:1025–8.

19. Glueck CJ, Gartside P, Fallat RW, et al. Longevity syndromes: familial hypobeta and familial hyperalpha lipoproteinemia. J Lab Clin Med 1976;88:941–57.

20. Patsch W, Kuisk I, Glueck C, et al. Lipoproteins in familial hyperalphalipoproteinemia. Arteriosclerosis 1981;1:156–61.

21. Johanson J, Carlson LA, Landou C, et al. High-density lipoproteins and coronary atherosclerosis: a strong inverse relation with the largest particles is confined to normotriglyceridemic patients. Arterioscler Thromb 1991;11:174–82.

22. Stampfer MJ, Sacks FM, Salvini S, et al. A prospective study of cholesterol, apolipoproteins, and the risk of myocardial infarction. N Engl J Med 1991;325:377–81.

23. Cheung MC, Brown BG, Wolf AC, Albers JJ. Altered particle size distribution of apolipoprotein A-I-containing lipoproteins in subjects with coronary artery disease. J lipid Res 1991;32:383–94.

24. Blanche PJ, Gong EL, Forte TM, et al. Characterization of human high-density lipoproteins by gradient gel electrophoresis. Biochimica et Biophysica Acta 1981;665:408–19.

25. Cheung MC, Segrest JP, Albers JJ, et al. Characterization of high-density lipoprotein subspecies: structural studies by single vertical spin ultracentrifugation and immunoaffinity chromatography. J Lipid Res 1987;28:913–29.

26. Li Z, McNamara JR, Ordovas JM, et al. Analysis of high-density lipoproteins by a modified gradient gel electrophoresis method. J Lipid Res 1994;35:1698–1711.

27. Sundaram GS, Mackenzie SL, Sodhi HS. Preparative isoelectric focusing of human serum high-density lipoprotein (HDL3). Biochim Biophys Acta 1974;337:196–203.

28. Mackenzie SL, Sundaram GS, Sodhi HS. Heterogeneity of human serum high-density lipoprotein (HDL2). Clin Chim Acta 1973;43:223–9.

29. Nestruck AC, Niedmann PD, Wieland H, Seidel D. Chromatofocusing of human high-density lipoproteins and isolation of lipoproteins A and A-I. Biochim Biophys Acta 1983;753:65–73.

30. Cheung MC, Albers JJ. Distribution of cholesterol and apolipoprotein A-I and A-II in human high-density lipoprotein subfractions separated by CsCl equilibrium gradient centrifugation: evidence for HDL subpopulations with differing A-I/A-II molar ratios. J Lipid Res 1979;20:200–7.

31. Cheung MC, Albers JJ. Characterization of lipoprotein particles isolated by immunoaffinity chromatography: Particles containing A-I and A-II and particles containing A-I but not A-II. J Biol Chem 1984;259:12201–09.

32. Ohta T, Hattori S, Nishiyama S, Matsuda I. Studies on the lipid and apolipoprotein compositions of two species of apo A-I-containing lipoproteins in normolipidemic males and females. J Lipid Res 1988;29:721–28.

33. James RW, Hochstrasser D, Tissot JD et al. Protein heterogeneity of lipoprotein particles containing apolipoprotein A-I without apolipoprotein A-II and apolipoprotein A-I with apolipoprotein A-II isolated from human plasma. J Lipid Res 1988;29: 1557–71.

34. Fruchart JC, Bard JM. Lipoprotein particle measurement: an alternative approach to classification of lipid disorders. Curr Opin Lipidol 1991;2:362–6.

35. Huang Y, von Eckardstein A, Wi S, et al. A plasma lipoprotein containing only apolipoprotein E and with γ mobility on electrophoresis releases cholesterol from cells. Proc Natl Acad Sci USA 1994;91:1834–8.

36. Havel RJ, Eder HA, Bragdon JH. The distribution and chemical composition of ultracentrifugally separated lipoproteins in human serum. J Clin Invest 1955;34:1345.

37. Eisenberg S. Plasma lipoproteins. In: Albers JJ, Segrest JP, eds. Methods in enzymology, Vol. 129, Orlando, FL: Academic Press, 1986:347–66.

38. Patsch JR, Gotto AM, Olivercrona T, et al. Formation of high-density-lipoprotein-2-like particles during the lipolysis of very-low-density lipoprotein in vitro. Proc Nat Acad Sci 1978;75:4519–23.

39. Tall AR, Krumholz S, Olivercrona T. Plasma phospholipid transfer protein enhances transfer and exchange of phospholipids between very low density lipoproteins and high density lipoproteins during lipolysis. J Lipid Res 1985;26:842–51.

40. Tollefson JH, Ravnik S, Albers JJ. Isolation and characterization of a phospholipid transfer protein (LTP-II) from human plasma. J Lipid Res 1988;29:1593–602.

41. Cheung MC, Wolfbauer G, Albers JJ. Plasma phospholipid mass transfer rate: relationship to plasma phospholipid and cholesteryl ester transfer activities and lipid parameters. Biochim Biophys Acta 1996;1303:103–10.

42. Wolfbauer G, Albers JJ, Oram JF. Phospholipid transfer protein enhances removal of cellular cholesterol and phospholipids by high-density lipoprotein apolipoproteins. Biochim Biophys Acta 1999;1439:65–76.

43. Glomset JA. The plasma lecithin:cholesterol acyltransferase reaction. J Lipid Res 1968;9:155–67.

44. Marzetta CA, Meyers TJ, Albers JJ. Lipid transfer protein-mediated distribution of HDL-derived cholesteryl esters among plasma apoB-containing lipoprotein subpopulations. Arteriocler Thromb 1993;13:834–41.

45. Acton S, Rigotti A, Landschulz et al. Identification of scavenger receptor SR-BI as a high-density lipoprotein receptor. Science 1996;271:518–20.

46. Tall AR. Plasma lipid transfer proteins. J lipid Res 1986;27:361–66.

47. Tollefson JH, Albers JJ. Isolation, characterization, and assay of plasma lipid transfer proteins. Methods Enzymol 1986;129:797–816.

48. Colvin PL, Moriguchi E, Barrett H, Parks J, Rudel L. Production rate determines plasma concentration of large high-density lipoprotein in non-human primates. J Lipid Res 1998;39:2076–85.

49. Colvin PL, Moriguchi E, Barrett PHR et al. Small HDL particles containing two apoA-I molecules are precursors in vivo to medium and large HDL particles containing three and four apoA-I molecules in nonhuman primates. J Lipid Res 1999;40:1782–92.

50. Krauss RM. Regulation of high-density lipoprotein levels. Med Clin North Amer 1982;66:403–30.

51. Knopp RH. Cardiovascular effects of endogenous and exogenous sex hormones over a woman's lifetime. Am J Obstet Gynecol, 1988;158:1630–43.

52. Wood PD, Haskell WL, Blair SN, et al. Increased exercise level and plasma lipoprotein concentrations: a one-year, randomized, controlled study in sedentary middle-aged men. Metabolism 1983;32:31–9.

53. Klatsky AL, Friedman GD, Siegelaub AB. Alcohol consumption before myocardial infarction: results from the Kaiser-Permanente epidemiologic study of myocardial infarction. Ann Intern Med 1974;81:294–301.

54. Dyer AR, Stamler J, Paul O, et al. Alcohol consumption and 17-year mortality in the Chicago Western Electric Company study. Prev Med 1980;9:78–90.

55. Haskell WL, Camargo C, Williams PT, et al. The effect of cessation and resumption of moderate alcohol in take on serum high-density-lipoprotein subfractions. N Engl J Med 1984;310:805–10.

56. Haffner SM, Applebaum-Bowden D, Wahl PW, et al. Epidemiological correlates of high-density-lipoprotein subfractions; apolipoproteins A-I, A-II, and D; and lecithin cholesterol acyltransferase: effects of smoking, alcohol, and adiposity. Arteriosclerosis 1985;5:169–77.

57. Albers JJ, Warnick GR, Nichols AV. Laboratory measurement of HDL. In Miller NE, Miller GJ, eds. Clinical and metabolic aspects of high-density lipoproteins. New York: Elsevier Science Publishers B.V., 1984.

58. Kunitake ST, Kane JP. Factors affecting the integrity of high-density lipoproteins in the ultracentrifuge. J Lipid Res 1982;23:936–40.

59. Cheung MC, Wolf AC. Differential effect of ultracentrifugation on apolipoprotein A-I-containing lipoprotein subpopulations. J Lipid Res 1988;29:15–25.

60. Kirstein P, Carlson K. Determination of the cholesterol content of high-density lipoprotein subfractions HDL2 and HDL3, without contamination of Lp(a) in human plasma. Clin Chim Acta 1981;113:123–34.

61. Wallentin L, Fåhraes L. HDL3 and HDL2 determination by a combined ultracentrifugation and precipitation procedure. Clin Chim Acta 1981;116:199–208.

62. Eyre J, Hammett F, Miller NE. A micro-method for the rapid ultracentrifugal separation of human plasma high-density lipoprotein subfractions, HDL2 and HDL3. Clin Chim Acta 1981;114:225–31.

63. März W, Groß W. Ultracentrifugal determination of high-density lipoprotein subfractions HDL2 and HDL3 in a high-capacity fixed-angle rotor. Ärztl Lab 1988;34: 265–70.

64. Rifai N, King ME. Further evidence for the heterogeneity of high-density lipoprotein isolates: HDL2:HDL3 cholesterol ratios and the presence of apolipoprotein B. Annals of Clinical and Laboratory Science 1987;17:345–9.

65. Asayama K, Miyao A, Kato K. High-density lipoprotein (HDL), HDL2, and HDL3 cholesterol concentrations determined in serum of newborns, infants, children, adolescents, and adults by use of a micromethod for combined precipitation ultracentrifugation. Clin Chem 1990;36:29–131.

66. Demacker PN, van Sommeren-Zondag DF, Stalenhoef AF, et al. Ultracentrifugation in swinging-bucket and fixed-angle rotors evaluated for isolation and determination of high-density lipoprotein subfractions HDL2 and HDL3. Clin Chem 1983;29:656–63.

67. Kostner G, Alaupovic P. Studies of the composition and structure of plasma lipoproteins: separation and quantification of the lipoprotein families occurring in the high-density lipoproteins of human plasma. Biochemistry 1972;11:3419–28.

68. Anderson DW, Nichols AV, Forte TM, et al. Particle distribution of human serum high-density lipoproteins. Biochim Biophys Acta 1977;493:55–68.

69. Redgrave TG, Roberts DCK, West CE. Separation of plasma lipoproteins by density gradient ultracentrifugation. Anal Biochem 1975;65:42–9.

70. Foreman JR, Karlin JB, Edelstein C, et al. Fractionation of human serum lipoproteins

by single-spin ultracentrifugation: quantification of apolipoproteins B and A-I and lipid components. J Lipid Res 1977;18:759–67.

71. Chapman MJ, Godstein S, Lagrange D, et al. A density gradient ultracentrifugal procedure for the isolation of the major lipoprotein classes from human serum. J Lipid Res 1981;22:339–58.

72. Terpstra AHM, Woodward CJH, Sanchea-Munz FJ. Improved techniques for the separation of serum lipoproteins by density gradient ultracentrifugation: visualization by prestaining and rapid separation of serum lipoproteins from small volumes of serum. Anal Biochem 1981;111:149–57.

73. Nilsson J, Mannickarottu V, Edelstein C, et al. An improved detection system applied to the study of serum lipoproteins after single-step density gradient ultracentrifugation. Anal Biochem 1981;110:342–8.

74. Groot PHE, Scheek LM, Havekes L, et al. A one-step separation of human serum high-density lipoproteins 2 and 3 by rate-zonal density gradient ultracentrifugation in a swinging bucket rotor. J Lipid Res 1982;23:1342–53.

75. Chung BH, Segrest JP, Cone JT, et al. High-resolution plasma lipoprotein cholesterol profiles by a rapid, high-volume semi-automated method. J Lipid Res 1981;22:1003–14.

76. Cone JT, Segrest JP, Chung BH, et al. Computerized rapid high resolution quantitative analysis of plasma lipoproteins based upon single vertical spin centrifugation. J Lipid Res 1982;23:923–35.

77. Patsch JR, Sailer S, Kostner G, et al. Separation of the main lipoprotein density classes from human plasma by rate-zonal ultracentrifugation. J Lipid Res 1974;15:356–66.

78. Patsch W, Schonfeld G, Gotto AM (Jr.), et al. Characterization of human high-density lipoproteins by zonal ultracentrifugation. J Biol Chem 1980;255:3178–85.

79. Schmitz G, Assmann G. Isolation of human serum HDL1 by zonal ultracentrifugation. J Lipid Res 1982;23:903–10.

80. Patsch W, Brown SA, Morrisett JD, et al. A dual-precipitation method evaluated for measurement of cholesterol in high-density lipoprotein subfractions HDL2 and HDL3 in human plasma. Clin Chem 1989;35:265–70.

81. Patsch JR, Patsch W. Zonal ultracentrifugation. In: Albers JJ, Segrest JP, eds. Methods in enzymology, Vol. 129. Orlando, FL: Academic Press, 1986:3–26.

82. Nichols AV, Blanche PJ, Gong EL. Gradient gel electrophoresis of human plasma high-density lipoproteins. In: L Lewis, Opplt JJ, eds. CRC handbook of electrophoresis, Vol. III. Boca Raton, FL: CRC Press, 1980:29–47.

83. Verdery RB, Benham DF, Baldwin HL, et al. Measurement of normative HDL subfraction cholesterol levels by Gaussian summation analysis of gradient gels. J Lipid Res 1989;30:1085–95.

84. Williams PT, Dreon DM, Blanche PJ, Krauss RM. Variability of plasma HDL subclass concentrations in men and women over time. Arterscler Thromb Vasc Biol 1997;17:702–06.

85. Lefevre M, Goudey-Lefevre JC, Roheim PS. Gradient gel electrophoresis-immunoblot analysis (GGEI): a sensitive method for apolipoprotein profile determinations. J Lipid Res 1987;28:1495–1507.

86. Cheung MC, Nichols AV, Blanche PJ, et al. Characterization of A-I-containing lipoproteins in subjects with A-I Milano variant. Biochim Biophys Acta 1988;960:73–82.

87. Williams P, Krauss R, Vranizan K, et al. Associations of lipoproteins and apolipoproteins with gradient gel electrophoresis estimates of high-density lipoprotein subfractions in men and women. Arterioscler Thromb 1992;12:332–40.

88. Williams P, Vranizan K, Austin M, et al. Familial correlations of HDL subclasses based on gradient gel electrophoresis. Arterioscler Thromb 1992;12:1467–74.

89. Krauss R, Williams P, Blanche P, et al. Lipoprotein subclasses in genetic studies: the Berkeley data set. Genet Epidemiol 1993;10:523–8.

90. Rainwater DL, Blangero J, Moore PH Jr. Genetic control of apolipoprotein A-I distribution among HDL subclasses. Atherosclerosis 1995;118:307–17.

91. Williams P, Haskell W, Vranizan K, et al The associations of high-density lipoprotein

subclasses with insulin and glucose levels, physical activity, resting heart rate, and regional adiposity in men with coronary artery disease: The Stanford Coronary Risk Intervention Project Baseline Survey. Metabolism 1995;44:1234–40.

92. Joven J, Vilella E, Ahmad S et al. Lipoprotein heterogeneity in end-stage renal disease. Kidney International 1993;43:410–18.

93. Cheung MC, Mendez AJ, Wolf AC, Knopp RH. Characterization of apolipoprotein A-I- and A-II-containing lipoproteins in a new case of high density lipoprotein deficiency resembling Tangier Disease and their effects on intracellular cholesterol efflux. J Clin Invest 1993;91:522–29.

94. Cheung MC, Austin MA, Moulin P, et al. Effects of pravastatin on apolipoprotein-specific high-density lipoprotein subpopulations and low-density lipoprotein subclass phenotypes in patients with primary hypercholesterolemia. Atherosclerosis 1993;102:107–19.

95. Williams PT, Vranizan KM, Austin MA, Krauss RM. Associations of age, adiposity, alcohol intake, menstrual status, and estrogen therapy with high-density lipoprotein subclasses. Arterioscler Thromb 1993;13:1654–61.

96. Cheung MC, Walden CE, Knopp RH. Comparison of the effects of triphasic oral contraceptives with desogestrel or levonorgestrel on apolipoprotein A-I-containing high-density lipoprotein particles. Metabolism 1999;48:658–64.

97. Williams P, Dreon D, Krauss, R. Effects of dietary fat on high-density-lipoprotein subclasses are influenced by both apolipoprotein E isoforms and low-density-lipoprotein subclass patterns 1–3. Am J Clin Nutr 1995;61:1234–40.

98. Cheung MC, Lichtenstein AH, Schaefer EJ. Effects of a diet restricted in saturated fatty acids and cholesterol on the composition of apolipoprotein A-I-containing lipoprotein particles in the fasting and fed states. Am J Clin Nutr 1994;60:911–18.

99. Williams PT, Krauss RM, Vranizan KM, et al. Effects of weight loss by exercise and by diet on apolipoprotein A-I and A-II and the particle size distribution of high-density lipoproteins in men. Metabolism 1992;41:441–49.

100. Rainwater DL, Andres DW, Ford AL, et al. Production of polyacrylamide gradient gels for the electrophoretic resolution of lipoproteins. J Lipid Res 1992;33:1876–81.

101. Ishida BY, Frohlich J, Fielding CJ. Prebeta-migrating high-density lipoprotein: quantitation in normal and hyperlipidemic plasma by solid phase radioimmunoassay following electrophoretic transfer. J Lipid Res 1987;28:778–86.

102. O'Kane MJ, Wisdom GB, McEneny J, et al. Pre-beta high-density lipoprotein determined by immunoblotting with chemiluminescent detection. Clin Chem 1992;38:2273–77.

103. Castro GR, Fielding CJ. Early incorporation of cell-derived cholesterol into pre-β-migrating high-density lipoprotein. Biochemistry 1988;27:25–9.

104. Nowicka G, Brüning T, Böttcher A, et al. Macrophage interaction of HDL subclasses separated by free flow isotachophoresis. J Lipid Res 1990;31:1947–63.

105. Okazaki M, Itakura H, Shiraishi K, et al. Serum lipoprotein measurement: liquid chromatography and sequential flotation (ultracentrifugation) compared. Clin Chem 1983;29:768–73.

106. Clifton PM, MacKinnon AM, Barter PJ. Separation and characterization of high-density lipoprotein subpopulations by gel permeation chromatography. J Chromatography 1987;414:25–34.

107. Gidez LI, Miller GJ, Burstein M, et al. Separation and quantitation of subclasses of human plasma high-density lipoproteins by a simple precipitation procedure. J Lipid Res 1982;23:1206–23.

108. Simpson HS, Ballantyne FC, Packard CJ. High-density lipoprotein subfractions as measured by differential polyanionic precipitation and rate zonal ultracentrifugation. Clin Chem 1982;28:2040–3.

109. Daerr WH, Windler EET, Rohwer HD, et al. Limitations of a new double-precipitation method for the determination of high-density lipoprotein subfractions 2 and 3. Atherosclerosis 1983;49:211–13.

110. Martini S, Baggio G, Baroni L, et al. Evaluation of HDL2 and HDL3 cholesterol by a pre-cipitation procedure in a normal population and in different hyperlipidemic pheno-types. Clin Chim Acta 1984;137:291–8.

111. Demacker PNM, Hak-Lemmers HLM, Hijmans AGM, et al. Evaluation of the dual-pre-cipitation method for determination of cholesterol in high-density lipoprotein subfrac-tions HDL2 and HDL3 in serum. Clin Chem 1986;32:819–25.

112. Cloey TA, Bachorik PS. Use of a dual-precipitation procedure for measuring high-den-sity lipoprotein 3 (HDL3) in normolipidemic serum. Clin Chem 1989;35:1390–3.

113. Demacker PNM, Hak-Lemmers HLM, van Heijst PJ. Interference of blood-clotting fac-tors in the determination of HDL2- and HDL3-cholesterol by the dual precipitation method. Clin Chim Acta 1987;165:133–9.

114. Warnick GR, Benderson JM, Albers JJ. Quantitation of high-density-lipoprotein sub-classes after separation by dextran sulfate and Mg2 precipitation. [Abstract]. Clin Chem 1982;28:1574.

115. Bachorik PS, Albers JJ. Precipitation methods for quantification of lipoproteins. In: Albers JJ, Segrest JP, eds. Methods in enzymology, Vol. 129. Orlando, FL: Academic Press, 1986:78–100.

116. Nguyen T, Warnick GR. Improved methods for separation of total HDL and subclasses. [Abstract]. Clin Chem 1989;35:1086.

117. Lundberg B, Högström S., Pietiläinen P, et al. Separation of plasma high-density lipo-protein subclasses by a combined precipitation method using polyethylene glycol 6000 and dextran sulfate. Scan J Clin Lab Invest 1984;44:305–9.

118. Dias VC, Parsons HG, Boyd ND, et al. Dual-precipitation method evaluated for determi-nation of high-density lipoprotein (HDL), HDL2 and HDL3 cholesterol concentrations. Clin Chem 1988;34:2322–7.

119. Demacker PNM. Differential determination of HDL-subfractions in clinical laboratories. Clin Chem 1989;35:701–2.

120. Kostner GM, Molinari E, Pichler P. Evaluation of a new HDL2/HDL3 quantitation method based on precipitation with polyethylene glycol. Clin Chim Acta 1983;148:139–47.

121. Brugger P, Kostner GM, Kullich WC, et al. Plasma concentrations of high-density lipo-protein (HDL)- 2 and HDL-3 in myocardial infarction survivors and in control subjects. Clin Cardiol 1986;9:273–6.

122. Widhalm K, Pakosta R. Precipitation with polyethylene glycol and density-gradient ul-tracentrifugation compared for determining high-density lipoprotein subclasses HDL2 and HDL3. Clin Chem 1991;37:238–40.

123. Leino A, Viikari J, Koskinen P, et al. Problems with PEG-based precipitation methods in the determination of HDL2- and HDL3- cholesterol. Scand J Clin Lab Invest 1987;47: 705–8.

124. James RW, Proudfoot A, Pometta D. Immunoaffinity fractionation of high-density lipo-protein subclasses 2 and 3 using anti-apolipoprotein A-I and A-II immunosorbent gels. Biochim Biophys Acta 1989;1002:292–301.

125. Koren E, Puchois P, Alaupovic P et al. Quantification of two types of apolipo-protein-A-I-containing lipoprotein particles in plasma by enzyme-linked differential-an-tibody immunosorbent assay. Clin Chem 1987;33:38–43.

126. Parra HJ, Mezdour H, Ghalim N, et al. Differential electroimmunoassay of human Lp A-I lipoprotein particles on ready-to-use plates. Clin Chem 1990;36:1431–5.

Measurement and Clinical Significance of Low-Density Lipoprotein Subclasses

16

John E. Hokanson

✧   Low-density lipoprotein (LDL) heterogeneity has been recognized for many years.[1-4] There is now convincing evidence of a relationship between variations in the physical properties of LDL and coronary heart disease (CHD), though it remains to be determined if this relationship is independent of other cardiovascular disease risk factors. A number of techniques have been developed for detecting and characterizing the variation in LDL size, flotation rate, and density.[4] This chapter focuses on techniques for measuring LDL heterogeneity that are now widely used in research laboratories and that may have application in a clinical setting. Measurement of LDL heterogeneity based on methyl signal detected by proton nuclear magnetic resonance (NMR) will be discussed in chapter 28.

BLOOD COLLECTION AND STORAGE

Appropriate collection and handling of samples are important for maintaining the physical integrity of LDL. Blood should be drawn after a 12-h fast, collected in 0.1% EDTA, mixed gently by inverting to avoid hemolysis, and centrifuged immediately at 1000g for 15–20 min at 4°C. In some cases when chylomicrons are present, plasma may be centrifuged for 30 min at 20,000 rpm and the chylomicrons aspirated off the top. Plasma samples may be stored at 4°C for up to one week without altering the LDL subclass distribution. For long-term storage, samples should be stored at −70°C. Paired analyses comparing fresh plasma to aliquots stored at −70°C indicate the mean absolute value of the difference in LDL peak particle diameter was $0.9 \pm 0.6\%$, with no detectable difference in LDL flotation rate. LDL size and flotation rate are stable for at least 29 mo for samples stored[1] at −70°C.[5] Thus, fasting plasma samples collected in EDTA and stored at −70°C can be used for determining LDL subclass distribution.

LOW-DENSITY LIPOPROTEIN SIZE

Krauss and Burke[6] developed the gradient gel electrophoresis (GGE) procedure using non-denaturing conditions to characterize LDL particle size distribution. Polyacrylamide gradients (2%–14%) can be formed following the procedure developed by Rainwater et al.,[7] and modified for LDL.[8]

Electrophoresis is performed using tris(hydroxymethyl)aminomethane(0.09

mol/L)/boric acid (0.08 mol/L)/Na_2 EDTA (0.003 mol/L) electrophoresis buffer (pH 8.3) at 10°C. Five µL of plasma is diluted 4:1 with a 50% sucrose/0.01% bromophenol blue tracking solution in electrophoresis buffer. Ten µL of this sample is added to each well. Two quality-control LDL samples are run on each gel. Standards of known diameter— ferritin (12.2 nm), thyroglobulin (17.0 nm), thyroglobulin dimer (23.6 nm; Pharmacia, Piscataway NJ), and uniform latex microspheres of carboxylated polystyrene (38.0 nm; Duke Scientific, Palo Alto, CA), or lipoprotein standards calibrated by analytical ultracentrifugation[9]—are loaded onto each gel. Electrophoresis is maintained for 24 h at 125 volts (3,000 volt hours).

Gel cassettes are removed from the electrophoresis tank, and stained for lipid in 0.04% Oil Red O in 60% ethanol at 55–60°C for 24 h and destained using 5% acetic acid. Protein standards are stained using 1.0% Coomassie Brilliant Blue R250 (Sigma Chemical, St. Louis, MO) in 50% methanol and 10% acetic acid placed on a strip of filter paper over the standard lane and destained using a 20% methanol/9% acetic acid solution. The major peak particle diameter of LDL (LDL-PPD) is reproducible, with a coefficient of variation (CV) of 2.5% from 87 consecutive gels.[10]

In addition to the continuous LDL-PPD determination, a dichotomous classification of LDL heterogeneity can be used to identify LDL subclass patterns, or phenotypes, denoted A and B.[11,12] (See Figure 16–1.) LDL subclass phenotype A is characterized by a predominance of large LDL particles while LDL subclass phenotype B is characterized by a predominance of small LDL particles. A majority (85%–90%) of subjects can be classified as having either LDL subclass phenotype A or B, while the remainder have an intermediate phenotype.[12] In rare conditions, LDL plasma concentrations may be too low to determine LDL-PPD by GGE.[13]

An alternative GGE procedure has been developed by McNamara et al. to describe LDL heterogeneity by defining seven size subfractions of LDL.[14] Plasma samples are electrophoresed under similar conditions as described above for 6 h at 240 volts (2,700 volt hours) and subsequently stained for lipid using Sudan Black B. Gels are destained using ethylene glycol/monoethyl ether. A pooled plasma sample containing three of the seven major bands of LDL is also run on each gel to identify the sample LDL subfractions. The percent of total LDL is estimated for each LDL subfraction as the area under the peak for each subfraction divided by the total area for LDL. Each percentage is then weighted by multiplying it by the defined LDL subclass (1 through 7) to produce an overall LDL score.

A new GGE method has been recently described that uses a 3% to 7.5% polyacrylamide gradient, electrophoresed under similar conditions as described above.[15] In this gradient, LDL migrates over a larger range of the gel. This allows for a high degree of resolution of LDL particle sizes.

High-performance gel-filtration chromatography (HPGC) has recently been applied to LDL size determinations.[16,17] Five µL of whole plasma or serum is loaded onto a Superose 6 HR 10/30 column (Pharmacia) and eluted with phosphate-buffered saline (0.1 mol/L NaH_2PO_4-H_2O, 0.2 mol/L NaCl, 0.1 mmol/L disodium EDTA, pH 7.4) at a rate of 0.5 mL/min at 25°C for 30 min. A fluorescent probe (*cis*-parinaric acid) is added to the column effluent at a constant rate of 0.5 mL/min and fluorescence is measured with excitation at 324 nm and emission at 413 nm. The within-run CV was 0.22 %. The between-run CV was 0.21 % using isolated LDL.[17]

Figure 16–1 ✧ Examples of LDL Subclass Phenotypes A and B as Determined by GGE of LDL from Individual Study Subjects

Phenotype A is characterized by a predominance of large, buoyant LDL, while phenotype B is characterized by a predominance of small, dense LDL. The estimated diameter (Å) of the major LDL subclass is also shown for each scan.

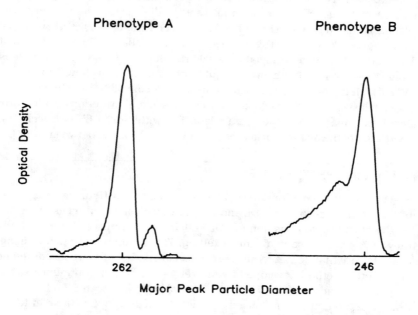

LOW-DENSITY LIPOPROTEIN FLOTATION RATE

Several different methods of density gradient ultracentrifugation have been used to characterize LDL flotation rate. Lipoproteins were first characterized by flotation rate (Svedberg flotation unit) using the analytical ultracentrifuge.[1] Subsequently Chung et al. developed a procedure using a vertical rotor in a preparative ultracentrifuge.[18] Methods for characterizing LDL subclasses based on flotation rates are modifications of this method.

One of these methods is designed to optimize the resolution of apolipoprotein B (apo-B)-containing lipoproteins.[19] A discontinuous salt gradient is produced by layering 1 mL of plasma adjusted to a density of 1.08 kg/L (total volume 5 mL) below 13 mL of a 1.006 kg/L NaCl solution in a Sorvall TV-865B tube (DuPont, Wilmington, DE). [This gradient may also be formed in a VTi 65.1 (Beckman Instruments, Palo Alto, CA) using 4 mL of $d = 1.08$ kg/L below 9.5 mL of $d = 1.006$ kg/L and centrifuged for 70 min at 65,000 rpm.[20]]

Samples are then centrifuged at 65,000 rpm for 90 min at 10°C. While maintaining temperature, centrifuge tubes are fractionated and cholesterol is measured in each fraction by enzymatic kit (Diagnostic Chemicals, Canada). LDL relative flotation (Rf) is calculated as the fraction number of the major peak of LDL divided by the total number of fractions. Recovery of cholesterol using this method is 92.5% ± 6.4% of total plasma cholesterol. The between-rotor CV of the LDL Rf is 3.5%. In addition, it is a highly reproducible method of determining the distribution of cholesterol in the apo-B-containing lipoprotein spectrum in a single ultracentrifugation step.

An alternative method for determining LDL Rf uses ultracentrifugation in a vertical rotor with a continuous flow auto-analyzer and mathematical curve deconvolution of 6 LDL subclasses.[21] A discontinuous salt gradient is formed by underlaying 70 μL of plasma adjusted to a density of 1.08 kg/L to a final volume of 650 μL under 4.65 mL of a 1.041 kg/L NaCl solution. Tubes are loaded into a Vti-80 rotor (Beckman Instruments, Palo Alto, CA) and centrifuged at 80,000 rpm for 1 h at 20°C. The sample is pumped from the bottom of the centrifuge tube into a continuous-flow cholesterol analyzer (VAP-II). Mathematical equations are used to deconvolute the cholesterol curve into six subclasses of LDL using exponential Gaussian distributions, which provided the best least-squares fit to the overall data. The within-rotor CV of the cholesterol concentration of the major subclass of LDL is 1.9% to 8.3%; the between-rotor CV is 5.2%.

LOW-DENSITY LIPOPROTEIN DENSITY

Several methods exist for determining the density of LDL subclasses. These methods often require pre-isolating LDL and long ultracentrifugation times. Important studies on the chemical composition of LDL subclasses have used these methods,[22–27] but they have limited use in a clinical setting. Three methods for determining LDL subclass density that do not require previous isolation of LDL are discussed here.

In the method developed by Marzetta et al.,[28] a discontinuous salt gradient is prepared by underlaying 3.7 mL of $d = 1.006$ kg/L NaCl with 5.7 mL of $d = 1.063$ kg/L KBr and 2.3 mL of plasma raised to a density of 1.21 kg/L with solid KBr. Tubes are placed in the SW41 swinging bucket rotor (Beckman Instruments) and centrifuged for 24 h at 41,000 rpm at 15°C. Tubes are fractionated from the top by pumping a dense solution of Fluorinert [1.85 kg/L;(3M, St. Paul, MN)] into the bottom of the centrifuge tube at a flow rate of 0.8 mL/min. The sample flows through a UV detector and absorbance at 280 nm is recorded. The density of each fraction is determined by refractometry of fractions collected from a tube under the same conditions in the absence of plasma. The densities of fractions in the LDL range (1.0203–1.0548 kg/L) have a CV of 0.2% to 0.06%, respectively.

In an alternate method for determining the density distribution of LDL, plasma is pre-stained with a 15 gm/L solution of Coomassie Brilliant Blue R250 (Sigma Chemical, St. Louis, MO), and 3.4 mL of stained plasma is raised to a density of 1.10 kg/L using solid KBr.[29] The sample is overlayered with 2.5 mL of $d = 1.065$ kg/L and 2.5 mL of $d = 1.020$ kg/L KBr solutions and 2.9 mL of $d = 1.006$ kg/L NaCl solution, all at pH 4.5–5.0. Tubes are centrifuged in a SW41 rotor (Beckman Instruments, Palo Alto, CA) at 37,000 rpm for 19.5 h with 15 min acceleration and 45 min deceleration time. The centrifuge tube is photographed, and a densitometric scan of this photograph yields a density distribution profile of LDL. LDL subclass peaks are identified and the area under each curve is calculated, assuming Gaussian curves. Finally, the area under each LDL subclass peak is expressed as percentage of the total area. Recovery of LDL (1.019 < d < 1.063 kg/L) cholesterol by this method was 86.4% ± 2.0%. The within-run CV for the

LDL cholesterol ranges from 3.0% to 7.8% and the between-run CV ranges from 1.8% to 2.3%.

Density gradient ultracentrifugation has been used to define three density subclasses of LDL.[30] A step-wise density gradient is layered in a centrifuge tube as follows:

- ✧ 0.5 mL of d = 1.182 Kg/L;
- ✧ 3.0 mL plasma adjusted to d = 1.09 kg/L;
- ✧ 1.0 mL of d = 1.060 kg/L;
- ✧ 1.0 mL of d = 1.056 kg/L;
- ✧ 1 mL of d = 1.045 kg/L;
- ✧ 2.0 mL of d = 1.034 kg/L;
- ✧ 2.0 mL of d = 1.024 kg/L; and
- ✧ 1 mL of d = 1.019 kg/L.

The gradient is centrifuged in an SW40 rotor (Beckman Instruments) for 24 h at 40,000 rpm at 23°C. Tubes are fractionated from the top and the effluent flows through a UV detector; absorbance at 280 nm is recorded. Three subclasses of LDL can be identified using this technique. The within-rotor CV is 5.4 % and the between-rotor CV is 6.5 %.[31]

RELATIONSHIP AMONG METHODS OF DETERMINING LDL SUBCLASSES

There is a high degree of correlation between these different methods of determining LDL subclasses, despite the fact that the methods use different physical properties of LDL and have different analytical strategies for reporting LDL heterogeneity. As shown in Figure 16–2, LDL Rf and LDL-PPD have a correlation coefficient of 0.68 ($p < 0.01$), and this relationship has been replicated in other studies.[13] In addition, LDL-PPD is significantly correlated with LDL peak density ($r = 0.88$).[19] LDL-PPD is also highly correlated with LDL-VAPII major peak Rf ($r = 0.86$).[21] LDL size measured by HPGC and LDL size measured by GGE show similar correlations ($r = 0.88$, $p<0.001$).[16] When subjects are classified as LDL subclass phenotype A or B, there are significant differences in LDL Rf[13] and the overall distribution of LDL. (See Figure 16–3.)

CLINICAL SIGNIFICANCE

A number of studies have investigated the relationship between variations in LDL physical characteristics and CHD (see Table 16–1). At last 12 cross-sectional studies, representing 2,792 subjects, reported variations in LDL among CHD cases and control subjects. In general these studies show an increased risk of CHD associated with smaller, more dense LDL. When other factors are included in the analysis [in particular triglyceride (TG) and HDL cholesterol (HDL-C)], these associations are attenuated. Thus, small, dense LDL may be an important marker for complex metabolic disturbances that lead to increased risk of CHD.

Figure 16–2 ✧ Relationship between LDL Peak Particle Diameter Estimated by GGE and LDL Buoyancy by Non-equilibrium DGUC

Results from 23 middle-aged males with normal lipid values.[22] The correlation coefficient is 0.68 ($p < .01$)

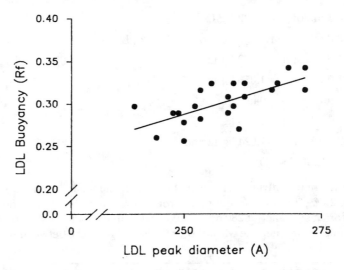

Fisher was the first to investigate the relationship between LDL distribution and CHD.[32] He reported a non-significant increase in risk associated with polydispersed LDL in normal cholesterolemic subjects. This potential risk was dramatically reduced when subjects were stratified based on hypertriglyceridemia. Even in this early report. the importance of other metabolic disturbances was recognized. More than 60% of these subjects with polydispersed LDL and glucose intolerance had atherosclerosis.

Crouse et al.[24] were the first to report a significant association between small LDL (defined as LDL molecular weight) and the presence of CHD. These CHD patients were more likely to have diabetes, and had higher TG and lower HDL-C in addition to having smaller LDL. There was a significant inverse relationship between LDL molecular weight and log TG ($r = -0.64$, $p<0.001$). After adjustment for TG, there was no longer a statistically significant difference in LDL molecular weight between patients and control subjects.

Austin et al.[11] confirmed the association between small LDL and CHD in a subset of subjects from the Boston Area Health Study. Using a dichotomous classification of LDL size distribution, LDL pattern B was associated with a three-fold increased risk of MI. This association however, was not independent of TG in multiple logistic regression analysis.

Overall, of the 12 cross-sectional studies investigating the relationship between LDL distribution and CHD,[11,24,26,33–40] nine have shown a significant relationship between small, dense LDL and CHD (see Table 16–1).[11,24,26,32–36,39,40] In assessing the in-

Figure 16–3 ✧ Mean Cholesterol Distribution by Non-equilibrium DGUC and Difference Plot Comparing Mean Values for Subjects with LDL Phenotype A and Phenotype B

Left view: Non-equilibrium DGUC of plasma from middle-aged males with normal lipid values.[22] Mean cholesterol values (mg/dL) are shown in each of 38 fractions in 9 males with LDL subclass phenotype A (solid symbols), and in 18 males with LDL subclass phenotype B (open symbols).

Right view: DGUC difference plot comparing mean values for subjects with LDL subclass phenotype B and those with phenotype A (B-A). Bars represent 95% confidence intervals of difference in means for each fraction. The plot shows that phenotype B subjects have more VLDL cholesterol, less buoyant LDL, more dense LDL, and less HDL cholesterol compared to phenotype A subjects.

To convert to mmol/L, multiply by 0.0259.

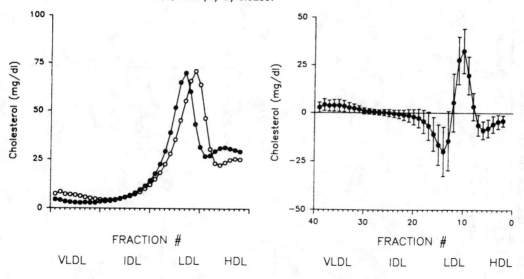

dependent relationship between small, dense LDL and CHD, the majority of these cross-sectional studies (six[11,24,26,32,35,40] of eight studies[11,24,26,32,35,36,39,40]) suggest the relationship between small LDL and CHD is intimately tied to other lipid abnormalities such as hypertriglyceridemia and low HDL-C.

Interestingly, in the three studies in which small, dense LDL was not associated with an increase in CHD,[32,27,38] study subjects were selected based on lipid levels. Two studies included only subjects with normal cholesterol levels,[32,37] and one also excluded subjects with hypertriglyceridemia (TG > 250 mg/dL, 2.83 mmol/L)[32]. The third study matched cases and control subjects for total cholesterol levels.[38] Using these selection criteria, the relationship between small, dense LDL and CHD may be obscured.

Table 16–1 ✧ Studies of Small, Dense LDL and Coronary Disease

Author (ref)	Year	Subjects	N =	Laboratory method	LDL Distribution			
					Trait definition	Univariate risk*	Multivariate risk*	Covariates
					Cross-sectional studies			
Fisher et al. (32)	1983	Normal cholesterolemic	187	DGUC	polydispersed	1.9 (0.8–4.5)[1]	0.6 (0.2–2.3)[1]	Hypertriglyceridemia[2]
Crouse et al. (24)	1985	CHD present CHD absent[7]	46 47	Gel chromotography	Molecular weight	P<0.001	0.075<p<0.10	TG
Austin et al. (11)	1988	MI cases, Controls	113 122	GGE	Phenotype B	3.0 (1.7–5.2)	1.6 (0.8–3.2)	TG, Quetelet index, age, sex
Griffin et al. (33)	1990	CHD cases, Controls	7 14	DGUC	Concentration of LDL III	P<0.05		
Tornvall et al. (34)	1991	MI cases, Controls[7]	36 14	DGUC	Apo B in dense LDL	P<0.001		
Campos et al. (35)	1992	CHD cases, Controls	280 822	GGE	Particle score	P<0.0001	P=0.5	TG[2], HDL-C[2], B-blocker use[2]
Coresh et al. (26)	1993	CHD present CHD absent[3]	107 91	GGE	Size	P<0.004	0.9 (0.5–1.7)	LogTG, DM, smoking, age, sex
Griffin et al. (36)	1994	Post MI Controls	40 58	DGUC	LDL III >100 mg/dL	6.9 (2.8–17.0)	Independent	TG, BMI, smoking, drugs, age
Campos et al. (37)	1995	CHD cases, Healthy controls[8]	92 92	GGE	Size	P=0.001[9]	P=0.0001[9]	HDL-C, HDL2-C[2], VLDL-C, BMI, age
Sherrard et al. (38)	1996	Asymptomatic CHD Matched controls	53 167	GGE	Size	NS		

Study	Year	Subjects	N	Method	Particle score			Adjusted variables
Rajman et al. (39)	1996	CHD present[11] / CHD absent[11]	46 / 21	GGE		P<0.001	P<0.001[12]	TG
Erbey et al. (40)	1999	IDDM	337	GGE	Size	P=0.03	0.8 (0.60–1.04)[10]	TG[2], family history of NIDDM
Prospective nested case/control studies								
Gardner et al. (41)	1996	Incident CHD / Matched controls	124 / 124	GGE	Size	P<0.001	P<0.004	Non-fasting TG[4], HDL-C, and non-HDL-C; SBP, smoking, BMI
Stampfer et al. (42)	1996	Incident MI / Matched controls	266 / 308	GGE	Size	1.4 (1.2–1.6)	1.1 (0.9–1.4)	TG[2], HDL-C, TC, TG-TC interaction
Lamarche et al. (43)	1997	Incident IHD / Matched controls	114 / 114	GGE	< 25.64 nm: lower tertile	3.6 (1.5–8.8)[5]	2.5 (0.9–6.8)[6]	TG[4], HDL-C[4], Apo B[2], TC/HDL-C
Mykkanen et al. (44)	1999	Incident CHD / Matched controls	58 / 116	GGE	Size	0.96 (0.72–1.27)[15]	NS	TG[4], TC/HDL-C ratio[2], apo B[4], SPB[2], smoking[2], age[4]

*Odds ratio (95% confidence intervals).
1 Calculated from table 3.
2 Significantly related to coronary disease in multivariate analysis that includes LDL distribution.
3 Subjects with TgG> 500 mg/dL (5.65 mmmol/L) were excluded.
4 Not significantly related to coronary disease in multivariate analysis that includes LDL distribution.
5 Model includes middle tertile of LDL size.
6 P = 0.08
7 Excluded if on lipid-lowering therapy.
8 Excluded if total cholesterol > 200 mg/dL (5.18 mmol/L) or TG > 250 mg/dL (2.83 mmol/L).
9 LDL size *larger* in cases compared to controls.
10 Odds ratio for an *increase* in LDL size.
11 Subjects with TG > 204 mg/dL (2.3 nmol/L) were excluded
12 By ANCOVA
13 Relative risk for a 1 standard deviation (8.7 Å) *increase* in LDL size.

Three[41–43] of four[41–44] prospective studies have reported that small LDL precedes CHD. These studies selected cases and matched controls from prospective cohorts and examined the relationship between LDL size and subsequent CHD events.

The Stanford Five-City Project[41] is a long-term community-based trial evaluating the effect of health promotion programs on cardiovascular disease. Incident cases of CHD were identified and controls were matched for age, sex, ethnicity, treatment or control city, and time of surveillance. Baseline non-fasting blood samples were collected from study subjects. Altogether, 124 case-control pairs were identified: 90 pairs of men and 34 pairs of women. For men and women combined, LDL-PPD was significantly smaller among cases compared to control subjects (26.17 nm versus 26.68 nm, p<0.001). In multiple logistic regression analysis, LDL size was independent of non-fasting TG, HDL-C, smoking, systolic blood pressure, and body mass index (BMI). This independent effect of LDL size on subsequent CHD appears to be limited to men, and is not seen among the smaller number of pairs of women.

In the Physicians Health Study,[42] 266 men with incident CHD were identified during a seven-year follow up. Control subjects were matched for age, smoking, and time of randomization. Only 15% of the blood samples were collected after a 12-h fast. An 0.8-nm decrease in LDL size was associated with a 38% increase in CHD risk (RR = 1.38, 95% CI = 1.18–1.62, p<0.001). In multivariate analysis, LDL size was not significantly associated with CHD (p=0.46), while TG remained related to incident CHD (RR = 1.33, 95% CI = 1.05–1.68, p=0.009 for a 1 S.D. increase in TG).

The Quebec Cardiovascular Study[43] followed 2,103 men for five years. One hundred and three incident cases of ischemic heart disease (IHD) were matched with control subjects (1:1) for age, cigarette smoking, BMI, and alcohol intake. There was no significant difference in the mean LDL-PPD between cases and control subjects, however, when LDL-PPD was broken into tertiles, small LDL was significantly associated with IHD (RR = 3.6, 95% CI = 1.5–8.8, $p < 0.01$). In step-wise multivariate logistic regression, small LDL remained significantly associated with IHD when TG or HDL-C was added to the model. However after controlling for TG, apo B, and HDL-C simultaneously, the risk of IHD associated with small LDL was reduced to marginal significance (RR = 2.5, 95% CI = 0.89–6.8, p=0.08). When 25 pairs were excluded because one subject of the pair was taking beta-blockers or diuretics at baseline, the relative risk of IHD associated with small LDL was 3.9 (95% CI = 1.2–13.3, $p < 0.05$). Thus, the relationship between small LDL and IHD appears to be modified by lipids, apolipoproteins, and drug therapy.

A recent study in an elderly population from Finland showed no association between LDL size and incident CHD.[44] Over a 3.5-year period, 86 CHD case were identified and control subjects were matched (2:1) by sex and diabetes status. There was no difference in LDL particle size (268.2 Å versus 268.5 Å respectively, p=0.78), or LDL subclass phenotype (20.9% versus 21.5% respectively, p=0.91) between CHD cases and control subjects. These study subjects were elderly (ages ranged from 65 to 74 years old). This may suggest that the relationship between LDL size and CHD exists primarily in younger individuals.

There is now evidence that small LDL is associated with sub-clinical CHD.[15] Intima media thickening of the common carotid artery (CCA-IMT) was quantified using B-mode ultrasound in 94 healthy, 50-year-old men. LDL major peak size was correlated with CCA-IMT ($r = -0.40$, $p<0.001$). In multivariate analysis, the relationship between LDL-III (the major subfraction containing small LDL) and CCA-IMT was independent of TG, accounting for 10% of the variance in CCA-IMT. Thus, LDL size relates to sub-clinical vascular changes that precede CHD in an apparently healthy population of middle-aged men.

Important contributions to our understanding of the clinical relevance of small, dense LDL have come from CHD intervention trials. The Stanford Coronary Risk Intervention Project randomized 213 men with CHD who were undergoing angiography to usual care or to a CHD risk reduction program.[45] The risk-reduction program included diet, exercise, and lifestyle modifications, as well as lipid-lowering drugs if target lipid levels could not be met. Subjects received an annual coronary angiography over four years. Among subjects with buoyant LDL (measured by the analytical ultracentrifuge), there were no differences in annualized angiographic changes between the usual care and the risk reduction groups. In contrast, among subjects with dense LDL, those on the risk-reduction program showed less progression of coronary disease based on minimum artery diameter ($p < 0.007$), and marginally favorable differences in mean artery diameter ($p < 0.09$) and stenosis ($p < 0.08$).[45] Thus, LDL buoyancy predicts subsequent response to an aggressive CHD risk reduction program.

A recent intervention trial provides important evidence that changes in LDL buoyancy by intensive lipid-lowering therapy can significantly improve coronary stenosis. In the Familial Atherosclerosis Treatment Study, men undergoing coronary angiography were randomized to intensive lipid-lowering therapy or conventional therapy and followed for 2.5 years.[46] LDL Rf was measured in 44 men on and off drug therapy.[47] Patients on intensive lipid-lowering therapy improved in coronary disease stenosis while coronary stenosis worsened in patients receiving conventional therapy. The change in coronary stenosis was significantly related to changes in LDL Rf ($r = -0.61$, $p<0.001$). In multiple regression analysis, change in LDL Rf was the best predictor of changes in coronary stenosis, accounting for 37% of the change in stenosis in these patients (see Figure 16–4). This relationship was independent of changes in TG and changes in HDL-C. This study indicates that small, dense LDL is an important therapeutic target and that monitoring changes in LDL distribution may provide important clues as to the effectiveness of lipid-lowering therapy in the prevention of CHD.

The biological mechanism(s) underlying the association between small, dense LDL and atherosclerosis remain to be elucidated. Possible explanations for the link between small, dense LDL and atherosclerosis are that small, dense LDL has increased susceptibility to oxidation,[48–52] decreased affinity for the LDL receptor,[53] increased binding to vascular proteoglycans,[54] increased flux into the aortic intima,[55] and promoted cholesterol ester accumulation in human aortic intimal cells.[56] Increased small, dense LDL is also associated with the complex metabolic disturbances seen with increased visceral adiposity[57] and the insulin resistance syndrome.[58–60]

SUMMARY

Various methods are available for characterizing the distribution of LDL particles. These techniques use different physical properties of LDL that are highly correlated with each other. Epidemiological studies have demonstrated that small, dense LDL is

Figure 16–4 ✧ Step-wise multiple linear regression of changes in coronary stenosis (y-axis) with the sequential addition of predictive variables. (*p < 0.05, **p < 0.001). From Zambon et al.[47]

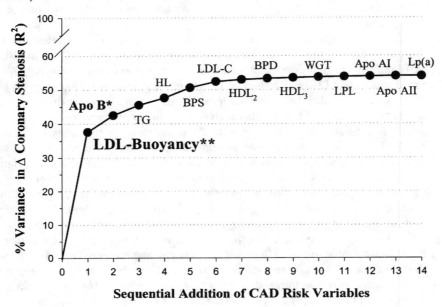

associated with increased risk of CHD, and the presence of small, dense LDL precedes clinical events. These studies indicate that small, dense LDL is a component of a complex physiologic syndrome: a set of interrelated abnormalities including elevated TG, low HDL-C, insulin resistance, and increased central obesity. These factors make it difficult to determine an "independent" risk of CHD associated with small, dense LDL. Intervention studies, however, have shown that small, dense LDL predicts the angiographic changes in response to lipid-lowering therapy, and that converting small, dense LDL to buoyant LDL is associated with CHD regression. The physiologic mechanism(s) underlying these observations remains to be clearly established. ✧

Acknowledgments: *The author would like to acknowledge John D. Brunzell, MD, and Melissa A. Austin, PhD, for their contributions to previous editions of this chapter.*

REFERENCES

1. Lindgren F, Jensen L, Wills R, Freeman N. Flotation rates, molecular weights, and hydrated densities of the low-density lipoproteins. Lipids 1969;4:337–44.
2. Adams G, Schumaker V. Polydispersity of human low-density lipoproteins. Ann NY Acad Sci 1969;164:130–46.
3. Hammond M, Fisher W. The characterization of a discrete series of low-density lipoproteins in the disease, hyper-pre-lipoproteinemia. J Biol Chem 1971;246:5454–65.

4. Krauss R, Blanche P. Detection and quantitation of LDL subfractions. Curr Opin Lipidol 1992;3:377–83.
5. Zambon A, Austin MA, Brown BG, Hokanson JE, Brunzell JD. Effect of hepatic lipase on LDL in normal men and those with coronary artery disease. Arterioscler Thromb 1993;13:147–53.
6. Krauss R, Burke D. Identification of multiple subclasses of plasma low-density lipoproteins in normal humans. J Lipid Res 1982;23:97–104.
7. Rainwater D, Andres D, Ford A, Lowe W, Blanche P, Krauss R. Production of polyacrylamide gradient gels for the electrophoretic resolution of lipoproteins. J Lipid Res 1992;33:1876–81.
8. Austin MA, Mykkanen L, Kuusisto J, Edwards KL, Nelson C, Haffner SM, Pyorala K, Laakso M. Prospective study of small LDLs as a risk factor for non-insulin-dependent diabetes mellitus in elderly men and women. Circulation 1995;92:1770–8.
9. La Belle M, Blanche PJ, Krauss RM. Charge properties of low-density-lipoprotein subclasses. J Lipid Res 1997;38:690–700
10. Hokanson JE, Austin MA, Zambon A, Brunzell JD. Plasma triglyceride and LDL heterogeneity in familial combined hyperlipidemia. Arterioscler Thromb 1993;13:427–34.
11. Austin M, Breslow J, Hennekens C, Buring J, Willett W, Krauss RM. Low-density-lipoprotein subclass patterns and risk of myocardial infarction. JAMA 1988;260:1917–21.
12. Austin M, King M-C, Vranizan K, Krauss RM. The atherogenic lipoprotein phenotype (ALP): a proposed genetic marker for coronary heart disease risk. Circulation 1990;82:495–506.
13. Capell WH, Zambon A, Austin MA, Brunzell JD, Hokanson JE. Compositional differences of LDL particles in normal subjects with LDL subclass phenotype A and LDL subclass phenotype B. Arterioscler Thromb Vasc Biol 1996;16:1040–6.
14. McNamara J, Campos H, Ordovas J, Peterson J, Wilson P, Schaefer E. Effect of gender, age, and lipid status on low-density-lipoprotein subfraction distribution: results of the Framingham Offspring Study. Arteriosclerosis 1987;7:483–90.
15. Skoglund-Andersson C, Tang R, Bond MG, de Faire U, Hamsten A, Karpe F. LDL particle size distribution is associated with carotid intima-media thickness in healthy 50-year-old men. Arterioscler Thromb Vasc Biol. 1999;19:2422–30.
16. Scheffer PG, Bakker SJ, Heine RJ, Teerlink T. Measurement of low-density-lipoprotein particle size by high-performance gel-filtration chromatography. Clin Chem. 1997;43:1904–12.
17. Scheffer PG, Bakker SJ, Heine RJ, Teerlink T. Measurement of LDL particle size in whole plasma and serum by high performance gel-filtration chromatography using a fluorescent lipid probe. Clin Chem. 1998;44:2148–51.
18. Chung BH, Segrest JP, Cone JT, Pfau J, Geer JC, Duncan LA. High-resolution plasma lipoprotein cholesterol profiles by a rapid, high-volume semi-automated method. J Lipid Res 1981;22:1003–14.
19. Auwerx JH, Marzetta CA, Hokanson JE, Brunzell JD. Large buoyant LDL-like particles in hepatic lipase deficiency. Arteriosclerosis 1989;9:319–25.
20. Purnell JQ, Marcovina SM, Hokanson JE, Kennedy H, Cleary PA, Steffes MW, Brunzell JD. Levels of lipoprotein(a), apolipoprotein B, and lipoprotein cholesterol distribution in IDDM: results from follow-up in the Diabetes Control and Complications Trial. Diabetes 1995;44:1218–26.
21. Kulkarni KR, Garber DW, Jones MK, Segrest JP. Identification and cholesterol quantification of low-density-lipoprotein subclasses in young adults by VAP-II methodology. J Lipid Res 1995;36:2291–302.
22. Shen MM, Krauss RM, Lindgren FT, Forte TM. Heterogeneity of serum low-density lipoproteins in normal human subjects. J Lipid Res 1981;22:236–44.
23. Teng B, Thompson GR, Sniderman AD, Forte TM, Krauss RM, Kwiterovich PO, Jr. Composition and distribution of low-density lipoprotein fractions in hyperapobetalipoproteinemia, normolipidemia, and familial hypercholesterolemia. Proc Natl Acad Sci USA 1983;80:6662–6.

24. Crouse J, Parks J, Schey H, Kahl FR. Studies of low-density lipoprotein molecular weight in human beings with coronary artery disease. J Lipid Res 1985;26:566–74.

25. Chapman M, Laplaud P, Luc G,et al. Further resolution of the low-density-lipoprotein spectrum in normal human plasma: physicochemical characteristics of discrete subspecies separated by density gradient ultracentrifugation. J Lipid Res 1988;29: 442–58.

26. Coresh J, Kwiterovich PJ, Smith H, Bachorik P. Association of plasma triglyceride and LDL particle diameter, density, and chemical composition with premature coronary artery disease in men and women. J Lipid Res 1993;34:1687–97.

27. Hokanson JE, Krauss RM, Albers JJ, Austin MA, Brunzell JD. LDL physical and chemical properties in familial combined hyperlipidemia. Arterioscler Thromb Vasc Biol 1995; 15:452–9.

28. Marzetta CA, Foster DM, Brunzell JD. Relationships between LDL density and kinetic heterogeneity in subjects with normolipidemia and familial combined hyperlipidemia using density gradient ultracentrifugation. J Lipid Res 1989;30:1307–17.

29. Swinkels D, Hak-Lemmers H, Demacker P. Single spin density gradient ultracentrifugation method for the detection and isolation of light and heavy low-density-lipoprotein subfractions. J Lipid Res 1987;28:1233–9.

30. Griffin BA, Caslake MJ, Yip B, Tait GW, Packard CJ, Shepherd J. Rapid isolation of low-density-lipoprotein (LDL) subfractions from plasma by density gradient ultracentrifugation. Atherosclerosis. 1990;83:59–67.

31. Griffin BA, Freeman DJ, Tait GW, Thomson J, Caslake MJ, Packard CJ, Shepherd J. Role of plasma triglyceride in the regulation of plasma low-density-lipoprotein (LDL) subfractions: relative contribution of small, dense LDL to coronary heart disease risk. Atherosclerosis. 1994;106:241–53.

32. Fisher WR. Heterogeneity of plasma low-density lipoproteins manifestations of the physiologic phenomenon in man. Metabolism 1983;32:283–91.

33. Griffin B, Caslake M, Yip B, Tait G, Packard C, Shepherd J. Rapid isolation of low-density-lipoprotein (LDL) subfractions from plasma by density gradient ultracentrifugation. Atherosclerosis 1990;83:59–67.

34. Tornvall P, Karpe F, Carlson L, Hamsten A. Relationship of low-density-lipoprotein subfractions to angiographically defined coronary artery disease in young survivors of myocardial infarction. Atherosclerosis 1991;90:67–80.

35. Campos H, Genest JJ, Blijlevens E, et al. Low-density-lipoprotein particle size and coronary artery disease. Arterioscler Thromb 1992;12:187–95.

36. Griffin BA, Freeman DJ, Tait GW, Thomson J, Caslake MJ, Packard CJ, Shepherd J. Role of plasma triglyceride in the regulation of plasma low-density-lipoprotein (LDL) subfractions: relative contribution of small, dense LDL to coronary heart disease risk. Atherosclerosis 1994;106:241–53.

37. Campos H, Roederer GO, Lussier-Cacan S, Davignon J, Krauss RM. Predominance of large LDL and reduced HDL2 cholesterol in normolipidemic men with coronary artery disease. Arterioscler Thromb Vasc Biol. 1995;15:1043–8.

38. Sherrard B, Simpson H, Cameron J, Wahi S, Jennings G, Dart A. LDL particle size in subjects with previously unsuspected coronary heart disease: relationship with other cardiovascular risk markers. Atherosclerosis. 1996 25;126:277–87.

39. Rajman I, Kendall MJ, Cramb R, Holder RL, Salih M, Gammage MD. Investigation of low-density-lipoprotein subfractions as a coronary risk factor in normotriglyceridemic men. Atherosclerosis. 1996;125:231–42.

40. Erbey JR, Robbins D, Forrest KY, Orchard TJ. Low-density-lipoprotein particle size and coronary artery disease in a childhood-onset type 1 diabetes population. Metabolism. 1999;48:531–4.

41. Gardner CD, Fortmann SP, Krauss RM. Association of small low-density-lipoprotein particles with the incidence of coronary artery disease in men and women. JAMA 1996;276:875–81.

42. Stampfer MJ, Krauss RM, Ma J, Blanche PJ, Holl LG, Sacks FM, Hennekens CH. A pro-

spective study of triglyceride level, low-density-lipoprotein particle diameter, and risk of myocardial infarction. JAMA 1996;276:882–8.

43. Lamarche B, Tchernof A, Moorjani S, Camtin B, Dagenais G, Lupien P, Despres J-P. Small, dense low-density-lipoprotein particles as a predictor of risk of ischemic heart disease in men: prospective results from the Quebec Cardiovascular Study. Circulation 1997;95:69–75.

44. Mykkanen L, Kuusisto J, Haffner SM, Laakso M, Austin MA. LDL size and risk of coronary heart disease in elderly men and women. Arterioscler Thromb Vasc Biol. 1999;19:2742–8.

45. Miller BD, Alderman EL, Haskell WL, Fair JM, Krauss RM. Predominance of dense low-density-lipoprotein particles predicts angiographic benefit of therapy in the Stanford Coronary Risk Intervention Project. Circulation 1996;94:2146–53.

46. Brown G, Albers JJ, Fisher LD, Schaefer SM, Lin JT, Kaplan C, Zhao XQ, Bisson BD, Fitzpatrick VF, Dodge HT. Regression of coronary artery disease as a result of intensive lipid-lowering therapy in men with high levels of apolipoprotein B. N Engl J Med 1990;323:1289–98.

47. Zambon A, Brown BG, Hokanson JE, Brunzell JD. Evidence for a new pathophysiological mechanism for coronary artery disease regression: hepatic lipase-mediated changes in LDL density. Circulation. 1999;99:1959–64.

48. de Graaf J, Hak-Lemmers H, Hectors M, Demacker P, Hendriks J, Stalenhof AFH. Enhanced susceptibility to in vitro oxidation of the dense low-density-lipoprotein subfraction in healthy subjects. Arterioscler Thromb 1991;11:298–306.

49. Chait A, Brazg R, Tribble D, Krauss R. Susceptibility of small, dense, low-density lipoproteins to oxidative modification in subjects with the atherogenic lipoprotein phenotype, pattern B. Am J Med 1993;94:350–6.

50. Tribble D, Holl L, Wood P,Krauss RM. Variations in oxidative susceptibility among six low-density-lipoprotein subfractions of differing density and particle size. Atherosclerosis 1992;93:189–99.

51. Dejager S, Bruckert E, Chapman J. Dense low-density-lipoprotein subspecies with diminished oxidative resistance predominate in combined hyperlipidemia. J Lipid Res 1993;34:295–308.

52. de Graaf J, Hendriks J, Demacker P, Stalenhoef A. Identification of multiple dense LDL subfractions with enhanced susceptibility to in vitro oxidation among hypertriglyceridemic subjects: normalization after clofibrate treatment. Arterioscler Thromb 1993;13:712–19.

53. Galeano NF, Milne R, Marcel YL, Walsh MT, Levy E, Ngu'yen TD, Gleeson A, Arad Y, Witte L, al Haideri M, et al. Apoprotein B structure and receptor recognition of triglyceride-rich low-density lipoprotein (LDL) is modified in small LDL but not in triglyceride-rich LDL of normal size. J Biol Chem 1994;269:511–9.

54. Anber V, Griffin BA, McConnell M, Packard CJ, Shepherd J. Influence of plasma lipid and LDL-subfraction profile on the interaction between low-density lipoprotein with human arterial wall proteoglycans. Atherosclerosis 1996;124:261–71.

55. Bjornheden T, Babyi A, Bondjers G, Wiklund O. Accumulation of lipoprotein fractions and subfractions in the arterial wall, determined in an in vitro perfusion system. Atherosclerosis 1996;123:43–56.

56. Jaakkola O, Solakivi T, Tertov V, Orekhov A, Miettinen T, Nikkari T. Characteristics of low-density-lipoprotein subfractions from patients with coronary artery disease. Coronary Artery Disease 1993;4:379–85.

57. Fujimoto W, Abbate S, Kahn S, Hokanson JE, Brunzell JD. The visceral adiposity syndrome in Japanese-American men. Obesity Research 1994;2:364–71.

58. Selby J, Austin M, Newman B, Mayer E, Krauss RM. LDL subclass phenotypes and the insulin resistance syndrome in women. Circulation 1993;88:381–7.

59. Howard BV, Mayer-Davis EJ, Goff D, Zaccaro DJ, Laws A, Robbins DC, Saad MF, Selby J, Hamman RF, Krauss RM, Haffner SM. Relationships between insulin resistance and lipoproteins in nondiabetic African Americans, Hispanics, and non-His-

panic whites: the Insulin Resistance Atherosclerosis Study. Metabolism 1998;47: 1174–9.

60. Ambrosch A, Muhlen I, Kopf D, Augustin W, Dierkes J, Konig W, Luley C, Lehnert H. LDL size distribution in relation to insulin sensitivity and lipoprotein pattern in young and healthy subjects. Diabetes Care. 1998;21:2077–84.

Lipoprotein(a): Structure, Measurement, and Clinical Significance

17

Santica M. Marcovina and Marlys L. Koschinsky

✧　In 1963, Kåre Berg observed that rabbits immunized with human low-density lipoproteins (LDL) produced an antiserum that reacted with an antigenic component that appeared to be present within the LDL fraction of some but not all of the individuals tested.[1] Berg called this newly discovered antigen lipoprotein(a) [Lp(a)], and he found that the presence of this antigen was genetically determined by an autosomal dominant mode of inheritance.[2] Subsequent studies provided evidence that Lp(a) is a specific family of lipoprotein particles whose protein moiety is comprised of at least two major proteins: a single copy of apolipoprotein B-100 (apo B) linked to a single copy of a protein of variable mass that has not been found in any other lipoprotein. This protein, which is responsible for the peculiar characteristics of Lp(a), is called apolipoprotein(a) [apo(a)].

Over the past several decades, numerous studies have established that increased Lp(a) concentrations are associated with increased risk of cardiovascular and cerebral vascular disease. Although the mechanism of Lp(a) atherogenicity or thrombogenicity has yet to be clarified, numerous structural, genetic, and metabolic studies have provided some intriguing possibilities to explain its association with atherosclerosis.

STRUCTURE OF LIPOPROTEIN(A)

Lp(a) is formed by joining a lipoprotein that is structurally very similar to LDL in protein and lipid composition to a carbohydrate-rich, highly hydrophilic protein named apo(a). Lp(a) particles contain apo(a) and apo B in a 1:1 apo(a)/apo B molar ratio.[3] In the Lp(a) particle, apo(a) is covalently linked to apo B by a single disulfide bridge;[4,5] the cysteine residues in each molecule that are involved in the disulfide linkage have been identified.[4–7] Non-covalent interactions, required for the initial association of the two proteins,[8–11] precedes specific disulfide bond formation. Recent studies have revealed that sequences in the amino-terminus of apo B are required for its non-covalent interaction with apo(a),[12] while covalent bond formation involves sequences within the C-terminal half of the apo B molecule.[6,7,13] This has been confirmed by scanning atomic force microscopy (SAFM) in which apo(a) appears to be linked to apo B at two distinct sites.[14] The majority of studies to date suggest that the associa-

345

tion of apo(a) and apoB-100 to form Lp(a) particles occurs extracellularly,[4,9,15–17] perhaps on the plasma membrane of hepatoctyes.[18]

Lp(a) has peculiar characteristics and, unlike the other human plasma lipoproteins, it cannot be classified on the basis of its physical-chemical properties as defined by the classical lipoprotein separation methods, such as density gradient ultracentrifugation and electrophoretic separation. In fact, in electrophoresis Lp(a) has a pre-beta mobility similar to very-low-density lipoproteins (VLDL),[19] and in ultracentrifugation its density spans both the LDL and high-density lipoprotein (HDL) range, with most of the Lp(a) found within the 1.050–1.100 kg/L density range.[20] However, Lp(a) can be detected in small amounts in all density intervals in the range of 1.000–1.210 kg/L,[21,22] and the concentration of Lp(a) appears to besignificantly increased in the triglyceride-rich < 1.006 kg/L density fraction after a fatty meal.[23,24]

Given that treatment of Lp(a) with reducing agents yields a lipoprotein particle that is essentially indistinguishable from LDL in its physical chemical properties, it is evident that the peculiar characteristics and the size and density heterogeneity of Lp(a) are almost entirely accounted for by the presence of its distinct protein component, apo(a). Apo(a) is a carbohydrate-rich protein that exhibits both intra- and inter-individual variations in size. The mean carbohydrate content has been estimated to be 28% by weight with a molar ratio of 3:7:5:4:7 for mannose, galactose, galactosamine, glucosamine, and sialic acid, respectively.[25] Although differences in apo(a) size are primarily related to differences in the length of the polypeptide chain,[26,27] a contribution of carbohydrate heterogeneity to the size heterogeneity cannot be excluded. The analysis of the apo(a) cDNA isolated from human liver libraries led to the discovery that apo(a) shares a high degree of homology with the serine protease zymogen plasminogen.[28] Plasminogen contains a protease domain and one copy each of five domains called kringles, designated as kringle 1 through kringle 5. A kringle is a highly conserved, tri-loop polypeptide structure stabilized by three disulfide bridges also found in other proteins involved in hemostasis and fibrinolysis.[29,30] The tri-loop structure is similar in shape to the Danish pastry called a kringle, from which its name derives.

The basic structure of apo(a) is graphically represented in Figure 17–1. Apo(a) contains a kringle domain and a carboxyl-terminal protease domain with 85% amino acid identity with the plasminogen protease domain. Despite the high degree of sequence conservation between the apo(a) and plasminogen protease domain, there is no proteolytic activity associated with apo(a) due to critical amino acid substitutions within this domain.[31] The kringle domain is composed of 11 distinct kringle types, ten of which are similar but not identical to each other and to plasminogen kringle 4, and one that shares over 85% amino acid identity with plasminogen kringle 5. The ten plasminogen kringle 4-like domains are identified as kringle 4 (K4) type 1 through type 10, and their sequence identity with plasminogen K4 ranges between 78% and 88%.[28,32,33] Apo(a) K4 type 1 and types 3 through 10 appear to have only one copy present per apo(a) molecule, while K4 type 2 is present in multiple repeats varying in number from as few as 3 to as many as 40.[34,35] The number of K4 type 2 repeats is therefore responsible for the size heterogeneity of apo(a) and ultimately of Lp(a) and for the different apo(a) isoforms.

Based on the cloned sequence,[28] the molecular mass of apo(a) protein varies from 187 kDa for an apo(a) that contains 12 K4 domains, to 662 kDa for an apo(a) that

Figure 17–1 ✧ Schematic Representation of the Lp(a) Particle. Lp(a) Is Distinguishable from LDL by the Presence of Apo(a), Which Is Covalently Linked to the ApoB Component of the LDL-like Moiety by a Single Disulfide Bond. The Structure of Apo(a) is Characterized by the Presence of Multiply-repeated Copies of Kringle Motifs that Resemble Plasminogen Kringle 4 (K4), Followed by a Single Copy of the Plasminogen Kringle 5-like (K5) and Protease-like Domains (PD)

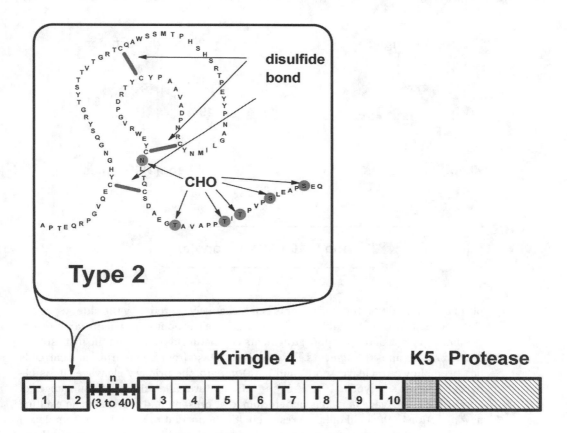

contains 50 K4 domains. Therefore, the weight ratio of apo(a) to apo B varies significantly in Lp(a) particles. For example, Lp(a) particles with 20 apo(a) K4 domains have about 64% of their protein mass as apo B and 36% as apo(a). In contrast, large Lp(a) particles containing 40 apo(a) K4 domains contain approximately an equal proportion of apo(a) and apo B protein (see Figure 17–2).

Fragments of apo(a) ranging in size from 85–215 kDa that correspond to apo(a) K4 types 1 and 2 have been detected immunochemically in concentrated human urine, and lack sequences downstream of the apo(a) K4 type 4 sequence;[36] it was subsequently demonstrated that apo(a) urine fragments are not derived from intact

Figure 17–2 ✧ Schematic Representation of the Relative Proportion of Apo(a) and Apo B in Lp(a) of Different Sizes

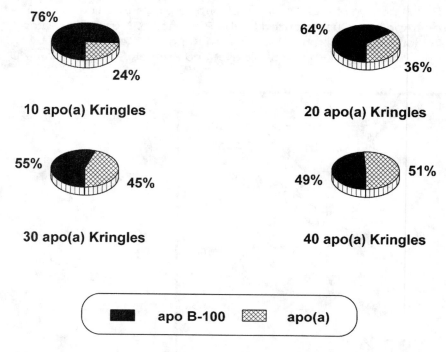

plasma Lp(a) and that these fragments can be actively secreted by the kidney.[36] It has also been shown that both full-length apo(a), as well as apo(a) fragments, are present in human plasma, and that apo(a) fragments circulating in plasma are the main source of the urinary apo(a) fragments.[37] Recently, elastase from polymorphonuclear cells has been shown to cleave apo(a) and Lp(a) *in vitro*; the primary cleavage site is between apo(a) K4 types 4 and 5.[38,39] The nature and clinical significance of apo(a)/Lp(a) cleavage *in vivo* is undetermined at present, and represents an exciting new direction in the field of Lp(a) research. It is important to note that uncomplexed apo(a) as well as apo(a) fragments have been identified in arterial lesions;[40,41] the fragments may correspond to cleavage products of Lp(a) generated by elastase-like enzymes present at the sites of local inflammation. This in turn may indicate a link between Lp(a) function and the inflammatory state.[42] The potential role of apo(a)/Lp(a) fragments in angiogenesis has been suggested owing to the similarity of these apo(a) fragments to proteolytic fragments of plasminogen that have been implicated in the inhibition of the process of angiogenesis.[43]

THE APO(a)-PLASMINOGEN GENE FAMILY

The apo(a) gene can be considered one of the most polymorphic transcribed genes in the human genome. The apo(a) gene can be divided into four main regions: the sequence coding for the signal peptide, the plasminogen-like K4 domain coding sequence containing several tandem repeats of a 5.5 Kb sequence encoding a cysteine-rich motif, the plasminogen-like K5 domain coding sequence, and the plasminogen-like protease domain coding sequence.[28] The apo(a) gene resides on chromosome 6q 26–27 in linkage with the plasminogen gene.[44] The proximity of the two genes and their remarkable sequence homology suggest a common origin, either from duplication of the plasminogen gene or from a common ancestral precursor. Other members of the apo(a)-plasminogen gene family have also been characterized;[45–47] to date, the family includes at least seven closely related genes and/or pseudogenes that have likely arisen by gene duplication and exon shuffling of the ancestral plasminogen gene.

GENETIC DETERMINANTS OF LIPOPROTEIN(a) LEVELS

Early family studies using diffusion in agarose gels indicated that the presence of Lp(a) segregated in a Mendelian autosomal-dominant fashion that was determined by two alleles: Lp(a$^+$) and Lp(a^0), or null, allele.[2] At that time, Lp(a) was found in only 30–40% of the subjects studied in different populations.[2] Numerous studies in which quantitative immunochemical methods have been used to measure Lp(a) have firmly established that Lp(a) concentrations, which range from <0.1 mg/dL to > 100 mg/dL, are strongly influenced by genetic factors.[48–50]

Discovery of genetic size polymorphism of apo(a) by Utermann and colleagues provided new insights into the genetic control of Lp(a). Apo(a) isoforms were determined by the mobility of apo(a) in sodium dodecylsulphate polyacrylamide gel electrophoresis (SDS-PAGE) under reducing conditions. Six different apo(a) isoforms were initially identified: F, B, S1, S2, S3, and S4.[51] The apo(a) isoforms are specified by alleles at a single apo(a) locus. These studies indicated that apo(a) isoforms are specified at a single locus by multiple autosomal alleles co-dominantly expressed. Additionally, it was shown that the size of the apo(a) isoforms were, in general, inversely correlated with the Lp(a) plasma concentrations. This inverse correlation may be attributable at least in part to less efficient secretion of larger apo(a) isoforms from hepatocytes.[52]

Gaubatz et al.[53] resolved 11 different apo(a) isoforms using PAGE combined with a sensitive detection system. Kamboh et al.,[54] using an improved separation technique, were able to distinguish as many as 23 apo(a) isoforms by SDS agarose gel electrophoresis followed by immunoblotting. Marcovina et al.[55] developed a modification of the Kamboh et al. procedure, using agarose gel electrophoresis followed by immunoblotting with ^{125}I-labeled monoclonal antibody and autoradiography. This approach allowed the identification of 34 apo(a) isoforms in a biracial population and is entirely consistent with the observations of Lackner et al.,[34] in which a total of 34 apo(a) alleles could be distinguished.

By using pulsed-field gel electrophoresis and genomic blotting,[56] it was determined that 94% of Whites are heterozygous at the apo(a) locus.[57] Examination of Lp(a) concentrations and apo(a) genotypes in 48 nuclear White families indicates that the apo(a) gene accounts for greater than 90% of the variation in plasma Lp(a) concentrations.[57] The number of K4 repeats in the apo(a) gene accounted for about 70%

of the Lp(a) variation, and the other factors at the apo(a) locus accounted for about 20% of the inter-individual variation in plasma Lp(a) concentrations. Interestingly, however, the extent to which variation in the size of the apo(a) gene accounts for the variability in plasma Lp(a) levels varies greatly among different ethnic populations.[58–60] The apo(a) gene is also the major determinant of plasma Lp(a) levels in the Black American population,[61] but has been reported to account for only half of the genetic variance in Africans.[62] In this population, unlike Whites, genetic factors other than the apo(a) locus itself, as well as non-genetic factors may contribute to the determination of Lp(a) levels.

A null allele(s) has been postulated to account for the absence of detectable apo(a) in individuals.[63] It has subsequently been shown that such "operational" null alleles can be associated with either the absence or presence of a transcript. A transcript positive null allele in which a splice mutation in the protease domain results in lack of secretion of the corresponding apo(a) isoform has recently been identified in baboons.[64] Although the molecular basis of operational null alleles in the human population is largely unknown, a recent study has identified a mutation that accounts for approximately 25% of the null alleles in the White population.[65] This mutation corresponds to a single base change that results in alternative splicing of the intron in apo(a) K4 type 8, and the insertion of a premature stop codon immediately following the apo(a) K4 type 8 sequence. The corresponding truncated apo(a) species appears to be secreted, but cannot be covalently linked to apo B to form Lp(a) particles and is likely rapidly degraded.[65]

Sequence variations in the coding and non-coding regions of the apo(a) gene have been reported to contribute to variations in plasma Lp(a) levels.[66–70] For example, a recently identified repeat polymorphism of the pentanucleotide sequence TTTTA present at –1371 upstream of the translational start site in the apo(a) gene may account for 10%–14% of the inter-individual variations in Lp(a) levels in Whites.[66] It has been shown that the number of pentanucleotide repeats (PNR), 6–11, correlate inversely with plasma Lp(a) levels in Whites; this correlation was not observed in Black African subjects. Whether or not the effect of the PNR polymorphism depends on the number of K4 repeats in apo(a) remains unclear at present, and the direct role of this sequence in determining Lp(a) levels remains to be addressed. In addition to the TTTTA polymorphism, a +93 C/T substitution has been reported that decreases apo(a) translation efficiency *in vitro*,[71] and affects Lp(a) plasma concentrations in the African but not White population.[72] Most recently, an apo(a) gene enhancer element has been identified in the intergenic region between the apo(a) and plasminogen genes[73]; the contribution of this element to plasma Lp(a) levels remains to be determined.

There have been several reports of the effects of other genes on plasma Lp(a) levels. Although mutations in the LDL receptor gene have been reported to elevate Lp(a) levels,[74,75] this is contradicted by a number of other studies that suggest no role for this receptor in Lp(a) catabolism (reviewed in ref. 76). Similarly, although an association between apo E isoform type and plasma Lp(a) levels has been suggested, the results of independent studies addressing this relationship are conflicting (reviewed in ref. 77). The role of apo B-100 in determining plasma Lp(a) levels was initially suggested by studies in which patients heterozygous for genetic defects in apo B-100 synthesis had lower Lp(a) levels than their unaffected relatives.[78] However, it has recently been reported that low LDL levels present in patients with hypobetalipoproteinemia had no effect on corresponding Lp(a) levels.[79]

NON-GENETIC DETERMINANTS OF LIPOPROTEIN(a) LEVELS

While it is generally accepted that moderate exercise does not modulate plasma Lp(a) levels,[80] there are several reports that diet may modulate plasma Lp(a) concentrations (reviewed in ref. 81). It appears that diets high in trans-fatty acids may raise Lp(a) levels,[82,83] while diets high in n-3 polyunsaturates may lower Lp(a) levels.[84] This is reinforced by the results of the Lugalawa study in which Lp(a) levels were found to vary in two racially homogenous Bantu populations that differed in their dietary habits. When subjects from the two groups were matched for apo(a) isoform type, the median Lp(a) level was found to be 40% lower in Bantus on fish diets rich in n-3 polyunsaturates than in Bantus on a vegetarian diet.[85]

There is evidence that hormones can modulate plasma Lp(a) concentrations. For example, thyroid hormone appears to affect Lp(a) levels, with lower values observed in patients with hyperthyroidism.[86,87] Growth hormone has been shown to significantly increase plasma Lp(a) levels.[88,89] A decrease in Lp(a) concentrations in women on hormone replacement therapy has been reported in a number of studies, with the majority of studies indicating that estrogen and progestin combination therapy is not more effective in lowering Lp(a) levels than estrogen alone (reviewed in ref. 90). The PEPI (postmenopausal estrogen/progestin intervention) study, the largest randomized placebo-controlled study to date, has been performed to determine the long-term effect of hormone replacement therapy on Lp(a) concentrations.[91] The results of this study indicate that hormone replacement therapy produced a 17%–23% reduction in Lp(a) levels after one year, which was maintained over the three-year follow-up period. There were no significant differences observed among the different treatment regimens utilized in this study (estrogen, continuous or cyclical progestin, or combination therapy).

MEASUREMENT OF LIPOPROTEIN(a)

The high size heterogeneity of apo(a), the distinct protein component of Lp(a), its association with apo B to form a single macromolecular complex, and the amino acid sequence homology with plasminogen constitute major challenges to the development of suitable immunoassays for the quantitative measurement of Lp(a) in human plasma. To obtain purified apo(a), reducing agents are used to dissociate apo(a) from apo B. However, the use of reducing agents markedly decreases apo(a) immunoreactivity, probably due to the cleavage of the intrachain disulfide bonds of the kringle domains.[92] The fact that the structure of isolated apo(a) is immunochemically different from apo(a) in Lp(a) has been further demonstrated by the observation that monoclonal antibodies raised against purified apo(a) have limited reactivity with native Lp(a).[93] Therefore, antibodies against apo(a) are generated by immunizing animals with intact Lp(a). If the generated antibodies are polyclonal, they need to be absorbed against apo B. Additionally, their immunoreactivity should also be tested against plasminogen in the assay format in which the antibodies are intended to be used, and, if cross-reactivity is detected, the antibodies should be absorbed against plasminogen. Similarly, when monoclonal antibodies against apo(a) are produced, they should be selected to react to epitopes present only in apo(a), so as to prevent cross-reactivity with plasminogen.

A major problem in the generation of antibodies for measuring apo(a) derives from the size heterogeneity of apo(a), which is due to the variable number of K4 type 2 repeats present in the various apo(a) polymorphs.[34,35] In fact, repeated antigenic determinants are present in variable numbers in different apo(a) particles, and therefore the immunoreactivity of the antibodies directed to these repeated epitopes will vary depending on the size of apo(a). As a consequence, it is expected that immunoassays using polyclonal antibodies or monoclonal antibodies directed to epitopes present in K4 type 2 will tend to underestimate apo(a) concentration in subjects with apo(a) of a smaller size than the apo(a) present in the assay calibrator, and to overestimate the apo(a) concentration of the larger apo(a) particles.

The problem of variable immunoreactivity of the antibodies can be solved by selecting monoclonal antibodies directed to apo(a) antigenic determinants not expressed in K4 type 2. One of the potential drawbacks of monoclonal antibodies is that their use limits the choice of the assay format mainly to enzyme-linked immunosorbent assay or radioimmunoassay. However, the coupling of high-affinity monoclonal antibodies to latex particles can make the monoclonal antibodies well suited for assays based on immunoprecipitation in liquid-phase. A monoclonal antibody-based turbidimetric assay for the measurement of Lp(a), potentially insensitive to apo(a) size, has been recently introduced in the United States. Oxidative modification of Lp(a) may produce significant changes in Lp(a) conformation,[94] and the same may occur with carbohydrate removal. The immunoreactivity of some of the monoclonal antibodies produced in our laboratory was differentially affected by carbohydrate removal and Lp(a) oxidation. The removal of sialic acid, for example, resulted in total loss of immunoreactivity for one monoclonal antibody, while the immunoreactivity of other antibodies was significantly higher (unpublished observations). Therefore, to avoid technical artifacts and lack of comparability of values, the monoclonal antibodies to be used in Lp(a) immunoassays should be selected after a careful characterization of their epitope specificity and immunochemical properties.

Specific recommendations for selecting and characterizing monoclonal antibodies for measuring apo AI and B are contained in a document of the International Federation of Clinical Chemistry.[95] Most of the recommendations made in this document are also applicable to monoclonal antibodies to apo(a).

A second approach to solve the effect of the size heterogeneity of apo(a) on the antibody immunoreactivity has been proposed by several investigators.[96–100] This approach involves the use of a sandwich-type ELISA in which the Lp(a) particles in plasma are captured by monoclonal or polyclonal antibodies against apo(a), and then Lp(a) concentration is measured by enzyme-conjugated monoclonal or polyclonal antibodies against the apo B component of Lp(a). It should be noted that even though the immunoreactivity of apo B in Lp(a) has been found to be only modestly lower than that in LDL,[101] studies performed with monoclonal antibodies clearly indicate that the epitope expression of apo B in Lp(a) is different from that in LDL.[102,103] Therefore, the anti-apo B antibodies to be used in Lp(a) assays, particularly monoclonal antibodies generated against LDL–apo B, should be carefully characterized.

Conceptually, it is true that Lp(a) assays using anti-apo B antibodies or anti-apo(a) monoclonal antibodies directed to epitopes present in apo(a) domains other than K4 type 2 are not affected by variation in Lp(a) size. However, the results of Lp(a) concentration in different samples will depend on the isoforms in the assay calibrator. In the immunoassays, the concentration of an analyte is obtained by comparing the immunoreactivity of the samples with that of the calibrator, which contains a known concentration of the analyte. Therefore, the composition of the assay calibrator should be very similar to that of the samples being analyzed. Considering the high heterogeneity of apo(a) size, this requirement is impossible to attain; therefore, the composition of the calibrator in the immunoassays is an arbitrary choice that will influence the values obtained in the samples.

Following the approach of Albers et al.,[104] the values assigned to Lp(a) assay calibrators, and consequently Lp(a) concentrations in the measured samples, historically have been expressed in terms of total lipoprotein mass. However, obtaining an accurate determination of Lp(a) particle mass is difficult in that it requires the summation of the independent determination of Lp(a) protein, lipid, and carbohydrate components.

Because Lp(a) is a heterogeneous complex of two proteins, the total protein mass is determined in the primary standard, usually by the Lowry method or, more accurately by amino acid analysis. However, considering the size heterogeneity of apo(a), the ratio of apo(a) to apo B in Lp(a) particles is highly variable, as illustrated in Figure 17–2. Therefore, it is evident that, independent of whether the values are expressed in terms of lipoprotein or protein mass, the ratio of apo(a) to apo B in the calibrator will affect the results for the samples. This concept is illustrated by the following example:

Lp(a) analyses are performed by the same ELISA, using an anti-apo-B antibody enzyme-conjugate for detection; calibration is performed using two different Lp(a) preparations; and total protein mass is determined by the Lowry method. The first preparation is an Lp(a) in which apo B is 70% of the total protein mass, and the second preparation is an Lp(a) in which apo B is 50% of the total protein mass. Considering the higher proportion of apo B in the first preparation, it is evident that the anti-apo-B antibodies will have a higher reactivity than with the second preparation. As a consequence, the same samples will have lower Lp(a) values in the assay calibrated with the first standard than those obtained by the assay calibrated with the second standard. Therefore, it is misleading to state that Lp(a) concentration may be accurately quantified regardless of the apo(a) isoforms with values expressed in terms of Lp(a) mass.[99] The only potentially accurate measurements, independent of apo(a) size polymorphism, are those obtained by methods using monoclonal antibodies specific to epitopes that are not present in K4 type 2, or antibodies to apo B using calibrators with value assigned in terms of nmol/L.

To quantify the influence of apo(a) size polymorphism on the accuracy of Lp(a) values, we produced, selected, and extensively characterized several monoclonal antibodies for their immunochemical properties and apo(a) domain specificity.[105] We developed and optimized three sandwich ELISA systems using monoclonal antibodies (MAb) or polyclonal antibodies (PAb) with different specificities as detection antibodies: MAb a-5, specific for apo(a) K4 types 1 and 2, MAb a-40, specific for apo(a) K4 type 9, and a PAb specific for apo B-100. The measurements were performed on microtiter plates coated with MAb a-6, specific to K4 type 2, to capture the Lp(a) particles. The assays were calibrated with the same serum containing apo(a) with 21 K4 domains and with an Lp(a) value assigned in nmol/L. Using all three ELISAs, we measured Lp(a) in a group of 723 subjects selected to have a single apo(a) isoform, as determined by a high-resolution phenotyping system.[55] Essentially identical results were obtained by the two methods that measured Lp(a) by using either a polyclonal antibody against apo B or the monoclonal antibody against K4 type 9, which is present only once per apo(a) particle. In contrast, the ELISA using MAb a-5, specific for apo(a) K4 type 2 repeats, overestimated Lp(a) concentration in samples containing apo(a) with more than 21 K4 repeats and underestimated Lp(a) samples containing apo(a) with fewer than 21 K4 repeats. The results of this study clearly demonstrate that antibody specificity and apo(a) size heterogeneity can significantly affect Lp(a) measurements.

Despite all of the above-mentioned problems, numerous immunochemical methods for the measurement of Lp(a) in a wide variety of formats, some of which are commercially available, have been reported.[106,107] Albers et al. were the first to report the development of a radial immunodiffusion (RID) and subsequently of a radio-immunoassay (RIA) for the measurement of Lp(a).[104, 108] Other assay formats include electroimmunodiffusion,[109,110] ELISA,[96–99,111–113] latex immunoassay,[114] immunonephelometric assay,[115] immunoturbidimetric assay,[116] and fluorescence assay.[100]

We have compared Lp(a) values obtained by two direct binding ELISA methods developed in our laboratory and seven commercially available methods, all calibrated with the same fresh-frozen serum with an intermediate-size apo(a) isoform.[117] Despite the significant differences in antibody source and in assay format, a common calibrator was able to decrease the differences in Lp(a) values obtained by the different methods. The results of two international surveys of Lp(a) measurements indicated that the lack of a common primary standard and poor assay precision were the main factors responsible for the high inter-laboratory variation observed in the surveys.[118]

A potential approach to bypass the problems of the immunochemical determination of Lp(a) could be to quantify Lp(a) by its cholesterol content. To this end, two methods were recently reported. In one method, cholesterol is enzymatically measured by a continuous flow analyzer in lipoprotein classes separated by single-spin vertical rotor ultracentrifugation.[119] The second reported method is based on the use of lectin affinity to separate Lp(a) from other lipoproteins with measurement of Lp(a) cholesterol by enzymatic assay.[120] Both of these methods could be used for screening subjects who have high Lp(a) concentrations. However, further studies are required to compare the clinical significance of Lp(a) cholesterol with that of Lp(a) mass or Lp(a) particle number.

We previously evaluated[106] the problems that must be addressed in order to standardize Lp(a) measurement. The major points that need to be considered can be summarized as follows:

1. Careful selection and characterization of the antibodies, optimization of the assay format; and demonstration that apo(a) size heterogeneity does not affect the accuracy of the results.

2.　Selection of the apo(a) polymorph in the primary standard, reference material, and assay calibrators.

3.　Development of a common, validated method for isolation of Lp(a) to be used as primary standard.

4.　Development of suitable reference material.

5.　Expression of apo(a) values.

6.　Development of a reference method.

Considering the major impact that the lack of comparability of data may have on the clinical interpretation of Lp(a) values, the NIH/NHLBI has recently awarded a four-year contract to our laboratory for the standardization of Lp(a) analytical methods. As recently reported,[121] the IFCC Working Group on Lp(a), whose aim was to make available a suitable secondary reference material for Lp(a), has extensively evaluated and characterized several candidate reference materials. The best performance was obtained by a preparation in lyophilized form that has been designated as IFCC proposed reference material for Lp(a) (IFCC-PRM).[121] As part of the NIH/NHLBI contract, we have actively collaborated with the IFCC Working Group by assigning an accuracy-based Lp(a) value to the IFCC-PRM. Our monoclonal antibody-based ELISA insensitive to apo(a) size polymorphism[76] and calibrated with a purified Lp(a) preparation was used as reference method for the value assignment. Based on 144 replicate analyses, a target value of 107 nmol/L was assigned to the IFCC-PRM. The assignment of a target value to the IFCC-PRM in nmol/L is an important step toward a scientifically sound approach in reporting Lp(a) data. To evaluate to what extent the use of a common reference material would contribute to comparability of Lp(a) values, we sent the IFCC-PRM, three quality control samples and 30 individual samples, encompassing a broad range of Lp(a) values and apo(a) isoforms, to 15 manufacturers and six research laboratories. A detailed protocol and report forms were also provided. Among the methods evaluated, two exhibited a very high correlation with our reference method (r=0.999 and 0.995, respectively) with minimum bias between the obtained and the assigned value related to apo(a) size. In contrast, a highly significant apo(a) size-dependent bias for the 30 samples was observed in most systems. The among-method CV for each of the 30 samples ranged from 6% to 31%, while the among-system CV for the IFCC-PRM was only 3%. The high comparability of values obtained with two of the methods and the very low among-method CV for the reference material seem to clearly indicate the suitability of the IFCC-PRM for use as secondary reference material for Lp(a). However, as noted previously and confirmed by this study, the availability of a common reference preparation can only reduce the variability due to the calibration component of the different assays. The major problem in the lack of comparability of Lp(a) values is represented by the overestimation or underestimation of Lp(a) values due to apo(a) size polymorphism. Even methods that are affected by apo(a) size do not produce comparable results, because each method has a different degree of apo(a) size dependency. We are now further evaluating and standardizing those methods that do not appear to be affected by apo(a) size polymorphism. Manufacturers of Lp(a) test kits should include standardization as one of their primary design goals by making available to clinical chemistry laboratories Lp(a) assays documented to be unaffected by apo(a) size polymorphism. As part of the NIH/NHLBI-supported activity, we are available to closely work with manufacturers or laboratories that want to develop accurate Lp(a) methods. The availability of the IFCC reference material for such assays would greatly contribute to the comparability of Lp(a) values.

POPULATION STUDIES

As we have discussed, Lp(a) concentrations in the White population are almost entirely genetically determined, and variation at the apo(a) locus contributes significantly to this heritability.[57,122] Numerous studies[58–60,123–130] also reported that Lp(a) values vary greatly between ethnic groups, and that this variability cannot be entirely explained by differences in apo(a) isoform size. The frequency distribution of Lp(a) in Whites is highly skewed toward the low concentrations. In contrast, in the Black population the distribution is almost Gaussian, and the median Lp(a) value in Blacks is nearly three times as high as in Whites.[130] In both Black and White infants, Lp(a) concentrations are lower at birth and rise to adult concentrations by the age of two.[131] A more recent study performed consecutively in a series of 1032 babies reported longitudinal changes in Lp(a) concentrations during the first year of life.[132] Lp(a) concentrations measured during the first postnatal week predicted the concentrations at 8.5 months, at which time Lp(a) concentrations were of the same order of magnitude as those of the parents.

After the initial rise in early childhood, Lp(a) concentrations were reported to be stable throughout adulthood, with no significant gender-related differences.[104,124] However, results from four major population-based studies do not entirely confirm these findings.

In the CARDIA study,[130] Lp(a) concentrations were determined in a group of 4165 young adults comprising approximately the same number of Blacks and Whites and men and women. In this study, no gender-related difference in Lp(a) concentrations was found among Whites. Among Blacks, a small but statistically significant ($p < .05$) difference was found, with concentrations of Lp(a) higher in women than in men. In the PROCAM study,[133] Lp(a) concentrations were measured in 1865 White males (age 20–64 years) and 819 females (age 20–59 years). The gender-related mean values were not significantly different. However, in men, Lp(a) concentrations remained constant with age, while Lp(a) concentrations in postmenopausal women were 2.1 mg/dL higher. The same observation was made in the ARIC study,[129] in which Lp(a) concentrations were determined in a large cohort of Black and White subjects. Premenopausal women from both races had lower Lp(a) concentrations than postmenopausal women. Additionally, it was found that both Black and White postmenopausal women on hormone replacement therapy had lower Lp(a) concentrations than women not on hormone therapy.[134]

Among 1284 White men and 1394 White women participating in the Framingham Offspring Study,[135] no gender-related differences in Lp(a) values were found. Although Lp(a) concentrations were 8% higher in postmenopausal women than in premenopausal women, this difference was not statistically significant. Furthermore, there was no significant difference in Lp(a) concentration between postmenopausal women on estrogen therapy and those not taking estrogen. The findings of this study contradict previous reports[90,91] and are rather surprising in view of the fact that hormone replacement therapy has been shown to lower plasma Lp(a) levels in a number of independent studies.

Data from all the population-based studies indicate that Lp(a) concentrations are race-related, with Blacks having the most striking difference compared to other races, both in terms of Lp(a) values and distribution. In this regard, it has recently been demonstrated that the Black American population has an increased frequency of intermediately-sized alleles, whereas Whites have a higher frequency of both small and large alleles;[136] the major determinant of increased Lp(a) levels in the Black population was found to be attributable to a four- to fivefold increase in the Lp(a) levels associated with intermediate apo(a) isoform sizes relative to Whites.[136] It is also likely that differences in Lp(a) concentration may be observed among ethnic groups within the same race. Therefore, population-based reference values, as well as the concentration at which Lp(a) is considered to be a risk factor, should be established for each ethnic group.

THROMBOTIC AND ATHEROGENIC ACTIVITIES OF LIPOPROTEIN(a)

Components of Lp(a) resemble both LDL and plasminogen, suggesting that Lp(a) may represent a bridge between the fields of atherosclerosis and thrombosis.[137] It is well-documented that Lp(a) is present in the arterial wall at the sites of atherosclerotic lesions,[40,41,138–142] and that Lp(a) accumulates at these sites to an extent that is proportional to plasma Lp(a) concentration.[139,140] A recent study found that Lp(a) is ubiquitous in coronary atheroma specimens and is detectable in larger amounts in the tissue from culprit lesions in patients with unstable angina compared to tissue from patients with stable angina.[143] Additionally, correlations were observed between plasma Lp(a) concentration and both the amount and location of plaque macrophages, as well as between plaque α-actin (a marker for smooth muscle cells) and the area of Lp(a) deposition.[143] The association of Lp(a) with the extent of infiltration of arterial wall macrophages is in keeping with a previous report that apo(a)/Lp(a) induces monocyte chemotactic activity in cultured endothelial cells.[144]

With respect to its direct effect on fibrinolytic parameters, Lp(a) has been shown to regulate the expression of plasminogen activator inhibitor-1 (PAI-1) in endothelial cells, which in turn inhibits the generation of plasmin by complexing and inactivating tissue-type plasminogen activator (tPA).[145] Another study reported that Lp(a) can inhibit the production and/or secretion of tPA from human endothelial cells,[146] which may also lead to impaired plasminogen activation and inhibition of fibrinolysis. A number of studies have suggested that Lp(a) may inhibit fibrinolysis by competing with plasminogen for binding to fibrin[147–149] and to cell surfaces,[150–152] thereby interfering with plasminogen activation on these surfaces. A very recent study has shown that apo(a) may interfere with plasminogen activation by complexing with plasminogen in solution; this complex binds poorly to the fibrin surface, which may inhibit plasmin formation on this surface *in vivo*.[153] There have been conflicting reports on the effect of Lp(a) on the lysis of fibrin clots. Although studies have reported that apo(a)/Lp(a) interferes with the lysis of fibrin clots *in vitro*,[154] as well as the lysis of fibrin clots introduced into mice over-expressing apo(a) from a transgene[155] and the lysis of clots containing human recombinant apo(a) in a rabbit vein fibrinolysis model,[156] other studies have reported either no effect of Lp(a) on this process,[157] or a stimulatory effect on clot lysis.[158] These discrepancies may be attributable to differences in experimental methodologies and/or the source of Lp(a)/apo(a) used for these studies. Harpel et al.[159,160] have shown that sulfhydryl compounds such as homocysteine, known to be associated with atherosclerosis and thromboembolic disease, and glutathione increase the affinity of Lp(a) for fibrin. They further propose that following vascular injury, partial plasmin degradation of the thrombus formed at the vessel wall produces a substrate that binds Lp(a) with a higher affinity than intact fibrin.[117] Increased concentrations of homocysteine and glutathione leaking from red cells and platelets in the thrombus increase the affinity of Lp(a) for fibrin. During the repair process, the Lp(a)-fibrin complex is incorporated into the vessel intima, contributing to the formation of an atheromatous plaque. A recent study has shown that apo(a)/Lp(a) potentiates *in vitro* responses of platelets to the thrombin-receptor agonist peptide SFLLRN, which may also contribute to the thromboembolic complications of Lp(a) *in vivo*.[161] Clearly, further studies are required to evaluate the prothrombotic/antifibrinolytic role of Lp(a) in atherogenesis.

In terms of its contribution to lesion growth, Lp(a) may promote the growth of plaques by inhibiting plasmin-dependent activation of transforming growth factor beta (TGF-β), thereby promoting proliferation of smooth muscle cells[162–164]; the role of Lp(a) in plaque growth is also suggested by the co-localization of apo(a) with plaque α-actin in atheromatous lesions.[143] It has also been suggested that formation of an insoluble complex of Lp(a) with calcium in atherosclerotic lesions may contribute to plaque growth.[165] Preliminary studies suggest that the formation of *in vitro* apo(a)- elastin complexes is potentiated by calcium (co-author's unpublished data), which contributes to the retention of Lp(a) in the intima. The incorporation of Lp(a)-derived cholesterol into plaque has also been documented.[166] Additionally, the ability of native Lp(a) to be a ligand for cholesteryl-ester-loaded macrophages has been described.[167] Thus, Lp(a) is thought to contribute to the continuous growth of the lesion as well as the acute thrombotic event that occurs after a plaque ruptures perhaps by inhibiting the activation of plasminogen by tPA. It is still possible, however, that localization of apo(a)/Lp(a) in plaque may represent a secondary phenomenon, and that Lp(a) is not causally related to lesion development. The latter hypothesis is supported by recent studies (see below) in which elevated Lp(a) levels were no longer atherogenic if LDL levels were substantially reduced, suggesting that Lp(a) may not be a primary causative agent in atherogenesis. Additionally, the results of a recent study indicate that elevated Lp(a) levels do not confer risk by contributing to the early functional or structural changes of atherosclerosis such as endothelial function, smooth muscle responses, or carotid wall thickness.[168] Scanu has suggested that the action of Lp(a) at the cell surface may be related to focal events rather than plasma concentrations of the lipoprotein;[169] this may also explain why Lp(a) levels are not generally correlated with fibrinolytic parameters such as α2-antiplasmin/plasmin complexes[170] or fibrin degradation products such as D-dimer.[171]

Results from these and other studies have prompted investigators to examine the relationship of Lp(a) concentration in plasma and the success of thrombolytic therapy. Five studies have shown that baseline Lp(a) concentrations do not affect the outcome of thrombolytic therapy.[172–176] Reports of Lp(a) concentrations during thrombolytic therapy are contradictory. Qiu et al. reported no effect of streptokinase or single-chain form tPA therapy on plasma Lp(a) concentrations in unstable angina,[174] while Hegele et al. reported acute reduction of Lp(a) concentrations by the two-chain form of tPA.[177] Comparison of these studies is difficult because one study sampled Lp(a) concentrations 6 h after therapy while the other sampled after 12 h, and different forms of tPA were used. Di Lorenzo et al. reported acute lowering of Lp(a) concentrations by heparin in patients undergoing percutaneous transluminal coronary angioplasty (PTCA),[178] but Hegele et al. observed that heparin alone had no effect.[177] All of these studies were done with small numbers of patients and must be repeated with sample sizes adequate to represent the different isoforms of apo(a). This may be important in light of several reports that suggest that smaller apo(a) isoforms bind more avidly to fibrin *in vitro*.[179,180]

CLINICAL SIGNIFICANCE OF LIPOPROTEIN(a)

Lp(a) Concentrations and Coronary Heart Disease: Perspective

In the early 1970s, several studies reported the association between coronary heart disease (CHD) and a plasma lipoprotein that was detected by electrophoresis and named pre-beta-1 lipoprotein because of its mobility relative to LDL in gels.[181–183] Subsequent studies demonstrated that pre-beta-1 was Lp(a) and confirmed its association with CHD.[184–186] In 1977, Albers et al. were the first to report the association between high concentrations of Lp(a), determined by an immunochemical method, and CHD.[108] The distribution of Lp(a) was measured in 90 myocardial infarction (MI) survivors and in their healthy spouses, and was found to be shifted to higher concentrations in MI survivors than in the spouse controls. In another study of MI survivors performed in 1981, Kostner et al. found that the relative risk for MI in subjects with Lp(a) concentrations > 30 mg/dL, expressed in terms of total Lp(a) mass, were 1.75-fold higher than in subjects with Lp(a) concentrations < 30 mg/dL.[187]

More recently, Dahlen and coworkers studied 307 patients who underwent coronary angiography and reported that the coronary lesion score significantly correlated with Lp(a) values; multivariate analysis demonstrated that high Lp(a) concentrations were associated significantly and independently with CHD.[188] In a study aimed at evaluating Lp(a) in the context of other risk factors, Armstrong et al. found that Lp(a) was an even stronger predictor of CHD if other risk factors were also present.[189]

Interest in Lp(a) increased with the discovery that apo(a) has a high homology with plasminogen,[28] and numerous clinical studies subsequently reported the association of Lp(a) with CHD,[190–194] MI,[195–197] stenosis following coronary artery bypass graft surgery (CABG),[198,199] restenosis after PTCA,[200–204] progression of CHD in familial hypercholesterolemia (FH),[205–208] peripheral vascular disease[209] and stroke.[210–216] One study reported no significant difference in Lp(a) concentrations between CABG patients and controls, although a trend toward higher Lp(a) concentrations with increasing severity of disease was reported.[217]

Two preliminary studies examined the utility of acutely lowering Lp(a) and LDL concentrations in patients by LDL-apheresis, before and after PTCA, for preventing restenosis.[218,219] In one study, in patients with Lp(a) concentration of > 30 mg/dL, restenosis rates were lower in those patients in whom a reduction of 50% or more of the initial Lp(a) concentration was achieved.[218] In the second study, restenosis was observed in only one out of ten patients treated once every 2 weeks for three to four months; three patients pheresed for two years did not restenose.[219] Similarly, Walzl et al. reported that plasmapheretic reduction of lipids, including Lp(a), in patients shortly after a stroke contributed to improved neurological recovery.[220] These are the first studies to show an improvement in clinical outcome as a result of lowering Lp(a) concentrations.

Lp(a) Concentrations As a Predictor of CHD Risk

Among numerous retrospective case-control studies, virtually all have shown a strong association between elevated Lp(a) levels and CHD (reviewed in ref. 221). A smaller number of prospective studies have been performed over the past 10 years to assess the contribution of plasma Lp(a) concentrations to the future development of CHD. The results of these studies have been somewhat discordant compared with those of the retrospective studies. In fact, while nine large prospective studies concluded that Lp(a) concentration is an independent risk factor for MI or CHD in men,[194,222–229] four other nested case-control studies reached opposite conclusions.[230–233] However, recent meta-analysis of prospective studies done between 1991 and 1997 indicated that plasma Lp(a) concentration is an independent risk factor for CHD in both men and women and that there is a dose-response relationship between plasma Lp(a) levels and CHD risk.[234] Several provocative editorials and reviews have critically evaluated the possible explanations for the discordant findings in individual prospective studies.[235–237]

There is mounting evidence to suggest that Lp(a) is a significant cardiovascular risk factor for women younger than 65. The Framingham Heart Study[225] has provided the only large prospective study of elevated levels and risk for CHD in women. In this study, the presence of a band representing sinking pre-beta lipoprotein was found to be a strong, independent predictor of myocardial infarction, intermittent claudication, and CHD in 3003 women observed for a mean period of 12 years. Orth-Gomer et al.[238] found in a study of CHD risk in young women that median Lp(a) levels were 38% higher in case compared to control subjects. In the Stanford Five-City Project study,[229] median Lp(a) concentrations were greater than 34% higher in female CHD cases than in control individuals. This difference was not statistically significant, however, probably due to the low number of case-control pairs in this study. Clearly, these observations merit further investigation in larger studies.

Historically, the large majority of clinical studies relating Lp(a) to risk of disease have been performed in White populations. More recently, a number of investigators have begun to evaluate the clinical significance of Lp(a) in other ethnic groups.[123–125,239–244] Sandholzer et al.[125] reported the results of a multicenter prospective case-control study that looked at apo(a) phenotypes and Lp(a) concentrations in six ethnic populations. These authors reported a consistent association of low-molecular-weight polymorphs with CHD across populations. However, plasma samples from all of the populations were not stored in the same way; the German samples were improperly stored at –20°C for two years and therefore were not analyzed for Lp(a) concentration, and the Israeli samples were stored at –20°C for six months. In addition, in one of the six populations, samples were from non-fasting individuals. This may be an important consideration if particles enriched with triglyceride containing Lp(a) react differently with antibodies used in Lp(a) assays. Abe and Noma found that the distribution of Lp(a) concentrations, apo(a) phenotype, and allele frequencies in healthy Japanese were not significantly different from White European populations, but were significantly different from other Asian populations, including Chinese, Indians, and Malaysians.[241] Further findings showed Lp(a) concentrations significantly higher in patients with CHD compared to healthy controls, a higher frequency of double-banded phenotypes in CHD patients, the same frequency of apo(a) alleles in CHD patients as in healthy individuals, and higher Lp(a) concentrations in CHD patients than in healthy people who had the same phenotype.[242]

The most interesting and intriguing results are those obtained in the few studies in which the clinical significance of Lp(a) was evaluated in Black and White subjects. In the Bogalusa Heart Study,[243] Lp(a) concentrations in White and Black children, and incidence of MI in their parents, were used as a measure of future risk for the children. Lp(a) concentrations in White children with parental MI were significantly higher than in White children without parental MI. In addition, the prevalence of parental MI in Whites was significantly higher in subjects with Lp(a) concentrations > 25 mg/dL. No relationship of Lp(a) concentration to incidence of parental MI was observed in Blacks. Guyton et al.[123] and Sorrentino et al.[244] studied the relationship between Lp(a) concentrations and CHD in Blacks and Whites and reported identical conclusions. White and Black patients with CHD had higher Lp(a) concentrations than Blacks and Whites without CHD. Although the Lp(a) concentrations in Blacks averaged twice those of Whites, the incidence of CHD between the two groups did not differ, and Blacks did not appear to experience increased atherosclerotic progression and mortality. Based on these findings, Guyton et al. concluded that the atherogenicity of Lp(a) in Blacks is decreased or is counterbalanced by other factors.[123] Clearly, basic studies are required to investigate the reasons for the apparent difference in the predictive value of Lp(a) concentrations in Blacks versus Whites.

Epidemiologic data have also been presented which suggest that Lp(a) may contribute to CHD in cooperation with other lipid or non-lipid risk factors (reviewed in ref. 245). Several studies have suggested that the CHD risk attributable to Lp(a) may be dependent on or enhanced by facilitating factors such as dyslipidemia. There is evidence that plasma Lp(a) and LDL can act additively in the development of angiographically-detectable CHD,[189] that Lp(a) and cholesterol levels act synergistically,[246] and that Lp(a) levels in men were no longer predictive of CHD severity, progression, and event rate when plasma LDL concentrations were decreased.[247] This has been interpreted to suggest that Lp(a) may not be a primary causative agent in atherogenesis. A case-control study by Hopkins et al.[248] revealed that patients with elevated levels of both Lp(a) and total cholesterol had a relative CHD risk of 13.8; the relative risk attributable to elevated total cholesterol was 1.6 and that attributable to elevated Lp(a) was 6.0, further suggesting an interaction between Lp(a) and other risk factors in determining CHD risk. An interesting study by Solymoss and coworkers[249] indicated that in women, an elevated ratio of total cholesterol to HDL cholesterol together with elevated Lp(a) levels markedly increased CHD risk. Most recently, the results of the Quebec Cardiovascular Study[250] suggest that Lp(a) is not an independent risk factor for ischemic heart disease in men, but increases the risk associated with elevated apo B and total cholesterol, and appears to attenuate the beneficial effects of elevated HDL. Plasma Lp(a) may also increase the risk associated with non-lipid CHD risk factors such as cigarette smoking, diabetes, hypertension and plasma homocysteine levels.[248]

Predictive Role of apo(a) Isoform Size on CHD Risk

Only a few studies have looked at the relationship of Lp(a) phenotype to CHD. Kark and co-workers reported a significantly higher prevalence of low-molecular-weight apo(a) isoforms in female, but not in male, MI survivors compared to controls.[196] Similarly, two studies reported a higher prevalence of low-molecular-weight isoforms in FH patients with CHD compared to those without disease.[205,206] Guo et al. reported the interesting finding that in FH patients heterozygous for apo(a) isoform, the different isoforms resided on distinct lipoprotein particles.[206] Another prospective study by Wild and coworkers suggests that Lp(a) levels are an independent risk factor for the development of CHD in men and also suggests that the size of apo(a) may also play a role in this process.[229]

In a large, population-based study, Marcovina et al. reported that the distribution of Lp(a) levels and apo(a) isoform size was significantly different between black and white Americans.[136] Blacks were found to have a lower frequency of small apo(a) isoform as compared to Whites and within the small size range, Lp(a) values were not significantly different between the two racial groups. In the range of intermediate apo(a) size however, Blacks had median Lp(a) values that were almost four times that of Whites. Considering that despite the high levels of Lp(a) the incidence of CHD in Blacks is the same if not less than in Whites, Marcovina et al.[136] hypothesized that Lp(a) levels and small apo(a) isoforms may synergistically contribute to Lp(a) pathogenicity. This hypothesis is interesting in light of recent reports by Kronenberg and Colleagues[251,252] in which they demonstrate that small apo(a) isoform size (<22 kringles) is a powerful predictor of risk for advanced atherosclerosis in the Bruneck study group, particularly when associated with high plasma Lp(a) concentrations; Lp(a) levels in conjunction with elevated LDL concentrations, but not apo(a) isoform size, were predictive of early atherosclerosis in this group. Because advanced atherosclerosis is associated with thrombotic events, this study suggests an isoform-dependent role for Lp(a) in these events.

Taken together, it is clear from these studies that the clinical significance of Lp(a) concentration and apo(a) isoform size in each ethnic group must be determined separately. Additionally, the predictive value of small apo(a) isoform sizes in men and women clearly merits further investigation in further large prospective studies using populations of varying ethnic composition.

Lp(a) Concentrations in Patients with Diabetes

The literature is contradictory in describing the potential role of Lp(a) as a contributing risk factor to the development of cardiovascular complications in patients with diabetes mellitus.[253] Numerous groups have reported that Lp(a) concentrations are increased in patients with insulin-dependent diabetes (IDDM),[254–258] and that Lp(a) concentration was[254,256,259] or was not[260–263] related to the degree of glycemic control. The recent Diabetes Control and Complications Trial (DCCT) examined plasma Lp(a) concentrations in 1299 patients with diabetes and 2158 controls.[264] There was no difference in mean plasma Lp(a) concentrations between controls (18.2 mg/dL) and patients receiving intensive insulin therapy (18.5 mg/dL). Mean plasma Lp(a) concentrations were significantly higher ($p < 0.05$) in patients receiving conventional insulin therapy (22.0 mg/dL) than in controls. However, other studies reported that Lp(a) concentrations were not increased in IDDM patients compared to healthy control subjects.[260,265–267] Two studies have compared apo(a) phenotype frequencies in IDDM patients and controls: no differences in either apo(a) phenotype frequency or plasma Lp(a) levels were found.[268,269] In a study of 45 identical twin pairs discordant for IDDM, Dubrey et al. reported no relationship between genetic susceptibility to IDDM and apo(a) phenotype or Lp(a) concentration; in this study, Lp(a) concentrations in patients with diabetes were also found to be similar to those found in the control population.[270] It is reasonable to conclude from the available data that IDDM has a modest effect, if any at all, on plasma Lp(a) levels. With two exceptions,[256,271] there seems to be general agreement that Lp(a) concentrations in non-insulin-dependent diabetes (NIDDM) are not increased.[259,260,272–274]

It is possible that Lp(a) may increase in patients with diabetes as a result of the renal complications of this disease, rather than as a direct result of diabetes *per se*. The studies to date examining a relationship between plasma Lp(a) levels and microalbuminuria or albuminuria in patients with diabetes have been inconclusive,[264,275–277] possibly as a consequence of small study size.[275,276] However, in a longitudinal study of patients with diabetes who were undergoing dialysis, decreased proteinuria resulted in significantly decreased Lp(a) levels.[278]

Even if diabetes does not result in elevated plasma Lp(a), this lipoprotein may contribute to the increased vascular risk observed in these patients. If this is the case, an association between Lp(a) levels and diabetic complications would be expected. In diabetic patients, associations were observed between high plasma Lp(a) and CHD,[279,280] ischemic heart disease or macroangiopathy,[281] arteriosclerosis obliterans and carotid atherosclerosis.[282] Increased concentrations of Lp(a) have also been reported in patients suffering from diabetic retinopathy.[283–285] A number of studies have reported that other risk factors surpassed the significance of Lp(a) in patients with diabetes. Ritter and co-workers studied the relationship between Lp(a) concentration and late diabetic complications, including diabetic polyneuropathy, autonomic neuropathy, nephropathy, peripheral occlusive disease, diabetic gangrene, CHD, and retinopathy.[286] No significant increases in Lp(a) correlated with any of these complications except for retinopathy, and this correlation was not significant when the duration of diabetes was factored into logistic regression analysis.[286] Similarly, in a more recent study, Lp(a) levels were not found to be a significant risk factor for retinopathy in neither young- nor older-onset diabetes.[287]

These studies collectively suggest that Lp(a) may not be a risk factor directly related to diabetes. Rather, Lp(a) concentrations may be elevated in some individuals independent of the diabetic condition, and may thus pose an additional risk for atherosclerotic disease. Although the incidence of increased concentrations of Lp(a) in the population with diabetes may be the same as that in the general population, it remains to be determined whether the atherogenicity of Lp(a) in patients with diabetes is increased, which may reflect altered biochemical properties of this lipoprotein in the diabetic condition.

Lp(a) Concentrations in Patients with Renal Disease

Several studies have revealed that plasma Lp(a) levels are increased in proteinuria or the nephrotic syndrome[278,288–290] (reviewed in ref. 291). Stenvinkel reported significant reduction of Lp(a) concentrations in patients with nephrotic syndrome after remission.[292] One small study[278] investigated the role of apo(a) phenotype in elevated Lp(a) in the nephrotic syndrome and found that Lp(a) was elevated in each apo(a) size class.

Using Lp(a) labeled with stable isotopes in a turnover study, the mechanism underlying the elevation of Lp(a) in the nephrotic syndrome has been investigated. The fractional catabolic rate of Lp(a) was not different between patients and controls, indicating that the elevation of Lp(a) in the nephrotic syndrome results from increased synthesis of Lp(a) rather than from reduced catabolism.[293] The increased synthesis of Lp(a) could be explained by the stimulation of hepatic protein synthesis that occurs as a consequence of the hypoalbuminuria and the reductions of oncotic pressure that accompany renal disease, as has been observed for other apolipoproteins.[294]

Lp(a) Concentrations in Patients Receiving Renal Replacement Therapy

A number of recent studies have found significantly higher concentrations of Lp(a) in patients receiving hemodialysis (HD), continuous ambulatory peritoneal dialysis (CAPD), or transplant therapy compared to healthy control subjects.[295–306]

Irish and co-workers reported significantly higher concentrations of Lp(a) in patients with chronic renal disease and in those undergoing CAPD compared to healthy controls, but found no difference between control subjects and patients undergoing hemodialysis or transplant therapy.[307] However, a recent report found that, relative to control subjects, Lp(a) levels were more elevated in CAPD patients than in HD patients.[308] Interestingly, analysis of apo(a) phenotypes in CAPD and HD patients revealed that plasma Lp(a) concentrations were specifically increased in patients with large apo(a) isoform sizes,[308–310] although this has not been a universal finding.[305,306] Dieplinger and coworkers reported increased Lp(a) values in patients with end-stage renal disease compared to controls, but found no difference in frequency of apo(a) isoforms between the groups. Concentrations of Lp(a) were increased two- to threefold in patients with high-molecular-weight apo(a) isoforms, while in patients with small isoforms, Lp(a) concentrations were comparable to those found in controls.[309]

Numerous studies have found that Lp(a) concentration declines following renal transplantation,[311–314] again underscoring the role of kidney function in determining plasma Lp(a) levels. In accordance with the renal replacement studies, lowering of plasma Lp(a) following transplantation was observed specifically in the large apo(a) isoform group.[314,315] Collectively, these results suggest that non-genetic factors related to renal insufficiency are responsible for increased Lp(a) concentrations in these populations.

Haffner et al. proposed that increased Lp(a) concentrations in chronic renal failure must occur early or contribute to its development, since Lp(a) concentration did not correlate with creatinine concentrations, was similarly increased in different ethnic groups, and was not affected by diet, hemodialysis, or CAPD treatment.[316] Sato and coworkers demonstrated co-localization of apo(a) and apo B-100 in the mesangial area and capillary loops in glomeruli from patients with glomerular diseases, and proposed that Lp(a) might advance glomerular disease by interfering with activation of TGF-β, thereby interfering with repair of injured cells or tissue.[317] It was recently reported that the binding of Lp(a) to the extracellular mesangial matrix is enhanced relative to LDL.[318] Although the significance of Lp(a) trapping in the mesangial matrix is unclear at present, it has been demonstrated that Lp(a) has both stimulatory (at low concentrations) and cytotoxic (at high concentrations) effects on cultured mesangial cells, both of which may negatively impact the course of renal disease *in vivo*.[319] However, a small prospective study failed to find any association between plasma Lp(a) levels and an increased progression of renal disease.[320]

The mechanism underlying changes in plasma Lp(a) concentrations in renal failure, renal replacement therapy, and renal transplantation, and the role of apo(a) isoform size, remains obscure. The release of tumor necrosis factor alpha, interleukin 1, and interleukin 6,[321] along with increased concentrations of C-reactive protein,[322] have been reported in hemodialysis patients. The release of cytokines has been attributed to chronic exposure to dialysis membranes.[323] Interleukin 6 is a potent activator of the synthesis of acute phase proteins by hepatocytes.[324,325] Lp(a) has been shown to behave like an acute phase protein after MI, stroke, or CABG surgery,[211,326–328] and may also play a role in inflammation.[329,330]

Lp(a) and Atherosclerotic Risk in Renal Riseases

Individuals with renal diseases are at a greatly increased risk of atherosclerotic complications, and the elevated levels of Lp(a) observed in renal diseases may contribute to this risk (reviewed in ref. 291). Cressman et al. reported that Lp(a) concentration and the presence of a previous CHD-related clinical event were the only independent risk factors for predicting CHD in hemodialysis patients in a multiple logistic regression model.[223] In a follow-up study, Lp(a) concentration was demonstrated to be an independent predictor of fatal events attributable to CHD.[331] Examination of the extracranial carotid arteries of patients undergoing hemodialysis revealed an association between the presence of atherosclerosis and the presence of small apo(a) isoforms.[332] In addition, both Lp(a) levels and frequency of small apo(a) isoforms were increased as the number of atherosclerotic sites increased. Similarly, in CAPD patients, plasma Lp(a) levels, and to an even greater extent, the frequency of small apo(a) isoforms, were increased in patients with CHD.[333] In another study, patients with symptomatic arterial disease in renal replacement therapy had significantly higher plasma Lp(a) levels and a higher frequency of smaller apo(a) isoforms than asymptomatic patients.[334] Interestingly, apo(a) phenotype was more predictive than plasma Lp(a) concentrations for CHD in HD patients as assessed by stepwise logistic regression analysis.[335] This finding can be explained by the specific elevation of Lp(a) levels associated with large apo(a) isoforms in end-stage renal disease patients. Therefore, the component of arterial risk attributable to small apo(a) isoforms[251] would be more apparent since the association between small apo(a) isoforms and elevated plasma Lp(a) levels is blunted in this population.[291]

Requirements for Clinical Studies of Lp(a) and Atherosclerotic Disease

The lack of standardization of both Lp(a) measurement and apo(a) phenotype determination makes it difficult to compare clinical studies. Further, until the development of Lp(a) assays that are not sensitive to apo(a) size, no conclusion can be reached regarding the independent effects of Lp(a) concentration and apo(a) phenotype on the risk for atherosclerotic disease. The following guidelines are proposed for designing future studies of Lp(a) and atherosclerotic disease:

1. Sample size, estimated by appropriate power calculations, must be large enough to adequately represent the numerous apo(a) isoforms[55] and the most common of the possible polymorphic combinations. This will prevent possible selection bias due to phenotype.

2. Isoform studies should use the technique with the highest resolution,[54,55] and a standardized approach for evaluating and reporting apo(a) isoforms should be used to achieve among-study comparability.[336]

3. Antibodies used for the measurement of Lp(a) concentrations in clinical studies must be characterized with regard to the epitope recognized, and a clear demonstration of the effect of isoform size must be demonstrated in order to be able to interpret Lp(a) concentrations.

4. The ethnic composition of all study populations must be defined.

5. To avoid possible confounding effects of the acute phase response on Lp(a) concentrations, Lp(a) should not be measured during an active inflammatory state.

6. Because of the non-Gaussian distribution of Lp(a) levels, medians should be reported rather than means.

7. Nonparametric statistics must be used for analysis of Lp(a) data.

Screening for Lipoprotein(a) Concentrations

Based on the contradictory results of the epidemiologic studies, the problems inherent in the immunochemical measurement of Lp(a), and the lack of a clearly defined threshold for clinical decision, screening of the general population for Lp(a) concentration is not recommended. However, in some clinical situations, the measurement of plasma Lp(a) concentration might be appropriate. For example, we do suggest that Lp(a) levels be measured in patients with existing CHD or in individuals at increased risk for developing CHD. These may include subjects with a family history of CHD or stroke, siblings and offspring of individuals with increased concentrations of Lp(a), patients with FH, and patients with renal dysfunction accompanied by proteinuria. However, considering the numerous methodological problems, Lp(a) measurement on this high-risk group of subjects should be performed only by specialized lipid research laboratories. These laboratories should have population-based reference values determined by their method for different ethnic groups. To enable the physician to estimate the patient's risk, Lp(a) values should be reported with the indication of the corresponding percentile of the general population. Based on the outcome of the clinical studies, it appears reasonable to consider patients with Lp(a) values above the 80th percentile at increased risk for CHD.

With respect to clinical directives for patients with elevated Lp(a) levels, larger prospective studies utilizing Lp(a) measurement techniques that are insensitive to apo(a) isoform size variability are required in order to more clearly define the basis of the risk relationship between Lp(a) and atherosclerotic disease. Elucidation of the mechanism underlying the pathophysiology of Lp(a) will also be useful in suggesting directions for the design of therapeutic strategies specifically aimed at lowering Lp(a) levels. Currently, the most effective way to decrease Lp(a) concentrations by 50% or more is by LDL- or Lp(a)-apheresis procedures. However, these techniques are expensive and are reserved for the extreme cases of hetero- and homozygous FH.[337–339] Although several pharmacological agents that lower Lp(a) levels such as niacin and neomycin (either separately or in combination),[340–342] bezafibrate,[343] as well as estrogen, tamoxifen, and combination hormone therapy in healthy postmenopausal women have been identified,[344,345] the long-term benefits of Lp(a)-lowering therapy are currently unknown and as such their routine use cannot be recommended. There is, however, encouraging preliminary evidence to suggest that decreasing Lp(a) concentrations utilizing apheresis procedures before and after PTCA and during recovery after stroke may improve outcome.[337–339]

It is reasonable at this time to consider the use of therapeutic regimens for patients with a predisposition for developing atherosclerotic disease and with increased Lp(a) concentrations in order to minimize lipid- and non-lipid-related risk factors that can be modified; this may include the use of diet, hydroxymethylglutaryl-CoA (HMG-CoA) reductase inhibitors, bile acid sequestrants, and probucol, all of which do not affect Lp(a) concentrations.[346] This approach may be particularly important in view of the fact that evidence has been presented suggesting that Lp(a) synergistically contributes to CAD by potentiating the effect of other lipid risk factors.[189,250] Although it is a logical therapeutic goal to decrease Lp(a) in patients with multiple cardiovascular risk factors, specific goals or targets have not been established due to the lack of reference ranges for different ethnic groups.

Despite the suggestion that small apo(a) isoforms are predictive of advanced stenotic atherosclerosis,[221] it is likely not cost effective at this time to add the determination of apo(a) isoform size to CHD risk assessment. We recommend that clinicians decide, on an individual case basis, whether the determination of apo(a) isoform size is necessary in order to generate a more complete risk profile.

SUMMARY

Lp(a) is a cholesterol-rich plasma lipoprotein, the levels of which are under relatively strict genetic control in the White population. The results from a number of studies suggest that elevated Lp(a) concentrations are a risk factor for premature atherosclerosis. Although Lp(a) has been hypothesized to represent a bridge between the fields of atherosclerosis and thrombosis, studies of the effect of Lp(a) on fibrinolysis *in vitro* have been somewhat inconsistent, and no effect on fibrinolysis *in vivo* has been demonstrated to date. Standardization of Lp(a) measurement and apo(a) phenotype determination must be developed in order to provide clinical investigators with the tools they need to elucidate the true relationship of Lp(a) to atherosclerotic disease. Currently the majority of measurements of Lp(a) concentration reported in clinical studies in the literature is confounded by isoform size, making it difficult to come to a sound conclusion regarding the role of Lp(a) concentration in disease. Measurement of Lp(a) concentrations with methods not sensitive to isoform size and determination of apo(a) phenotypes in different ethnic groups are required before specific recommendations can be made regarding screening of the general population for Lp(a).

At the present time, screening for Lp(a) concentration is recommended for patients with existing CHD, or in individuals at high risk for CHD including those with a family history of CHD, stroke, MI, or FH and renal dysfunction accompanied by proteinuria. Within this subset, management of individuals with high Lp(a) concentrations should be directed at minimizing all other lipid- and non-lipid risk factors for atherosclerotic disease. Despite recent studies that suggest a predictive role for small apo(a) phenotypes in advanced atherosclerosis, we do not recommend the determination of apo(a) isoforms in CHD risk assessment at this time. Ongoing studies related to probing the mechanism(s) of Lp(a) pathogenicity may provide defined indications for the clinical determination of Lp(a) concentrations and apo(a) isoform sizes   ✧

Acknowledgments. *Dr. Marcovina's Lp(a) standardization work cited in this review was supported by Contract N01-HV-88175 from the National Heart, Lung, and Blood Institute, U.S. Public Service. Original work cited for Dr. Koschinsky was supported by the Medical Research Council of Canada and the Heart and Stroke Foundation of Ontario.*

REFERENCES

1. Berg K. A new serum type system in man: the Lp system. Acta Pathol Microbiol Scand 1963;59:362–82.
2. Berg K. The Lp system. [Review]. Ser Haemotol 1968;1:111–36.
3. Albers, JJ, Kenedy, H, Marcovina, SM. Evidence that Lp(a) contains one molecule of

apo(a) and one molecule of apo B: evaluation of amino acid analysis data. J Lipid Res 1996;37:192–196.

4. Koschinsky ML, Marcovina SM. Lipoprotein(a): structural implications for pathophysiology. Int J Clin Lab Res 1997;27:14–23.

5. Brunner C, Kraft H-G, Utermann G, Muller H-J. Cys4057 of apolipoprotein(a) is essential for lipoprotein(a) assembly. Proc Natl Acad Sci USA 1993;90:11643–11647.

6. Callow MJ, Rubin EM. Site-specific mutagenesis demonstrates that cystein 4326 of apolipoprotein B is required for covalent linkage with apolipoprotein(a) *in vivo*. J Biol Chem 1995;270:23914–23917.

7. McCormick SPA, Ng JK, Taylor S, Flynn LM, Hammer RE, Young SG. Mutagenesis of the human apolipoprotein B gene in a yeast artificial chromosome reveals the site of attachment for apolipoprotein(a). Proc Natl Acad Sci 1995; 92:10147–10151.

8. Ernst A, Helmhold M, Brunner C, Petho-Schramm P, Armstrong VW, Muller H-J. Identification of two functionally distinct lysine-binding sites in kringle 37 and in kringles 32–36 of human apolipoprotein(a). J Biol Chem 1994;270:6227–34.

9. Trieu VN, McConathy WJ. A two-step model for lipoprotein(a) formation. J Biol Chem 1995;270:15471–4.

10. Gabel BR, May LF, Marcovina SM, Koschinsky ML. Lipoprotein(a) Assembly. Quantitative assessment of the role of apo(a) kringle IV types 2–10 in particle formation. Arterioscler Thromb Vasc Biol 1996;16:1559–67.

11. Gabel BR, Koschinsky ML. Sequences within apolipoprotein(a) kringle IV types 6–8 bind directly to low-density lipoprotein and mediate noncovalent association of apolipoprotein(a) with apolipoproteinB-100. Biochemistry 1998;37:7892–7898.

12. Gabel BR, McLeod, RS, Yao Z, Koschinsky ML. Sequences within the amino terminus of apoB100 mediate its noncovalent association with apo(a). Arterioscler Thromb Vasc Biol 1998;18:1738–1744.

13. Gabel BR, Yao Z, McLeod RS, Young SG, Koschinsky ML. Carboxyl-terminal truncation of apolipoproteinB-100 inhibits lipoprotein(a) particle formation. FEBS Letts 1994;350:77–81.

14. Xu S. Apolipoprotein(a) binds to low-density lipoprotein at two distant sites in lipoprotein(a). Biochemistry 1998;37:9284–9294.

15. Chiesa G, Hobbs, HH, Koschinsky, ML, Lawn, RM, Maika, SD, and Hammer, RE. Reconstitution of lipoprotein(a) by infusion of human low-density lipoprotein into transgenic mice expressing human apolipoprotein(a). J Biol Chem 1992;267:24369–24374.

16. White AL, Rainwater DL, Lanford RE. Intracellular maturation of apolipoprotein(a) and assembly of lipoprotein(a) in primary baboon hepatocytes. J Lipid Res 1993;34:509–517.

17. Frank S, Krasznai K, Durovic S, Lobentanz E-M, Dieplinger H, Wagner E, Zatloukal K, Cotten M, Utermann G, Kostner GM, Zechner R. High-level expression of various apolipoprotein(a) isoforms by "transferrinfection": the role of kringle IV sequences in the extracellular association with low-density lipoprotein. Biochemistry 1994;33:12329–12339.

18. White, AL and Lanford, RE. Cell surface assembly of lipoprotein(a) in primary cultures of baboon hepatocytes. J Biol Chem 1994;269:28716–28723.

19. Albers JJ, Cabana VG, Warnick GR, Hazzard WR. Lp(a) lipoprotein: relationship to sinking pre-β lipoprotein, hyperlipoproteinemia, and apolipoprotein B. Metabolism 1975;24:1047–54.

20. Gaubatz JW, Heideman C, Gotto AM Jr, Morrisett JD, Dahlen GH. Human plasma lipoprotein(a): structural properties. J Biol Chem 1983;258:4582–9.

21. Fless GM, Rolih CA, Scanu AM. Heterogeneity of human plasma lipoprotein(a): isolation and characterization of the lipoprotein subspecies and their apoproteins. J Biol Chem 1984;259:11470–8.

22. Fless GM. Heterogeneity of particles containing the apo B-apo(a) complex. In: Scanu AM, ed. Lipoprotein(a). San Diego: Academic Press, 1990:41–51.

23. Pfaffinger D, Schuelke J, Kim C, Fless GM, Scanu AM. Relationship between apo(a)

isoforms and Lp(a) density in subjects with different apo(a) phenotype: a study before and after a fatty meal. J Lipid Res 1991;32:679–83.

24. Cohn JS. Lam CWK, Sullivan DR, Hensley WJ. Plasma lipoprotein distribution of apolipoprotein(a) in the fed and fasted states. Atherosclerosis 1991;90:59–66.

25. Fless GM, ZumMallen ME, Scanu AM. Physicochemical properties of apolipoprotein(a) and lipoprotein(a-) derived from the dissociation of human plasma lipoprotein(a). J Biol Chem 1986;261:8712–18.

26. Hixson JE, Britten ML, Manis GS, Rainwater DL. Apolipoprotein(a) (Apo(a)) glycoprotein isoforms result from size differences in apo(a) mRNA in baboons. J Biol Chem 1989; 264:6013–16.

27. Koschinsky ML, Beisiegel U, Henne-Bruns D, Eaton DL, Lawn RM. Apolipoprotein(a) size heterogeneity is related to variable number of repeat sequences in its mRNA. Biochemistry 1990;29:640–4.

28. McLean JW, Tomlinson JE, Kuang W-J, Eaton DL, Chen EY, Fless GM, Scanu AM, and Lawn RM. cDNA sequence of human apolipoprotein(a) is homologous to plasminogen. *Nature* 1987;330:132–137.

29. Magnusson S, Sottrup-Jensen L, Petersen TE, Dudek-Wojciechowska G, Claeys H. Homologous "kringle" structures common to plasminogen and prothrombin: substrate specificity of enzymes activating prothrombin and plasminogen. In: Ribbons DW, Brew K. eds. Proteolysis and physiological regulation. New York: Academic Press, 1976: 203–38.

30. Castellino FJ, Beals JM. The genetic relationships between the kringle domains of human plasminogen, prothrombin, tissue plasminogen activator, urokinase, and coagulation factor XII. J Mol Evol 1987;26:358–69.

31. Gabel BR, Koschinsky ML. Analysis of the proteolytic activity of a recombinant form of apolipoprotein(a). Biochemistry 1995;34:15777–84.

32. Guevara J Jr, Knapp RD, Honda S, Northup SR, Morrisett JD. A structural assessment of the apo(a) protein of human lipoprotein(a). Proteins 1992;12:188–99.

33. Guevara J Jr, Jan AY, Knapp R, Tulinsky A, Morrisett JD. Comparison of ligand-binding sites of modeled apo(a) kringle-like sequences in human lipoprotein(a). Arterioscler Thromb 1993;13:758–70.

34. Lackner C, Cohen JC, Hobbs HH. Molecular definition of the extreme size polymorphism in apolipoprotein(a). Hum Mol Genet 1993;2:933–40.

35. van der Hoek YY, Wittekoek ME, Beisiegel U, Kastelein JJ, Koschinsky ML. The apolipoprotein(a) kringle IV repeats which differ from the major repeat kringle are present in variably-sized isoforms. Hum Mol Genet 1993;2:361–66.

36. Mooser V, Seabra MC, Abedin M, Landschulz KT, Marcovina S, Hobbs HH. Apolipoprotein(a) kringle 4-containing fragments in human urine. J Clin Invest 1996;97: 858–864.

37. Mooser V, Marcovina SM, White AL, Hobbs HH. Kringle-containing fragments of apolipoprotein(a) circulate in human plasma and are excreted into the urine. J Clin Invest 1996;98:2414–2424.

38. Edelstein C, Italia JA, Klezovitch O, Scanu AM. Functional and metabolic differences between elastase-generated fragments of human lipoprotein(a) and apolipoprotein(a). J Lipid Res 1996;37:1786–1801.

39. Edelstein C, Italia JA, Scanu AM. Polymorphonuclear cells isolated from human peripheral blood cleave lipoprotein(a) and apolipoprotein(a) at multiple interkringle sites via the enzyme elastase. J Biol Chem 1997;272:11079–11087.

40. Reblin T, Meyer N, Labeur C, Henne-Bruns D, Beisiegel U. Extraction of lipoprotein(a), apo B, and apo E from fresh human arterial wall and atherosclerotic plaques. Atherosclerosis 1995;113:179–188.

41. Hoff HF, O'Neil J, Yashiro A. Partial characterization of lipoproteins containing apo(a) in human atherosclerotic lesions. J Lipid Res 1993;34:789–98.

42. Scanu AM. Proteolytic modifications of lipoprotein(a): potential relevance to its postulated atherothrombogenic role. J Investig Med 1998;46:359–363.

43. O'Reilly MS, Holmgren L, Shing, Y, Chen C,Rosenthal RA, Moses M, Lane WS, Cao Y, Sate EH, Folkman J. Angiostatin: A novel angiogenesis inhibitor that mediates the suppression of metastases by a Lewis lung carcinoma. Cell 1994;79:315–328.

44. Frank SL, Klisak I, Sparkes RS, et al. The apolipoprotein(a) gene resides on human chromosome 6q26–27, in close proximity to the homologous gene for plasminogen. Hum Genet 1988;79:352–6.

45. Malgaretti N, Acquati F, Magnaghi P, Bruno L, Pontoglio M, Rocchi M, saccone S, Della Valle G, K'Urso M, LePaslier D, Ottolenghi S, Taramelli R. Characterization by yeast artificial chromosome cloning of the linked apolipoprotein(a) and plasminogen genes and identification of the apolipoprotein(a) 5' flanking region. Proc Natl Acad Sci USA 1992;89:11584–11588.

46. Magnaghi P, Citterio E, Malgareti N, Acquati F, Ottolenghi S, Taramelli R. Molecular characterization of the human apo(a)-plasminogen gene family clustered on the telomeric region of chromosome 6 (6q26–27). Hum Mol Genet 1994;3:437–442.

47. Takabatake N, Souri M, Ichinose A. Multiple novel transcripts for apolipoprotein(a)-related gene II generated by alternative splicing in tissue-and cell type-specific manners. J Biochem 1998;124:540–546.

48. Albers JJ, Wahl P, Hazzard WR. Quantitative genetic studies of the human plasma Lp(a) lipoprotein. Biochem Genet 1974;11:475–86.

49. Iselius L, Dahlen G, DeFaire U, Lundman T. Complex segregation analysis of the Lp(a)/ pre-beta 1-lipoprotein trait. Clin Genet 1981;20:147–51.

50. Morton NE, Berg K, Dahlen G, Ferrel RE, Rhoads GG. Genetics of the Lp lipoprotein in Japanese-Americans. Genet Epidemiol 1985;2:113–21.

51. Utermann G, Menzel HJ, Kraft HG, Duba HC, Kemmler HG, Seitz C. Lp(a) glycoprotein phenotypes: inheritance and relation to Lp(a)-lipoprotein concentrations in plasma. J Clin Invest 1987;80:458–65.

52. Gavish D, Azrolan N, Breslow JL. Plasma Lp(a) concentration is inversely correlated with the ratio of kringle IV/kringle V encoding domains in the apo(a) gene. J Clin Invest 1989;84:2021–2027.

53. Gaubatz JW, Ghanem KI, Guevara J Jr, et al. Polymorphic forms of human apolipoprotein(a): inheritance and relationship of their molecular weights to plasma concentrations of lipoprotein(a). J Lipid Res 1990;31:603–13.

54. Kamboh MI, Ferrell RE, Kottke BA. Expressed hypervariable polymorphism of apolipoprotein(a). Am J Hum Genet 1991;49:1063–74.

55. Marcovina SM, Zhang ZH, Gaur VP, Albers JJ. Identification of 34 apolipoprotein(a) isoforms: differential expression of apolipoprotein(a) alleles between American Blacks and Whites. Biochem Biophys Res Commun 1993;191:1192–6.

56. Lackner C, Boerwinkle E, Leffert CC, Rahmig T, Hobbs HH. Molecular basis of apolipoprotein(a) isoform size heterogeneity as revealed by pulsed-field gel electrophoresis. J Clin Invest 1991;87:2153–61.

57. Boerwinkle E, Leffert CC, Lin J, Lackner C, Chiesa G, Hobbs HH. Apolipoprotein(a) gene accounts for greater than 90% of the variation in plasma lipoprotein(a) concentrations. J Clin Invest 1992;90:52–60.

58. Kraft HG, Cochl S, Menzel HJ, Sandholzer C, Utermann G. The apolipoprtoein(a) gene: a transcribed hypervariable locus controlling plasma lipoprotein(a) concentration. Hum Genet 1992;90:52–60.

59. Kraft HG, Lingenhel A, Pang RW, Delport R, Trommsdorff M, Vermaak H, Janus ED, Utermann G. Frequency distributions of apolipoprotein(a) kringle IV repeat alleles and their effects on lipoprotein(a) levels in Caucasian, Asian, and African popoulations: the distribution of null alleles is non-random. Eur J Hum Genet 1996;4: 74–87.

60. Sandholzer C, Hallman DM, Saha N, Sigurdsson G, Lackner C, Csaszar A, Boerwinkle E, Utermann G. Effects of the apolipoprotein(a) size polymorphism on the lipoprotein(a) concentration in seven ethnic groups. Hum Genet 1991;86:607–614.

61. Mooser V, Scheer D, Marcovina SM, Wang J, Guerra R, Cohen J, Hobbs HH. The Apo(a)

gene is the major determinant of variation in plasma Lp(a) levels in African Americans. 1997;61:402–417.

62. Scholz M, Kraft HG, Lingenhel A, Deport R, Vorster EH, Bickeboller H, Utermann G. Genetic control of lipoprotein(a) concentrations is different in Africans and Caucasians. Eur J Hum Genet 1999; 7:169–178.

63. Utermann G, Duba C, Menzel HJ. Genetics of the quantitative Lp(a) lipoprotein trait. II. Inheritance of Lp(a) glycoprotein phenotypes. Hum Genet 1988;78:47–50.

64. Cox LA, Jett C, Hixson JE. Molecular basis of an apolipoprotein(a) null allele: a splice site mutation is associated with deletion of a single exon. J Lipid Res. 1998;39: 1319–1326.

65. Ogorelkova M, Gruber A, Utermann, G. Molecular basis of congenital Lp(a) deficiency: a frequent apo(a) "null" mutation in Caucasians. Hum Mol Genet. 1999;8:2087–2096.

66. Trommsdorff M, Kochl S, Lingenhel A, Kronenberg F, Delport R, Vermaak H, Lemming L, Clausen IC, Faergeman O, Utermann G, Kraft H-G. A pentanucleotide repeat polymorphism in the 5' control region of the apolipoprotein(a) gene is associated with lipoprotein(a) plasma concentrations in Caucasians. J Clin Invest 1995;96:150–57.

67. Cohen JC, Chiesa G, Hobbs HH. Sequence polymorphisms in the apolipoprotein(a) gene. Evidence for dissociation between apolipoprotein(a) size and plasma lipoprotein(a) levels. J Clin Invest 1993;91:1630–1636.

68. Mancini FP, Mooser V, Guerra R, Hobbs HH. Sequence microheterogeneity in apolipoprotein(a) gene repeats and the relationship to plasma Lp(a) levels. Hum Mol Genet 1995;4:1535–1542.

69. Mooser V, Mancini FP, Bopp S, Petho-Schramm A, Guerra R, Boerwinkle E, Muller H-J, Hobbs HH. Sequence polymorphisms in the apo(a) gene associated with specific levels of Lp(a) in plamsa. Hum Mol Genet 1995;4:173–181.

70. Suzuki K, Kuriyama M, Saito T, Ichinose A. Plasma lipoprotein(a) levels and expression of the apolipoprotein(a) gene are dependent on the nucleotide polymorphisms in its 5'-flanking region. J Clin Invest 1997;99:1361–1366.

71. Zysow BR, Lindahl GE, Wade DP, Knight BL, Lawn RM. C/T polymorphism in the 5' untranslated region of the apolipoprotein(a0 gene introduces an upstream ATG and reduces *in vitro* translation. Arterioscler Thromb Vasc Biol. 1995;15:58–64.

72. Kraft HG, Windegger M, Menzel HJ, Utermann G. Significant impact of the +93 C/T polymorphism in the apolipoprotein(a) gene on Lp(a) concentrations in Africans but not in Caucasians: confounding effect of linkage disequilibrium. Hum Mol Genet. 1998;7:257–264.

73. Yang Z, Boffelli D, Boonmark N, Schwartz K, Lawn RM. Apolipoprotein(a) gene enhancer resides within a LINE element. J Biol Chem 1998;273:891–897.

74. Utermann G, Hoppichler F, Dieplinger H, Seed M, Thompson G, Boerwinkle E. Defects in the low-density-lipoprotein receptor gene affect lipoprotein(a) levels: multiplicative interaction of two gene loci associated with premature atherosclerosis. Proc Natl Acad Sci USA 1989;86:4171–4.

75. Lingenhel A, Kraft HG, Kotze M, Peeters AV, Kronenberg F, Kruse R, Utermann G. Concentrations of the atherogenic Lp(a) are elevated in FH. Eur J Hum Genet 1998;6:50–60.

76. Koschinsky ML, Marcovina SM. Lipoprotein(a): structural implication for pathophysiology. Int J Clin Lab Res 1997;27:14–23.

77. Koschinsky ML, Ramharack R. Structure, Function and Regulation of Lipoprotein(a). Curr Pharm Des 1996;2:121–138.

78. Hegele RA, Sutherland S, Robertson M, Wu L, Emi M, Hopkins PN, Williams RR, Lalouel JM. The effect of genetic determinants of low-density-lipoprotein levels on lipoprotein(a). Clin Invest Med 1991;14:146–152.

79. Averna M, Marcovina SM, Noto D, Cole TG, Krul ES, Schonfeld G. Familial hypobetalipoproteinemia is not associated with low levels of lipoprotein(a). Arterioscler Thromb Vasc Biol 1995;15:2165–75.

80. Thomas TR, Ziogas G, Harris WS. Influence of fitness status on very-low-density lipoprotein subfractions and lipoprotein(a) in men and women. metabolism 1997;46: 1178–1183.

81. Puckey L, Knight B. Dietary and genetic interactions in the regulation of plasma lipo-protein(a). Curr Opin Lipidol 1999;10:35–40.

82. Katan MB, Zock PL, Mensink RP. Trans-fatty acids and their effects on lipoproteins in humans. Annu Rev Nutr 1995;15:473–493.

83. Mensink RP, Zock PL, Katan MB, Hornstra G. Effect of dietary cis- and trans-fatty acids on serum lipoprotein(a) levels. J Lipid Res 1992;33:1493–1501.

84. Herrmann W, Biermann J, Kostner GM. Comparison of the effects of N-3 to N-6 fatty acids on serum level of lipoprotein(a) in patients with coronary artery disease. Am J Cardiol 1995;76:459–462.

85. Marcovina SM, Kennedy H, Bittolo-Bon G, Cazzolato G, Galli C, Casiglia E, Puato M, Pauletto P. Fish intake, independent of apo(a) isoform size, accounts for lower plasma lipoprotein(a) levels in Bantu fisherman of Tanzania: The Lugalawa Study. Arterioscler Thromb Vasc Biol 1999;19:1250–1256.

86. De Bruin TWA, van Barlingen H, Van Linde-Sibenius Trip M, Van Vruust de Vries A-RR, Akveld MJ, Erkelens DW. Lipoprotein(a) and apolipoprotein B plasma concentrations in hypothyroid, euthyroid, and hyperthyroid subjects. J Clin Endocrinol Metab 1993;76: 121–126.

87. Hoppichler F, Sandholzer C, Moncayo R, Utermann G, Kraft HG. Thyroid hormone (fT4) reduces lipoprotein(a) plasma levels. Atherosclerosis 1995;115:65–71.

88. Eden S, Wiklund O, Oscarsson J, Rosen T, Bengtsson BA. Growth hormone treatment of growth hormone-deficient adults results in a marked increase in Lp(a) and HDL cho-lesterol concentrations. Arterioscler Thromb Vasc Biol 1993;13:296–301.

89. Olivecrona H, Johansson AG, Lindh E, Ljunghall S, Berglund L, Angelin B. Arterioscler Thromb Vasc Biol. 1995;15:847–849.

90. Marcovina SM, Koschinsky ML. The effect of hormone replacement therapy on lipo-protein(a) levels in postmenopausal women. Cardiovascular Reviews and Reports, 1999 (in press).

91. Espeland MA, Marcovina SM, Miller V, et al. Effect of postmenopausal hormone ther-apy on lipoprotein(a) concentration. Circulation 1998;97:979–986.

92. Scanu AM, Pfaffinger D, Fless GM, Makino K, Eisenbart J, Hinman J. Attenuation of im-munologic reactivity of lipoprotein(a) by thiols and cysteine-containing compounds: structural implications. Arterioscler Thromb 1992;12:424–9.

93. Guo H-C, Armstrong VW, Luc G, et al. Characterization of five mouse monoclonal anti-bodies to apolipoprotein(a) from human Lp(a): evidence for weak plasminogen reactiv-ity. J Lipid Res 1989;30:23–37.

94. Naruszewicz M, Giroux L-M, Davignon J. Oxidative modification of Lp(a) causes changes in the structure and biological properties of apo(a). Chem Phys Lipids 1994; 67/68:167–74.

95. Marcovina SM, Curtiss LK, Milne R, Albers JJ. Selection and characterization of mono-clonal antibodies for measuring plasma concentrations of apolipoproteins A-I and B. Scientific Division, Committee on Apolipoproteins, Working Group on antibody re-agents, IFCC document. JIFCC 1990;2:138–44.

96. Rainwater DL, Manis GS. Immunochemical characterization and quantitation of lipo-protein(a) in baboons: development of an assay depending on two antigenically dis-tinct proteins. Atherosclerosis 1988;73:23–31.

97. Fless GM, Snyder ML, Scanu AM. Enzyme-linked immunoassay for Lp(a). J Lipid Res 1989;30:651–62.

98. Vu-Dac N, Mezdour H, Parra HJ, Luc G, Luyeye I, Fruchart JC. A selective bi-site immunoenzymatic procedure for human Lp(a) lipoprotein quantification using monoclonal antibodies against apo(a) and apo B. J Lipid Res 1989;30:1437–43.

99. Taddei-Peters WC, Butman BT, Jones GR, Venetta TM, Macomber PF, Ransom H. Quantification of lipoprotein(a) particles containing various apolipoprotein(a) isoforms by a monoclonal anti-apo(a) capture antibody and a polyclonal anti-apo-lipoprotein B detection antibody sandwich enzyme immunoassay. Clin Chem 1993;39:1382–9.

100. Kottke BA, Bren ND. A particle concentration fluorescence immunoassay for Lp(a). Chem Phys Lipids 1994;67/68:249–56.

101. Fless GM, Pfaffinger DJ, Eisenbart JD, Scanu AM. Solubility-, immunochemical-, and lipoprotein-binding properties of apo B-100-apo(a), the protein moiety of lipoprotein(a). J Lipid Res 1990;31:909–18.

102. Zawadzki Z, Tercé F, Seman LJ, et al. The linkage with apolipoprotein(a) in lipoprotein(a) modifies the immunochemical and functional properties of apolipoprotein B. Biochemistry 1988;27:8474–81.

103. Gries A, Fievet C, Marcovina S, et al. Interaction of LDL, Lp(a), and reduced Lp(a) with monoclonal antibodies against apo B. J Lipid Res 1988;29:1–8.

104. Albers JJ, Hazzard WR. Immunochemical quantification of human plasma Lp(a) lipoprotein. Lipids 1974;9:15–26.

105. Marcovina SM, Albers JJ, Gabel B, Koschinsky ML, Gaur VP. Effect of the number of apolipoprotein(a) kringle 4 domains on immunochemical measurements of Lipoprotein(a) Clin Chem 1995;41:246–55.

106. Albers JJ, Marcovina SM, Lodge MS. The unique lipoprotein(a): properties and immunochemical measurement. Clin Chem 1990;36:2019–26.

107. Labeur C, Shepherd J, Rosseneu M. Immunological assays of apolipoproteins in plasma: methods and instrumentation. Clin Chem 1990;36:591–7.

108. Albers JJ, Adolphson JL, Hazzard WR. Radioimmunoassay of human plasma Lp(a) lipoprotein. J Lipid Res 1977;18:331–8.

109. Molinari E, Pichler P, Krempler F, Kostner G. A rapid screening method for pathological lipoprotein Lp(a) concentrations by counterimmunoelectrophoresis. Clin Chim Acta 1983;128:373–8.

110. Gaubatz JW, Cushing GL, Morrissett JD. Quantitation, isolation, and characterization of human lipoprotein(a). Methods Enzymol 1986;129:167–86.

111. Labeur C, Michiels G, Bury J, Usher DC, Rosseneu M. Lipoprotein(a) quantified by an enzyme-linked immunosorbent assay with monoclonal antibodies. Clin Chem 1989; 35:1380–4.

112. Abe A, Maeda S, Makino K, et al. Enzyme-linked immunosorbent assay of lipoprotein(a) in serum and cord blood. Clin Chim Acta 1988;177:31–40.

113. Wong WLT, Eaton DL, Berloui A, Fendly B, Hass PE. A monoclonal antibody-based enzyme-linked immunosorbent assay of lipoprotein(a). Clin Chem 1990;36:192–7.

114. Vu-Dac N, Chekkor A, Parra H, Duthilleul P, Fruchart JC. Latex immunoassay of human serum Lp(a+) lipoprotein. J Lipid Res 1985;26:267–9.

115. Cazzolato G, Prakasch G, Green S, Kostner GM. The determination of lipoprotein Lp(a) by rate and endpoint nephelometry. Clin Chim Acta 1983;135:203–8.

116. Levine DM, Sloan BJ, Donner JE, Lorenz JD, Henzerling R. Automated measurement of Lp(a) by immunoturbidimetric analysis. Int J Clin Lab Res 1992;22:173–8.

117. Albers JJ, Marcovina SM. Standardization of Lp(a) measurement. Chem Phys Lipids 1994;67/68:257–63.

118. Labeur C, Rosseneu M, Henderson O. International Lp(a) standardization. Chem Phys Lipids 1994;67/68:265–70.

119. Kulkarni KR, Garber DW, Marcovina SM, Segrest JP. Quantification of cholesterol in all lipoprotein classes by the VAP-II method. J Lipid Res 1994;35:159–68.

120. Seman LJ, Jenner JL, McNamara JR, Schaefer EJ. Quantification of lipoprotein(a) in plasma by assaying cholesterol in lectin-bound plasma fraction. Clin Chem 1994;40:400–3.

121. Tate et al., IFCC Standardization Project for the Measurement of Lipoprotein(a). Phase 2. Selection and properties of a proposed secondary reference material for lipoprotein(a). Clin Chem Lab Med (in press).

122. Austin MA, Sandholzer C, Selby JV, Newman B, Krauss RM, Utermann G. Lipoprotein(a) in women twins: heritability and relationship to apolipoprotein(a) phenotypes. Am J Hum Genet 1992;51:829–40.

123. Guyton JR, Dahlen GH, Patsch W, Kautz JA, Gotto AM, Jr. Relationship of plasma

lipoprotein Lp(a) levels to race and to apolipoprotein B. Arteriosclerosis 1985;5: 265–72.

124. Helmhold M, Bigge J, Muche R, et al. Contribution of the apo(a) phenotype to plasma Lp(a) concentration shows considerable ethnic variation. J Lipid Res 1991;32:1919–28.

125. Sandholzer C, Saha N, Kark JD, et al. Apo(a) isoforms predict risk for coronary heart disease: a study in six populations. Arterioscler Thromb 1992;12:1214–26.

126. Cobbaert C, Kesteloot H. Serum lipoprotein(a) levels in racially different populations. Am J Epidemiol 1992;136:441–9.

127. Parra HJ, Luyeye I, Bouramoue C, Demarquilly C, Fruchart JC. Black-White differences in serum Lp(a) lipoprotein levels. Clin Chim Acta 1987;168:27–31.

128. Srinivasan SR, Dahlen GH, Jarpa RA, Webber LS, Berenson GS. Racial (Black-White) difference in serum lipoprotein(a) distribution and its relation to parental myocardial infarction in children. Bogalusa Heart Study. Circulation 1991;84:160–7.

129. Brown SA, Hutchinson R, Morrisett J, et al. Plasma lipid, lipoprotein cholesterol, and apoprotein distributions in selected US communities: the Atherosclerosis Risk in Communities (ARIC) study. Arterioscler Thromb 1993;13:1139–58.

130. Marcovina SM, Albers JJ, Jacobs DR, Jr, et al. Lipoprotein(a) concentrations and apolipoprotein(a) phenotypes in Caucasians and African Americans: the CARDIA study. Arterioscler Thromb 1993;13:1037–45.

131. Rifai N, Heiss G, Doetsch K. Lipoprotein(a) at birth, in Blacks and Whites. Atherosclerosis 1992;92:123–9.

132. Wilcken DEL, Wang XL, Dudman NPB. The relationship between infant and parent Lp(a) concentrations. Chem Phys Lipids 1994;67/68:299–304.

133. Sandkamp M, Assmann G. Lipoprotein(a) in PROCAM participants and young myocardial infarction survivors. In: Scanu AM, ed. Lipoprotein(a). San Diego: Academic Press, 1990:205–9.

134. Nabulsi AA, Folsom AR, White A, et al. Association of hormone-replacement therapy with various cardiovascular risk factors in postmenopausal women. N Engl J Med 1993;328:1069–75.

135. Jenner JL, Ordovas JM, Lamon-Fava S, et al. Effects of age, sex, and menopausal status on plasma lipoprotein(a) levels: The Framingham Offspring Study. Circulation 1993;87:1135–41.

136. Marcovina SM, Albers JJ, Wijsman E, Zhang Z-H, Chapman NH, Kennedy H. Differences in Lp(a) concentrations and apo(a) polymorphs between Black and White Americans. J Lipid Res 1996;37:2569–85.

137. Scanu AM. Lipoprotein(a): a potential bridge between the fields of atherosclerosis and thrombosis. Arch Pathol Lab Med 1988;112:1045–7.

138. Cushing, GL, Gaubatz JW, Nava ML, et al. Quantitation and localization of apolipoproteins(a) and B in coronary artery bypass vein grafts at re-operation. Arteriosclerosis 1989;9:593–603.

139. Rath M, Niendorf A, Reblin T, Dietel M, Krebber HJ, Beisiegel U. Detection and quantification of lipoprotein(a) in the arterial wall of 107 coronary artery bypass patients. Arteriosclerosis 1989;9:579–92.

140. Niendorf A, Rath M, Wolf K, et al. Morphological detection and quantification of lipoprotein(a) deposition in atheromatous lesions of human aorta and coronary arteries. Virchows Archiv Pathol Anat 1990;417:105–11.

141. Beisiegel U, Niendorf A, Wolf K, Reblin T, Rath M. Lipoprotein(a) in the arterial wall. Eur Heart J 1990;11(supplement E):174–83.

142. Wolf K, Rath M, Niendorf A, Beisiegel U, Dietel M. Morphological co-localization of apoprotein(a) and fibrin(ogen) in human coronary atheromas. Circulation 1989;80: II-522.

143. Dangas G, Mehran R, Harpel PC, et al. Lipoprotein(a) and inflammation in human coronary atheroma: association with the severity of clinical presentation. J Am Coll Cardiol 1998;32:2035–2042.

144. Poon M, Zhang X, Dunsky KG, Taubman MB, Harpel PC. Apolipoprotein(a) induces

monocyte chemotactic activity in human vascular endothelial cells. *Circulation* 1997; 96:2514–2519.

145. Etingin OR, Hajjar DP, Hajjar KA, Harpel PC, Nachman RL. Lipoprotein(a) regulates plasminogen activator inhibitor-1 expression in endothelial cells: a potential mechanism in thrombogenesis. J Biol Chem 1991;266:2459–65.

146. Levin EG, Miles LA, Fless GM, Scanu AM, Baynham P, Curtiss LK, Plow EF. Lipoproteins inhibit the secretion of tissue plasminogen activator from human endothelial cells. Arterioscler Thromb 1994;14:438–42.

147. Harpel PC, Gordon BR, Parker TS. Plasmin catalyzes binding of lipoprotein(a) to immobilized fibrinogen and fibrin. Proc Natl Acad Sci USA 1989;86:3847–51.

148. Loscalzo J, Weinfeld M, Fless GM, Scanu AM. Lipoprotein(a), fibrin binding, and plasminogen activation. Arteriosclerosis 1990;10:240–5.

149. Rouy D, Koschinsky ML, Fleury V, Chapman J, Angles-Cano E. The binding of human recombinant apolipoprotein(a) and plasminogen to fibrin surfaces. Biochemistry 1992; 3:6333–39.

150. Gonzalez-Gronow M, Edelberg JM, Pizzo SV. Further characterization of the cellular plasminogen binding site: evidence that plasminogen 2 and lipoprotein(a) compete for the same site. Biochemistry 1989;28:2374–7.

151. Miles LA, Fless GM, Levin EG, Scanu AM, Plow E. A potential basis for the thrombotic risks associated with lipoprotein(a). Nature 1989;339:301–3.

152. Hajjar KA, Gavish D, Breslow JL, Nachman RL. Lipoprotein(a) modulation of endothelial cell surface fibrinolysis and its potential role in atherosclerosis. Nature 1989; 339:303–5.

153. Sangrar W, Gabel BR, Boffa MB, Walker JB, Hancock MA, Marcovina SM, Horrevoets AJG, Nesheim ME, Koschinsky ML. The solution phase interaction between apolipoprotein(a) and plasminogen inhibits the binding of plasminogen to a plasmin-modified fibrinogen surface. Biochemistry 1997;34:10353–10363.

154. Sangrar W, Bajzar L, Nesheim ME, Koschinsky ML. Antifibrinolytic effect of recombinant apolipoprotein(a) *in vitro* is primarily due to attenuation of tPA-mediated Glu-plasminogen activation. Biochemistry 1995;34:5151–5157.

155. Palabrica TM, Liu AC, Aronovitz MJ, Furie B, Lawn RM, Furie BC. Antifibrinolytic activity of apolipoprotein(a) *in vivo*: human apolipoprotein(a) transgenic mice are resistant to tissue plasminogen activator-mediated thrombolysis. Nature Medicine 1995;1: 256–259.

156. Biemond BJ, Friederich PW, Koschinsky ML, Sangrar W, Xia J, Levi M, Buller HR, ten Cate JW. Apolipoprotein(a) attenuates fibrinolysis in the rabbit jugular vein thrombosis model *in vivo*. Circulation 1997;96:1612–1615.

157. Halvorsen S, Skjonsberg OH, Berg K, Ruyter R, Godal HC. Does Lp(a) lipoprotein inhibit the fibrinolytic system? Thromb Res 1992;68:223–32.

158. Mao SJ, Tucci MA. Lipoprotein(a) enhances plasma clot lysis *in vitro*. FEBS Lett 1990; 267:131–4.

159. Harpel PC, Chang VT, Borth W. Homocysteine and other sulfhydryl compounds enhance the binding of lipoprotein(a) to fibrin: a potential biochemical link between thrombosis, atherogenesis and sulfhydryl compound metabolism. Proc Natl Acad Sci USA 1992;89: 10193–7.

160. Harpel PC, Borth W. Fibrin, lipoprotein(a), plasmin interactions: a model linking thrombosis and atherogenesis. Ann NY Acad Sci 1992;667:233–8.

161. Rand ML, Sangrar W, Hancock MA, Taylor DM, Marcovina SM, Packham MA, and Koschinsky ML. Apolipoprotein(a) enhances platelet repsonses to the thrombin receptor-activating peptide, SFLLRN. Arterioscler Thromb Vasc Biol 1998;18:1393–1399.

162. Kojima S, Harpel PC, Rifkin DB. Lipoprotein(a) inhibits the generation of transforming growth factor beta: an endogenous inhibitor of smooth muscle cell migration. J Cell Biol 1991;113:1439–45.

163. Grainger DJ, Kirschenlohr HL, Metcalfe JC, Weissberg PL, Wade DP, Lawn RM. The pro-

liferation of human smooth muscle cells is promoted by lipoprotein(a). Science 1993;260:1655–8.

164. Grainger DJ, Kemp PR, Liu AC, Lawn RM, Metcalfe JC. Activation of transforming growth factor-beta is inhibited in transgenic apolipoprotein(a) mice. Nature 1994;370: 460–62.

165. Yashiro A, O'Neil J, Hoff HF. Insoluble complex formation of lipoprotein(a) with low-density lipoprotein in the presence of calcium ions. J Biol Chem 1993;268: 4709–15.

166. Smith EB, Cochran S. Factors influencing the accumulation in fibrous plaques of lipid derived from low-density lipoprotein. II. Preferential immobilization of lipoprotein(a) (Lp(a)). Atherosclerosis 1990;84:173–81.

167. Keesler GA, Gabel BR, Devlin C, Koschinsky ML, Tabas I. The binding activity of the macrohage lipoprotein(a)/apolipoprotein(a) receptor is induced by cholesterol via a post-translational mechanism and recognizes distinct kringle domains on apolipoprotein(a). J Biol Chem 1996;271:32096–32104.

168. Raitakari OT, Adams MR, Celermajer DS. Effect of Lp(a) on the early functional and structural changes of atherosclerosis. Arterioscler Thromb Vasc Biol 1999;19:990–995.

169. Scanu AM. Structural basis for the presumptive atherothrombogenic action of lipoprotein(a). Facts and speculations. Biochem Pharmacol 1993;46:1675–80.

170. Oshima S, Uchida K, Yasu T, Uno K, Nonogi H, Haze K. Transient increase of plasma lipoprotein(a) in patients with unstable angina pectoris: does lipoprotein(a) alter fibrinolysis? Arterioscler Thromb 1991;11:1772–7.

171. Donders SH, Lustermans FA, Van Wersch JW. Coagulation factors and lipid composition of the blood in treated and untreated hypertensive patients. Scand J Clin Lab Invest 1993;53:179–86.

172. Armstrong VW, Neubauer C, Schutz E, Tebbe U. Lack of association between raised serum Lp(a) concentration and unsuccessful thrombolysis after acute myocardial infarction. Lancet 1990;336:1077.

173. von Hodenberg E, Kreuzer J, Hautmann KJM, Nordt T, Kubler W, Bode C. Effects of lipoprotein(a) on success rate of thrombolytic therapy in acute myocardial infarction. Am J Cardiol 1991;67:1349–53.

174. Qiu S, Theroux P, Genest J Jr, Solymoss BC, Robitaille D, Marcil M. Lipoprotein(a) blood concentrations in unstable angina pectoris, acute myocardial infarction, and after thrombolytic therapy. Am J Cardiol 1991;67:1175–9.

175. von Hodenberg, Pestel E, Kreuzer J, Freitag M, Bode C. Effects of lipoprotein(a) on thrombolysis. Chem Phys Lipids 1994;67/68:381–5.

176. Tranchesi B, Santos-Filho RS, Vinagre C, et al. Lipoprotein(a) concentrations do not influence the outcome of rt-PA therapy in acute myocardial infarction. Ann Hematol 1991;62;141–2.

177. Hegele RA, Freeman MR, Langer A, Connelly PW, Armstrong PW. Acute reduction of lipoprotein(a) by tissue-type plasminogen activator. Circulation 1992;85:2034–8.

178. Di Lorenzo M, Salvini P, Levi-Della-Vida M, Maddaloni E. Acute reduction of lipoprotein(a) by tissue-type plasminogen activator. Circulation 1993;87:1052–3.

179. Hervio L, Chapman MJ, Thillet J, Loyau S, Anglés-Cano E. Does apolipoprotein(a) heterogeneity influence lipoprotein(a) effects on fibrinolysis? Blood 1993;82:392–7.

180. Hervio L, Girard-Globia A, Durlach V, Anglés-Cano E. The antifibrinolytic effect of lipoprotein(a) in heterozygous subjects is modulated by the relative concentration of each of the apolipoprotein(a) isoforms and their affinity for fibrin. Eur J Clin Invest 1996;26: 411–17.

181. Dahlen G, Ericson C, Furberg C, Lundkvist L, Svardsudd K. Angina of effort and an extra pre-beta lipoprotein fraction. Acta Med Scan 192;531(Suppl):6.

182. Papadopoulos NM, Bedynek JL. Serum lipoprotein patterns in patients with coronary atherosclerosis. Clin Chim Acta 1973;44:153.

183. Insull W, Najmi M, Vloedman DA. Plasma pre-beta lipoprotein subfractions in diagnosis of coronary artery disease. Circulation 1972;45(suppl II):II–170.

184. Berg K, Dahlen G, Frick MH. Lp(a) lipoprotein and pre-beta1-lipoprotein in patients with coronary heart disease. Clin Genet 1974;6:230–5.

185. Dahlen G, Berg K, Gillnas T, Ericson C. Lp(a) lipoprotein/pre-beta1-lipoprotein in Swedish middle-aged males and in patients with coronary heart disease. Clin Genet 1975;7:334–41.

186. Dahlen G, Frick MH, Berg K, Valle M, Wiljasalo M. Further studies of Lp(a) lipoprotein/pre-beta1-lipoprotein in patients with coronary heart disease. Clin Genet 1975;8:183–9.

187. Kostner GM, Avogaro P, Cazzolato G, Marth E, Bittolo-Bon G, Qunici GB. Lipoprotein Lp(a) and the risk for myocardial infarction. Atherosclerosis 1981;38:51.

188. Dahlen GH, Guyton JR, Mohammad A, Farmer JA, Kautz JA, Gotto AM. Association of levels of lipoprotein Lp(a), plasma lipids, and other lipoproteins with coronary artery disease documented by angiography. Circulation 1986;74:758–65.

189. Armstrong VW, Cremer P, Eberle E, et al. The association between serum Lp(a) concentrations and angiographically assessed coronary atherosclerosis: dependence on serum LDL levels. Atherosclerosis 1986;62:249–57.

190. Hearn JA, DeMaio SJ Jr, Roubin GS, Hammarstrom M, Sgoutas D. Predictive value of Lipoprotein(a) and other serum lipoproteins in the angiographic diagnosis of coronary artery disease. Am J Cardiol 1990;66:1176–80.

191. Genest J Jr, Jenner JL, McNamara JR, et al. Prevalence of lipoprotein(a) [Lp(a)] excess in coronary artery disease. Am J Cardiol 1991;67:1039–45.

192. Genest JJ Jr, Martin-Munley SS, McNamara JR, et al. Familial lipoprotein disorders in patients with premature coronary artery disease. Circulation 1992;85:2025–33.

193. Genest JJ Jr, McNamara JR, Ordovas JM, et al. Lipoprotein cholesterol, apolipoprotein A-I and B and Lipoprotein(a) abnormalities in men with premature coronary artery disease. J Am Coll Cardiol 1992;19:792–802.

194. Rosengren A, Wilhelmsen L, Eriksson E, Risberg B, Wedel H. Lipoprotein (a) and coronary heart disease: a prospective case-control study in a general population sample of middle-aged men. BMJ 1990;301:1248–51.

195. Sandkamp M, Funke H, Schulte H, Kohler E, Assmann G. Lipoprotein(a) is an independent risk factor for myocardial infarction at a young age. Clin Chem 1990;36:20–23.

196. Kark JD, Sandholzer C, Friedlander Y, Utermann G. Plasma Lp(a), apolipoprotein(a) isoforms and acute myocardial infarction in men and women: a case-control study in the Jerusalem population. Atherosclerosis 1993;98:139–51.

197. Graziani MS, Zanolla L, Righetti G, et al. Lipoprotein(a) concentrations are increased in patients with myocardial infarction and angiographically normal coronary arteries. Eur J Clin Chem Clin Biochem 1993;31:135–7.

198. Hoff HF, Beck GJ, Skibinski CI, et al. Serum Lp(a) level as a predictor of vein graft stenosis after coronary artery bypass surgery in patients. Circulation 1988;77:1238–44.

199. Solymoss BC, Marcil M, Wesolowska E, Lesperance J, Pelletier LC, Campeau L. Risk factors of venous aortocoronary bypass graft disease noted at late symptom-directed angiographic study. Can J Cardiol 1993;9:80–84.

200. Hearn JA, Donohue BC, Baalbaki H, et al. Usefulness of serum lipoprotein(a) as a predictor of restenosis after percutaneous transluminal coronary angioplasty. Am J Cardiol 1992;69:736–9.

201. Tenda K, Saikawa T, Maeda T, et al. The relationship between serum lipoprotein(a) and restenosis after initial elective percutaneous transluminal coronary angioplasty. Jpn Circ J 1993;57:789–95.

202. Desmarais RL, Sarembock IJ, Ayers CR, Vernon SM, Powers ER, Gimple LW. Elevated serum lipoprotein(a) as a risk factor for clinical recurrence after coronary balloon angioplasty. Circulation 1995;91:1403–1409.

203. Yamamoto H, Imazu M, Yamabe T, Ueda H, Hattori Y, Yamakido M. Risk factors for restenosis after percutaneous transluminal coronary angioplasty: role of lipoprotein(a). Am Heart J 1995;130:1168–1173.

204. Miyata M, Biro S, Arima S, Hamasaki S, Kaieda H, Nakao S, Kawataki M, Nomoto K,

Hanaka H. High serum concentration of lipoprotein(a) is a risk factor for restenosis after percutaneous transluminal coronary angioplasty in Japanese patients with single vessel disease. Am Heart J 1996;132:269–273.

205. Seed M, Hopplicher F, Reaveley D, et al. Relation of serum lipoprotein(a) concentration and apolipoprotein(a) phenotype to coronary heart disease in patients with familial hypercholesterolemia. N Engl J Med 1990;322:1494–9.

206. Guo HC, Chapman MJ, Bruckert E, Farriaux JP, De-Gennes JL. Lipoprotein Lp(a) in homozygous familial hypercholesterolemia: density profile, particle heterogeneity, and apolipoprotein(a) phenotype. Atherosclerosis 1991;86:69–83.

207. Hegele RA, Connelly PW, Cullen-Dean G, Rose V. Elevated plasma lipoprotein(a) associated with abnormal stress thallium scans in children with familial hypercholesterolemia. Am J Cardiol 1993;72:402–6.

208. Sorensen KE, Celermajer DS, Georgakopoulos D, Hatcher G, Betteridge DJ, Deanfield JE. Impairment of endothelium-dependent dilation is an early event in children with familial hypercholesterolemia and is related to the lipoprotein(a) level. J Clin Invest 1994;93:50–55.

209. Cheng SW, Ting AC, Wong J. Lipoprotein(a) and its relationship to risk factors and severity of atherosclerotic peripheral vascular disease. Eur J Vasc Endovasc Surg 1997; 14:17–23.

210. Koltringer P, Jurgens G. A dominant role of lipoprotein(a) in the investigation and evaluation of parameters indicating development of cervical atherosclerosis. Atherosclerosis 1985;58:187–98.

211. Jurgens G, Koltringer P. Lipoprotein(a) in ischemic cerebrovascular disease: a new approach to the assessment of risk for stroke. Neurology 1987;37:513–15.

212. Woo J, Lau E, Lam CWK, et al. Hypertension, lipoprotein(a), and apolipoprotein A-I as risk factors for stroke in the Chinese. Stroke 1991;22:203–8.

213. Shintani S, Kikuchi S, Hamaguchi H, Shiigai T. High serum lipoprotein(a) concentrations are an independent risk factor for cerebral infarction. Stroke 1993;24:965–9.

214. Jovicic A, Ivanisevic V, Ivanovic I. Lipoprotein(a) in patients with carotid atherosclerosis and ischemic cerebrovascular disorders. Atherosclerosis 1993;98:59–65.

215. Nagayama M, Shinohara Y, Nagayama T. Lipoprotein(a) and ischemic cerebrovascular disease in young adults. Stroke 1994;25:74–78.

216. Peynet J, Beaudeux JL, Woimant F, Flourie F, Giraudeauz V, Vicaut E, Launay JM. Apolipoprotein(a) size polymorphism in young adults with ischemic stroke. Atherosclerosis 1999;142:233–239.

217. Averna MR, Barbagallo CM, Ocello S, et al. Lp(a) concentrations in patients undergoing aorto-coronary bypass surgery. Eur Heart J 1992;13:1405–9.

218. Yamaguchi H, Lee YJ, Daida H, et al. Effectiveness of LDL-apheresis in preventing restenosis after percutaneous transluminal coronary angioplasty (PTCA): LDL-apheresis angioplasty restenosis trial (L-ART). Chem Phys Lipids 1994;67/68: 399–403.

219. Kanemitsu S, Tekekoshi N, Murakami E. Effects of LDL apheresis on restenosis after angioplasty. Chem Phys Lipids 1994;67/68:339–43.

220. Walzl M, Lechner H, Walzl B, Schied G. Improved neurological recovery of cerebral infarctions after plasmapheretic reduction of lipids and fibrinogen. Stroke 1993;24: 1447–51.

221. Durrington PN. Lipoprotein(a). Ballieres Clin Endocrinol Metab 1995;9:773–795.

222. Sigurdsson G, Baldursdottir A, Sigvaldason H, Agnarsson U, Thorgeirsson G, Sigfusson N. Predictive value of apolipoproteins in a prospective survey of coronary artery disease in men. Am J Cardiol 1992;69:1251–4.

223. Cressman MD, Heyka RJ, Paganini EP, O'Neil J, Skibinski CI, Hoff HF. Lipoprotein(a) is an indipendent risk factor for cardiovascular disease in hemodialysis patients. Circulation 1992;86:475–482.

224. Cremer P, Nagel D, Labrot B, Mann H, Muche R, Elster H, Seidel D. Lipoprotein Lp(a) as predictor of myocardial infarction in comparison to fibrinogen, LDL cholesterol, and

other risk factors: results from the prospective Gottingen Risk, Incidence and Prevalence Study (GRIPS). Eur J Clin Invest 1994;24:444–53.

225. Boston AG, Gagnon DR, Cupples A, Wilson PWF, Jenner FL, Ordovas JM, Schaefer EJ, Castelli WP. A prospective investigation of elevated lipoprotein(a) detected by electrophoresis and cardiovascular disease in women: The Framingham Heart Study. Circulation 1994;90:1688–95.

226. Schaefer EJ, Lamon-Fava S, Jenner JL, et al. Lipoprotein(a) levels and risk of coronary heart disease in men. JAMA 1994;271:999–1003.

227. Assmann G, Schulte H, Von Eckardstein A. Hypertrigyceridemia and elevated lipoprotein(a) are risk factors for major coronary events in middle-aged men. Am J Cardiol 1996;77:1179–1184.

228. Bostom AG, Cupples LA, Jenner JL, Ordovas JM, Seman LJ, Wilson PWF, Schaefer EJ, Castelli WP. Elevated plasma lipoprotein(a) and coronary heart disease in men aged 55 years and younger. JAMA 1996;276:544–8.

229. Wild SH, Fortmann SP, Marcovina SM. A prospective case-control study of lipoprotein levels and apo(a) size and risk of coronary heart disease in Stanford Five-City Project participants. Arterioscler Thromb Vasc Biol 1997;17:239–45.

230. Jauhiainen M, Koskinen P, Ehnholm C, et al. Lipoprotein (a) and coronary heart disease risk: a nested case-control study of the Helsinki Heart Study participants. Atherosclerosis 1991;89:59–67.

231. Coleman MP, Key TJ, Wang DY, Hermon C, Fentiman IS, Allen DS, Jarvis M, Pike MC, Sanders TA. A prospective study of obesity, lipids, apolipoproteins, and ischaemic heart disease in women. Atherosclerosis 1992;92:177–185.

232. Ridker PM, Hennekens CH, Stampfer MJ. A prospective study of lipoprotein(a) and the risk of myocardial infarction. JAMA 1993;270:2195–9.

233. Alfthan G, Pekkanen J, Jauhiainen M, Pitkdniemi J, Karvonen M, Tuomilehto J, Salonen JT, Ehnholm C. Relation of serum homocysteine and lipoprotein(a) concentrations to atherosclerotic disease in a prospective Finnish population based study. Atherosclerosis 1994;106:9–19.

234. Craig WY, Neveux LM, Palomaki GE et al. Lipoprotein(a) as a risk factor for ischemic heart disease: metaanalysis of prospective studies. Clin Chem 1998;44:2301–2306.

235. Barnathan ES. Has lipoprotein "little" (a) shrunk? JAMA 1993;270:2224–5.

236. Gurewich V, Mittleman M. Lipoprotein(a) in coronary heart disease: is it a risk factor after all? JAMA 1994;271:1025–6.

237. Marcovina SM, Koschinsky ML. Lipoprotein(a) as a risk factor for coronary artery disease. Am J Cardiol 1998;82:57U–66U.

238. Orth-Gomer K, Mittleman MD, Schenk-Gustafsson K et al. Lipoprotein(a) as a determinant of coronary heart disease in young women. Circulation 1997;95:329–334.

239. Kim JQ, Song JH, Lee MM, et al. Evaluation of Lp(a) as a risk factor of coronary artery disease in the Korean population. Ann Clin Biochem 1992;29:226–8.

240. Sandholzer CH, Boerwinkle E, Saha N, Tong MC, Utermann G. Apolipoprotein(a) phenotypes, Lp(a) concentration and plasma lipid levels in relation to coronary heart disease in a Chinese population: evidence for the role of the apo(a) gene in coronary heart disease. J Clin Invest 1992;89:1040–46.

241. Abe A, Noma A. Studies on apolipoprotein(a) phenotypes. Part 1. Phenotype frequencies in a healthy Japanese population. Atherosclerosis 1992;96:1–8.

242. Abe A, Noma A, Lee YJ, Yamaguchi H. Studies on apolipoprotein(a) phenotypes. Part 2. Phenotype frequencies and Lp(a) concentrations in different phenotypes in patients with angiographically defined coronary artery diseases. Atherosclerosis 1992; 96:9–15.

243. Srinivasan SR, Dahlen GH, Jarpa RA, Webber LS, Berenson L. Racial (black-white) differences in serum lipoprotein(a) distribution and its relation to parental myocarial infarction in children. Bogalusa Heart Study. *Circulation* 1991;84:160–167.

244. Sorrentino MJ, Vielhauer C, Eisenbart JD, Fless GM, Scanu AM, Feldman T. Plasma lipoprotein (a) protein concentration and coronary artery disease in black patients compared with white patients. Am J Med 1992;93:658–62.

245. Marcovina SM, Hegele RA, Koschinsky ML. Lipoprotein(a) and coronary heart disease risk. Curr Cardiol Rep 1999;1:105–111.

246. Dahlen GH, Weinehall L, Stenlund H, et al. Lipoprotein(a) and cholesterol levels act synergistically and apolipoprotein A1 protects against primary acute myocardial infarction in middle-aged males. An incident case-control study from Sweden. J Intern Med 1998;244:425–430.

247. Maher VM, Brown BG, Marcovina SM, Hillger LA, Zhao XQ, Albers JJ. Effects of lowering elevated LDL cholesterol on the cardiovascular risk of lipoprotein(a). JAMA 1995;274:1771–4.

248. Hopkins PN, Wu LL, Hunt SC, et al. Lipoprotein(a) interactions with lipid and nonlipid risk factors in early familial coronary artery disease. Arterioscler Thromb Vasc Biol 1997;17:2783–2792.

249. Solymoss BC, Marcil M, Wesolowska E et al. Relation of coronary artery disease in women 60 years of age to the combined elevation of serum lipoprotein(a) and total cholesterol to HDL cholesterol ratio. Am J Cardiol 1993;72:1215–1219.

250. Cantin B, Gagnon F, Moorjani S et al. Is lipoprotein(a) an independent risk factor for ischemic heart disease in men? The Quebec Cardiovascular Study. J Am Coll Cardiol 1998;31:519–525.

251. Kronenberg F, Kronenberg MF, Kiechl S, Trenkwalder E, Santer P, Oberhollenzer F, Egger G, Utermann G, Willeit J. Role of lipoprotein(a) and apolipoprotein(a) phenotype in atherogenesis: prospective results from the Bruneck Study. Circulation 1999;100: 1154–1160.

252. Marcovina SM, Koschinsky ML. Lipoprotein(a) concentration and apolipoprotein(a) size. A synergistic role in advanced atherosclerosis? (Editorial) Circulation 1999;100: 1151–1153.

253. Jenkins AJ, Best JD. The role of lipoprotein(a) in the vascular complications of diabetes mellitus. J Int Med 1995;237:359–65.

254. Bruckert E, Davidoff P, Grimaldi A, et al. Increased serum levels of lipoprotein(a) in diabetes mellitus and their reduction with glycemic control. JAMA 1990;263: 35–36.

255. Haffner SM, Tuttle KR, Rainwater DL. Decrease of lipoprotein(a) with improved glycemic control in IDDM subjects. Diabetes Care 1991;14:302–7.

256. Guillausseau PJ, Peynet J, Chanson P, et al. Lipoprotein(a) in diabetic patients with and without chronic renal failure. Diabetes Care 1992;15:976–9.

257. Couper JJ, Bates DJ, Cocciolone R, et al. Association of lipoprotein(a) with puberty in IDDM. Diabetes Care 1993;16:869–73.

258. Salzer B, Stavljenic A, Jurgens G, Dumic M, Radica, A. Polymorphism of apolipoprotein E, lipoprotein(a), and other lipoproteins in children with type I diabetes. Clin Chem 1993;39:1427–32.

259. Nagashima K, Yutani S, Miyake H, Onigata K, Yagi H, Kuroume T. Lipoprotein(a) levels in Japanese children with IDDM. Diabetes Care 1993;16:846.

260. Ritter MM, Richter WO, Lyko K, Schwandt P. Lp(a) serum concentrations and metabolic control. Diabetes Care 1992;15:1441–2.

261. Maser RE, Usher D, Becker DJ, Drash AL, Kuller LH, Orchard TJ. Lipoprotein(a) concentration shows little relationship to IDDM complications in the Pittsburgh Epidemiology of Diabetes Complications Study cohort. Diabetes Care 1993;16:755–8.

262. Heller FR, Jamart J, Honore P, et al. Serum lipoprotein(a) in patients with diabetes mellitus. Diabetes Care 1993;16:819–23.

263. Perez A, Carreras G, Caixas A, Castellvi A, Caballero A, Bonet R, Ordonez-Llanos J, de Leiva A. Plasma lipoprotein(a) levels are not influenced by glycemic control in type I diabetes. Diabetes Care 1998;21:1517–1520.

264. Purnell JQ, Marcovina SM, Hokanson JE, Kennedy H, Cleary PA, Steffes MW, Brunzell JD. Levels of lipoprotein(a), apolipoprotein B, and lipoprotein cholesterol distribution in IDDM. Results from follow-up in the Diabetes Control and Complications Trial. Diabetes 1995;44:1218–1226.

265. Levitsky LL, Scanu AM, Gould SH. Lipoprotein(a) levels in black and white children and adolescents with IDDM. Diabetes Care 1991;14:283–7.

266. Austin A, Warty V, Janosky V, Arslanian S. The relationship of physical fitness to lipid and lipoprotein(a) levels in adolescents with IDDM. Diabetes Care 1993;16:4215.

267. Winocour PH, Durrington PN, Bhatnagar D, et al. A cross-sectional evaluation of cardiovascular risk factors in coronary heart disease associated with type 1 (insulin-dependent) diabetes mellitus. Diabetes Res Clin Pract 1992;18:173–84.

268. Klausen IC, Schmidt EB, Lervang HH, Gerdes LU, Ditzel J, Faergeman O. Normal lipoprotein(a) concentrations and apolipoprotein(a) isoforms in patients with insulin-dependent diabetes mellitus. Eur J Clin Invest 1992;22:538–41.

269. Császár A, Dieplinger H, Sandholzer C, et al. Plasma lipoprotein (a) concentration and phenotypes in diabetes mellitus. Diabetologia 1993;36:47–51.

270. Dubrey SW, Reaveley DA, Leslie DG, O'Donnell M, O'Connor BM, Seed M. Effect of insulin-dependent diabetes mellitus on lipids and lipoproteins: a study of identical twins. Clin Sci 1993;84:537–42.

271. Ramirez LC, Arauz-Pacheco C, Lackner C, Albright G, Adams BV, Raskin P. Lipoprotein(a) levels in diabetes mellitus: relationship to metabolic control. Ann Intern Med 1992;117: 42–7.

272. Joven J, Vilella E. Serum levels of lipoprotein(a) in patients with well-controlled non-insulin-dependent diabetes mellitus. JAMA 1991;265:1113–14.

273. Wolffenbuttel BH, Leurs PB, Sels JP, Rondas-Colbers GJ, Menheere PP, Nieuwenhuijzen-Kruseman AC. Improved blood glucose control by insulin therapy in type 2 diabetic patients has no effect on lipoprotein(a) concentrations. Diabet Med 1993; 10:427–30.

274. Velho G, Erlich D, Turpin E, et al. Lipoprotein(a) in diabetic patients and normoglycemic relatives in familial NIDDM. Diabetes Care 1993;16:742–7.

275. Jenkins AJ, Steele JS, Janus ED, Best JD. Increased plasma apolipoprotein(a) levels in IDDM patients with microalbumineria. Diabetes 1991;40:787–790.

276. Kapelrud H, Bangstead H-J, Dahl-Jorgensen K, Berg K, Hanssen KF. Serum Lp(a) lipoprotein concentrations in insulin-dependent diabetic patients with microalbumineria. Br Med J 1991;303:675–678.

277. Gall M-A, Rossing P, Hommel E, Voldsgaard AI, Andersen P, Nielsen FS, Dyerberg J, Parving H-H. Apolipoprotein(a) in insulin-dependent diabetic patients with and without diabetic nephropathy. Scand J Clin Lab Invest 1992;52:513–521.

278. Wanner C, Rader D, Bartens W, Kramer J, Brewer HB, Schollmeyer P, Wieland H. Elevated plasma lipoprotein(a) in patients with the nephrotic syndrome. Ann Intern Med 1993;119:263–269.

279. Ruiz J, Thillet J, Huby T, James RW, Erlich D, Flandre P, Froguel P, Chapman J, Passa P. Association of elevated lipoprotein(a) levels and coronary heart disease in NIDDM patients. Relationship with apolipoprotein(a) phenotypes. Diabetologia 1994;37:585–591.

280. Hiraga T, Kobayashi T, Okubo M, Nakanishi K, Sugimoto T, Ohashi Y, Murase T. Prospective study of lipoprotein(a) as a risk factor for atherosclerotic cardiovascular disease in patients with diabetes. Diabetes Care 1995;18:241–244.

281. James RW, Boemi M, Sirolla C, Amadio L, Fumelli P, Pometta D. Lipoprotein(a) and vascular disease in diabetic patients. Diabetologia 1995;38:711–714.

282. Yamamoto M, Egusa G, Yamakido M. Carotid atherosclerosis and serum lipoprotein(a) concentrations in patients with NIDDM. Diabetes Care 1997;20:829–831.

283. Maioli M, Tonolo G, Pacifico A, et al. Raised serum apolipoprotein (a) in active diabetic retinopathy. Diabetologia 1993;36:88–90.

284. Muller HM, Diekstall FF, Schmidt E, Marz W, Canzler H, Demeler U. Lipoprotein (a): a risk factor for retinal vascular occlusion. Ger J Ophthalmol 1992;1:338–41.

285. Tomikawa S, Mezawa M, Yoshida Y, Saiga T, Shimizu Y. Lipoprotein (a) and sclerotic changes in retinal arterioles. Nippon Ganka Gakkai Zasshi 1993;97:967–74.

286. Ritter MM, Loscar M, Richter WO, Schwandt P. Lipoprotein(a) in diabetes mellitus. Clin Chim Acta 1993;214:45–54.

287. Haffner SM, Klein BE, Moss SE, Klein R. Lp(a) is not related to retinopathy in diabetic subjects. Eur J Ophthalmol 1995;5:119–23.

288. Takegoshi T, Kotoh C, Haba T, et al. A study of the clinical significance of lipoprotein(a) in nephrotic syndrome. Jpn J Med 1991;30:21–5.

289. Thomas ME, Freestone A, Varghese Z, Persaud JW, Moorhead JF. Lipoprotein(a) in patients with proteinuria. Nephrol Dial Transplant 1992;7:597–601.

290. Faucher C, Doucet C, Baumelou A, Chapman J, Jacobs C, Thillet J. Elevated lipoprotein(a) levels in primary nephrotic syndrome. Am J Kidney Dis 1993;22:808–813.

291. Dieplinger H, Kronenberg F. Genetics and metabolism of lipoprotein(a) and their clinical implications. (Part 2). Wien Klin Wochenschr 1999;111/2:46–55.

292. Stenvinkel P, Berglund L, Heimburger O, Pettersson E, Alvestrand A. Lipoprotein(a) in nephrotic syndrome. Kidney Int 1993;44:1116–23.

293. De Sain-Van Der Velden MG, Reijngoud DJ, Kaysen GA, Gadellaa MM, Voorbij H, Stellaard F, Koomans HA, Rabelink TJ. Evidence for increased synthesis of lipoprotein(a) in the nephrotic syndrome. J Am Soc Nephrol 1998;9:1474–1481.

294. Appel GB, Blum CB, Chien S, Kunis CL, Appel AS. The hyperlipidemia of the nephrotic syndrome: relation to plasma albumin concentration, oncotic pressure and viscosity. N Engl J Med 1985;312:1544–1548.

295. Parra HJ, Mezdour H, Cachera C, Dracon M, Tacquet A, Fruchart JC. Lp(a) lipoprotein in patients with chronic renal failure treated by hemodialysis. Clin Chem 1987;33:721.

296. Heimann P, Josephson MA, Felner SK, Thistlethwaite JR Jr, Stuart FP, Dasgupta A. Elevated lipoprotein(a) levels in renal transplantation and hemodialysis patients. Am J Nephrol 1991;11:470–4.

297. Cressman MD, Heyka RJ, Paganini EP, O'Neil J, Skibinski CI, Hoff HF. Lipoprotein(a) is an independent risk factor for cardiovascular disease in hemodialysis patients. Circulation 1992;86:475–82.

298. Barbagallo CM, Averna MR, Scafidi V, Galione A, Notarbartolo A. Increased lipoprotein(a) levels in subjects with chronic renal failure on hemodialysis. Nephron 1992;62:471–2.

299. Webb AT, Reaveley DA, O'Donnell M, O'Connor B, Seed M, Brown EA. Lipoprotein (a) in patients on maintenance haemodialysis and continuous ambulatory peritoneal dialysis. Nephrol Dial Transplant 1993;8:609–13.

300. Thillet J, Faucher C, Issad B, Allouache M, Chapman J, Jacobs C. Lipoprotein(a) in patients treated by continuous ambulatory peritoneal dialysis. Am J Kidney Dis 1993; 22:226–32.

301. Takegoshi T, Kitoh C, Shimada T, Kawai K, Yamazaki Y, Mabuchi H. Alterations of Lp(a) lipoprotein in patients with chronic renal failure treated by continuous ambulatory peritoneal dialysis. Nippon Jinzo Gakkai Shi 1993;35:757–63.

302. Anwar N, Bhatnagar D, Short CD, et al. Serum lipoprotein (a) concentrations in patients undergoing continuous ambulatory peritoneal dialysis. Nephrol Dial Transplant 1993;8: 71–74.

303. Webb AT, Plant M, Reaveley DA, et al. Lipid and lipoprotein(a) concentrations in renal transplant patients. Nephrol Dial Transplant 1992;7:636–41.

304. Murphy BG, McNamee P, Duly E, Henry W, Archbold P, Trinick T. Increased serum apolipoprotein(a) in patients with chronic renal failure treated with continuous ambulatory peritoneal dialysis. Atherosclerosis 1992;93:53–57.

305. Hirata K, Kikuchi S, Saku K, Jimi S, Zhang B, Naito S, Hamaguchi H, Arakawa K. Apolipoprotein(a) phenotypes and serum lipoprotein(a) levels in maintenance hemodialysis patients with/without diabetes mellitus. Kidney Int 1993;44:1062–1070.

306. Auguet T, Senti M, Rubies-Prat J, Pelegri A, Pedro-Botet J, Nogues X, Romero R. Serum lipoprotein(a) concentration in patients with chronic renal failure receiving hemodialysis and continuous ambulatory peritoneal dialysis. Nephrol Dial Transplant 1993;8:199–1103.

307. Irish AB, Simons LA, Savdie E, Hayes JM, Simons J. Lipoprotein(a) concentrations in chronic renal disease states, dialysis and transplantation. Aust NZ J Med 1992;22: 243–8.

308. Kronenberg F, Konig P, Neyer U, Auinger M, Pribasnig A, Lang U, Reitinger J, Pinter G, Utermann G, Dieplinger H. Multicenter study of lipoprotein(a) and apolipoprotein(a) phenotypes in patients with end-stage renal disease treated by hemodialysis or continuous ambulatory peritoneal dialysis. J Am Soc Nephrol 1995;6:110–120.

309. Dieplinger H, Lackner C, Kronenberg F, Sandholzer Ch, Lhotta K, Hoppichler F, Graff H, Konig P. Elevated plasma concentrations of plasma lipoprotein(a) in patients with end-stage renal disease are not related to the size polymorphism of apolipoprotein(a). J Clin Invest 1993;91:397–401.

310. Zimmermann J, Herrlinger S, Pruy A, Wanner C. Mechanism of high serum lipoprotein(a) in hemodialysis patients. J Am Soc Nephrol 1997;8:260A (abstract).

311. Black IW, Wilcken DE. Decreases in apolipoprotein(a) after renal transplantation: implications for lipoprotein(a) metabolism. Clin Chem 1992;38:353–7.

312. Kronenberg F, Konig P, Lhotta K, Konigsrainer A, Sandholzer Ch, Utermann G, Dieplinger H. Cyclosporin and serum lipids in renal transplant recipients. Lancet 1993;341:765.

313. Azrolan N, Brown CD, Thomas L, Hayek T, Zhao ZH, Roberts KG, Scheiner C, Friedman EA. Cyclosporin A has divergent effects on plasma LDL cholesterol (LDL-C) and lipoprotein(a) (Lp(a)) levels in renal transplant recipients: evidence for renal involvement in the maintenance of LDL-C and the elevation of Lp(a) concentrations in hemodialysis patients. Arterioscler Thromb 1994;14:1393–1398.

314. Kronenberg F, Konig P, Lhotta K, Ofner D, Sandholzer Ch, Margreiter R, Dosch E, Utermann G, Dieplinger H. Apolipoprotein(a) phenotype-associated decrease in lipoprotein(a)plasma concentrations after renal transplantation. Arterioscler Thromb 1994;14:1399–1404.

315. Kerschdorfer L, Konig P, Neyer U, Bosmuller C, Lhotta K, Auinger M, Hohenegger M, Riegler P, Margreiter R, Utermann G, Dieplinger H, Kronenberg F. Lp(a) plasma concentrations after renal transplantation: a prospective evaluation after four years of follow-up. Atherosclerosis 1999; in press.

316. Haffner SM, Gruber KK, Aldrete G Jr, Morales PA, Stern MP, Tuttle KR. Increased lipoprotein(a) concentrations in chronic renal failure. J Am Soc Nephrol 1992;3:1156–62.

317. Sato H, Suzuki S, Ueno M, et al. Localization of apolipoprotein(a) and B-100 in various renal diseases. Kidney Int 1993;43:430–5.

318. Kramer-Guth A, Greiber S, Pavenstadt H, Quaschning T, Winkler K, Schollmeyer P, Wanner C. Interaction of native and oxidized lipoprotein(a) with human mesangial cells and matrix. Kidney Int 1996;49:1250–61.

319. Greiber S, Kramer-Guth A, Pavenstadt H, Gutenkunst M, Schollmeyer P, Wanner C. Effects of lipoprotein(a) on mesangial cell proliferation and viability. Nephrol Dial Transplant 1996;11:778–85.

320. Samuelsson O, Attman PO, Knight-Gibson C, Larsson R, Mulec H, Wedel H, Weiss L, Alaupovic P. Plasma levels of lipoprotein(a) do not predict progression of human chronic renal failure. Nephrol Dial Transplant 1996;11:2237–2243.

321. Cavaillon JM, Poignet JL, Fitting C, Delons S. Serum interleukin-6 in long-term hemodialyzed patients. Nephron 1992;60:307–13.

322. Docci D, Bilancioni R, Buscaroli A, et al. Elevated serum levels of C-reactive protein in hemodialysis patients. Nephron 1990;56:364–7.

323. Mege JL, Olmer M, Purgus R, et al. Haemodialysis membranes modulate chronically the production of TNF alpha, IL1beta and IL6. Nephrol Dial Transplant 1991;6:868–75.

324. Le JM, Vilcek J. Interleukin-6: a multifunctional cytokine regulating immune reactions and the acute phase response. Lab Invest 1989;61:588–602.

325. Kishimoto T. The biology of interleukin-6. Blood 1989;74:1–10.

326. Sonoda M, Sakamoto K, Miyauchi T, et al. Changes in serum lipoprotein(a) and C4b-binding protein levels after acute myocardial infarctions. Jpn Circ J 1992;56:1214–20.

327. Slunga L, Johnson O, Dahlen GH, Eriksson S. Lipoprotein(a) and acute-phase proteins in acute myocardial infarction. Scand J Clin Lab Invest 1992;52:95–101.

328. Cobbaert C, Sergeant P, Meyns B, Szecsi J, Kesteloot H. Time course of serum Lp(a) in men after coronary artery bypass grafting. Acta Cardiol 1992;47:529–42.

329. Rantapaa-Dahlqvist S, Wallberg-Jonsson S, Dahlen G. Lipoprotein(a), lipids, and lipoproteins in patients with rheumatoid arthritis. Ann Rheum Dis 1991;50:366–8.

330. Maeda S, Abe A, Seishima M, Makino K, Noma A, Kawade M. Transient changes of serum lipoprotein(a) as an acute phase protein. Atherosclerosis 1989;78:145–50.

331. Cressman MD, Abood D, O'Neil J, Hoff HF. Lp(a) and premature mortality during chronic hemodialysis treatment. Chem Phys Lipids 1994;67/68:419–27.

332. 303. Kronenberg F, Kathrein H, Konig P, Neyer U, Sturm W, Lhotta K, Grochenig E, Utermann, G, Dieplinger H. Apolipoprotein(a) phenotypes predict the risk for carotid atherosclerosis in patients with end-stage renal disease. Arterioscler Thromb 1994; 14:1405–1411.

333. Wanner C, Bartens W, Walz G, Nauck M, Schollmeyer P. Protein loss and genetic polymorphism of apolipoprotein(a) modulates serum lipoprotein(a) in CAPD patients. Nephrol Dial Transplant 1995;10:75–81.

334. Webb AT, Reaveley DA, O'Donnell M, O'Connor B, Seed M, Brown EA. Lipids and lipoprotein(a) as risk factors for vascular disease in patients on renal replacement therapy. Nephrol Dial Transplant 1995;10:354–357.

335. Koch M, Kutkuhn B, Trenkwalder E, Bach D, Grabensee B, Dieplinger H, Kronenberg F. Apolipoprotein B, fibrinogen, HDL cholesterol, and apolipoprotein(a) phenotypes predict coronary artery disease in hemodialysis patients. J Am Soc Nephrol 1997;8: 1889–1898.

336. Marcovina SM, Hobbs HH, Albers JJ. Relationship between the number of apolipoprotein(a) kringle 4 repeats and mobility of the isoforms in agarose gel: bases for a standardized isoform nomenclature. Clin Chem 1996;42:436–9.

337. Armstrong VW, Schleef J, Thiery J, et al. Effect of HELP-LDL-apheresis on serum concentrations of human lipoprotein(a): kinetic analysis of the post-treatment return to baseline levels. Eur J Clin Invest 1989;19:235–40.

338. Pokrovsky SN, Adamova IY, Afanasieva OY, Benevolenskaya GF. Immunosorbent for selective removal of lipoprotein(a) from human plasma: *in vitro* study. Artif Organs 1991;15:136–46.

339. Gordon BG, Kelsey SF, Bilheimer DW, et al. Treatment of refractory familial hypercholesterolemia by low-density lipoprotein apheresis using an automated dextran sulfate cellulose adsorption system: The Liposorber Study Group. Am J Cardiol 1992;70: 1010–16.

340. Gurakar A, Hoeg JM, Kostner GM, Papadopoulos NM, Brewer HB Jr. Levels of lipoprotein Lp(a) decline with neomycin and niacin treatment. Atherosclerosis 1985;57: 293–301.

341. Kostner GM. The affection of lipoprotein-a by lipid lowering drugs. In: Widholm K, Naito HK, eds. Recent aspects of diagnosis and treatment of lipoprotein disorders: impact on prevention of atherosclerotic diseases. New York: Alan R. Liss, 1988:255–63.

342. Carlson LA, Hamsten A, Asplund A. Pronounced lowering of serum levels of lipoprotein Lp(a) in hyperlipidemic subjects treated with nicotinic acid. J Intern Med 1989;226: 271–6.

343. Pelegri A, Romero R, Senti M, Nogues X, Pedro-Botet J, Rubies-Prat J. Effect of bezafibrate on lipoprotein(a) and triglyceride-rich lipoproteins, including intermediate-density lipoproteins, in patients with chronic renal failure receiving haemodialysis. Nephrol Dial Transplant 1992;7:623–6.

344. Shewmon DA, Stock JL, Rosen CJ, Heiniluoma KM, Hogue MM, Morrison A, Doyle EM, Ukena T, Weale V, Baker S. Tamoxifen and estrogen lower circulating lipoprotein(a) concentrations in healthy postmenopausal women. Arterioscler Thromb 1994;14:1586–93.

345. Soma MR, Meschia M, Bruschi F, Morrisett JD, Paoletti R, Fumagalli R, Crosignani P. Hormonal agents used in lowering lipoprotein(a). Chem Phys Lipids 1994;67/68:345–50.

346. Brewer HB. Effectiveness of diet and drugs in the treatment of patients with elevated Lp(a) levels. In: Scanu AM, ed. Lipoprotein(a). New York: Academic Press, 1990:211–20.

Immunological Assays of Apolipoproteins A-II, A-IV, C-I, C-II, and C-III in Plasma: Methods and Applications

18

Christine Labeur and Maryvonne Rosseneu

✧ In atherosclerosis research, quantification of both the lipid and protein content of the lipoproteins has gained importance in the eighties.[1–3] All of the major apolipoproteins have been isolated, purified, and sequenced, and most of their physiological functions have been elucidated.

Given the metabolic role of apolipoproteins as lipid carriers, as ligands for receptors, and as enzyme activators, the measurement of the apolipoprotein concentrations in plasma should usefully complement that of the lipids with which they are associated. Because several of these apolipoproteins are present on the same lipoprotein particles, they are best measured in whole plasma by immunological techniques requiring the use of monoclonal antibodies or polyclonal antisera.[4–6] These methods have already been applied to the quantification of most of the apolipoproteins in plasma, including apolipoprotein (apo) A-I, A-II, A-IV, B, C-I, C-II, C-III, D, E, and lipoprotein(a) [Lp(a)].[7–9] In general terms, the plasma concentration of the smaller apolipoproteins—apo C-I, C-II, C-III, A-II, A-IV, and E—are within the range of 5–50 mg/dL. This range offers few difficulties for most of the current immunological techniques.

The various methodological aspects of immunological assays for apolipoproteins AII, AIV, CI, CII, and CIII, and their current applications in research and clinical chemistry laboratories, are described in this chapter.

GENERAL ASPECTS OF APOLIPOPROTEIN QUANTIFICATION

Immunological assays of apolipoproteins require some specific considerations.[4–6] Because of the lipid-binding properties of the apolipoproteins and their presence on the surface of lipoprotein particles, some of the antigenic sites are susceptible to partial or complete masking by lipids.[4,5,10] Therefore, accurate quantification of apolipoproteins requires pretreatment of the plasma or lipoprotein samples to completely expose the antigenic sites by delipidation or, on a more practical basis, by exposure to enzymes, denaturing agents, or detergents.[10] The presence of a given apolipoprotein on several lipoprotein fractions raises corollary problems. This effect is less pronounced for the smaller apolipoproteins, such as apo C-II and C-III, which are probably equally exposed at the surface of all particles.[11,12]

Antisera for Apolipoprotein Assays

Immunological assays of apolipoproteins seem quite sensitive to the nature of the antisera used in the measurement; these vary with the kind of antigen used in the immunization procedure, the species of host animal, and the dose of antigen injected. Significant differences between antisera have been reported. Monoclonal antibodies have been investigated as a possible approach to circumventing this problem. Apparently, however, the exposure of epitopes may vary in lipoprotein particles from different individuals. Optimal quantification of apolipoproteins will therefore require a mixture of several monoclonal antibodies.

Standards for Apolipoprotein Assays

Selection and quantification of a suitable primary standard has been a major problem in the development and standardization of apolipoprotein assays. Purified apolipoproteins have been chosen as primary standards for the apolipoproteins considered here. These purified apolipoprotein fractions were obtained from plasma lipoproteins separated by flotation ultracentrifugation.[7–10] For apo A-II isolation, the high-density lipoproteins (HDL) were isolated from normolipemic plasma, while for purification of the C apolipoproteins, the very-low-density lipoprotein (VLDL) fraction was recovered from hypertriglyceridemic plasma. All lipoproteins were subsequently delipidated with ether/ethanol,[9] and the HDL apolipoproteins and VLDL apolipoproteins were obtained. Apo A-II was further isolated from other HDL apolipoproteins by ion-exchange chromatography on a DEAE Sepharose column.[10] VLDL apolipoproteins were fractionated by gel filtration on a Sephacryl S200 column,[11,12] yielding three major fractions. Apo C-III was isolated from the apo C-containing fraction by ion-exchange chromatography on a DEAE Sepharose column,[12] while apo C-II was recovered from the same fraction by chromatofocusing.[11]

A different purification strategy had to be applied for apo A-IV, as this apolipoprotein is only partially associated with lipoproteins in plasma.[13] Apo A-IV was purified from lymph chylomicrons obtained from a patient who had lymph carcinoma,[13] or was recovered from plasma after adsorption on a triglyceride (TG) emulsion.[14] Further purification was performed by preparative gel electrophoresis in sodium dodecyl sulphate, and the protein was recovered by electroelution.[13] The mass of the primary standard was determined either by protein quantitation according to the method of Lowry[15] with bovine serum albumin as a standard, or preferably by quantitative amino acid analysis or by phenylalanine quantitation by high-performance liquid chromatography (HPLC).[16]

TECHNIQUES FOR THE QUANTIFICATION OF APO A-II, A-IV, C-I, C-II, AND C-III

Techniques for the quantification of apo A-II, A-IV, C-I, C-II and C-III include radioimmunoassay (RIA); enzyme immunoassays, particularly enzyme-linked immunosorbent assay (ELISA); electroimmunoassay (EIA); radial immunodiffusion (RID); and immunoprecipitin assays, including nephelometric and turbidimetric procedures.

The characteristics of these assays are summarized in Table 18–1 and their advantages and disadvantages are given in Table 18–2.

Radioimmunoassay (RIA)

This technique, which can detect as little as a few nanograms of protein, has been applied to the assay of apo A-II,[17–20] A-IV,[21,22] C-I,[23,24] C-II,[23,25,26] and C-III.[23,25] RIAs are of either the liquid or the solid-phase type and use either monoclonal antibodies or polyclonal antisera. However, RIAs require the iodination of pure apolipoprotein, a procedure that might decrease the reactivity of the standard compared to that of the lipoproteins, owing to self-association and aggregation of the isolated apolipoprotein. Another drawback of this technique is the need for high dilutions, which might lead to substantial experimental errors. The equipment needed for the RIA assay includes a gamma counter for radioactivity measurement and an automated dilutor and pipetting station for precise handling of the high dilutions and small volumes. Calculation of the concentrations of unknown samples is preferably carried out by a curve-fitting procedure after log-logit transformation of the measured values.

These assays can be easily automated, but are not convenient for clinical laboratories, owing to the safety requirements inherent to the handling and disposal of radioactive samples.

Enzyme Immunoassay

Several types of enzyme immunoassays, either direct or competitive, have been reported for the apolipoproteins. The sensitivity of these assays is similar to that of RIAs, but no radioactive tracers are required. These assays have enabled the quantification of apo A-II,[27–29] A-IV,[13] C-I,[30–32] C-II,[11,30,31] and C-III.[11,30,31]

Most assays begin with the preparation of affinity-purified antibodies, which are subsequently labeled with either peroxidase or alkaline phosphatase, using either periodate or other classical coupling procedures.[9] Recently, an ELISA procedure involving monoclonal antibodies was reported for apo A-II.[29] The nature of the monoclonal antibody seems crucial for the recognition of all apo A-II present in plasma, so that a combination of several antibodies seems preferable to only one.

Two types of ELISA assays are currently used: the "sandwich" type and the competitive type. In the sandwich-type ELISAs, a polystyrene plate is coated with affinity-purified antibodies prepared against the apolipoprotein to be measured. After blocking all residual binding sites on the plate with either albumin or casein,[9] the plasma is incubated with the immobilized antibody for 2 h at 37°C. After extensive washing, the antibody-antigen complex on the plate is incubated with a second detecting antibody which is enzyme labeled. The amount of bound conjugated antibody is a direct measure of the antigen concentration. This assay is very sensitive, with a detection limit of 0.5–1 ng and has the major advantage of easy and stable coating of the plates with affinity-purified antibodies.[9,10]

In the competitive type of assay, the plates are coated with the antigen and the plasma antigen and the antigen immobilized on the plate compete for conjugated antibody. This assay is about 10–20 times less sensitive than the sandwich-type ELISA. Its

Table 18–1 ✧ Characteristics of Immunological Assays for Apolipoproteins*

	RIA	ELISA	EIA	RID	Nephelometry	Turbidimetry
APO A-II						
Sensitivity (ng)	0.5	1	20	5	30	20
Intra-assay CV (%)	7	8	5	5	5	5
Inter-assay CV (%)	9	7	8	—	7	6
Normal values (mg/dL) mean ± SD	25– 4	35– 5	76– 2	29– 2	37– 9	38– 3
APO A-IV						
Sensitivity (ng)	5	0.2	20	—	25	—
Intra-assay CV (%)	5	4	5	—	2.0	—
Inter-assay CV (%)	7	8	9	—	2.4	—
Normal values (mg/dL) mean ± SD	17– 3	14– 5	14– 4	—	19– 3	—
APO C-1						
Sensitivity (ng)	15	5	50	—	—	—
Intra-assay CV (%)	7	3	5	—	—	—
Inter-assay CV (%)	9	5	8	—	—	—
Normal values (mg/dL) mean ± SD	5– 3	6– 2	6– 1	—	—	4– 1
APO C-II						
Sensitivity (ng)	1	0.3	45	—	—	10
Intra-assay CV (%)	6	3	6.5	—	—	3.3
Inter-assay CV (%)	10	8	8.2	—	—	6.2
Normal values (mg/dL) mean ± SD	4– 1	3– 1	4– 2	—	—	4– 1
APO C-III						
Sensitivity (ng)	0.3	10	20	—	15	—
Intra-assay CV (%)	9	3.6	6	—	2.2	2.8
Inter-assay CV (%)	13	4.3	8	—	6.3	5.2
Normal values (mg/dL) mean ± SD	15– 6	16– 3	12– 4	—	12– 3	11– 3

*RIA = Radioimmunoassay
ELISA = Enzyme-linked Immunosorbent Assay
EIA = Electroimmunoassay
RID = Radial Immunodiffusion
CV = Coefficient of Variance
SD = Standard Deviation
— = No data available

Table 18–2 ✧ Advantages and Disadvantages of Immunological Assays for Apolipoproteins*

Technique	Advantages	Disadvantages
RIA	High sensitivity High specificity	High dilution Uses isotope
ELISA	High sensitivity High specificity No isotope	High dilution
RID	Easy Low dilution No isotope	Incubation time 48h Not easy to automate
EIA	Low dilution No isotope	No monoclonal antibody 10 samples per plat Not easy to automate
Nephelometry	Low dilution No isotope Easy to automate	Special equipment No monoclonal antibody Specific polyclonal antibodies required
Turbidimetry	Low dilution No isotope Easy to automate	No monoclonal antibody Specific polyclonal antibodies required

*RIA = Radioimmunoassay
ELISA = Enzyme-linked Immunosorbent Assay
RID = Radial Immunodiffusion
EIA = Electroimmunoassay

major drawback for apolipoprotein measurement is the requirement for purified apolipoproteins for plate coating. As these apolipoproteins normally occur as lipid-bound components of lipoproteins, their antigenic properties when immobilized on the plate might differ from those in their native state.

ELISA assays, especially those of the sandwich type, are well suited to the quantification of apolipoproteins; they require a minimal amount of antiserum compared to nephelometry, RID, or EIA, and have the great advantage of not being affected by sample turbidity.[10] They are also easy to automate, and their accuracy and reproducibility compares well to that of other assays, provided the dilutions are made accurately. These assays should become more widely used in the future, especially for quantification of the smaller apolipoproteins such as apo C-II, and C-III, whose plasma concentrations are around 10 mg/dL or less. ELISA processes can be partially or fully automated, including sample dilution, dispensing the samples into the plates, and plate washing. The plates can be read after the colorimetric reaction, either manually or by an automated reader that is connected to a personal computer or hard-wired to its own computing device. Fully automated systems perform all operations automatically after programming for the application of the samples, the incubation times, wash cycles, volumes of reagents, and other factors.

Several types of calculations are available for computing results, depending upon the type of assay. In the sandwich-type direct assay, the curve can be fitted to a four-parameter equation[9] and the concentrations of the samples calculated from the fitted curve. For the competitive-type assay (as in RIAs), a log-logit transformation is used to linearize the curve before the concentration of test samples is calculated.

Electroimmunoassay (EIA)

This technique has also been used to quantify most apolipoproteins, including apo A-II,[33,34] A-IV,[35–37] C-I,[38] C-II,[34,38–40] and C-III.[34,40,41] The coefficient of variation (CV) for this assay is significantly higher than that obtained using other techniques. This method is difficult to automate and is therefore more limited in its application.

Radial Immunodiffusion (RID)

This method has been used to assay apo A-II,[42–45] C-I,[45] C-II,[44,45] and C-III.[44,45] Although RID is simple in principle, its applicability depends upon the ability to obtain sharp precipitin rings of sufficient diameter. However, silver staining of the immuno-precipitates can enhance the sensitivity tenfold, bringing the threshold level of detection to 10 ng.[45] The migration of VLDL is slow in comparison to that of low-density lipoprotein (LDL), and 72h–96h diffusion is required to reach an equilibrium. Although the technique is easy to perform, its accuracy is questionable; moreover, it is not readily applicable to large population studies that generate a large number of samples.

Immunoprecipitation Assays

These assays include both nephelometric and turbidimetric procedures and have been applied to the measurement of most apolipoproteins. Nephelometric assays have been described for apo A-II,[46,47] apo AI-V,[48] and for apo C-III.[49] These apolipoproteins were assayed by endpoint nephelometry,[46–49] where the concentration is proportional to turbidity after the formation of the antigen antibody complex is complete.

In the turbidimetric assay, absorption of the antigen antibody complex is measured at 340 nm in a spectrophotometer. In the nephelometric assay, the intensity of the scattered light is measured at an angle 30°–90° to that of the incident beam. These techniques are fast, accurate, and reproducible.[10,16] However, they have drawbacks in that they are extremely sensitive to sample turbidity and require enzymes or detergents when TG concentrations exceed 200 mg/dL. Measuring apo C-II, C-III, and A-IV in hyperlipemic samples by turbidimetry can be inaccurate. Turbidimetry has been used to quantify apo A-II,[50,51,53] C-II,[51–53] and C-III.[51,53] This technique has been adapted to most of the available clinical analyzers and is especially suited to the measurement of large sample numbers with good reproducibility.

CLINICAL APPLICATIONS

Apolipoproteins and Cardiovascular Disease

Apolipoprotein assays have found three major fields of application: in the assessment of risk for cardiovascular disease in myocardial infarction survivors, in patients with evidence of coronary heart disease (CHD) as diagnosed by coronary angiography, and in offspring of patients with CHD. Apo A-I and B were the major parameters measured in most case-control studies, showing that the concentrations of these apolipoproteins differ significantly from the values measured in a control group.[8,55] These studies were further extended to the measurement of apo A-II, C-II, and C-III.[10,16]

In a case-control study[55] comparing 70 male survivors of myocardial infarction to an equal number of healthy controls matched for age and body-mass index, apo B was shown to be significantly increased and apo A-I significantly decreased in the cases compared to controls. A multivariate analysis indicated that the apo A-I/B ratio, HDL-cholesterol (HDL-C), and the apo A-I/A-II ratio contributed independently to the discrimination of cases from controls, with an overall classification of 82% of the cases. Similar results were obtained by other investigators (Table 18–3). In most of these studies, the apo A-I/B ratio was the best discriminator between cases and controls, while apo A-II was a less powerful parameter.

Apolipoproteins were further measured in a group of patients with coronary lesions assessed by coronary angiography (Table 18–3). In most studies, a statistically significant negative correlation between the apo A-I/B ratio and the severity of CHD was reported.[56–60] Other investigators found that apo A-I plasma concentrations relate better to the presence or absence of CHD than to the severity of the disease, while apo A-II was a poor discriminator.[57,60]

In a study of 2020 patients aged 31–70 years who underwent coronary angiography, the patients were classified as having one-, two-, or three-vessel disease according to the extent of the lesions.[61] When compared to age-matched controls free of angiographically detected lesions, a significant decrease in the apo A-I/B ratio was observed in the cases with two- and three-vessel disease. Further, there was a tendency toward a decrease of the apo A-I/B ratio with an increasing severity of the lesions. Among the other apolipoproteins and lipids, apo B was the best discriminator, while apo A-I, A-II, total cholesterol (TC), and TG did not differ significantly among the four groups of patients.[61]

More recent studies that included the measurements of apo A-II, C-III, and A-IV in either plasma or lipoprotein particles[62–65] showed increased apo CIII concentrations in the patients. Studies conducted in patients with peripheral vascular disease[8] are difficult to evaluate due to complications such as diabetes, hypertension, and obesity that are often present in such patients.

A further application for plasma apolipoprotein assays is monitoring and early detection of hereditary risk for CHD. In one study, young adults whose fathers suffered a well-documented myocardial infarction below age 50 were compared to age- and sex-matched controls who had no familial history of CHD.[66] Lower apo A-I concentrations were the only significant difference in the lipid and apolipoprotein values between the cases and the controls. This difference in apo A-I concentrations is not

Table 18–3 ✧ Lipids and Apolipoprotein Measurements in Patients with Coronary Heart Disease

Author	Variables	Principal Findings
De Backer et al.[55]	Apo A-1, A-II, B TC, TG, HDL-C	Apo A-I, A-I/B, HDL-C lower Apo B higher in cases
Leitersdorf et al.[54]	Apo A-1, A-II, B, E TC, TG, HDL-C	Apo A-I lower Apo B, E higher in cases
Riesen et al.[56]	Apo A-1, A-II, B TC, TG, LDL-C, HDL-C	Apo A-I, A-II lower Apo B, LDL-C, TC higher in cases
Miller et al.[57]	Apo A-1, A-II, E TC, TG, LDL2-C, HDL2-C	HDL2-C lower in severe cases
Noma et al.[58]	Apo A-1, A-II, B TC, TG, LDL-C, HDL-C	LDL/HDL-C higher in cases Apo B/A-I, B/A-II higher in cases
Kottke et al.[60]	Apo A-1, A-II, B TC, TG, HDL-C	Apo A-I, A-II, B best discriminators
Sedlis et al.[59]	Apo A-1, A-II, B, E TC, TG, HDL-C	Apo A-I/B best discriminator Apo E higher in cases with total occlusion
Labeur et al.[61]	Apo A-1, A-II, B TC, TG, HDL-C	Apo A-I/B best discriminator

reflected in either the HDL-C or apo A-II concentrations. In a comprehensive study (based on the same design) that was carried out in students of 12 European countries, results showed that apo B and LDL-C were the best discriminators between students with and without a paternal history of CHD.[67]

Early screening of neonates, including assays for apolipoproteins and TC, can be carried out on a minimal quantity of blood[68] to detect increased apo B and decreased apo A-I plasma concentrations. Other apolipoproteins, including A-II, C-II, C-III, and A-IV, can also be measured in newborns.[69–71]

Apolipoproteins and Primary Dyslipidemias

Patients with Type I dyslipidemia are characterized by significantly decreased plasma concentrations of apo A-I and apo B, but normal apo A-I/B ratios. When lipoprotein lipase deficiency is responsible for this pattern, apo C-II and C-III are increased about threefold compared to normals. Apo C-II deficiency can also induce this type of dyslipidemia, in which case apo C-II concentrations are undetectable even by the most sensitive ELISA or RIA assays.[9,10]

In Type II hyperlipoproteinemia, the plasma apo B concentrations are severely increased while the apo A-I concentrations are slightly decreased. A strong positive correlation between plasma TG and apo C-II and C-III concentrations exists in these hypercholesterolemic patients, so that a distinction between Type IIa and Type IIb patients can be made on the basis of the increased plasma concentrations of these apolipoproteins. In addition to a two- to threefold increase of plasma apo B concentrations, Type III patients are characterized by increased apo E concentrations, whereas apo C-II and apo C-III increase about fourfold above normal. In Type IV patients, the apo AI/B ratio is significantly reduced, whereas apo C-II and apo C-III are increased by a factor of two to three.

The most pronounced increase in plasma apolipoproteins is observed in Type V patients. In these patients, plasma TG are positively correlated with apo C-III and inversely correlated with apo C-II.

In hypobetalipoproteinemic patients, plasma apo B concentrations are strongly reduced, whereas apo A-I concentrations are normal. In addition, apo C-II concentrations are reduced by about 50%, whereas apo CIII concentrations are decreased about fourfold compared to normals.

Plasma concentrations of the C apolipoproteins are thus increased most significantly in the hypertriglyceridemic states, whereas apo A-IV concentrations are not significantly different in dyslipoproteinemic patients compared to controls.[13,14] However, Brewer et al.[72] studied the *in vivo* metabolism of apo A-IV in severe hypertriglyceridemia and demonstrated that plasma levels of apo A-IV are significantly elevated in hypertriglyceridemic patients due to a delayed catabolism of apo A-IV. Apo A-IV concentrations seem sensitive to the state of alimentary lipemia,[73] and this apolipoprotein was reported to decrease food intake in rats.[74]

Well-controlled studies on the genetic polymorphism of apo A-IV and its influence on plasma lipid levels reported by the European Atherosclerosis Research Group[75] showed that the apo A-IV polymorphism does not influence HDL-C and apo A-IV plasma levels. Apo A-IV levels were lower in females than in males. In females, oral contraceptive users had significantly lower apo A-IV levels than non-users. When myocardial infarction survivors were compared to controls, no differences in apo A-IV levels and phenotypic distribution were observed, suggesting that the apo A-IV gene is not a major determinant of the risk for myocardial infarction and/or coronary heart disease.

Apolipoproteins and Secondary Dyslipidemias

In addition to the primary dyslipidemias, which are mostly due to genetic factors, a number of pathologies and dietary factors are responsible for inducing secondary dyslipidemias. These have essentially the same features and lead to the same phenotypes as the primary dyslipidemias. These are, however, reversible and should normalize upon treatment of the underlying disease. Secondary dyslipidemias can occur as a result of renal disease, alcohol consumption, liver disease, thyroid dysfunction, and diabetes mellitus.[7–10]

Chronic renal failure can be treated either by hemodialysis or by continuous ambulatory peritoneal dialysis (CAPD). Both types of treatment decrease the HDL fraction, which can be accompanied by an accumulation of VLDL and an increase of apo C-II and C-III.[76] The secondary dyslipidemia is usually more severe in CAPD patients, in whom a Type IIb or even a Type V dyslipidemia can occur.

In patients with nephrotic syndrome, pronounced secondary dyslipidemia develops readily due to decreased LDL-receptor synthesis and to apo B overproduction.

HDL and especially apo AI are lost through the kidneys, accounting for the low apo AI and AII concentrations in these patients.[77]

Alcohol influences the lipoprotein patterns according to frequency and volume of consumption. Acute consumption increases HDL concentrations, especially that of apo A-II.

Secondary dyslipidemias can occur in diabetes mellitus. In Type I, insulin-dependent diabetes mellitus (IDDM), Type IV pattern is frequent, characterized by decreased apo A-I and A-II concentrations and increased apo B, C-II, and C-III concentrations.[7–10] In Type II non-insulin dependent diabetes mellitus (NIDDM), a Type V hyperlipoproteinemia is frequently observed. In both cases, this secondary dyslipidemia results in CHD, which represents a major complication in diabetics. Apo A-IV levels and apo A-IV phenotypes were studied in NIDDM patients.[78,79] Apo A-IV levels were higher both in male and female diabetic patients compared to controls, while there was no difference between the apo A-IV phenotypic distribution. Apo A-IV levels could be corrected with the hypertriglyceridemia in these patients.

Among liver diseases, acute hepatitis decreases the apo A-I and A-II concentrations due to impaired HDL synthesis, while a decrease in hepatic lipase activity increases the apo C-II and C-III concentrations. In chronic hepatitis, hepatic lipase activity is decreased while apo A-I and A-II synthesis is normal. In liver cirrhosis, protein synthesis is impaired and the concentrations of the liver-synthesized apolipoproteins—A-I, A-II, B, and the C apolipoproteins—are significantly decreased.

In thyroid disorders, hyperthyroidism is accompanied by a large decrease in apo B concentrations due to increased LDL catabolism. In non-obese hypothyroid patients, apo B is increased and a Type IIa phenotype is most common due to reduced LDL catabolism.[80] In obese hypothyroid patients, apo C-II and C-III can accumulate due to impaired IDL-to-LDL conversion, inducing a Type V dyslipidemia.

SUMMARY

Apolipoproteins can be routinely assessed by a variety of immunological procedures and can be usefully combined with lipid quantitation for the characterization of primary and secondary dyslipidemias. Since the apolipoproteins constitute the physiological carriers of the plasma lipids, their plasma concentration and lipoprotein distribution are sensitive to hormonal, functional, and dietary regulation. As a consequence, different patterns arise. The combination of apolipoprotein and lipid assays provides a more sensitive and accurate way of monitoring primary and secondary dyslipidemias, as well as of evaluating a patient's risk of developing cardiovascular diseases.   ✧

REFERENCES

1. Rifkind BM. The Lipid Research Clinics Primary Prevention Trial results. I. Reduction in incidence of coronary heart disease. J Amer Med Assoc 1984;251:351–64.
2. Rifkind BM. The Lipid Research Clinics Coronary Primary Prevention Trial results. II. The relationship of reduction in incidence of coronary heart disease to cholesterol lowering. J Amer Med Assoc 1984;251:365–74.

3. De Backer G, Rosseneu M, Deslypeze JP. Discriminative value of lipids and apoproteins in coronary heart disease. Atherosclerosis 1982;42:197–203.

4. Steinberg KK, Cooper GR, Rosseneu M. Evaluation and standardization of apolipoprotein A-I immunoassays. Clin Chem 1983;29:415–26.

5. Rosseneu M, Vercaemst R, Steinberg KK, Cooper GR. Some considerations of methodology and standardization of apolipoprotein B immunoassays. Clin Chem 1983;29:427–33.

6. Naito HK. The Clinical significance of apolipoprotein measurements. J Clin Immunoassay 1986;9:11–20.

7. Rosseneu M, Bury J. Apolipoproteins assays for the diagnosis of hyperlipidemias. In: Naito H, ed. Recent aspects on diagnosis and treatment of lipid disorders: Impact on prevention of atherosclerotic diseases. New York: A. R. Liss, 1988;143–5.

8. Kostner GM. Apolipoproteins and lipoproteins of human plasma: significance in health and disease. Adv Lipid Res 1983;20:1–43.

9. Bury J, Rosseneu M. Apolipoprotein quantitation by ELISA: technical aspects and clinical applications. Rev Immunoassay Techn 1988;1:1–25.

10. Labeur C, Shepherd J, Rosseneu M. Immunological assays of lipoproteins in plasma: Methods and instrumentation. Clin Chem 1990;36:591–7.

11. Bury J, Michiels G, Rosseneu M. Human apolipoprotein C-II quantitation by sandwich-enzyme-linked immunosorbent assay. J Clin Chem Clin Biochem 1986;24:457–61.

12. Bury J, Rosseneu M. Enzyme immunosorbent assay for human apolipoprotein C-III. J Clin Chem Clin Biochem 1985;23:63–8.

13. Rosseneu M, Michiels G, De Keersgieter W, et al. Human apolipoprotein A-IV quantitation by sandwich-enzyme-linked immunosorbent assay. Clin Chem 1988;34:739–43.

14. Weinberg RB, Scanu AM. Isolation and characterization of human apolipoprotein A-IV from lipoprotein-depleted serum. J Lipid Res 1983;24:54–9.

15. Lowry OH, Rosebrough NJ, Farr AL, Randall RJ. Protein measurement with the Folin reagent. J Biol Chem 1951;193:265–75.

16. Rosseneu MY, Labeur C. Apolipoprotein structure, function, and measurement. Curr Opin Lipidol 1990;1:508–13.

17. Mordasini RC, Riesen WF. Electroimmunoassay and radioimmunoassay for the quantitation of high-density apolipoproteins AI and AII. J Clin Chem Clin Biochem 1980;18:917–20.

18. Mao SJT, Gotto AM Jr, Jackson RL. Immunochemistry of human plasma high-density lipoproteins: radioimmunoassay of apolipoprotein A-II. Biochemistry 1975;14:4127–31.

19. Schonfeld G, Chen J, McDonell WF, Jeng I. Apolipoprotein A-II content of plasma high-density lipoproteins measured by radioimmunoassay. J Lipid Res 1977;18:645–54.

20. Goldberg RB, Karlin JB, Juhn DJ, Scanu AM, Edelstein C, Rubenstein AH. Characterization and measurement of human apolipoprotein A-II by radioimmunoassay. J Lipid Res 1980;21:902–12.

21. Ghiselli G, Krishnan S, Beigel Y, Gotto AM Jr. Plasma metabolism of apolipoprotein A-IV in humans. J Lipid Res 1986;27:813–27.

22. Bisgaier CL, Sachdev OP, Lee ES, Williams KJ, Blum CB, Glickman RM. Effect of lecithin:cholesterol acyltransferase on distribution of apolipoprotein A-IV among lipoproteins of human plasma. J Lipid Res 1987;28:693–703.

23. Bren ND, Rastogi A, Kottke BA. Quantification of human apolipoproteins C-I, C-II, and C-III by radioimmunoassay. Mayo Clinic Proc 1993;68:657–64.

24. Polz E, Kotite L, Havel RJ, Kane JP, Sata T. Human apolipoprotein C-I: concentration in blood serum and lipoproteins. Biochem Med 1980;24:229–37.

25. Schonfeld G, George PK, Miller J, Reilly P, Witztum J. Apolipoprotein C-II and C-III levels in hyperlipoproteinemia. Metabolism 1979;28:1001–10.

26. Barr SI, Kottke BA, Chang JY, Mao SJT. Immunochemistry of human plasma

apolipoprotein C-II as studied by radioimmunoassay. Biochem Biophys Acta 1981; 663:491–505.

27. Dubois DY, Cantraine F, Malmendier CL. Comparison of different sandwich immuno-assays for the quantitation of human apolipoproteins A-I and A-II. J Immunol Meth 1987;96:115–20.

28. Dufaux B, Ilsemann K, Assmann G. Competitive enzyme immunoassay for apolipoprotein A-II. J Clin Chem Clin Biochem 1983;21:39–43.

29. Stein EA, Dipersio L, Pesce AJ, et al. Enzyme-linked immunoabsorbent assay of apolipoprotein A-II in plasma with use of a monoclonal antibody. Clin Chem 1986;32:967–71.

30. Holmquist L. Quantitation of human serum very-low-density apolipoprotein B, C-I, C-II, C-III, and E by enzyme immunoassay. J Immunol Meth 1980;34:243–51.

31. Carlson LA, Holmquist L. Concentrations of apolipoproteins B, C-I, C-II, C-III and E in sera from normal men and their relation to serum lipoprotein levels. Clin Chim Acta 1982;124:163–78.

32. Riesen WF, Sturzenegger E. Enzyme-linked immunosorbent assay for apolipoprotein C-I. J Clin Chem Clin Biochem 1986;24:723–7.

33. Curry MD, Alaupovic P, Suenram CA. Determination of apolipoprotein A and its consti-tutive A-I and A-II polypeptides by separate electroimmunoassays. Clin Chem 1976;22:315–22.

34. Alaupovic P, Curry MD, McConathy WJ. Quantitative determination of human plasma apolipoproteins by electroimmunoassay. Intern Confer Atheroscl 1978;109–15.

35. Utermann G, Beisiegel U. Apolipoprotein A-IV: a protein occurring in human mesenteric lymph chylomicrons and free in plasma. Eur J Biochem 1979;99:333–43.

36. Green PHR, Glickman RM, Riley JW, Quinet E. Human apolipoprotein A-IV. J Clin Invest 1980;65:911–9.

37. Bisgaier CL, Sachdev OP, Megna L, Glickman RM. Distribution of apolipoprotein A-IV in human plasma. J Lipid Res 1985;26:11–25.

38. Curry MD, McConathy WJ, Fesmire JD, Alaupovic P. Quantitative determination of apolipoproteins C-I and C-II in human plasma by separate electroimmunoassays. Clin Chem 1981;27:543–8.

39. Jauhiaianen M, Laitinen M, Penttilö I, Puhakainen E, Hietanen E. Determination of hu-man apolipoprotein C-II by electroimmunoassay: studies on standardization and deter-mination before and after physical training. Int J Biochem 1983;15:501–6.

40. Mörz W, Schenk G, Gross W. Apolipoproteins C-II and C-III in serum quantified by zone immunoelectrophoresis. Clin Chem 1987;33:664–9.

41. Curry MD, McConathy WJ, Fesmire JD, Alaupovic P. Quantitative determination of hu-man apolipoprotein C-III by electroimmunoassay. Biochem Biophys Acta 1980;617:503–13.

42. Albers JJ, Cheung MC, Wahl PW. Effect of storage on the measurement of apolipoproteins A-I and A-II by radial immunodiffusion. J Lipid Res 1980;21:874–8.

43. Cheung MC, Albers JJ. The measurement of apolipoprotein A-I and A-II levels in men and women by immunoassay. J Clin Invest 1977;60:43–50.

44. Goto Y, Akanuma Y, Harano Y. Determination by the SRID method of normal values of serum apolipoproteins (A-I, A-II, B, CII, CIII and E) in normolipidemic healthy Japanese subjects. J Clin Biochem Nutr 1986;1:73–88.

45. Ishida BY, Paigen B. Silver-enhanced radial immunodiffusion assay of plasma apolipo-proteins. J Lipid Res 1992;33:1073–8.

46. Kuusi T, Palosuo T, Ehnholm C. Immunonephelometric measurements of human plasma apolipoproteins A-I and A-II: an assay performed by consecutive addition of the two antisera to a single specimen. Scand J Clin Lab Invest 1985;45:245–53.

47. Rosseneu M, Vinaimont N, Musliner TA, Bernier D, Herbert PN, Belpaire F. Immuno-nephelometry of apolipoprotein A-II in plasma. Clin Chem 1984;30:234–7.

48. Schwarz S, Haas B, Luley C, Schafer JR, Steinmetz A. Quantification of apolipoprotein A-IV in human plasma by immunonephelometry. Clin Chem 1994;40:1717–21.

49. Bury J, De Keersgieter W, Rosseneu M, Belpaire F, Christophe J. Immunonephelo-metric quantitation of the apolipoprotein C-III in human plasma. Clin Chim Acta 1985;145:249–58.

50. Rifai N, King ME. Immunoturbidimetric assays of apolipoproteins A, AI, AII, and B in serum. Clin Chem 1986;32:957–61.

51. Noma A, Haras Y, Goto Y. Quantification of serum apolipoprotein A-I, A-II, B, C-II, C-III, and E by turbidimetric immunoassay: reference values and age- and sex-related differences. Clin Chim Acta 1991;199:147–57.

52. Rifai N, Silverman LM. Immunoturbidimetric techniques for quantifying apolipoproteins CII and CIII. Clin Chem 1986;32:1969–72.

53. Ikeda T, Shibuya Y, Senba U, et al. Automated immunoturbidimetric analysis of six plasma apolipoproteins: correlation with radial immunodiffusion assays. J Clin Lab Anal 1991;5:90–5.

54. Leitersdorf E, Gottehrer N, Fainaru M, et al. Analysis of risk factors in 532 survivors of first myocardial infarction hospitalized in Jerusalem. Atherosclerosis 1986;59:75–93.

55. De Backer G, Rosseneu M, Deslypere JP. Discriminative value of lipids and apoproteins in coronary heart disease. Atherosclerosis 1982;42:197–203.

56. Riesen WF, Mordasini R, Salzmann C, Theler A, Gurtner HP. Apolipoproteins and lipids as discriminators of severity of coronary heart disease. Atherosclerosis 1980;37: 157–62.

57. Miller NE, Hammett F, Saltissi S, et al. Relation of angiographically defined coronary artery disease to plasma lipoprotein subfractions and apolipoproteins. British Med J 1981;282:1741–4.

58. Noma A, Yokosuka T, Kitmra K. Plasma lipids and apolipoproteins as discriminators for presence and severity of angiographically defined coronary artery disease. Atherosclerosis 1983;49:1–7.

59. Sedlis SP, Schechtman KB, Ludbrook PA, Sobel BE, Schonfeld G. Plasma apoproteins and the severity of coronary artery disease. Circulation 1986;73:978–86.

60. Kottke BA, Zinsmeister AR, Holmes DR, Kneller RW, Hallaway BJ, Mao ST. Apolipoproteins and coronary artery disease. Mayo Clin Proc 1986;61:313–20.

61. Labeur C, Vincke J, Muyldermans L, et al. Plasma lipoprotein (a) values and severity of coronary artery disease in a large population of patients undergoing coronary angiography. Clin Chem 1992;38:2261–6.

62. Genest JJ Jr, Bard JM, Fruchart JC, Ordovas JM, Wilson PF, Schaefer EJ. Plasma apolipoprotein A-I, A-II, B, E and CIII containing particles in men with premature coronary artery disease. Atherosclerosis 1991;90:149–57.

63. Kottke BA, Moll PP, Michels VV, Weidman WH. Levels of lipids, lipoproteins, and apolipoproteins in a defined population. Mayo Clin Proc 1991;66:1198–208.

64. Chivot L, Mainard F, Bigot E, et al. Logistic discriminant analysis of lipids and apolipoproteins in a population of coronary bypass patients and the significance of apolipoproteins C-III and E. Atherosclerosis 1990;82:205–11.

65. Ordovas JM, Civeira F, Genest J Jr, et al. Restriction-fragment-length polymorphisms of the apolipoprotein A-I, C-III, A-IV gene locus: relationships with lipids, apolipoproteins, and premature coronary artery disease. Atherosclerosis 1991;87: 75–86.

66. De Backer G, Hulstaert F, De Munck K, Rosseneu M, Van Parijs L, Dramaix M. Serum lipids and apoproteins in students whose parents suffered prematurely from a myocardial infarction. Am Heart J 1986;112:478–84.

67. Rosseneu, M, Fruchart JC, Bard JM, Nicaud V, Vinaimont N, Cambien F. On behalf of the EARS group: plasma apolipoprotein concentrations in young adults with a parental history of premature coronary heart disease and in controls: The EARS Study. Atherosclerosis 1994;108:127–36.

68. Van Biervliet JP, Vinaimont N, Caster H, Rosseneu M. A screening procedure for dyslipoproteinemia in newborns: apoprotein quantitation on dried-blood spots. Clin Chim Acta 1982;120:191–200.

69. Averna MR, Barbagallo CM, Di Paola G. et al. Lipids, lipoproteins and apolipoproteins AI, AII, B, CII, CIII and E in newborns. Biol Neonate 1991;60:187–92.

70. Boediman D, Murakami R, Nakamura H. Relationship between plasma triglycerides and apolipoprotein CII in infants during the first year of life. J Pediatr Gastroenterol Nutr 1993;17:82–5.

71. Van Biervliet JP, Rosseneu M, Bury J, Caster H, Stul MS, Lamote R. Apolipoprotein and lipid composition of plasma lipoproteins in neonates during the first month of life. Pediatric Res 1986;20:324–8.

72. Verges B, Rader D, Schaefer J, Zech L, Kindt M. Fairwell T, Gambert P, Brewer HB Jr. In vivo metabolism of apolipoprotein A-IV in severe hypertriglyceridemia: a combined radiotracer and stable isotope kinetic study. J Lipid Res 1994;35:2280–91.

73. Annuzzi G, Holmquist L, Carlson LA. Concentrations of apolipoproteins B, C-I, C-II, C-III, E, and lipids in serum and serum lipoproteins of normal subjects during alimentary lipaemia. Scand J Clin Lab Invest 1989;49:73–81.

74. Fujimoto K, Fukagawa K, Sakata T, Tso P. Suppression of food intake by apolipoprotein A-IV is mediated through the central nervous system in rats. J Clin Invest 1993;91:1830–3.

75. Ehnholm C, Tenkanen H, de Knijff P, Havekes L, Rosseneu M, Menzel JJ, Tiret L. Genetic polymorphism of apolipoprotein A-IV in five different regions of Europe. Relations to plasma lipoproteins and to history of myocardial infarction: the EARS study. European Atherosclerosis Study, Atherosclerosis 1994;107:229–38.

76. Alsayed N, Rebourcet R. Abnormal concentrations of CII, CIII, and E apolipoproteins among apolipoprotein B-containing, B-free, and A-I-containing lipoprotein particles in hemodialysis patients. Clin Chem 1991;37:387–93.

77. Muls E, Rosseneu M, Daneels R, Schurgers M, Boelaert J. Lipoprotein distribution and composition in the human nephrotic syndrome. Atherosclerosis 1985;54:225–37.

78. Verges BL, Vaillant G, Goux A, Lagrost L, Brun JM, Gambert P. Apolipoprotein A-IV levels and phenotype distribution in NIDDM. Diabetes Care 1994;17:810–7.

79. Verges B. Apolipoprotein A-IV in diabetes mellitus. Diabete Metab 1995;21:99–105.

80. Muls E, Rosseneu M, Lamberigts G, De Moor P. Changes in the distribution and composition of high-density lipoproteins in primary hypothyroidism. Metabolism 1985;34:345–53.

Apolipoprotein E: Laboratory Determinations and Clinical Interest

Gérard Siest, Alexandra Schlenck, Marjorie Starck, Monique Vincent-Viry, Françoise Schiele, and Sophie Visvikis

❖ Apolipoprotein E (apo E), an arginine (Arg)-rich glycoprotein (34.2 kilodaltons) is involved in two major processes:

> ❖ It plays an endocrine-like function and transports lipids from their site of synthesis, or absorption, to the organs and cells where the lipids are used, stored, and excreted.

> ❖ It has a paracrine-like role and transports lipids between cells and, in particular, transports cholesterol from the peripheral organs to the hepatocytes for excretion.

Apo E is also implied in other biological processes such as regeneration of the peripheral nerve cells, and proliferation and differentiation of smooth muscle cells. Apo E also has an immunoregulatory role;[1,2] it also modulates the activity of some lipid metabolism enzymes such as lipoprotein lipase (LPL), lecithin cholesterol acyl transferase (LCAT), and cholesteryl ester transfer protein (CETP).

Apo E is a major constituent of chylomicrons, very-low-density lipoproteins (VLDL), and intermediate-density lipoproteins (IDL). It is also found in high density lipoproteins (HDL) and at very low level in low-density lipoproteins (LDL). Apo E is a ligand for many lipoprotein receptors. The first discovered was the LDL (apo B/E)-receptor (LDLR). Later, other receptors of the same family were identified: the LDL-receptor-related protein (LRP), the VLDL-receptor (VLDLR), and the apolipoprotein E receptor 2 (apo ER2), a new member of the apo E family of receptors found on the platelet surface that might be involved in the inhibition by apo E of platelet reactivity by stimulating intracellular nitric oxide synthase (eNOS or NOSIII).[3] It also seems to participate in the development of the nervous system. The scavenger receptor type I class B (SR-BI)[4] is also able to bind apo E. The quantity and localization of plasma apo E in the lipoproteins are important for the interaction of apo E with these receptors.

Recent studies suggested that apo E, probably together with LPL, could be mediating an intracellular pathway of lipoproteins independent of the specific membrane receptors. Apo E interacts with the heparin sulfate proteoglycans (HSPG) localized on the surface of the cells.[5]

THE APO E GENE

Apo E belongs to a multigenic family that comprises the following apoprotein genes: A-I, A-II, C-I, C-II, and C-III. The gene apo R, 4 exons and 3 introns (Figure 19–1), is located as a cluster E–C–I–C-II in the proximal area of the long arm of the chromosome 19 at 19q13.2.[6] It is a small gene of 3597 base pairs (bp) that is transcribed into mRNA containing 1163 nucleotides.

The first exon is non-coding. Exon 2 codes for the first 14 amino acids of the signal peptide. Exon 3 codes for signal peptide end and the first 61 residues of the mature protein. Exon 4 codes for the major part of the mature protein.[7] It contains hundreds of non-coding nucleotides in the 3′ area, and 66-nucleotide repeats coding for the α-amphiphilic helix. This last area is very rich in guanine-cytosine (GC) and constitutes one of the cytosine-phosphate-guanine (CpG) islets identified in the human genome. There are also several *Alu* sequences, one located at approximately 370 nucleotides upstream of the initiation codon, two others within intron 2, and the last one localized 150 nucleotides after exon 4.[8]

Many positive and negative regulatory elements were described in the 5′ flanking and intronic areas of the gene.[7] A positive estrogen response element (ERE) and one sterol response element (SRE) were identified. Some elements described in the 5′ region and in the 3′ region are also tissue specific. A "cap" messenger ribonucleic acid (mRNA) consensus sequence exists at nucleotide +1 of the first exon, and a eucaryotic promoter TATAATT consensus sequence is present at 33 bp above the initiation site of the transcription.

THE APO E PROTEIN

Apo E is synthesised as a pre-protein containing a signal peptide (of 18 amino acids[9]) that is cleaved in the endoplasmic reticulum. Apo E is then secreted as a sialylated mature protein made up of a single chain of 299 amino acids (Figure 19–2). This chain contains two thrombin cleavage sites at residues 191 and 215, two heparin-binding sites at residues 142–147 and 192–215, and an o-glycosylation site at residue threonine 194.[10]

Figure 19–1 ✦ Schematic representation of the apo E gene. The values in base-pairs of the introns and exons are indicated

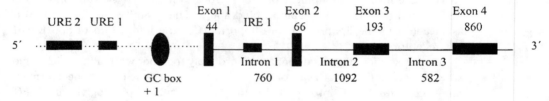

URE 2, URE 1: Upstream regulatory element
IRE 1: Intron regulatory element
(Paik YK et al., J Biol Chem 1988;263:13340–13349)

Figure 19–2 ✧ Schematic Representation of the Apo E3/3 Protein (Apo E)

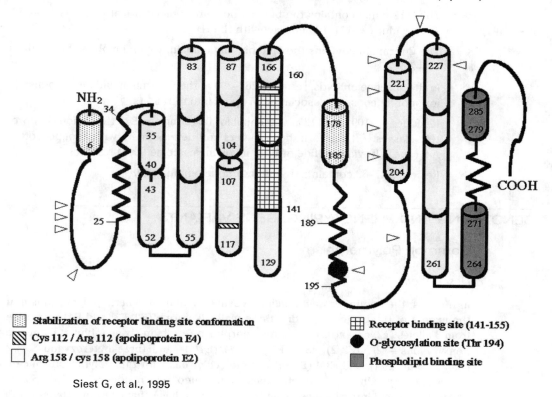

Stabilization of receptor binding site conformation

Cys 112 / Arg 112 (apolipoprotein E4)

Arg 158 / cys 158 (apolipoprotein E2)

Receptor binding site (141–155)

O-glycosylation site (Thr 194)

Phospholipid binding site

Siest G, et al., 1995

The mature protein has a molecular mass of 34200 Da. Apo E is secreted in mono or dimeric sialylated forms,[10] the sialic acid residues giving it an increased acidic character and adding a chemical heterogeneity to the protein in addition to its genetic polymorphism.[9] However, only 25% of apo E circulating in plasma is sialylated. Desialylation occurs after secretion. The role of glycosylation has not yet been clearly established. It is not necessary for the secretion of the protein,[9] but could influence the hepatic capture of VLDL.[11] Ikewaki et al.[12] proposed that a high sialylation could prevent the formation of dimers, help bind apo E to the receptors, and consequently accelerate its catabolism.

Apo E is expressed in many tissues (brain, lung, kidney, ovary, muscle) but more than 90% of plasma apo E comes from the liver. Apo E secretion is increased by cholesterol and fatty acids and decreased by substances such as insulin, thyroid hormones, or estrogens.[13–15] The mature macrophages derived from the human monocytes also produce a large quantity of apo E. In human brain, astrocytes and glial cells constitute the second major site of synthesis of apo E. Apo E also represents one of the main proteins of cerebrospinal fluid.

Different functions are attributed to specific domains of this protein:

✧ The N-terminal contains the binding domain to receptors at residues 136–158. The residues at 171–183 interact with HSPG.

✧ The C-terminal contains the lipid-binding domain, which involves the residues 245–299.

✧ In the absence of lipids, residues 267–299 at the C-terminal end are responsible for spontaneous self-association of apo E into tetramers.[16]

✧ Residues 61, 109, and 112 are essential for targeting apo E to the various lipoprotein classes.[17] It can form homodimers and heterodimers with apolipoprotein A-II (apo A-II) via disulfide bridges involving cysteine (Cys) residues.

✧ Residues 21–62 contain a thyroid hormone binding site.[18]

GENOTYPING AND PHENOTYPING: GENE VARIANTS

Common Polymorphism

Description

In humans, the apolipoprotein E gene presents a common genetic polymorphism in the exon 4 of the protein, creating three major isoforms (E2, E3, and E4) that arise from 3 alleles (ε2, ε3, and ε4). This polymorphism results in six genotypes. Three are homozygous—ε2/2 (E2/2), ε3/3 (E3/3), ε4/4 (E4/4)—and three heterozygous: ε3/2 (E3/2), ε2/4 (E2/4), and ε3/4 (E3/4). The molecular basis for this polymorphism centers around cysteine-arginine interchanges at amino acid residues 112 and 158.[7,19] These amino acid interchanges result from the single-base change from a thymine (T) to a cytosine (C) at the relevant position in the gene's coding region in exon 4 (Figure 19–3).

Figure 19–3 ✧ Schematic representation of the common apo E polymorphism localized in exon 4 (↓: specific site of the HhaI endonuclease)

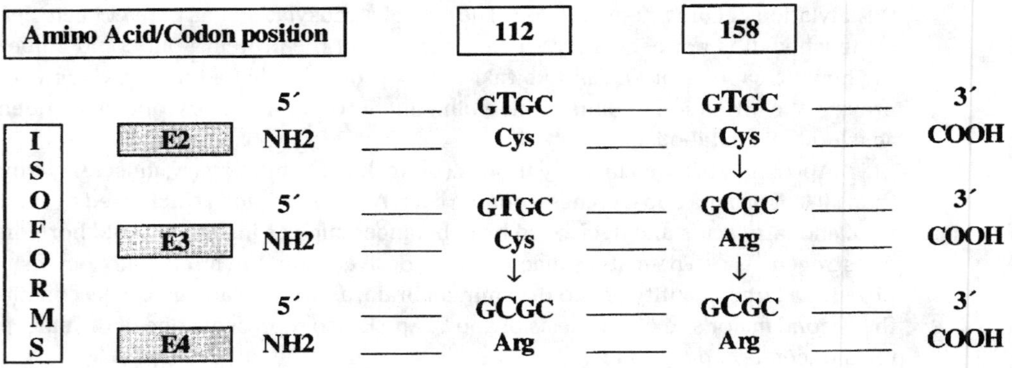

Table 19–1 ✧ Isoelectric Points of ApoE Common Isoforms	
Isoform	*Apparent pI*
E2	5.68 – 5.9
E3	5.81 – 6.0
E4	5.95 – 6.1

Phenotyping

The initial procedure of apo E polymorphism typing was developed at the protein level. Because the amino acid interchanges modify the protein charge, the three isoforms can be identified on the basis of their isoelectric point (pI) (Table 19–1) by isoelectrofocusing[20] or by two-dimensional electrophoresis.

ISOELECTROFOCUSING (IEF)

Numerous procedures have been developed.[21] The early method was based on apo E isolation from delipidated VLDL, initially separated by ultracentrifugation[22] or precipitation. IEF was performed in denaturing conditions with urea and dithiothreitol (DTT) in polyacrylamide gels (5%–7.5%) containing an ampholyte gradient (2%) (pH 4–6). Proteins were stained with Coomassie Brillant Blue.

As a consequence of the presence of sialylated apo E3 that focuses at the apo E2 position (23), the differentiation of genotypes must be based on the relative intensities of the bands quantified by densitometric scanning. However, there are multiple sources of possible misinterpretation/misclassification:

✧ the large volume of plasma required (~\14 ml),

✧ the lack of sensitivity and specificity of the protein staining,

✧ the presence of contaminating protein bands besides apo E isoforms (serum amyloid A, pro-apo A-I),[24]

✧ the loss of apo E during the ultracentrifugation step, and

✧ the presence of more acidic sialylated apo E forms.

Various investigators have proposed improvements at different stages of the procedure:

Pre-analytical steps. Sample volumes and pre-analytical steps may be reduced by directly applying small volumes of unfractionated plasma or serum with or without delipidation, dialysis, and addition of DTT Tween, guanidine/HCl, and ampholytes.

Gel isoelectric focusing. Agarose gels (2%) may replace polyacrylamide gels.[25]

pH gradient. Immobilines may be used instead of carrier ampholytes to form a high-resolution immobilized pH gradient in polyacrylamide gels. This process avoids pH gradient drift during electrofocusing, and allows the separation of proteins with very small differences in isoelectric point, thus improving separation between parent apo E isoforms and their post-translational variants. Ampholyte pH range is usually 4.5–6.5 or 5–8, and occasionally 3–10. Focusing time is usually three hours, with many variations.

Isoform detection. Sensitivity and specificity can be improved by immunodetection. For immunoblotting after electrophoresis, proteins are transferred to nitrocellulose membranes, and treated with monoclonal or polyclonal anti-apo E antibodies.[26] A second antibody coupled to alkaline phosphatase or horseradish peroxidase is then added to follow the reaction. An immunofixation with polyclonal anti-apo E antibodies is also possible on agarose gels, where proteins are Silver stained without transferring onto a membrane.

These procedures may be partially automated by using gel bond for casting ultrathin gel plates or using the commercial Phast System format, each of which increases the number of samples that could simultaneously be analyzed by IEF. The methods seem to be unaffected by differences in apo E isoform distribution between VLDL and HDL fractions and by lower Apo E4 plasma concentration,[27] but remain sensitive to electroblotting efficiency.

Interpretation. Interpretative difficulties that may arise from the presence of sialylated apo E forms may be resolved by neuraminidase and/or cysteamine pretreatment. Neuraminidase removes sialic acid residues and simplifies patterns.[23,25] This can be combined with cysteamine pretreatment. Cysteamine reacts specifically with cysteine residues and creates a supplementary positive charge.

TWO-DIMENSIONAL ELECTROPHORESIS

A second electrophoresis in sodium dodecylsulphate-polyacrylamide gel can be linked to the first IEF step to separate proteins with similar pI according to their molecular mass. Proteins are detected by Silver-staining the gel or by immunoblotting, as previously mentioned.

This seems to be the procedure with the best resolution for efficiently separating genetic and post-translationally modified apo E isoforms. However, it is expensive and tedious, and difficult to implement in population screening or in non-specialized laboratories.

Misclassification of the apo E phenotype could be a consequence of nonenzymatic glycation,[28] charge modifications due to amino acid substitutions of residues other than 112 and 158, and artifacts caused by prolonged storage of the plasma.[25,29] One group did not observe any effect of plasma freezing at $-70°C$. We observed that, provided there are not too many cycles of freezing and thawing, phenotyping could be done on frozen samples.

Genotyping

Several methods have been developed to directly detect nucleotide substitutions at the gene level after amplification of the apo E genomic sequence containing the polymorphic sites by polymerase chain reaction (PCR).

Table 19–2 ✧ Specific Endonuclease Digestion Linked to Polymorphic Site Located in Codons 112 and 158 of the Exon 4 of ApoE Gene		
Endonuclease	*Codon 112*	*Codon 158*
Hhal, CfoI	GCG*C	GCG*C
AflIII	A*CGTGT	
HaeII		AGCGCC

PCR-RESTRICTION FRAGMENT LENGTH POLYMORPHISM (PCR-RFLP)

This method is based on the appearance or disappearance of specific endonuclease restriction sites (Table 19–2) induced by C↔T substitutions in the gene's coding region.

After PCR amplification of a fragment of 206–267 bp,[30,31] the PCR product is digested by HhaI[26,30] or CfoI,[31] or simultaneously by AflIII and HaeII.[32,33] The restriction fragments are separated by electrophoresis on slab polyacrylamide gel[30] or agarose gel.[31] Visualization occurs by ultaviolet (UV) illumination of ethidium bromide (EtBr) stained gel or by Silver staining. Each of the six common apo E genotypes is distinguishable by a unique combination of restriction fragment sizes.

The most common method is based on digestion of a 244 bp PCR fragment with HhaI linked to polyacrylamide slab gel electrophoresis and UV illumination of the EtBr stained gel[30] (Figure 19–4). However, because of the demand for high-yield PCR, high resolution, detection sensitivity, and high-throughput electrophoresis, several improvements to this approach have been presented.

Figure 19–4 ✧ Combination of H*hal*-restriction fragment sizes characterizing the six common apo E genotypes in polyacrylamide slab gel electrophoresis and made visible by UV illumination after EtBr staining

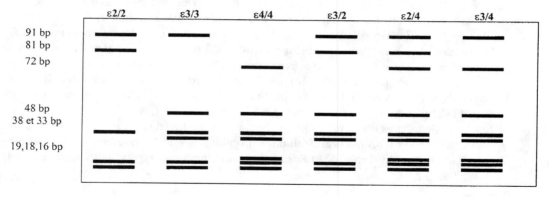

Despite its relative ease and simplicity, Hixson and Vernier's method shows several drawbacks:

❖ It needs highly concentrated and purified DNA.

❖ Apo E gene PCR is particularly prone to low yield and misproducts, possibly because of high percentage of (G+C) nucleotide content.[34,35]

❖ The H*hal* digestion generates several small restriction fragments including non-informative ones, which may give rise to faint bands.

❖ The interpretation of electropherograms relies entirely on complete H*hal* digestion of the PCR product. Consequently, the unequivocal genotyping of apo E is impossible, and the results may be biased towards less frequently occurring alleles, particularly in genotypes with a single allele coding for Arg 158 (ε3/2 and ε2/4).[36]

To reduce the heavy expenditure in staff time inherent in previous approaches, a microplate array diagonal gel electrophoresis (MADGE) linked to gel image analysis[34] allows 96 restriction analyses to be performed simultaneously (see Chapter 34).

Improvement in the sensitivity of H*hal* restriction isotyping may be obtained by performing two consecutive PCR steps or by adding an end-labeled primers step. However, these procedures are time-consuming and lead to nonspecific amplification. Also their applications in clinical and epidemiological laboratories are limited by the use of radioactivity. Recently, the restriction fragment analysis (by capillary gel electrophoresis [CGE] in a replaceable non-gel sieving matrix) streamlined the genotyping of apo E in large-scale population and diagnostic studies because of high resolution (1bp), automation, and speed (12–20 minutes per sample).[36–38] Linked to laser-induced fluorescence (LIF) detection of the restriction fragments, it gave the same high sensitivity as radiolabeling methods. The CGE-LIF analysis ensures the accurate classification of rare genotypes (ε2/2, ε3/2, and ε2/4), although errors can occur when samples have low concentration, when DNA is poorly purified, and when PCR is inefficient or endonuclease digestion is incomplete.[36,39]

AMPLIFICATION REFRACTORY MUTATION SYSTEM (ARMS)

This technique is based on a batch PCR, performed in parallel reactions, and uses different primers complementary to one of the alleles, assuming that elongation occurs only when primer and target sequences match completely. Wenham et al.[40] proposed to genotype apo E using the ARMS approach based on four PCR reactions and five primers. One is common to the entire PCR reaction while two specific primer pairs (one per polymorphic site) are chosen in order to complement sites GCGC or GTGC in codons 112 or 158 respectively. Each system may amplify two sequences, one of 181 bp and the other of 319 bp.

Genotypes are determined by the pattern produced on agarose gel electrophoresis of the PCR products and ethidium bromide staining. Homozygous genotypes are characterized by 2 specific PCR fragments, and the heterozygous genotypes by 3 or 4 (ε2/4).

The major limitation of ARMS is the possibility of false positives or false negatives, which necessitates internal controls. Analytical time may be restricted by designing a multiplex PCR approach and automating the analysis of the PCR products by CGE.[41]

HYBRIDIZATION WITH ALLELE-SPECIFIC OLIGONUCLEOTIDE (ASO)

This method is based on spotting PCR-amplified apo E polymorphic sequence on nitrocellulose or nylon membrane, followed by hybridization with different labeled ASO probes. The two polymorphic sites may be amplified in a common PCR reaction or in two separate reactions.[42] The sequence is identified by using four different probes with sequences corresponding to the coding regions of Cys 112, Cys 158, Arg 112, and Arg 158, or in the latter by using only two specific probes corresponding to coding sequences of Cys or Arg. Both procedures use radioactively labeled ASO probes and dot pattern detection by autoradiography.

Development of systems in microplate format linked to colorimetric detection has simplified and automated the procedure. Biotinylated amplified products are generated by incorporation of fluorescent labeled primers[43] or of dinitrophenyl (DNP)-labeled nucleotides (Affigene®Apo E commercial kit) and are immobilized on streptavidine-coated microplates. The genotype is identified, in the first case by a selective hybridization immunoassay with 5′-fluorescein isothiocyanate (FITC)–labeled probes complementary to either Arg 112 or Arg 158, followed by H*hal* cleavage of the correctly matched hybrids and measurement of the remaining microplate-absorbed signal by using anti-FITC, Fab-horseradish peroxidase conjugate. In the second case, apo E genotypes are determined by mini-sequencing reactions on the DNA bound to the solid phase linked to an ELISA–like assay utilizing anti-DNP alkaline phosphatase conjugate and a substrate (Affigene®Apo E). The signal (at 409 nanometers wavelength) will depend on genotype.

Another commercialized kit (Affigene®, InnoLIPA-Apo E) proceeds to a reverse dot blot by hybridization of biotinylated-PCR fragments on four different membrane strips, where specific oligonucleotide probes are immobilized (Cys 112, Cys 158, Arg 112, and Arg 158). Alleles are then detected by binding alkaline phosphatase-labeled conjugate to biotinylated hybrids, producing with the 5-bromo-4-chloro-3-indolyl phosphate/nitroblue tetrazolium (BCIP/NBT) substrate, a purple/brown precipitate. This procedure allowed apo E genotyping to be included in a multiplex PCR of 23 polymorphisms.[44]

The real-time fluorescence PCR detection of apo E genotypes is based on specific hybridization of probes to PCR product at the annealing temperature of the mutation. The melting behavior of one of the hybridized oligonucleotide is identified and the substance undergoes fluorescence monitoring. Apo E genotyping performed in a new high-speed thermal cycler (LightCycler, Roche Diagnostics, Mannheim, Germany) may be a promising system.

OLIGONUCLEOTIDE LIGATION ASSAY (OLA)

In this procedure two primers are hybridized to complementary stretches of DNA at sites of polymorphism. Primers are created so that the 3′-end of the first primer is located immediately adjacent to the 5'-end of the second primer. Assuming that the 3'-end of the first primer matches the target DNA perfectly, both primers can be ligated by T4-DNA ligase. (No ligation will be obtained when a mismatch occurs at the 3'-end of the first primer.) Baron et al.[45] proposed a multiplex OLA system containing three synthetic oligonucleotide primers per polymorphic site: two allele-specific and one common fluorescently labeled reporter probe, hybridized to one strand of the PCR product.

The multiplex OLA product is subsequently denatured and electrophoresed on polyacrylamide slab gel linked to a Genescan software to analyze peak color and fragment size. Homozygous genotypes are characterized by two specific peaks and the heterozygous genotypes by three or four (ϵ2/4) peaks.

SINGLE STRAND CONFORMATION POLYMORPHISM ANALYSIS (SSCP)

The SSCP analysis perceives nucleotide variations as mobility shifts that are caused by secondary conformational changes of single-stranded amplification products. These changes are a consequence of hydrogen and electrostatic links inside the primary structure. Amplified double-stranded DNA (dsDNA) fragments are denatured and single-stranded DNA (ssDNA) are separated by polyacrylamide slab gel electrophoresis under non-denaturing conditions. Their detection involves either radio-labeled primers or Silver staining.

The two apo E polymorphic sites may be amplified in separated sets of PCR[46,47] where ϵ4 is distinguished from ϵ2 and ϵ3, and ϵ3 and ϵ2 are distinguished from ϵ3 and ϵ4, respectively. Aozaki et al. achieved a single PCR amplification of the two polymorphic regions simultaneously.[48] Homozygous genotypes are characterized by two bands and the heterozygous genotypes by three or four (ϵ2/4) bands.

ISOTHERMAL PRIMER OLIGO BASE EXTENSION (PROBE)

Recently, the ϵ2/3, ϵ3/3, ϵ3/4, and ϵ4/4 genotypes were simultaneously determined by utilizing temperature-cycled PROBE combined with matrix-assisted laser desorption/ionization time-of-flight mass spectrometry.[49]

The choice of the methods needs to be directed by the type of application of the apo E genotyping (individual diagnosis or population screening) by the logistic capacities of the laboratory (Table 19–3). In general, results obtained from different methods of population screening for common apo E polymorphisms are in complete agreement. No differences between ASO and ARMS, H*hal*-restriction isotyping (H*hal*-RI) and ASO, or H*hal*-RI and SSCP were observed.[48,50]

Recommended Procedure: PCR-RFLP

The H*hal*-RI appears to be the most convenient approach for detecting the common apo E polymorphisms (Figure 19–5).

Table 19–3 ✧ Performance and Quality Assessment of the ApoE Genotyping Methods

Methods	Advantages	Drawbacks
PCR-RFLP	Simple and robust Non-radioactive Automation feasible	Long Lack of sensitivity Nonspecific alteration of restriction sites may lead to misclassification
ARMS	Non-radioactive Automation feasible	False positive and negative values
ASO	Sensitive	Tedious and expensive Radioactive Uncertain hybridization creates false positive
Kits	High-throughput analysis Automate	Uncertain hybridization creates false positive
OLA	High sensitivity Automation feasible	Non-specific Specialized material
SSCP	Sensitive	Radioactive or tedious Silver staining Difficult to develop Lack of reproducibility

Sample: Genomic DNA

We have demonstrated that processing and storage of DNA source significantly affect the quality of the genomic material and consequently its suitability for apo E polymorphism analysis by Hha*I*-RI.

ORIGINAL SOURCE

✧ Buffy coat (stored at −70°C or −196°C)

✧ Whole blood (fresh, refrigerated no longer than 48h, or frozen at −70°C or −196°C for no longer than 1 week) 39

✧ Clotted whole blood

DNA ISOLATION

Salting out with 6M sodium chloride (NaCl) after Proteinase K digestion.[51] Commercially available kits may be used (QiaAmp blood kit).

Figure 19–5 ✧ General Diagram of the Reference Method

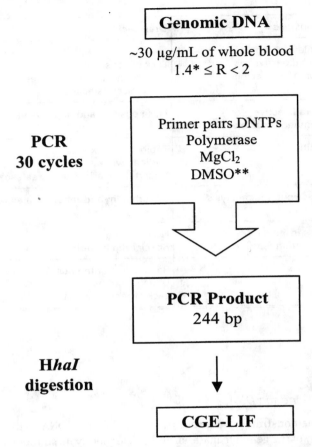

Genomic DNA

~30 μg/mL of whole blood
1.4* ≤ R < 2

**PCR
30 cycles**

Primer pairs DNTPs
Polymerase
MgCl₂
DMSO**

PCR Product
244 bp

***Hha*I
digestion**

CGE-LIF

* a purity index of 1.8–1.4 does not seem affected H*hal*-RI and may be accept-able
** because of the high (G+C) content of apo E gene, successful PCR amplifica-tion needs rigorously control conditions. Presence of dimethylsulfoxide (DMSO) is a critical point of optimisation.
R : purity index of DNA, ratio between absorbance at 260 nm and absorbance at 280 nm
CGE-LIF: capillary gel electrophoresis linked to laser-induced fluorescence

PCR Amplification[30]

Primers	
F4 (Hixson and Vernier, 1990)	5'ACA GAA TTC GCC CCG GCC TGG TAC AC3'
F6 (Hixson and Vernier, 1990)	5'TAA GCT TGG CAC GGC TGT CCA AGG A3'
PCR mixture	**Final concentration**
Buffer PCR (Appligène)	1X
Desoxynucleotide triphosphate (dNTP)	150 μM
Primers	0,5 μM
Dimethylsulfoxide (DMSO)	10%
DNA	1 μg
Taq polymerase (Appligène)	0,025 U/μl
Thermal cycling parameters	
DNA denaturation (before addition of Taq)	95°C, 5 min
Taq polymerase addition	
Amplification	30 cycles
Denaturation	95°C, 1 min
Annealing	60°C, 1 min
Elongation	70°C, 2 min

Restriction Enzyme Digestion (HhaI Gibco)

10 μl of PCR product is digested by 0.5 U of H*hal in enzyme buffer, at* +37°C for one night.

Restriction site: 5'GCGKC3'
       3'CGC↑G 5'

Capillary Gel Electrophoresis

A few nanoliters of digested PCR are injected into a stacking gel. DNA fragments are separated at 9.4 kilovolts in linear polyacrylamide gel buffer and detected on-line (Figure 19–6) by laser-induced fluorescence.[36,52]

Comments

There is a need for rapid, non-invasive, and economical methods to obtain DNA samples for genetic studies, especially for apo E genotyping. Capillary blood collected on

Figure 19–6. ✦ Characterization of the Six Common Apo E Genotrypes by H*hal*-RI Linked to CGE-LIF

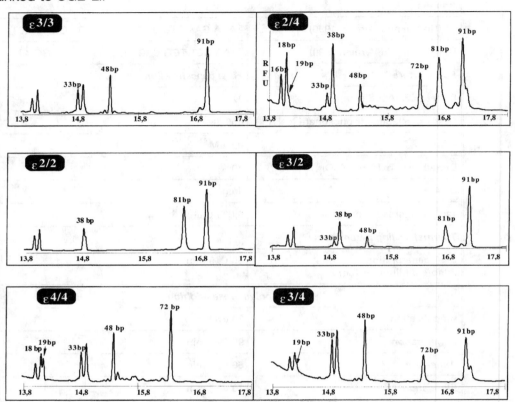

absorbent paper[53] and buccal swabs[54] may be the best procedures to easily collect DNA samples. This avoids venipuncture and storage difficulties, and allows transmission by mail and prolonged preservation of samples at room temperature. However, original samples respond differently to DNA extraction procedures, and may produce DNA samples unsuitable for usual analysis (low yield, degradation, and low purity).

Development of a nested PCR using two apo E gene-specific primer pairs and providing specific high-yield apo E-PCR products has resolved these problems. This may also be a robust assay for retrospective apo E genotyping of DNA from difficult templates such as archival fixed brain[55] and formaldehyde-fixed pathology specimens.[56]

Promoter-Region Polymorphisms

Description

The existence of genetic variants within the apo E gene regulatory region has been explored by systematically screening the region comprising nucleotides −1017 to +406, using denaturing gradient gel electrophoresis (DGGE) (−491A/T, −427 C/T, and −219 G/T) or the direct DNA sequencing (IE1) approach.

Four new polymorphic sites have been found in the transcriptional regulatory region:

❖ *A/T and C/T polymorphisms* have been described at position −491 and −427, respectively.[57]

❖ A *G/T polymorphism* at position −219[57] corresponds to site −186 bp of the apo E gene TATA box.[58] It is located in a potential binding sequence of the Th1/E47 heterodimer transcriptional factor and is named Th1/E47cs.

❖ A *C/G polymorphism* has been also identified at position −113 of the apo E mRNA in the apo E intron promoter enhancer element (IE1).[59,60] It is located 1.15 kb downstream of the Th1/E47cs.[58]

Apo E-Promoter Genotyping

The two polymorphisms −491A/T and −427C/T may be identified simultaneously by endonuclease digestion after a nested PCR approach in the region of nucleotides −1017 to +406, and using two apo E promoter-specific primer pairs. The −427C/T substitution creates an *AluI* restriction enzyme site (AG↓CT) while the −491A/T characterization needs the design of a mismatch primer, producing a *DraI* cut site (TTT↓AAA) when an A is present in the PCR product.[57,61]

Because the Th1/E47cs polymorphism did not create or destroy any restriction enzyme sites, two techniques may be used to identify it. The first one consists of designing a mismatch primer that contains one mismatched base pair, four bases away from the 3′ end of the forward primer and five bases away from the polymorphism. When incorporated into a PCR product, this primer produces a *BstnI* cut site when a G is present, and no cut site when T is present at the polymorphic site. The second approach consists of performing an ASO hybridization. Allele identification is performed with the digoxigenine (DIG) system of labeling and detection. The IE1 polymorphism is determined by a PCR-RFLP approach using the restriction enzyme NlaIV (restriction site GGN↓NCC).[60]

Rare Variants

Description

More than 30 apo E variants have been described.[62,63] They can differ from the three common isoforms by their molecular mass as a consequence of deletions, insertions, frameshifts, or stop codon formation or, most commonly, by their charge as a consequence of single nucleotide substitution and alteration of their amino acids composition.

Apo E variants are designated according to their relative position on isoelectric focusing. Variants with more acidic charge than apo E2 are named apo E1, while variants with a more basic charge relative to apo E4 are designated apo E5 or E7. So far, no apo E6 has been reported. Variants with a relative position intermediate between two isoforms were designated apo E3+ (more basic than apo E3), apo E4− (more acidic than apo E4). Some variants show more than one amino acid substitution and this leads to a similar isoelectric mobility. They are included in the same variant name.

Most of the rare variants of apo E have been identified in exon 4, which codes for the major part of the mature protein. Eight variations are described in exon 3, while no variant have been detected in exon 2 (Table 19–4).

Detection of Rare Apo E Variants

The majority of rare apo E variants have been identified at a protein level by two-dimensional electrophoresis or by isoelectrofocusing. However, only peptide mapping by high performance liquid chromatography (HPLC) or mass spectrometry specifically distinguishes different protein structures in a variant that shows a difference in charge.

Most genotyping methods omit new and rare variants. Only direct DNA sequencing can identify them. However this is tedious and expensive, and cannot be used as a screening method for unknown variants. SSCP analysis is usually considered the method of choice to identify unknown mutations; however, only an apo E4*Pittsburg variant has been detected by this approach.[64]

Some genotyping methods can specifically identify rare variants. All nucleotide substitutions that alter H*hal* restriction site at codons 99, 100, 106, 135, 136[65] or 141, and 142[66] may be identified by PCR-RFLP. Apo E1$_{Weisgraber}$, apo E2$_{(Arg145 \rightarrow Cys)}$, and apo E4$_{Philadelphia}$ may be identified by endonuclease digestion respectively with *Taq1* (67), B*bvI* and F*n4II*,[68] A*val*, and B*bvI*.[69] Apo E2$_{(Lys146 \rightarrow Gln)}$ identification by P*vuII* digestion is based on a preliminary mutagenic amplification assay by PCR.

Genotyping methods may represent a powerful complement to phenotyping when certain structural variants of apo E have the same net charge as the three common isoforms. Combining IEF and PCR-RFLP procedures can identify apo E1$_{Weisgraber}$,[70] apo E1$_{Hammersmith}$,[71] and apo E2$_{Fukuoka}$.[72]

APO E CONCENTRATION

Apo E concentration in human serum as well as in lipoprotein particles is measured by different methods.

The Measurement of Total APO E in Serum

Reviews of radial immunodiffusion, electroimmunoassay, radioimmunoassay, immunonephelometry or immunoturbidimetry, and enzyme-linked immunosorbent assays can be found in the literature.

Radial Immunodiffusion (RID)

This method, developed by Mancini, was applied to apo E measurement for the first time by Kushwaha.[73] A 3% agarose gel is impregnated with rabbit anti-human apo E antibody. The samples, delipidated with tetramethylurea, are placed in a central well in the gel. For 48 hours at 37°C, apo E diffuses outside the wells and forms an immune

Table 19–4 ✧ ApoE Variants

Variant name	Exon/Intron	Codon	Nucleotide change	Codon change
Apo E0	I-3	3592	A→G	Splice donor defect
E0	3	31–60	∆G	Gly→FS→stop at codon 60
E0	4	209–212	2919 or 2020 or 2921 10 bp deletion ∆(4037–4046)	Leu→FS→stop at codon 229
Apo E1 Weisgraber (Gly127→Asp)	4	127	GGC→GAC	Gly→Asp
E1	4	142	CGC→CTC	Arg→Leu
E1 Harrisburg	4	146	AAG→GAG	Lys→Glu
E1 Hammersmith	4	146	G→C	Lys→Asn
		147	C→T	Arg→Trp
E1(Leu252→Glu)	4	252	CTG→GAG	Leu→Glu
Apo E2 Kyoto (Arg134→Gln)	3	25	C→T	Arg→Cys
Apo E2 (Arg134→Gln)	4	134	CGG→CAG	Arg→Gln
E2(Arg136→Cys)	4	136	CGC→TGC	Arg→Cys
E2Christchurch	4	136	CGC→AGC	Arg→Ser
Apo E2(Arg145→Cys)	4	145	CGT→TGT	Arg→Cys
E2Sendai	4	145	CGT→CCT	Arg→Pro
Apo E2(Lys146→Gln)	4	146	AAG→CAG	Lys→Gln
E2Fukuoka	4	224	CGG→CAG	Arg→Gln
E2Dunedin	4	228	CGC→TGC	Arg→Cys
E2(Val236→Glu)	4	236	GTG→GAG	Val→Glu
Apo E3 Freiburg	3	42	ACA→GCA	Thr→Ala
E3(Ala99→Thr; Ala152→Pro	4	99	GCG→ACG	Ala→Thr
	4	152	GCC→CCC	Ala→Pro
E3Leiden	4	120–126 or 121–127	Duplication 21 bp	Tandem Duplication
E3(Arg136→His)	4	136	CGC→CAC	Arg→His
E3(Arg142→Cys)	4	142	CGC→TGC	Arg→Cys
E3Kochi	4	145	CGT→CAT	Arg→His
E3Washington	4	210	TGG→TAG	Trp→stop
E3(Arg251→Gly)	4	251	CGC→GGC	Arg→Gly
Apo E4 Philadelphia	3	13	GAG→AAG	Glu→Lys
E4Freiburg E4Pittsburg	3	28	CTG→CCG	Leu→Pro
E4(Arg274→His)	4	274	CGC→CAC	Arg→His
E4(Ser296→Arg)	4	296	ACG→CGC	Ser→Arg

Table 19–4 ✧ Continued				
Apo E5 Japan(Glu3→Lys)	3	3	GAG→AAG	Glu→Lys
E5Canada (Glu13→Lys)	3	13	GAG→AAG	Glu→Lys
E5Frankfurt	4	81	CAG→AAG	Gln→Lys
E5(Pro84→Arg)	4	84	CCG→CGG	Pro→Arg
E5(Glu212→Lys)	4	212	CAG→AAG	Glu→Lys
ApoE7 Suita	4	244	GAG→AAG	Glu→Lys
		245	GAG→AAG	Glu→Lys

Δ : deletion; FS: frameshift; aa: amino acids; bp: base-pairs

complex, which appears as a precipitation ring at the equilibrium point. The ring size is proportional to apo E concentration. This method is time consuming, needs large amounts of antibody, and is less precise than other methods.

Electroimmunoassay (EIA)

This assay, developed by Laurell, was used for the first time by Curry et al.[74] A 2% agarose gel is impregnated with rabbit or sheep-anti-apo E antibodies. During electrophoresis, apo E migrates and forms an immunoprecipitate with antibody. This complex is stained with Coomassie blue and the precipitation line determines the peak or rocket height in proportion to apo E concentration. The method was optimized in 1988 by Boerwinkle et al.[27] This method is sensitive but needs large amount of antibody.

Radioimmunoassay (RIA)

The principle of this assay is based on the reaction of a rabbit antiserum with buffer-diluted samples during an overnight pre-incubation at $+4°C$. Iode 125 (^{125}I)–labeled apo E is added to the preparation and incubated for various times, from 36 hours at $+4°C$ to overnight at room temperature. The separation of free and bound radioactivity is achieved by incubating the samples overnight at $+4°C$ with rabbit or goat anti-immunoglobulin type G (IgG). The ^{125}I-apo E/antibody complex and apo E/antibody are separated from the ^{125}I-apo E and the free apo E by centrifugation at 2000 g over 25 min.[74] The resulting pellet is washed and its radioactivity counted to quantify apo E. This very sensitive method can detect nanograms of apo E. It uses very small quantities of antibody, but the large dilution of the samples could lead to poor precision and inaccuracy.

Immunoprecipitation Assay

This method includes immunonephelometry and immunoturbidimetry. These automated methods are largely used in clinical laboratories. The former measures the light scattering of the particles whereas the latter measures the decrease in light transmission. The second technique is less sensitive than the first one.

The first protocol proposed rabbit antiserum diluted in phosphate buffer, mixed with the sample diluted in the same buffer, but containing sodium chloride, polyethylene glycol, and Tween 20. After two hours at 23°C, the light scatter produced by the apo E/antibody complex was measured with a laser nephelometer in order to calculate apo E concentration.

In 1986, Rifai developed an immunoturbidimetric method using commercially available reagents,[76] and Japanese groups performed automated procedures using kits from Daiichi.[77] Recently, in our laboratory, an immunoturbidimetric assay was adapted on the Cobas Mira.[78] Both assays are fast, precise, and can be easily automated, but elevated serum triglyceride concentration affects apo E measurement especially by immunoturbidimetry.

Enzyme-Linked Immunosorbent Assay (ELISA)

In this assay, antibodies are first coated to the wall of the microplate well; then samples and enzyme-conjugated anti-human apo E antibody are added. The concentration of apo E is measured after reaction with a substrate.

COMPETITIVE ELISA

Polystyrene tubes are washed with buffered Tween 20 and coated with rabbit anti-human apo E polyclonal antibody. Then, samples containing apo E and solutions with apo E-VLDL labeled with alkaline phosphatase are added. As the labeled apo E-VLDL presents in excess, it can displace the apo E present in the samples. After appropriate washing, quantification is performed (using the reaction with nitrophenylphosphate as substrate for alkaline phosphatase). This technique has been improved using tubes precoated with cellulose nitrate.

INDIRECT SANDWICH ELISA

Wells of a microtiter plate are coated with polyclonal rabbit, goat, or sheep, or monoclonal mouse, antibodies. Samples are added after the well is saturated with apo E-free bovine serum albumin solution. The samples are then incubated and washed, and combined with polyclonal anti-human apo E antibody labeled with horseradish peroxidase. The concentration of apo E is quantified by reaction with *o*-phenylene-diamine and hydrogen peroxide.

Rouis et al.[79] used 2,2'-azido-di-3-ethyl-benzylthiazalin-6-sulfonate and hydrogen peroxide as substrates. Kee et al.[80] optimized this procedure by using two polyclonal antibodies for the apo E detection: a goat polyclonal anti-human apo E antibody to recognize apo E, and a rabbit anti-goat IgG antiserum conjugated with horseradish peroxidase to quantify apo E concentration.

The analytical performance of each of these methods is acceptable. The within-run coefficients of variation (CV) are $< 9\%$ for RIA and ELISA and $< 5\%$ for other techniques. The between-run CV is $< 20\%$ for RIA, 6%–13% for ELISA, and 3%–8%

for the other assays. RIA and ELISA have the lowest detection limits (1–15 ng and 0.2–2 ng, respectively).

The measurement of Apo E concentration by these methods in healthy subjects differs according to the measurement technique:

- ❖ with RID, serum apo E concentrations vary from 36 mg/L[81] to 246 mg/L;[73]

- ❖ with RIA, they vary from 36–60 mg/L[82] (but several authors measured up to 95[83] and 100 mg/L.[84]);

- ❖ with EIA, the highest results are obtained with values of 119 mg/L;[85]

- ❖ with immunoprecipitation, the average was about 40 mg/L;[76–78,86] and

- ❖ with ELISA, the mean values can be divided into two groups: the first one presents values ranging from 20–40 mg/L[87–91] whereas the second group has values from 50–75 mg/L.[80,92–95]

The above results are very discrepant. Different factors can affect the measurement of apo E, for example, apo E phenotype, the preanalytical procedure (fresh or frozen samples, delipidation, detergent use), and the avidity and quality of antibodies. In addition, the lack of standardized methodology, the use of in-house reagents, and the difference in protocols established by individual research groups contribute to these variations.

The Measurement of Apo E in Lipoprotein Particles

Lipoproteins are classified according to their physico-chemical characteristics or their composition (see Chapter 1). We can distinguish apo E-contained in apo B lipoproteins (LpB:E; VLDL; and LDL) and apo E in non-apo B lipoproteins (LpE-non-B; HDL).

Two-Site Enzyme Immunoassay

This assay was developed first by Kandoussi[96] to measure the concentrations of apo E and apo C-III in apo B-containing lipoproteins. Wells of a microtiter plates were coated with either anti-apo C-III or anti-apo E polyclonal antibody and incubated overnight at room temperature. The appropriately diluted samples were incubated in wells for two hours at 37°C. After incubation, a horseradish peroxidase-conjugated anti-apo B polyclonal antibody was added to the wells. After two hours at 37°C, the enzymatic reaction quantified the apo E and apo C-III in the apo B-containing lipoproteins. This method was modified by Yang et al.,[90] who changed the coating antibody to quantify LpB:E and LpE:B (apo B in apo E-containing lipoproteins) and was used by Li et al.[97] This assay is difficult to use in the routine laboratory, because it is very sensitive and because of the sample dilution.

Electro-Immunodiffusion (EID)

Duriez and Fruchart[98] developed this assay in 1994 to measure lipoparticles AI (LpA-I) and lipoparticles AI:AII (LpA-I:A-II) concentrations in HDL (see Chapter 27). In theory, this assay could be applied to other lipoproteins. An agarose gel was impregnated with anti-apo A-I and anti-apo A-II antibodies. Samples were added to the wells and anti-apo A-II antibody was added in excess. During the electrophoresis, lipoproteins migrate and form a complex LpA-I:A-II/anti-apo A-II antibody that precipitates close to the wells. LpA-I continue to migrate until, at the equilibrium, a complex apo A-I/anti-apo A-I antibody forms and precipitates. The heights of the apo A-I rockets are proportional to the apo A-I concentration in LpA-I.[97]

Recently, a variant commercially available method that employs ready-to-use plates has been proposed to measure LpB:E and LpE-non-B. In this method, the agarose gel contains an anti-apo E polyclonal antibody. The native sample and the sample pre-incubated with an anti-apo B antibody are placed in wells in the gel. During the electrophoresis, apo E migrates until it forms a complex with the anti-apo E antibody. The gel is stained with violet acid. The height of the rockets is measured and compared with the calibration curve to determine the total apo E and LpE-non-B concentrations in the sample. The LpB:E concentration is calculated by measuring the difference between total apo E and LpE-non-B concentrations.[99,100]

The concentrations measured by these two methods are relatively similar. CVs are acceptable. The intra-assay CV is below 3%, whereas the inter-assay CV is between 5% and 8.5%. By differential ELISA and EID, the LpB:E concentrations varied from 13–20 mg/L.

STANDARDIZATION OF THE MEASUREMENT OF APO E CONCENTRATION

Because the measurement of apo E concentration has not been standardized, the literature shows a large variation in reported values. Today there are no recommended reference methods, no accepted specifications for the antibodies, and no reference materials (RM) available. Apo E purified from human plasma VLDL or produced by genetic engineering and human serum pools spiked with purified apo E are used as calibrators. Moreover, every research group and manufacturer produces its own calibrators. The behavior of the calibrators may differ from that of human serum samples due to their physico-chemical properties related, for example, to aggregates of the purified protein or to the lyophilization process, and to their immunoreactivity towards polyclonal or monoclonal antibodies (matrix effect). There is, consequently, a need to prepare a stable RM with a certified assigned value, as had been done for apolipoproteins A-I and A-II.

For this purpose, we carried out, with the support of the European Union, a feasibility study for the preparation of a candidate apo E RM.[101] Human apo E3 was produced using recombinant DNA technology. Using the bacterial expression system in *E. coli* and one-step affinity chromatography, large quantities of apo E could be obtained and purified (> 95% purity). The protein exhibited physical, biological, and immunological properties close to that of the human apo E purified from VLDL.[102] To ensure acceptable stability, a batch of lyophilized material containing the purified recombinant apo E added to a matrix was then prepared. The apo E concentration was determined by capillary electrophoresis, using Apo A-I certified reference material as the calibrator, which was shown to be a suitable method to assign a value to RM.[103]

Other non-immunological methods (such as Lowry's method or HPLC quantitation of the phenylamine content) can be used to determine protein concentration. The use of this material as a common calibrator between various methods and laboratories improved the accuracy of apo E measurement in serum or plasma.

The preparation of an apo E reference material thus seems to be feasible and will be useful not only to individual clinical laboratories for standardizing their assays, but also to the diagnostics industry to calibrate the standards it provides with reagent kits. As a result, the accuracy of apo E measurements will improve and the dispersion of results among laboratories will substantially decrease.

BIOLOGICAL VARIATION AND CLINICAL SIGNIFICANCE OF APO E

Genetic and Environmental Factors Affecting Variation

Apo E Polymorphism and Ethnic Variations

The distribution of the apo E alleles is highly variable among the different populations throughout the world (Figure 19–7). The frequency of the ε4 allele varies from about 5%–7% in Chinese populations to about 10% in other Asian and American Indian groups, and reaches close to 37% in Papua New Guineans. It is also elevated in black American and African groups with a frequency of about 20% and 30% respectively. In Australian Aborigines, and in Inuits from Greenland, the ε4 frequency is about 25%; it is 30% in Lapps from Finland. In Caucasian populations outside of Europe (Canada, USA, New-Zealand), the ε4 frequency varies from 9%–15%.[104–117] In European countries, a clear, decreasing North/South gradient in the frequency of the ε4 allele was described (Figure 19–8). The frequency of ε4 is high in northern Europe (Finland, Sweden, Norway, Iceland, and Denmark) but also in Scotland, The Netherlands, and Belgium: the frequency there is about 15%–20%.[104,114,118–122] in Northern Ireland, Germany, Tyrol, Hungary, Poland, Switzerland, northern France, and northern Spain an intermediate frequency of ε4 is observed.[78,104,123–126] The lowest frequencies of ε4 (about 8% to 5%) are found in southern Europe (southern France, Italy, southern Spain, Canary Islands, Crete, Cyprus, or Sardinia).[127–134] In addition, some differences are observed among different geographical areas within a country. Specific studies investigating the factors responsible for the difference in apo E allele frequencies among populations have not been carried out. Some have suggested that differences of ε4 allele frequency between populations explain in part the different prevalence rates of cardiovascular disease (CVD).

Apo E Polymorphism and Apo E Concentration

Distribution of serum apo E values in presumably healthy, subjects does not fit a Gaussian curve, and is skewed towards elevated values. The total inter-individual variation of serum apo E is considerable (25%–32%), but similar to that reported for other apolipoproteins such as apo A-I and apo B. Apo E genotype is an important de-

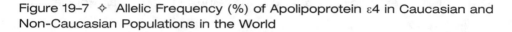

Figure 19–7 ✧ Allelic Frequency (%) of Apolipoprotein ε4 in Caucasian and Non-Caucasian Populations in the World

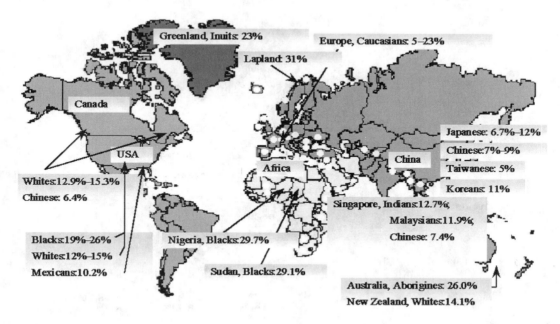

terminant of apo E concentration itself, and 6%–30% of its total variability has been attributed to the common apo E polymorphism. The ε2, ε4 alleles have an increasing and decreasing effect respectively on serum apo E concentration (the highest apo E values are found in the ε2/2 genotype and the lowest in the ε4/4 genotype). Subjects with the ε2/2 genotype exhibit apo E values 1.5- to 2.5-fold higher than subjects having the ε3/3 genotype. Conversely, subjects with the ε4/4 genotype present with apo E values 5%–10% lower than subjects with the e3/3 genotype.[78]

In addition, the non-additive effect of ε2 and ε4 alleles was clearly demonstrated.[135] Moreover, apo E polymorphism also influences the distribution of apo E concentration among apo B- and non-apo B-containing lipoprotein particles. The proportion of apo E in non-apo B-containing lipoprotein particles is lower in subjects carrying the ε2; the opposite is observed for the apo B-containing lipoproteins.[98]

Apo E Concentration and Non-Genetic Factors Affecting Variation

Apo E concentration is determined in part by the genetic variations at the apo E locus. However, this explanation does not account for a large part of the variation, suggesting that other genetic and environmental components are major determinants of its concentration in serum.

Figure 19-8 ◇ Allelic Frequency (%) of Apolipoprotein ε4 in Caucasian Populations in Europe

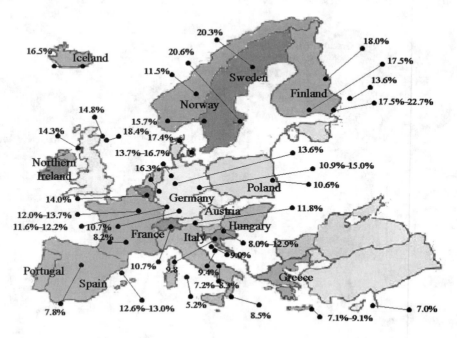

PREANALYTICAL VARIATION

Preanalytical factors that could modify the apo E concentration were recently listed in the ApoEurope project.[137] Several reports agree that apo E can be stored frozen between −20°C and −80°C, at least for three months, without deterioration. Our recent results show that serum samples can be kept at −196°C for up to four years without significant alteration. At +4°C, apo E is stable for one week. However, the effect of storage depends on various factors (antibodies, temperature and length of storage, apo E polymorphism, distribution among lipoproteins, etc.) and must be assessed in each case.

Fasting and length of fast before blood sampling have a noticeable effect on lipid and lipoprotein concentrations. A significant increase in total apo E level was reported two hours after a test meal without excess fat, corresponding to a conventional French breakfast. *In vitro* studies have shown that insulin may accelerate the catabolism of LDL. The transfer of apo E from HDL to triglyceride-rich lipoproteins might explain in part this increase of apo E concentration. Data obtained from the ApoEurope project showed no significant effect of fasting time on apo E concentration (comparing ≤ 2 h, 2–6 h, and > 6 h) and a significant effect on triglyceride concentration in both sexes.

Posture is another important factor affecting preanalytical variation. These changes occur rapidly within five minutes of altering the posture, a time frequently equivalent to the duration of the blood sampling. It was reported that serum apolipoprotein A-I and B concentrations decrease by 5% and 9%, respectively, in subjects who change from standing to sitting, or from standing to reclining. However no data are available for apo E. Seasonal changes in apo E concentration could exist as they do for total cholesterol and triglyceride concentrations but, to our knowledge, no relevant data have been published.

BIOLOGICAL VARIATION

Age and gender are related both to the allelic frequencies of the common apo E polymorphisms and the serum apo E concentration. Because the ε4 allele is associated with cardiovascular disease or dementia, the literature generally describes a decrease with age in the frequency of the ε4 allele. The ε2 allele might be associated with longevity in humans and was reported to be more frequent in centenarians.[2] The prevalence of ε2 allele in subjects older than 80 years is double that in younger individuals. This association might be explained by the protective effect of the ε2 allele. In addition, the impact of the allelic effects could increase with age[136] and the influence of the apo E polymorphism could differ by gender, with a more pronounced effect in women than in men.[111]

Moreover, age itself significantly influences serum apo E concentration. Apo E seems to decrease from birth and childhood until the age of 20–30 years. Also, the effect of age differs between males and females: in men, serum apo E concentration increases linearly up to the ages of 40–44, but seems to tail off thereafter. In women, apo E values continue to increase after the age of 44. This age-related gender effect could be related to hormonal changes associated with the menopause in women. In very elderly subjects (above 80 years), apo E concentration seems to be lower than in subjects aged 50–60 years. Lower apo E values are observed in boys than in girls. In adults older than 26 years, serum apo E concentration is higher in men than in women up to the age of 40 years. It is similar in men and women in middle-aged persons, and it is lower in persons over 50 years of age. Such changes with age and gender resemble those observed for other plasma lipids and lipoproteins (total and LDL-cholesterol, triglycerides, apo A-I and apo B) and are universal. In addition to the effect of age, puberty itself significantly decreases serum apo E concentration in both sexes.[2,78,137]

Increased body mass index (BMI) and waist-to-hip ratio (WHR) are associated with increased apo E concentration.[78,122] BMI and/or WHR were positively correlated with triglycerides, LDL-cholesterol, and apo B, and negatively correlated with HDL-cholesterol and apo A-I. Relationships between BMI, triglycerides, and some hepatic enzymes, especially alanine aminotransferase and γ-glutamyltransferase, were described some years ago. In non-insulin-dependent diabetic patients, γ-glutamyltransferase activity is often increased. This increase could be related in part to modified lipid metabolism in patients with the syndrome of insulin resistance. The association between adiposity and total cholesterol and apo B concentrations appears to be altered in young adults carrying the e2 allele.[138]

In certain populations, serum apo E concentration is not strongly influenced by socio-economic and lifestyle factors such as smoking, drinking, dietary habits, and physical activity. Although moderate drinking and smoking do not seem to significantly modify the concentration of apo E, it has been reported that alcohol abuse increases apo E concentration and that 80% of smokers have higher apo E concentration than non-smokers matched by age and sex.[78,122,138]

Recently, in the ApoEurope project, we found an increasing north-south gradient in serum apo E concentration throughout Europe. This gradient is inverse to that reported for the ε4 allele. It is not solely due to the effect of apo E polymorphism, and is independent of age. This study underlines the importance of the geographical area as a determinant of the total variability of the apo E concentration.[137]

In conclusion, in presumably healthy subjects, the polymorphism of apo E is mainly associated with ethnicity, and the major factors determining biological variation of serum apo E are, in decreasing order of importance: genetic polymorphism of apo E (mainly ε2/2 genotype), WHR or obesity, age, sex, and geographic area.

Clinical Significance

Lipoprotein Metabolism

Numerous population studies have reported the effects of apo E alleles on plasma lipid concentrations.[2] On average, the ε4 allele increases the concentration of total cholesterol and LDL-cholesterol in a healthy population, thus conferring a relative predisposition to atherosclerosis. Apo E4 is associated not only with increase in LDL cholesterol but also with decreased LDL size.[139] In contrast, the ε2 allele usually decreases cholesterol concentration, an effect, depending on the population studied, two to three times the cholesterol-increasing effect of the ε4 allele. Eight percent of total cholesterol variability was attributable to apo E polymorphism. Other authors obtained similar results, finding differences in total and LDL-cholesterol that were highly significant in males, but not in females. There was no effect of apo E phenotype on HDL-cholesterol.

Allelic variation in apo E also affects the apo B concentration, the ε2 allele being associated with lower values and the 94 allele with higher ones. Apo E polymorphism accounts for 12% of the total apo B variability. Apo A-I concentration does not show significant variation with the apo E phenotype. With regard to the effect of the apo E phenotype on lipoprotein(a) [Lp(a)] concentration, either no effect or higher concentration in individuals with the ε4 allele were observed, but these findings are still controversial.[2,111,115,140]

The ε2 and ε4 alleles are also associated with an increase in plasma triglyceride concentrations in the general population. Phenotype E3/3 is associated with the lowest triglyceride concentration and phenotypes E2/2, E4/4, and E2/4 are associated with higher concentrations. A meta-analysis including 45 population samples from 17 countries confirmed that serum triglyceride concentration is significantly higher in subjects with ε2/2, ε3/2, ε4/3, and ε4/2 apo E genotypes than in those with the apo E ε3/3 genotype (2/2: + 32 mg/dL [0.42 mmol/L; 2/3: + 12 mg/dL (0.14 mmol/L)]); 4/3: + 11 mg/dL (0.13 mmol/L); 4/2: + 17 mg/dL (0.19 mmol/L). This trend was observed in normolipemic children and adults, in diabetic obese patients, and in hyperlipidemic subjects.[141] However, triglyceride concentration is the result of numerous genetic and environmental interactions. The presence of a single ε2 allele is perhaps sufficient to account for a delayed clearance of chylomicrons and VLDL remnants from plasma.

During a five-year follow-up of a series of relatives, we found that individuals carrying the ε4 allele had a significantly greater weight-related increase in triglyceride concentration than did individuals without the ε4 allele. Thus, obese individuals with an ε4 allele may be at increased risk for clinically significant hypertriglyceridemia. This adds to the atherogenic potential of the ε4 allele.[2]

The apo E 4/4 and 4/3 phenotypes also appear to be related to higher systolic blood pressure than phenotypes 3/3, 3/2, or 4/2, which suggests that apo E might be one of the factors behind the observed association between serum cholesterol concentration and blood pressure.[142,143]

Cardiovascular Disease

A number of studies have suggested that the ε4 allele is related to an increased risk of coronary heart disease (CHD).[2,118,119,123,144] It is unclear whether this relationship is mediated through the effect of the apo E genotype on lipids, or by other mechanisms. The different prevalence of apo E genotypes across Europe may partly explain the differing rates of CHD. The frequency of this allele presents large geographical variations: it is more frequent in northern European countries than in Mediterranean ones.

Epidemiological studies have demonstrated a consistent positive relationship between coronary artery disease (CAD) and ε4 frequency.[104,123,145,146] The European Atherosclerosis Research Study, based on comparing offspring aged 18–26 years who had a familial history of premature CAD with age- and sex-matched control subjects, demonstrated a significant association of the apo E polymorphism with paternal history of myocardial infarction (MI).[118] Clinical studies have reported that the frequency of the ε4 allele is higher in individuals with CHD, e.g., in MI survivors or subjects with angiographic evidence of atherosclerosis, than in control subjects.[2] Apo E ε4/3 heterozygosity has been also associated with MI at an earlier age than the ε3/2 and ε3/3 genotypes, and the ε4 allele was shown to be associated with an increased risk for exercise-induced silent myocardial ischemia in older, healthy, normocholesterolemic men. In a young population, aged 15–34 years, apo E genotype affects both cholesterol concentrations and the extent of early-stage atherosclerotic lesions: ε2/3 heterozygotes had the least involvement of thoracic and abdominal aortas with lesions, whereas ε4/3 had the greatest involvement, and ε3/3 had intermediate involvement. However, a population followed for four to six years showed no significant variation among phenotypes with regard to either the number of coronary lesions or the within-person mean percentage diameter of stenosis at baseline, as compared to the follow-up angiography.[2] Recently, it was demonstrated that the apo E ε4 allele was a genetic risk factor for coronary atherosclerosis in middle-aged, but not in older, men suggesting that at an older age, other CAD risk factors play a more important role in the atherosclerotic process than apo E polymorphism.[147]

Moreover, a meta-analysis of the epidemiological studies showed that generally, apo E4 allele was associated with cardiac risk in men and women (the odds ratio was 1.44).[148] These data underline the importance of apo E4 in public health.[145] On the contrary, the association of the ε2 allele with CVD is presently not established, except for its role in the pathology of type III hyperlipoproteinemia.[149]

Historically, the link between apo E polymorphism and atherosclerosis was first established with the observation that patients with type III hyperlipoproteinemia and with the apo E 2/2 phenotype had premature CAD. However, some authors have proposed that the ε2 allele may have a protective effect on the development of coronary atherosclerosis. The role of apo E serum concentration as a risk factor for CAD has not been yet investigated. However, there is increasing evidence that serum apo E concentrations may be directly involved in the pathogenesis of CAD.[2,150,151]

Alzheimer's

Alzheimer's (AD) is the most common cause of dementia in the aged population. The cause of AD remains unknown. Epidemiological studies have demonstrated several risk factors for AD, including advanced age, female gender, low education level, and a positive family history of dementia.[152] Among known genetic markers, the most important is the apo E polymorphism, particularly the ε4 allele, as a susceptibility gene for the early- and late-onset familial AD, as well as for sporadic AD.[153,154] However, the mechanisms and associations linking these risk factors to the pathogenesis of the disease are not fully understood.

The first observation of increased HDL-cholesterol concentration in patients with AD was made in 1985. This observation was confirmed some years later by an observation of an increase of cholesterol and apo B concentrations in both AD and stroke patients. The relation between AD and ε4 allele was first described in 1989 by Shimano et al.,[155] who found a two-fold greater relative frequency of the ε4 allele in AD patients (20.8 % vs. 8.6%–11.7% [Japanese controls]). In 1993, the increased frequency of ε4 in late-onset familial AD was discovered. During the same year, numerous papers confirmed the link between ε4 allele and AD. The ε4 allele frequency in patients with AD differs among the various studies from 27%–62%, depending on the classification of AD (sporadic, familial, late-onset, autopsy-confirmed), ethnic effects, and differences in the age of patients and controls.[2] As in healthy subjects, a north-south geographical gradient of the ε4 frequency was shown in European AD patients.[156] A gene dose effect was clearly demonstrated.[157] The earliest onset of AD was described in subjects with two ε4 alleles, followed by those with one ε4 and by the subjects without ε4 allele.[158] More recently, the association between several apo E polymorphisms in the promoter region of the gene and AD was discussed.[57,58,60,159,160] In addition, a novel mutation in exon 3 of the apo E gene (apo E4*Pittsburgh) was demonstrated to be associated with a high risk of developing AD.[64]

The role of serum apo E concentration as a risk factor for AD is unclear. The lack of standardization of apo E measurements and, in general, the small size of studied patient groups does not permit a clear conclusion about changes in apo E concentration. Recently a European study[156] revealed that serum apo E concentration is decreased in both men and women with AD.

Data on apo E concentration in cerebrospinal fluid (CSF) in AD are controversial: no change,[161] decreased,[162] and increased[163] values have been reported. In healthy subjects, the CSF apo E concentration increases with age and this increase is not influenced by sex or by apo E polymorphism.

Other Pathologies

NEUROLOGICAL DISEASE

One of the main difficulties in the study of dementia is the clinical classification of patients into distinct pathological groups. To investigate the specific role of apo E in AD, we must determine the prevalence of apo E alleles in the other neurodegenerative disorders.

The atherosclerotic process affecting cerebral arteries broadly resembles that affecting the coronary arteries. It is perhaps not surprising that three studies show a similarly increased prevalence (by ~119%) of the ε4 allele in both conditions.[2] Two other syndromes show high ε4 allele frequency comparable with those found in AD: vascular dementia with values varying from 19% to 45% and cortical Lewy Body disease with values of 35%–40%. In addition, the presence of ε4 allele enhances the extent of brain abnormalities in various vascular diseases.[27,164] However, more recently, a lack of association between ε4 frequency and family history of dementia was observed, supporting the view that, in a general population, apo E4 cannot explain a large proportion of the dementias.[165]

No significant difference in the distribution of apo E phenotypes between patients with Creutzfeldt-Jacob disease (CJD) and control subjects was found.[166] The authors concluded that apo E concentration in CSF cannot be taken as a biochemical marker for CJD, that apo E phenotype had no influence on the duration of CJD, and that there is no association of apo E4 with either the duration or time of onset of CJD.

In a similar manner, no increase in ε4 frequency was found in familial amyloidotic polyneuropathy, Down's syndrome, amyotrophic lateral sclerosis (Guam dementia), and in Huntington's disease. No significantly different prevalence of ε4 has been observed in Parkinson disease patients compared with controls (19%, 7%, and 13%) except for one Japanese study that showed a positive shift of 32% when dementia is associated.[2]

In multiple sclerosis (MS), the ε4 allele was more common in patients with a more severe type of disease. Although apo E does not seem to be implicated in the early pathogenesis of the disease, patients possessing the ε4 allele might have a reduced capacity for neuronal remodeling after relapse. A significant decrease in CSF apo E concentration was observed in MS linked to a decrease in intrathecal apo E. This decrease occurred independently of the apo E genotype.[167]

DIABETES MELLITUS

Cardiovascular disease is one of the principal complications of diabetes mellitus and a major cause of morbidity and mortality. The main changes in the lipid profile of diabetic patients relate to the altered metabolism of VLDL, HDL, and, to a lesser extent, LDL. The frequency distribution of the apo E phenotypes is similar in the non-diabetic population, in insulin-dependent diabetic patients, and in type 2 (non-insulin-dependent diabetes mellitus, NIDDM) patients, at least in men. The ε4 allele frequency is not increased in familial NIDDM, despite the presence of apo E in pancreatic islet amyloid. However, the association between the ε2 allele and hypertriglyceridemia might be stronger in diabetic patients than in non-diabetic populations. In addition, the ε2 allele is related to type III and type IV hyperlipidemia in NIDDM patients, whereas the ε4 allele is related to type IIb and type V hyperlipidemia, the two alleles contributing to hypertriglyceridemia and probably atherosclerosis.[2]

In patients with insulin-dependent diabetes mellitus (IDDM), Werle et al.[168] showed an association between apo E genotypes and creatinine clearance with a decreasing glomerular filtration rate in the following order of genotypes: ε4/4 and ε4/3 > ε3/3 > ε2/2 and ε2/3. These authors suggested that apo E polymorphism might be a clinically relevant renal risk factor in normolipidemic patients with IDDM.

MISCELLANEOUS

Apo E4 was said to be associated with a four-fold risk of self-reported fractures in hemodialysis patients younger than 80 years.[169] Similarly, a 16% lower lumbar spine bone mineral density (BMD) was reported among Japanese women carrying the ε4 allele.[170] A seven-year follow-up of women older than 65 years concluded that women with the ε4 allele are at increased risk of hip and wrist fracture.[171]

Other studies have shown relationships between apo E polymorphism and various pathologies such as retinis pigmentosa,[172] nephrotic syndrome,[173] and hypertension.[142] These last results were not confirmed by De Knijff et al.[63] Serum apolipoprotein E concentration may also be altered in several diseases, such as multiple sclerosis, severe cholestasis, and deficiency in LCAT or apolipoprotein C-III.

INVOLVEMENT IN DIETARY AND DRUG RESPONSES

Apolipoprotein E is a good candidate for the study of gene-environment interactions, both at the gene and protein level. Apo E common polymorphism influences the responses to cholesterol-lowering diets and to phytosterols. The study by Sarkkinen et al.[174] demonstrated that patients with the genotype ε4/4 are good responders to a low-fat diet plan to decrease cholesterol. Similar results have been reported by Miettinen et al.[175] using sitostanol. Apo E genotype modulates the effect of black tea; subjects with ε3/4 genotype reduced their HDL cholesterol after four weeks of drinking six mugs of black tea each day.[176] The response to lipid-lowering drugs is also, in many studies, apo E phenotype-dependent.

Nestel et al.[177] found that patients with the ε2/3 genotype were better responders to gemfibrozil. Ordoras et al.[178] in a meta-analysis of five studies demonstrated that the decrease in LDL cholesterol caused by statins is in the order ε4<ε3<ε2. However, here again there is a high variability between studies and subjects. Very often the investigated groups were too small to reach statistical significance.

The efficiency of drugs used to treat Alzheimer's also depends on common polymorphisms of Apo E. Poirier et al.[179] showed that tacrine, a cholinomimetic drug, is more efficient in non-ε4 patients, particularly in women.[179–181]

With non-cholinomimetic drugs, xanomeline, or S.12024 drugs, a better improvement is obtained inversely in ε4 patients.[181] For a patient with Alzheimer's, apo E genotyping could clearly help the clinician prescribe a more appropriate medication.

The effect of combined estrogen-progesterone preparations and hormonal replacement therapy are also influenced by apo E polymorphism. The degree to which these drugs elevate triglycerides or lipoproteins and LpB:E differs between women with ε2 and those with ε4 alleles.

SUMMARY

The apo E gene and proteins are both surprising and promising molecules. The gene provides important information in dyslipidemia and Alzheimer's. The common apo E polymorphism is also central in the pharmacogenomic evolution, due to the interest in lipid-lowering and Alzheimer drugs. The protein is heavily involved in lipid metabolism, acting in concert with apo C-III, LPL, proteoglycans, and other proteins and enzymes. The binding of the protein to receptors, amyloid proteins, or other intracellular molecules must be studied in more detail. The apo E concentration in tissues and blood is critical: higher concentration could be protective but depends on the isoform conformation. The protein is also altered by oxidation or glycation, which could also represent a protective mechanism. The physico-chemical properties of this amphiphatic molecule could be useful for the vectoring of drugs and DNA in cells. The use of plasma apo E concentration in clinical situations must be validated. ✧

REFERENCES

1. Mahley RW. Apolipoprotein E: Cholesterol transport protein with a role in cell biology. Science 1988;240:622–30.
2. Siest G, Pillot T, Regis-Bailly A, Leininger-Muller B, Steinmetz J, Galteau MM, Visvikis S. Apolipoprotein E: An important gene and protein to follow in laboratory medicine. Clin Chem 1995;41:1068–86.
3. Riddell DR, Owen JS. Nitric oxide and platelet aggregation. Vitam Horm 1999;57:25–48.
4. St. Clair RW, Beisiegel U. What do all the apolipoprotein E receptors do? Curr Opinion Lipid. 1997;8:243–5.
5. Mahley RW, Ji ZS. Remnant lipoprotein metabolism: key pathways involving cell–surface heparin sulfate proteoglycans and apolipoprotein E. J Lipid Res 1999;40:1–16.
6. Myklebost O, Rognes A. A physical map of the apolipoprotein gene cluster on human chromosome 19. Hum Genet 1988;78:244–7.
7. Paik YK, Chang DJ, Reardon CA, Davies GE, Mahley RW, Taylor JM. Nucleotide sequence and structure of the human apolipoprotein E gene. Proc Natl Acad Sci USA 1985;82:3445–9.
8. Benlian P. Génétique et dyslipidémies. Approche gène candidat. Edition INSERM, 1996.
9. Zannis VI, McPherson J, Goldberger G, Karathanasis SK, Breslow JL. Synthesis, intracellular processing, and signal peptide of human apoE. J Biol Chem 1984;259:5495–9.
10. Wernette-Hammond ME, Lauer SJ, Corsini A, Walker D, Taylor JM, Rall SC. Glycosylation of human apolipoprotein E. The carbohydrate attachment site is threonine 194. J Biol Chem 1989;264:9094–9101.
11. Ito H, Naito C, Nakamura K, Nagase M. Postprandial triglyceride-rich lipoprotein metabolism: possible role of sialylated apolipoprotein E isoproteins. Eur J Clin Invest 1994;24:468–75.
12. Ikewaki K, Rader DJ, Zech LA, Brewer HB. *In vivo* metabolism of apolipoproteins A-I

and E in patients with a beta-lipoproteinemia: implications for the roles of apolipo-proteins B and E in HDL metabolism. 1994;35:1809–19.

13. Patsch W, Franz S, Schonfeld G. Role of insulin lipoprotein secretion by cultured rat hepatocytes. J Clin Invest 1983;71:1161–74.

14. Patsch W, Gotto AM, Patsch JR. Effects of insulin on lipoprotein secretion in rat hepatocyte cultures. J Biol Chem 1986;261:9603–6.

15. Ogbonna G, Theriault A, Adeli K. Hormonal regulation of human apolipoprotein E gene expression in HepG2 cells. Int J Biochem 1993;25:636–40.

16. Aggerbeck LP, Wetterau JR, Weisgraber KH, Wu CSC, Lindgren FT. Human apolipoprotein E3 in aqueous solution. II. Properties of the amino- and carboxyl-termi-nal domains. J Biol Chem 1988;263:6249–58.

17. Dong LM, Wilson C, Wardell MR, Simmons T, Mahley RW, Weisgraber KH, Agard DA. Human apolipoprotein E: role of arginine 61 in mediating the lipoprotein preferences of the E3 and E4 isoforms. J Biol Chem 1994;269:22358–65.

18. Benvenga S, Cahnmann HJ, Robbins J. Characterization of thyroid hormone binding to apolipoprotein-E: localization of the binding site in the exon 3-coded domain. Endocri-nology 1993;133:1300–5.

19. Das HK, McPherson J, Bruns GAP, Karathanasis SK, Breslow JL. Isolation, characteriza-tion, and mapping to chromosome 19 of the human apolipoprotein E gene. J Biol Chem 1985;260:6240–7.

20. Brouwer DAJ, Van Doormal JJ, Muskiet FAJ. Clinical chemistry of common apolipoprotein E isoforms. J Chromatogr B. 1996;678:23–41.

21. Steinmetz A. Clinical implications of the apolipoprotein E polymorphism and genetic variants: current methods for apoE phenotyping. Ann Biol Clin 1991;49:1–8.

22. Warnick GR, Mayfield C, Albers JJ, Hazzard WR. Gel isoelectric focusing method for specific diagnosis of familial hyperlipoproteinemia type 3. Clin Chem 1979;25:279–84.

23. Snowden C, Houlston RS, Harif MH, Laker MF, Humphries SE, Aberti KGMM. Disparity between apolipoprotein E phenotypes and genotypes (as determineted by polymerase chain reactionn and oligonucleotide probes) in patients with non-insulin-dependent di-abetes mellitus. Clin Chim Acta 1991;196:49–58.

24. Steinmetz A, Jakobs C, Motzny S, Kaffarnik H. Differential distribution of apolipo-protein E isoforms in human plasma lipoproteins. Atherosclerosis 1989;9:405–11.

25. McDowell IF, Wisdom GB, Trimble ER. Apolipoprotein E phenotype determined by agarose gel electrofocusing and immunoblotting. Clin Chem 1989;35:2070–73.

26. Havekes LM, De Knijff P, Beisiegel U, Havinga J, Smit M, Klasen E. A rapid micromethod for apolipoprotein E phenotyping directly in serum. J Lipid Res 1987;28:455–63.

27. Boerwinkle E, Utermann G. Simultaneous effects of the apolipoprotein E polymor-phism on apolipoprotein E, apolipoprotein B, and cholesterol metabolism. Am J Hum Genet 1988;42:104–12.

28. Wenham PR, Newton CR, Price WH. Analysis of apolipoprotein E genotypes by the am-plification refractory mutation system. Clin Chem 1991;37:241–4.

29. Lehtimäki T. Determination of apolipoprotein E phenotypes from stored or postmor-tem serum samples. Clin Chim Acta 1991;203:177–82.

30. Hixson JE, Vernier DT. Restriction isotyping of human apolipoprotein E by gene ampli-fication and cleavage with *Hhal*. J Lipid Res 1990;31:545–8.

31. Reymer WA, Groenemeyer BE, Van De Burg R, Kastelein JJP. Apolipoprotein E geno-typing on agarose gel. Clin Chem 1995;41:1046–7.

32. Chapman J, Etupinan J, Asherov A, Goldfarb LG. A simple and efficient method for apolipoprotein E genotype determination. Neurology 1996;46:1484.

33. Zivelin A, Rosenberg N, Peretz H, Amit Y, Kornbrot N, Seligsohn U. Improved method for genotyping apolipoprotein E polymorphisms by a PCR-based assay simultaneously utilizing two distinct restriction enzymes. Clin Chem 1997;43:1657–9.

34. Bolla MK, Haddad L, Humphries SE, Winder AF, Day INM. High-throughput for determi-nation of apolipoprotein E genotypes with use of restriction digestion analysis by microplate array diagonal gel electrophoresis. Clin Chem 1995;41:1599–1604.

35. Lahoz C, Osgood D, Wilson PWF, Schaefer EJ, Ordovas JM. Frequency of phenotype-genotype discrepancies at the apolipoprotein E locus in a large population study. Clin Chem 1996;42:1817–23.

36. Schlenck A, Bohnet K, Aguillon D, Lafaurie C, Siest G, Visvikis S. High sensitivity of laser-induced fluorescence detection in capillary gel electrophoresis for accurate apolipoprotein E genotyping. Biotechniques 1997;22:736–42.

37. Baba Y, Yoshinobu B, Tomisaki R, Tetsuro M, Ogihara T. High-resolution separation of PCR product and gene diagnosis by capillary gel electrophoresis. Biomed Chromatogr 1994;8:291–3.

38. Sell SM, Ren K. Automated capillary electrophoresis in the genotyping of apolipoprotein E. Genomics 1997;46:163–4.

39. Visvikis S, Schlenck A, Maurice M. DNA extraction and stability for epidemiological studies. Clin Chem Lab Med 1998;36:551–5.

40. Wenham PR, Price WH, Blundell G. Apolipoprotein E genotyping by one-stage PCR. Lancet 1991;337:1158.

41. Donohoe GG, Salomaki A, Lehtimaki T, Pulkki K, Kairisto V. Rapid identification of apolipoprotein E genotypes by multiplex amplification refractory mutation system PCR and capillary gel electrophoresis. Clin Chem 1999;45:143–6.

42. Green EK, Bain SC, Day PJR, Barnett AH, Charleson F, Jones AF, Walker MR. Detection of human apolipoprotein E3, E2, and E4 genotypes by an allele-specific oligonucleotide-primed polymerase chain reaction assay: development and validation. Clin Chem 1991;37:1263–8.

43. Kohler T, Rost AK, Purschwitz K, Vondran S, Remke H, Wagner O, Richter V. Genotyping of human apolipoprotein E alleles by the new qualitative, microplate-based CASSI-detection assay. Biotechniques 1998;25:80–5.

44. Cheng S, Pallaud C, Grow MA, Scharf SJ, Erlich HA, Klitz W, Pullinger CR, Malloy MJ, Kane JP, Siest G, Visvikis S. A multi-locus genotyping assay for cardiovascular disease. Clin Chem Lab Med 1998;36:561–6.

45. Baron H, Fung S, Aydin A, Bähring S, Jeschke E, Luft FC, Schuster H. Oligonucleotide ligation assay for detection of apolipoprotein E polymorphisms. Clin Chem 1997;43:1984.

46. Tsai MY, Suess P, Schwichtenberg K, Eckfeldt JH, Yuan J, Tuchman M, Hunninghake D. Determination of apolipoprotein E genotypes by single strand conformation polymorphism. Clin Chem 1993;39:2121–4.

47. Wilton S, Lim L. Rapid identification of apoE allele by multiple single strand conformation polymorphism (SSCP) analysis. Trends Genet 1995;11:341.

48. Aozaki R, Kawaguchi R, Ogasa U, Hikiji K, Kubo N, Sakurabayashi I. Rapid identification of the common apo E isoform genotype using polymerase chain reaction–single strand conformation polymorphism (PCR–SSCP). Mol Cell Probes 1994;8:51–4.

49. Little DP, Braun A, Darnhofer-Demar B, Koster H. Identification of apolipoprotein E polymorphisms using temperature-cycled primer oligo base extension and mass spectrometry. Eur J Clin Chem Clin Biochem 1997;35:545–8.

50. Maekawa B, Cole TG, Seip RL, Bylund D. Apolipoprotein E genotyping methods for the clinical laboratory. J Clin Lab Anal 1995;9:63–9.

51. Miller SA, Dykes DD, Polesky HF. A simple salting out procedure for extracting DNA from human nucleated cells. Nucl Acid Res 1988;16:1215.

52. Schlenck A, Visvikis S, O'Kane M, Siest G. High-resolution separation of PCR product and gene diagnosis by capillary gel electrophoresis. Biomed Chromatogr 1996;10:48–50.

53. Lagarde JP, Benlian P, Zekraoui L, Raisonnier A. Genotyping of apolipoprotein E (alleles epsilon2, epsilon3, and epsilon4) from capillary blood. Ann Biol Clin 1995;53:15–20.

54. Ilveskoski E, Lehtimaki T, Erkinjuntti T, Koivula T, Karhunen PJ. Rapid apolipoprotein E genotyping from mailed buccal swabs. J Neurosci Meth 1998;79:5–8.

55. Gioia L, Vogt LJ, Freeman WM, Flood A, Vogt BA, Vrana KE. PCR-based apolipoprotein E genotype analysis from archival fixed brain. J Neurosci Meth 1998;80:209–14.

56. Ghebremedhin E, Braak H, Braak E, Sahm J. Improved method facilitates reliable apo E genotyping of genomic DNA extracted from formaldehyde-fixed pathology specimens. J Neurosci Meth 1998;79:229–31.

57. Artiga MJ, Bullido MJ, Sastre I, Recuero M, Garcia MA, Aldudo J, Vazquez J, Valdivieso F. Allelic polymorphisms in the transcriptional regulatory region of apolipoprotein E gene. FEBS Lett 1998;421:105–8.

58. Lambert JC, Pasquier F, Cottel D, Frigard B, Amouyel P, Chartier-Harlin MC. A new polymorphism in the Apo E promoter associated with risk of developing Alzheimer's disease. Hum Mol Genet 1998;7:533–40.

59. Betard C, Gee M, Robitaille Y, Cholette AL, Roy P, Gauvreau D. Linkage diseuilibrium between a newly identified polymorphism in the apo enhancer region and apo epsilon allele in Alzheimer patients. In: Roses A, Weisgraber K, Christen Y (eds.). Apolipoprotein E and Alzheimer's disease. New York: Springer Verlag, 1996.

60. Mui S, Briggs M, ChuNG H, Wallace RB, Gomez-Isla T, Rebeck GW, Hyman BT. A newly identified polymorphism in the apolipoprotein E enhancer gene region is associated with Alzheimer's disease and strongly with the epsilon 4 allele. Neurology 1996; 47:196–201.

61. Bullido MJ, Artiga MJ, Recuero M, Sastre I, Garcia MA, Aldudo J, Lendon C, Han SW, Morris JC, Frank A, Vazquez J, Goate A, Valdivieso F. A polymorphism in the regulatory region of Apo E associated with risk for Alzheimer's dementia. Nat Genet 1998;18: 69–71.

62. Rall SC, Mahley RW. The role of apolipoprotein genetic variants in lipoprotein disorders. J Intern Med 1992;231:653–9.

63. De Knijff P, Van den Maadenberg AMJM, Frants RR, Havekes LM. Genetic heterogeneity of apolipoprotein E and its influence on plasma lipid and lipoprotein levels. Hum Mut 1994;4:178–94.

64. Kamboh MI, Aston CE, Perez-Tur K, Kokmen E, Ferrell RE, Hardy J, De Kosky ST. A novel mutation in the apolipoprotein E gene (Apo E4*Pittsburgh) is associated with the risk of late-onset Alzheimer's disease. Neurosci Lett 1999;263:129–32.

65. Minnich A, Weisgraber KH, Newhouse Y, Dong LM, Fortin LJ, Tremblay M, Davignon J. Identification and characterization of novel apolipoprotein E variant, apolipoprotein E3 (Arg136 His): association with mild dyslipidemia and double prebeta very-low-density lipoproteins. J Lipid Res 1995;36:57–65.

66. Richard P, De Zelueta MP, Beucler I, De Gennes JL, Cassaigne A, Iron A. Identification of a new apolipoprotein E variant (E2 Arg142 Leu) in type III hyperlipidemia. Atherosclerosis 1995;112:19–28.

67. Steinmetz A, Assefbarkhi N, Eltze C, Ehlenz K, Funke H, Pies A, Assmann G, Kaffarnik H. Normolipemic dysbetalipoproteinemia and hyperlipoproteinemia type III subjects homozygous for a rare genetic apolipoprotein E variant (apoE1). J Lipid Res 1990; 31:1005–13.

68. Hsia SH, Connely PW, Hegele RA. Restriction isotyping of apolipoprotein E R145C in type III hyperlipoproteinemia. J Invest Med 1995;43:187–94.

69. Lohse P, Mann WA, Stein EA, Brewer HB. Apolipoprotein E4*Philadelphia (Glu13 Lys, Arg145 Cys). Homozygousity for two rare point mutations in the apolipoprotein E gene combined with severe type III hyperlipoproteinemia. J Biol Chem 1991;266:10479–84.

70. Feussner G, Lohrmann J, Dobmeyer J. Rapid and reliable identification of human apolipoprotein E1 (Gly127 Asp, Arg158 Cys) variant. Clin Chem 1995;41:1043–5.

71. Hoffer MJV, Niththyananthan S, Naoumova RP, Kibirige MS. Apolipoprotein E-I–hammersmith (Lys146àAsn; Arg147àTrp), due to a dinucleotide substitution, is associated with early manifestation of dominant type III hyperlipoproteinaemia. Atherosclerosis. 1996;124:183–9.

72. Moriyama K, Sasaki J Matsunaga A, Arakawa F Takada Y, Araki K, Kaneko S, Arakawa K. Apolipoprotein E-1 Lys–146–Glu with type III hyperlipoproteinemia. Biochim Biophys Acta 1992;1128:58–64.

73. Kushwaha RS, Hazzard WR, Wahl PW, Hoover JJ. Type III hyperlipoproteinemia: diag-

nosis in whole plasma by apolipoprotein E immunoassay. Ann Intern Med 1977;87: 509–16.

74. Curry MD, McConnathy WJ, Alaupovic P, Ledford JH, Popovic M. Determination of human apolipoprotein E by electroimmunoassay. Biochim Biophys Acta 1976;439: 413–25.

75. Applebaum-Bowden D, McLean P, Steinmetz A, Fontana D, Mathys C, Warnick GR, Chung M, Albers JJ, Hazzard WR. Lipoprotein, apolipoprotein, and lipolytic enzyme changes following estrogen administration in post-menopausal women. J Lipid Res 1989;30:1895–1906.

76. Rifai N, Christenson RH, Gelman BB, Silverman LM. Automated determination of apolipoprotein A-I and apolipoprotein E in cerebrospinal fluid. Clin Chem 1986;32: 2207–15.

77. Noma A, Hata Y, Goto Y. Quantitation of serum apolipoproteins A-I, A-II, B, C-II, C-III, and E in the healthy Japanese by turbidimetric immunoassay: reference values and age- and sex-related differences. Clin Chim Acta 1991;199:147–58.

78. Vincent-Viry M, Schiele F, Gueguen R, Bohnet K, Visvikis S, Siest G. Biological variations and genetic reference values for apolipoprotein E serum concentrations: results from the Stanislas Cohort Study. Clin Chem 1998;445:957–65.

79. Rouis M, Nigon F, Eggerman TL, Brewer JC, Chapman JB. Apolipoprotein E expression by human monocyte-derived macrophages modulation by opsonized zymosan and cholesterol. Eur J Biochem 1990;189:447–53.

80. Kee P, Bais R, Sobecki SK, Branford S, Rye KA, Barter JP. Indirect sandwich enzyme-linked immunosorbent assay (ELISA) for plasma apolipoprotein E. Ann Clin Biochem 1996;33:119–26.

81. Eto M, Watanabe K, Iwashima Y, Morikawa A, Oshima E, Sekiguchi M, Ishii K. Apolipoprotein E phenotypes and plasma lipid in young and middle-aged subjects. Tohoku J Exp Med 1990;148:25–34.

82. Kaprio J, Ferell RE, Kottke BA, Kamboh MI, Sing SF. Effects of polymorphisms in apolipoproteins E, A-IV, and H on quantitative traits related to risk for cardiovascular disease. Arterioscler Thromb Vasc Biol 1991;11:1330–48.

83. Mackie A, Caslake M, Packard C, Shepherd J. Concentration and distribution of human plasma apolipoprotein E. Clin Chim Acta 1981;116:35–45.

84. Yamada N, Murase T, Akanuma Y, Itakura H, Kosaka K. Plasma apolipoprotein E levels in hypertriglyceridemia. Horm Metab Res 1982;14:303–6.

85. Bittolo-Bon G, Cazzollato M, Kostner G, Avogaro P. Total plasma apo E and high-density-lipoprotein apo E in survivors of myocardial infarction. Atherosclerosis 1984;44: 223–35.

86. Chiba H, Akizawa K, Fujisawa SI, Osaka-nakamori T, Iwasaki N, Suzuki H, Intoh S, Matsuno K, Mitamura T, Kobayashi K. A rapid and simple quantification of human apolipoprotein E-rich high-density lipoproteins in serum. Biochem Med Metab Biol 1992;47:31–7.

87. Bury J, Vercaemst R, Rosseneu M, Belpaire F. Apolipoprotein E quantified by enzyme-linked immunosorbent assay. Clin Chem 1986;32:265–70.

88. Alsayed N, Rebourcet R, Chapman J. Concentrations of apolipoprotein C-II, C-III and E in total serum and in the apolipoprotein B-containing lipoproteins, determined by a new enzyme-linked immunosorbent assay. Clin Chem 1990;12:2047–52.

89. Wilson HM, Patel JC, Russel D, Skinner ER. Alterations in the concentration of an apolipoprotein E-containing subfraction of plasma high-density lipoprotein in coronary heart disease. Clin Chim Acta 1993;220:175–87.

90. Yang C, Xie Y, Yang M, Quion JA, Gotto J. ELISA quantitation of apolipoproteins in plasma lipoprotein fractions: apoE in apoB-containing lipoproteins (LpB:E) and apoB in apo E-containing lipoproteins (LpE:B). J Prot Chem 1995;14:503–8.

91. Krul ES, Cole TG. Quantitation of apoE. Meth Enzymol 1996;263:170–87.

92. Havekes LM, De Knijff P, Smit M, Frants RR. The effect of apolipoprotein E allele substitution on plasma lipid and apolipoprotein levels. Adv Exp Med Biol 1988;243:87–93.

93. Genest JJ, Bard JM, Fruchart JC, Ordovas JM, Wilson PF, Shaefer EJ. Plasma apolipoprotein A-I-, A-II-, B-, E- and C-III-containing particles in men with premature coronary artery disease. Atherosclerosis 1991;90:149–57.

94. Gracia V, Fiol C, Hurtado I, Pinto X, Argimon JM, Castinieras MJ. An enzyme-linked immunosorbent assay method to measure human apolipoprotein E levels using commercially available reagents: effect of apolipoprotein E concentration. Anal Biochem 1994;223:212–17.

95. Krassnoff P, Pisani T, Long S. Quantitative assay for the determination of apo E in serum and plasma. J Clin Ligand Assay 1996;19:172–76.

96. Kandoussi A, Cachera C, Parsy D, Bard JM, Fruchart JC. Quantitative determination of different apolipoprotein-B-containing lipoproteins by an enzyme-linked immunosorbent assay: apo B with apoC-III and apo B with apo E. J Immunoassay 1991;12:305–23.

97. Li Z, McNamara J, Fruchart JC, Luc G, Bard J, Ordovas J, Wilson P, Schaefer J. Effects of gender and menopausal status on plasma lipoprotein subspecies and particle sizes. J Lipid Res 1996;37:886–89.

98. Duriez P, Fruchart JC. Dosage des lipoprotéines définies selon leur composition en apolipoprotéines en vue de la prédiction du risque cardiovasculaire. Ann Biol Clin 1994;52:179–83.

99. Luc G, Fievet C, Arveiler D, Evans A, Bard JM, Cambien F, Fruchart JC, Ducimetière P. Apolipoproteins C-III and apo E in apo-B- and non-apoB-containing lipoproteins in two populations at contrasting risk for myocardial infarction: the ECTIM Study. J Lipid Res 1996;37:508–17.

100. Luc G, Ducimetiere P, Bard JM, Arveiler D, Evans A, Cambien F, Fruchart JC, Fiever C. Distribution of apolipoprotein E between apo-B- and non-apo-B-containing lipoproteins according to apo E phenotype. Atherosclerosis 1997;131:257–62.

101. Schiele F, Barbier A, Visvikis A, Aggerbeck L, Rosseneu M, Havekes LM, Huttinger M, Profilis C, Siest G. Feasibility of a recombinant human apolipoprotein E reference material. Fresenius J Anal Chem 1998;360:501–4.

102. Barbier A, Visvikis A, Mathieu F, Diez L, Havekes LM, Siest G. Characterization of three human apolipoprotein E isoforms (E2, E3, and E4) expressed in Escherichia Coli. Eur J Clin Chem Clin Biochem 1997;35:581–9.

103. Schlenck A, Schiele F, Barbier A, Shuvaev V, Visvikis S, Siest G. Capillary electrophoretic analysis of recombinant human apolipoprotein E. Calibration mode of a protein reference material. J Chromatogr 1999;851:237–41.

104. Gerdes LU, Klausen IC, Sihm I, Faegerman O. Apolipoprotein E polymorphism in a Danish population compared to findings in 45 other study populations around the world. Genet Epidemiol 1992;9:155–67.

105. Kao JT, Tsai KS, Chang CJ, Huang PC. The effects of apolipoprotein E polymorphism on the distribution of lipids and lipoproteins in the Chinese population. Atherosclerosis 1995;114:55–9.

106. Tai DY, Su FH, Chang KH, Lee-Chen GJ. Human apolipoprotein E: correlation of polymorphisms and serum lipid concentrations in Chinese. Chung Hua I Hsueh Tsa Chih (Taipei) 1999;62:133–9.

107. Yamanoushi Y, Arinami T, Tsuchiya S, Miyazaki R, Takaki H, Takano T, Hamaguchi H. Apolipoprotein E5 and E7 in apparently healthy Japanese males: frequencies and relation to plasma lipid levels. Jpn J Human Genet 1994;39:315–25.

108. Kim HS, Kamboh MI. Genetic polymorphisms of apolipoproteins A-IV, E, and H in Koreans. Hum Hered 1998;48:313–7.

109. Sanghera DK, Ferrell RE, Aston CE, McAllister AE, Kamboh MI, Kimm SY. Quantitative effects of the apolipoprotein E polymorphism in a biracial sample of 9–10-year-old girls. Atherosclerosis 1996;126:35–42.

110. Kamboh MI, Evans RW, Aston CE. Genetic effect of apolipoprotein(a) and apolipoprotein E polymorphisms on plasma quantitative risk factors for coronary heart disease in American black women. Atherosclerosis 1995;117:73–81.

111. Howard BV, Gidding SS, Liu K. Association of apolipoprotein E phenotype with plasma lipoproteins in African-American and White young adults. The CARDIA Study. Am J Epidemiol 1998;148:859–68.

112. Kamboh MI, Serjeantson SW, Ferrell RE. Genetic studies of human apolipoproteins. XVIII. Apolipoprotein polymorphisms in Australian Aborigines. Hum Biol 1991;63: 179–86.

113. Gerdes LU, Gerdes C, Hansen PS, Klausen IC, Faergeman O, Dyerberg J. The apolipoprotein E polymorphism in Greenland Inuit in its global perspective. Hum Genet 1996;98:546–50.

114. Lehtinen S, Luoma P, Lehtimäki T, Näyhä S, Hassi J, Nikkari T. Differences in genetic variation of apolipoprotein E in Lapps and Finns (abstract). 10th Symp Atherosclerosis, Montreal, 1994;p 263.

115. Schaefer EJ, Lamon–Fava S, Johnson S, Ordovas JM, Schaefer MM, Castelli WP, Wilson PWF. Effects of gender and menopausal status on the association of apolipoprotein E phenotype with plasma lipoprotein levels. Results from the Framingham offspring study. Arterioscler Thromb 1994;14:1105–13.

116. Cauley JA, Eichner JE, Kamboh MI, Ferrell RE, Kuller LH. Apo E allele frequencies in younger (age 42–50) vs. older (age 65–90) women. Genet Epidemiol 1993;10:27–34.

117. Kamboh MI, Aston CE, Hamman RF. The relationship of apo E polymorphism and cholesterol levels in normoglycemic and diabetic subjects in a biethnic population from the San Luis Valley, Colorado. Atherosclerosis 1995;112:145–59.

118. Tiret L, de Knijff P, Menzel HJ, Ehnholm C, Nicaud V, Havekes LM for the EARS group. Apo E polymorphism and predisposition to coronary heart disease in youths of different European populations, the EARS study. Arterioscler Thromb 1994;14:1617–24.

119. Stengard JH, Zerba KE, Pekkanen J, Ehnholm C, Nissinen A, Sing CF. Apolipoprotein E polymorphism predicts death from coronary heart disease in a longitudinal study of elderly Finnish men. Circulation 1995;91:265–9.

120. Eggersten G, Tegelman R, Ericsson S, Angelin B, Berglund L. Apolipoprotein E polymorphism in a healthy Swedish population: variation of allele frequency with age and relation to serum lipid concentrations. Clin Chem 1993;39:2125–9.

121. De Knijff P, Boomsma DI, De Wit E, Kempen HJM, Leuven JAG, Frants RR, Havekes LM. The effect of the apolipoprotein E phenotype on plasma lipids is not influenced by environmental variability: results of a Dutch twin study. Hum Genet 1993;91:268–72.

122. Braeckman L, De Bacquer D, Rosseneu M, De Backer G. Apolipoprotein E polymorphism in middle-aged Belgian men: phenotype distribution and relation to serum lipids and lipoproteins. Atherosclerosis 1996;120:67–73.

123. Luc G, Bard JM, Arveiler D, Evans E, Cambou JP, Bingham A, Amouyel P, Schaffer P, Ruidavets JB, Cambien F et al. Impact of apolipoprotein E polymorphism on lipoproteins and risk of myocardial infarction. The ECTIM study. Arterioscler Thromb 1994;14:1412–9.

124. Kalman J, Juhasz A, Csaszar A, Kanka A, Rimanoczy A, Janka Z, Rasko I. Increased apolipoprotein E4 allele frequency is associated with vascular dementia in the Hungarian population. Acta Neurol Scand 1998;98:166–8.

125. Kowalska A, Wiechmann I, Walter H. Genetic variability of apolipoprotein E in a Polish population. Hum Biol 1998;6:1093–9.

126. Gene M, Moreno P, Ezquerra M, Prat A, Huguet E, Adroer R, Oliva R. Low apolipoprotein E epsilon4 allele frequency in the population of Catalonia (Spain) determined by PCR–RFLP and laser fluorescent sequencer. Eur J Epidemiol 1997;13:841–3.

127. Xu CF, Talmud PJ, Angelico F, Ben MD, Savill J, Humphries SE. Apolipoprotein E polymorphism and plasma lipid, lipoprotein, and apolipoprotein levels in Italian children. Genet Epidemiol 1991;8:389–98.

128. Corbo RM, Scacchi R, Mureddu L, Mulas G, Alfano G. Apolipoprotein E polymorphism in Italy investigated in native plasma by a simple polyacrylamide gel isoelectric focusing technique. Comparison with frequency data of other European populations. Ann Hum Genet 1995;59:197–209.

129. James RW, Boemi M, Giansanti R, Fumelli P, Pometta D. Underexpression of the apolipoprotein E4 isoform in an Italian population. Arterioscler Thromb 1993;13: 1456–9.

130. Margaglione M, Seripa D, Gravina C, Grandone E, Vecchione G, Cappucci C, Merla G, Papa S, Postiglione A, Di Minno G, Fazio VM. Prevalence of apolipoprotein E alleles in healthy subjects and survivors of ischemic stroke. An Italian case-control study. Stroke 1998;29:399–403.

131. Gomez-Coronado D, Alvarez JJ, Entrala A, Olmos JM, Herrera E, Lasuncion MA. Apolipoprotein E polymorphism in men and women from a Spanish population: allele frequencies and influence on plasma lipids and apolipoproteins. Atherosclerosis 1999;147:167–76.

132. Muros M, Rodriguez-Ferrer CR. Underexpression of apo E4 allele in a population living in a European ultraperipheral region (abstract). Atherosclerosis 1995;115 (Suppl):S116.

133. Cariolou MA, Kokkofitou A, Manoli P, Christou S, Karagrigoriou A, Middleton L. Underexpression of the apolipoprotein E2 and E4 alleles in the Greek Cypriot population of Cyprus. Genet Epidemiol 1995;12:489–97.

134. Kafatos A, Moschandreas J, Hatzis C, Linardakis M, Visvikis S, Siest G and the ApoEurope group. Apolipoprotein E polymorphisms in Crete and relation to lipoprotein concentrations and other coronary heart disease risk factors. World Nutr Diet 2000; accepted for publication.

135. Bohnet K, Regis-Bailly A, Vincent-Viry M, Schlenk A, Gueguen R, Siest G, Visvikis S. Apolipoprotein E genotype ε4/ε2 in the STANISLAS Cohort Study— Dominance of the E2 allele? Ann Hum Genet 1996; 60:509–16.

136. Haviland MB, Lussier-Cacan S, Davignon J, Sing CF. Impact of apolipoprotein E genotype variation on means, variances, and correlations of plasma lipid, lipoprotein, and apolipoprotein traits in octogenarians. Am J Med Genet 1995;58:315–31.

137. Schiele F, De Bacquer D, Vincent-Viry M, Beisiegel U, Ehnholm C, Evans A, Kafatos A, Martins MC, Sans S, Sass C, Visvikis S, De Backer G, Siest G, and the ApoEurope group. Apolipoprotein E serum concentration and polymorphism in six European countries: the ApoEurope project. Atherosclerosis 2000; accepted for publication.

138. Boer JMA, Ehnholm C, Menzel HJ, Havekes LM, Rosseneu M, O'Reilly DStJ, Tiret L, for the EARS Group. Interactions between lifestyle-related factors and the apo E polymorphism on plasma lipids and apolipoproteins. The EARS study. Arterioscler Thromb Vasc Biol 1997;17:1675–81.

139. Haffner SM, Stern MP, Miettinen H, Robbins D, Howard BV. Apolipoprotein E polymorphism and LDL size in a biethnic population. Arterioscler Thromb Vasc Biol 1996;16:1184–8.

140. Heng CK, Saha N, Tay JS. Lack of association of apolipoprotein E polymorphism with plasma Lp(a) levels in the Chinese. Clin Genet 1995;48:113–9.

141. Dallongeville J, Lussier-Cacan S, Davignon J. Modulation of plasma triglyceride levels by apo E genotype: a meta-analysis. J Lipid Res 1992;33:447–54.

142. Uusitupa M, Sarkkinen E, Kervinen K, Kesaniemi YA. Apolipoprotein E phenotype and blood pressure. Lancet 1994;343:57.

143. Shiwaku K, Gao TQ, Hojo N, Fukushima T, Yamane Y. Low levels of serum cholesterol and systolic blood pressure in Japanese with the apolipoprotein E3/2 genotype. Clin Chim Acta 1999;284:15–23.

144. Stengard JH, Pekkanen J, Ehnholm C, Nissinen A, Sing CF. Genotypes with the apolipoprotein ε4 allele are predictors of coronary heart disease mortality in a longitudinal study of elderly Finnish men aged 65–84 years. Hum Genet 1996;97:677–84.

145. Couderc R, Bailleul S. L'apolipoprotéine E et ses allèles chez le sujet sain et au cours de l'athérosclérose. Ann Biol Clin 1998;56:651–9.

146. Wilson PWF, Myers RH, Larson MG, Ordovas JM, Wolf PA, Schaefer EJ. Apolipoprotein E alleles, dyslipemia, and coronary heart disease. The Framingham offspring study. JAMA 1994;272:1666–71.

147. Ilveskoski E, Perola M, Lehtimaki T, Laippala P, Savolainen V, Pajarinen J, Penttilä A,

Lalu KH, Männikkö A, Liesto KK, Koivula T, Karhunen PJ. Age-dependent association of apolipoprotein E genotype with coronary and aortic atherosclerosis in middle-aged men. An autopsy study. Circulation 1999;100:608–13.

148. Wilson PWF, Schaefer EJ, Larson MG, Ordovas JM. Apolipoprotein E alleles and risk of coronary disease: a meta-analysis. Arterioscl Thromb Vasc Biol 1996; 16:1250–5.

149. Mahley RW, Huang Y, Rall SC. Pathogenesis of type III hyperlipoproteinemia (dysbetalipoproteinemia). Questions, quandaries, and paradoxes. J Lipid Res 1999;40:1933–49.

150. Mahley RW, Huang Y. Apolipoprotein E: from atherosclerosis to Alzheimer's disease and beyond. Curr Opin Lipidol 1999;10:207–17.

151. Jarvik GP, Goode EL, Austin MA, Auwerx J, Deeb S, Schellenberg GD, Reed T. Evidence that the apolipoprotein E genotype effects on lipid levels can change with age in males: a longitudinal analysis. Am J Hum Genet 1997;61:171–81.

152. Alloul K, Sauriol L, Kennedy W, Laurier C, Tessier G, Novosel S, et al. A. Alzheimer's disease: a review of the disease, its epidemiology and economic impact. Arch Gerontol Geriatr 1998; 27:189–221.

153. Higgins GA, Large CH, Rupniak HT, Barnes JC. Apolipoprotein E and Alzheimer's disease: a review of recent studies. Pharmacol Biochem Behavior 1997;56:675–85.

154. Farrer LA, Cuplles LA, Haines JL, Hyman B, Kukull WA, Mayeux R, Myers RH, Pericak-Vance MA, Risch N, van Duijn CM. Effects of age, sex, and ethnicity on the association between apolipolipoprotein E genotype and Alzheimer's. A meta-analysis. JAMA 1997;278:1349–56.

155. Shimano H, Ishibashi S, Murase T, Gotohda T, Yamada N, Takaku F, Ohtomo E. Plasma apolipoproteins in patients with multi-infarct dementia. Atherosclerosis 1989;79: 257–60.

156. Siest G, Qin B, Bertrand P, Herbeth B, Serot JM, Masana L et al. Apolipoprotein E polymorphism and serum level in Alzheimer's disease in nine European countries: the ApoEurope project. Clin Chem Lab Med; submitted.

157. Lucotte G, Turpin JC, Landais P. Apolipoprotein E ε4 allele doses in late-onset Alzheimer's disease. Ann Neurol 1994;36:681–2.

158. Breitner JC, Wyse BW, Anthony JC, Welsh-Bohmer KA, Steffens DC, Norton MC, Tschanz JT, Plassman BL, Meyer MR, Skoog I, Khachaturian A. Apo E-epsilon4 count predicts age when prevalence of AD increases, then declines: the Cache County Study. Neurology 1999;53:321–31.

159. Town T, Paris D, Fallin D, Duara R, Barker W, Gold M, Crawford F, Mullan M. The −491 A/T apolipoprotein E promoter polymorphism association with Alzheimer's disease: independent risk and linkage disequilibrium with the known Apo E polymorphism. Neuroscience Lett 1998;252:95–8.

160. Licastro F, Pedrini S, Govoni M, Pession A, Ferri C, Annoni G, Casadei V, Veglia F, Bertolini S, Grimaldi LM. Apolipoprotein E and alpha-antichymotrypsin allele polymorphism in sporadic and familial Alzheimer's disease. Neurosci Lett 1999;270:129–32.

161. Hahne S, Nordstedt C, Ahlin A, Nybäck H. Levels of cerebrospinal fluid apolipoprotein E in patients with Alzheimer's disease and healthy controls. Neurosc Lett 1997;224:99–102.

162. Blennow K, Hesse C, Fredman P. Cerebrospinal fluid apolipoprotein E is reduced in Alzheimer's disease. Neuro Report 1994;5:2534–6.

163. Merched A, Blain H, Visvikis S, Herbeth B, Jeandel C, Siest G. Cerebrospinal fluid apolipoprotein E level is increased in late-onset Alzheimer's disease. J Neurol Sci 1997;145:33–9.

164. Kalman J, Juhasz A, Csaszar A, Kanka A, Rimanoczy A, Janka Z, Rasko I. Increased apolipoprotein E4 allele frequency is associated with vascular dementia in the Hungarian population. Acta Neurol Scand 1998;98:166–8.

165. Danet S, Brousseau T, Richard F, Amouyel P, Berr C. Risk of dementia in parents of probands with and without the apolipoprotein E4 allele. The EVA study. J Epidemiol Community Health 1999;53:393–8.

166. Zerr I, Helmhold M, Poser S, Armstrong VW, Weber T. Apolipoprotein E phenotype frequency and cerebrospinal fluid concentration are not associated with Creutzfeldt-Jacob disease. Arch Neurol 1996;53:1233–8.

167. Gaillard O, Gervais A, Meillet D, Plassart E, Fontaine B, Lyon-Caen O, Delattre J, Schuller E. Apolipoprotein E and multiple sclerosis: a biochemical and genetic investigation. J Neurol Sci 1998;158:180–6.

168. Werle E, Fiehn W, Hasslacher C. Apolipoprotein E polymorphism and renal function in German type 1 and type 2 diabetic patients. Diabetes Care 1998;21:994–8.

169. Kohlmeier M, Saupe J, Schaefer K, Asmus G. Bone fracture history and prospective bone fracture risk of hemodialysis patients are related to apolipoprotein E genotype. Calcif Tissue Int 1998;62:278–81.

170. Shiraki M, Shiraki Y, Aoki C, Hosoi T, Inoue S, Kaneki M, Ouchi Y. Association of bone mineral density with apolipoprotein E phenotype. J Bone Miner Res 1997;12:1438–45.

171. Cauley JA, Zmuda JM, Yaffe K, Kuller LH, Ferrell RE, Wisnieswski SR, Cummings SR. Apolipoprotein E polymorphism: a new genetic marker of hip fracture risk—the study of osteoporotic fractures. J Bone Miner Res 1999;14:1175–81.

172. Huq L, McLachlan T, Hammer HM, Bedford D, Packard CJ, Shepherd J, Converse CA. An increased incidence of apolipoprotein E2/E2 and E4/E4 in retinis pigmentosa. Lipids 1993;28:995–8.

173. Lerique B, Moulin B, Delpéro C, Purgus R, Olmer M, Boyer J. Apolipoprotein E phenotype and hyperlipoproteinemia in nephrotic syndrome. Clin Chem 1994;40:849–50.

174. Sarkkinen E, Korhonen M, Erkkila A, Ebeling T, Uusitupa M. Effect of apolipoprotein E polymorphism on serum lipid response to the separate modification of dietary fat and dietary cholesterol. Am J Clin Nutr 1998;68:1215–1222.

175. Miettinen TA, VanHanen H.D. Dietary sitostanol related to absorption, synthesis, and serum level of cholesterol in different apo E phenotypes. Atherosclerosis 1994; 105:217–226.

176. Loktionov A, Bingham SA, Vorster H, Jerling JC, Runswick SA, Cummings JH. Apolipoprotein E genotype modulates the effect of black tea drinking on blood lipids and blood coagulation factors: a pilot study. Brit J Nutr 1998;79:133–139.

177. Nestel P, Simons L, Barter P, Clifton P, Colquhoun D, Hamilton-Craig I, Sikaris K, Sullivan D. A comparative study of the efficacy of simvastatin and gemfibrozil in combined hyperlipoproteinemia: prediction of response by baseline lipids, apo E genotype, lipoprotein(a), and insulin. Atherosclerosis 1997;120:231–239.

178. Ordovas JM, Lopez-Miranda J, Perez-Kimenez F, Rodriguez C, Park JS, Cole T, Schaefer EJ. Effect of apolipoprotein E and A-IV phenotypes on the low-density-lipoprotein response to HMG CoA reductase inhibitor therapy. Atherosclerosis 1995;113:157–166.

179. Poirier J, Delisle MC, Quirion R, Aubert I, Farlow M, Lahiri D, Hui S, Bertrand P, Nalbantoglu J, Gilfix BM. Apolipoprotein ε4 allele as a predictor of cholinergic deficits and treatment outcome in Alzheimer's. Proc Natl Acad Sci USA 1995;92:12260–12264.

180. Farlow MR, Lahiri DK, Poirier J, Davignon J, Schneider L, Hui SL. Treatment outcome of tacrine therapy depends on apolipoprotein genotype and gender of the subjects with Alzheimer's disease. Neurology 1998;50:669–677.

181. Poirier J. Apolipoprotein cholinergic integrity and the pharmacogenetics of Alzheimer's disease. J Psychiatr Neurosci 1999;34:147–153.

Indirect Assays of Lipid Peroxidation

20

Clodagh Loughrey and Ian Young

OXIDATIVE MODIFICATION OF LDL AND ATHEROSCLEROSIS

✧   Elevated serum cholesterol, particularly in the form of apolipoprotein B (apo B)-containing lipoproteins, is an important etiological factor in the pathogenesis of atherosclerosis. However, individuals with the highest low-density lipoprotein cholesterol (LDL-C) levels will not all develop coronary artery disease, and, conversely, atherosclerotic disease is not confined to those with elevated serum cholesterol levels. Other factors impact on the lipoprotein/arterial wall interaction, exacerbating or retarding the atherogenic process. Among these factors, it is now widely believed that oxidation of low-density lipoprotein (LDL) in the vessel wall is crucial to the cellular uptake of LDL in the first stages of atherosclerotic plaque development.[1]

A key early step in atherogenesis is the formation of the fatty streak consisting of a subendothelial collection of foam cells, which are cholesterol-laden macrophages or smooth muscle cells. Under normal circumstances, uptake of LDL-C via the native LDL receptor is downregulated with increasing intracellular cholesterol content, and internalization of cholesterol by this route does not form foam cells. The existence of an alternative pathway for cellular uptake of LDL is supported by the fact that patients who completely lack LDL receptors can form foam cells.[2] Scavenger receptor A (SRA) was first demonstrated when it was shown that LDL modified *in vitro* by acetylation was taken up avidly when incubated with macrophages.[2] Uptake was not downregulated by increasing intracellular cholesterol, so that the macrophages became lipid-laden, resembling foam cells. However, significant acetylation of LDL does not occur *in vivo* and it is now clear that there are other more physiologically relevant modifications of LDL that can result in cellular uptake via one of several types of scavenger receptor.[2] Incubation of LDL with endothelial cells or smooth muscle cells results in such a modification of LDL, and this modification was subsequently shown to be oxidative in nature. Although there are other candidate modifications that can enhance LDL uptake by macrophages *in vitro*, including glycation, self-aggregation, immune complex formation, complex formation with proteoglycans, and hydrolysis, most interest to date has focused on oxidation of LDL.

Atherogenic Properties of Oxidized LDL

The first pro-atherogenic property of oxidized LDL (oxLDL) to be noted was its ability to be taken up rapidly by macrophages to form foam cells. OxLDL has many characteristics that potentially promote atherogenesis, some of which are summarized in Figure 20–1. It is a chemo-attractant for circulating monocytes;[3] this occurs directly, and also via stimulation of the release of monocyte chemo-attractant protein (MCP-1) from endothelial cells.[4] OxLDL also promotes the differentiation of monocytes into tissue macrophages by enhancing release of macrophage colony-stimulating-factor (M-CSF) from endothelial cells[5] and inhibits the motility of resident macrophages.[3] It is a chemo-attractant for T cells,[6] although not for B cells, and it is worth noting that atherosclerotic plaque contains primarily monocytes and T cells. Unlike native LDL, oxLDL is immunogenic[7] and it is also cytotoxic to various cell types, including endothelial cells.[8] It inhibits tumor necrosis factor (TNF) expression,[9] stimulates release of interleukin-1 β[10] from monocyte-macrophages, and can inhibit endothelial cell-dependent arterial relaxation.[11]

Evidence Supporting LDL Oxidation *In Vivo*

That oxidation of LDL does indeed occur *in vivo* is supported by several strands of evidence:

✧ LDL gently extracted from both rabbit and human atherosclerotic lesions has been shown to be oxidatively modified to some extent.[12]

Figure 20–1 ✧ Atherogenic Properties of oxLDL

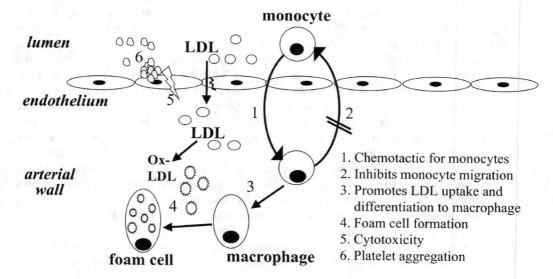

1. Chemotactic for monocytes
2. Inhibits monocyte migration
3. Promotes LDL uptake and differentiation to macrophage
4. Foam cell formation
5. Cytotoxicity
6. Platelet aggregation

✧ Immunohistochemical staining of atherosclerotic lesions with specific monoclonal antibodies has demonstrated the presence of oxLDL.[7]

✧ Circulating anti-oxLDL antibodies have been demonstrated in serum, and titers correlate with progression of atherosclerotic lesions.[7]

✧ Several studies in different animal models of atherosclerosis strongly suggest that progression of the lesions can be delayed by intervention with antioxidants.[1] The fact that several different antioxidants have been used (probucol, vitamin E, butylated hydroxytoluene, and diphenylphenylene-diamine) supports the implication that the anti-atherogenic effect is due to the antioxidant properties of these drugs, rather than any other biological effect.

✧ A significant role for LDL oxidation in the development of atherosclerosis is also supported by a substantial body of epidemiological evidence. Ecological, case-control, and prospective studies indicate that low antioxidant consumption is associated with an increased risk of cardiovascular disease.[13–15] The evidence is strongest in the case of vitamin E (α-tocopherol), with less consistent support for the protective role of vitamin C, carotenoids, and flavonoids.

Trials of Antioxidant Supplementation

The proposal that oxidative modification is important in atherosclerotic disease in humans will only be established conclusively in sufficiently large, randomized, double-blind clinical intervention trials, using as endpoints either altered progression of lesions, assessed by ultrasound or angiographically, or ischemic events. The results of several such studies have now been reported.

A trial of supplementation with four different vitamin and mineral combinations was carried out in almost 30,000 inhabitants of Linxian, an area of northern China where there is a chronically low intake of several nutrients.[16] It was found that supplementation with a multivitamin preparation including vitamin E (30 mg daily), β-carotene (15 mg daily), and selenium (50 μg daily), but not other combinations, over 5.25 yrs reduced total mortality, and in a subgroup with esophageal dysplasia, a reduction in cerebrovascular disease mortality was also observed. However in the ATBC study, which investigated heavy smokers in Scandinavia over 5–8 years, supplementation with neither 50 mg vitamin E or 20 mg β-carotene resulted in any decrease in cardiovascular events.[17]

A preliminary report of 333 men with coronary heart disease who entered the Harvard Physicians' Health Study indicated that there was a 40% reduction in major coronary events in those taking β-carotene (50 mg on alternate days). However this was not a primary endpoint of the initial study (which was to assess effect of β-carotene on cancer risk), and results were reported only on a subset of men with coronary heart disease. The results on the larger cohort of 22,000 healthy men subsequently showed no benefit conferred by β-carotene supplementation[18] in terms of total or cardiovascular mortality. The CARET trial of β-carotene and retinol supplementation was halted prematurely with the discovery of a 26% increase in cardiovascular mortality and 46% increase in lung cancer mortality in the active treatment group.[19]

In the CHAOS study, 2002 subjects with angiographically proven coronary heart disease were randomized to vitamin E (400–800 IU daily) or placebo and followed for a mean of 510 days.[20] There was a significant reduction in the incidence of non-fatal myocardial infarction in the intervention group, although the same group had a higher incidence of cardiovascular death. By contrast, the GISSI-P investigators recently published their findings of vitamin E supplementation in a study of 11,324 survivors of recent myocardial infarction.[21] Subjects were randomized to 300 mg vitamin E daily, versus n-3 polyunsaturated fatty acids (PUFAs) or placebo, and followed over 3.5 years. There was a reduction in ischemic events in the group randomized to vitamin E, but this was not statistically significant. The PQRST study investigated the effects of the antioxidant and lipid-lowering drug, probucol versus cholestyramine, a lipid-lowering drug with no antioxidant effect, in 303 hypercholesterolemic patients over 3 years.[22] Despite the reduction in LDL susceptibility to copper oxidation *in vitro* in the probucol group, as assessed by lag time, probucol failed to inhibit progression of angiographically-proven femoral atherosclerosis.

Observational epidemiologic data have consistently suggested that populations whose lifelong diet contains large amounts of antioxidant vitamins, such as those living in the Mediterranean area, have a lower-than-average risk of cardiovascular disease. A number of factors may therefore confound the results of the above studies. Subjects may have been observed over too short a period of time; the process of atherosclerotic plaque development occurs over many years, and antioxidants are likely to be of most value in the earliest stages, i.e., the formation of the fatty streak, rather than the later stages of plaque development or rupture. If myocardial infarction is the endpoint, a long treatment period may well be necessary to see any beneficial effect on plaque initiation. In the PQRST study, the probucol group had a significant decrease in HDL cholesterol, which might adversely affect atherosclerosis progression. In the ATBC study, the subjects were supplemented with relatively small doses of vitamin E, although the β-carotene dose was similar to the Harvard Physicians' Health Study. It is possible that atherosclerotic disease in the heavy smokers was so far advanced as to limit the validity of the study. The GISSI-P participants were all of Italian origin and consumed a diet that is unlikely to be as deficient in antioxidants as the diet consumed by the CHAOS study subjects, from the United Kingdom.

Despite these largely negative findings thus far, several large-scale clinical intervention trials of antioxidant supplementation are well under way, and further trial data should soon be available which will better define the role of antioxidant supplementation in the primary and secondary prevention of atherosclerotic disease.

Mechanisms of LDL Oxidation *In Vivo*

Many cell types are capable of oxidizing LDL, including monocytes, macrophages, neutrophils, endothelial cells, smooth muscle cells, and fibroblasts. However cell types that are involved in the atherosclerotic lesion in which oxLDL is found, i.e., macrophages, endothelial cells, and smooth muscle cells, would seem the most likely to contribute to LDL oxidation *in vivo*. It appears likely that LDL is oxidized in microdomains in the arterial wall, sequestered by proteoglycans and other extracellular matrix constituents, where it is protected from plasma antioxidants.[23] It is still unclear which oxidative mechanisms or radical species are involved; potential candidates to date include NADPH oxidase, myeloperoxidase, cytochrome P450, the mitochondrial electron transport chain, peroxynitrite, xanthine oxidase, and lipoxygenase (LO). The latter enzyme has received much attention with the discovery that, not only does LO modify LDL *in vitro* to a form taken up by the scavenger receptor,[24] but homozygous disruption of the LO gene diminishes atherosclerosis, with decreased titers of antibodies to oxLDL, in transgenic mice.[25]

Principles of Lipid Peroxidation and the Nature of Oxidized LDL

Oxidation of LDL is a free radical-driven lipid peroxidation chain reaction. A free radical, which by definition possesses at least one unpaired electron, can abstract electrons from non-radical species; in doing so, it creates another radical species, and sets up a self-propagating chain reaction. Free radicals react with a wide variety of molecules, including lipids, proteins, and DNA. Lipid peroxidation is initiated by free radical attack on a double bond associated with a PUFA. This causes the removal of a hydrogen atom from a methylene (CH_2) group, the rate of which determines rate of initiation, a key step. The lipid radical reacts very quickly with molecular oxygen, and the peroxyl radical thus formed is a crucial intermediate[26] (Figure 20–2).

A PUFA peroxyl radical in LDL may abstract a hydrogen atom from an adjacent PUFA to form a hydroperoxide and another lipid radical, a reaction that results in chain propagation. Removal of hydrogen atoms by the peroxyl radical from other lipids, including cholesterol, eventually yields oxysterols. Molecular rearrangement of the peroxyl radical results in a more stable configuration, a conjugated diene. Lipid hydroperoxides fragment to shorter-chain aldehydes, including malondialdehyde and 4-hydroxynonenal. These intermediates in turn may bind to amino acid side chains (e.g., ε-amino groups of lysine residues) of apo B-100, giving the protein an increased net negative charge. The classical LDL receptor recognizes a specific domain of positive charges from lysine, arginine, and histidine residues on apo B. Altering this domain causes binding by the apo B/E receptor to fail, and an increase in negative surface charge on apo B results in increased recognition by the scavenger receptor.

In the presence of a chain-breaking antioxidant such as vitamin E, the peroxyl radical may be scavenged. The tocopheroxyl radical thus formed has very low reactivity and will generally result in chain termination. LDL exposed to oxidative stress *in vitro* will not form significant amounts of hydroperoxides until it becomes depleted of chain-breaking antioxidants. *In vitro* studies of LDL oxidation have verified the existence of a 'lag phase,' during which significant oxidation of LDL cannot be detected, prior to the onset of the 'propagation phase,' presumably after the endogenous antioxidants have been consumed (see Figure 20–3). There follows a steady increase in the detectable byproducts of oxidation, until the substrate, i.e., the PUFAs, have been depleted, and a plateau phase is reached. Assessment of LDL resistance to oxidation has generally involved measuring the duration of the lag phase, although other variables, such as the rate of propagation, are also noted.

Figure 20–2 ✧ Lipid Peroxidation: A Chain Reaction

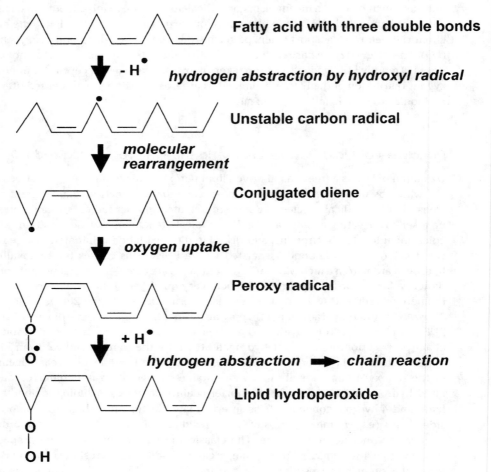

Fatty acid with three double bonds

↓ - H•   *hydrogen abstraction by hydroxyl radical*

Unstable carbon radical

↓ *molecular rearrangement*

Conjugated diene

↓ *oxygen uptake*

Peroxy radical

↓ + H•   *hydrogen abstraction* ➡ *chain reaction*

Lipid hydroperoxide

Factors Influencing Susceptibility of LDL to Oxidation

Factors Intrinsic to LDL

Many studies have examined the oxidative susceptibility of LDL in the context of the composition of the LDL particle and, as might be expected, it is clear that the composition has a highly significant effect on the lag time and on the extent to which the particle can be oxidized. Since the main substrate for oxidation is the PUFA double bond, the fatty acid composition of the lipoprotein is of prime importance, a high proportion of PUFAs conferring greater susceptibility to oxidation while a high proportion of mono-unsaturated fatty acids protects against oxidation.[27–29] This effect has been borne out in many case-control studies performed in various pathological conditions

Figure 20–3 ✧ Typical Graph of LDL Oxidation Using Copper Ions

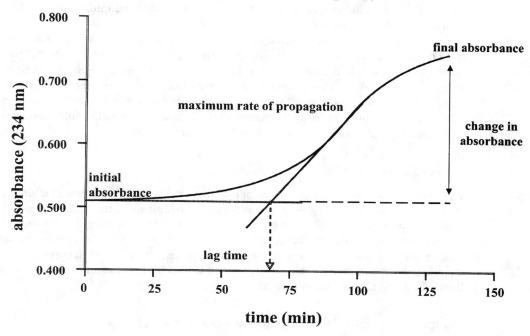

including coronary artery disease,[30] diabetes mellitus,[31] familial hypercholesterol-emia (FH),[32] and chronic renal failure.[33]

Since the propagation phase of LDL oxidation begins after the endogenous anti-oxidants are consumed, susceptibility to oxidation is also highly dependent on the an-tioxidant content, which in lipoproteins is mainly α-tocopherol (vitamin E), although ubiquinol-10 and carotenoids are also important.[34] The molar ratio of PUFA to total antioxidants in LDL is approximately 150:1, and just as there is considerable be-tween-subject variation in fatty acid content depending on diet, so lipophilic anti-oxidant intake also varies significantly from individual to individual.[35] LDL rich in vitamin E is less susceptible to oxidation,[29] and dietary supplementation with vitamin E has been shown to result in increased LDL resistance to copper oxidation *in vi-tro,*[36–38] an effect that is dose-dependent.[39] The increase in lag time associated with an intensive low-fat diet and exercise program in patients with coronary artery disease was also attributed to increased LDL antioxidant content.[40] The ability of carotenoid supplementation to increase the resistance of LDL to oxidation is more controversial, with variable results reported. For instance, supplementation of renal transplant re-cipients with tomato juice increased the LDL lycopene content but did not reduce the oxidative susceptibility.[41]

LDL size is another factor that has been shown to affect oxidative susceptibil-ity.[42] The small, dense subfractions of LDL are more susceptible to oxidation than large, less dense LDL particles, which may to a large extent be due to differences in antioxidant content.[43] Increased susceptibility to oxidation may therefore be viewed as part of the metabolic cardiovascular syndrome. For additional information on LDL subclasses, refer to chapter 16.

The concentration of pre-existing fatty acid peroxides in LDL also exerts an effect on the oxidative susceptibility of the particle, higher levels of these "seeding" peroxides being associated with a shorter lag time when transition metals are used to initiate oxidation.[44,45] In one study, treatment of athletes with β-carotene reduced LDL susceptibility to oxidation after, but not before, an acute bout of exercise.[46] This effect was attributed to prevention by β-carotene of the formation of seeding lipid peroxides during the oxidative stress associated with the acute exercise.

Factors Extrinsic to LDL

The *in vitro* assessment of LDL oxidizability takes into account only those factors *intrinsic* to LDL, as discussed above. It is important to bear in mind that LDL susceptibility to oxidation *in vivo* is likely to be heavily influenced by the molecule's immediate micro-environment, with respect to local antioxidant concentrations, transition metal availability, and presence of specific enzyme systems, among other factors. Understanding of these factors remains limited and it is difficult to make any assessment of their impact on LDL oxidizability *in vivo*.

Clinical Utility of LDL Oxidizability Assessment

Numerous studies to date have been carried out to assess the susceptibility of LDL to oxidation *in vitro* in a variety of situations. It is generally assumed that the more susceptible LDL is to oxidation, the greater the atherosclerotic risk in that individual, group, or condition. This assumption also provides a rationale for therapeutic manipulation of LDL oxidizability, with potential implications for atherosclerosis prevention, which has been investigated by many groups. However, to date, prospective studies linking increased susceptibility of LDL to oxidation to the subsequent development of atherosclerosis are lacking.

Case-Control Studies of LDL Oxidation in Subjects with Established Atherosclerosis

The susceptibility of LDL to oxidation in groups with established atherosclerosis has been investigated in several case-control studies. LDL was shown to be more susceptible to oxidation in a group of 73 patients with angiographically proven coronary artery disease, who demonstrated a reduction in lag time before conjugated diene production when LDL isolated from plasma was incubated with copper ions.[47] This trend was confirmed by van de Vijver et al.,[30] although not by Schreier who found no difference in lag time, but did demonstrate increased LDL malondialdehyde production in coronary artery disease subjects,[48] a finding also noted by Chiu et al.[49]

In a Finnish study of 40 hypercholesterolemic men with early carotid atherosclerosis, increased susceptibility of LDL plus VLDL to copper-induced oxidation, as shown by decreased lag time before onset of oxidation and high concentrations of

LDL hydroperoxides, was a strong predictor of increase in carotid wall thickness over three years.[50] Subjects with peripheral vascular disease have been shown to exhibit significantly increased LDL susceptibility to oxidation by copper ions *in vitro*, as evidenced by a shorter lag time, and increased maximum rate of propagation.[51]

Case-Control Studies of LDL Oxidation in Healthy Subjects at High Risk of Atherosclerosis

LDL isolated from subjects with both type 1 and type 2 diabetes mellitus has repeatedly been proven to be more susceptible to copper oxidation *in vitro*,[52] exhibiting reduced lag time before the onset of propagation phase, increased rate of production of conjugated dienes, and increased malondialdehyde production. This seems likely to be related to glycemic control, as oxidative susceptibility of LDL plus VLDL is reported to be increased in type 1 diabetics with high, as opposed to normal, blood ketone concentrations.[53] Indeed, in individuals with type 1 diabetes who exert good control, LDL appears to be no less resistant than controls to copper oxidation *in vitro*.[54]

Napoli et al. demonstrated increased LDL susceptibility to oxidation by copper in patients with homozygous familial hypercholesterolemia, as evidenced by a decreased lag time and an increased rate of propagation.[55] Levels of LDL malondialdehyde and lipid hydroperoxides were also higher in the FH group after oxidation. Cominacini et al. also confirmed a reduced lag phase in subjects with type 2a hyperlipoproteinemia,[47] but this was not substantiated in other studies of patients with either homozygous or heterozygous FH.[56–58]

Cigarette smoking has also been shown to be associated with increased LDL susceptibility to copper oxidation *in vitro*.[59] Greater oxidative susceptibility of LDL has been demonstrated repeatedly in renal transplant recipients, another high-risk group for atherosclerosis.[60–63] However, patients on long-term hemodialysis, who show even greater propensity to premature atherosclerosis than transplant recipients, do not exhibit an increased susceptibility to LDL oxidation in most studies.[33,63–65]

Assessment of Antioxidant Efficacy

Extrapolation of the findings outlined above leads to the assumption that manipulation of oxidative susceptibility of LDL using dietary or pharmacological intervention will exert an effect on the atherogenic risk of an individual. It has been demonstrated that increasing dietary monounsaturated fatty acid intake significantly decreases susceptibility to oxidation of LDL.[66,67] Conversely high PUFA intake has been associated with increased LDL oxidizability, assessed by shorter lag times.[27,28]

Many studies have focused on the possibility of prolonging lag time by supplementation with various antioxidant agents. Alpha-tocopherol (vitamin E) is the most abundant antioxidant in LDL, and unsurprisingly, lag time is highly correlated with LDL α-tocopherol.[68] In most studies, dietary supplementation with vitamin E, either alone,[38,69–72] or in combination with vitamin C and β-carotene[73,74] and selenium,[75] has caused LDL to be protected against oxidation. The effect of vitamin E on increasing lag time has been demonstrated not only in healthy subjects, but also in subjects with type 2 diabetes mellitus[76] and in cystic fibrosis patients.[77]

Beta-carotene is the next most abundant antioxidant compound in LDL. It has been shown that total carotenoids, as well as vitamin E, in plasma were strongly correlated with lag time of copper-induced oxidation of LDL subfractions.[78] Beta-carotene, lycopene, and β-cryptoxanthin were mainly located in the larger, less-dense LDL particles, whereas lutein and zeaxanthin were found preferentially in the smaller, more dense LDL particles. Total carotenoids and vitamin E were less concentrated in these latter particles, which were also found to be more susceptible to oxidation. However, unlike vitamin E, a beneficial effect of β-carotene supplementation on lag time has not been consistently demonstrated, and one study even indicated that LDL enriched with β-carotene *in vitro* displayed increased susceptibility to oxidation.[71] Hypercholesterolemic women supplemented with β-carotene displayed no increase in LDL resistance to oxidation.[79] Renal transplant recipients were unable to increase lag time by increasing LDL lycopene with tomato juice consumption.[41]

Although vitamin C exists only in the aqueous phase of plasma, and is not a constituent of lipoproteins, it does play a role in the regeneration of vitamin E, and supplementation with vitamin C has been found to prolong lag time in smokers.[80] Ubiquinol-10 is a lipophilic potent antioxidant, and is the first to be consumed during the oxidative process.[34] However, it is present in at most 10% of LDL particles and is likely to be of little impact in LDL resistance to oxidation. Dietary supplementation with the flavonoids quercetin and catechin in rats was shown to prolong lag time and total diene production in copper-induced oxidation of LDL,[81] though most studies in man have been negative.

Much interest has been shown in investigating possible antioxidant properties of drugs whose benefit in cardiovascular disease is already established. The effect of the lipid-lowering agent probucol on reduction in lag time is well recognized.[82] Some inhibition of LDL oxidation has also been reported to occur in treatment with fluvastatin,[83] pravastatin,[84,85] simvastatin,[84] metabolites of atorvastatin,[86] fenofibrate,[87] and gemfibrozil.[86] Treatment with the sulfonylurea gliclazide was shown to increase LDL oxidation resistance *in vitro*.[88] Similar results have been found in treatment with calcium-channel blockers nifedipine and lacidipine,[89] although not with doxazosin,[90] and with the β-blocker carvedilol.[89] Estrogens have been shown to inhibit both copper- and cell-mediated oxidation *in vitro*. However in women on hormone replacement therapy, a decreased susceptibility of LDL to oxidation could not be demonstrated.[91] Recently much attention has been focused on the effect of lowering LDL susceptibility to oxidation of plant-derived isoflavonoids, such as phytoestrogens.[92–95] The clinical relevance of these findings is not yet known.

METHODOLOGY

The general procedure for assessing LDL susceptibility to oxidation *in vitro* consists of several steps, which will be described in sequence:

- ❖ isolation of LDL;
- ❖ LDL purification;

❖ initiation of oxidation;

❖ monitoring of oxidation;

❖ expression, and interpretation of results.

The majority of work published in this field utilizes a kinetic method based on Esterbauer's work on copper-induced oxidation of LDL, with continuous monitoring of conjugated diene production.[68] The method is also applicable to investigation of oxidation of other lipoproteins, such as VLDL[96] and HDL.[97]

Equipment and Materials

❖ Polyallomer Belltop ultracentrifuge tubes (13 x 32mm; 3ml; Beckman 349621)

❖ Peristaltic pump [e.g., Gilson Miniplus 2 instrument (Gilson Medical Electronics, France)], fitted with narrow-bore AutoAnalyzer tubing (Bran & Luebbe, Germany)

❖ Beckman Table Top Ultracentrifuge (TL100), with fixed-angle rotor (TL100.3)

❖ Beckman Tube Topper Sealer including tube topper, stand, seal cap, seal guide, heat sink and removal tool (Beckman 348137) together with tube spacers (Beckman 355937) to prevent movement and distortion of the tubes within the rotor during ultracentrifugation

❖ Needle (21G) and 2-mL syringe for each LDL sample to be isolated, plus 2 extra needles per run

❖ O-ring tubes (2mL) for collecting crude LDL (Sarstedt Ltd 72.694). Tubes (10mL) for collecting desalted PD10-treated LDL (Sarstedt Ltd 57.469). Tubes (4-mL) for estimation of protein content and standard curve preparation (Sarstedt Ltd 55.478)

❖ PD10 columns containing Sephadex G25 (Pharmacia Ltd, Milton Keynes, UK). Although these columns are disposable, they can be reused many times by thorough rinsing with at least 25 mL phosphate-buffered saline after use and immediately prior to re-use. Columns must be stored and used at 4°C.

❖ Disposable semi-micro cuvettes, 1 mL (Sarstedt Ltd 67.746)

❖ Semi-micro quartz cuvettes (cells), 1 mL (Starna Ltd, Romford, Essex) (6 for a 6-cell spectrophotometer)

❖ Ultrasonic cleaner (e.g., Nusonics, Quayl Dental, Worthing, Sussex) plus disposable 20-ml cups for cleaning quartz cuvettes

❖ Thermostatically controlled spectrophotometer (37°C, Hitachi U-2000–1, HIT/121–0032), containing automatic 6-cell positioner (Hitachi HIT/121–0304) linked to a PC with software package for automatic data handling (Hitachi, Enzyme Kinetic Data system)

❖ Microsoft Excel software for computing raw data, utilizing a macro program written for this procedure (available from authors)

Reagents

- ✧ Millipore quality water (to reduce contamination by transition metal ions that can promote oxidation)
- ✧ potassium bromide (Sigma)
- ✧ sodium chloride (Sigma)
- ✧ bovine serum albumin solution (BSA) (Sigma A2153)
- ✧ Biorad dye reagent (Biorad 500–600, Biorad Hemel Hempstead, UK)
- ✧ saline solution 0.9% (BDH 10241AP)
- ✧ hydrochloric acid 37% (Janssen 12.463.47)
- ✧ copper chloride ($CuCl_2.2H_2O$) (BDH 10088)

Solutions

- ✧ sodium chloride solution, density 1.006 g/mL, 0.196 mol/L: made up by adding 11.42 g to 1 L deionized water and stable for 1 month stored at 4°C
- ✧ phosphate buffered saline (PBS) pH 7.4, 0.01 mol/L, stable for 1 month stored at 4°C
- ✧ BSA solution 25 µg/L, made by adding 12.5 mg to volumetric flask, gently (to avoid foaming) making up to 500 mL with deionized water, stable frozen at –20°C in 7-mL aliquots for 6 months
- ✧ hydrochloric acid (0.5 mol/L)
- ✧ copper chloride solution 40 µmol/L, made by serial dilution of a 33.2 mmol/L stock solution (0.567g $CuCl_2.2H_2O$ in 100 mL), stored at 4°C

Sample Type and Stability

Blood is taken (after overnight fasting) from a peripheral vein into glass tubes containing lithium heparin 50,000 U/L, on ice. (Heparinized plasma is used in preference to serum because serum collection lengthens total sample preparation time. However, using serum with this technique gives results that are indistinguishable from those obtained using heparinized plasma.) Plasma is isolated within 30 min of venisection by centrifugation at 1500 g for 10 min. Samples stored in 1-ml aliquots at −70°C are stable for 6 months.

Procedure

LDL Isolation

Separation of lipoprotein species is achieved by flotation non-equilibrium ultracentrifugation. Conventional methods of isolating LDL by ultracentrifugation take up to 24 h. If a prolonged ultracentrifugation step is employed, it is essential to use EDTA plasma to avoid artifactual LDL oxidation during purification. The EDTA should then be removed prior to the initiation of *in vitro* oxidation, either by Sephadex G25 chromatography (see below) or by prolonged dialysis against EDTA-free buffer. In our experience, the former procedure does not completely remove EDTA, increasing assay variability, while the latter has been reported to result in loss of antioxidants.[98]

Use of a benchtop ultracentrifuge in LDL oxidation studies is advantageous in that it allows rapid (< 2 h) isolation of LDL, greatly shortening the length of the procedure overall. The necessity of using EDTA samples to prevent interim oxidation of LDL is therefore avoided. Heparinized plasma (0.9 mL) is added to a Beckman 3-mL ultracentrifuge tube containing 0.4451g potassium bromide, using a 2.5-cm length of fine-bore tubing connected to a pipette tip. The tube is inverted gently several times to dissolve the salt, using Parafilm as a temporary seal, resulting in plasma with density 1.30 kg/L. Sodium chloride solution (d = 1.006 kg/L) is then gently overlaid, using the peristaltic pump and tubing connected to a 21G needle which has been bent to ensure that the saline trickles down the inside wall of the centrifuge tube. It is important that no mixing or distortion of the layers occurs during this step.

The tubes are then sealed and placed gently in the rotor. Ultracentrifugation is performed for 1 h at 541,000 g at 4°C. Use of acceleration and deceleration setting 6 prevents disturbing the density gradient created during ultracentrifugation. On completion of the run, the tubes are gently removed from the rotor and placed in the rack. The LDL band will be visible, in most cases as a discrete orange band located approximately one-third from the top of the tube. It is distinctly separate from the other lipoprotein species, VLDL now located at the top of the tube and HDL below LDL.

The LDL band is removed by aspiration, which minimizes contamination with other lipoproteins and plasma proteins, as can occur if collected by downward fractionation. The top of the ultracentrifugation tube is first punctured with 2x21G needles to release the vacuum. A small hole is then made in the side wall of the tube, just below the bottom edge of the LDL band, using another 21G needle, and a further fresh 21G needle attached to a 1-ml syringe is used to aspirate the LDL sample through this site. Aspiration of approximately 0.9 ml of the tube contents is sufficient to remove the whole LDL fraction, ensuring that the tip of the needle remains within the band. This "crude" (unpurified) LDL is placed on ice for immediate use (stable at 4°C for 2.5 h).

LDL Purification

Prior to oxidation, potassium bromide, as well as other small molecules such as urate that may affect the oxidation process, must be removed from the LDL sample. This is readily achieved by size exclusion chromatography.

PD10 columns should be prepared during the time taken for ultracentrifugation. One column per sample is prepared at 4°C by washing with 25 mL PBS prior to use. Crude LDL (0.5 mL) is added to the prewashed column and allowed to enter the gel bed prior to the addition of 2 ml PBS. The eluant is discarded. Purified LDL is obtained by adding a further 2 ml PBS and the eluant collected in a 10-ml tube. This "desalted" LDL is placed on ice until ready to be oxidized after determination of protein content. It is much less stable than "crude" LDL and must be used as rapidly as possible. All steps post-PD10 treatment must therefore be prepared in advance (during ultracentrifugation) where possible, i.e., LDL protein content estimation and preparation of quartz cells.

Oxidation of LDL

LDL PROTEIN CONTENT ESTIMATION

LDL concentration in the cuvette for oxidation is standardized by protein content, which is assessed spectrophotometrically by reading against a prepared BSA standard curve using Biorad as the indicator dye. Stock BSA (25 µg/mL) is used to prepare working standard solutions (0, 2.5, 10, 15, 20 µg/mL), 100µL of which are added to 1.1 mL water and 300 µL Biorad dye reagent. Absorbance of standards is read at 595 nm within 5–60 min, and used to calculate protein concentration of desalted LDL treated similarly. Dilution of LDL during the protein assay is accounted for by multiplying the result obtained by a factor of 15, as 100 µL of desalted LDL is added to 1100 µL water and 300 µL Biorad reagent, to total 1500 µL.

PREPARATION OF QUARTZ CELLS

A rigorous cleaning regime must be followed to avoid contaminating the oxidation mixture by seeding lipoperoxides, a relic of previous oxidation assays, and adherent to the sides of the cells, which would artefactually increase measured susceptibility to oxidation. After each use, or prior to first use, each cell is

1. rinsed at least 10 times before use with distilled water;
2. covered in separate disposable containers with 4% Decon-90 and sonicated for 5 min;
3. inverted within the containers and sonicated for a further 5 min before
4. rinsing again at least 10 times with distilled water. The cells are next
5. soaked in 0.5 mol/L HCl for at least 1 h (or stored in this when not in use).

The acid-soaked cells must then be thoroughly cleaned prior to use in the oxidation assay. Steps (1) to (4) are repeated before the cells are inverted on absorbent paper to drain, and are then ready for use.

CHOICE OF OXIDIZING AGENT

As discussed previously, it is likely that LDL is oxidized *in vivo* by macrophages, endothelial cells, and smooth muscle cells; such oxidation depends on the presence of traces of transition metals. Oxidation of LDL can also occur *in vitro* in a cell-free medium, in which the oxidation process is strongly catalyzed by transition metals alone. The properties of cell-oxidized LDL are very similar, if not identical, to LDL oxidized by copper in a cell-free environment.[24] It is on the basis of this premise that most studies are presently performed, copper ions being currently the most commonly used agent for initiating LDL oxidation. The presence in plasma of proteins that chelate metals implies that copper-dependent oxidation of LDL is unlikely to occur *in vivo*. However, the fact that redox active copper and iron ions have been obtained from "gruel" made from advanced atherosclerotic plaque provides some support for their role in oxidation of LDL *in vivo*.[99] It has been proposed that these metal ions might be released from ceruloplasmin and transferrin by pro-oxidant reactions occurring in the developing plaque.[100–102]

Alternative promoters of oxidation include the free radical generator 2,2′-azobis-[2-amidinopropane hydrochloride (AAPH)], as well as potentially more physiologically relevant pro-oxidants such as myeloperoxidase, lipoxygenase, hemin, ceruloplasmin, and cell systems. The precise mechanisms of how different oxidizing agents initiate LDL oxidation remain unclear, although lipoxygenases may play a more prominent role in cell-mediated oxidation of LDL. However, once the process is under way, peroxidation will likely proceed by a free radical-mediated chain reaction in a similar fashion regardless of the nature of the initial oxidizing insult. The method described here employs copper as the oxidizing agent but can easily be modified to use these alternative initiators of oxidation.

THE OXIDATION MIXTURE

The final concentration of desalted LDL in the cuvette is 50 µg LDL protein/mL, in a total volume of 1000 µL, which also includes 50 µL of 40 µmol/L copper(II) chloride, the remainder consisting of PBS. The respective volumes of LDL (Y) and PBS (Z) required are calculated as follows, where X is the desalted LDL protein concentration:

$$Y\ \mu L = 1000 \times (50/X\ \mu g/mL)$$

$$Z\ \mu L = 1000 - (Y\ \mu L + 50\ \mu L\ Cu^{2+})$$

Dilution of the LDL sample with PBS is carried out in the quartz cuvette, the copper chloride being added last. The solution is mixed by pipette action, expelling and drawing in 50 µL of the cell contents several times when adding the copper solution. The samples are then placed in the spectrophotometer and data collection initiated.

MONITORING OXIDATION

The previous discussion of the nature of LDL oxidation indicates the diversity of measurable modifications and byproducts that result when the LDL particle undergoes oxidation, providing a variety of methods for assessing rate and extent of oxidation. Theoretically, measurement of any byproduct of lipid (or protein) peroxidation may be used to monitor oxidation of LDL in a closed system. This may entail removing an aliquot of the oxidation mixture at regular timed intervals, stopping the reaction with an antioxidant such as butylated hydroxytoluene and measuring the chosen product—e.g., lipid hydroperoxides,[103] malondialdehyde, thiobarbituric-reactive species (TBARS), 4-hydroxynonenal, amino groups (see chapter 21 for details of these assays) or change in fluorescence at 430 nm (increases due to loss of free lysine residues). Increase in electronegativity of LDL is an alternative means of assessing LDL oxidation that relies on modification of the lipoprotein particle; measuring the relative decrease of polyunsaturated fatty acids or lipophilic antioxidants at various time points also indicates rate and extent of oxidation.[104] Both macrophage modification and copper-catalyzed oxidation of LDL diminish polyunsaturated fatty acids, notably arachidonic and linoleic acid,[105] and it is accepted that the propagation phase of LDL oxidation does not begin until its antioxidants are consumed.

These methods have several drawbacks, not least of which is that monitoring is discontinuous. Large sample sizes are also required and the repeated sampling is highly labor-intensive. A method for continuously monitoring lipoprotein oxidation relies on the fact that oxidized LDL absorbs ultraviolet emissions maximally at 234 nm, unlike native LDL, which has an absorbance maximum of 222 nm.[68] It has been shown that this change in absorbance is due to the production of conjugated dienes, and it correlates well with increases in peroxides, TBARS, and fluorescence at 430nm.[106] Thus the continuous recording of absorbance at 234 nm is an effective method of monitoring LDL oxidation *in vitro* and has the added advantage of allowing for more frequent readings and therefore more accurate monitoring. Continuous monitoring of protein fluorescence is an alternative method with the same advantages.

Expression and Interpretation of Results

Absorbance at 234 nm is measured every 2 min and the change is recorded on a personal computer using an appropriate software package. The spectrophotometer output is converted into ASCII file format and imported into the spreadsheet program Excel (Microsoft). The following parameters are automatically computed by a customized macro (available from the authors):

1. Lag time: calculated as the intercept between the line of maximum slope of the propagation phase and the baseline (see Figure 20–3)

2. Minimum absorbance

3. Maximum absorbance

4. Total increase in absorbance

5. Maximum slope of propagation phase

The key aspect of this analysis is the fitting of a straight line to the slope of the propagation phase. This line is determined by the least squares method. The point of maximum slope is found by repeated computation of the average slope for 11 consecutive points, thus allowing for deviations due to random noise from the spectrophotometer. In our laboratory, the within-assay coefficient of variation (C.V.) of the lag time as determined by analysis of duplicates is 7.9% (n = 101 pairs); the between-assay C.V. is 8.2%, calculated from repeated analysis of LDL from plasma samples stored at –70°C.[107]

The assay as described above is usually carried out using an automated spectrophotometer, and typically about six samples can be assessed simultaneously. However, for large-scale studies the assay can be modified to run on a microtiter plate if a plate reader capable of utilizing 234 nm is available.[108] Up to 96 samples could then be analyzed in a single run. The same basic methodology can also be applied to assess the susceptibility of VLDL, HDL, or other lipoproteins to oxidation, although these have been much less thoroughly investigated and their clinical utility is less well established.[50, 53, 96, 109–113]

SUMMARY

The importance of LDL oxidation in atherogenesis is being increasingly recognized. LDL undergoes a number of changes during the oxidative process, which allow monitoring the process *in vitro* when oxidation is initiated with copper or other agents. In many cases of established atherosclerosis, such as coronary artery disease, peripheral vascular disease, and cerebrovascular disease, LDL is more susceptible to oxidation, and therefore theoretically more atherogenic. Increased susceptibility of LDL to oxidation *in vitro* has also been noted in groups at high-risk of atherosclerosis, notably type 1 and type 2 diabetics, smokers, and patients with FH. Decrease in oxidative susceptibility with dietary manipulation or pharmacological supplementation with antioxidants has been demonstrated in some of these patient groups. However, despite promising results from animal work showing delayed progression of atherosclerosis with antioxidant supplementation, results of the few published large-scale trials on antioxidant intervention in human atherosclerotic disease have failed to demonstrate any significant benefit thus far. It is possible that the supplementation and observation period were too short, and further trials are ongoing.

Advances in the understanding of the nature of LDL oxidation *in vivo* in the past decade are currently driving experiments to improve methods of assessing LDL susceptibility *in vitro*. The continued and expanding worldwide interest in oxidation of lipoproteins in atherogenesis implies that continued efforts are likely to be made to design effective therapeutic measures to inhibit this process. Assessment of ability of any such measures to inhibit LDL oxidation *in vitro* will be an integral part of gauging effectiveness of any such measures. ✧

REFERENCES

1. Steinberg D, Lewis A. Conner Memorial Lecture. Oxidative modification of LDL and atherogenesis. Circulation 1997;95:1062–71.
2. Brown MS, and Goldstein JL. Lipoprotein metabolism in the macrophage: implications for cholesterol deposition in atherosclerosis. Annu Rev Biochem 1983;52:223–61.
3. Quinn MT, Parthasarathy S, Fong LG, and Steinberg D. Oxidatively modified low-density lipoproteins: a potential role in recruitment and retention of monocyte/macrophages during atherogenesis. Proc Natl Acad Sci U S A 1987;84:2995–8.
4. Cushing SD, Berliner JA, Valente AJ et al. Minimally modified low-density lipoprotein induces monocyte chemotactic protein 1 in human endothelial cells and smooth muscle cells. Proc Natl Acad Sci U S A 1990;87:5134–8.
5. Rajavashisth TB, Andalibi A, Territo MC, Berliner JA, Navab M, Fogelman AM, Lusis AJ. Induction of endothelial cell expression of granulocyte and macrophage colony-stimulating factors by modified low-density lipoproteins. Nature 1990;344:254–7.
6. McMurray HF, Parthasarathy S, Steinberg D. Oxidatively modified low-density lipoprotein is a chemo-attractant for human T lymphocytes. J Clin Invest 1993;92:1004–8.
7. Palinski W, Rosenfeld ME, Yla-Herttuala S et al. Low-density lipoprotein undergoes oxidative modification *in vivo*. Proc Natl Acad Sci USA 1989;86:1372–6.

8. Hessler JR, Morel DW, Lewis LJ, Chisolm GM. Lipoprotein oxidation and lipoprotein-induced cytotoxicity. Arteriosclerosis 1983;3:215–22.

9. Hamilton TA, Ma GP, Chisolm GM. Oxidized low-density lipoprotein suppresses the expression of tumor necrosis factor-alpha mRNA in stimulated murine peritoneal macrophages. J Immunol 1990;144:2343–50.

10. Thomas CE, Jackson RL, Ohlweiler DF, Ku G. Multiple lipid oxidation products in low-density lipoproteins induce interleukin-1 beta release from human blood mononuclear cells. J Lipid Res 1994;35:417–27.

11. Ohgushi M, Kugiyama K, Fukunaga K, Murohara T, Sugiyama S, Miyamoto E, Yasue H. Protein kinase C inhibitors prevent impairment of endothelium-dependent relaxation by oxidatively modified LDL. Arterioscler Thromb 1993;13:1525–32.

12. Yla-Herttuala S, Palinski W, Rosenfeld ME, et al. Evidence for the presence of oxidatively modified low-density lipoprotein in atherosclerotic lesions of rabbit and man. J Clin Invest 1989;84:1086–95.

13. Gey KF and Puska P. Plasma vitamins E and A inversely correlated to mortality from ischemic heart disease in cross-cultural epidemiology. Ann N Y Acad Sci 1989; 570:268–82.

14. Rimm EB, Stampfer MJ, Ascherio A, Giovannucci E, Colditz GA, Willett WC. Vitamin E consumption and the risk of coronary heart disease in men. N Engl J Med 1993;328:1450–6.

15. Stampfer MJ, Hennekens CH, Manson JE, Colditz GA, Rosner B, Willett WC. Vitamin E consumption and the risk of coronary disease in women. N Engl J Med 1993;328: 1444–9.

16. Blot WJ, Li JY, Taylor PR, Guo W, Dawsey SM, Li B. The Linxian trials: mortality rates by vitamin-mineral intervention group. Am J Clin Nutr 1995;62:1424S–1426S.

17. The Alpha-Tocopherol, Beta Carotene Cancer Prevention Study Group. The effect of vitamin E and beta carotene on the incidence of lung cancer and other cancers in male smokers. N Engl J Med 1994;330:1029–35.

18. Hennekens CH, Buring JE, Manson JE et al. Lack of effect of long-term supplementation with beta carotene on the incidence of malignant neoplasms and cardiovascular disease. N Engl J Med 1996;334:1145–9.

19. Redlich CA, Chung JS, Cullen MR, Blaner WS, Van Bennekum AM, Berglund L. Effect of long-term beta-carotene and vitamin A on serum cholesterol and triglyceride levels among participants in the Carotene and Retinol Efficacy Trial (CARET). Atherosclerosis 1999;143:427–34.

20. Stephens NG, Parsons A, Schofield PM, Kelly F, Cheeseman K, Mitchinson MJ. Randomized controlled trial of vitamin E in patients with coronary disease: Cambridge Heart Antioxidant Study (CHAOS). Lancet 1996;347:781–6.

21. Gruppo Italiano per lo Studio della Sopravvivenza nell'Infarto miocardico. Dietary supplementation with n-3 polyunsaturated fatty acids and vitamin E after myocardial infarction: results of the GISSI-Prevenzione trial. Lancet 1999;354:447–55.

22. Walldius G, Regnstrom J, Nilsson J et al. The role of lipids and antioxidative factors for development of atherosclerosis. The Probucol Quantitative Regression Swedish Trial (PQRST). Am J Cardiol 1993;71:15B–19B.

23. Steinberg D, Parthasarathy S, Carew TE, Khoo JC, Witztum JL. Beyond cholesterol. Modifications of low-density lipoprotein that increase its atherogenicity. N Engl J Med 1989;320:915–24.

24. Parthasarathy S, Fong LG, Quinn MT, Steinberg D. Oxidative modification of LDL: comparison between cell-mediated and copper-mediated modification. Eur Heart J 1990;11 Suppl E:83–7.

25. Steinberg, D. At last, direct evidence that lipoxygenases play a role in atherogenesis. J Clin Invest 1999;103:1487–8.

26. Abuja PM and Esterbauer H. Simulation of lipid peroxidation in low-density lipoprotein by a basic "skeleton" of reactions. Chem Res Toxicol 1995;8:753–63.

27. Reaven P, Parthasarathy S, Grasse BJ et al. Feasibility of using an oleate-rich diet to re-

duce the susceptibility of low-density lipoprotein to oxidative modification in humans. Am J Clin Nutr 1991;54:701–6.

28. Reaven P, Parthasarathy S, Grasse BJ, Miller E, Steinberg D, Witztum JL. Effects of oleate-rich and linoleate-rich diets on the susceptibility of low-density lipoprotein to oxidative modification in mildly hypercholesterolemic subjects. J Clin Invest 1993;91: 668–76.

29. Thomas MJ and Rudel LL. Dietary fatty acids, low-density lipoprotein composition, and oxidation and primate atherosclerosis. J Nutr 1996;126:1058S–62S.

30. van de Vijver LP, Kardinaal AF, van Duyvenvoorde W, Kruijssen DA, Grobbee DE, van Poppel G, Princen HM. LDL oxidation and extent of coronary atherosclerosis. Arterioscler Thromb Vasc Biol 1998;18:193–9.

31. Dimitriadis E, Griffin M, Owens D, Johnson A, Collins P, Tomkin GH. Oxidation of low-density lipoprotein in NIDDM: its relationship to fatty acid composition. Diabetologia 1995;38:1300–6.

32. Donner MG, Parhofer KG, Richter WO, Schwandt P. Low-density lipoprotein (LDL) oxidizability before and after LDL apheresis. Metabolism 1999;48:881–6.

33. Loughrey CM, Young IS, McEneny J, McDowell IF, McMaster C, McNamee PT, Trimble ER. Oxidation of low-density lipoprotein in patients on regular haemodialysis. Atherosclerosis 1994;110:185–93.

34. Stocker R, Bowry VW, Frei B. Ubiquinol-10 protects human low-density lipoprotein more efficiently against lipid peroxidation than does alpha-tocopherol. Proc Natl Acad Sci USA 1991;88:1646–50.

35. Klatt P and Esterbauer H. Oxidative hypothesis of atherogenesis. J Cardiovasc Risk 1996;3:346–51.

36. Reaven PD and Witztum JL. Comparison of supplementation of RRR-alpha-tocopherol and racemic alpha-tocopherol in humans. Effects on lipid levels and lipoprotein susceptibility to oxidation. Arterioscler Thromb 1993;13:601–8.

37. Wiseman SA, Van den Boom MA, De Fouw NJ, Wassink MG, Op den Kamp JA, Tijburg LB. Comparison of the effects of dietary vitamin E on *in vivo* and *in vitro* parameters of lipid peroxidation in the rabbit. Free Radic Biol Med 1995;19:617–26.

38. Suzukawa M, Ishikawa T, Yoshida H, Nakamura H. Effect of *in-vivo* supplementation with low-dose vitamin E on susceptibility of low-density lipoprotein and high-density lipoprotein to oxidative modification. J Am Coll Nutr 1995;14:46–52.

39. Ziouzenkova O, Gieseg SP, Ramos P, Esterbauer H. Factors affecting resistance of low-density lipoproteins to oxidation. Lipids 1996;31:S71–6.

40. Parks EJ, German JB, Davis PA et al. Reduced oxidative susceptibility of LDL from patients participating in an intensive atherosclerosis treatment program [see comments]. Am J Clin Nutr 1998;68:778–85.

41. Sutherland WH, Walker RJ, De Jong SA, Upritchard JE. Supplementation with tomato juice increases plasma lycopene but does not alter susceptibility to oxidation of low-density lipoproteins from renal transplant recipients. Clin Nephrol 1999;52:30–6.

42. Chait A, Brazg RL, Tribble DL, Krauss RM. Susceptibility of small, dense, low-density lipoproteins to oxidative modification in subjects with the atherogenic lipoprotein phenotype, pattern B. Am J Med 1993;94:350–6.

43. Tribble DL, van den Berg JJ, Motchnik PA, Ames BN, Lewis DM, Chait A, Krauss RM. Oxidative susceptibility of low-density-lipoprotein subfractions is related to their ubiquinol-10 and alpha-tocopherol content. Proc Natl Acad Sci U S A 1994;91:1183–7.

44. O' Leary V, Darley-Usmar VM, Russell LJ, Stone D. Pro-oxidant effects of lipoxygenase-derived peroxides on the copper-initiated oxidation of low-density lipoprotein. Biochemical Journal 1992;282:631–4.

45. Santanam N and Parthasarathy S. Parodoxical actions of antioxidants in the oxidation of low-density lipoprotein by peroxidases. J Clin Invest 1995;95:2594–600.

46. Wetzstein CJ, Shern-Brewer RA, Santanam N, Green NR, White-Welkley JE, Parthasarathy S. Does acute exercise affect the susceptibility of low-density lipoprotein to oxidation? Free Radic Biol Med 1998;24:679–82.

47. Cominacini L, Garbin U, Pastorino AM et al. Predisposition to LDL oxidation in patients with and without angiographically established coronary artery disease. Atherosclerosis 1993;99:63–70.

48. Schreier LE, Sanguinetti S, Mosso H, Lopez GI, Siri L, Wikinski RL. Low-density lipoprotein composition and oxidability in atherosclerotic cardiovascular disease. Clin Biochem 1996;29:479–87.

49. Chiu HC, Jeng JR, Shieh SM. Increased oxidizability of plasma low-density lipoprotein from patients with coronary artery disease. Biochim Biophys Acta 1994;1225:200–8.

50. Salonen JT, Nyyssonen K, Salonen R, Porkkala-Sarataho E, Tuomainen TP, Diczfalusy U, Bjorkhem I. Lipoprotein oxidation and progression of carotid atherosclerosis. Circulation 1997;95:840–5.

51. van de Vijver LP, Kardinaal AF, van Duyvenvoorde W, Kruijssen DA, Grobbee DE, van Poppel G, Princen HM. Oxidation of LDL and extent of peripheral atherosclerosis. Free Radic Res 1999;31:129–39.

52. Tsai EC, Hirsch IB, Brunzell JD, Chait A. Reduced plasma peroxyl radical-trapping capacity and increased susceptibility of LDL to oxidation in poorly controlled IDDM. Diabetes 1994;43:1010–4.

53. Jain SK, McVie R, Jaramillo JJ, Chen Y. Hyperketonemia (acetoacetate) increases the oxidizability of LDL + VLDL in type 1 diabetic patients. Free Radic Biol Med 1998;24:175–81.

54. Jenkins AJ, Klein RL, Chassereau CN, Hermayer KL, Lopes-Virella MF. LDL from patients with well-controlled IDDM is not more susceptible to *in vitro* oxidation. Diabetes 1996;45:762–7.

55. Napoli C, Postiglione A, Triggiani M, et al. Oxidative structural modifications of low-density lipoprotein in homozygous familial hypercholesterolemia. Atherosclerosis 1995;118:259–73.

56. Raal FJ, Areias AJ, Waisberg R, von Arb M. Susceptibility of low-density lipoprotein to oxidation in familial hypercholesterolemia. Atherosclerosis 1995;115:9–15.

57. Karabina SA, Elisaf M, Bairaktari E, Tzallas C, Siamopoulos KC, Tselepis AD. Increased activity of platelet-activating factor acetylhydrolase in low-density-lipoprotein subfractions induces enhanced lysophosphatidylcholine production during oxidation in patients with heterozygous familial hypercholesterolemia. Eur J Clin Invest 1997;27:595–602.

58. Sanchez-Quesada JL, Otal-Entraigas C, Franco M, Jorba O, Gonzalez-Sastre F, Blanco-Vaca F, and Ordonez-Llanos J. Effect of simvastatin treatment on the electronegative low-density lipoprotein present in patients with heterozygous familial hypercholesterolemia. Amer J Cardio 1999;84:655–9.

59. Harats D, Ben-Naim M, Dabach Y, Hollander G, Havivi E, Stein O, Stein Y. Effect of vitamin C and E supplementation on susceptibility of plasma lipoproteins to peroxidation induced by acute smoking. Atherosclerosis 1990;85:47–54.

60. Ghanem H, van den Dorpel MA, Weimar W, Man in't Veld AJ, El-Kannishy MH, Jansen H. Increased low-density-lipoprotein oxidation in stable kidney transplant recipients. Kidney Int 1996;49:488–93.

61. van den Dorpel MA, Ghanem H, Rischen-Vos J, Man in't Veld AJ, Jansen H, Weimar W. Low-density lipoprotein oxidation is increased in kidney transplant recipients. Transpl Int 1996;9:S54–7.

62. Varghese Z, Fernando RL, Turakhia G et al. Calcineurin inhibitors enhance low-density lipoprotein oxidation in transplant patients. Kidney Int Suppl 1999;71:S137–40.

63. Sutherland WH, Walker RJ, Ball MJ, Stapley SA, Robertson MC Oxidation of low-density lipoproteins from patients with renal failure or renal transplants. Kidney Int 1995;48:227–36.

64. Schulz T, Schiffl H, Scheithe R, Hrboticky N, Lorenz R. Preserved antioxidative defense of lipoproteins in renal failure and during hemodialysis. Am J Kidney Dis 1995;25:564–71.

65. Westhuyzen J, Saltissi D, Healy H. Oxidation of low-density lipoprotein in hemodialysis

patients: effect of dialysis and comparison with matched controls. Atherosclerosis 1997;129:199–205.

66. Aviram M, Eias K. Dietary olive oil reduces low-density lipoprotein uptake by macrophages and decreases the susceptibility of the lipoprotein to undergo lipid peroxidation. Ann Nutr Metab 1993;37:75–84.

67. Berry EM, Eisenberg S, Friedlander Y, Harats D, Kaufmann NA, Norman Y, Stein Y. Effects of diets rich in monounsaturated fatty acids on plasma lipoproteins—the Jerusalem Nutrition Study. II. Monounsaturated fatty acids vs. carbohydrates. Am J Clin Nutr 1992;56:394–403.

68. Esterbauer H, Striegl G, Puhl H, and Rotheneder M. Continuous monitoring of *in vitro* oxidation of human low-density lipoprotein. Free Radic Res Commun 1989;6:67–75.

69. Kleinveld HA, Demacker PN, Stalenhoef AF. Comparative study on the effect of low-dose vitamin E and probucol on the susceptibility of LDL to oxidation and the progression of atherosclerosis in Watanabe heritable hyperlipidemic rabbits. Arterioscler Thromb 1994;14:1386–91.

70. Li D, Devaraj S, Fuller C, Bucala R, Jialal I. Effect of alpha-tocopherol on LDL oxidation and glycation: *in vitro* and *in vivo* studies. J Lipid Res 1996;37:1978–86.

71. Bowen HT, Omaye ST. Oxidative changes associated with beta-carotene and alpha-tocopherol enrichment of human low-density lipoproteins. J Am Coll Nutr 1998;17:171–9.

72. Porkkala-Sarataho EK, Nyyssonen MK, Kaikkonen JE, Poulsen HE, Hayn EM, Salonen RM, Salonen JT. A randomized, single-blind, placebo-controlled trial of the effects of 200 mg alpha-tocopherol on the oxidation resistance of atherogenic lipoproteins. Am J Clin Nutr 1998;68:1034–41.

73. Abbey, M., Nestel, P.J. and Baghurst, P.A. Antioxidant vitamins and low-density-lipoprotein oxidation. Am J Clin Nutr 1993;58:525–32.

74. Woodside JV, Young IS, Yarnell JW et al. Antioxidants, but not B-group vitamins, increase the resistance of low-density lipoprotein to oxidation: a randomized, factorial design, placebo-controlled trial. Atherosclerosis 1999;144:419–27.

75. Nyyssonen K, Porkkala E, Salonen R, Korpela H, Salonen JT. Increase in oxidation resistance of atherogenic serum lipoproteins following antioxidant supplementation: a randomized double-blind placebo-controlled clinical trial. Eur J Clin Nutr 1994;48:633–42.

76. Reaven PD, Herold DA, Barnett J, Edelman S. Effects of Vitamin E on susceptibility of low-density lipoprotein and low-density-lipoprotein subfractions to oxidation and on protein glycation in NIDDM. Diabetes Care 1995;18:807–16.

77. Winklhofer-Roob BM, Ziouzenkova O, Puhl H et al. Impaired resistance to oxidation of low-density lipoprotein in cystic fibrosis: improvement during vitamin E supplementation. Free Radic Biol Med 1995;19:725–33.

78. Lowe GM, Bilton RF, Davies IG, Ford TC, Billington D, Young AJ. Carotenoid composition and antioxidant potential in subfractions of human low-density lipoprotein. Ann Clin Biochem 1999;36:323–32.

79. Nenseter MS, Volden V, Berg T, Drevon CA, Ose L, Tonstad S. No effect of beta-carotene supplementation on the susceptibility of low-density lipoprotein to *in vitro* oxidation among hypercholesterolemic, postmenopausal women. Scand J Clin Lab Invest 1995;55:477–85.

80. Fuller CJ, Grundy SM, Norkus EP, Jialal I. Effect of ascorbate supplementation on low-density lipoprotein oxidation in smokers. Atherosclerosis 1996;119:139–50.

81. Fremont L, Gozzelino MT, Franchi MP, Linard A. Dietary flavonoids reduce lipid peroxidation in rats fed polyunsaturated or monounsaturated fat diets. J Nutr 1998;128:1495–502.

82. Regnstrom J, Walldius G, Nilsson S et al. The effect of probucol on low-density lipoprotein oxidation and femoral atherosclerosis. Atherosclerosis 1996;125:217–29.

83. Leonhardt W, Kurktschiev T, Meissner D et al. Effects of fluvastatin therapy on lipids, antioxidants, oxidation of low-density lipoproteins, and trace metals. Eur J Clin Pharmacol 1997;53:65–9.

84. Kleinveld HA, Demacker PN, De Haan AF, Stalenhoef AF. Decreased *in vitro* oxidizability of low-density lipoprotein in hypercholesterolemic patients treated with 3-hydroxy-3-methylglutaryl- CoA reductase inhibitors. Eur J Clin Invest 1993;23: 289–95.

85. Chen MF, Hsu HC, Lee YT. Short-term treatment with low-dose pravastatin attenuates oxidative susceptibility of low-density lipoprotein in hypercholesterolemic patients. Cardiovasc Drugs Ther 1997;11:787–93.

86. Aviram M, Rosenblat M, Bisgaier CL, Newton RS. Atorvastatin and gemfibrozil metabolites, but not the parent drugs, are potent antioxidants against lipoprotein oxidation. Atherosclerosis 1998;138:271–80.

87. Chaput E, Maubrou-Sanchez D, Bellamy FD, Edgar AD. Fenofibrate protects lipoproteins from lipid peroxidation: synergistic interaction with alpha-tocopherol. Lipids 1999;34:497–502.

88. O'Brien R and Luo M. The effects of gliclazide and other sulfonylureas on low-density lipoprotein oxidation *in vitro*. Metabolism 1997;46:22–5.

89. Napoli C, Salomone S, Godfraind T et al. 1,4-Dihydropyridine calcium channel blockers inhibit plasma and LDL oxidation and formation of oxidation-specific epitopes in the arterial wall and prolong survival in stroke-prone spontaneously hypertensive rats. Stroke 1999;30:1907–15.

90. Brude IR, Drevon CA, Viken K, Arnstad JE, Valnes KN, Nenseter MS. Doxazosin treatment and peroxidation of low-density lipoprotein among male hypertensive subjects: *in vitro* and *ex vivo* studies. Biochem Pharmacol 1999;58:183–91.

91. Mc Manus J, Mc Eneny J, Thompson W, Young IS. The effect of hormone replacement therapy on the oxidation of low-density lipoprotein in postmenopausal women. Atherosclerosis 1997;135:73–81.

92. Ruiz-Larrea MB, Mohan AR, Paganga G, Miller NJ, Bolwell GP, Rice-Evans CA. Antioxidant activity of phytoestrogenic isoflavones. Free Radic Res 1997;26:63–70.

93. Tikkanen MJ, Wahala K, Ojala S, Vihma V, Adlercreutz H. Effect of soybean phytoestrogen intake on low-density lipoprotein oxidation resistance. Proc Natl Acad Sci USA 1998;95:3106–10.

94. Wiseman H. The bioavailability of non-nutrient plant factors: dietary flavonoids and phytoestrogens. Proc Nutr Soc 1999;58:139–46.

95. Clarkson TB and Anthony MS. Phytoestrogens and coronary heart disease. Baillieres Clin Endocrinol Metab 1998;12:589–604.

96. McEneny J, Trimble ER, Young IS. A simple method for assessing copper-mediated oxidation of very-low-density lipoprotein isolated by rapid ultracentrifugation. Ann Clin Biochem 1998;35:504–14.

97. Rifici VA and Khachadurian AK. Oxidation of high-density lipoproteins: characterization and effects on cholesterol efflux from J774 macrophages. Biochim Biophys Acta 1996;1299:87–94.

98. Scheek LM, Wiseman SA, Tijburg LB, van Tol A. Dialysis of isolated low-density lipoprotein induces a loss of lipophilic antioxidants and increases the susceptibility to oxidation *in vitro*. Atherosclerosis 1995;117:139–44.

99. Smith C, Mitchinson MJ, Aruoma OI, Halliwell B. Stimulation of lipid peroxidation and hydroxyl-radical generation by the contents of human atherosclerotic lesions. Biochem J 1992;286:901–5.

100. Swain JA, Darley-Usmar V, Gutteridge JM. Peroxynitrite releases copper from caeruloplasmin: implications for atherosclerosis. FEBS Lett 1994;342:49–52.

101. Lamb DJ and Leake DS. Iron released from transferrin at acidic pH can catalyze the oxidation of low-density lipoprotein. FEBS Lett 1994;352:15–8.

102. Lamb DJ and Leake DS. Acidic pH enables caeruloplasmin to catalyze the modification of low-density lipoprotein. FEBS Lett 1994;338:122–6.

103. el-Saadani M, Esterbauer H, el-Sayed M, Goher M, Nassar AY, Jurgens, G. A spectrophotometric assay for lipid peroxides in serum lipoproteins using a commercially available reagent. J Lipid Res 1989;30:627–30.

104. Esterbauer H, Quehenberger O, Jurgens G. In: Rice-Evans C. and Halliwell B (eds.). Free Radicals: Methodology and Concepts. London: The Richelieu Press, 1988:243–268.
105. Carpenter KL, Wilkins GM, Fussell B, Ballantine JA, Taylor SE, Mitchinson MJ, Leake DS. Production of oxidized lipids during modification of low-density lipoprotein by macrophages or copper. Biochem J 1994;304:625–33.
106. Esterbauer H, Gebicki J, Puhl H, Jurgens G. The role of lipid peroxidation and antioxidants in oxidative modification of LDL. Free Radic Biol Med 1992;13:341–90.
107. McDowell IF, McEneny J, Trimble ER. A rapid method for measurement of the susceptibility to oxidation of low-density lipoprotein. Ann Clin Biochem 1995;32:167–74.
108. Wallin B, Rosengren B, Shertzer HG, Camejo G. Lipoprotein oxidation and measurement of thiobarbituric-acid-reacting substances formation in a single microtiter plate: its use for evaluation of antioxidants. Anal Biochem 1993;208:10–5.
109. Jurgens G, Ashy A, Esterbauer H. Detection of new epitopes formed upon oxidation of low-density lipoprotein, lipoprotein (a), and very-low-density lipoprotein. Use of an antiserum against 4-hydroxynonenal-modified low-density lipoprotein. Biochem J 1990;265:605–8.
110. Louheranta AM, Porkkala-Sarataho EK, Nyyssonen MK, Salonen RM, Salonen JT. Linoleic acid intake and susceptibility of very-low-density and low-density lipoproteins to oxidation in men. American Journal of Human Nutrition 1996;63:698–703.
111. Van Gaal LF, Vertommen J, De Leeuw IH. The *in vitro* oxidizability of lipoprotein particles in obese and non-obese subjects. Atherosclerosis 1998;137:S39–44.
112. Hasselwander O, McEneny J, McMaster D, Fogarty DG, Nicholls DP, Maxwell AP, Young IS. HDL composition and HDL antioxidant capacity in patients on regular hemodialysis. Atherosclerosis 1999;143:125–33.
113. McEneny J, O'Kane M, McMaster C, McMaster D, Mercer C, Trimble E, Young I. VLDL subfractions (A–D) in type 2 diabetes: their susceptibility to oxidation and lipid composition. Atherosclerosis 1999;144(S1):125.

Direct Measures of Lipid Peroxidation

21

Sridevi Devaraj and Ishwarlal Jialal

❖   Data continue to accrue supporting the hypothesis that oxidative stress is pivotal in the genesis of the atherosclerotic lesion. There are several direct as well as indirect measures for assaying oxidative stress. An overview of LDL oxidation and clinical applicability of the assessment of LDL oxidizability, utilizing indirect measures of oxidation, has been outlined in Chapter 20. Thus, this chapter will focus on direct measures of oxidative stress.

F2-ISOPROSTANES

F2-isoprostanes are prostaglandin-like compounds formed *in vivo* from free radical catalyzed peroxidation of arachidonic acid, mainly via a non-cycloxygenase-dependent mechanism. F2-isoprostanes are found in body tissues in the esterified form and in biological fluids, such as plasma and urine, in the free form.[1–3] F2-isoprostanes can be measured accurately and extremely sensitively by a solid-phase extraction procedure, followed by selective ion-monitoring gas chromatography negative chemical ionization/mass spectrometry (GC/MS), employing tritiated PGF2-alpha as the internal standard.

Recently, enzyme immunoassays have been developed to detect F2-isoprostanes.[4] In these assays, which correlate well with GC/MS values, urinary F2-isoprostanes are first extracted by passing through C18 and silica columns. This process is then followed by enzyme immunoassay using 8-epi F2-isoprostane as standard.

A potential drawback to measuring F2-isoprostanes as an index of endogenous lipid peroxidation is that they can be readily generated *ex vivo* in biological fluids such as plasma in which arachidonyl-containing lipids are present. This occurs when plasma is left at room temperature. Whereas plasma must be snap-frozen for accurate measurement of F2-isoprostanes, urinary F2-isoprostanes are extremely stable and can be frozen for later analysis. While the ideal specimen is a 24-h urine, urinary F2-isoprostanes can also be measured in first-morning urine. The amount of urinary F2-isoprostanes is expressed per mg urinary creatinine.

The relevance of measuring urinary F2-isoprostanes with regard to atherosclerosis has been brought out in many studies.[1–6] F2-isoprostanes are increased following LDL oxidation by macrophages, endothelial cells, or by copper[5,6] and they localize in foam cells in human atherosclerotic lesions.[7,8] Increased concentrations have been detected in oxidized LDL (Ox-LDL) and also in patients who are smokers or who have established risk factors for premature atherosclerosis, such as diabetes and hyper-cholesterolemia.[9-12] Compared to a control group, subjects who have hypercholester-olemia have increased urinary F2-isoprostanes;[10] Davi et al. have shown that levels of F2-isoprostanes are significantly increased in patients with Type 2a hypercholesterol-emia compared to controls.[10] Diabetic subjects also have increased levels of iso-prostanes compared to matched controls.[11,12]

Levels of isoprostanes are increased in the urine of patients undergoing angio-plasty; they double six hours after angioplasty and return to pre-angioplasty values within 24 hours. Morrow et al.[13] have shown that plasma levels of free and esterified F2-isoprostanes were significantly higher in smokers than in age- and sex-matched non-smokers. Also, in a cross-sectional study of 24 chronic smokers and matched con-trols, Reilly et al.[14] showed that smokers had significantly increased urinary excretion of F2-isoprostanes compared to non-smokers. Thus, F2-isoprostanes are increased in subjects with established risk factors for premature coronary heart disease (CHD) such as smoking, hypercholesterolemia, and diabetes.

In addition to serving as a direct measure of *in vivo* oxidative stress, certain isoprostanes have biological activity,[1-3] for example, the 8-epi F2-isoprostane pro-duces potent vasoconstrictor activity, modulates platelet aggregation, and stimulates smooth muscle cell proliferation. Furthermore, alpha tocopherol supplementation has been found to suppress F2-isoprostanes and atherogenesis in apolipoprotein E-(apo-E) deficient mice.[15] In human subjects, alpha tocopherol supplementation has been shown to lower urinary F2-isoprostanes in subjects with hypercholesterolemia or diabetes.[10-12] Also, in a recent report, we have shown that alpha tocopherol supplementation (400 IU/day) can decrease urinary F2-isoprostanes in normal volun-teers.[16] Vitamin C supplementation for 28 days has also been shown to reduce the lev-els of F2-isoprostanes and the titer of antiphospholipid antibodies in patients with systemic lupus erythematosus.[17]

Thus, the measurement of F2-isoprostanes may provide a sensitive, specific, and non-invasive method for the assessment of *in vivo* lipid peroxidation in humans. While F2-isoprostanes are a direct measure of lipid peroxidation and whole body oxi-dative stress, their assessment does not allow one to infer the site or locality of the in-creased oxidative stress.

AUTO-ANTIBODIES TO OXIDIZED LDL

Another way to evaluate lipoprotein oxidation is by measuring auto-antibodies against epitopes on Ox-LDL.[18] Alteration of LDL by oxidative modification alters the apo B-100 structure. This alteration makes LDL more immunogenic. Monoclonal antibodies to Ox-LDL recognize material from atherosclerotic lesions, but not normal arteries. Circu-lating auto-antibodies to Ox-LDL have been demonstrated and found to be increased in patients with myocardial infarction, diabetes, renal failure, or hypertension, along with a concomitant increase in LDL oxidation.[19-23] The presence of auto-antibodies to Ox-LDL has been positively correlated with the progression of atherosclerosis, as man-ifested by carotid artery stenosis.[24] However, while some studies have shown signifi-cant associations between auto-antibody titer and severity of coronary or carotid

Figure 21-1 ✧ ELISA for Auto-Antibodies to Ox-LDL

Antigen-coated plate
(N-LDL/Ox-LDL*/Blank)
↓
Incubate overnight at 4°C
Wash 3 times with PBS-EDTA and 3 times with distilled water
(PBS containing 0.27 mmol/L EDTA, 20 umol/L BHT, 0.05% Tween)
↓
Block with PBS with 2%BSA
↓
Incubate for 2 h at 4°C
Wash 3 times as above
↓
Add plasma (1:50 in PBS with 1%BSA)
↓
Incubate overnight at 4°C
Wash 3 times as above
↓
Add HRP-conjugated rabbit anti-human IgG (1: 2000)
↓
Incubate for 4 h at 4°C
Wash 3 times as above
↓
Add substrate (o-phenylene diamine in citrate buffer)
↓
Incubate for 15 min at room temperature
↓
Stop with sulfuric acid (2 mmol/L)
↓
Read at absorbance 492 nm
↓
Calculate antibodies to Ox-LDL Ratio
(Ox-LDL-Blank)/(N-LDL-Blank)

Abbreviations: N-LDL, native low-density lipoproteins; OX-LDL, oxidized low-density lipoproteins; PBS, phosphate buffered saline; BSA, bovine serum albumin; HRP, horse radish peroxidase.

*25 ug of OX-LDL is prepared with equal amounts of LDL oxidized for 2h and 24 h with copper (5 umol/L).

atherosclerosis, others have not. A schema used in the authors' laboratory for measurement of auto-antibodies to Ox-LDL by ELISA is shown in Figure 21–1. (For additional information on this ELISA assay, contact the author directly: jialal.i@pathology. swmed.edu.)

To date, there is no agreement on the standardization of the antigen (Ox-LDL). Also, there is no standard method, reference material, or control for assays of antibodies to Ox-LDL. In the present form, most immunoassays for antibodies to Ox-LDL depend on different reactivities of immunoglobulin from patients' serum with antigen that is either in the native (unmodified) form or with LDL that has been modified (malondi-aldehyde-LDL, i.e., MDA-LDL or Ox-LDL). However, differences may occur due to inter-individual variations in the immune response to a given level of antigen and secondly, these auto-antibodies may be removed from the circulation due to tissue binding.

While this assay shows a lot of promise, it needs to be standardized. Further-more, the assay must be carefully designed to avoid changes in the LDL oxidation state (from different temperatures used in the various assay incubation steps) during the assay, which could alter the results. Also, there may be interferences from immune complexes. Data can be reported either as the ratio of modified LDL to native LDL (mLDL/nLDL) or as the difference of binding between modified LDL and native LDL (mLDL–nLDL). A blank plate is employed in the assay that consists only of coating buffer and can thus decrease assay variability due to non-specific binding. Once the assay is well-standardized, it could become an important and sensitive direct measure of oxidative stress.

MEASUREMENT OF MODIFIED LDL IN PLASMA

The development of monoclonal antibodies to Ox-LDL has given investigators a rela-tively new method of measuring Ox-LDL by ELISA. Epitopes produced by covalent binding of 4-hydroxynonenal or MDA have received considerable attention. Using one such assay, Holvoet et al.[25,26] developed a competitive ELISA in which a monoclonal antibody recognizing an epitope found in MDA-modified LDL (mAb-1H11) and a mono-clonal antibody recognizing an epitope in Ox-LDL (mAb-4E6) were used to detect mod-ified LDL in plasma. Each antibody was pre-incubated with patient or control plasma and added to microplates coated with MDA-modified LDL or Ox-LDL respectively; the bound antibody was detected using a horse radish peroxidase-labeled anti-mouse IgG conjugate. They showed that oxidized LDL levels are increased in patients with unsta-ble angina, carotid atherosclerosis, and acute myocardial infarction, while MDA-modi-fied LDL is increased only in acute coronary syndromes, e.g,. unstable angina and acute myocardial infarction. From these studies it appears that Ox-LDL correlated with the progression of the lesion while MDA-LDL correlated with acute events.

Itabe et al.[27] have developed a sandwich ELISA using an anti-human apo B anti-body. Using this assay, they were able to detect as low as 0.5 ng protein of copper-induced Ox-LDL. Also, they found significantly increased levels of Ox-LDL in hemo-dialysis patients compared to controls. However, these findings, while offering great promise, need to be confirmed by other groups.

BREATH-VOLATILE HYDROCARBONS

Breakdown products of lipid hydroperoxides can be measured in exhaled breath as volatile hydrocarbons. This is a very sensitive and non-invasive measure of lipid peroxidation in humans. Ethane and pentane are end-products of the peroxidation of w-3 and w-6 polyunsaturated fatty acids (PUFA) respectively. Breath sampling for hy-drocarbon assessment can be performed by one of two techniques.[28]

In the first, single aliquots of expired breath are sampled from an unprepared individual. It is essential to purify the inspired air because of the risk of hydrocarbon contamination arising from exogenous sources (motor vehicles, cigarette smoke, etc.) that create a high background. In the second method, expired breath is collected and measured quantitatively following a wash-out period in which the subject inhales hydrocarbon-free air. Hydrocarbons in breath are then separated by gas chromatography using a flame-ionization detector or GC/MS techniques. However, only materials such as glass, stainless steel, and water that are non-permeable to hydrocarbons may be used for tubing and sampling material.

Breath hydrocarbons have been shown to increase with age and smoking status.[29,30] They are apparently not influenced by fasting, and short-term changes in diet do not influence hydrocarbon concentrations.[31] However, both the type and amount of PUFA in the diet and intake of antioxidant vitamins such as E, C, and beta-carotene can influence hydrocarbon concentrations.[32] Thus, although this method is non-invasive, it is tedious and technically demanding because of its numerous pitfalls. Moreover, in recent years, it has become clear that assessment of pentane may be hampered because its separation from isoprene, which is present in human breath at concentrations far above that of pentane, has not been adequately obtained.[33] Thus, the role of breath hydrocarbon testing as a measure of lipid peroxidation clearly needs to be established by further research.

ASSESSMENT OF ANTIOXIDANT STATUS

Halliwell and Gutteridge defined an antioxidant as any substance that delays or inhibits damage to a target molecule. The balance between pro-oxidant challenge and the presence of antioxidants determines net oxidative stress.

Antioxidants may be present within cells, in cell membranes, or in extracellular fluids; may be hydrophilic or lipophilic; and may be endogenously produced or derived from the diet. Intracellular antioxidants include glutathione and enzymes such as glutathione peroxidase, superoxide dismutase, and catalase. Membrane-bound antioxidants include alpha tocopherol, beta-carotene and ubiquinone. Many antioxidants that are derived from the diet including ascorbate, polyphenols and flavonoids are hydrophilic and carried in plasma, while the lipophilic tocopherols and carotenoids are carried by lipoproteins. Other predominantly extracellular antioxidants are bilirubin and uric acid. Some weaker antioxidants include chelating proteins such as albumin, transferrin, lactoferrin, and ceruloplasmin. Assessment of antioxidant status may include either the measurement of each individual antioxidant or may employ methods to measure total antioxidant capacity.

TOTAL ANTIOXIDANT CAPACITY

All published methods of estimating antioxidant capacity of a solution measure the inhibition of an artificially generated species.[34] A free radical species is generated in a solution containing an oxidation target; antioxidants in the added sample quench the target response by interacting with the reactive oxygen species. Published methods differ in the choice of free radical generator used, target, and type of measurement used to detect the oxidized product.

One of the most widely adapted techniques is the total peroxyl radical-trapping antioxidant parameter (TRAP).[35]. In this assay, the water-soluble compound, 2,2'-azobis(2-amidinopropane hydrochloride) (AAPH), undergoes thermal decomposition to produce peroxyl-free radicals. The rate of oxygen uptake is monitored by performing the reaction in an oxygen-electrode chamber. The measurement is calibrated using Trolox, a water-soluble alpha tocopherol analog.

In an effort to improve this assay, a method has been developed for use on a centrifugal analyzer with plasma volumes as low as 3 µL.[36] In this assay, 2,2'-azinobis-(3-ethylbenzothiazoline-6-sulphonic acid) (ABTS) is incubated with metmyoglobin (this acts as a peroxidase) and hydrogen peroxide, forming the long-lived cation, ABTS+. The presence of an antioxidant in heparinized plasma reduces this radical cation, the concentration of which is measured by absorbance. The clinical utility of this approach needs to be assessed.

Another widely used method for determining total antioxidant capacity is the ORAC (oxygen radical absorbance capacity) assay based on the procedure described by Cao et al.[37] The method utilizes β-phycoerythrin (β-PE) as an indicator protein and AAPH as a peroxyl radical generator. Under appropriate conditions, the loss of β-PE fluorescence in the presence of reactive species is an index of oxidative damage of the protein. The inhibition by an antioxidant, which is reflected in the protection against the loss of β-PE fluorescence in the ORAC assay, is a measure of its antioxidant capacity.

Minor dietary constituents that are gaining considerable attention as potential antioxidants include polyphenols. These compounds are usually not measured directly; they are measured by assays that assess total antioxidant capacity. For these antioxidants, plasma total and conjugated phenols can be measured by the method described by Serafini et al.[38] To measure total phenols, 500 µL of plasma is acidified and complexed phenols are extracted with alcoholic sodium hydroxide. Proteins are then precipitated using 0.75 mol/L metaphosphoric acid, and phenols are re-extracted with a mixture of acetone:water (1:1). The phenol content is then determined by the method of Folin and Denis,[39] using resveratrol or gallic acid as a standard. Free phenols can also be measured by the Folin and Denis method following precipitation of proteins with 0.75 mol/L metaphosphoric acid. The level of conjugated phenols is then assessed by subtracting free phenols from total phenols.

Ingestion of pure vitamin C and red or white wine in healthy volunteers has been shown to increase antioxidant capacity as measured by TRAP and ORAC activities. Also, antioxidant capacity has been shown to be reduced in conditions associated with oxidative stress such as diabetes, myocardial infarction, reperfusion injury, hemodialysis, and rheumatoid arthritis.[40] However, further research is required to assess the utility of these measures in determining antioxidant capacity at various stages of disease or therapy.

MEASUREMENT OF INDIVIDUAL ANTIOXIDANTS

Glutathione

Glutathione, a substrate of glutathione peroxidase, plays an important role in maintaining redox status; a decrease in intracellular glutathione is clearly an early consequence of oxidative stress. When glutathione oxidizes, it forms glutathione disulfide and other mixed disulfides. These can be measured as ophthalaldehyde reactive material released from precipitated protein after reduction with borohydride.[41] Protein sulphydryls can be measured by reacting with 5,5'dithiobis-2-nitrobenzoic acid (DTNB).[42] Problems with measurement include the short half-life of glutathione (less than two minutes) and the fact that red blood cells have 100-fold higher levels of glutathione than plasma has. The ratio of oxidized to reduced glutathione is a useful indicator of oxidative stress and can be measured by coupling the Ellman reaction to oxidation of NADPH to NADP and following the decrease in absorbance at 340 nm.[43] Recent methods offer high levels of specificity and sensitivity and employ high-performance liquid chromatography (HPLC) techniques.[44]

Alpha-Tocopherol

Alpha-tocopherol, the most active and the most abundant isomer of the vitamin E family, is the principal lipid-soluble antioxidant in tissues and plasma.[45] It is also the predominant antioxidant in the LDL particle. Alpha-tocopherol, a chain-breaking antioxidant, traps peroxyl free radicals. Several studies have associated low alpha-tocopherol levels with the development of atherosclerosis.[46–50] Furthermore, in a cross-sectional study of 16 European populations, a significant inverse correlation was found between alpha-tocopherol levels and CHD mortality.[49] Also, plasma alpha tocopherol levels correlate inversely with the risk of angina pectoris.[48] The Cambridge Heart Anti-Oxidant Study (CHAOS) has shown that in 2,002 patients with angiographically proven myocardial infarction, administration of alpha-tocopherol (400 or 800 IU/day) for 17 months significantly reduced non-fatal myocardial infarction by 76%.[51] Data from some animal studies have also shown that dietary alpha-tocopherol can retard the progression of atherosclerosis.[52,53]

Studies by many different laboratories have shown that alpha-tocopherol, *in vitro* and in vivo, can inhibit the oxidative susceptibility of LDL. In a dose-response study, Jialal et al.[54,55] showed that at least 400 IU/day of alpha tocopherol was required to see a significant beneficial effect on LDL oxidation. Also, by decreasing LDL oxidation in normal volunteers, alpha tocopherol has been shown to prevent the cytotoxic effects of Ox-LDL on endothelial cells.[56]

Alpha tocopherol may have additional benefits in preventing cardiovascular disease.[57] Alpha tocopherol

- ❖ alone or in combination with ascorbate and beta-carotene, has been shown to reduce platelet adhesion;
- ❖ inhibits smooth muscle proliferation and protein kinase C activity in vitro;
- ❖ when used as a supplement preserves endothelium-dependent vasodilation in hypercholesterolemic subjects and smokers;[58,59]
- ❖ decreases monocyte-endothelial adhesion *in vitro*;
- ❖ when supplemented at 1200 IU/day decreases monocyte pro-atherogenic activities such as superoxide anion and lipid oxidation via inhibition of protein kinase

C, decreases interleukin-1β release via inhibition of 5-lipoxygenase, and decreases monocyte adhesion to endothelium via inhibition of adhesion molecules, CD11b, and VLA-, and transcription factor, NFκb.[60–62]

Older methods for measuring vitamin E used fluorescence; however, they were very non-specific and have been replaced by HPLC methods in which retinol, alpha tocopherol, and carotenoids are measured simultaneously. Common to most versions of the HPLC methods is the addition of an organic solvent (containing the internal standard) to serum or plasma, which aids deproteinization, followed by separation of the organic layer containing the alpha tocopherol. The organic extract is evaporated to dryness, brought up in the mobile phase, and separated chromatographically. The recovery of extraction is 95%–100% and the run-to-run reproducibility is < 6%. Samples must be stored at −70°C.

Alpha tocopherol, being lipid-soluble, is often expressed as a portion of lipid content.[63] A standard reference material (for retinol, alpha tocopherol, and carotenoid analyses) that is serum-based is available from the National Institute of Standards and Technology, Gaithersburg, MD.

Carotenoids

Carotenoids belong to a large group of compounds that are responsible for pigmentation of most fruits and vegetables. The most widely studied carotenoid is beta-carotene, a precursor of vitamin A.[64] Carotenoids are known to quench singlet oxygen.

Beta-carotene is a hydrophobic member of the carotenoid family. Increased beta-carotene intake has been inversely linked to the risk of angina. The effect of beta-carotene on LDL oxidizability is, however, controversial. Also, in the alpha-tocopherol beta-carotene (ATBC) study,[65] beta-carotene supplementation in Finnish smokers increased the incidence of cancer. Carotenoids are unstable when stored longer than six months at −20°C. Serum or heparinized plasma is recommended for their measurement by HPLC.

Ascorbate

Ascorbate is a water-soluble, chain-breaking antioxidant that regenerates alpha tocopherol from its chomanoxyl radical form.[66] Low levels of ascorbate have been identified as a risk factor for atherosclerosis and are associated with increased CHD mortality.[67] Atheromatous aortas have lower ascorbate concentrations than control vessels. Furthermore, smokers, diabetics, and patients with CHD have lower plasma ascorbate levels.[68–70]

Physiological concentrations of ascorbate inhibit metal-catalyzed and cell-mediated LDL oxidation.[71,72] Also, dietary ascorbate supplements have been shown to prevent LDL oxidation induced by acute cigarette smoking.[73] Early methods of ascorbate analysis were based on fairly non-specific reactions such as ascorbate reduction of 2,6-dichloroindophenol. In recent years, HPLC methods employing UV, fluorimetric, or electrochemical detection have been developed.[74]

Because ascorbate oxidizes easily (temperature and pH greatly influence its stability), dehydroascorbate may form during sample preparation or storage. Most HPLC methods involve initially determining ascorbate levels, then reducing dehydroascorbate to ascorbate and repeating the measurement.[75] Most methods involve acid stabilization of ascorbate with perchloric or metaphosphoric acid being added to serum or plasma immediately following separation from blood cells. Antioxidants such as dithiothreitol have also been used to prevent degradation.

OTHER MEASURES:

Electron Spin Resonance

Other direct measures of oxidative stress include direct measurement of free radicals by electron spin resonance (ESR). ESR is often presented as "the gold standard" for identification of free radicals.[76] When present in a magnetic field, the unpaired electron of the free radical can occupy one of two energy states. The amount of splitting of the two energy levels depends on the strength of the magnetic field applied. By applying electromagnetic radiation of certain energy, the electron can move from the lower to the higher energy level and this absorption of radiation is recorded as a spectrum.

A useful technique in ESR is the use of spin traps such as nitrones or nitroso compounds, which react with the free radical to form a more stable radical adduct. However, while ESR is a sensitive measure of free radicals, very few clinical studies have demonstrated its relevance. Furthermore, the method requires considerable expertise and is not suitable for the clinical laboratory.

Protein Oxidation

Proteins are particularly attractive targets for product analyses because *in vitro*, different oxidative insults create similar end products in lipids, but distinct patterns of oxidation products in model proteins.[77,78] Specific fluorescence patterns can be produced when certain amino acids react with peroxides. Phagocytes secrete myeloperoxidase that produces the powerful cytotoxin, hypochlorous acid, from hydrogen peroxide and chloride ion.

Also, myeloperoxidase, can oxidize L-tyrosine in plasma in the presence of hydrogen peroxide to the tyrosyl radical. *In vitro*, tyrosyl radical cross-links tyrosine residues on proteins forming o,o'-dityrosine. Also, hypochlorous acid generated by myeloperoxidase converts L-tyrosine to 3-chlorotyrosine.[77,78] In vivo, LDL isolated from atherosclerotic lesions exhibits a 100-fold increase in dityrosine levels compared with circulating LDL. Also, dityrosine levels are increased in the tissue of fatty streaks as well as in advanced atherosclerotic lesions. Since dityrosine is protease-resistant, stable to acid hydrolysis, and intensely fluorescent, its identification may pinpoint targets where phagocytes inflict oxidative damage in vivo. Dityrosine levels are typically measured by isotope dilution GC/MS,[79] but HPLC methods with fluorescent detection have also been used.

A potent protein-nitrating reagent is peroxynitrite.[80] Nitric oxide released by endothelial cells plays a critical role in normal physiology. When nitric oxide reacts with superoxide released from phagocytes, it produces peroxynitrite that nitrates proteins, forming 3-nitrotyrosine. Immunohistochemical studies have detected 3-nitrotyrosine in human atherosclerotic lesions. Also, levels of 3-nitrotyrosine in lesion LDL were 80-fold higher compared to circulating LDL; 3-nitrotyrosine and 3-chlorotyrosine can be detected by GC-MS or HPLC, with fluorimetric detection.[81]

Another measure of protein oxidation is to determine the amount of protein carbonyls formed. Protein carbonyls are markers of oxidative stress; they are increased in smokers and associated with aging.[82-85] The conventional colorimetric assay that measures reactive protein carbonyls using 2,4-dinitrophenyl hydrazine (DNPH) is labor intensive, time consuming, and requires extensive washing that decreases the sensitivity of the assay.

Reactive protein carbonyls can also be measured by HPLC, using sodium dodecyl sulfate in the mobile phase. With the availability of specific anti-DNP antibodies, Western blotting as well as ELISA assays that efficiently detect protein carbonyls have recently been developed.[82-85]

SUMMARY

Oxidative stress is increasingly recognized in the pathogenesis of atherosclerosis. Although direct measures such as urinary F2-isoprostanes are emerging as good markers of oxidative stress, there is clearly an urgent need for improved and simplified techniques to measure oxidative stress in vivo. Thus, the search continues for a single, rapid, specific, and convenient test of oxidative stress that could become part of the laboratory repertoire in the assessment of oxidative stress, especially as it relates to atherosclerosis. ✧

REFERENCES

1. Pratico D. F2-isoprostanes: sensitive and specific non-invasive indices of lipid peroxidation in vivo. Atheroscler 1999;147:1–10.
2. Roberts LJ II, Morrow J. The generation and actions of isoprostanes. Biochim Biophys Acta 1997;1345:121–35.
3. Patrono C, Fitzgerald G. Isoprostanes—potential markers of oxidant stress in atherothrombotic disease. Arterioscler Thromb Vasc Biol 1997;17:2309–15.
4. Wang Z, Ciabettoni J. Immunological characterization of urinary F2-isoprostane excretion in man. J Pharmac Exp Therap 1995;275:94–100.
5. Gopaul NK, Nourooz-Zadeh J, Mallett AI et al. Formation of F2-isoprostanes during aortic endothelial-cell-mediated LDL oxidation. FEBS Lett 1994;348:297–300.
6. Lynch SM, Morrow JD, Roberts LJ, Frei B. Formation of F2-isoprostanes in plasma and LDL exposed to oxidative stress *in vitro*. J Clin Invest 1994;93:998–1004.
7. Pratico D, Juliano L, Mauriello A, Spagnoli L, Lawson JA et al. Localization of F2-isoprostanes in human atherosclerotic lesions. J Clin Invest 1997;100:2028–34.
8. Gniwotta C, Morrow JD, Roberts LJ, Kuhn H. PGF2-like compounds, F2-isoprostanes are present in increased amounts in human atherosclerotic lesions. Arterioscler Thromb Vasc Biol 1997;17:3236–41.
9. Reilly MP, Pratico D, Delanty N, DiMinnio G, Tremoli E et al. Increased formation of F2-isoprostanes in hypercholesterolemia. Circ 1998;98:2822–28.
10. Davi G, Alessandrini P, Mezzatti P, Minotti G, Bucciarelli T et al. In vivo formation of 8-ep

PGF2-alpha is increased in hypercholesterolemia. Arterioscler Thromb Vasc Biol 1997; 17:3230–35.

11. Davi G, Ciabattoni G, Consoli A, Mezzetti A, Falco A et al. In vivo formation of 8-ep PGF2-alpha and platelet activation in diabetes mellitus: effect of improved metabolic control and vitamin E supplementation. Circulation 1999;99:224–9.

12. Gopaul NK, Anggard EE, Mallet AI, Betteridge DJ, Wolff SP, Nourooz-zadeh J. Plasma 8-epi PGF2 alpha levels are elevated in individuals with NIDDM. FEBS Lett 1995;368: 225–9.

13. Morrow JD, Frei B, Longmire AW. Increase in circulating products of F2-isoprostanes in smokers. N Engl J Med 1995;332:1198–203.

14. Reilly MP, Lawson JA, Fitzgerald GA. Eicosanoids and isoecosanoids: indices of cellular function and oxidant stress. J Nutr. 1998;128:434–438S.

15. Pratico D, Tangirala RK, Radar RJ, Rokach J, Fitzgerald JA. Vitamin E suppresses isoprostane generation in vivo and reduces atherosclerosis in apo E-deficient mice. Nature Med 1998;4:1189–92.

16. Marangon K, Devaraj S, Tirosh O, Packer L, Jialal I. Comparison of the effect of alpha-lipoic acid and alpha-tocopherol supplementation on measures of oxidative stress. Free Radical Biol Med 1999;27:1114–21.

17. Pratico D, Ferro D, Juliano L, Rokach J, Conti F et al. Systemic clotting activation in patients with antiphospholipid antibodies: a role for lipid peroxidation. Blood 1999;93: 3931–5.

18. Yla-Herttuala S. Is oxidized low-density lipoprotein present in vivo? Curr Opinion in Lipidol 1998;9:337–44.

19. Maggi E, Chiesa R, Melissano G et al. LDL oxidation in patients with severe carotid atherosclerosis. Arterioscler Thromb 1994;14:1892–9.

20. Yla Herttuala S, Palinski W, Rosenfeld M et al. Evidence for the presence of oxidatively modified LDL in atherosclerotic lesions of rabbit and man. J Clin Invest 1989;284: 1086–95.

21. Maggi E, Bellazzi R, Gazo A et al. Auto-antibodies against Ox-LDL in uremic patients undergoing dialysis. Kidney Inter 1994;46:869–76.

22. Bellomo G, Maggi E, Poli M et al. Auto-antibodies against Ox-LDL in NIDDM. Diabetes 1995;44:60–66.

23. Puurunen M, Manttari M, Manninen M et al. Antibodies against Ox-LDL predicting myocardial infarction. Arch Intern Med 1994;154:2605–09.

24. Salonen JT, Yla Herttuala S, Yamamoto R et al. Auto-antibodies to Ox-LDL and progression of carotid atherosclerosis. Lancet 1992;339:883–7.

25. Holvoet P, Perez G, Zhao Z et al. MDA-LDL in patients with atherosclerotic disease. J Clin Invest 1995;95:2611–9.

26. Holvoet P, Vanhaecke J, Janssens S et al. Ox-LDL and MDA-LDL in patients with acute coronary syndromes and stable CAD. Circ 1998;98:1487–94.

27. Itabe H, Yamamoto H, Imanaka T, Shimamura K, Uchiyama H, Kimura J, Sanaka T, Hata Y, Takano T. Sensitive detection of oxidatively modified low-density lipoprotein using a monoclonal antibody. J Lipid Research 1996;37:45–53.

28. Kneepkens CMF, Lepage G, and Roy CC. The potential of the hydrocarbon breath test as a measure of lipid peroxidation. Free Rad Biol Med 1994;17:1271–60.

29. Sohal RS, Muller A, Koletzko B, Sies H. Effect of age and ambient temperature on pentane production in adult housefly. Mech Aging Develop 1985;29:317–26.

30. Schwarz KB, Cox JM, Sharma S et al. Elevation of breath ethane in pregnant women who smoke. Pediatr Res 1993;33:310a.

31. Zarling EJ and Clapper M. Technique for gas chromatograhic measurement of volatile alkanes from single breath samples. Clin Chem 1987;33:140–1.

32. Lemoyne M, Van Gossum A, Kurian R et al. Breath pentane analysis as an index of lipid peroxidation. Am J Clin Nutr 1987;46:267–72.

33. Springfield JR and Levitt MD. Pitfalls in the use of breath pentane measurements to assess lipid peroxidation. J Lipid Res 1994;35:1497–1504.

34. Rice-Evans C, Miller NJ. Total antioxidant status in plasma and body fluids. Meth Enzymol 1994;234:279–93.

35. Wayner DDM, Burton GW, Ingold KU, Barclay LRC, Locke SJ. The relative contribution of vitamin E, urate, asorbate, and proteins to TRAP in human blood plasma. Biochim Biophys Acta 1987;924:408–19.

36. Miller NJ, Rice-Evans C, Davies MJ, Gopinathan V, Milner A. A novel method for measuring antioxidant capacity and its application for monitoring the antioxidant status in premature neonates. Clin Sci 1993;84:407–12.

37. Cao, G, Prior R.L. Measurement of oxygen radical absorbance capacity in biological samples. Methods in Enzymol 1999;299: 50–62.

38. Serafini M, Maiani G, Ferro-Luzzi A. Alcohol-free red wine enhances plasma antioxidant capacity in humans J Nutr 1998;128:1003–7.

39. Swain T, Hillis WE. Estimation of total phenols. J Sci Food Agric 1959;10:63–68.

40. Woodford FP, Whitehad TP. Is measuring serum antioxidant capacity clinically useful? Ann Clin Biochem 1998;35:48–56.

41. Brigelius R, Lenzen R, Sies H. Increase in hepatic mixed disulphides and glutathione disulphide elicited by paraquat. Biochem Pharmacol 1982;31:1637–41.

42. Ellman GL. Tissue sulphydryl groups. Arch Biochim Biophys 1984;235:334–42.

43. Tietze F. Enzymatic method for quantitative determination of nanogram amounts of total and oxidized glutathione. Anal Biochem 1969;27:502–22.

44. Reed DJ, Babson JR, Beatty BW, Brodie AE, Ellis WW, Potter DW. HPLC analyses of nanogram levels of glutathione, disulphide, and mixed disulphides. Anal Biochem 1980;106:55–62.

45. Esterbauer H, Dieber Rotheneder H, Waeg G, Puhl H, Tatzber F. Endogenous antioxidants and LDL oxidation. Biochem Soc Transac 1990;18:1059–61.

46. Gey, KF, Puska, P, Jordon, P, and Moser U. Inverse correlation between vitamin E and mortality from ischemic heart disease in cross-cultural epidemiology. Am J Clin Nutr 1992;53:326–30.

47. Riemersma RA, Wood DA, MacIntyre CCA, Elton RA, Gey KF, and Oliver MF. Risk of angina pectoris and plasma concentrations of vitamins A, C, and E, and carotene. Lancet 1997;37:1–4.

48. Rimm, EB, Stampfer M., Ascherio A, Giovannucci E, Colditz GA, and Willett WC. Vitamin E consumption and the risk of coronary heart disease in men. N. Engl J Med 1993;328:1450–54.

49. Losonczy KG, Harris TB, HavlikRJ. Vitamin E and C supplement use and risk of all-cause and coronary heart disease mortality in older persons: the established populations for Epidemiologic Studies of the Elderly. Am J Clin Nutr 1996;64:190–4.

50. Hodis HN, Mack WJ, LaBree L et al. Serial coronary angiographic evidence that antioxidant vitamin intake reduces progression of coronary artery atherosclerosis. JAMA 1995;273:1849–53.

51. Stephens MG, Parsons A, Schofield PM, Kelly F, Cheeseman K, Mitchinson MJ, Brown MJ. Randomized controlled trial of vitamin E in patients with coronary disease: Cambridge Heart Antioxidant Study (CHAOS). Lancet 1996;347:781–6.

52. Verlangieri AJ, Buxh MJ. Effect of d-AT supplementation on experimentally induced primate atherosclerosis. J Am Coll Nutr 1992;11:131–8.

53. Williams RJ, Motteram JM, Sharp CH, Gallagher PJ. Dietary AT and attenuation of early lesion development in modified Watanabe rabbits. Atheroscler 1992;94:153–9.

54. Jialal I, Fuller CJ, Huet BA. The effect of alpha-tocopherol supplementation on LDL oxidation: a dose-response study. Arterioscler Thromb Vasc Biol 1995;15:90–7.

55. Devaraj S, Huet BA, Fuller CJ, Jialal I. A dose-response comparison of RRR-AT and all rac AT on LDL oxidation Arterioscler Thromb Vasc Biol 1997;17:2273–9.

56. Belcher JD, Balla J, Balla G, Jacobs DR, Gross M, Jacobs HS, Vercellotti GM. Vitamin E, LDL, and endothelium: brief oral supplementation prevents oxidized LDL-mediated vascular injury *in vitro*. Arterioscler Thromb 1993;13:1779–89.

57. Devaraj S, Jialal I. The effect of AT on crucial cells in atherogenesis. Curr Opin Lipidol 1998;9:11–5.

58. Green D, O' Driscoll G, Rankin JM, Maiorana AJ, Taylor RR. Beneficial effects of AT administration on NO function in subjects with hypercholesterolemia. Clin Sci 1998; 95:361–7.

59. Heitzer T, Yla Herttuala S, Wild E, Luoma J, Drexler H. Effect of AT on endothelial vasodilator function in patients with hypercholesterolemia, chronic smoking, or both. J Amer Coll Cardiol 1999;33:499–505.

60. Devaraj S, Li D, Jialal I. The effects of alpha tocopherol supplementation on monocyte function: decreased lipid oxidation, IL-1b secretion, and monocyte adhesion to endothelium. J Clin Invest 1996;98:756–61.

61. Islam KN, Devaraj S, Jialal I. Alpha-tocopherol enrichment of monocytes decreases agonist-induced adhesion to human endothelial cells. Circulation 1998;98:2255–61.

62. Devaraj S, Jialal I. AT decreases IL-1b release from activated human monocytes by inhibition of 5-lipoxygenase. Arterio Thromb Vasc Biol 1999;19:1125–33.

63. Thurnham DI, Davies JA, Crump BJ, Situnayake RD, Davis M. The use of different lipids to express serum tocopherol. Ann Clin Biochem 1986;23:514–20.

64. Burton GW, Ingold KU. An unusual type of lipid antioxidant. Science 1984;224:569–73.

65. Jialal I, Fuller CJ. The effect of vitamin E, vitamin C, and beta-carotene on LDL oxidation and atherosclerosis. Can J Cardiol 1995;11(Suppl):97G–103G.

66. Packer JE, Slater TF, Wilson RL. Direct observation of a free radical interaction between vitamin C and vitamin E. Nature 1979;278:737–8.

67. Dubick M, Hunter G, Casey S, Keen C. Aortic ascorbic acid, trace elements, and SOD activity in human aneurysmal and occlusive diseases. Proc Soc Expt Biol 1987;84: 138–143.

68. Stankova L, Riddle M, Larned J, Burry K, Menashe D et al. Plasma ascorbate concentrations and blood cell dehydroascorbate transport in patients with diabetes mellitus. Metabolism 1984;33:347–53.

69. Chow CK, Thacker RR, Changchit C, Bridges RB, Rehm SR, Humble J, Turbok J. Lower levels of vitamin C and carotenoids in plasma of cigarette smokers. J Am Coll Nutr 1986;3:305–12.

70. Ramirez J, Flowers N. Leukocyte ascorbic acid and its relationship to coronary artery disease in man. Am J Clin Nutr 1980;33:2079–87.

71. Jialal I, Vega GL, Grundy SM. Physiologic levels of ascorbic acid inhibit the oxidative modification of LDL. Atherosclerosis 1990;82:185–91.

72. Frei B. Ascorbic acid protects lipids in human plasma and LDL against oxidative modification. Am J Clin Nutr 1991;54:1113–8S.

73. Harats D, Ben Naim M, Debach Y, Hollander G, Havivi E et al. Effect of vitamin C and E supplementation on susceptibility of plasma lipoproteins to oxidation induced by acute smoking. Atheroscler 1990;85:47–54.

74. Sauberlich H, Goad WC, Skala H, Waring PP. Procedure for mechanized measurement of vitamin C. Clin Chem 1976;22:105–10.

75. Cammack J, Oke A, Adams RN. Simultaneous HPLC measurement of ascorbate and dehydroascorbate. J Chromatogr 1991;565:529–32.

76. Swartz HM, Swartz SM. Biochemical and biophysical applications of ESR. In: Methods of biochemical analysis 1985;29:207–323.

77. Heinecke JW. Oxidants and antioxidants in the pathogenesis of atherosclerosis: implications for the oxidized LDL hypothesis. Atherosclerosis 1998;141:1–15.

78. Heinecke JW. Mechansims of oxidative damage of LDL in human atherosclerosis. Curr Opin Lipidol 1997;8:268–74.

79. Leuwenburgh C, Rasmussen JE, Hsu FF, Mueller DM, Pennathur S, Heinecke JW. MS-quantification of protein oxidation by tyrosyl radical, copper, and hydroxyl radical in LDL isolated from human atherosclerotic plaques. J Biol Chem 1997;272:3250–6.

80. Beckman JS, Ye YZ, Anderson PG, Chen J, Accavitti MA, Tarpey MM, White CR. Exten-

sive nitration of protein tyrosines in human atherosclerosis detected by immuno-histochemistry. Biol Chem Hoppe Seyler 1994;375:81–7.

81. Beckman JS, Chen J, Ischiropoulos H, Crow JP. Oxidative chemistry of peroxynitrite. Meth Enzymol 1994;233:229–58.

82. Stadtman ER, Oliver CN. Metal-catalyzed oxidation of protein-physiological conse-quences. J Biol Chem 1991;266:2005–8.

83. Levine RL, Garland D, Oliver C, Amici AA, Climent I, Lenz AG et al. Determination of carbonyl content in oxidatively modified proteins. Meth Enzymol 1990;186:464–8.

84. Reznick AZ, Cross CE, Hu ML, Suzuki YJ, Khwaja S, Safadi A et al. Modification of plasma proteins by cigarette smoke as measured by protein carbonyl formation. Biochem J 1992;286:607–11.

85. Marangon K, Devaraj S, Jialal I. Measurement of protein carbonyls in plasma of smok-ers and in Ox-LDL by an ELISA. Clin Chem 1999;45:577–8.

Determination and Clinical Significance of Lipoprotein Lipase and Hepatic Lipase

22

Thomas Olivecrona and Gunilla Olivecrona

✧ Lipoprotein lipase (LPL) and hepatic triglyceride lipase (HTGL) are related enzymes that carry out the quantitatively major steps in lipoprotein metabolism. The delipidation process is illustrated in Figure 22–1. Note that HTGL can also hydrolyze phospholipids. LPL hydrolyzes triglycerides (TG) carried in chylomicrons and VLDL. This occurs at "binding-lipolysis sites" on the vascular endothelium, where the enzyme is anchored to heparan sulfate proteoglycans. The reaction releases fatty acids for use in cellular metabolic reactions and transforms the TG-rich primary lipoproteins into cholesterol-rich remnant lipoproteins. This process is completed within a timeframe of a few minutes to a few hours after the lipoproteins have entered circulation. Some of the remnants are rapidly removed from the circulation by receptor-mediated endocytosis, but some are transformed into low-density lipoproteins (LDL) and high-density lipoproteins (HDL).

The role of HTGL remains somewhat enigmatic. Studies on lipoprotein kinetics in patients with HTGL deficiency[1] and studies on the effects of addition of purified HTGL to plasma[2] indicate that the enzyme acts on HDL and LDL and that it may be involved in the terminal stages of delipidation of chylomicron and VLDL remnants.

LPL action can be viewed as the general reaction in lipoprotein metabolism. In accord with this, LPL activity is high in most species. Table 22–1 shows the lipase activities in post-heparin plasma of man, rat, dog, guinea pig, and calf. Heparin (100 IU/kg b.w., about 0.65 mg) was injected intravenously, and a plasma sample was taken 10 or 15 min later. HTGL was assayed using a gum arabic-stabilized TG emulsion in the presence of 1 mol/L NaCl to suppress LPL activity. LPL was assayed with a phosphatidylcholine-stabilized TG emulsion using rat serum as source of activator. To assay LPL activity in human and rat plasma, HTGL was suppressed by immunoinhibition using anti-HTGL serum. For dog, guinea pig, and calf plasma, LPL activity represents the difference in activity between samples treated with anti-LPL antibody and control serum.

HTGL acts upon the remnants formed by LPL for degradation or remodeling (see Figure 22–1). Its activity varies widely among species (Table 22–1). It is high in humans and in rats, moderately high in dogs, low in guinea pigs and virtually non-existent in calves, fishes, and birds.[3] Similar observations have been made for other factors involved in remodeling and metabolism of the cholesterol-rich lipoproteins. For instance, lipid transfer activity in plasma differs widely among species.[4] The con-

Figure 22–1 ✦ Delipidation of Triglyceride-Rich Lipoproteins by the Lipases

A. Exogenous pathway.   B. Endogenous pathway.

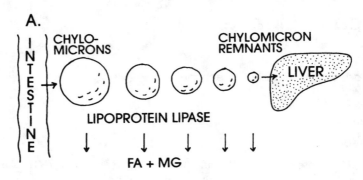

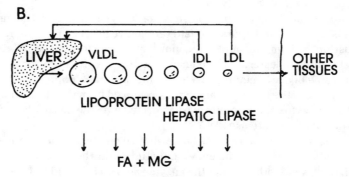

Source: Olivecrona and Bengtsson-Olivecrona[5]

Table 22–1 ✦ Lipase Activities in Post-Heparin Plasma of Some Species (values in mU/mL)		
	LPL	*HTGL*
Man	350	370
Rat	440	700
Dog	630	170
Guinea pig	790	70
Calf	530	< 5

centrations of LDL cholesterol (LDL-C) and HDL cholesterol (HDL-C) in plasma also vary widely: LDL-C and HDL-C are both relatively high in humans; dogs have low LDL-C but high HDL-C; and guinea pigs have high LDL-C and low HDL-C. There is apparently considerable latitude in how animals handle the metabolism of remnant particles and of LDL-C and HDL-C, and consequently in their need for HTGL activity. In contrast, the LPL reaction is indispensable.

There are many excellent reviews to which the reader is referred for information on the molecular structure, kinetic properties, physiological regulation, and postulated pathophysiological roles of the two lipases.[5–9] In this chapter we refer only to studies directly relevant to the measurement and clinical relevance of the lipases. Several recent reviews and handbook chapters on assay methods for the lipases are available.[10–14]

PROPERTIES OF LPL AND HTGL

LPL is present in most extra-hepatic tissues. The enzyme is synthesized in parenchymal cells, transferred to the vascular endothelium, and anchored to heparan sulfate proteoglycans. The enzyme can move along the endothelium by jumping from one binding site to the next, and may perhaps move to other tissues with blood. Removal and degradation in the liver conclude its life cycle. This process is illustrated in Figure 22–2.

The enzyme requires apolipoprotein (apo) C-II for activity. It is strongly inhibited by fatty acids, which has been suggested to be a mechanism for feedback control of the enzyme activity. The main substrates for LPL are TG in chylomicrons and VLDL. LPL is regulated in a tissue-specific manner, mainly by factors that relate to energy metabolism.

HTGL is present in the liver, in the adrenal cortex, and in ovaries, but it is absent in most other tissues. In contrast to LPL, it does not require apo C-II and acts on smaller, denser lipoproteins such as chylomicron remnants, intermediate-density lipoproteins (IDL), LDL, and HDL. Steroid and other hormones regulate HTGL activity.

Non-Catalytic Functions

LPL enhances binding of lipoproteins to cells. This enhancement can be substantial, several hundred-fold, and involves at least two separate mechanisms.

In one mechanism, LPL binds to cell surface heparan sulfate and to the lipoprotein particle.[15] This is of obvious physiological importance for the transient binding of chylomicrons and VLDL to "binding-lipolysis sites" at the endothelium. However, this bridging can also be demonstrated for LDL and HDL with a large variety of cells as well as the intercellular matrix.[15] The physiological and/or pathophysiological importance of this mechanism is not yet established, but some authors ascribe to it an important role in atherogenesis.[7]

In the other mechanism, LPL binds to a group of cell surface receptors in the LDL-receptor family.[16] Most studied is the binding of LPL to the LDL receptor-related protein (LRP). This mechanism is believed to play an important role in the catabolism of remnant lipoproteins.

Figure 22–2 ✧ Transport of LPL in Blood

The enzyme is produced in parenchymal cells, illustrated here by an adipocyte on the right. It is released from these cells and transferred to the binding sites at the nearby vascular endothelium. From here, LPL can dissociate into the circulating blood and bind to endothelial sites in other tissues, as illustrated in the left part of the figure. Avid uptake by the liver keeps the blood concentration of LPL low.

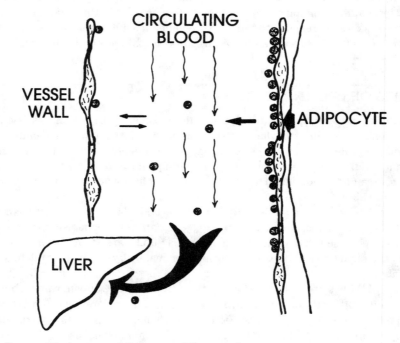

Source: Olivecrona and Bengtsson-Olivecrona[5]

LPL in Adipose Tissue

Some of the fatty acids generated by LPL action are directly taken up into the subjacent tissue, but some are released back into blood as albumin-bound free fatty acids (FFA).[17] This split must reflect a balance between LPL-mediated lipolysis and metabolic processes in the cells. In the fed state, fatty acids from chylomicrons are taken up and stored in adipose tissue much more efficiently than albumin-bound FFA.[18,19] In this sense, LPL directs fatty acids to the adipose tissue. For fatty acid storage to occur, other signals must make the tissue ready to esterify the fatty acids into TG.[17,20] The regulation of these processes, which are obviously central to regulation of energy metabolism and to the size of adipose tissue, has generated much interest.

LPL activity in adipose tissue is regulated by several mechanisms acting at different levels. For example, there is long-term regulation of LPL mRNA by hormones such as insulin[21] and cortisol.[22] There are differences between adipose tissue localities, and these have been suggested to be affected by sex steroid hormones, perhaps contributing to the male and female patterns of obesity.

Two mechanisms for short-term regulation have been described. There is a protein in adipocytes that binds specifically to the 3'-untranslated region of LPL mRNA and prevents its translation into protein.[23] This process is triggered by adrenergic stimulation. Another mechanism affects the maturation of LPL. The default pathway, which operates in other tissues and in adipose tissue in the fed state, processes the enzyme into its active form. During fasting, however, a mechanism in the adipose tissue is switched on. This channels the enzyme into an inactive form, which is then degraded.[24]

LPL as a Possible Rate-Limiter for the Turnover of Triglyceride-Rich Lipoproteins

TG clearance is usually a very efficient process. Results from studies using oral fat loads imply that most individuals can easily transport 10 g TG per hour. This is more than enough to cover resting energy expenditure and about 100 times the LDL-C transport rates. The question arises whether LPL activity sets the upper limit for the transport rate. As a first approximation one could use post-heparin LPL activity as a measure of LPL available at endothelial sites. A recent study showed an activity of 483 $\pm$ 180 mU/mL for a group of middle-aged, healthy, normolipidemic men.[25] This assay was performed with a phospholipid-stabilized TG emulsion at 25°C and pH 8.5. The activity would be higher at 37°C but lower at pH 7.4; these factors roughly equal out. (The activity is somewhat higher with rat chylomicrons than with the synthetic emulsion. Nonetheless, the value should give an estimate of the capacity for TG hydrolysis *in vivo*.)

The enzyme splits two ester bonds for each TG molecule. Therefore, the activity corresponds to clearing roughly 250 nmol TG per mL and min, or about 40 g of TG per hour. The concentrations of TG-rich lipoproteins in normal plasma are well above the K_m values measured *in vitro*. Hence, if the particles had free access to the lipase, the system would operate at a rate much above that observed for TG transport. Perhaps the most direct evidence for this is that plasma TG levels quickly drop after heparin injection. This demonstrates that the limiting factor is not the amount of lipase but its access to the lipoprotein particles.[26] Lipoproteins spend most of their time in the circulating blood where there is little or no LPL; lipase action requires that the particles bind to the endothelium. In most cases, this "margination" of lipoproteins to endothelial sites may be the limiting factor. Whether it is related to the amount of LPL available at the sites is presently not known.

LPL Deficiency

More than 40 mutations in LPL that result in inactive enzyme have been described.[27] Some are major rearrangements of the gene, but most are point mutations.

Homozygotes or compound heterozygotes develop massive hypertriglyceridemia. This illustrates that the LPL reaction is necessary for normal clearance of

TG-rich lipoproteins. Predictably, patients have low levels of LDL-C and HDL-C. Other clinical signs include eruptive xanthomas and lipemia retinalis. The major pathology is related to recurrent episodes of pancreatitis. Otherwise, patients are relatively healthy and there is no evidence that they develop premature atherosclerosis.

Heterozygotes should have half-normal LPL activity. Studies to date indicate that most of the heterozygotes have normal lipid levels, but they tend to develop hyperlipidemia when exposed to other metabolic stress situations such as obesity[28] and pregnancy.[29] Hence, half-normal LPL activity is usually compatible with relatively normal lipoprotein metabolism. Interestingly, the lipoprotein phenotype that the heterozygotes tend to develop is similar to that encountered in the so-called metabolic syndrome[30] and is quite different from the phenotype seen in homozygotes. Along the same line, in mice with targeted inactivation of the LPL gene, the heterozygotes had a mild phenotype with moderate increase of plasma TG and a decrease of HDL-C.[31] Individuals with defects in apo C-II have a similar clinical picture as those with defects in LPL.[27] Heterozygotes for apo C-II defects do not present any clinical symptoms.

HTGL Deficiency

Fewer cases of HTGL deficiency than of LPL deficiency have been described. This is probably because the phenotype is less dramatic,[32] and therefore identifying individuals for DNA sequence analysis has not been so easy.

Accessing Lipases for Measurement

LPL is present in many extra-hepatic tissues, but its main sites of action are in muscles and adipose tissue. It is, therefore, logical to measure the enzyme in these tissues if biopsies can be obtained. Theoretically, HTGL could be measured in the liver, but it is not realistic to obtain liver biopsies for this purpose.

Fortunately, there is a simpler method to sample the lipases. Heparin releases them from their tissue-binding sites in the form of enzyme-heparin complexes.[33] Therefore, post-heparin plasma provides convenient access to the lipases for clinical studies.

LPL and HTGL activity are interesting parameters in population studies[34] but generally do not yield information that is relevant to treatment strategies for individual patients. The only situation in which the clinician needs a measure of the lipases is when a deficiency state is suspected from the plasma lipoprotein profile. In general, patients with genetic deficiencies have no or very low activity in post-heparin plasma. For LPL, the differential diagnosis is to find whether the case is a deficiency of the enzyme or of its activator, apo C-II.

HTGL in Pre- and Post-Heparin Plasma

HTGL activity in plasma is low but significant. Heparin increases the activity several hundred-fold. A positive, linear correlation exists between plasma HTGL activities before and after injection of heparin.[35,36] This suggests that plasma HTGL is in equilibrium with HTGL in the liver, and that the effect of heparin is to shift the equilibrium towards soluble complexes in blood. In accord with this, a study in which human HTGL was injected in mice showed that the enzyme rapidly became bound in the liver, from which it could be released again by heparin.[37] The turnover rate for HTGL is relatively slow; the $T_{1/2}$ has been estimated to 4.6 h in rats[38] and 3 h in mice.[37] Hence, relatively small amounts would be expected to turn over during the 15–60 min that are usually studied after heparin injection. Plasma HTGL curves tend to follow the heparin concentration fairly closely.[39] HTGL remains in blood for as long as heparin remains.

Because of the strong linear correlation between HTGL activity before and after heparin injection, one could measure this enzyme in regular plasma samples. However, the activity is so low that it is at or beyond the limit of current methodologies. Since the uncertainties in measuring HTGL activity in regular plasma are so great, we recommend that it be measured in post-heparin plasma.

Clinical Significance of Post-Heparin HTGL Activity

Many studies have demonstrated an inverse relationship between HTGL activity and HDL-C levels.[40,41] Based on the observation that HTGL acts on HDL, it has been argued that high HTGL activity leads to a generally enhanced catabolism of the particles.[40] Alternatively, it has been suggested that the major impact of high HTGL activity is to enhance hydrolysis of TG transferred into the particles with cholesteryl ester transfer protein (CETP), and hence drive depletion of HDL core lipids through exchange with TG-rich lipoproteins.[42–44]

LPL Activity in Pre- and Post-Heparin Plasma

As with HTGL, the level of LPL activity in plasma is very low.[25] The origin and fate of plasma LPL is more complex than for HTGL. LPL is produced in extra-hepatic tissues, taken up from blood, and degraded in the liver. The concentration of LPL in plasma does not reflect an equilibrium situation but represents a continuous flow of lipase molecules.[7] The processes involved are likely influenced by a number of physiological parameters. Although one early study claimed a correlation between LPL activity in pre- and post-heparin plasma,[36] most studies have not supported this finding.[25,45] It is now clear that LPL activity in pre- and post-heparin plasma are two separate parameters, the more useful of which is the activity in post-heparin plasma. The activity in pre-heparin plasma is difficult to measure with precision, and its clinical significance has not been established.

LPL is thought to be anchored to vessel walls by interaction with heparan sulphate proteoglycans on endothelial cells. An additional 116,000-dalton protein may be involved in the binding.[46] The enzyme at the endothelium is often referred to as "functional LPL" because it can act on lipoproteins, in contrast to LPL located within cells or in transit to the endothelium.

Studies with perfused rat hearts have led to the concept that heparin-releasable LPL is equal to functional LPL. Borensztajn and Robinson reported that when rat hearts are perfused and heparin is added to the medium, a burst of LPL activity occurs during the first two minutes.[47] It is reasonable to assume that this is the enzyme that was directly exposed at the endothelium. If the perfusion continues, the enzyme continues to be released, but at a much lower level.[48] Hence, heparin can recruit LPL from sites not immediately exposed to blood. This may represent the pool of LPL located along cell surfaces in the tissue, as shown by electron microscopic immunostaining,[49] and perhaps LPL recycling in the endothelial cells.[50] Translating this mechanism to the whole animal, we might expect to see a quick rise of LPL activity after heparin injection, followed by a continued rise. This is exactly what one sees in animals in which the liver has been excluded from the circulation.[51] In an intact animal, the situation is more complex: The liver extracts LPL even in the presence of heparin,[52] so that post-heparin LPL soon reaches a plateau. This value does not represent all the LPL that was exposed at endothelial sites, but a balance between release from peripheral tissues and extraction in liver.

Heparin is a polydisperse mixture of molecules varying in length and degree of sulfation. We have recently compared the effects of size-fractionated heparins on LPL.[26,39] Shorter heparins were quite effective in releasing the enzyme from peripheral tissues, but were relatively less efficient in retarding the uptake of the enzyme by the liver. Hence, plasma LPL activity fell off more rapidly after infusion of the shorter heparins. This led to a period of depletion of functional LPL, with impeded TG-clearing ability.

In conclusion, it is not clear how post-heparin LPL relates to functional LPL. The activity in a sample of post-heparin plasma underestimates functional, endothelium-bound LPL because the liver has extracted some of the released enzyme. On the other hand, heparin recruits enzyme from deeper layers in the tissue. The balance between these processes depends on the type of heparin used. In particular, low-molecular-weight heparin preparations yield different results compared to regular heparin.

Clinical Significance of Pre- and Post-Heparin LPL Activity

Post-heparin LPL activity varies a great deal among individuals. A three-fold range of activities is not unusual in a population sample.[25,34] If LPL activity were the major determinant for catabolism of TG-rich lipoproteins, one would expect a strong association between measures of LPL activity and plasma TG. However, this relationship was found to be weak or non-significant in most studies.[14,25,45,53–56] Taskinen et al. found a strong correlation between postprandial TG and post-heparin LPL activity in normal individuals.[57] In men with non-insulin-dependent diabetes mellitus (NIDDM), the relationship was weaker and not statistically significant, and in men with NIDDM and coronary artery disease no relationship was found. Likewise, Tornvall et al. found a rather strong inverse correlation between fasting plasma TG and post-heparin LPL activity in normal men, but no relation in young survivors of myocardial infarction.[25] These results reinforce the hypothesis that metabolic factors can override LPL activity as the rate-limiting factor in TG lipolysis.

Increases of LPL activity by several mechanisms have been found to lower plasma TG, improving capacity to handle lipid loads, and increasing HDL-C levels. This is true in transgenic mice that over-express LPL;[58–60] in rats treated with a novel drug, NO-1886,[61] which increases tissue LPL mRNA and activity; and in humans treated with fenofibrate.[62]

In the general population, the parameter that correlates most consistently with LPL activity has been HDL-C, particularly HDL_2-C.[41,63,64] The molecular mechanisms behind this relation have been discussed extensively.[4,41–43] One line of thought is based on the fact that surface components transfer from TG-rich lipoproteins to HDL as a result of LPL-mediated hydrolysis of core TG. Hence, efficient delipidation, as opposed to early receptor-mediated particle removal, would channel more phospholipids, cholesterol, and apolipoproteins to HDL. Another line of thought stresses the role of CETP, which catalyzes homo- and hetero-exchange of cholesteryl esters and TG between lipoproteins. Increased levels of TG-rich lipoproteins (basal or postprandial) would cause increased flow of cholesteryl esters from LDL and HDL into the TG-rich lipoproteins. On the other hand, TG transferred to LDL and HDL would be susceptible to hydrolysis by HTGL. The result would be a preponderance of small HDL (HDL_3), and small LDL (pattern B). Recent studies, in fact, have demonstrated an association between LPL activity and small, dense LDL.[54,65]

LPL Mass in Pre- and Post-Heparin Plasma

There is more LPL protein mass in plasma than corresponds to the active enzyme.[25,66] LPL mass can be separated into two fractions by chromatography on heparin-agarose. One fraction corresponds to a small amount of active lipase. The other fraction is a larger amount of catalytically inactive lipase protein, probably in monomeric form.[66] The origin and turnover of this inactive lipase is not clear. Heparin increases the level only about two-fold, most of it bound to lipoproteins, predominantly to LDL in fasting plasma.[67] The amount corresponds to about one lipase monomer for each 500 to 1000 apo B molecules. Model experiments have shown that monomeric LPL bound to lipoproteins enhances their interaction with heparan sulphate but does not mediate binding to LRP. The monomer has much lower affinity for heparin/heparan sulphate than the dimer.

LPL mass is readily measured by an ELISA.[14,67] The clinical significance of this measure has not been established. Much research remains before we understand the physiology of this inactive mass. One study found a strong correlation between this measure and the level of HDL cholesterol in myocardial infarct survivors.[25,41]

LPL activity and mass in post-heparin plasma correlate rather closely.[14,25] This suggests that LPL released by heparin is almost exclusively the active species. These relationships are illustrated in Figure 22–3, which shows separation of pre- and post-heparin plasma on heparin-agarose. In post-heparin plasma, peaks of lipase activity and mass coincided at around 0.9 mol/L NaCl in the gradient. There was also an earlier peak of inactive lipase that eluted around 0.5 mol/L NaCl. In pre-heparin plasma only the inactive peak was observed, since the amount of active lipase in pre-heparin plasma after distribution into the chromatography fractions is below the limit of detection in the assays. In this experiment, the ratio between the mass of active LPL and the mass of inactive LPL in post-heparin plasma was 3.6. Though the lipase activity in plasma increased 325-fold after heparin, the inactive LPL mass increased only two-fold. In analysis of post-heparin plasma from six individuals, the ratio between the active peak and the inactive peak was 2.9 ± 0.5. The inactive LPL peak increased 3.0 ± 0.4-fold after heparin infusion.

Figure 22-3 ✧ Separation of Active and Inactive Forms of LPL in Plasma by Chromatography on Heparin-Agarose

Ten mL of plasma were loaded on a small column of heparin-agarose and eluted using a gradient of NaCl. LPL mass was determined by ELISA.

○ LPL mass in pre-heparin plasma

● LPL mass in plasma obtained 10 minutes after i.v. injection of 100 IU heparin/kg body weight

◆ LPL activity in post-heparin plasma.

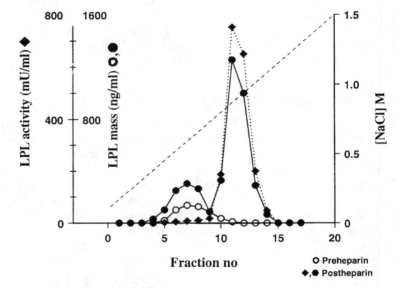

Source: Olivecrona et al.[66]

DESCRIPTION AND DISCUSSION OF CURRENT METHODS

Different assay procedures result in widely varying values for lipase activities. For instance, Taskinen[68] surveyed the literature and found that values reported for LPL in post-heparin plasma from normal individuals differed about ten-fold between laboratories. The difference for adipose tissue LPL was even greater, at 6–110 mU/g.

We recommend that the clinical laboratory measure LPL and HTGL activities in post-heparin plasma as the first choice. For studies on patients suspected to be deficient in either LPL or HTGL, we recommend that the samples be shipped to a laboratory experienced in this methodology. For this purpose, post-heparin plasma can be frozen. For research projects, it is often more appropriate to study LPL in tissue extracts; one single method cannot be recommended (see discussion below). We refer readers to the literature for conditions suitable for the particular project.

The two main approaches to estimating tissue LPL activity are to measure total activity and/or heparin-releasable activity. The latter is assumed to be the sum of endothelial LPL and some intracellular LPL that has been secreted during the extraction, balanced by inactivation/degradation in the medium. The most efficient extraction/solubilization of total tissue LPL is obtained with detergent-containing buffers. A further advantage is that LPL is usually stable for hours at 4°C in these buffers.

Several different detergent cocktails have been described. Most of these contain protease inhibitors. For this we use

✧ one pill of protease inhibitors (CompleteMini®Boehringer no. 1836153) per 50 mL of buffer or the following concentrations (per L) of individual inhibitors:

  ✧ 10 mg leupeptin (Boehringer),

  ✧ 1 mg pepstatin (both from the Peptide Institute, Osaka, Japan), and

  ✧ 25 KIU Trasylol (Sigma).

✧ Stock solutions of leupeptin and pepstatin (1 mg/mL) are made in ethanol (95%). A suitable buffer composition is:

  ✧ 25 mmol/L ammonia adjusted with HCl to pH 8.2 containing 5 mmol/L EDTA and, per mL,

   ✧ 10 mg Triton X-100,

   ✧ 1 mg SDS (higher proportions of SDS will denature LPL), and

   ✧ 5 IU heparin.

This buffer is suitable also for immunoassay and immunoprecipitation. It is excellent for diluting purified LPL, and therefore for assay purposes. LPL solubilized as described above can bind to heparin-agarose, but for this purpose heparin should be omitted from the buffer. Whenever the protein concentrations of the extracts are low, increased recovery and stability are obtained if bovine serum albumin (1 mg/mL) is included in the buffer. The heparin-detergent buffer also works well for extracting of HTGL from liver and steroid-producing glands.

Substrate Emulsions

The substrates commonly used for measurement of LPL and HTGL are long-chain TG emulsified with phospholipids or other surface-active components (e.g., gum arabic). For LPL, the reaction rates with synthetic emulsions are comparable to those obtained with VLDL or chylomicrons. For convenience, and to increase assay sensitivity, labeled TG (^{3}H or ^{14}C in the fatty acid moiety) are often used. Triolein is preferable to saturated TG (e.g., tripalmitin), since it is melted at assay temperatures, and is preferable to more unsaturated TG (e.g., trilinolein) because it is less prone to oxidative damage.

Emulsions stabilized by gum arabic are recommended for assaying HTGL and can also be used for measuring LPL. This emulsion is prone to absorption of non-specific proteins (e.g., from tissue homogenates), which may inhibit lipase activity by covering the oil-water interface. With LPL, the basal activity (in the absence of apo C-II or serum) is high. The stimulation by apo C-II is consequently less (1.5- to 2.5-fold) than with other types of emulsions.

To prepare such an emulsion, perform the following actions.

❖ Mix 25 mg unlabeled triolein (e.g., from a heptane solution containing 25 mg/mL) with ^{3}H-labeled triolein (~50 × 10^6 d.p.m.) in a round-bottomed, 30-mm diameter glass vessel suitable for sonication.

❖ Evaporate solvent under N_2 at room temperature.

❖ Add 1 mL 10 % (w/v) gum arabic in water (Sigma). (Gum arabic takes some time to dissolve with magnetic stirring.)

❖ Add 1.25 mL 1 mol/L Tris-HC1 buffer pH 8.5 and 2 mL water.

❖ Chill the vessel in ice water and sonicate for 10 min in a 50%-pulsed mode (Soniprep 150, MSE, Crawley, Sussex, UK) with a 9.5 mm diameter flat-tipped probe at medium setting placed a few mm below the surface of the liquid. (It is important to standardize conditions of vessel geometry, volume, tip placement, energy, and time.)

❖ Inspect the emulsion. If oil droplets float on the surface, sonication is insufficient. Try other settings.

The emulsion is now ready to be mixed with other constituents of the incubation medium. Use this emulsion on the same day it is prepared.

Corey and Zilversmit[69] pointed to the possibility of dispersing TG in glycerol with phospholipids as stabilizers. Nilsson-Ehle and Schotz[70] used this idea to develop a stable stock emulsion for assay of LPL. This convenient method is now widely used.

In our laboratory, the most reproducible measurements of LPL are obtained with the commercial emulsion Intralipid® and manual titration of the released fatty acids. The sensitivity in such assays is too low for many applications, however. Yet this can be overcome by incorporating labeled TG into Intralipid by sonication. The activities obtained by quantitating the release of labeled fatty acids are comparable to those obtained by titration. This indicates that the labeled triolein mixes well with the lipids in the Intralipid solution. The sonicated emulsion is stable for about 2 wks. Intralipid 10% is an emulsion of soya bean TG in egg yolk phosphatidyl choline used for parenteral nutrition. It contains 100 g TG and 12 g phospholipid per liter. Presumably, other lipid emulsions for parental nutrition can be used.

To incorporate the labeled lipid, perform the following actions:

❖ Evaporate labeled triolein (~10^6 d.p.m.) under N_2 on the walls of a round-bottomed, 30-mm diameter glass vessel suitable for sonication.

❖ Add 5 mL Intralipid (10%, Fresenius-Kabi, Stockholm, Sweden).

❖ Chill the vessel in ice water and sonicate for 10 min in a 50%-pulsed mode (MSE Soniprep 150 at medium setting with a flat tip 9.5 mm probe placed a few mm below the surface of the liquid).

❖ It is important to standardize conditions of vessel geometry, volume, tip placement, energy, and time. After sonication, the emulsion is less stable, but can be stored at 4°C for 1–2 wks without changing substrate properties.

The reactions involved in lipase assays are complex. TG are sequentially hydrolyzed to diglycerides, monoglycerides, and free glycerol. The action on each of these intermediary products differs, due to properties of the enzyme's active site (low activity against 2-monoglycerides but high activity against 1,3-monoglycerides) and also because of the different physical properties of the products. Usually the rate-limiting step is hydrolysis of the first ester bond in the TG.

Substrate Concentration

The relevant factor is the amount of lipid-water interface, not the total amount of emulsified lipid. One cannot use data on substrate requirements from the literature; one must determine this experimentally, because it depends on the physical properties of the homemade emulsion.

Albumin

Both LPL and HTGL are inhibited by fatty acids. It is therefore necessary to include albumin in the reaction mixture, to bind the fatty acids. Furthermore, albumin at concentrations of a few mg per mL is useful to prevent adsorption of the lipases to glass. The molar ratio of free fatty acids to albumin should not exceed 5:1 at any time. Incubation systems for hydrolysis of triglycerides usually contain 30–60 mg albumin per mL. For most purposes it is not necessary to use fatty acid-free albumin.

pH

The activity of both lipases is usually measured at alkaline pH (8.2–8.6) because the higher rate makes the assays more sensitive. It should be pointed out, however, that the enzymes have a relatively high activity also at physiological pH (7.4), which is approximately half of that observed at pH 8.5. Other aspects of the reaction may be sensitive to pH, such as lipid packing, lipid-protein interactions, and the rate at which partial glycerides/lysophospholipids are isomerized. Therefore, pH 7.4 is recommended for studies that explore physiological reactions, such as lipoprotein interconversions.

Temperature

An early study[71] noted that LPL-catalyzed release of fatty acids was linear with time at room temperature, but not at 37°C under the assay conditions used. This important observation has been overlooked in many subsequent studies. Unless there is a specific reason to use 37°C, such as studying lipid transitions, it is recommended that the incubation temperature be 25°C.

Buffer Composition

It is considered a characteristic of LPL, "the salt-sensitive lipase," that it is inhibited by 0.5–1 mol/L NaCl. This is due to an irreversible denaturation of the enzyme molecule and depends on a combination of the high salt concentration and a high temperature (e.g., 37°C). If this is avoided, for instance by incubating at low temperature, the enzyme can exert full catalytic activity even in the presence of 1 mol/L NaCl. For most purposes, NaCl concentrations of 0.05–0.15 result in optimal activity and stability of LPL for kinetic studies. The activity of HTGL, "the salt-resistant lipase," is not affected much by 1.0 mol/L NaCl.

Activator

With TG emulsions as substrates, the activity of LPL (but not of HTGL) is increased several-fold by apo C-II. For assay purposes, whole serum or HDL can be used to provide activation. Similar results are obtained with plasma as with serum. Due to the presence of low lipase activities, the serum should be heat-inactivated at 56°C for 30 min. Serum from most mammals, with the exception of cows and guinea pigs, can probably be used, but the most common sources are fasting humans or rats. Due to individual variation in the amounts of activator, it is recommended that the laboratory prepare a large pool of serum and test out the optimal amount to be used in the assay (usually 5%–10% v/v). The serum can be stored at −20°C for years.

Heparin

The LPL-heparin complex is more stable and soluble than the enzyme alone and is catalytically active.[33] Therefore, heparin is included in most buffers used to extract LPL from tissues and for incubation of the enzyme in kinetic studies. Plasma samples for analysis should preferentially be collected in heparinized tubes.

Selective Measurement of LPL and HTGL

There are two approaches to measuring LPL and HTGL: either to use assay conditions that favor one of the enzymes, or to use antibodies that inhibit the activity of one of them. The activity of LPL can be readily suppressed by 1 mol/L NaCl. The remaining activity, measured using the gum arabic-stabilized emulsion in the absence of serum or apo C-II, is a good measure of HTGL. Note that the mechanism of suppression of LPL is an irreversible change of conformation. For this to work, the pH should be relatively high (8.5–8.6), the temperature should be at least 25°C, and the emulsion should not contain phospholipids.

We advocate immunoinhibition of HTGL for routine assays of LPL. This is accomplished by mixing the sample with an appropriate amount of antiserum, or preferably immune IgG, and incubating for 2 h on ice. LPL in plasma or in tissue extracts in the heparin-detergent buffer does not lose appreciable activity during this time. Centrifugation before assay is not needed and does not change the results. As a control, incubate some samples after immunoinhibition under conditions used for HTGL determination. There should be little or no activity. Otherwise, one has to determine whether the immunoinhibition was incomplete (> 5% activity remaining) and/or whether LPL was fully suppressed by 1 mol/L NaCl.

Sometimes one needs to differentiate LPL from other lipases—for instance, in tissue homogenates. Some information can be obtained by testing the effects of including 1 mol/L NaCl in the assay, and/or excluding serum (apo C-II). This should suppress the LPL activity. A more direct approach is to pre-treat the enzyme source with antibodies that inhibit LPL.

For assaying LPL, we recommend the following method:

❖ Prepare a batch of assay medium that can then be stored in suitable aliquots at −20°C. The composition is 0.3 mol/L Tris with 0.2 mol/L NaCl, 0.02% (w/v) heparin and 12% (w/v) bovine serum albumin.

❖ Adjust the pH to 8.5 with HCl.

❖ Mix appropriate volumes of assay medium, heat-inactivated serum, and labeled emulsion at room temperature. This solution is stable for one day. A typical ratio of components is 10 parts assay medium, 1 part rat serum, and 1 part ³H-labeled Intralipid.

❖ Pipette 120 µL into each assay tube. The total volume should be 200 µL. Hence, a maximum of 80 µL sample can be added. For plasma and tissue homogenates, one should preferably use less than 10 µL to avoid interference by other sample components. The rest of the volume can be made up with water.

❖ Incubate the tubes at 25°C for 5 min before adding the enzyme source. Continue incubation in a shaking water bath. For longer times (1–2 h), it may be necessary to cover the tubes to prevent evaporation.

❖ Run blank incubations (without lipase) for each assay and preferably also reference sample(s).

❖ Assay samples in duplicate or triplicate.

❖ Stop the reaction after the desired time by adding solvents to extract fatty acids.[10,72]

To assay HTGL:

❖ Mix one batch of the gum arabic-stabilized emulsion with 2.5 mL each of 5 mol/L NaCl and of 10% (w/v) bovine serum albumin in water (titrated to pH 8 with NaOH, stored frozen).

❖ Add 3.25 mL water, for a total volume of 12.5 mL. Use on the same day only.

❖ Pipette 150 µL substrate into each tube.

❖ Add water and/or buffer to make 200 µL when the sample has been added.

❖ Incubate at 25°C for 5 min before the enzyme source is added.

❖ Continue as under assay for LPL.

Units

Unfortunately, several different units are used to express lipase activities. We advocate the definition of a mU as the release of 1 nmol fatty acid per minute at 25°C and pH 8.5.

Standardization of the Assay and Quality Control

Using the procedures described above, the intra-assay variation is usually ± 5%. However, due to the complex nature of the substrate, the inter-assay variation can be substantial: up to ± 25%. It is important to quantify the specific radioactivity of the substrate accurately (d.p.m. per nmol fatty acid). As a quality control, one should occasionally determine the amount of fatty acids released in some samples that have been titrated manually, and compare this to the release of fatty acids calculated from radioactivity. One should also check the efficiency of the extraction procedure for fatty acids by adding a known amount of labeled fatty acid to some samples and performing the assay procedure. It is advisable to include a reference sample in each assay and to use this to correct for between-assay variation. Whenever the reference sample activity deviates by more than 25% from the expected value, one should review the optimization of the assay.

Due to the instability of the enzymes, a good standard is hard to find. For LPL, we and others use bovine skim milk frozen in portions at –70°C. For HTGL, and for assays of LPL in human pre- or post-heparin plasma, the best reference is a batch of human post-heparin plasma stored at –70°C. Our experience is that the assay must be thoroughly and continuously controlled, since many components of the system may vary.   ⟡

REFERENCES

1. Demant T, Carlson LA, Holmquist L et al. Lipoprotein metabolism in hepatic lipase deficiency: studies on the turnover of apolipoprotein B and on the effect of hepatic lipase on high-density lipoprotein. J Lipid Res 1988;29:1603–11.
2. Clay MA, Hopkins GJ, Ehnholm C, Barter PJ. The rabbit as an animal model of hepatic lipase deficiency. Biochim Biophys Acta 1989;1002:173–81.
3. Lindberg A, Olivecrona G. Lipase evolution: Trout, *Xenopus* and chicken have lipoprotein lipase and apolipoprotein C-II-like activity but lack hepatic lipase-like activity. Biochim Biophys Acta Lipids Lipid Metab 1995;1255:205–11.
4. Barter PJ. Enzymes involved in lipid and lipoprotein metabolism. Curr Opin Lipidol 1990;1:518–23.
5. Olivecrona T, Bengtsson-Olivecrona G. Lipoprotein lipase and hepatic lipase. In: Schettler G, Habenicht AJR (eds). Handbook of experimental pharmacology. Volume 109. Principles and treatment of lipoprotein disorders. Heidelberg: Springer-Verlag, 1994;175–205.
6. Santamarina-Fojo S, Dugi KA. Structure, function and role of lipoprotein lipase in lipoprotein metabolism. Curr Opin Lipidol 1994;5:117–25.
7. Olivecrona G, Olivecrona T. Triglyceride lipases and atherosclerosis. Curr Opin Lipidol 1995;6:291–305.
8. Goldberg IJ. Lipoprotein lipase and lipolysis: Central roles in lipoprotein metabolism and atherogenesis. J Lipid Res 1996;37:693–707.
9. Bensadoun A, Berryman DE. Genetics and molecular biology of hepatic lipase. Curr Opin Lipidol 1996;7:77–81.
10. Bengtsson-Olivecrona G, Olivecrona T. Assay of lipoprotein lipase and hepatic lipase. In: Converse CA, Skinner ER (eds). Lipoprotein analysis: A practical approach. New York: Oxford University Press, 1992;169–85.
11. Vilella E, Joven J. In vitro measurement of lipoprotein and hepatic lipases. In: Ordovas JM (ed). Lipoprotein protocols. Totowa, NJ: Humana Press, 1998;243–51.
12. Briquet-Laugier V, Ben-Zeev O, Doolittle MH. Determining Lipoprotein Lipase and

Hepatic Lipase Activities Using Radio-labeled Substrates. In: Doolittle M, Reue K. (eds.). Lipase and Phospholipase Protocols. Totowa, NJ: Humana Press, 1999;81–94.

13. Holm C, Olivecrona G, Ottosson M. Assays of lipolytic enzymes. In: Ailhaud G (ed.). Adipose tissue Protocols. Volume 155, Methods in Molecular Biology. Totowa, NJ: Humana Press, 2000; (in press).

14. Taskinen M-R, Antikainen M. Measurement of enzymes in lipoprotein metabolism. In: Betteridge DJ, Illingworth DR, Shepherd J (eds.). Lipoproteins in health and disease. London: Arnold, 1999;433–43.

15. Eisenberg S, Sehayek E, Olivecrona T, Vlodavsky I. Lipoprotein lipase enhances binding of lipoproteins to heparan sulfate on cell surfaces and extracellular matrix. J Clin Invest. 1992;90:2013–21.

16. Beisiegel U. Receptors for triglyceride-rich lipoproteins and their role in lipoprotein metabolism. Curr Opin Lipidol 1995;6:117–22.

17. Frayn KN, Coppack SW, Fielding BA, Humphreys SM. Coordinated regulation of hormone-sensitive lipase and lipoprotein lipase in human adipose tissue *in vivo:* implications for the control of fat storage and fat mobilization. Advan Enzyme Regul 1995;35:163–78.

18. Bragdon JH, Gordon RS. Tissue distribution of C^{14} after the intravenous injection of labeled chylomicrons and unesterified fatty acids in the rat. J Clin Invest 1958;37:574–8.

19. Hultin M, Savonen R, Olivecrona T. Chylomicron metabolism in rats: Lipolysis, recirculation of triglyceride-derived fatty acids in plasma FFA, and fate of core lipids as analyzed by compartmental modeling. J Lipid Res 1996;37:1022–36.

20. Sniderman AD, Baldo A, Cianflone K. The potential role of acylation-stimulating protein as a determinant of plasma triglyceride clearance and intracellular triglyceride synthesis. Curr Opin Lipidol 1992;3:202–7.

21. Farese RV, Jr., Yost TJ, Eckel RH. Tissue-specific regulation of lipoprotein lipase activity by insulin/glucose in normal-weight humans. Metabolism 1991;40:214–6.

22. Ottosson M, Vikman-Adolfsson K, Enerbäck S, Olivecrona G, Björntorp P. The effects of cortisol on the regulation of lipoprotein lipase activity in human adipose tissue. J Clin Endocrinol Metab 1994;79:820–5.

23. Ranganathan G, Vu D, Kern PA. Translational regulation of lipoprotein lipase by epinephrine involves a trans-acting binding protein interacting with the 3′ untranslated region. J Biol Chem 1997;272:2515–9.

24. Bergö M, Olivecrona G, Olivecrona T. Forms of lipoprotein lipase in rat tissues: In adipose tissue the proportion of inactive lipase increases on fasting. Biochem J 1996;313:893–8.

25. Tornvall P, Olivecrona G, Karpe F, Hamsten A, Olivecrona T. Lipoprotein lipase mass and activity in plasma and their increase after heparin are separate parameters with different relations to plasma lipoproteins. Arterioscler Thromb Vasc Biol. 1995;15:1086–93.

26. Chevreuil O, Hultin M, Østergaard PB, Olivecrona T. Biphasic effects of low-molecular-weight and conventional heparins on chylomicron clearance in rats. Arterioscler Thromb 1993;13:1397–403.

27. Brunzell JD. Familial lipoprotein lipase deficiency and other causes of the chylomicronemia syndrome. In: Scriver CR, Beaudet AL, Sly WS, Valle D (eds.). Metabolic basis of inherited disease. New York: McGraw-Hill, Inc., 1995;1913–32.

28. Julien P, Vohl MC, Gaudet D, et al. Hyperinsulinemia and abdominal obesity affect the expression of hypertriglyceridemia in heterozygous familial lipoprotein lipase deficiency. Diabetes 1997;46:2063–8.

29. Hayden MR, Liu MS, Ma Y. Gene environment interaction and plasma triglyceride levels: the crucial role of lipoprotein lipase. Clin Genet 1994;46:15–8.

30. Wilson DE, Emi M, Iverius P-H, et al. Phenotypic expression of heterozygous lipoprotein lipase deficiency in the extended pedigree of a proband homozygous for a missense mutation. J Clin Invest 1990;86:735–50.

31. Coleman T, Seip RL, Gimble JM, Lee D, Maeda N, Semenkovich CF. COOH-terminal

disruption of lipoprotein lipase in mice is lethal in homozygotes, but heterozygotes have elevated triglycerides and impaired enzyme activity. J Biol Chem 1995;270: 12518–25.

32. Connelly PW, Hegele RA. Hepatic lipase deficiency. Crit Rev Clin Lab Sci 1998;35:547–72.

33. Olivecrona T, Bengtsson-Olivecrona G. Heparin and lipases. In: Lane D, Lindahl U (eds.). Heparin. London, England: Edward Arnold Publishers Ltd., 1989;335–361.

34. Henderson HE, Kastelein JJP, Zwinderman AH, et al. Lipoprotein lipase activity is decreased in a large cohort of patients with coronary artery disease and is associated with changes in lipids and lipoproteins. J Lipid Res 1999;40:735–43.

35. Karpe F, Olivecrona T, Walldius G, Hamsten A. Lipoprotein lipase in plasma after an oral fat load: relation to free fatty acids. J Lipid Res 1992;33:975–84.

36. Glaser DS, Yost TJ, Eckel RH. Preheparin lipoprotein lipolytic activities: relationship to plasma lipoproteins and postheparin lipolytic activities. J Lipid Res 1992;33:209–14.

37. Peterson J, Bengtsson-Olivecrona G, Olivecrona T. Mouse preheparin plasma contains high levels of hepatic lipase with low affinity for heparin. Biochim Biophys Acta 1986;878:65–70.

38. Schoonderwoerd K, Hülsmann WC, Jansen H. Stabilization of liver lipase in vitro by heparin or by binding to non-parenchymal liver cells. Biochim Biophys Acta 1981;665: 317–21.

39. Chevreuil O, Hultin M, Østergaard P, Olivecrona T. Heparin-decasaccharides impair the catabolism of chylomicrons. Biochem J 1996;320:437–44.

40. Taskinen M-R, Kuusi T. Enzymes involved in triglyceride hydrolysis. Baillieres Clin Endocrinol Metab 1987;1:639–66.

41. Tornvall P, Karpe F, Proudler A, et al. High-density lipoprotein: relations to metabolic parameters and severity of coronary artery disease. Metabolism: Clinical and Experimental 1996;45:1375–82.

42. Deckelbaum RJ, Olivecrona T, Eisenberg S. Plasma lipoproteins in hyperlipidemia: roles of neutral lipid exchange and lipase. In: Carlson LA, Olsson AD (eds.). Treatment of Hyperlipoproteinemia. New York: Raven Press, 1984;85–93.

43. Miesenböck G, Patsch JR. Postprandial hyperlipemia: the search for the atherogenic lipoprotein. Curr Opin Lipidol 1992;3:196–201.

44. Clay MA, Newnham HH, Barter PJ. Hepatic lipase promotes a loss of apolipoprotein A-I from triglyceride-enriched human high-density lipoproteins during incubation in vitro. Arteriosclerosis 1991;11:415–22.

45. Watson TDG, Tan C-E, McConnell M, Clegg SK, Squires LF, Packard CJ. Measurement and physiological significance of lipoprotein and hepatic lipase activities in preheparin plasma. Clin Chem 1995;41:405–12.

46. Sivaram P, Klein MG, Goldberg IJ. Identification of a heparin-releasable lipoprotein lipase-binding protein from endothelial cells. J Biol Chem 1992;267:16517–22.

47. Borensztajn J, Robinson DS. The effect of fasting on the utilization of chylomicron triglyceride fatty acids in relation to clearing factor lipase (lipoprotein lipase) releasable by heparin in the perfused rat heart. J Lipid Res 1970;11:111–7.

48. Liu G, Olivecrona T. Synthesis and transport of lipoprotein lipase in perfused guinea pig hearts. Am J Physiol 1992;263:H438–46.

49. Blanchette-Mackie EJ, Masuno H, Dwyer NK, Olivecrona T, Scow RO. Lipoprotein lipase in myocytes and capillary endothelium of heart: Immunocytochemical study. Am J Physiol 1989;256:E818–28.

50. Saxena U, Klein MG, Goldberg IJ. Transport of lipoprotein lipase across endothelial cells. Proc Natl Acad Sci U S A 1991;88:2254–8.

51. Ehnholm C, Schröder T, Kuusi T, et al. Studies on the effect of hepatectomy on pig post-heparin plasma lipases. Biochim Biophys Acta 1980;617:141–9.

52. Vilaró S, Ramírez I, Bengtsson-Olivecrona G, Olivecrona T, Llobera M. Lipoprotein lipase in liver. Release by heparin and immunocytochemical localization. Biochim Biophys Acta 1988;959:106–17.

53. Jansen H, Hop W, Van Tol A, Bruschke AVG, Birkenhäger JC. Hepatic lipase and lipo-

protein lipase are not major determinants of the low-density lipoprotein subclass pattern in human subjects with coronary heart disease. Atherosclerosis 1994;107:45–54.

54. Campos H, Dreon DM, Krauss RM. Associations of hepatic and lipoprotein lipase activities with changes in dietary composition and low-density-lipoprotein subclasses. J Lipid Res 1995;36:462–72.

55. St-Amand J, Després J-P, Lemieux S, et al. Does lipoprotein or hepatic lipase activity explain the protective lipoprotein profile of premenopausal women? Metabolism 1995;44:491–8.

56. Jeppesen J, Hollenbeck CB, Zhou M-Y, et al. Relation between insulin resistance, hyperinsulinemia, postheparin plasma lipoprotein lipase activity, and postprandial lipemia. Arterioscler Thromb Vasc Biol 1995;15:320–4.

57. Taskinen M-R. Postprandial lipemia and lipoprotein lipase. In: Woodford FP, Davignon J, Sniderman A (eds.). Atherosclerosis X. Amsterdam: Elsevier, 1995;758–62.

58. Shimada M, Ishibashi S, Gotoda T, et al. Over-expression of human lipoprotein lipase protects diabetic transgenic mice from diabetic hypertriglyceridemia and hypercholesterolemia. Arterioscler Thromb Vasc Biol 1995;15:1688–94.

59. Liu M-S, Jirik FR, LeBoeuf RC, et al. Alteration of lipid profiles in plasma of transgenic mice expressing human lipoprotein lipase. J Biol Chem 1994;269:11417–24.

60. Zsigmond E, Scheffler E, Forte TM, Potenz R, Wu W, Chan L. Transgenic mice expressing human lipoprotein lipase driven by the mouse metallothionein promoter. A phenotype associated with increased perinatal mortality and reduced plasma very-low-density lipoprotein of normal size. J Biol Chem 1994;269:18757–66.

61. Hara T, Cameron-Smith D, Cooney GJ, Kusunoki M, Tsutsumi K, Storlien LH. The actions of a novel lipoprotein lipase activator, NO-1886, in hypertriglyceridemic fructose-fed rats. Metabolism: Clinical and Experimental 1998;47:149–53.

62. Simpson HS, Williamson CM, Olivecrona T, et al. Postprandial lipemia, fenofibrate, and coronary artery disease. Atherosclerosis 1990;85:193–202.

63. Patsch JR, Prasad S, Gotto AM, Jr., Patsch W. High-density lipoprotein 2. Relationship of the plasma levels of this lipoprotein species to its composition, to the magnitude of postprandial lipemia, and to the activities of lipoprotein lipase and hepatic lipase. J Clin Invest 1987;80:341–7.

64. Kuusi T, Ehnholm C, Viikari J, et al. Postheparin plasma lipoprotein and hepatic lipase are determinants of hypo-and hyperalphalipoproteinemia. J Lipid Res 1989;30:1117–26.

65. Karpe F, Tornvall P, Olivecrona T, Steiner G, Carlson LA, Hamsten A. Composition of human low-density lipoprotein: Effects of postprandial triglyceride-rich lipoproteins, lipoprotein lipase, hepatic lipase and cholesteryl ester transfer protein. Atherosclerosis 1993;98:33–49.

66. Olivecrona G, Hultin M, Savonen R, Chevreuil O, Olivecrona T. Transport of LPL in plasma and lipoprotein metabolism. In: Woodford J, Davignon J, Sniderman A (eds.). Atherosclerosis X. Amsterdam: Elsevier, 1995;250–3.

67. Vilella E, Joven J, Fernández M, et al. Lipoprotein lipase in human plasma is mainly inactive and associated with cholesterol-rich lipoproteins. J Lipid Res 1993;34:1555–64.

68. Taskinen M-R. Lipoprotein lipase in hypertriglyceridemias. In: Borensztajn J (ed.) Lipoprotein Lipase. Chicago: Evener Publishers, 1987;201–28.

69. Corey JE, Zilversmit DB. Validation of a stable emulsion for the assay of lipoprotein lipase activity. J Lab Clin Med 1977;89:666–74.

70. Nilsson-Ehle P, Schotz MC. A stable, radioactive substrate emulsion for assay of lipoprotein lipase. J Lipid Res 1976;17:536–41.

71. Greten H, Levy RI, Fredrickson DS. A further characterization of lipoprotein lipase. Biochim Biophys Acta 1968;164:185–94.

72. Belfrage P, Vaughan M. Simple liquid-liquid partition system for isolation of labeled oleic acid from mixtures with glycerides. J Lipid Res 1969;10:341–4.

Determination and Clinical Significance of Cholesteryl Ester Transfer Protein

23

Christopher J. Fielding

❖ Cholesteryl ester transfer protein (CETP) is a 74-kda glycoprotein catalyzing the equilibration of nonpolar lipids (particularly triglyceride [TG] and cholesteryl ester [CE]) between plasma lipoprotein particles.[1,2] Genomic and cDNA base sequences have been reported.[3,4]

CETP is one member of a family of mammalian lipid transfer proteins including plasma phospholipid transfer protein (PLTP), lipopolysaccharide binding protein, and permeability increasing factor.[5] CETP mRNA is widely expressed in sites such as adipose tissue, muscle, liver, and placenta; the majority of circulating CETP probably originates from the liver. CETP may play an intracellular role in neutral lipid transfer between lipid droplets and other organelles; however, individuals with genetic CETP deficiency, who completely lack neutral lipid transfer activity in plasma, had no reported defect in cellular neutral lipid metabolism.[6] CETP may contribute to the transfer of phospholipids between plasma lipoproteins, although the greatest part of phospholipid transfer is now assigned to PLTP.[7] CETP is active in the "idle" exchange of CE between all lipoprotein classes. It is mainly because of CETP activity that the cholesteryl ester fatty acyl composition of very-low-density lipoproteins (VLDL), low-density lipoproteins (LDL), and high-density lipoproteins (HDL) is identical in human plasma. In terms of *net* lipid transfer, the exchange of HDL-CE for VLDL- and LDL-TG has the greatest magnitude.[8]

The clinical significance of CETP has been controversial.[9] This is, in part, because the protein seems to play two separate roles in plasma lipid metabolism. When CETP catalyzes the net exchange of VLDL-TG for HDL-CE, the TG-rich HDL produced are a substrate for hepatic TG lipase. Hydrolysis of this TG by hepatic lipase reduces HDL "core" volume, accompanied by an excess of "surface" protein and phospholipid. HDL protein (apolipoprotein A-I [apo A-I]) is released. The small pre-beta-migrating HDL produced are an effective acceptor of free cholesterol (FC) unloaded from peripheral cells, and promote reverse cholesterol transport.[10]

Other reactions also contribute to prebeta-HDL production. For example, the transfer of phospholipid to HDL by PLTP can displace pre-beta-migrating, lipid-poor apo A-I from HDL.[11] Nevertheless, on present evidence, the role of CETP in HDL metabolism would be considered anti-atherogenic, because of the potentially protective effect against cellular cholesterol accumulation.

The second product of the CETP reaction is a CE-enriched VLDL or LDL. VLDL newly secreted from the liver contains some CE, but this mass is significantly increased by CETP-mediated transfer from HDL. As a result, human LDL contain about twice the CE content (relative to LDL protein, apo B) as VLDL.[12] CE-enriched LDL react relatively poorly with hepatic LDL receptors.[13] As a result, increased levels of CETP would be expected to lead to the appearance of large CE-rich LDL. These "beta-VLDL" are usually considered pro-atherogenic.

However, several other factors complicate this picture. Only part of VLDL is converted to LDL; the balance is removed by the liver as soon as TG hydrolysis is complete.[14] CE-rich VLDL bind apo E more effectively than normal VLDL.[15] Apo E-rich VLDL are cleared more efficiently than normal VLDL by hepatic LDL receptors.[16] This reaction sequence could counteract the effect of increased CETP activity, by decreasing the proportion of VLDL converted to LDL.

Large, CE-rich LDL with the expected properties are induced in cholesterol-fed lower primates.[17] CETP activity is increased in the plasma of these animals.[18] However, similar particles are not normally seen in human plasma. In fact, in the presence of documented coronary heart disease (CHD), small, dense LDL are typically observed.[19] Finally, in most individuals, the mass of CETP protein in plasma does not determine the rate of CETP activity.[20] Instead, this more often reflects the composition of the donor and acceptor lipoprotein classes, HDL and VLDL.

In summary, a cause-and-effect relationship between increased CETP concentrations and human atherosclerosis has not yet been convincingly shown. Consistent with this lack of relationship, the incidence of CHD in CETP-deficient human subjects was no less than that of controls.[21,22]

CLINICAL RELEVANCE, FREQUENCY DISTRIBUTION, REFERENCE RANGES, AND INTERPRETATION

CETP protein concentration in normolipemic human plasma has been assayed with monoclonal antibodies by several laboratories. Mean values ranged from a high of 2.8 ± 0.6 mg/dL[23] to a low of 0.9 ± 0.4 mg/dL.[24] Most studies used the same proprietary monoclonal antibody (TP-2). The weighted mean in different studies was about 1.8 mg/dL. The plasma concentration of CETP protein was mildly elevated (less than twofold) in several hyperlipidemic syndromes, including combined hyperlipidemia, hypercholesterolemia, dysbetalipoproteinemia, and hyperchylomicronemia. The mean of plasma CETP mass in these groups was generally within two standard deviations of normal values.[25]

CETP mass in plasma has also been measured indirectly.[25,26] This assay uses exogenous donor and recipient lipoproteins, usually HDL and LDL, which are isolated by ultracentrifugal flotation. In most studies, HDL was directly labeled with ^{3}H-cholesteryl oleate. The correlation coefficient of activity and mass assays was about 0.85.[25,26] Unlabeled cholesteryl ester in plasma will dilute isotopically labeled HDL-CE by CETP-mediated exchange as a function of time. As a result, the kinetics of this assay are potentially quite complex. Because of difficulties in isolating and storing fully active CETP protein, indirect measurement of CETP mass is made relative to a normal plasma pool.

Endogenous plasma CETP activity reflects the net rate at which CE mass is transferred in native plasma samples between lipoprotein classes. This rate has been assayed enzymatically, as the rate of change in CE mass in donor and acceptor lipoproteins as a function of time.[27] It has also been measured isotopically, in plasma in which CE has been pre-labeled to equilibrium.[28]

Much of the net transfer of CE represents an exchange with TG. It is still unclear whether CETP can catalyze unidirectional neutral lipid transfer. CETP also catalyzes the nonproductive (bi-directional) exchange of CE between lipoprotein particles. As a result, endogenous CETP activity is strongly influenced by plasma TG concentration. As plasma TG concentration rises, an increased proportion of nonproductive CE exchange is transformed to the productive transfer of CE for TG.

Endogenous CETP activity is conventionally defined as the net rate at which HDL-CE mass is transferred to VLDL and LDL. Using this definition, CETP rate can sometimes have a zero or negative value.[29] This reflects net transfer of VLDL and LDL-CE to HDL.

A second influence on CETP activity that is independent of CETP protein levels is the activity of lecithin:cholesterol acyltransferase (LCAT).[10] Essentially the whole of HDL-CE is generated by the LCAT. As a result, regardless of the level of CETP protein in plasma, the molar rate of CETP-mediated transfer of HDL-CE cannot exceed that of LCAT because HDL-CE levels would become zero. In normal fasting plasma, the molar rate of net transfer of HDL-CE to VLDL and LDL was 10%–50% of the rate of LCAT (5–25 nmol/mL/h).[27,30] The balance of LCAT-derived CE remains in HDL. It is probably removed by the liver via the selective transfer pathway.[31]

CETP activity is increased postprandially, but CETP mass was not significantly increased.[32,33] The postprandial stimulation of CETP activity in normal plasma was coincident with, and probably entirely dependent on, the post-absorptive rise in VLDL-TG. In nephrotic syndrome[34] and combined hyperlipidemia,[35] hypertriglyceridemia was also associated with a change in CETP activity.

ADVANTAGES AND DISADVANTAGES OF CURRENT METHODOLOGIES

Measurements of plasma CETP mass have been carried out with monoclonal antibodies directed against the intact purified protein[23–25] or against a synthetic polypeptide representing residues 131–142 of the CETP amino acid sequence.[36] The mAb against CETP protein can be obtained from Dr. Y. L. Marcel, Ottawa Heart Institute, Ottawa, Canada, and the antipeptide mAb is available from Affinity Bioreagents, Golden, Colorado. Both assays use standard ELISA procedures[23] and measure CETP protein mass at 20–400 ng/well.

In view of the availability of CETP mABs, and the widespread use of automated immunoassay procedures in the analytical laboratory, assays of CETP mass using purified and labeled exogenous lipoproteins offer no obvious advantage. These assays are empirical, difficult to standardize between laboratories, expensive in isotope costs, and time-consuming.

Measurement of CETP activity in native plasma, particularly if coupled with assay of LCAT activity, offers insight into the flow of cholesterol between plasma lipoproteins not available from other procedures. It would be interesting to measure this under conditions where plasma lipoprotein concentrations were modified, for example during cholesterol lowering by diet or drugs. Three methodologies have been described. Two involve the enzymatic measurement of CE mass in HDL or VLDL+LDL as a function of time. The third measures the movement of ^{3}H-cholesteryl esters in prelabeled plasma.

Enzymatic Method 1[30]

The principle of this method is that when LCAT activity is inhibited, total CE in plasma is unchanged during incubation at 37°C. The CETP-mediated transfer of CE from HDL to VLDL+LDL can be conveniently determined as the rate of decrease in HDL-CE mass. This can be measured in a standard laboratory chemistry analyzer as the difference between total and free cholesterol in the soluble (HDL) fraction of plasma following precipitation of VLDL and LDL with heparin-MnCl$_2$ or MgCl$_2$-dextran sulfate.[36] This assay depends on the assumption that CETP activity is independent of HDL-CE mass, and the accumulation of CE in VLDL, over the period of assay. It also assumes that CETP activity is unaffected by the inhibition of LCAT. In practice, rates are often only briefly linear, as the compositional gradient between HDL and VLDL becomes dissipated as a function of time, and in the absence of hepatic lipase activity.

Enzymatic Method 2[27]

The principle of this method is that the increased CE in plasma incubated *in vitro* as a result of LCAT activity is associated with an equivalent molar *decrease* in FC. The rate of CETP-mediated transfer of CE from HDL to VLDL and LDL is then the difference between the rate of *decrease* in FC in whole plasma, and the rate of *increase* of CE in HDL, as a function of time.

Molar CETP activity = [Total increase in plasma CE] − [Increase in HDL-CE]
                     = [Decrease in plasma FC] − [Increase in HDL-CE]
                     = [(Initial plasma FC − final plasma FC)]
                         − [(final HDL-TC − final HDL-FC)
                         − (initial HDL-TC − initial HDL-FC)]

where CE is cholesteryl ester, FC is free cholesterol, HDL is high-density lipoprotein, and TC is total cholesterol.

While these measurements can all be made with a standard laboratory chemistry analyzer, the variances are additive. Six assays are needed at each time point, compared to the four needed in the first enzymatic method. Nevertheless, this assay provides unique information on the interplay between the LCAT and CETP reactions.

Isotopic Method[28]

Plasma FC is pre-equilibrated with ^{3}H-FC in the presence of a sulfhydryl inhibitor of LCAT, to prevent synthesis of labeled CE during equilibration. LCAT activity is restored by adding excess mercaptoethanol or dithiothreitol. A portion of the labeled CE synthesized is transferred by CETP to VLDL+LDL. At intervals, total labeled CE, and labeled CE in VLDL+LDL, are determined. Because FC is also labeled in this method, esterified and ^{3}H-FC must be separated by thin-layer chromatography prior to determinating CETP activity.

This assay assumes that the activity of CETP, and the gradient of CE between HDL and VLDL, are not modified by the pre-equilibration of plasma with ^{3}H-FC in the presence of DTNB.

DISCUSSION OF RECOMMENDED METHODS

For determining CETP mass, immunoassay using available reagents is clearly preferable to the less direct isotopic method. Each of the three methods to determine CETP activity gave qualitatively similar results in individual studies in the assay of normal plasma, but there has been to date no systematic comparison between them, either with normal or with hyperlipidemic plasma samples. Methodological details are given in the individual references cited.   ✧

REFERENCES

1. Tall A. Plasma lipid transfer proteins. Ann Rev Biochem 1995;64:235–57.
2. Lagrost L. Regulation of cholesteryl ester transfer protein (CETP) activity: review of in vitro and in vivo studies. Biochim Biophys Acta 1994;1215:209–36.
3. Drayna D, Jarnagin AS, McLean J, Henzel W, Kohr W, Fielding C, Lawn R. Cloning and sequencing of human cholesteryl ester transfer protein cDNA. Nature 1987;327:632–4.
4. Agellon L, Quinet E, Gillette T, Drayna D, Brown M, Tall AR. Organization of the human cholesteryl ester transfer gene. Biochemistry 1990;29:1372–6.
5. Day JR, Albers JJ, Lofton-Day CE, Gilberg TL, Ching AFT et al. Complete cDNA encoding human phospholipid transfer protein from human endothelial cells. J Biol Chem 1994;269:9388–91.
6. Inazu A, Brown ML, Hesler CB, Agellon LB, Koizumi J, Takata K, Moruhama Y et al. Increased high-density-lipoprotein levels caused by a common cholesteryl ester transfer gene mutation. N Engl J Med 1990;323:1234–8.
7. Speijer H, Groener JEM, van Ramshorst E, van Tol A. Different locations of cholesteryl ester transfer protein and phospholipid transfer protein activities in plasma. Atherosclerosis 1991;90:159–68.
8. Morton RE, Zilversmit DB. Interrelationship of lipids transferred by the lipid transfer protein isolated from human lipoprotein-deficient plasma. J Biol Chem 1983;258:11751–7.
9. Fielding CJ, Havel RJ. Cholesteryl ester transfer protein: friend or foe? J Clin Invest 1996 97:2687–8.
10. Fielding CJ, Fielding PE. Molecular physiology of reverse cholesterol transport. J Lipid Res 1995;36:211–28.
11. Von Eckardstein A, Jauhiainen M, Huang YD, Metso J, Langer C, Pussinen P, Wu SL et al. Phospholipid-transfer-protein-mediated conversion of high-density lipoprotein generates prebeta(1) HDL. Biochim Biophys Acta 1996;1301:255–62.
12. Fielding PE, Ishikawa Y, Fielding CJ. Apolipoprotein E mediates binding of normal very-low-density lipoprotein to heparin but is not required for high-affinity receptor binding. J Biol Chem 1989;264:12462–6.
13. Schechtman G, Boerboom LE, Hannah J, Howard BV. Dietary fish oil decreases low-density lipoprotein clearance in nonhuman primates. Am J Clin Nutr 1996;64:215–21.
14. Kesaniemi YA, Vega G, Grundy SM. Kinetics of apolipoprotein B in normal and hyper-triglyceridemic man: review of current data. In: Berman M, Grundy SM, Howard BV, (eds). Lipoprotein kinetics and modeling. New York: Academic Press, 1982:181–205.

15. Pagnan A, Havel RJ, Kane JP, Kotite L. Characterization of human very-low-density lipoproteins containing two electrophoretic populations: double prebeta lipoproteinemia and primary dysbetalipoproteinemia. J Lipid Res 1977;18:613–22.

16. Windler EET, Kovanen PT, Chao YS, Brown MS, Havel RJ, Goldstein JL. The estradiol-stimulated lipoprotein receptor of rat liver: a binding site that mediates the uptake of rat lipoproteins containing apolipoproteins B and E. J Biol Chem 1980; 255:10464–71.

17. Tall AR, Small DM, Atkinson D, Rudel L. Studies on structure of low-density lipoprotein isolated from *Macaca fascicularis* fed an atherogenic diet. J Clin Invest 1978;62: 1354–63.

18. Quinet E, Tall AR, Ramakrishnan R, Rudel L. Plasma lipid transfer protein as a determinant of the atherogenicity of monkey plasma lipoproteins. J Clin Invest 1991;87: 1559–66.

19. Krauss RM. Low-density lipoproteins and coronary artery disease. Am J Cardiol 1995; 75:53B–57B.

20. Mann CJ, Yen FT, Grant AM, Bihain BE. Mechanism of plasma cholesteryl ester transfer in hypertriglyceridemia. J Clin Invest 1991;88:2059–66.

21. Hirano KS, Yamashita S, Kuga Y, Sakai N, Nozahi S, Kihara T, Arai K et al. Atherosclerotic disease in marked hyperalphalipoproteinemia: combined reduction of cholesteryl ester transfer protein and hepatic lipase. Arterio Thromb Vasc Dis 1995;15: 1840–56.

22. Zhong S, Sharp DS, Grove JS, Bruce C, Yano K, Curb JB, Tall AR. Increased coronary artery disease in Japanese-American men with mutation in the cholesteryl ester transfer protein gene despite increased HDL levels. J Clin Invest 1996;97:2917–23.

23. Glenn KC, Melton MA. Quantification of cholesteryl ester transfer protein: activity and immunochemical assays. Methods Enzymol 1996;263:339–51.

24. Guyard-Dangrement V, Lagrost L, Gambert P, Lallemand C. Competitive enzyme-linked immunoabsorbent assay of the human cholesteryl ester transfer protein. Clin Chim Acta 1995;231:147–60.

25. McPherson R, Mann CJ, Tall AR, Hogue M, Martin L, Milne RW, Marcel YL. Plasma concentrations of cholesteryl ester transfer protein in hyperlipoproteinemia. Arterio Thromb 1991;11:797–804.

26. Tato F, Vega GL, Tall AR, Grundy SM. Relation between cholesteryl ester transfer protein activities and lipoprotein cholesterol in patients with hypercholesterolemia and combined hyperlipidemia. Arterio Thromb Biol 1995;15:112–20.

27. Fielding CJ, Havel RJ, Todd KM, Yeo KE, Schloetter MC, Weinberg V, Frost PH. Effects of dietary cholesterol and fat saturation on plasma lipoproteins in an ethnically diverse population of healthy young men. J Clin Invest 1995;95:611–18.

28. Channon KM, Clegg RJ, Bhatnagar D, Ishola M, Arrol S, Durrington PN. Investigation of lipid transfer in human serum leading to the development of an isotopic method for the determination of endogenous cholesterol esterification and transfer. Atherosclerosis 1990;80:217–26.

29. Van Tol A, Schenk LM, Groener JEM. Net mass transfer of cholesteryl esters from low-density lipoproteins to high-density lipoproteins in plasma from normolipemic subjects. Arterio Thromb Vasc Biol 1994;11:55–63.

30. Fielding PE, Fielding CJ, Havel RJ, Kane JP, Tun P. Cholesterol net transport, esterification and transfer in human hyperlipemic plasma. J Clin Invest 1983;71:449–60.

31. Acton S, Rigotti A, Lanschutz KT, Xu S, Hobbs HH, Krieger MM. Identification of scavenger receptor SB-1 as a high-density-lipoprotein receptor. Science 1996;271:518–20.

32. Castro GR, Fielding CJ. Effects of postprandial lipemia on plasma cholesterol metabolism. J Clin Invest 1985;75:874–82.

33. Tall A, Sammett D, Granot E. Mechanisms of enhanced cholesteryl ester transfer from high-density lipoproteins to apolipoprotein B-containing lipoproteins during alimentary lipemia. J Clin Invest 1986;77:1163–72.

34. Moulin P, Appekl GB, Ginsberg HN, Tall AR. Increased concentration of plasma

cholesteryl ester transfer protein in nephrotic syndrome: role in dyslipoproteinemia. J Lipid Res 1992;33:1817–22.

35. Guerin ME, Bouchert E, Dolphin PJ, Chapman MJ. Absence of cholesteryl ester transfer protein-mediated cholesteryl ester mass transfer from high-density lipoprotein to low-density lipoprotein particles is a major feature of combined hyperlipidemia. Eur J Clin Invest 1996;26:485–94.

36. Thomas AP, Cumming RI, Jones C, Thomas RC, Pleasant KT, Barakat H. Mouse monoclonal antipeptide antibodies specific for cholesteryl ester transfer protein (CETP). Hybridoma 1996;15:359–64.

Measurement and Clinical Significance of Lecithin: Cholesterol Acyltransferase

24

P. Haydn Pritchard

✧ Lecithin:cholesterol acyltransferase (LCAT) is the enzyme responsible for the synthesis of the majority of plasma cholesteryl esters in plasma by the transfer of fatty acid from phosphatidylcholine to the 3-hydroxyl group of cholesterol (see Figure 24–1).

A great deal of information on the biochemistry and pathophysiology of this enzyme is now available, and it has been the topic of numerous reviews.[1,2,3] It is generally believed that LCAT regulates the transport of cholesterol between extravascular and intravascular pools. In the theoretical pathway, known as reverse cholesterol transport, cholesterol is moved from peripheral tissues to the liver for catabolism. The esterification of cholesterol by LCAT in plasma serves to maintain a chemical concentration gradient for unesterified cholesterol between peripheral cells and plasma.[4] LCAT therefore plays a central role in the initial steps of this process. Studies on patients who have the familial LCAT deficiency have clearly identified the central role this enzyme plays in plasma cholesterol homeostasis.[5] However, the exact role LCAT plays in reverse cholesterol transport is far from clear.

The purpose of this chapter is to describe how measurement of LCAT activity in plasma can be used in the differential diagnosis of familial LCAT deficiency and its variant, fish-eye disease.[6,7] In addition, the chapter discusses how LCAT activity might be used as a biological probe to predict HDL particle size and, potentially, the risk of coronary heart disease (CHD).[8]

BIOCHEMISTRY OF LECITHIN:CHOLESTEROL ACYLTRANSFERASE

LCAT is a glycoprotein with an apparent molecular weight of 67,000 dalton, and the human enzyme has been purified to homogeneity in a number of laboratories. In plasma. LCAT protein is bound to high-density lipoproteins (HDL) and it esterifies cholesterol primarily in this class of lipoproteins. However, several investigators have provided evidence that plasma or recombinant LCAT may act directly on lower-density lipoproteins.[9–11] The major structural protein of HDL, apolipoprotein (apo) A-I, is believed to be the principal activator of LCAT. In addition, our observation that 90% of LCAT activity is removed from plasma by anti-A-I immunoaffinity column chromatography[12] suggests a physical association and functional interdependence.

The gene for the human LCAT has been sequenced.[13,14] It consists of 6 exons and 5 introns and encodes an mRNA of 1,550 nucleotides, which is expressed primarily in

Figure 24–1 ✧ Cholesterol Esterification by Lecithin:Cholesterol Acyltransferase

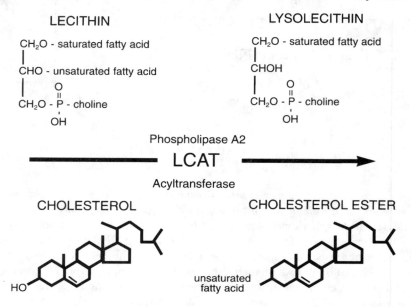

the liver. The mature protein contains 416 amino acids and a hydrophobic lead sequence of 24 amino acids. Amino acid sequence analysis indicates homology with the active site of a variety of other lipases.[15] This suggests that serine 181 is the reactive residue of LCAT. Francone and Fielding[16] used site-directed mutagenesis and *in vitro* expression to probe the role of these two serine residues. Exchange of serine 181 for either threonine, glycine, or alanine caused the complete loss of activity. Substitution of serine 216 with threonine only modestly decreased LCAT activity. Remarkably, substitution of serine 216 by an alanine residue increased activity ten-fold. Yang and Pownall[17] have analyzed the secondary structure based on the amino acid sequence and the identification of disulfide bridges. Spectrofluorometric studies have demonstrated that a substantial portion of the tryptophan residues are exposed on the outside of porcine LCAT. These hydrophobic residues are usually assumed to be within the inner domains of proteins. The high degree of glycosylation may account for this unusual structure. The LCAT protein is readily soluble in water, yet its hydropathic index is far greater than that of the plasma apolipoproteins such as apo A-I. The carbohydrate groups of LCAT may therefore play a major role in the structure and function of this protein. We have demonstrated by site-directed mutagenesis[18,19] that LCAT is glycosylated at all four potential N-glycosylation sites. No data exists on the tertiary structure of LCAT, and no crystals of purified plasma LCAT have been reported in the literature.

MOLECULAR PATHOLOGY OF THE LCAT GENE

It is now 35 years since a Norwegian patient with familial LCAT deficiency was described by Kare Norum and collaborators. Since that time, the study of LCAT deficiency has received a great deal of attention from clinical and basic scientists. These research efforts have provided information on the clinical presentation and laboratory findings in affected individuals, which have led to a better understanding of the pathological changes that are common in this rare yet instructive disease process. Accordingly, a number of review articles have been published.[4,20,21]

Familial LCAT deficiency is characterized biochemically by the absence of LCAT activity in plasma. This results in a grossly abnormal lipoprotein structure and, most significantly, HDL deficiency. Extensive genetic studies have clearly demonstrated that both LCAT deficiency and its related disorder, fish-eye disease, are caused by one of a number of mutations that occur within the LCAT gene. In affected individuals, LCAT in plasma is either absent, present but inactive, or present but dysfunctional.[20]

Over the last ten years, several laboratories have reported the gene defects that appear to be causative for LCAT deficiency and fish-eye disease. In our recent review[20] we identified all the published mutations of the LCAT gene and classified them according to the biochemical phenotype. The causative nature of these mutations has been established from the fact that none of these defects have been identified in a normal population and, in most cases, the observed mutation was the only one found on each allele analyzed. The absolute assignment of these mutations to either LCAT deficiency or fish-eye disease is not straightforward, and caution should be used in such a segregation. This is especially true in cases where the clinical phenotype appears to be caused by compound heterozygosity. In the first instance, however, the relationship between the structural defect and the function of LCAT is more easily studied in patients who are homozygous for a single genetic defect.

In general, mutations that are likely to have a major effect on the structure of LCAT, such as frame shifts, premature stop codons, or the introduction of a proline residue, appear to be associated with a near absence of LCAT enzyme protein in plasma; consequently, LCAT activity is absent. By contrast, single amino acid changes are more often associated with higher levels of LCAT mass and activity. The ability of some LCAT mutants to utilize lipoproteins other than HDL to synthesize cholesteryl esters, as reflected by a higher proportion of endogenous activity, is directly related to the clinical phenotype. In addition, mutations of this type, particularly the fish-eye disease defects, would not be expected to disrupt the structural integrity of the catalytic site but may represent abnormalities associated with the binding of LCAT to HDL. It is possible that this class of mutation may prevent LCAT from making a conformational change that is necessary for normal interaction with HDL but not with low-density lipoproteins (LDL). Several mutations have been identified in compound heterozygotes, indicating that the number of mutations of the LCAT gene is greater than originally predicted.

The number of different molecular defects identified in the LCAT gene so far is consistent with heterogeneity of the phenotypic expression seen in these disorders. However, it is likely that the additional effects of the environment and other genes will also influence the expression of the clinical and biochemical phenotypes. The presence of widely spaced mutations throughout the LCAT gene, and the knowledge that the sequence of the LCAT gene is virtually conserved in humans, suggest that the normal function of LCAT is very sensitive to changes throughout its primary amino acid sequence. From the biochemical analysis of fish-eye disease defects, it appears that LCAT has at least two functionally important domains, the catalytic center and the recognition site for HDL substrates. However, without the knowledge of the three-dimensional structure of this protein and the definition of specific structural domains, it remains difficult to resolve how mutations that are seemingly very close to one another can cause dramatic differences in the properties of this enzyme.

TYPES OF ASSAYS USED IN THE ASSESSMENT OF LCAT ACTIVITY

The three assays for the measurement of LCAT activity described below were established initially for the differential diagnosis of HDL deficiency syndromes. We have previously reported a process for investigating such conditions; the discussion herein is confined to the specific methods used. It is important, however, that the investigator be clear in understanding the different types of assays used and the limitations of the results obtained. This is especially important in choosing the correct assay to use for studying LCAT activity in patients who are not being investigated for LCAT deficiency syndromes. A summary of the methods and their uses is presented in Table 24–1.

LCAT Activity

In this assay, the activity of LCAT in plasma is defined using an exogenous substrate (specifically an HDL analog) that has been labeled with ^{3}H-cholesterol. The results are generally equivalent to the amount of LCAT enzyme present in the plasma. In most

Table 24–1 ✧ Summary of Methods Used to Measure Cholesterol Esterification

Assay	Source of LCAT	Substrate	Interpretive Use	Comments
LCAT Activity	plasma	exogenous HDL analog	Measurement of homozygous or heterozygous LCAT deficiency	Activity generally reflects the amount of wild-type LCAT in plasma
Cholesterol Esterification Rate (CER)	plasma	endogenous lipoproteins	Low normal activities in the absence of LCAT activity are diagnostic for fish-eye disease	This method has limited use with the exception of differential diagnosis of LCAT deficiency syndromes. The method likely overestimates the true molar rate of esterification in plasma.
Fractional Esterification Rate in HDL (FER$_{HDL}$)	phosphotungstic acid-treated plasma (i.e., plasma that has been depleted of VLDL and LDL)	HDL in plasma	Activity measure is proportional to the relative amount of small HDL particles.	Potentially, a highly informative assay. High activities are associated with small HDL, low levels of HDL, and the presence or risk of CHD.

cases, the LCAT activity measured by this method varies very little between individuals.

The assay is based on the ability of a sample of plasma to esterify ^{3}H-cholesterol in an exogenously provided analog of HDL that also contains a known amount of unlabeled unesterified cholesterol (UC), phosphatidylcholine, and apo A-I. The calculation of the activity assumes that during the incubation, the ^{3}H-cholesterol does not equilibrate with the endogenous cholesterol pool of the plasma sample. This is generally acceptable for most samples, but isotope dilution might occur in samples with very high lipid levels. Such problems can be exacerbated by the precipitation of LDL and very-low-density lipoproteins (VLDL) by phosphotungstic acid treatment of the plasma prior to the addition of the substrate. Since greater than 95% of the LCAT protein is bound to HDL or is free in plasma, the LCAT is not significantly reduced by removal of the less dense lipoproteins.

Cholesterol Esterification Rate (CER)

In this assay, the rate of observed cholesterol ester synthesis is a function of both the amount and activity of LCAT in plasma, together with the endogenous plasma lipoprotein substrate composition and properties. The principle of the assay is straightforward. The sample of plasma is equilibrated with a trace amount of ^{3}H-cholesterol and incubated at 37 C. The amount of ^{3}H-cholesterol ester produced is measured as a function of the total radioactivity.

This fractional rate of esterification depends on a number of factors, most importantly the availability of the ^{3}H-cholesterol for esterification by LCAT. Thus, if the plasma sample has high levels of total cholesterol (and hence of unesterified cholesterol), the relative rate of esterification will fall since proportionally more of the cholesterol will be less available for esterification due to its location in larger lipoproteins. This "isotope dilution effect" also impacts the calculated rate of (endogenous) cholesterol esterification.

In the calculation described below,[7] the CER is calculated from the fractional esterification rate (FER) and the total amount of unesterified cholesterol in the plasma sample. This calculation assumes that all molecules of cholesterol are equally available for esterification during the incubation. This is not accurate, and the true rate of esterification is likely far lower than that estimated by this method. In my opinion, the only method that can definitively measure the true rate of esterification is one that chemically measures the increase in cholesteryl esters or the decrease in unesterified cholesterol during the incubation. Such methods are not yet available. Thus, I believe that the primary use of measuring LCAT activity and the CER is in the differential diagnosis of LCAT deficiency syndromes.

FER$_{HDL}$

As indicated above, all assays of LCAT function that use ^{3}H-cholesterol as a marker for the esterification of the total UC pool in the assay may yield erroneous results. This fact was observed by Dobiasova, who correctly identified the fraction esterification rate (FER) as having great potential for the study of cholesterol esterification in individuals who are not being investigated for LCAT deficiency syndromes.[6,22–25] Dobiasova's strategy has been to measure the FER in only the HDL fraction of plasma. This is achieved by removing lower-density lipoproteins by precipitation with phosphotungstic acid prior to labeling the endogenous lipoproteins with ^{3}H-cholesterol. Thus, all of the radiolabel is confined to the HDL particles and the assumption that all of the radiotracer is available for esterification is more valid. This has revealed more significant changes in apparent LCAT activity in conditions where there is proven CHD or increased risk of disease. Specifically, the FER_{HDL} is significantly higher in patients with CHD or at risk of CHD from hyperlipidemia or hypertension. In contrast, octogenarians who have no evidence of CHD have very low levels, as do women compared to age-matched men.

These changes in FER_{HDL} appear to be related to the size distribution of the HDL, i.e., the smaller the HDL particles, the higher the FER_{HDL}. This makes sense, since LCAT prefers to esterify cholesterol in smaller particles. This unique property of LCAT can be used as a biological probe for the estimation of lipoprotein particle size. Since smaller HDL particles are seen in patients at risk of CHD, this assay may be merely a measure of size heterogeneity of HDL rather than a reflection of a true increase in the rate of cholesterol esterification in the plasma of such subjects. This notion, however, should not be forgotten: If the high FER_{HDL} does indeed reflect a high endogenous esterification rate in the HDL fraction, this finding disagrees with the generally accepted opinion that LCAT activity is beneficial to the process of reverse cholesterol transport. Such a paradox requires further investigation.

METHODS

LCAT Activity

This assay uses ethanolosome (proteoliposome) substrates to measure LCAT activity in plasma. The results obtained generally reflect the amount of LCAT protein in plasma and hence do not vary greatly between normal individuals. A normal range of 25–35 nmol/h/mL plasma can be expected; however, this *must* be established in-house since preparations of apo A-I vary in their ability to activate LCAT. Both familial LCAT activity and fish-eye disease will give values < 2 nmol/h/mL. Heterozygotes for both disorders will be approximately 50% of normal. Usually, an LCAT of < 20 nmol/h/mL in a first-degree relative of a patient with LCAT deficiency or fish-eye disease indicates the heterozygous state. Care should be taken in interpreting low (but not absent) LCAT activity, since this can also be associated with extremely high triglyceride levels or with poor sample storage. It is crucial that the samples have been frozen only once prior to analysis.

Stock Solutions and Equipment

✧ Egg yolk phosphatidylcholine (EYPC): Sigma Type III-E, 5 mg/mL in absolute ethanol. Store at –20°C.

✧ Unesterified cholesterol (UC): Sigma CH-S, 1 mg/mL in absolute ethanol. Store at –20°C.

✧ Tritiated unesterified cholesterol ([7(n)-^{3}H] cholesterol, 1 m Ci/mL) (Amersham Catalog No. TRK 122).

✧ Apo A-I (purified by PBE 94 chromatofocusing), 1.5 mg/mL in 0.15 mol/L NaCl, 1 mmol/L EDTA, 0.03% azide. Store at 4°C.

✧ Assay buffer: 10 mmol/L Tris-HCl, pH 7.4 (1.211 g/L), 5 mmol/L EDTA (1.861 g/L), 0.15 mol/L NaCl (8.783 g/L). Store at 4°C.

✧ 8% BSA: 0.8 of BSA (essentially fatty-acid-free) dissolved in 10 mL assay buffer. Store at 4°C.

✧ M β-mercaptoethanol: 35 μL undiluted β-mercaptoethanol in 5 mL freshly made assay buffer

✧ UC/CE standard: 20 mg cholesterol and 20 mg cholesteryl oleate (or palmitate) 98% pure in 10 mL chloroform.

✧ TLC plates: Merck 20 × 20 cm silica gel 60 F$_{254}$.

✧ Amicon ultrafiltration cell, model 12, and Amicon YM30 membranes.

✧ Fisher disposable culture tubes (borosilicate glass, Catalog No. 14–961–26)

Production of Ethanolosomes

1. Mix 260 μL EYPC, 150 μL UC, 12 μL ^{3}H-UC (1 m Ci/mL) in a 12 × 75 mm test tube and dry under nitrogen gas. This gives a PC:UC molar ratio of 4:1.

2. Place 10 mL of assay buffer in a test tube. Dissolve the dried lipid residue in 125 μL absolute ethanol. Take this up in a 1-mL syringe with a small gauge needle (> 25) and, while vortexing, inject this solution in the 10 mL assay buffer.

3. Concentrate the solution on an Amicon YM-30 membrane.

4. Place the Amicon ultrafiltration cell (model 12) on a stirrer.

5. Place a YM-30 membrane (carefully check that the membrane is intact!) in the ultrafiltration cell, shiny part up. (Be careful. The filter is very fragile.)

6. Wash the membrane twice with 1 volume Milli-Q water (MQ) under nitrogen pressure of ± 18–20 psi (with slow gas flow and slow stirring).

7. After the second wash step, apply the sample solution and let the sample flow through (under the same conditions as for wash steps) until no more than 2 mL are left on the membrane. Collect the buffer that flows through.

8. Take up the remaining 2 mL using a pipette fitted with a small piece of rubber tubing to prevent damage to the membrane.

9. Store the membrane in 70% ethanol.

10. Adjust to a final volume of 2.5 mL with assay buffer. This solution should be water clear or slightly turbid.

11. Check that all activity is retained in the sample by counting 10 μL of the filtered sample solution and 10 μL of the "flow-through."

12. Store ethanolosomes at 4°C and use within 14 days.

Assay Procedure

1. Run duplicates for each sample, including quality controls (15 μL serum).

2. Determine the number of samples to be measured. Make a premix containing liposomes, apo A-I, and assay buffer, according to Table 24–2.

3. Add 100 μL of the premix to each test tube and incubate for 30 min at 37°C to allow for possible association of apo A-I with liposomes. Do not place the samples on ice after incubation; leave them at room temperature.

4. Make a mixture of 5 volumes 8% BSA and 1 volume 0.1 mol/L β-mercaptoethanol (5:1 ratio), enough for all samples (see Table 24–2). Add 60 μL of this mixture to each tube.

5. Add 15 μL of plasma sample to each tube and incubate at 37°C for the time indicated in Table 24–2.

6. Terminate the reaction by adding 1 mL of 100% ethanol. Leave the samples at room temperature for 15 min.

7. Vortex the samples and centrifuge at 4,000 rpm for 20 min at room temperature in a standard tabletop centrifuge to separate phases.

8. Pour the liquid phase in new test tubes and evaporate to dryness under N_2.

9. While the samples are drying, set up a glass tank for the chromatography of TLC plates. Make a mixture of 105 mL petroleum ether, 18 mL diethyl ether, and 1.56 mL acetic acid. Mix well, pour into the tank and close the lid tightly to obtain saturation in the tank.

Table 24–2 ✧ Assay Parameters and Conditions	
Liposomes	30 μL
Apo A-I	± 10 μL*
Assay buffer	85 μL
BSA/β-mercaptoethanol mix	60 μL
Plasma sample	15 μL
Incubation temperature	37°C
Incubation time	30 min

*The amount of apo A-I to be used depends on the optimal activation of the apo A-I preparation, which varies from batch to batch.

> *Caution: Pour in the middle, not on the wall, and do not apply grease to the lid of the tanks.*

10. Prepare the TLC plates: Mark the 1.5-, 9.0-, 10.0-, 11.0-, and 18.5-cm points on two ends of the plates. Draw corresponding lines by connecting the points (the middle line is used to cut the plate in half.) Mark 2.5-cm segments for each line, for 8 segments per plate.

11. When the samples are completely dry, add 10 μL UC/CE standard and 50 μL of chloroform to each sample to make the bands visible and to provide a carrier for more efficient extraction.

12. Apply the samples to the TLC plate as streaks (20 μL at a time) in the fume hood. Include a control lane (UC/CE standard) on each plate.

13. Run in the glass tank until the solvent front reaches the top line. This may take approximately 10 min. Dry the plates in the fume hood.

14. The cholesterol and cholesteryl ester bands can be visualized with the aid of light or iodine vapor (use I_2 crystals).

15. Outline the UC and CE bands with pencil. The highest band is the cholesteryl ester band, which is the most hydrophobic. If iodine vapor was used to make the bands appear, leave the plates in the fume hood until the iodine has completely disappeared. Presence of I_2 will quench the counts.

16. Carefully cut out squares containing the UC and CE bands and place them in 5-mL scintillation vials. Add 5 mL scintillation fluid (toluene containing 4 g/L omnifluor or xylene-based Instafluor), preferably in the fume hood. Leave the samples at room temperature for at least 1 hour before starting to count, or, if you are in a hurry, shake well and count.

Calculation

LCAT activity is expressed in nmol of cholesterol esterified per hour per mL plasma. It is calculated from:

$$[CE/(CE + UC)] \times 1/I \times 4.66 \times 1000/sv$$

where CE is the disintegrations per minute (DPM) recovered in cholesteryl ester after the incubation, UC is the DPM recovered in cholesterol after the incubation, I is the time of incubation (usually 30 min), sv is the sample volume (usually 15 μL), and 4.46 is the total amount of unesterified cholesterol (in nmols) added to the incubation in the ethanolosome substrate.

Cholesterol Esterification Rate (CER) in Plasma

The methods by which this assay is used to investigate families with fish-eye disease has been extensively reported.[26-31] Specifically, in patients with LCAT deficiency, both the LCAT activity and the CER are virtually nonexistent. However, in the case of fish-eye disease, the LCAT activity is close to zero, yet the CER remains at 50%–70% of normal. *This paradoxical esterification of cholesterol in the plasma of patients with fish-eye disease is diagnostic.*

Reagents

❖   [7(n)^{3}H] cholesterol (specific activity 5 Ci/mmol) (Amersham Corp.).

❖   Unesterified cholesterol assay kit (Wako Chemicals, Richmond VA).

❖   Tris Buffer, pH 7.4

Labeling of Plasma

1.   Prepare paper disc from Whatmann 1 filter paper using a hole punch.

2.   Dry 10 μL of ^{3}H-cholesterol under N_2.

3.   Reconstitute in 200 μL of absolute ethanol.

4.   Add 3 μL to each disc and allow the discs to air dry for 10 min.

5.   Transfer the discs into 12× 75 glass tubes.

6.   Close the tubes with parafilm. Store at 4°C. (These discs will last 3 months at 4°C.)

7.   Add a minimum of 100 μL of plasma sample to each tube. Seal with parafilm and incubate overnight on ice.

8.   Transfer 50 μL of the labeled sample to a new tube.

9.   Incubate at 37°C for 30 min.

10.   Terminate the reaction by adding 1 mL of 100% ethanol. Leave the samples at room temperature for 15 min.

11.   Vortex the samples and centrifuge at 4,000 rpm for 20 min at room temperature in a standard tabletop centrifuge to separate phases.

12.   Pour the liquid phase into new test tubes and evaporate to dryness under N_2.

13.   While the samples are drying, set up a glass tank for the chromatography of TLC plates. Make a mixture of 105 mL petroleum ether, 18 mL diethyl ether, and 1.56 mL acetic acid. Mix well. Pour the mixture into the tank and close the lid tightly to obtain saturation in the tank.
      Caution: Pour in the middle, not on the wall, and do not apply grease to the lid of the tanks.

14.   Prepare the TLC plates: Mark the 1.5-, 9.0-, 10.0-, 11.0-, and 18.5-cm points on two ends of the plates. Draw corresponding lines by connecting the points (the middle line is used to cut the plate in half). Mark 2.5-cm segments for each line, for 8 segments per plate.

15.   When the samples are completely dry, add 10 μL UC/CE standard and 50 μL of chloroform to each sample to see the heights of the bands and to provide a carrier medium for a more efficient way of extraction.

16. Apply the samples to the TLC plate as streaks, 20 μL at a time, in the fume hood. Include a control lane (UC/CE standard) on each plate.

17. Run in the glass tank until the solvent front reaches the top line. This may take approximately 10 min. Dry the plates in the fume hood.

18. The cholesterol and cholesteryl ester bands can be made to appear with the aid of light or iodine vapor (use I_2 crystals). Outline the UC and CE bands with pencil. The highest band is the cholesteryl ester band, which is the most hydrophobic. If iodine vapor was used to materialize the bands, leave the plates in the fume hood until the iodine has completely disappeared. Presence of I_2 will quench the counts.

19. Carefully cut out squares containing the UC and CE bands and place them in 5-mL scintillation vials. Add 5 mL scintillation fluid (toluene containing 4 g/L omnifluor), preferably in the fume hood. Leave the samples at RT for at least 1 h before starting to count.

Calculation

The plasma CER is expressed in nmol/h/mL plasma. It requires prior knowledge of the concentration of unesterified cholesterol in the test sample. CER is calculated as follows:

$$[CE/(CE + UC)] \times 1/I \times puc \times 1000/sv$$

where CE is the DPM (disintegrations per min) recovered in cholesteryl ester after the incubation, UC is the DPM recovered in cholesterol after the incubation, I is the time of incubation (usually 0.5 h), sv is the sample volume, and puc is the total amount of unesterified cholesterol (in nmol) added to the incubation mixture with the plasma sample.

Fractional Esterification Rate (FER$_{HDL}$) in HDL

Preparation of VLDL- and LDL-Depleted Plasma

Reagents

✧ Phosphotungstate solution (PTA): 4 g of phosphotungstic acid and 16 mL of 1 mol/L NaOH. Bring the solution to 100 mL with deionized distilled water.

✧ 2 mol/L $MgCl_2$

Precipitation Procedure

✧ To 1 mL of plasma (in 1.5 mL eppendorf tubes)

✧ Add 100 μL of PTA and vortex.

✧ Add 25 μL of 2 mol/L $MgCl_2$ and vortex.

✧ Incubate at 4°C for 20 min.

✧ Centrifuge at 12,000 rpm at 4°C (precise temperature is important) for 10 minutes.

✧ Remove supernate to a new tube. This fraction contains the HDL particles; always store on ice.

Determination of FER in PTA-Treated Plasma

This procedure is conducted exactly as that described for CER above.

Calculation

Since the FER_{HDL} is independent of the amount of unesterified cholesterol in the incubation, the calculation simply reflects the fraction of the total radiolabel that was esterified. It is calculated as follows:

$$[CE/(CE + UC)] \times 1/I \times 100$$

where CE is the DPM recovered in cholesteryl ester after the incubation, UC is the DPM recovered in cholesterol after the incubation, and I is the time of incubation (usually 30 min).

SUMMARY

LCAT is clearly an important plasma enzyme that plays a major role in cholesterol metabolism. The assay of LCAT activity and the cholesterol esterification rate described in this chapter are primarily used in the differential diagnosis of HDL deficiency syndromes. However, for the assessment of patients at risk of CAD, the measurement of FER_{HDL} has greater potential use in the clinical management and in the elucidation of the true role of LCAT in the protection against CHD.   ✧

Acknowledgments: *These studies have been funded through grants from the British Columbia Heart and Stroke Foundation.*

REFERENCES

1. Jonas A. Lecithin-cholesterol acyltransferase in the metabolism of high-density lipoproteins. Biochim Biophys Acta 1991;1084:205–20.
2. Applebaum-Bowden D. Lipases and lecithin:cholesterol acyltransferase in the control of lipoprotein metabolism. Curr Opin Lipidol 1995;6:130–5.
3. Marcel YL, Vezina CA, Weech PK et al. Lecithin:cholesterol acyltransferase: a review and immunochemical studies. Adv Exper Med Biol 1986;201:163–79.
4. Fielding CJ. Factors affecting the rate of catalyzed transfer of cholesteryl esters in plasma. Am Heart J 1987;113:532–7.
5. Frohlich J, McLeod R. Lecithin:cholesterol acyltransferase (LCAT) deficiency syndromes. Adv Exper Med & Biol 1986;201:181–94.

6.   Frohlich JJ, Pritchard PH. The clinical significance of serum high-density lipoproteins. Clin Biochem 1989;22:417–23.

7.   Frohlich J, Westerlund J, Sparks D, Pritchard PH. Familial hypoalphalipoproteinemias. Clin Invest Med 1990;13:202–10.

8.   Dobiasova M, Frohlich J. Measurement of fractional esterification rate of cholesterol in plasma depleted of apoprotein-B-containing lipoprotein: methods and normal values. Phys Res 1996;45:65–73.

9.   Rajaram OV, Barter PJ. Reactivity of human lipoproteins with purified lecithin: cholesterol acyltransferase during incubations in vitro. Biochim Biophys Acta 1985;835:41–49.

10. Carlson LA, Holmquist L. Evidence for the presence in human plasma of lecithin:cholesterol acyltransferase activity (beta-LCAT) specifically esterifying free cholesterol of combined pre-beta- and beta-lipoproteins: studies of fish-eye disease patients and control subjects. Acta Med Scand 1985;218:197–205.

11. OK Hill JS, Wang X, Pritchard PH. Recombinant lecithin:cholesterol acyltransferase containing a Thr123 → Ile mutation esterifies cholesterol in low-density lipoprotein but not in high-density lipoprotein. J Lipid Res 1993;34:81–8.

12. Pritchard PH, McLeod RM, Frohlich JJ et al. Lecithin:cholesterol acyltransferase in familial HDL deficiency (Tangier disease). Biochem Biophys Acta 1988;958:227–34.

13. McLean J, Fielding C, Drayna D et al. Cloning and expression of human lecithin-cholesterol acyltransferase cDNA. PNAS USA 1986;83:2335–9.

14. McLean J, Wion K, Drayna D et al. Human lecithin-cholesterol acyltransferase gene: complete gene sequence and sites of expression. Nucl Acid Res 1986;14:9397–406.

15. Warden CH, Langner CA, Gordon JI et al. Tissue-specific expression, developmental regulation, and chromosomal mapping of the lecithin:cholesterol acyltransferase gene: evidence for expression in brain and testes as well as liver. J Biol Chem 1989;264: 21573–81.

16. Francone OL, Fielding CF. Structure-function relationships in human lecithin:cholesterol acyltransferase: site-directed mutagenesis at serine residues 181 and 216. Biochem 1991;30:1074–7.

17. Yang CY, Mangoogian D, Pao Q, et al. Lecithin:cholesterol acyltransferase: functional regions and a structural model of the enzyme. J Biol Chem 1987;262:3086–91.

18. OK Hill JS, Wang X, McLeod R, Pritchard PH. Lecithin:cholesterol acyltransferase: role of N-linked glycosylation in enzyme function. Biochem J 1993;294:879–84.

19. OK Hill JS, Pritchard PH. Role of N-linked glycosylation of lecithin:cholesterol acyltransferase in lipoprotein substrate specificity. Biochim Biophys Acta 1995;1254: 193–7.

20. Kuivenhoven JA, Pritchard PH, Hill JS, Frohlich J, Assmann G, Kastelein JJ. The molecular pathology of lecithin:cholesterol acyltransferase deficiency syndromes. J Lipid Res 1997;38:191–205.

21. Kuivenhoven JA, Stalenhoef AF, Hill JS, Demacker PN, Errami A, Kastelein JJ, Pritchard PH. Two novel molecular defects in the LCAT gene are associated with fish-eye disease. Arterioscler Thromb Vasc Biol 1996;16:294–303.

22. Dobiasova M, Stribrna J, Sparks DL et al. Cholesterol esterification rates in very-low-density-lipoprotein- and low-density-lipoprotein-depleted plasma: relation to high-density lipoprotein subspecies, sex, hyperlipidemia, and coronary artery disease. Arterioscler Thromb 1991;11:64–70.

23. Dobiasova M, Stribrna J, Pritchard PH et al. Cholesterol esterification rate in plasma depleted of very-low and low-density lipoproteins is controlled by the proportion of HDL2 and HDL3 subclasses: study in hypertensive and normal middle-aged and septuagenarian men. J Lipid Res 1992;33:1411–8.

24. Dobiasova M, Frohlich JJ. Structural and functional assessment of high-density lipoprotein heterogeneity. Clin Chem 1994;40:1554–8.

25. Dobiasova M, Stribrna J, Frohlich JJ. Relation of cholesterol esterification rate to the plasma distribution of high-density lipoprotein subclasses in normal and hypertensive women. Clin Invest Med 1995;18:449–54.

26. Funke H, von Eckardstein A, Pritchard PH et al. The molecular defect causing fish-eye disease. Proc Natl Acad Sci 1991;88:4855–9.

27. Klein H-G, Lohse P, Pritchard PH et al. Two different allelic mutations in the lecithin:cholesterol acyltransferase (LCAT) gene associated with the fish-eye syndrome. J Clin Invest 1992;89:499–506.

28. Funke H, von Eckardstein A, Pritchard PH et al. Genetic and phenotypic heterogeneity in familial lecithin:cholesterol acyltransferase (LCAT) deficiency: six newly identified defective alleles further contribute to the structural heterogeneity in this disease. J Clin Invest 1993;91:677–83.

29. Kastelein JJP, Pritchard PH, Erkelens DW et al. Familial high-density-lipoprotein deficiency causing corneal opacities (fish-eye disease) in a kindred of Dutch descent. J Intern Med 1992;231:413–19.

30. Kuivenhoven JA, Weibusch H, Pritchard PH et al. An intronic mutation in the lariate branch point sequence is a direct cause of an inherited human disorder (fish-eye disease). J Clin Invest 1996;98:358–64.

31. Kuivenhoven JA, Voorst tot Vorst E, Weibusch H et al. A unique genetic and biochemical presentation of fish-eye disease. J Clin Invest 1995;96:2783–91.

Determination and Clinical Significance of Phospholipids

25

Papasani V. Subbaiah

✧ Phospholipids are integral and essential components of all lipoproteins and cell membranes. In quantitative terms, the amount of phospholipids in fact exceeds that of triglycerides (TG) as well as cholesterol (measured as unesterified) in normal human plasma. However, phospholipids are chemically more diverse than the neutral lipids, and are composed of several subclasses with distinct physicochemical properties. There are two major classes of phospholipids in plasma lipoproteins: glycerophospholipids, which have a glycerol backbone, and sphingophospholipids, which have a sphingosine backbone. One sphingophospholipid—sphingomyelin (SPH)—and five subclasses of glycerophospholipids are found in plasma. These subclasses include

✧ phosphatidyl choline (PC),

✧ lysophosphatidyl choline (LPC),

✧ phosphatidyl ethanolamine (PE),

✧ phosphatidyl serine (PS), and

✧ phosphatidyl inositol (PI)

Each subclass of phospholipids is actually composed of several molecular species that differ from each other in their fatty acid composition. The structures of the major phospholipids in human plasma and their normal concentrations are shown in Figure 25–1.

Despite their high concentration in plasma, phospholipid measurement is not routinely performed in the clinical chemistry laboratory. One reason is that most methods for the measurement of total phospholipids have been rather time consuming and tedious, and they are less amenable to automation, compared to the methods for the measurement of the neutral lipids. Another reason is that the phospholipid concentration in plasma is not altered as markedly as that of cholesterol and TG in various pathological conditions. However, the following considerations show that the estimation of lipoprotein phospholipids provides information that is not merely supplemental to the neutral lipid values, but at times more important than either cholesterol or TG concentration.

1. Only 10%–20% of the total weight of high-density lipoprotein (HDL) is cholesterol, but 25%–30% of it is phospholipids.[1] Although HDL concentration is ex-

Figure 25–1 ✧ Structures of Major Phospholipids of Normal Plasma

General Structure of Phosphoglyceride

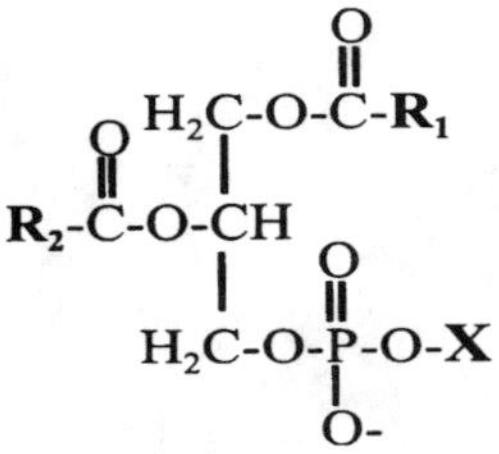

R_1 = Usually saturated fatty acid

R_2 = Usually unsaturated fatty acid
(absent in LPC)

Phosphoglyceride	Structure of X	Conc. in normal plasma mmol/L (% of total)
Phophatidyl choline (PC)	$H_2C\text{-}H_2C\text{-}\overset{+}{N}(CH_3)_3$	1.795 (68.4)
Lysophosphatidyl choline (LPC)	$H_2C\text{-}H_2C\text{-}\overset{+}{N}(CH_3)_3$	0.178 (6.8)
Phosphatidyl ethanolamine (PE)	$H_2C\text{-}H_2C\text{-}\overset{+}{N}H_3$	0.115 (4.4)
Phosphatidyl serine (PS)	$H_2C\text{-}HC\text{-}\overset{+}{N}H_3$ COO-	0.021 (0.8)
Phosphatidyl inositol (PI)	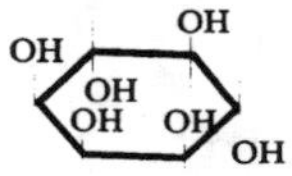	0.060 (2.3)

Structure of Sphingomyelin (SPH)

0.454 (17.3)

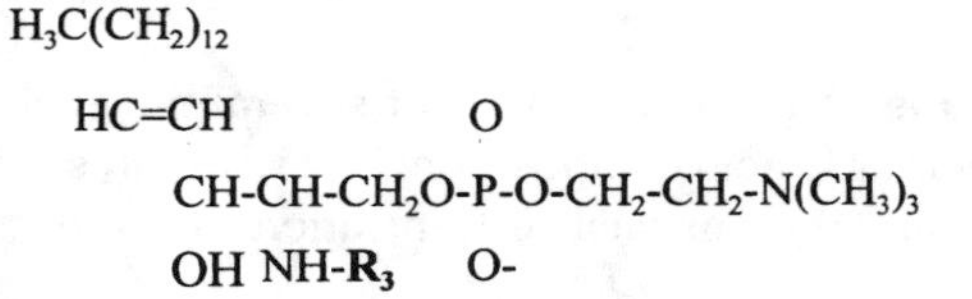

R_3 = Long-chain saturated fatty acid

pressed routinely in terms of its cholesterol content, the phospholipid content reflects the concentration of HDL much more accurately.

2.   Functionally, the phospholipids of HDL are more important than cholesterol or even apolipoprotein A-I in reverse cholesterol transport.[2] Abnormalities in phospholipid composition affect the function of HDL more than abnormalities in TG or cholesterol concentration.

3.   Phospholipids are substrates for several important enzymes in plasma such as lecithin:cholesterol acyltransferase (LCAT), lipoprotein lipase, and hepatic lipase, and therefore changes in their composition may affect the activities of these enzymes.

4. Unlike TG or cholesteryl esters, phospholipids exchange more readily with cell membranes and therefore alterations in plasma phospholipid composition likely reflect possible alterations in cell membrane composition and function in various pathological states.

5. Since the polyunsaturated fatty acids in plasma are mainly carried by the phospholipids, the long-term dietary status of essential fatty acids is more accurately assessed by the fatty acid composition of phospholipids rather than that in total lipids. The saturated fatty acid content of plasma phospholipids has been reported to be an independent risk factor for atherosclerosis.[3,4] Table 25–1 lists some of the pathological conditions in which the plasma phospholipid composition has been shown to be altered.

Table 25–1 ✧ Pathological Significance of Plasma Phospholipids (PL)

Disease	Effects on plasma phospholipids	Reference
Coronary heart disease (CHD)	PC/FC ratio significantly lower in ischemic heart disease.	36
	HDL phospholipids correlate with atherogenic risk even in normolipidemics.	37
	PC/SPH ratio decreased in HDL.	38,39
	Decrease in HDL phospholipids is more significant than the decrease in HDL cholesterol.	40
	Free cholesterol/PL ratio increased in HDL in ischemic heart disease.	41
Hyperlipidemia	35% increase in cholesterol/PL in LDL (Type IIa hyperlipidemia).	42
Insulin-dependent diabetes	Decrease in choline PL in apo B-containing lipoproteins.	43
	Increase in glycated aminophospholipids.	11
	Free cholesterol/PL ratio increased.	44
Liver diseases	HDL-PL correlate better than HDL cholesterol with liver disease.	45
	Free cholesterol and PL increased in cholestatic liver disease.	46
Cancer	Decreased PL in hematologic cancer.	47
	Decrease in plasma PL in acute leukemia and malignant lymphoma. LPC peak most sensitive indicator for monitoring treatment.	23
	Increase in lysophosphatidic acid in ovarian cancer, multiple myeloma.	48,49
Cerebrovascular disease	HDL PL significantly decreased.	50
Cystic fibrosis	Polyunsaturated phospholipids correlate with pulmonary function.	51
Schistosomiasis infection	Phospholipid concentration elevated.	52
Trauma (burns)	Elevated PC, and decreased SPH and lyso PC.	53

Review of Existing Methods for Phospholipid Estimation

Methods for phospholipid estimation can be divided into two groups: (1) estimation of total phospholipid concentration in plasma or lipoproteins, and (2) estimation of the composition of individual phospholipid subclasses. In addition, there are special methods (which will not be discussed here) to determine the molecular species composition of individual phospholipid subclasses,[5] and to estimate the concentration of minor phospholipids with specific biological functions, such as platelet-activating factor,[6] disaturated PC,[7] plasmalogens,[8] phospholipid – hydroperoxides,[9] truncated (oxidized) PCs,[10] glycated aminophospholipids,[11] and lysophosphatidic acid.[12]

Total Phospholipids of Plasma

The only unique structural feature common to all phospholipids is the presence of lipid-bound phosphate. Therefore most of the methods originally designed to determine plasma phospholipids depended upon the estimation of lipid phosphorus. In general, the total lipids are first extracted from the plasma, the lipid phosphorus is released by acid-digestion, and then the released phosphorus is estimated by colorimetric methods. The various methods differ from each other in the reagents used to release the inorganic phosphate (Pi): sulfuric acid and hydogen peroxide, perchloric acid, mixtures of perchloric and sulfuric acids, with vanadium pentoxide as catalyst. The most common reagent used for color is ammonium molybdate, which forms a phosphomolybdate complex with the phosphate, which is then reduced by stannous chloride-hydrazine sulfate or aminonapthol sulfonate at high temperature.

Phospholipids have also been estimated without acid digestion, by complexing the intact lipids with chromogenic reagents such as ammonium ferrothiocyanate[13] and prussian blue complex[14] or fluorogenic reagents such as diphenylhexatriene.[15]

Because about 95% of the total plasma phospholipids contain choline as the base (PC, LPC, SPH), many laboratories use the measurement of lipid-bound choline as a close approximation of total phospholipids. The method is based on the release of choline by phospholipase D from *Streptomyces chromofuscus*, which acts on all three choline-containing phospholipids. The released choline is oxidized with choline oxidase to produce betaine and hydrogen peroxide. The hydrogen peroxide is then reacted with peroxidase in the presence of 4-amino antipyrene and phenol to produce a red quinone complex, which is measured at 505 mm.

$$PC \xrightarrow{\text{Phospholipase D}} \text{Phosphatidic acid} + \text{choline}$$

$$LPC \xrightarrow{\text{Phospholipase D}} \text{Lysophosphatidic acid} + \text{choline}$$

$$SPH \xrightarrow{\text{Phospholipase D}} \text{Ceramide phosphate} + \text{choline}$$

$$\text{Choline} \xrightarrow{\text{Choline oxidase}} \text{Betaine} + H_2O_2$$

$$2\,H_2O_2 + \text{Phenol} + 4\text{-aminoantipyrene} \xrightarrow{\text{Peroxidase}} \text{Quinineimine}$$
$$(\lambda\text{max 505 nm}) + 2H_2O$$

This method has the advantage of not requiring lipid extraction and not involving corrosive reagents such as perchloric acid and a special fume hood. The drawback is that the method does not measure PS, PI, and PE. High concentrations of bilirubin and ascorbic acid have been reported to interfere in color development, although the concentrations encountered in most clinical samples are without effect. Interference by high concentration of EDTA in plasma has been reported,[16] but including sufficient $CaCl_2$ in the buffer overcomes this.

Choline can also be estimated with choline kinase by the following sequence of reactions.

$$Choline + ATP \xrightarrow{\text{Choline kinase}} Cholinephosphate + ATP$$

$$ATP + phosphoenol\ pyruvate \xrightarrow{\text{Pyruvate kinase}} ATP + Pyruvate$$

$$Pyruvate + NADH + H^+ \xrightarrow{\text{Lactate dehydrogenase}} Lactate + NAD^+$$

The NADH consumed is measured at 340 nm. The main advantage of this method is that it can be used on dilute solutions where the interference from bilirubin and ascorbate may be more problematic. However, the requirement for additional enzymes and for a UV range spectrophotometer are disadvantages.

Quantitation of Individual Phospholipid Classes

As mentioned earlier, the total PC *concentration* of whole plasma or lipoproteins does not change as dramatically as either cholesterol or TG, and therefore, the quantitation of phospholipids as potential markers of disease has been neglected. However, the *composition* of phospholipids may be more important than the total amount of phospholipids in some cases. The importance of determining the SPH/PC ratio in amniotic fluid for the estimation of lung maturity of the fetus is well established.[17] Table 25–1 lists other pathological conditions, several of which are characterized by abnormalities in individual phospholipid subclasses. About 70% of plasma PE is in the plasmalogen form,[18] which is considered to have strong anti-oxidant properties. Therefore the estimation of plasma PE provides an indirect measure of the anti-oxidant reserve of the plasma. Furthermore, since LPC is the product of lipolytic actions in the plasma, an increase in its concentration may indicate increased lypolysis.

Separation of phospholipids into individual classes has been performed by classical chromatographic procedures using silicic acid column, silicic acid-impregnated paper, and silica gel thin layer chromatography (TLC),[19] as well as high-performance liquid chromatography (HPLC),[20] and capillary gas-liquid chromatography (GLC).[21] In addition, nuclear magnetic resonance (NMR) methods that do not require the physical separation of the phospholipids from each other for quantitation have been developed.[22,23] At present, the TLC and HPLC methods are the most widely used. TLC separation is performed on silica gel-coated plates, with a variety of solvent systems, the most effective being those containing chloroform, methanol, and water. The quantitation of individual phospholipid spots after TLC separation is performed either by densitometry after color development on the plate[24] or by determining the lipid phosphorus in individual spots after scraping from the plate.[25] A combination of TLC and flame ionization detection is used in the Iatroscan method, employing silica-coated chromarods.[26] While this method has high sensitivity, in our experience it suffers from poor reproducibility. HPLC separation is usually carried out on normal phase silica columns with a variety of solvent systems, the choice of which is dictated by the detection method used. The various methods for quantitation following HPLC separation include UV absorbance,[20] post-column fluorescence derivatization,[27] electrochemical detection,[28] flame ionization,[29] mass spectroscopy,[30] light-scattering detection,[31] and refractive index.[32] Although the UV detection method has been used by several investigators, its drawback is that it is mainly dependent upon the number of double bonds in the acyl chains, and is, therefore, highly variable. In addition, the choice of solvents is limited because the most effective solvents interfere in UV measurements at the low wavelengths. The molar extinction coefficients are also very low with consequent low sensitivity. However, if the fatty acid composition is not significantly different among samples, one can use calibrated standards of similar composition and quantitate the phospholipids quite accurately. The refractive index method is not dependent upon the structure of the phospholipid, but its sensitivity is very low and it is unsuitable for gradient separation of the phospholipids. The electrochemical method is also independent of the phospholipid structure, but suffers from poor reproducibility and interference from other solutes.[28] While mass spectroscopy yields detailed information that is not obtainable with other methods, the instrumentation is expensive and difficult to operate. The flame ionization technique is very sensitive, and allows the use of most solvents for HPLC separation. Although this method is promising, it has not yet gained wide acceptance for phospholipid estimations. In our experience the light-scattering detection method is more practical and reproducible and the results correlate highly with the estimation of lipid phosphorus.

Enzymatic methods to estimate the major phospholipids of plasma without prior chromatographic separation have also been reported. Blaton et al.[33] used phospholipase C and sphingomyelinase from *B. cereus*, which release choline phosphate specifically from PC and SPH respectively, to determine these phospholipids separately. LPC concentration can be determined as the difference between the total lipid-bound choline as estimated by the phospholipase D method, and the PC and SPH values as determined by this procedure. One drawback of this procedure is that since both phospholipase C and sphingomyelinase are from the same source, the possible cross-contamination of the enzymes can give rise to spurious results for either PC or SPH, or both.

Recommended Methods for Total Phospholipid Estimation

ESTIMATION OF LIPID PHOSPHORUS BY CHEMICAL METHOD

Apparatus Required

✧   Heating block with thermostatic control

✧   Spectrophotometer

- ✧ Perchloric acid fume hood
- ✧ Water bath
- ✧ N_2 evaporator

Reagents

- ✧ Perchloric acid (70%)
- ✧ Ammonium molybdate (2.5% w/v in de-ionized water)
- ✧ ANSA (1-amino-naphtol-4-sulfonic acid) reagent: Dissolve 12 g of $NaHSO_3$ in about 80 mL de-ionized water by stirring at room temperature. Then add 2.4 g of Na_2SO_3 and 0.2 g of ANSA. After further stirring for about 10 min to dissolve all ingredients, filter the solution through a Whatman No. 1 filter paper, and bring the volume to 100 mL with de-ionized water. Store at 4°C in a brown bottle, protected from light. This solution is stable for a least one month.

Standard Solution

- ✧ *Stock:* Dissolve 43.9 g of KH_2PO_4 (10 mg Pi) in deionized sterile water in a 100 mL volumetric flask. Bring the volume to 100 mL with deionized water and store at 4°C. If kept sterile, this solution is stable for at least six months.
- ✧ *Working solution*: Dilute 2.5 mL stock phosphorus standard to 25 mL with de-ionized sterile water, and store at 4°C. This solution contains 10 µg Pi/ mL and is stable for one month.

Lipid Extraction

Extract the total lipids from plasma or lipoprotein samples by the modified Bligh and Dyer procedure[34] as follows.

- ✧ Dilute aliquots of plasma or lipoprotein sample (equivalent to 25–100 µL plasma) to 0.4 mL with 0.15 mmol/L NaCl-1mmol/L EDTA in 13 × 100 mm disposable glass tubes.
- ✧ Add 1.0 mL methanol to each tube and vortex briefly (10 sec).
- ✧ Then add 0.5 mL chloroform, vortex, and let stand for 15 sec.
- ✧ Add another 0.5 mL chloroform and 0.5 mL water, briefly mixing after each addition.
- ✧ Centrifuge the tubes at 1000 × g at room temperature to separate the chloroform and aqueous layers.
- ✧ Using a Pasteur pipette, transfer the chloroform layer into a clean glass tube; add another 0.5 mL of chloroform to the original tube, vortex, and centrifuge.
- ✧ Combine the chloroform layer from this extract with the first extract.
- ✧ Evaporate the combined extracts under N_2 and redissolve in 100 µL of chloroform: methanol (2:1 v/v).

Lipid Digestion and Color Development

✧ Transfer aliquots of lipid extract (equivalent to 25 μL whole plasma) into disposable glass tubes (13 × 100 mm), and evaporate the solvent completely under a stream of nitrogen.

✧ Similarly, transfer KH_2PO_4 standards containing 0.5 to 5.0 μg Pi, and a reagent blank containing 100 μL water.

✧ Using a glass pipette and Pipet-Aid dispenser, add 0.4 mL of 70% perchloric acid to each tube, including the standards and blanks.

✧ Place all tubes in a block heater that has been pre-heated to 200° C in a perchloric acid hood and digest the samples for 20 min, or until all the yellow color disappears from the sample tubes.

✧ Cool the tubes to room temperature (in the fume hood) and add 3 mL de-ionized water, followed by 0.2 mL of ammonium molybdate solution and 80 μL of the ANSA reagent.

✧ Mix the tubes by vortexing and place them in a boiling water bath for 10 min.

✧ Remove the tubes from the water and allow to cool to room temperature.

✧ Take the readings in a spectrophotometer at 830 nm, adjusted for the reagent blank. The blue color is stable for at least 24h and therefore, analysis of several samples in the same batch is possible without loss of sensitivity or accuracy.

Calculations

From the optical density (OD) values of the standards, calculate the absorbance units/μg phosphorus. Divide the OD of the unknown sample by the above value to obtain the μg of lipid phosphorus in the unknown sample (25 μL plasma). Because there is one atom of phosphorus per mole of phospholipid, dividing the phosphorus value by 31 (atomic weight of phosphorus) gives the μmol of phospholipid in the sample. To convert μg phosphorus into mg weight percentage of phospholipids, multiply by 25 (taking the average mol weight of the phospholipid as 775) and the dilution factor.

$$\frac{\text{O.D of unknown (25 μL plasma)}}{\text{O.D of standard per μg Pi}} \times \frac{40}{31} = \text{mmol / L of plasma}$$

$$\frac{\text{O.D of unknown (25 μL plasma)}}{\text{O.D of standard per μg Pi}} \times \frac{25 \times 40 \times 100}{1000} = \text{mg phospholipid / dL plasma}$$

ESTIMATION OF LIPID-BOUND CHOLINE BY ENZYMATIC METHOD

Reagents

All reagents described here are based on the "phospholipids B" kit supplied by Wako Chemicals, Inc. (Richmond, VA). These reagents can be purchased in kit form from this company, or prepared in the laboratory, using ingredients purchased from other manufacturers (e.g., Sigma Chemical Co, St. Louis, MO; Roche Diagnostics, Indianapolis, IN).

1. Buffer (200 mL): 0.5 mmol/L Tris-Cl buffer, pH 8.0, containing 50 µg/mL $CaCl_2.H_2O$ and 0.05% phenol. Store at 4°C. This solutions is stable for at least two months.

2. Color reagent (50 mL):

    Phospholipase D from *Streptomyces chromofuscus* (EC 3.1.4.4)   24 units

    Choline oxidase (EC 1.1.3.17)   100 units

    Horse radish Peroxidase (EC 1.11.1.7)   270 units

    4-amino antipyrene   750 mg

    Make up all the ingredients in 50 mL of the above buffer solution (1). This solution is stable for at least two weeks at 4°C.

3. Standard solution (10 mL):

    Choline chloride: 3.87 mmol/L (equivalent to 300 mg/dL of phospholipid)

    Phenol: 0.1% (w/v)

    This solution is stable for at least one month at 4°C.

Procedure

Transfer 20 µL aliquots of plasma, standard solution, and 0.15 mol/L NaCl (reagent blank) into disposable glass tubes (13 × 100 mm). Add 3.0 mL of color reagent and mix the contents by vortexing. Place all the tubes in a water bath at 37°C for 10 min. Take the readings at 505 nm in a spectrophotometer adjusted for the reagent blank. The color is stable for more than two hours at room temperature.

Calculation

$$\frac{\text{O.D of sample}}{\text{O.D of standard}} \times 300 = \text{mg phospholipid / dL}$$

The above value may be converted to SI units by dividing by 77.5:

phospholipids (mg/dL)/77.5 = phospholipids (mmol/L)

When lipoprotein fractions are assayed, use samples equivalent to 50 µL of plasma.

Interfering Substances

Bilirubin up to 20 mg/dL (342 µmol/L) does not affect the reaction. However, ascorbic acid above 5 mg/dL (284 µmol/L) inhibits the color development. The presence of free choline in plasma gives spuriously high values, but less than 1% of total choline in plasma is known to be in free form. The reported inhibition of color development by EDTA in plasma samples[16] is overcome by the presence of $CaCl_2$ in the dilution buffer.

Measurement of Phospholipid Composition

While there are several methods for the quantitation of phospholipid subclasses, especially following their separation by HPLC, the following two methods are recommended, based on experience in the author's laboratory.

TLC SEPARATION AND PHOSPHORUS ESTIMATION:

Apparatus and Reagents:

These are the same as those used for the estimation of total phospholipids by the phosphate assay. The only additional pieces of equipment needed are a TLC chamber, an iodine chamber, a dry-air oven, and silica gel-coated TLC plates (commercially obtained from Whatman Inc, #K6 silica gel 60A).

Activate the TLC plate by placing in a dry air oven at 105° C for 30 min and cool to room temperature. Make lanes of 2 cm each on the plate by scoring with a needle. Using a capillary pipette, spot the lipid extracts, equivalent to 100 μL of whole plasma, on the lanes. Standards (50 μg each) of PC, LPC, and PE should be spotted on a separate lane to identify the spots. Develop the plate in the solvent system of chloroform:methanol:water (65:25:4 v/v) until the solvent reaches about 2 cm from the top of the plate. Lining the TLC chamber with filter paper increases the saturation of the chamber with solvent vapors and improves the reproducibility.

Remove the plate from the chamber and let it dry in a fume hood for a few minutes until the solvent smell is gone. Place the plate in an iodine chamber for about 30 sec; the lipids will appear as yellow spots. A TLC chamber with about 50 g of iodine crystals in the bottom and a glass lid is appropriate as an iodine chamber. Mark the spots corresponding to standard PC, LPC, and PE with a needle (Figure 25–2). The spot between LPC and PC is the SPH, which usually appears as a double spot. The faint spot between PE and PC is the mixture of PI and PS. These two lipids do not separate from each other in this solvent system. Since their concentrations in human plasma are very low, they are routinely estimated together.

After the iodine color disappears, scrape the spots with the help of a razor blade into individual glass tubes (13 × 100 mm). Add 0.4 mL of 70% perchloric acid into each tube, digest the lipids, and measure phosphorus as described for the total phospholipids. The presence of silica gel does not interfere with the color development, and the only extra step needed is to centrifuge the tubes at 1000 × g for 5 min to sediment the silica gel before taking the readings of the supernatant solutions in a spectrophotometer. For each batch of plates, estimate phosphorus from an area of the blank plate 4 cm^2, to correct for any interference from silica gel. Most commercially available plates do not show any phosphorus.

Figure 25–2 ✧ Schematic Diagram of TLC Separation of Plasma Phospholipids (not drawn to scale)

Abbreviations:

LPC = lysophosphatidyl choline

PC = phosphatidyl choline

PE = phosphatidyl ethanolamine

PI = phosphatidyl inositol

PS = phosphatidyl serine

SPH = sphingomyelin

Neutral
Lipids

PE

PI+PS

PC

SPH

LPC

Calculations:

$$\frac{\text{OD of unknown (100 } \mu\text{L plasma)}}{\text{OD}/\mu\text{g Pi standard}} \times \frac{10}{31} = \text{mmol}/\text{L of plasma}$$

To calculate the mg% value, multiply the above value (mmol/ L) by 77.5 for PC, PE, PI+PS, and SPH, and by 50 for LPC.

HPLC SEPARATION AND QUANTITATION BY
A LIGHT-SCATTERING DETECTOR

Apparatus

✧   HPLC machine with gradient capabilities

✧   Evaporative light scattering detector (ELSD) (Alltech Associates, Deerfield, IL)

✧   HPLC column (46 × 250 mm) silica column (5 μ), with a guard column

Solvent Mixture

Use only HPLC-grade solvents. All solvents must be filtered through 0.45-μ filters, and degassed by bubbling helium or nitrogen before use.

The gradient system described by Becart et al[35] is recommended with the flow rate set at 1.0 mL/min throughout.

Solvent A: chloroform: methanol: 30% ammonium hydroxide (80: 19.5: 0.5 v/v)

Solvent B: chloroform: methanol: water: 30% ammonium hydroxide (60: 34: 5.5: 0.5 v/v)

Set the gradient program as follows:

Time (min)	% of A	% of B
0	100	0
14	0	100
23	0	100
29	100	0
34	100	0

The last step returns the column to the initial setting, ready for the injection of the next sample.

Figure 25–3 ✧ HPLC Separation of Human Plasma Phospholipids, and Quantitation by a Light-Scattering Detector

A: Neutral lipids, including free and esterified cholesterol, and triglycerides.
B: Free fatty acids and unidentified neutral lipids.
The detector response is in arbitrary units.

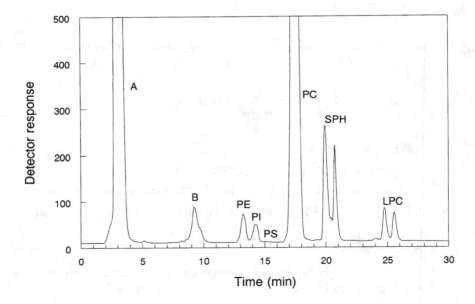

ELSD Detector Settings

N$_2$ gas flow, 1.6 L/min; drift tube temperature, 50° C.

Inject total lipid extract corresponding to 50 μl plasma into the column and record the detector output using a computer-based data management system.

The response factor for each phospholipid should be determined by using standards, and the concentrations of various phospholipids should then be calculated by entering the predetermined response factors into the program. Figure 25–3 shows a typical chromatogram for the separation of human plasma phospholipids (corresponding to 50 μl plasma). The peak for PS is barely visible at this concentration, between PC and PI. Both SPH and LPC appear as double peaks, and the two peaks are combined for the calculation.

The concentrations determined by this method agree closely with those measured by the TLC method. However, because the factors are non-linear and vary significantly among different phospholipids, it is important to determine these factors in the ranges expected in the samples and with the specific data management program employed. It should be pointed out that the response factors are lower for the phospholipids normally present in low concentrations in human plasma (PI, PS, LPC), than for PC, PE, and SPH. ✧

Acknowledgments: *The original research referred to in this chapter was supported by a grant from the National Institutes of Health, #HL 52597. The technical assistance of Mr. Wilfred Buchanan is gratefully acknowledged.*

REFERENCES

1. Edelstein C. General properties of plasma lipoproteins and apolipoproteins. In: Scanu AM, Spector AA, eds. Biochemistry and biology of plasma lipoproteins. New York: Marcel Dekker, 1986:495–505.
2. Fournier N, de la Llera Moya M, Burkey BF, Swaney JB, Paterniti J Jr, Moatti N et al. Role of HDL phospholipid in efflux of cell cholesterol to whole serum: studies with human apo A-I transgenic rats. J Lipid Res 1996;37:1704–11.
3. Gershfeld NL. Selective phospholipid adsorption and atherosclerosis. Science 1979;204:506–8.
4. Miettinen A, Naukkarinen V, Huttunen JK, Mattila S, Kumlin T. Fatty acid composition of serum lipids predicts myocardial infarction. Br Med J 1982;285:993–6.
5. Blank ML, Robinson M, Fitzearald V, Snyder F. Novel quantitative method for determination of molecular species of phospholipids and diglycerides. J Chromatogr 1984;298:473–82.
6. Shinozaki K, Kawasaki T, Kambayashi J, Sakon M, Shiba E, Uemura Y et al. A new method of purification and sensitive bioassay of platelet-activating factor (PAF) in human whole blood. Life Sci 1994;54:429–37.
7. Sestak TL, Subbaiah PV, Jaskowiak NT, Bagdade JD. A high-performance liquid chromatographic procedure for the determination of disaturated phosphatidylcholine in human plasma. Anal Biochem 1990;191:156–9.
8. Schulz R, Strynadka KD, Panas DL, Olley PM, Lopaschuk GD. Analysis of myocardial plasmalogen and diacyl phospholipids and their arachidonic acid content using high-performance liquid chromatography. Anal Biochem 1993;213:140–6.
9. Miyazawa T, Fujimoto K, Oikawa S. Determination of lipid hydroperoxides in low-den-

sity lipoprotein from human plasma using high-performance liquid chromatography with chemiluminescence detection. Biomed Chromatogr 1990;4:131–4.

10. Schlame M, Haupt R, Wiswedel I, Kox WJ, Rustow B. Identification of short-chain oxidized phosphatidylcholine in human plasma. J Lipid Res 1996;37:2608–15.

11. Ravandi A, Kuksis A, Marai L, Myher JJ, Steiner G, Lewisa G, Kamido H. Isolation and identification of glycated aminophospholipids from red cells and plasma of diabetic blood. FEBS Letters 1996;381:77–81.

12. Jalink K, Hordijk PL, Moolenaar WH. Growth-factor-like effects of lysophosphatidic acid, a novel lipid mediator. Bba-Rev Cancer 1994;1198:185–96.

13. Stewart JCM. Colorimetric determination of phospholipids with ammonium ferrothiocyanate. Anal Biochem 1980;104:10–4.

14. Sandhu RS. Serum phospholipids determined without acid digestion. Clin Chem 1976;22:1973–5.

15. Jouanel P, Motta C, Delattre J, Dastugue B. A rapid and sensitive fluorometric assay of serum phospholipid. Clin Chim Acta 1980;105:173–81.

16. Cham BE, Mahon M, Kostner K, Dwivedy A, Fang NX, Iannuzzi C. Phospholipids in EDTA-treated plasma and serum. Clin Chem 1993;39:2347–8.

17. Gluck L, Kulovich MW, Borer RC. Diagnosis of the respiratory distress syndrome by amniocentesis. Am J Obstet Gynecol 1971;109:440–5.

18. Myher JJ, Kuksis A, Pind S. Molecular species of glycerophospholipids and sphingomyelins of human plasma: comparison to red blood cells. Lipids 1989;24:408–18.

19. Kates, M. Techniques of lipidology. Isolation, analysis, and identification of lipids. In: Work TS and Work E (eds.). Laboratory techniques in biochemistry and molecular biology.New York: North Holland Publishing Co., 1972;[3]393–465.

20. Patton GM, Fasulo JM, Robins SJ. Analysis of lipids by high-performance liquid chromatography: Part I. J Nutr Biochem 1990;1:493–500.

21. Kuksis A, Myher JJ, Geher K, Jones GJL, Shepherd J, Packard CJ et al. Effect of saturated and unsaturated fat diets on lipid profiles of plasma lipoproteins. Atherosclerosis 1982;41:221–40.

22. Nourisorkhabi MH, Agar NS, Sullivan DR, Gallagher C, Kuchel PW. Phospholipid composition of erythrocyte membranes and plasma of mammalian blood including Australian marsupials; Quantitative P-31 NMR analysis using detergent. Comp Biochem Physiol [B] 1996;113:221–7.

23. Kuliszkiewicz-Jaus M, Janus W, Baczynski S. Application of 31P NMR spectroscopy in clinical analysis of changes of serum phospholipids in leukemia, lympoma, and some other non-haematologic cancers. Anticancer Res 1996;16:1587–94.

24. Bovet P, Darioli R, Essinger A, Golay A, Sigwart U, Kappenberger L. Phospholipids and other lipids in angiographically assessed coronary artery disease. Atherosclerosis 1989;80:41–7.

25. Subbaiah PV, Davidson MH, Ritter MC, Buchanan W, Bagdade JD. Effects of dietary supplementation with marine lipid concentrate on the plasma lipoprotein composition of hypercholesterolemic patients. Atherosclerosis 1989;79:157–66.

26. Sebedio JL. Utilization of thin-layer chromatography-flame ionization detection for lipid analysis. In: Sebedio JL, Perkins EG, eds. New trends in lipid and lipoprotein analyses. Champaign, IL: AOCS press, 1995:24–37.

27. Bernhard W, Linck M, Creutzburg H, Postle AD, Arning A, Martin-Carrera I, Sewing KF. High-performance liquid chromatographic analysis of phospholipids from different sources with combined flourescence and ultraviolet detection. Anal Biochem 1994;220:172–1780.

28. Boswart J, Schmidt T, Kostiuk P, Pacakova V, Stulik K. High-performance liquid chromatographic determination of some polar phospholipids in serum. J Chromatogr 1989;495:61–70.

29. Maxwell RJ, Nungesser EH, Marmer WN, Foglia TA. HPLC with flame ionization detection: class separation, linearity of response, and quantification of sterols, glycerides, and phospholipids. LC-GC 1987;5:829–33.

30. Kuypers FA, Bütikofer P, Shackleton CHL. Application of liquid chromatography-thermospray mass spectrometry in the analysis of glycerophospholipid molecular species. J Chromatogr Biomed Appl 1991;562:191–206.

31. Christie WW. Rapid separation and quantification of lipid classes by high-performance liquid chromatography and mass (light-scattering) detection. J Lipid Res 1985;26:507–12.

32. Porter NA, Wolf RA, Nixon JR. Separation and purification of lecithins by high-pressure liquid chromatography. Lipids 1978;14:20–4.

33. Blaton V, DeBuyzere M, Spincemaille J, Declercq B. Enzymic assay for phosphatidyl-choline and sphingomyelin in serum. Clin Chem 1996;29:806–9.

34. Bligh EG, Dyer WJ. A rapid method of total lipid extraction and purification. Can J Biochem Physiol 1959;37:911–7.

35. Becart J, Chevalier C, Biesse JP. Quantitative analysis of phospholipids by HPLC with a light-scattering evaporative detector. Application to raw materials for cosmetic use. J High Res Chromatogr 1990;13:126–9.

36. Kuksis A, Myher JJ, Geher K, Jones GJL, Breckenridge WC, Feather T et al. Decreased plasma phosphatidyl choline/free cholesterol ratio as an indicator of risk for ischemic vascular disease. Atherosclerosis 1982;2:296–302.

37. Perova NV, Shcherbakova IA, Nechaev AS, Nikitina NA, Metel'skaia VA. Indicators of the atherogenic properties of plasma lipoproteins and coronary atherosclerosis (selective angiography data). Kardiologiia 1985;25:91–5.

38. Mai FT, Liakishev AA, Polesskii VA, Sidorenko BA, Gerasimova EN. Phospholipid content of subfractions of high-density lipoproteins in women with angiographically documented coronary arteriosclerosis. Kardiologiia 1983;23:33–7.

39. Ozerova IN, Gerasimova EN, Mai FT, Kurdanov KhA. Esterifying activity of the plasma in patients with ischemic heart disease. Vopr Med Khim 1984;30:118–23.

40. Kunz F, Pechlaner C, Erhart R, Fend F, Muhlberger V. HDL and plasma phospholipids in coronary artery disease. Arterioscler Thromb 1994;14:1146–50.

41. Pham TM, Torkhovskaia TI, Ozerova IN, Polesskii VA, Kurdanov KhA. Changes in the indices affecting the phospholipid structure of high-density lipoprotein subfractions in ischemic heart disease. Vopr Med Khim 1981;27:701–6.

42. Shattil SJ, Bennett JS, Colman RW, Cooper RA. Abnormalities of cholesterol-phospholipid composition in platelets and low-density lipoproteins of human hyperbetalipoproteinemia. J Lab Clin Med 1977;89:341–53.

43. Ziegler O, Mejean L, Igau B, Fruchart JC, Drouin P, Fievet C. Accessibility of human apolipoprotein B-100 epitopes in insulin-dependent diabetes: Relation with the surface lipid environment of atherogenic particles. Diabetes Metab 1996;22:179–84.

44. Bagdade JD, Subbaiah PV. Abnormal high-density lipoprotein composition in women with insulin-dependent diabetes. J Lab Clin Med 1989;113:235–40.

45. Akaike M, Kikuchi K, Aramaki T, Okumura H. High-density lipoprotein phospholipid concentrations in serum of patients with liver disease. Clin Chem 1985;31:1083–4.

46. Miller JP. Dyslipoproteinaemia of liver disease. Baillieres Clin Endocrinol Metab 1990;4:807–32.

47. Dessi S, Batetta B, Spano O, Sanna F, Tonello M, Giacchino M et al. Clinical remission is associated with restoration of normal high-density lipoprotein cholesterol levels in children with malignancies. Clin Sci 1995;89:505–10.

48. Xu Y, Shen ZZ, Wiper DW, Wu MZ, Morton RE, Elson P et al. Lysophosphatidic acid as a potential biomarker for ovarian and other gynecologic cancers. JAMA 1998;280:719–23:15.

49. Sasagawa T, Okita M, Murakami J, Kato T, Watanabe A. Abnormal serum lysophospholipids in multiple myeloma patients. Lipids 1999;34:17–21:7.

50. Sall ND, Toure M, Fall S, Sarr NG, Ndiaye NM, Seck I, Ndiaye IP. Phospholipid levels in exploration of cerebral atherosclerosis in African Senegalese population. Dakar Medical 1994;39:77–80.

51. Gibson RA, Teubner JK, Haines K, Cooper DM, Davidson GP. Relationships between

pulmonary function and plasma fatty acid levels in cystic fibrosis patients. J Pediatr Gastroenterol Nutr 1986;5:408–15.

52. Owen JS, Gillett MP. Lecithin:cholesterol acyltransferase deficiency associated with hepatic schistosomiasis mansoni. Scand J Clin Lab Invest - Supplement 1978;150:194–8.

53. Harris RL, Cottam GL, Johnston JM, Baxter CR. The pathogenesis of abnormal erythrocyte morphology in burns. J Trauma-Injury Infect Crit Care 1981;21:13–21.

Determination and Clinical Significance of Nonesterified Fatty Acids

26

Henry J. Pownall

✧   Nonesterified fatty acids (NEFA), or free fatty acids, are fundamental units in the structure of lipids in membranes and lipoproteins. NEFA form esters of cholesterol and glycerol, which ultimately form the fatty inclusions of hepatocytes[1] and adipocytes, the cores of low-density and very-low-density lipoproteins (LDL and VLDL),[2] and the lipid droplets in the foam cells of atherosclerotic lesions.[3] They are also an important source of energy for the heart and for aerobically conditioned skeletal muscle.

Plasma NEFA concentrations are increased in three related pathologic states that tend to cluster in individuals and that have been implicated in premature coronary artery disease: obesity, type 2 diabetes mellitus, and elevated plasma triglyceride.[4–8] Among other factors included in the cluster—termed the cardiovascular metabolic syndrome, insulin resistance syndrome, or metabolic syndrome X—is a reduced concentration of high-density lipoprotein (HDL) cholesterol, a reduction that occurs through the exchange of HDL cholesteryl ester for triglyceride in VLDL and chylomicrons.[9,10] In type 2 diabetes mellitus, insulin resistance in multiple tissue sites, especially adipose tissue, leads to impaired NEFA uptake and a rise in plasma NEFA and triglyceride concentrations.[11–13] In vitro studies have shown that several important cell types, including hepatocytes,[14] adipocytes,[6,7,12,13] smooth muscle cells,[15] and neutrophils,[16] exhibit an active NEFA metabolism that may be impaired in pathologic states.

The mechanism of NEFA transfer between lipoproteins and between lipoproteins and cell membranes is important to our understanding of lipid metabolism. There is some consensus that fatty acids transfer between lipid and protein surfaces by means of rate-limiting desorption followed by diffusion-controlled uptake by an acceptor lipid surface or protein. This rate increases or decreases according to the degree of unsaturation and the chain length of the fatty acids, respectively.[17–19]

The mechanism of lipid translocation across cell membranes remains unresolved. Some evidence favors a protein-mediated translocation mechanism. Candidate proteins include FAT/CD36, which is a receptor for oxidized LDL; plasma membrane fatty acid–binding protein (FABP$_{pm}$), which is a membrane-bound form of mitochondrial aspartate aminotransferase; and fatty acid transport protein (FATP) and the yeast homologue FAT1, both of which appear to be fatty acyl-coenzyme A synthases.[20] Convincing evidence that any of them are directly involved in fatty acid translocation is lacking. Most evidence for assignment of these proteins as fatty acid translocators has been obtained in living cells in which the protein might increase fatty acid transport by an indirect effect such as activation of NEFA utilization or conversion to glycerolipids. Indeed, none of the candidate translocators have been shown to catalyze fatty acid transport in a system in which no other proteins are present. Finally, more recent evidence suggests that only long-chain fatty acids require a translocator. This may be due, however, to a chain length effect on desorption following translocation and not the flip-flop step itself.[17-19] Other evidence suggests that fatty acids spontaneously transfer across cell membranes and that differences in rates of transfer of fatty acids are simply a reflection of the metabolic state of the cell.[11]

In humans, the major fatty acids contain an even number of carbon atoms in straight chains. Each chain contains 14 to 22 carbon atoms and may have from zero to six double bonds; fatty acids with zero, one, two, and three or more are called saturated, monounsaturated, di-unsaturated, and polyunsaturated. The physical effect of increasing the number of double bonds in a fatty acid is a reduction in the melting point. The physiologic effects of unsaturation are much broader. Many of the acyltransferases that utilize fatty acids or their acyl-coenzyme A analogues have a specificity that varies according to unsaturation and chain length. In addition, some fatty acids are precursors to other bioregulatory molecules such as the eicosanoids and prostaglandins.

Fatty acids are usually described in terms of the number of carbon atoms (n) and the number of double bonds (m); they are named according to the location of the double bonds. Carboxyl-carbon, for example, is C_1. The double bonds in nearly all naturally occurring fatty acids are in the *cis* configuration.

Fat that is intended for human consumption is frequently hydrogenated to improve its shelf life. This has two important effects: decreasing the number of double bonds and converting the fats from liquid to solid form. A side reaction is the conversion of some double bonds from the *cis* to the *trans* configuration; the resulting more solid product appears to be nearly as atherogenic as saturated fatty acids.[21]

Cold-water fish such as salmon contain a special class of fatty acids, to which another nomenclature has been applied: they are called omega-3, or n-3, fatty acids. In this system, the location of double bonds is indicated by counting from the last carbon (omega, n = 1), which is typically in a methyl group, to the position of the first carbon atom in each double bond. Fish oil has important physiologic effects that may reduce risk for cardiovascular disease, among them reductions of blood pressure,[22] plasma triglyceride,[23] and platelet aggregation.[24] Omega-3 fatty acids reduce plasma concentrations of soluble forms of the cellular adhesion molecules ICAM-1 (intracellular adhesion molecule 1) and E-selection, thereby possibly altering vascular cell activation.[25]

Representative examples of fatty acids found in human plasma and tissues are shown in Table 26–1. In humans, the fatty acid composition of plasma NEFA, plasma lipoproteins, and, to a lesser extent, adipose tissue, is a function of the fatty acid composition of the diet. The effects of diets rich in saturated, monounsaturated, polyunsaturated, and omega-3 fatty acids on NEFA and on the composition of classes of lipoproteins have been reported.[26] For the sake of brevity and illustration, only effects on NEFA composition are shown in Table 26–2. Plasma NEFA and lipoproteins contain a higher fraction of those fatty acids increased in the diet. Effects are likely to be con-

Table 26–1 ✧ Structures of Typical Fatty Acids Found in Human Diets, Plasma, and Tissues

Fatty Acid		Structure
Saturated	Palmitic	$CH_3(CH_2)_{14}COOH$
	Stearic	$CH_3(CH_2)_{16}COOH$
Monounsaturated	Oleic	$CH_3(CH_2)_7CH= CH(CH_2)_7COOH$
	Linoleic	$CH_3(CH_2)_7CH= CH(CH_2)_7COOH$
Omega-6 polyunsaturated	Linoleic	$CH_3(CH_2)_4(CH=CHCH_2)_2(CH_2)_6COOH$
	Linolenic	$CH_3(CH_2)_4(CH=CHCH_2)_3(CH_2)_3COOH$
	Arachidonic	$CH_3(CH_2)_4(CH=CHCH_2)_4(CH_2)_2COOH$
Omega-3 polyunsaturated	Eicosapentaenoic	$CH_3(CH_2)_4(CH=CHCH_2)_5(CH_2)_2COOH$
	Docosahexaenoic	$CH_3(CH_2)_4(CH=CHCH_2)_6(CH_2)_2COOH$

nected to the cholesterol-lowering effects of diets in which polyunsaturated fatty acids replace saturated fatty acids; according to the Hegsted equation,[27] the change in total plasma cholesterol concentration (ΔTC, mg/dL) in response to a change in the composition of the diet is given by the following equation:

$$\Delta TC = 2.16\ \Delta S - 1.65\ \Delta P + 0.068\ \Delta C,$$

where S and P are the percentages of calories derived from saturated and polyunsaturated fatty acids, and C is the daily consumption of cholesterol (mg/day).

EXPERIMENTAL PLAN AND SAMPLING

From the brief summary given above, it is clear that fatty acid analyses provide important information about lipid metabolism for both clinical and basic research. In particular, because of the possible role of NEFA in the pathogenesis of obesity and type 2 diabetes mellitus, and ultimately atherosclerosis, accuracy in measurement in vitro and in vivo is crucial. Relevant analyses include those that provide the fatty acid compositions of total NEFA, of unbound NEFA, and of cholesteryl, glyceryl, and phosphoglyceryl esters. The analyses may be performed in tissue culture medium, plasma, and cell membranes, each of which may require special handling to prevent changes in fatty acid composition. Such changes may result from a variety of lipolytic processes occurring between the time of sampling and analysis. For longitudinal trials in which some analytes are not measured for several weeks or even months after collection, it is important to collect and store samples under conditions that minimize degradation.

Table 26–2 ✧ Nonesterified Fatty Acids in Plasma Following Four Dietary Interventions in Normolipidemic Men (N=20)

Fatty Acid[a]	Dietary Fat (30% of Calories) Consisting Mainly of			
	Saturated Fat	Monounsaturated Fat	Polyunsaturated Fat	Polyunsaturated Fat + n-3 Fatty Acids
14:0 (S)	2.49	2.14	1.94	2.17
16:0 (S)	23.95	25.10	23.03	27.78
16:1 (M)	3.40	2.42	2.93	3.02
18:0 (S)	9.07	8.10	10.13	8.26
18:1 (M)	38.43	38.15	32.17	31.69
18:2 (P)	19.71	20.07	23.47	19.20
18:3 (P)	0.22	0.07	0.60	0.48
18:4 (P)	0.00	0.00	0.52	0.07
20:3 (P)	0.73	0.00	0.99	0.00
20:4 (P)	0.54	1.82	1.99	1.51
20:5 (n)	0.20	1.25	0.00	2.73
22:6 (n)	1.24	0.89	0.24	3.10

Source: Data from Pownall et al.[26]
[a]S = saturated; M = monounsaturated; P = polyunsaturated; n = omega-3

Plasma NEFA concentration is difficult to quantify validly by a single measurement because of intraindividual biologic variation. In a study of 12 healthy subjects (6 men and 6 women, mean age 22.7 ± 1.5 years), day-to-day variation of NEFA on 12 consecutive days following an overnight fast was 376 µmol/L or 45% (means of within-subject biologic variation).[28] Therefore, it is advised that multiple measurements on different days be made to obtain more accurate values.

Zambon et al. assessed a number of techniques for reliability in determining plasma NEFA concentration.[29] One of the problems that had to be resolved was the artifactual elevation of plasma NEFA as the result of in vitro lipolysis following blood collection. The problem was particularly acute in hypertriglyceridemic plasma or following the administration of heparin. To minimize in vitro hydrolysis, paraoxon, a cholinesterase inhibitor, was added to the plasma sample immediately after blood collection and separation. Paraoxon proved to be an effective inhibitor of lipolysis in preheparin plasma at room temperature for 2 hours and in postheparin plasma stored immediately at $-20°C$. Inhibition with paraoxon was not necessary for preheparin samples that were collected and immediately transferred to ice and assayed or stored at $-70°C$ for up to 60 days before assaying. Thus, it is advisable to use paraoxon as an inhibitor of lipolytic activity in postheparin plasma and to store these samples at $-70°C$ if analyses are to be performed at a later date. (Note to the reader: Paraoxon is a nerve agent—use a fume hood if you plan to follow this procedure.)

If plasma is to be analyzed for NEFA after long-term storage, verify that the analyte concentration remains stable for the term of storage. Optimal handling would probably involve blood collection in paraoxon-coated tubes, immediate transfer to ice, separation at $0°C$ to $4°C$, and storage at $-70°C$.

NEFA ANALYSIS

Several methods are commonly used for NEFA analysis; each has its advantages and disadvantages. Before a method is chosen, consider the skill of the technical personnel, the cost of reagents, the instrumentation needed, and the precision and accuracy of the method. In choosing a method for clinical studies, consider and evaluate each method to determine which best addresses the study's objectives.

Direct Chemical Analysis

The titration method of Dole[30] is a proven method that involves the extraction of plasma with 40 parts 2-propanol, 10 parts heptane, and 1 part sulfuric acid. The acid provides the protons that give NEFA the neutrality necessary for solubilization in the organic phase. Typically, 5 parts of the extraction mixture are mixed with 1 part plasma by vortexing. The organic phase is collected, and thymol blue indicator blanks without fatty acids and palmitic acid standards within the range of normal, hypertriglyceridemic, or diabetic plasma (0.3–1.0 mmol/L) are treated in the same way. Freshly prepared NaOH in absolute ethanol is used to titrate the samples while the sample is gently agitated. The volume of the titrant is recorded at the endpoint, and the NEFA concentration measured on the basis of the calibration curve that is recorded with a range of palmitic acid concentrations.

This method requires very little specialized equipment and is a direct chemical method in which the stoichiometry between titrant and NEFA is known. It is, however, time-consuming, requires greater technical skill than some other methods, and does not give the concentration of individual fatty acid species.

High-Performance Liquid Chromatographic Analysis of Fluorescent NEFA Esters

Several methods in which NEFA are derivatized with a fluorescent reagent have been described. The reagents include 5-bromomethyl fluorescein,[31] 9-anthryldiazomethane

(ADAM),[32] 4-(2-carbazoylpyrrolidin-1-yl)-7-(*N,N*-dimethylaminosulfonyl)-2,1,3-benzoxadiazole,[33] 2-(4-hydrazinocarbonylphenyl)-4,5-diphenylimidazole,[34] and *p*-bromophenacyl bromide.[35] All these derivatives are suitable for the determination of total fatty acid concentration and fatty acid composition. However, the conditions have been best detailed for ADAM[32] and *p*-bromophenacyl bromide.[35] Both procedures begin with a Dole extraction followed by derivatization to the fluorescent ester, which can be detected by monitoring the fluorescence of the effluent from a reverse-phase high-performance liquid chromatography column. The limits of sensitivity are a function of the absorption and fluorescence properties of the derivative. An optimal derivatizing agent would selectively react with fatty acids, and it would have a high extinction coefficient in a spectral range where light sources have their most intense outputs. Furthermore, the fluorescence of the derivatized fatty acid should have a high quantum yield that is independent of the structure of the acyl chain, and appear in a spectral range where detectors have high sensitivity. As the cost of lasers falls and their power and reliability improve, it is likely that more commercial instruments will use a laser source.[31]

The advantages of high-performance liquid chromatographic methods combined with fluorescence detection are high sensitivity and discrimination of most fatty acid species. As technology improves, it is likely that newer methods with improved molecular species discrimination and sensitivity will be developed. The disadvantages of these methods are that they require expensive instrumentation and sophisticated technical support, and their results may be confounded by other carboxyl-containing species that form fluorescent derivatives. Before these methods are embraced for any study, they should be thoroughly evaluated in systems with a predetermined fatty acid composition and concentration.

Analysis of Unbound Fatty Acids

In plasma, most NEFA are associated with albumin and plasma lipoproteins. The fraction associated with lipoproteins is greatly increased in physiologic states (such as diabetes) in which there are high plasma concentrations of fatty acids.[36] However, as with all sparingly soluble substances, a small fraction of the NEFA circulates in the hydrated and unbound state. The concentration of this fraction may be very important physiologically, because the transport of those NEFA is very close to diffusion controlled. As a consequence, the concentration of unbound NEFA is an important determinant of fatty acid flow into cells.

In the past, the concentration of unbound fatty acids could be determined only by methods such as equilibrium dialysis, gel filtration, and ultracentrifugation, all of which are model dependent and require some expensive instrumentation. Recently, Richieri and Kleinfeld described a fluorescence method that gives the concentration of unbound NEFA.[37] The method uses intestinal fatty acid–binding protein that has been tagged with the fluorescent probe acrylodan. The labeled protein, ADIFAB, is nonfluorescent in the absence of NEFA and exhibits increasing fluorescence as the NEFA concentration increases. On the basis of this method the mean concentration of unbound NEFA in serum was 7.5 nmol/L, which was six orders of magnitude lower than the mean concentration of total serum NEFA.[37]

Because the concentration of unbound NEFA increases exponentially with the ratio of total NEFA to albumin, the method is a sensitive one for assessment of physiologic status. It is anticipated that these measurements will be increasingly applied to the study of obesity, diabetes, and atherosclerosis.

Gas Chromatographic Analysis

Several methods for the gas chromatographic analysis of fatty acids have been described. Most are laborious because they involve an extraction method.[38–41] A more recent report describes a procedure in which plasma NEFA are directly esterified by a 2% solution of acetyl chloride in methanol that contains an internal standard.[42] The resulting esters are extracted into hexane and an aliquot is injected into a gas chromatograph. The concentrations of the fatty acids are calculated by comparing the integrated area under their respective peaks with an internal standard (tridecanoic acid) of known concentration.

This procedure has the advantages of relative simplicity and the ability to provide the concentrations of individual fatty acid classes. The disadvantages are that it requires a gas chromatograph and it is not as sensitive as some of the fluorescence-based assays. In addition, according to one report[43] and our experiences with this assay, the treatment of plasma with methanolic acetyl chloride is associated with some hydrolysis of plasma acyl esters. Nevertheless, the procedure is useful if the spontaneous hydrolysis is less than the amount of analyte being estimated. Additional method development is needed to improve this otherwise convenient assay.

Enzymatic Analysis

Several procedures for the enzymatic determination of NEFA have been reported,[44–46] and with the availability of commercial kits these methods have enjoyed wide use. Like other kits, the one supplied by Wako Chemicals (Richmond, VA) involves a complex and yet reliable chemistry. The method relies on the formation of acyl-coenzyme A from NEFA and coenzyme A in the presence of acyl-coenzyme A synthase. The resulting acyl-coenzyme A is treated with acyl-coenzyme A oxidase, thereby liberating hydrogen peroxide, which in the presence of peroxidase leads to the oxidative condensation of 3-methyl-N-ethyl-N-(β-hydroethyl)-aniline, with 4-aminoantipyrine giving a colored adduct that can be quantified spectrophotometrically. The amount of NEFA in the sample can be calculated on the basis of absorption at 550 nm, and a calibration curve prepared with standards having known concentrations.

The advantages of the procedure are its simplicity; it requires only a spectrophotometer. The disadvantages are the low sensitivity (>0.1 mmol/L) and the inability to quantify individual NEFA species. In addition, there is reduced sensitivity against long-chain polyunsaturated fatty acids such as arachidonate, eicosapentaenoate, and docosahexaenoate, so that the plasma NEFA of patients on diets containing long-chain omega-3 fatty acids will be underreported.

Colorimetric Methods

Several colorimetric methods have been reported.[47–49] They are generally indirect methods based on the partitioning of copper into soaps formed by fatty acids. They are time-consuming and not very sensitive. Any future development of a NEFA assay that might employ an absorbance measurement is likely to be displaced by a more sensitive fluorescence method based on similar chemistry.

Mass Spectrometric Methods

Over the past few years, the mass spectrometer has risen to a new level of popularity as a laboratory tool because of declining instrument costs and simpler instrument operation. In most mass spectrometric applications, NEFA are separated by either gas chromatography or high-performance liquid chromatography that is in line with the mass spectrometer.

Mass spectrometric methods are very sensitive and can easily detect 1 pmol/L. In addition, there is no ambiguity with respect to the identity of the fatty acid because the mass spectrometer, which is used as the detector, gives the molecular mass. Finally, NEFA assays based on high-performance liquid chromatography or gas chromatography can also be used to determine isotope ratios in stable-isotope metabolic studies of NEFA turnover.[50]

FINAL PERSPECTIVES

Some of the methods cited here are also applicable to the analysis of fatty acids liberated from glycerol esters such as triglyceride and phosphatidylcholine by treatment with a base or with an enzyme. However, gas chromatographic analysis of fatty acid methyl esters liberated by treatment with methanolic base and boron trifluoride is likely to be simpler than fluorescence or colorimetric methods. Given the relatively high concentrations of fatty acid esters compared with NEFA in most biologic fluids, much smaller sample volumes can usually be used.

The choice of method in a given application will depend on the number of samples to be run, the amount of sample available, and the possible need to measure all NEFA species. In all cases it is advisable to collect samples and cool immediately with an ice bath to minimize lipolysis. If samples cannot be analyzed immediately, they should be stored in the presence of paraoxon at −70°C, particularly if they are from hypertriglyceridemic and/or postheparin plasma. If an enzymatic method is used, the paraoxon could interfere with the assay and storage will have to be at −70°C in the absence of paraoxon. For small studies, it is more economical to separate fatty acids from other lipids by thin-layer or high-performance liquid chromatography and to analyze the respective band or peak by a gas chromatography of methyl esters or similarly formed fluorescent derivatives. For large studies, it is usually more economical to use one of the enzymatic kits. In all cases, the appropriate quality assurance and quality control measures should be in place before such a study is begun. ✧

REFERENCES

1. Goldblatt PJ, Gunning WT III. Ultrastructure of the liver and biliary tract in health and disease. Ann Clin Lab Sci 1984;14:159–67.

2. Miller KW, Small DW. Structure of triglyceride-rich lipoproteins: an analysis of core and surface phases. In: Gotto AM Jr (ed.). Plasma Lipoproteins. New Comprehensive Biochemistry, vol. 14. New York: Elsevier, 1987:1–71.

3. Tabas I. The stimulation of the cholesterol esterification pathway by atherogenic lipoproteins in macrophages. Curr Opin Lipidol 1995;6:260–8.

4. Schneider DJ, Sobel BE. Synergistic augmentation of expression of plasminogen activator inhibitor type-1 induced by insulin, very-low-density lipoproteins, and fatty acids. Coron Artery Dis 1996;7:813–7.

5. Lewis GF, Uffelman KD, Szeto LW, Weller B, Steiner G. Interaction between free fatty acids and insulin in the acute control of very low density lipoprotein production in humans. J Clin Invest 1995;95:158–66.

6. Egan BM, Hennes MMI, Stepniakowski KT, O'Shaughnessy IM, Kissebah AH, Goodfriend TL. Obesity hypertension is related more to insulin's fatty acid than glucose action. Hypertension 1996;27:723–8.

7. Laws A. Free fatty acids, insulin resistance and lipoprotein metabolism. Curr Opin Lipidol 1996;7:172–7.

8. Hopkins PN, Hunt SC, Wu LL, Williams GH, Williams RR. Hypertension, dyslipidemia, and insulin resistance: links in a chain or spokes on a wheel? Curr Opin Lipidol 1996;7:241–53.

9. Deckelbaum RJ, Granot E, Oschry Y, Rose L, Eisenberg S. Plasma triglyceride determines structure-composition in low and high density lipoproteins. Arteriosclerosis 1984;4:225–31.

10. Patsch JR, Prasad S, Gotto AM Jr, Patsch W. High-density lipoproteins$_2$: relationship of the plasma levels of this lipoprotein species to its composition, to the magnitude of postprandial lipemia, and to the activities of lipoprotein lipase and hepatic lipase. J Clin Invest 1987;80:341–7.

11. Civelek VN, Hamilton JA, Tornheim K, Kelly KL, Corkey BE. Intracellular pH in adipocytes: effects of free fatty acid diffusion across the plasma membrane, lipolytic agonists, and insulin. Proc Natl Acad Sci U S A 1996;93:10139–44.

12. Frayn KN, Williams CM, Arner P. Are increased plasma nonesterified fatty acid concentrations a risk factor for coronary heart disease and other chronic diseases? Clin Sci (Colch) 1996;90:243–53.

13. Schwartz MW, Brunzell JD. Regulation of body adiposity and the problem of obesity. Arterioscler Thromb Vasc Biol 1997;17:233–8.

14. Dixon JL, Furukawa S, Ginsberg HN. Oleate stimulates secretion of apolipoprotein B-containing lipoproteins from Hep G2 cells by inhibiting early intracellular degradation of apolipoprotein B. J Biol Chem 1991;266:5080–6.

15. Lu G, Morinelli TA, Meier KE, Rosenzweig SA, Egan BM. Oleic acid-induced mitogenic signaling in vascular smooth muscle cells: a role for protein kinase C. Circ Res 1996;79:611–8.

16. Li Y, Ferrante A, Poulos A, Harvey DP. Neutrophil oxygen radical generation: synergistic responses to tumor necrosis factor and mono/polyunsaturated fatty acids. J Clin Invest 1996;97:1605–9.

17. Zhang F, Kamp F, Hamilton JA. Dissociation of long and very long chain fatty acids from phospholipid bilayers. Biochemistry 1996;35:16055–60.

18. Pownall HJ, Hickson DM, Smith LC. Transport of biological lipophiles: effect of lipophile structure. J Am Chem Soc 1983;105:2440–5.

19. Massey JB, Bick DH, Pownall HJ. Spontaneous transfer of monoacyl amphiphiles between lipid and protein surfaces. Biophys J 1997;72:1732–43.

20. Abumrad N, Harmon C, Ibrahimi A. Membrane transport of long-chain fatty acids: evidence for a facilitated process. J Lipid Res 1998;39:2309–18.

21. Denke MA. Serum lipid concentrations in humans. In: *Trans* Fatty Acids and Coronary Heart Disease Risk: Report of the Expert Panel on *Trans* Fatty Acids and Coronary Heart Disease. Am J Clin Nutr 1995;62:693S–700S.

22. Mori TA, Bao DQ, Burke V, Puddey IB, Beilin LJ. Docosahexaenoic acid but not eicosapentaenoic acid lowers ambulatory blood pressure and heart rate in humans. Hypertension 1999;34:253–60.

23. Pownall HJ, Brauchi D, Kilinc C, Osmundsen K, Pao Q, Payton-Ross C, Gotto AM Jr, Ballantyne CM. Correlation of serum triglyceride and its reduction by omega-3 fatty acids with lipid transfer activity and the neutral lipid compositions of high-density and low-density lipoproteins. Atherosclerosis 1999;143:285–97.

24. Mori TA, Beilin LJ, Burke V, Morris J, Ritchie J. Interactions between dietary fat, fish, and fish oils and their effects on platelet function in men at risk of cardiovascular disease. Arterioscler Thromb Vasc Biol 1997;17:279–86.

25. Abe Y, El-Masri B, Kimball KT, Pownall H, Reilly CF, Osmundsen K, Smith CW, Ballantyne CM. Soluble cell adhesion molecules in hypertriglyceridemia and potential significance on monocyte adhesion. Arterioscler Thromb Vasc Biol 1998;18:723–31.

26. Pownall HJ, Raynaud AS, Harper E, Choi S, Rohrbach K, Pao Q, Reeves RS, Gotto AM Jr. Effects of twelve weeks of dietary fish oil, polyunsaturated fat, monounsaturated fat, and saturated fat on human plasma lipoprotein structure and composition. In: Pownall HJ, Spector AS (eds.). Omega-3 Fatty Acids in Nutrition, Vascular Biology and Medicine. Dallas: American Heart Association, 1995:64–78.

27. Hegsted DM, McGandy RB, Myers ML, Stare FJ. Quantitative effects of dietary fat on serum cholesterol in man. Am J Clin Nutr 1965;17:281–95.

28. Widjaja A, Morris RJ, Levy JC, Frayn KN, Manley SE, Turner RC. Within- and between-subject variation in commonly measured anthropometric and biochemical variables. Clin Chem 1999;45:561–6.

29. Zambon A, Hashimoto SI, Brunzell JD. Analysis of techniques to obtain plasma for measurement of levels of free fatty acids. J Lipid Res 1993;34:1021–8.

30. Dole VP. A relationship between non-esterified fatty acids in plasma and the metabolism of glucose. J Clin Invest 1956;35:150–4.

31. Mukherjee PS, DeSilva KH, Karnes HT. 5-Bromomethyl fluorescein (5-BMF) for derivatization of carboxyl-containing analytes for use with laser-induced fluorescence detection. Pharm Res 1995;12:930–6.

32. Tojo H, Ono T, Okamoto M. Reverse-phase high-performance liquid chromatographic assay of phospholipases: application of spectrophotometric detection to rat phospholipase A_2 isozymes. J Lipid Res 1993;34:837–44.

33. Toyo'oka T, Takahashi M, Suzuki A, Ishii Y. Determination of free fatty acids in blood, tagged with 4-(2-carbazoylpyrrolidin-1-yl)-7-(N,N-dimethylaminosulfonyl)-2,1,3-benzoxadiazole, by high-performance liquid chromatography with fluorescence detection. Biomed Chromatogr 1995;9:162–70.

34. Nakashima K, Taguchi Y, Kuroda N, Akiyama S, Duan G. 2-(4-Hydrazinocarbonylphenyl)-4,5-diphenylimidazole as a versatile fluorescent derivatization reagent for the high-performance liquid chromatographic analysis of free fatty acids. J Chromatogr 1993;619:1–8.

35. Puttmann M, Krug H, von Ochsenstein E, Kattermann R. Fast HPLC determination of serum free fatty acids in the picomole range. Clin Chem 1993;39:825–32.

36. Cistola DP, Small DM. Fatty acid distribution in systems modeling the normal and diabetic human circulation. A ^{13}C nuclear magnetic resonance study. J Clin Invest 1991;87:1431–41.

37. Richieri GV, Kleinfeld AM. Unbound free fatty acid levels in human serum. J Lipid Res 1995;36:229–40.

38. MacGee J, Allen KG. Preparation of methyl esters from the saponifiable fatty acids in small biological specimens for gas-liquid chromatographic analysis. J Chromatogr 1974;100:35–42.

39. Tserng K-Y, Kliegman RM, Miettinen EL, Kalhan SC. A rapid, simple, and sensitive pro-

cedure for the determination of free fatty acids in plasma using glass capillary column gas-liquid chromatography. J Lipid Res 1981;22:852–8.

40. Lefèvre G, Tallet F, Baassou S, Agneray J, Yonger J, Raichvarg D. Free fatty acid microdetermination by gas-liquid chromatography without transmethylating effects of methylation procedure. J Biochem Biophys Methods 1985;11:133–6.

41. Höckel M, Dunges W, Holzer A, Brockerhoff P, Rathgen GH. A microliter method for the gas chromatographic determination of long-chain nonesterified fatty acids in human serum or plasma. J Chromatogr 1980;221:205–14.

42. Lepage G, Roy CC. Specific methylation of plasma nonesterified fatty acids in a one-step reaction. J Lipid Res 1988;29:227–35.

43. Hallaq Y, Becker TC, Manno CS, Laposata M. Use of acetyl chloride/methanol for as-sumed selective methylation of plasma nonesterified fatty acids results in significant methylation of esterified fatty acids. Lipids 1993;28:355–60.

44. Mulder C, Schouten JA, Popp-Snijders C. Determination of free fatty acids: a compara-tive study of the enzymatic versus the gas chromatographic and the colorimetric method. J Clin Chem Clin Biochem 1983;21:823–7.

45. Ramirez I. A problem with enzymatic determination of free fatty acids in rat and mouse blood. J Lipid Res 1984;25:92.

46. Degen AJM, Van der Vies J. Enzymatic microdetermination of free fatty acids in plasma of animals using paraoxon to prevent lipolysis. Scand J Clin Lab Invest 1985;45:283–5.

47. Lauwerys RR. Colorimetric determination of free fatty acids. Anal Biochem 1969;32:331–3.

48. Regouw BJM, Cornelissen PJHC, Helder RAP, Spijkers JBF, Weeber YMM. Specific de-termination of free fatty acid in plasma. Clin Chim Acta 1971;31:187–95.

49. Brunk SD, Swanson JR. Colorimetric method for free fatty acids in serum validated by comparison with gas chromatography. Clin Chem 1981;27:924–6.

50. Guo Z, Nielsen S, Burguera B, Jensen MD. Free fatty acid turnover measured using ultralow doses of [U-^{13}C] palmitate. J Lipid Res 1997;38:1888–95.

Measurement and Clinical Significance of Lipoprotein Particles LpA-I and LpA-I:A-II

27

Patrick Duriez and Jean-Charles Fruchart

❖ Many epidemiological studies have indicated that the plasma level of high-density lipoproteins (HDL) is inversely correlated with the risk for CHD.[1] It has been hypothesized that HDL exerts this protective effect by the "reverse" transport of excess cholesterol from peripheral tissues to the liver.[2]

HDL are conventionally isolated by ultracentrifugation in the density range of 1.063 to 1.21 kg/L. Two main subfractions have been identified as HDL2 ($1.063 < d < 1.125$ kg/L) and HDL3 ($1.125 < d < 1.21$ kg/L).

Ultracentrifugation is a valuable tool for HDL isolation, but this procedure alters the structure and composition of the particles.[3] Moreover, ultracentrifugation does not take into account the protein component of the lipoproteins, which plays a key role in their metabolism. The discovery that apolipoproteins play an essential metabolic role led to the realization that they could be used as specific markers for the identification of lipoprotein particles and as a new means for the characterization and classification of lipoproteins.[4] The availability of antibodies directed against specific apolipoproteins allowed lipoprotein particles to be isolated and characterized based on their apolipoprotein composition.

The purpose of this chapter is to review the clinical significance of HDL subfractions according to their apolipoprotein composition.

ISOLATION AND COMPOSITION OF HDL PARTICLES

Lipoproteins can be distinguished on the basis of their apolipoprotein composition. According to the concept developed by Alaupovic,[4] lipoproteins can be separated into simple lipoprotein particles that contain one apolipoprotein (LpB, LpA-I, etc.), and complex lipoprotein particles that contain two or more apolipoproteins (LpB:E, LpB:C-III, LpB:C-III:E, LpA-I:A-II, etc.).

We purified HDL particles from the plasma of normolipidemic subjects according to their content of apolipoproteins A-I, A-II, and A-IV using sequential immuno-affinity chromatography.[5] A flowchart of the process is given in Figure 27–1. We isolated four types of particles: LpA-I, LpA-I:A-II, LpA-IV, and LpA-IV:A-I. As shown in Table 27–1, all types had a similar proportion of protein but differed significantly in cholesterol and triglyceride content. LpA-I and LpA-I:A-II particles contained more cholesterol (approximately 11% of total weight) than LpA-IV and LpA-IV:A-I (4% and

Figure 27–1 ✧ Flow Diagram of Sequential Immunoaffinity Chromatogarphy

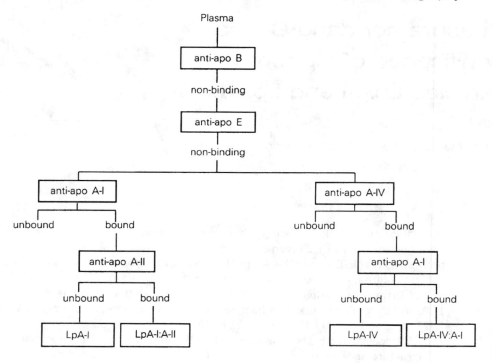

Table 27-1 ✧ Protein, Lipid, and Apolipoprotein Composition of LpA-I, LpA-I:A-II, LpA-IV, and LpA-IV:A-I Particles (Mass %)				
Component	*LpA-1*	*LpA-I:A-II*	*LpA-IV*	*LpA-IV:A-I*
Proteins	62.0 ± 7.4	65.2 ± 7.3	70.2 ± 20.1	61.3 ± 9.4
LIPIDS				
Total cholesterol	11.8 ± 4.1	11.5 ± 3.9	4.2 ± 3.5	8.0 ± 3.8
Free cholesterol	2.8 ± 4.1	1.6 ± 1.1	0.4 ± 0.2	1.2 ± 1.1
Triglycerides	5.0 ± 2.2	3.8 ± 1.8	9.4 ± 6.8	9.6 ± 5.7
Phospholipids	21.2 ± 4.4	19.5 ± 4.3	16.2 ± 10.5	21.1 ± 6.9
APOLIPOPROTEINS				
A-I	97.6 ±2.5	67.4 ± 13.3	—	57.8 ± 14.4
A-II	—	31.4 ± 13.5	0.4 ± 0.7	10.2 ± 2.7
A-IV	2.1 ± 2.4	1.0 ± 1.9	99.6 ± 0.8	31.5 ± 21.0
C-III	0.3 ± 0.3	1.2 ± 0.2	0.1 ± 0.1	0.4 ± 0.1
All values are given as mean ± SD				

8%, respectively). Conversely, the apo A-IV-containing particles had more triglyceride (10%).[6]

Particles were defined by their major apolipoprotein content: LpA-I and LpA-IV contained a single major apolipoprotein. LpA-I:A-II and LpA-IV:A-I were more complex particles, but both still had apolipoprotein A-I (apo A-I) as the major apolipoprotein. LpA-I:A-II particles contained apo A-I and apo A-II in a molar ratio of 4:3, whereas LpA-IV:A-I contained apo A-I, apo A-IV, and apo A-II in a molar ratio of approximately 3.5:1:1.

Of the total recovered weight of apo A-I, 65% was found in LpA-I:A-II, 25% in LpA-I, and only 1%–2% in LpA-IV:A-I particles. Most of the apo A-II was found in LpA-I:A-II, with a small proportion in LpA-IV. Of the total recovered weight of apo A-IV, 92% was found in LpA-IV and LpA-IV:A-I particles, 5% was associated with LpA-I:A-II, and 3% was associated with LpA-I. All particles contained a small proportion of apo C-III. In addition, sodium dodecylsulphate-polyacrylamide gel electrophoresis (SDS-PAGE) of the isolated particles revealed the presence of other proteins. The proline-rich protein lecithin-cholesterol acyltransferase (LCAT), cholesteryl ester-transfer protein (CETP), and apo D were made visible using immunoblotting with specific antibodies for each type of isolated particle[6] and then quantified.

The LCAT activity of the particles was measured by the method of Chen and Albers.[7] The specific activity of LCAT was expressed as the percentage of cholesterol esterified per 100 μg of protein. Under these conditions, and using the value for the LpA-I particle to represent 100% activity, cholesterol esterification never exceeded 16%. The LpA-IV particles demonstrated the most activity, followed by LpA-IV:A-I and LpA-I. LpA-I:A-II particles showed little LCAT activity. Of considerable significance was the finding that CETP was present in LpA-I, LpA-IV:A-I, and LpA-IV, but not in LpA-I:A-II particles (unpublished data).

Analysis of phospholipids revealed differences in the type of phospholipid constituents among the particles. The phosphatidylcholine/sphingomyelin ratio was 3.9:1 and 5.3:1 for Lp-I and LpA-I:A-II, respectively, and approximately 1:1 for the apo A-IV-containing particles.

PHYSIOLOGICAL ROLE OF APO A-I-CONTAINING PARTICLES

One of the key questions is whether the various HDL particles differ in their physiological roles. To gain insight into the mechanisms of cholesterol movement in peripheral cells, cultured adipose cells were studied. Adipose tissue is the main organ of cholesterol storage in the body and contains mostly non-esterified cholesterol. Moreover, rat adipocytes can accumulate and release, upon feeding and fasting respectively, large amounts of cholesterol, suggesting that these peripheral cells may represent a relaxed form of cholesterol homeostasis control. This observation has been advantageous in the study of cholesterol efflux from cholesterol-preloaded adipose cells in culture, using Ob1771 adipose cells.

A subclone of Ob17 cells established from the epididymal fat pad of the Ob/Ob mouse was used as a model of peripheral cells. In the presence of low-density lipoprotein (LDL), these cells accumulate cholesterol via the LDL receptor pathway. After cholesterol pre-loading with LDL, long-term exposure to LpA-I particles promoted cholesterol efflux. Such efflux was not observed in the presence of LpA-I:A-II.[8] The ligands that recognize the cell surface HDL binding sites have been identified as apo A-I, apo A-IV, and apo A-II.[9,10]

It has been proposed that apo A-I and apo A-IV play the role of agonists and apo A-II that of antagonist of cholesterol efflux.[10] HDL3 reportedly induces protein kinase C-dependent translocation of cholesterol from intracellular membrane to the cell surface in human fibroblasts or bovine endothelial cells.[11] We recently demonstrated that cholesterol efflux from adipose cells is coupled to diacylglycerol production and to protein kinase C activation.[12] The role of apo A-II as an antagonist in the generation of cholesterol efflux is strongly supported by the fact that the binding of apo A-I liposomes, but not apo A-II liposomes, results in diacylglycerol production. Huang et al.[13] confirm that LpA-I was more effective than LpA-I:A-II in both uptake and esterification of fibroblast-derived cholesterol. Nevertheless, different studies reported that both LpA-I and LpA-I:A-II demonstrate equal ability to promote efflux of cholesterol from several types of cells, such as fibroblasts, smooth muscle cells, and Fu5AH cells.[14,15]

QUANTIFICATION OF LPA-I AND LPA-I:A-II PARTICLES

Quantification of LpA-I and LpA-I:A-II lipoprotein particles is possible using techniques such as immunoprecipitation,[16] two-phase electroimmunoassay,[17] enzyme-linked differential antibody immunosorbent assay,[5] differential electroimmunoassay,[18] and immunoturbidimetric assay.[19] The three latter methods have been adapted for routine analysis and are described below.

Enzyme-Linked Differential Antibody Immunosorbent Assay

An enzyme-linked immunosorbent assay (ELISA) method has been described for the measurement of LpA-I:A-II particles.[5] The method consists of two steps: measurement of LpA-I:A-II and measurement of total apo A-I.

To measure LpA-I:A-II, wells of the plates were coated with rabbit antibodies to apo A-II (50 µL per well, diluted 100-fold in deionized water) for 18 h at 25°C in a humidified chamber. After blocking the non-reacted sites, and three washes with 1% rabbit serum in deionized water, 50 µL samples of non-delipidated plasma, diluted in 150 mmol/L Na_2HPO_4 buffer, pH 6.5, containing 1% of rabbit serum, were added to the wells and incubated for 18 h at 4°C. During this incubation step, only LpA-I:A-II were retained; LpA-I were removed during the subsequent washing with Na_2HPO_4 buffer.

After incubation with peroxidase-labeled antibodies to apo A-I, the measurement of retained peroxidase activity by addition of peroxidase substrate allows one to determine the amount of apo A-I associated with apo A-II. Quantitative recovery of known amounts of LpA-I:A-II isolated by immunoaffinity chromatography added to plasma varied from 95% to 102% ($n = 7$). The intra- and interassay coefficients of variation were 4.8% and 9.2%, respectively.

Total apo A-I was measured using a non-competitive enzyme-linked immunoassay. Here, the plates were coated with antibodies to apo A-I. After incubation with various dilutions of non-delipidated plasma, the total amount of apo A-I retained by these antibodies was evaluated using peroxidase-labeled antibodies to apo A-I

(LpA-I:A-II +1 LpA-I). The difference between total apo A-I (LpA-I:A-II + LpA-I) and apo A-I associated with apo A-II (LpA-I:A-II) represented the apo A-I (LpA-I) associated with particles without apo A-II. Addition of LpA-I isolated by immunoaffinity chromatography to the plasma with a known concentration of LpA-I resulted in an average recovery of 95% (93%–103%, $n = 7$). Intra- and interassay coefficients of variation were 5.1% and 9.6%, respectively.

Differential Electroimmunoassay

A rocket electroimmunoassay procedure has been developed to quantify LpA-I particles containing apo A-I but free of apo A-II.[18]

Preparation of Plates

Suitable concentrations of polyclonal antisera to apo A-I and to apo A-II were incorporated in a 9-g/L solution of buffered agarose (electrophoresis buffer, pH 8.6) at 55°C, poured onto plastic films, and allowed to gel at room temperature. Wells were punched in the gel (16 per film), and the plates were then ready to use. Samples were diluted 50-fold in isotonic saline, and 5 μL of the solution were placed in each well. Electrophoresis was carried out at 12.5 V/cm for 4 h in a pH 8.6 buffer containing Tris 7.05 g/L, glycine 5.65 g/L, barbital 0.285 g/L, and sodium barbital 1.62 g/L . When anti-apo A-II was used in very high amounts that exceeded anti-apo A-I, the LpA-I:A-II particles were retained near the wells, whereas LpA-I particles continued to migrate and react with anti-apo A-I. After electrophoresis, the remaining proteins were absorbed by placing on the gels one layer of thin filter paper soaked with isotonic saline and two layers of thick filter paper, all held in place under a pressure of 1 kg for 20 min. Thereafter, gels were vertically washed in isotonic saline for 60 min and the absorption process was repeated for 10 min. Plates were dried and stained with Coomassie Brilliant Blue. After destaining, "rockets" corresponding to LpA-I:A-II particles (low peaks) and to Lp-I particles (less-intensely colored high peaks) were visible.

Lp-I:A-II can be calculated as the difference between total apo A-I and Lp-I levels. LpA-I:A-II levels can be routinely measured using a commercialized kit (Sebia, Issy les Moulineaux, France).[18]

Primary and Secondary Standards

LpA-I particles isolated by immunoaffinity chromatography were used as a primary standard. They were concentrated under reduced pressure, and the concentration of apo A-I was determined by electroimmunoassay. This primary standard was used to measure the concentration of LpA-I in a lyophilized normolipidemic plasma, which was subsequently used as a secondary standard.

Precision

Within-run precision was estimated by repeated measurements ($n = 32$) of LpA-I concentrations in three plasma samples containing high, medium, and low amounts; resulting CVs were 1.51%, 2.57% and 3.72%, respectively. The between-run precision was assessed by performing 10 measurements of LpA-I in the same samples on four consecutive days; resulting CVs were 3.01%, 4.12%, and 4.56% for the high, medium, and low concentrations, respectively.

Sample Storage

The effect of freezing was investigated by comparing LpA-I results for fresh plasma samples and samples frozen (–20°C) for a four-month period ($n = 80$). Results were similar after the first freeze-thaw cycle. After the second freeze-thaw cycle, the results on frozen samples were significantly lower compared to fresh samples.

Comparison of the Two Methods

The ELISA method to measure LpA-I:A-II is very sensitive but difficult to implement in a routine laboratory. In our view, its use is limited to research laboratories. On the other hand, the differential immunoassay method is easy to use and highly reproducible, and comparable results are obtained among different routine laboratories. We think that this method is better suited for use in the clinical laboratories, but it is relatively expensive and difficult to automate.

Immunoturbidimetric Assay

Shishino et al.[19] developed an immunoturbidimetric assay method for LpA-I by treating sera with an anti-apolipoprotein A-II and A-I antibody sequentially. This essay was reported as sensitive, such that it could detect as little LpA-I as 0.155 g/L with good precision. There was a good correlation in the level of serum LpA-I between the present assay and a conventional differential electroimmunoassy on ready-to-use plates (r = 0.94, p < 0.001).

CLINICAL SIGNIFICANCE OF LPA-I AND LPA-I:A-II LEVELS

Distribution in Normolipidemic Men

HDL-cholesterol (HDL-C), apo A-I, and LpA-I were measured in 233 healthy normolipidemic young men (cholesterol < 250 mg/dL and triglycerides < 200 mg/dL).[20] Among these subjects, the composition of HDL was highly variable: the 10th and the 90th percentile values for the HDL-C/apo A-I ratio were 0.32 and 0.49, respectively. The 10th and 90th percentiles for apo A-I and LpA-I:A-II concentrations were 126 and 167 mg/dL and 83 and 116 mg/dL, respectively. On the other hand, LpA-I showed a much larger variation: the 10th and 90th percentiles were 33 and 62 mg/dL, respectively. The distribution of individual values of LpA-I showed that this fraction of apo A-I-containing particles was highly variable among subjects; the LpA-I/apo A-I ratio varied from 0.18 to 0.58. Triglyceride, LpA-I, and LpA-I:A-II concentrations correlated with HDL-C, but there was no correlation between apo A-I-containing particles and plasma triglyceride level.

Distribution in a Biracial Community

The distribution of serum LpA-I and LpAI-AII were examined in a random community-based subsample of black (n = 1021) and white (n = 1087) children aged 5 to 17 years.[21] Black children had significantly higher LpA-I levels than white children. With respect to LpA-I:A-II, prepubertal (aged 5 to 10 years) black males and pubertal (age 11 to 17 years) white children showed significantly higher values than their counterparts.

Effects of Sex and Hormonal Therapeutics on LpA-I and LpAI-AII Levels

In the previous study by Srinivasan et al.[21] on racial differences in serum levels of HDL particles, these authors reported that a significant sex differential (males > females) was noted among blacks and whites for LpA-I and LpA-I:A-II, with the exception of LpA-I levels at the pubertal age. Among the pubertal age group, a male-female crossover trend (females > males) in LpA-I levels was apparent after age 14. This study suggests that sexual hormones have a role in controlling LpA-I and LpA-I:AII levels. Oral estrogen (ethinyl estradiol 0.05 mg/d) replacement therapy significantly increased LpA-I by 66% and LpA-I:A-II by only 14% (nonsignificant) in postmenopausal women.[22] In this condition the LpA-I production rate (PR) significantly increased by 76%, whereas LpA-I:A-II PR showed only a nonsignificant increase of 22%. These data suggest that estrogen replacement therapy could have a potentially anti-atherogenic effect by largely and selectively increasing LpA-I levels. On the other hand the effects of continuous oral estrogen-progestin (17 beta-estradiol + norethisterone acetate) (E2NE) and transdermal estrogen with cyclic progestin regimens (17 beta-estradiol + medroxyprogesterone) (E2MP) reduced HDL-C levels in postmenopausal women.[23] LpA-I and LpA-I:A-II remained unchanged in the E2NE group while LpA-I:A-II but not LpA-I decreased in the E2MP group. Hyperlipidemia in pregnancy accompanying selectively raised concentrations of serum apo A-I and HDL2-C has been considered to be, at least in part, mediated by sex-hormones. Ikeda et al.[24] reported that pre-beta LpA-I plasma levels were significantly higher in normal full-term maternal blood. Administration of an antagonist of GnRH (Cetrorelix) suppressed testosterone secretion in men. In young men, suppression of testosterone was associated with increases in mean serum levels of HDL-C (+20%), apo A-I (10%), apo A-II (7%), LpA-I (23%) but not LpA-I:A-II.[25] The thyroid hormone triiodothyronine (T3) is known to be a potent mediator of apo A-I gene expression. Comuzzie et al.[26] showed that T3 accounted for 37% of the additive genetic variance in LpA-I.

Longevity

We hypothesized that octogenarians survive the age when the incidence of CHD is very high due to several protective factors. We compared HDL-C, HDL2-C, HDL3-C, apo A-I, and apo A-II in octogenarians and younger control subjects who smoked fewer than 10 cigarettes per day and were not taking drugs known to affect lipid metabolism.[27] We also compared the levels of LpA-I and LpA-I:A-II in these individuals using the differential immunoassay procedure. In men, the total HDL-C was similar in octogenarians and in controls aged 38 ± 8 years, while HDL2-C was higher and HDL3-C, apo A-I, and A-II were lower in octogenarians than in controls. In women, the levels of HDL-C and apo A-I were similar in pre-menopausal and octogenarian subjects, but were higher in postmenopausal women than in octogenarians. HDL2-C and apo A-II were similar in all three groups. In contrast, HDL3-C was higher in premenopausal and postmenopausal control women than in octogenarians. However, LpA-I was significantly elevated in octogenarian men and women (men: 61 ± 14 mg/dL; women 70 ± 14 mg/dL) compared to younger control subjects (men: 48 ± 12 mg/dL; pre-menopausal women: 53 ± 11 mg/dL; postmenopausal women: 63 ± 19 mg/dL). On the other hand, LpA-I:A-II was clearly lower in octogenarians. The distribution of LpA-I and LpA-I:A-II values also appeared to be modified by age, with a shift of the distribution toward higher values of LpA-I and lower values of LpA-I:A-II in octogenarians as compared with younger subjects. This could mean that individuals with low levels of LpA-I have a higher frequency of CHD during the sixth or seventh decade of life.

Brewer et al.[28] recently investigated LpA-I and LpA-I:A-II in a kindred population with hyperalphalipoproteinemia and a decreased risk of CHD. The selective increase in LpA-I in the 60-year-old putative homozygote proband with a family history of longevity supports the concept that these particles may represent the "anti-atherogenic" fraction of HDL.

CHD

LpA-I, but not LpA-I:A-II, was found to be lower in normolipidemic patients with angiographically documented CHD, compared to asymptomatic subjects and a group of patients with angiographically normal coronary arteries.[29] However, in a study that found triglyceride levels to be higher in the patients than in the controls, both LpA-I and LpA-I:A-II were reduced to a similar degree in patients with CHD.[22] O'Brien et al.[31] also reported that LpA-I and LpA-I:A-II were similarly reduced in subjects with coronary artery disease but that plasma apo A-I was the best predictor of CHD.

A case-control study of apo A-I-containing particles has been carried out in three populations with different CHD risk.[32] Male patients with myocardial infarction and controls were recruited in two French centers, Strasbourg and Toulouse, and in Belfast in Northern Ireland. The standardized CHD mortality rates in Belfast, Strasbourg, and Toulouse were, respectively, 348, 102, and 78 per 100,000. In Northern Ireland and France, patients had lower levels of HDL-C, apo A-I, apo A-II, LpA-I, and LpA-II:A-I in comparison to controls. In control subjects and in patients, the level of LpA-I was lower in Northern Ireland than in France. A high-risk profile, characterized by a low LpA-I level, was more frequent in Northern Ireland. Furthermore, multivariate analysis suggested that the LpA-I/HDL-C ratio is a significant marker of CHD risk. We have recently observed that the level of LpA-I (but not LpA-I:A-II) is lower in children whose parents had premature CHD than in a control group with no family history of CHD.[33]

Primary and Secondary Dyslipidemias

Some dyslipidemias have characteristic patterns of apo A-I particles. For instance, Type III dyslipidemia is characterized by a decrease of LpA-I and an increase of

LpA-I:A-II.[34] The HDL decrease observed in patients with chronic renal failure treated with hemodialysis is mainly due to a decrease in LpA-I:A-II.[35] Non-insulin-dependent diabetes mellitus is characterized by a specific decrease in LpA-I particles.[36]

Obesity

The android pattern of body fat distribution has been shown to increase the risk of metabolic disease and CHD. Regional distribution of adipose tissue was estimated by the waist-to-hip ratio (WHR) and overall obesity was estimated by the body mass index (BMI) in 98 obese normolipidemic, non-diabetic, non-smoker subjects over 18 years of age.[37] WHR was inversely correlated with LpA-I ($r = 0.46$) and HDL-cholesterol ($r = 0.37$). BMI was not correlated with protective lipid parameters but only with triglycerides. After adjustment, LpA-I was lower in men and in upper body obese women. LpA-I is a better indicator of body fat distribution than HDL-cholesterol or apo A-I.

Diabetes Mellitus

The high incidence and prevalence of CHD in diabetes mellitus is clearly established. The usual lipid pattern found in type II diabetic patients is a moderate increase in fasting triglyceride levels associated with low HDL-C levels. Brites FD et al.[38] showed that HDL-C and apo A-I were significantly decreased in diabetic patients due to a selective reduction in the LpA-I subfraction. The HDL-C / apo A-I + apo A-II ratio suggested an accelerated catabolism of apo A-I. For the first time these authors isolated a small apo A-I-containing particle (pre-beta) only in diabetic patients that might be associated with the poor capacity of serum samples of patients to promote cellular cholesterol efflux. This data confirms the results of the previous report of Cavallero et al.,[39] which showed that LpA-I of type II diabetic patients were protein enriched and phospholipid depleted and that the large LpA-I particles were absent from the population of LpA-I of these patients. Diabetes mellitus induces glycosylated protein formation. Igau et al.[40] isolated glycosylated and non-glycosylated LpA-I particle subfractions (GLpA-I and NGLpA-I) from patients with poorly controlled type I diabetes mellitus. GlpA-I bound less than NGLpA-I to Fu5AH rat hepatoma cells and induced a lower cellular cholesterol efflux, suggesting a decreased capacity of the glycosylated particles to induce the first step of the "reverse cholesterol transport."

Diet

Diet can also modify the LpA-I concentration. The effect of the ratio of dietary polyunsaturated fat to saturated fat (P/S) on apo A-I-containing particles has been investigated. With total fat and cholesterol intake kept constant, a high P/S diet led to a decrease in LpA-I but not LpA-I:A-II particles, compared to a low P/S diet.[41]

The effect of fasting in Ramadan (the ninth lunar month of the Muslim year) on plasma lipids was studied by Adlouni et al.[42] Ramadan fasting significantly reduced serum apo B while serum apo A-I was significantly increased compared with that measured during the pre-fasting period. Analysis of serum LpA-I and LpA-I:A-II showed that the levels of LpA-I:A-II were unchanged but those of LpA-I were significantly increased at the end of Ramadan compared with the pre-fasting period. The observed diet pattern during Ramadan showed an increase in total energy intake based on carbohydrates (+1.4%), proteins (+0.4%), but not on fat (−0.7%), compared with a usual diet used during the rest of the year. During Ramadan the fat diet is rich in monounsaturated and polyunsaturated fatty acid, in contrast to saturated fatty acid, which decreased during Ramadan.

Alcohol consumption increases circulating levels of HDL. Some authors suggest a beneficial effect of chronic alcohol consumption on CHD. We investigated the relationships between LpA-I and LpA-I:A-II concentrations and alcohol consumption in 344 men and found that LpA-I:A-II levels increased and LpA-I levels decreased with an increasing alcohol intake.[43] Nevertheless, Branchi et al.[44] and Lecomte et al.[45] showed that both LpA-I and LpA-I:A-II were significantly higher in moderate alcohol drinkers (20–50 g/d) than in non drinkers. Gottrand et al.[46] showed that moderate wine consumption in healthy volunteers reduced plasma clearance of apo A-II leading to increases in LpA-I:A-II plasma levels. In five males subjects, apo A-I and apo A-II increased significantly (20% and 60%, respectively) after the diet was supplemented with alcohol (50 g/d; 4 weeks). LpA-I:A-II increased by 32%, whereas alcohol had no effect on the concentration of LpA-I. The alcohol treatment did not significantly alter the metabolism of apo A-I. Conversely, the fractional catabolic rate of apo A-II decreased significantly (by 21%) with alcohol, whereas the production rate of apo A-II tended to increase by 18%. Therefore, the decrease in the fractional catabolic rate of apo A-II could lead to an accumulation of apo A-II-containing lipoproteins in plasma and account for the dramatic increase in LpA-I:A-II observed in the plasma of subjects consuming alcohol.

Studies of octogenarians and patients with CHD suggest that LpA-I is the main anti-atherogenic particle. Therefore, it seems unlikely that chronic alcohol consumption would have an anti-atherogenic effect, at least due to changes in LpA-I and LpA-I:A-II levels.

Cigarette Smoking

Cigarette smoking is associated with low plasma HDL-C and apo A-I levels, which may explain, in part, its deleterious effects on CHD. After smoking cessation, ex-smokers had higher plasma levels of HDL-C, apo A-I, and LpA-I:A-II than smokers and consumed more vegetable protein and polysaccharides.[47] Adjustment on nutritional variables did not show any additional difference between ex-smokers and smokers, suggesting that smoking *per se* affects LpA-I and LpA-I:A-II levels. Eliasson et al.[48] reported that smokers had lower HDL-C and LpA-I but higher fasting triglycerides, as well as an increased proportion of small, dense LDL particles. They had higher fasting and steady-state C-peptide levels during the euglycemic hyperinsulinemic clamp technique. The smokers were also insulin resistant and lipid intolerant with an impaired triglyceride clearance after a mixed test meal. Therefore, insulin resistance syndrome inducing decreases in LpA-I:A-II and LpA-I is likely to be an important reason for the increased cardiovascular morbidity in smokers.

Effects of Drugs on Apo A-I Particles

Considering that LpA-I is a potent marker of cardiovascular risk in clinical and in epidemiological studies, it is interesting to study the effect of drug therapy on LpA-I level. Two main questions concerning the effects of drugs arise:

✧   Do compounds with various mechanisms of action have different effects on HDL particles?

✧   Does pharmacological modulation of LpA-I concentration change cardiovascular morbidity and mortality?

We now have some data to answer the former question, but further research is still needed to answer the latter.

Atmeh et al.[17] showed that the use of nicotinic acid may increase LpA-I concentration, whereas probucol decreases the concentration of this particle. In contrast, nicotinic acid decreased LpA-I:A-II, and probucol had no major effect. We have shown that fenofibrate decreases LpA-I and increases LpA-I:A-II,[49] whereas hydroxymethylglutaryl-CoA reductase inhibitors (statins) such as simvastatin and pravastatin have different effects. Simvastatin increased LpA-I, particularly when baseline levels were low,[49] but had no effect on LpA-I:A-II. Pravastatin increased both LpA-I and LpA-I:A-II.[50] Treatment of hypercholesterolemic patients with fluvastatin significantly increased LpA-I and did not significantly modify LpA-I:A-II.[51] Atorvastatin[52] and cerivastatin[53] also increased LpA-I. The bile acid sequestrant, cholestyramine, also increased the concentration of these two particle types.

It has been suggested that LpA-I may represent the particle that is involved in cholesterol efflux from peripheral cells. We speculate that the observed increase in LpA-I may potentiate the beneficial cardiovascular effect of low-density-lipoprotein cholesterol reduction observed on statin measurement. Conversely, the decrease caused by fenofibrate might be considered a potentially harmful effect. However, kinetic studies are necessary to determine whether HMG-CoA reductase inhibitors and cholestyramine increase, and fenofibrate decreases, LpA-I level by inducing an excess synthesis of the particle or by inhibiting its catabolism.

The Role of Apo A-I and Apo A-II in Development of Atherosclerosis in Transgenic Animal Models

Transgenic animal models (mice[54–56] and rabbits[57]) clearly demonstrate that over-expression of apo A-I leading to a high concentration of HDL particles containing mainly apo A-I rich HDL (LpA-I) inhibits development of atherosclerosis when the plasma is rich in apo B-containing particles. On the other hand, the role of apo A-II is not clearly demonstrated. Some studies[56] have suggested that the transgenesis of apo A-II increases atherogenesis and that apo A-II rich HDL are atherogenic, while apo A-I/apo A-II HDL (LpA-I:A-II) are poorly anti-atherogenic in comparison with apo A-I rich HDL (LpA-I). These animal models suggest that lipoprotein particles mimicking what is called LpA-I in human clinical studies are highly anti-atherogenic. The role of LpA-I:A-II is not clearly demonstrated and depends on other metabolic factors.

SUMMARY

The introduction of immunological methods that allow the separation of various apo A-I-containing lipoprotein particles revealed the existence of their subpopulations with different lipid and apolipoprotein composition and with different metabolic functions. Quantification of LpA-I and LpA-I:A-II particles might allow more accurate prediction of the risk of developing premature atherosclerosis. This approach might also provide a new basis for the classification of dyslipidemias and for the study of the effects of lipid-lowering drugs. ✧

REFERENCES

1. Gordon T, Castelli WP, Hjortland MC, Kannel WB, Dawber TR. High-density lipoprotein as a protective factor against CHD: The Framingham Study. Am J Med 1977;62:707–14.
2. Glomset JA. The plasma lecithin-cholesterol acyltransferase reaction. J Lipid Res 1968;9:155–67.
3. Castro GR, Fielding CF. Evidence for the distribution of apolipoprotein E between lipoprotein classes in human normocholesterolemic plasma and for the origin of unassociated apolipoprotein E (LpE). J Lipid Res 1984;25:58–67.
4. Alaupovic P. The role of apolipoproteins in the lipid transport process. Ric Clin Lab 1982;12:3–21.
5. Koren E, Puchois P, Alaupovic P, Fesmire J, Kandoussi A, Fruchart JC. Quantification of two different types of apolipoprotein A-I-containing lipoprotein particles in plasma by enzyme-linked differential antibody immunosorbent assay. Clin Chem 1987;33:38–43.
6. Duverger N, Ghalim N, Theret N, Duchateau P, Aguie G, Ailhaud G, Castro G, Fruchart JC. Lipoprotein A-I-containing particles. In: Malmendier CL et al. (eds.). Hypercholesterolemia, hypocholesterolemia, hypertriglyceridemia. New York: Plenum Press, 1990: 93–99.
7. Chen CC, Albers JJ. Characterization of proteoliposomes containing apolipoprotein A-I: a new substrate for the measurement of lecithin-cholesterol acyltransferase activity. J Lipid Res 1982;23:680–91.
8. Barkia A, Puchois P, Ghalim N, Torpier G, Ailhaud G, Fruchart JC. Differential role of apolipoprotein A-I-containing particles in cholesterol efflux from adipose cells. Atherosclerosis 1991;87:135–46.
9. Steinmetz A, Barbaras R, Ghalim N, Clavey V, Fruchart JC, Ailhaud G. Human apolipoprotein A-IV binds to apolipoprotein A-I/A-II receptor sites and promotes cholesterol efflux from adipose cells. J Biol Chem 1990;265:7859–63.
10. Barbaras R, Puchois P, Fruchart JC, Pradines-Figueres A, Ailhaud G. Purification of an apolipoprotein-A-binding protein from mouse adipose cells. Biochem J 1990;269: 767–73.
11. Slotte JP, Oram JF, Bierman EL. Binding of high-density lipoproteins to cell receptors promotes translocation of cholesterol from intracellular membranes to the cell surface. J Biol Chem 1987;262:12904–7.
12. Theret N, Delbart C, Aguie G, Fruchart JC, Vassaux G, Ailhaud G. Cholesterol efflux from adipose cells is coupled to diacylglycerol production and protein kinase C activation. Biochem Biophys Res Commun 1990;173:1361–8.
13. Huang Y, von Eckardstein A, Wu S, Assmann G. Cholesterol efflux, cholesterol esterification, and cholesteryl ester transfer by LpA-I and LpA-I/A-II in native plasma. Arterioscler Thromb Vasc Biol 1995;15:1412–8.
14. Oikawa S, Mendez AJ, Cheung MC, Oram JF, Bierman EL. Effect of apo A-I and apo A-I:A-II HDL particles in intracellular cholesterol efflux. [Abstract 2711]. Circulation 1991;84(Suppl II):682.
15. Johnson WJ, Kilsdonk EPC, Van Tol A, Phillips MC, Rothblat GH. Cholesterol efflux

from cells to immunopurified subfractions of human high-density lipoprotein: LpA-I and LpA-I:A-II. J Lipid Res 1991;32:1993–2000.

16. Cheung MC, Albers JJ. Distribution of high-density lipoprotein particles with different apoprotein composition: particles with A-I and A-II and particles with A-I but no A-II. J Lipid Res 1982;23:747–53.

17. Atmeh RF, Shepherd J, Packard CJ. Subpopulations of apolipoprotein A-I in human high-density lipoproteins: their metabolic properties and response to drug therapy. Biochim Biophys Acta 1983;751:175–88.

18. Parra HJ, Mezdour H, Ghalim N, Bard JM, Fruchart JC. Differential electroimmunoassay of human LpA-I lipoprotein particles on ready-to-use plates. Clin Chem 1990;36:1431–5.

19. Shishino K, Hitsumoto Y, Osawa H, Makino H, Saheki S. Development of a serum lipoprotein A-I immunoassay method. Rinsh Byori 1999;47:579–9.

20. Luc G, Parra HJ, Zylberberg G, Fruchart JC. Plasma concentrations of apolipoprotein A-I-containing particles in normolipidemic men. Eur J Clin Invest 1991;21:118–22.

21. Srinivasan SR, Elkasabany A, Berenson GS. Distribution and correlates of serum high-density lipoprotein subclasses (LpA-I and LpA-I:A-II) in children from a biracial community. The Bogalusa Study. Metabolism 1998;47:757–63.

22. Brinton EA. Oral estrogen replacement therapy in postmenopausal women selectively raises levels and production rates of lipoprotein A-I and lowers hepatic lipase activity without lowering the fractional catabolic rate. Arterioscler Thromb Vasc Biol 1996;16:431–40.

23. Tilly-Kiesi M, Kahri J, Pyorala T, Puolakka J, Luotola H, Lappi M, Lahdenpera S, Taskinen MR. Responses of HDL subclasses, Lp(A-I) and Lp(A-I:A-II) levels and lipolytic enzyme activities to continuous oral estrogen-progestin and transdermal estrogen with cyclic progestrin regimens in postmenopausal women. Atherosclerosis 1997;129:249–259.

24. Ikeda H, Ikeda T. Pre-beta-migrating lipoprotein A-I concentration in normal full-term maternal blood. Rinsho Byori 1999;47:866–70.

25. Von Eckardstein A, Kliesch S, Nieschlag E, Chirazi A, Assmann G, Behre HM. Suppression of endogenous testosterone in young men increases serum levels of high-density lipoprotein subclass lipoprotein A-I and lipoprotein(a). J Clin Endocrinol Metab 1997;82:3367–72.

26. Comuzzie AG, Blangero J, Mahaney MC, Sharp RM, VandeBerg JL, Stern MP, MacCluer JW. Triiodothyronine exerts a major pleitropic effect on reverse cholesterol transport phenotypes. Arterioscler Thromb Vasc Biol 1996;16:289–93.

27. Luc G, Bard JM, Lussier-Cacan S, Bouthillier D, Parra HJ, Fruchart JC, Davignon J. High-density-lipoprotein particles in octogenarians. Metabolism 1991;40:1238–43.

28. Brewer HB, Rader D, Fojo S, Hoeg JM. Frontiers in the analysis of HDL structure, function, and metabolism. In: Carlson LA (ed.). Disorders of HDL. London: Smith-Gordon, 1990:51–58.

29. Puchois P, Kandoussi A, Fiévet P, Fourrier JL, Bertrand M, Koren E, Fruchart JC. Apolipoprotein A-I-containing lipoproteins in coronary artery disease. Atherosclerosis 1987;68:35–40.

30. Genest JJ, Bard JM, Fruchart JC, Ordovas JM, Wilson PFW, Shaefer GJ. Plasma apolipoproteins (a), A-I-, A-II-, B-, E- and C-III-containing particles in men with premature coronary artery disease. Atherosclerosis 1991;90:149–57.

31. O'Brien T, Nguyen TT, Hallaway BJ, Hodge D, Bailey K, Holmes D, Kottke BA. The role of lipoprotein A-I and lipoprotein A-I/A-II in predicting coronary artery disease. Arterioscler Thromb Vasc Biol 1995;15:228–31.

32. Cambien F, Parra HJ, Arveiler D, Cambou JP, Evans A, Bingham A. Lipoprotein particles in patients with myocardial infarction and controls. [Abstract 1380]. Circulation 1990;82(Suppl III):348.

33. Amouyel P, Isorez D, Bard JM, Goldman M, Lebel P, Zylberberg G, Fruchart JC. Parenteral history of early myocardial infarction is associated with decreased levels of lipoparticle A-I in adolescents. Arterioscler Thromb 1993;13:1640–4.

34. Lussier-Cacan S, Bard JM, Boulet L, Nestruck AC, Grother AM, Fruchart JC, Davignon J. Lipoprotein composition changes induced by fenofibrate in dysbetalipoproteinemia type III. Atherosclerosis 1989;78:167–82.

35. Cachera C, Kandoussi A, Equagoo K, Fruchart JC, Tacquet A. Evaluation of apolipoprotein A-I-containing particles in chronic renal failure patients undergoing hemodialysis. Am J Nephrol 1990;10:171–2.

36. Fruchart JC. Insulin resistance and lipoprotein abnormalities. Diabet Metab 1991; 17:244–8.

37. Lecerf JM, Masson A, Fruchart JC, Bard JM. Serum LpA-I lipoprotein particles and other antiatherogenic lipid parameters in normolipidemic obese subjects. Diabetes Metab 1996;22:331–40.

38. Brites FD, Cavallero E, de Geitere C, Nicolaiew N, Jacotot B, Rosseneu M, Fruchart JC, Wikinski RL, Castro GR. Abnormal capacity to induce cholesterol efflux and a new LpA-I pre-beta particle in type 2 diabetic patients. Clin Chim Acta 1999;279:1–14.

39. Cavallero E, Brites F, Delfly B, Nicolaiew N, Decossin C, de Geitere C, Fruchart JC, Wikinski R, Jacotot B, Castro G. Abnormal reverse cholesterol transport in controlled type 2 diabetic patients. Studies on fasting and postprandial LpA-I particles. Arterioscler Thromb Vasc Biol 1995;15:2130–5.

40. Igau B, Castro G, Clavey V, Slomianny C, Bresson R, Drouin P, Fruchart JC, Fievet C. In vivo glucosylated LpA-I subfraction. Evidence for structural and functional alterations. Arterioscler Thromb Vasc Biol 1997;17:2830–6.

41. Fumeron F, Brigant L, Parra HJ, Bard JM, Fruchart JC, Apfelbaum M. Lowering of HDL_2 cholesterol and lipoprotein A-I particle levels by increasing the ratio of polyunsaturated to saturated fatty acids. Am J Clin Nutr 1991;53:655–9.

42. Adlouni A, Ghalim N, Saile R, Hda N, Parra HJ, Benslimane A. Beneficial effect on serum apo A-I, apo B, and LpA-I levels of Ramadan fasting. Clin Chim Acta 1998;271:179–89.

43. Puchois P, Ghalim N, Zylberberg G, Fiévet P, Demarquilly C, Fruchart JC. Effect of alcohol intake on human apolipoprotein A-I-containing lipoprotein subfractions. Arch Intern Med 1990;150:1638–41.

44. Branchi A, Rovellini A, Tomella C, Sciariada L, Torri A, Molgora M, Sommariva D. Association of alcohol consumption with HDL subpopulations defined by apolipoprotein A-I and apolipoprotein A-II content. Eur J Clin Nutr 1997;51:362–5.

45. Lecomte E, Herbeth B, Paille F, Steinmetz J, Artur Y, Siest G. Changes in serum apolipoprotein and lipoprotein profile induced by chronic alcohol consumption and withdrawal: determinant effect on heart disease? Clin Chem 1996;42:1666–75.

46. Gottrand F, Beghin L, Duhal N, Lacroix B, Bonte JP, Fruchart JC, Luc G. Moderate red wine consumption in healthy volunteers reduced plasma clearance of apolipoprotein A-II. Eur J Clin Invest 1999;29:387–94.

47. Richard F, Marecaux N, Dallongeville J, Devienne M, Tiem N, Fruchart JC, Fantino M, Zylberberg G, Amouyel P. Effect of smoking cessation on lipoprotein A-I and lipoprotein A-I:A-II levels. Metabolism 1997;46:711–5.

48. Eliasson B, Mero N, Taskinen Mr, Smith U. The insulin resistance syndrome and posprandial lipid intolerance in smokers. Atherosclerosis 1997;129:79–88.

49. Bard JM, Parra HJ, Camare R, Luc G, Ziegler O, Dachet C, Bruckert E, Douste-Blazy P, Drouin P, Jacotot B, De Gennes JL, Keller U, Fruchart JC. A multi-center comparison of the effects of simvastatin and fenofibrate therapy in severe primary hypercholesterolemia, with particular emphasis on lipoproteins defined by their apolipoprotein composition. Metabolism 1992;4:498–503.

50. Bard JM, Parra HJ, Douste-Blazy P, Fruchart JC. Effect of pravastatin, an HMG CoA reductase inhibitor, and cholestyramine, a bile acid sequestrant, on lipoprotein particles defined by their apolipoprotein composition. Metabolism 1990;39:269–73.

51. Bard JM, Dallongeville J, Hagen E, Pfister, Ose L, Fruchart JC, Duriez P. Comparison of the effect of fluvastatin, an hydroxymethyl glutaryl Coenzyme A reductase inhibitor, and colestyramine, a bile acid sequestrant, on lipoprotein particles defined by apolipoprotein composition. Metabolism 1995;44:1447–54.

52. Dallongeville J, Fruchart JC, Maigret P, Bertollini S, Bittolo Bon G, Campbell MM, Farnier M, Langan J, Mahla G, Paucullo P, Sirtpri C. Double-blind comparison of apolipoprotein- and lipoprotein-particle-lowering effects of atorvastatin and prava-statin monotherapy in patients with primary hypercholesterolemia. J Cardiovasc Pharmacol Ther 1998;3:103–10.

53. Davignon J, Hanefeld M, Nakaya N, Hunninghake DB, Insull W Jr, Ose L. Clinical effi-cacy and safety of cerivastatin: summary of pivotal phase Iib/studies. Am J Cardiol 1998;82:32J–39J.

54. Rubin EM, Krauss RM, Spangler EA, Vertuyft JG, Clift SM. Inhibition of early athero-genesis in transgenic mice by human apolipoprotein A-I. Nature 1991;19:265–7.

55. Plump AS, Scott CJ, Breslow JL Human apolipoprotein A-I gene expression increases high-density lipoprotein and supresses atherosclerosis in the apolipoprotein-E-defi-cient mouse. Proc Natl Acad Sci USA 1994;91:9607–11.

56. Schultz JR, Verstuyft JG, Gong EL, Nichols AV, Rubin EM. Protein composition deter-mines the anti-atherogenic properties of HDL in transgenic mice. Nature 1993; 365:762–4.

57. Duverger N, Kruth H, Emmanuel F, Caillaud JM, Vigletta C, Castro G, Tailleux A, Fievet C, Fruchart JC, Houdebine LM, Denefle P. Inhibition of atherosclerosis development in cho-lesterol-fed human apolipoprotein A-I transgenic rabbits. Circulation 1996;94:713–7.

Determination and Clinical Significance of Triglyceride-Rich Lipoprotein Remnants

28

Richard J. Havel

✧ Plasma triglycerides (TG) are contained predominantly in two major lipoprotein classes: very-low-density lipoproteins (VLDL) and chylomicrons.[1] TG concentration is closely correlated with the concentration of these two TG-rich lipoproteins (TRL). TRL have a density of <1.006 kg/L and can therefore be separated by ultracentrifugal flotation at the non-protein solvent density of plasma. The clinical utility of plasma TG concentrations, measured in the post-absorptive state, remains somewhat controversial, although increasing evidence indicates that this analyte is an independent risk factor for coronary heart disease (CHD) and other atherosclerotic diseases.[2] Plasma TG are quantified clinically for this reason and also so that low-density lipoprotein cholesterol (LDL-C) can be estimated by the Friedewald formula.[3]

TRL comprise a heterogeneous group of particles of differing origin (chylomicrons from the intestine and VLDL from the liver), size (ranging in diameter from 300–800 Å or greater), and lipid and apolipoprotein composition.[1] (For additional information on lipoprotein composition, refer to Chapter 1.) Moreover, as described below, they include nascent particles and particles that have been partially metabolized by lipases (principally lipoprotein lipase and, to a lesser extent, hepatic lipase). The latter particles are generally referred to as remnants.[4] During the last 20 years, evidence has accumulated to suggest that remnant particles may constitute the atherogenic component of TRL.[5] Such particles, as compared with nascent TRL, are depleted of TG, phospholipids, and apolipoproteins A and C, and are relatively or absolutely enriched in cholesterol, cholesteryl esters, and apolipoprotein (apo) E.[4]

This chapter describes the basis for the distinguishing properties of TRL remnants, together with the most salient evidence for their atherogenicity. In addition, the chapter summarizes and evaluates various approaches that have been proposed to quantify remnant concentrations.

PHYSIOLOGICAL SIGNIFICANCE OF TRL REMNANTS

Remnant particles are produced from chylomicrons and VLDL during the course of TRL metabolism. Chylomicrons, which transport dietary and biliary lipids through the lymphatic system to the blood, are the vehicles of transport of exogenous long-chain fatty acids and cholesterol (Figure 28–1).[1] Chylomicrons are synthesized in the endoplasmic reticulum of intestinal absorptive cells (enterocytes), packaged in

Figure 28–1 ◆ The Pathway of Transport of Dietary Lipids in Chylomicrons and the Formation of Chylomicron Remnants

Triglycerides (stippled area) and cholesteryl esters (black area) are contained in the nonpolar core of the lipoprotein particles.

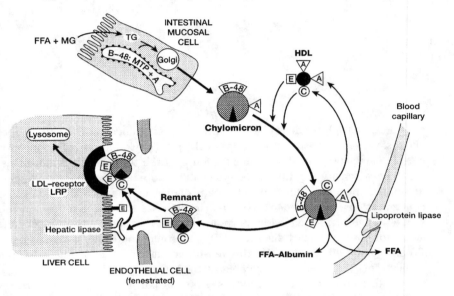

Source: *Medical Clinics of North America,* Vol. 66, 1982:319. Reproduced by permission of the publisher.

the Golgi apparatus, and then secreted into the interstitium of intestinal villi, where they enter lacteals and are delivered via the thoracic lymph duct to the blood.

Chylomicrons are secreted at all times, not only during active absorption of dietary fat.[6] For example, after an overnight fast, small chylomicrons (300–800 Å in diameter) that carry lipids derived from biliary phospholipids and cholesterol together with lipids derived from sloughed intestinal epithelial cells are produced. These small chylomicrons fundamentally resemble the much larger particles (up to 2000 Å in diameter or greater) that are produced during active dietary fat absorption.

Both small and large chylomicrons contain a single molecule of apo B-48, a truncated version of full-length apo B (B-100) secreted by the liver.[7] Apo B-48, like apo B-100, is required for the assembly and secretion of TRL particles. These particles are essentially microemulsions composed of a hydrophobic core containing predominantly TG with cholesteryl esters and some unesterified (free) cholesterol, surrounded by a monomolecular layer of phospholipids and free cholesterol, together with specific apoproteins. In chylomicrons, the latter are principally apo B-48, apo A-I, and apo A-IV.[1]

After secretion, chylomicrons acquire additional apoproteins, including apo E, apo C-I, apo C-II, and apo C-III from high-density lipoprotein (HDL) in lymph and blood plasma (Figure 28–1).[1] Chylomicrons bind rapidly to lipoprotein lipase, which in turn is bound to proteoglycans on the surface of blood capillaries, mainly in muscle and adipose tissue. This binding is followed by rapid hydrolysis of most of the component TG and some of the phospholipids in the particle. Apo C-II is an essential cofactor for efficient hydrolysis, which is accompanied by transfer of C apoproteins, together with essentially all of the A-I and apo A-IV on the chylomicron surface, to HDL. The chylomicron remnant, normally produced in only a few minutes, can be defined as a lipid-depleted chylomicron particle that retains its component cholesterol and cholesteryl esters, apo B-48 and apo E, and is depleted not only of triglycerides and phospholipids, but also of most of the C apoproteins; it essentially lacks A apoproteins.[4] The remnant particle dissociates from lipoprotein lipase on the capillary surface and is delivered to the liver, where it is efficiently captured by molecules residing on the surface of liver cells, including hepatic lipase and lipoprotein receptors, predominantly the LDL receptor and the LDL receptor-related protein.

Receptor-binding is followed by endocytosis of the remnant particles via coated pits on the surface of hepatocytes, leading to catabolism of the lipid components and apo B within 30–60 min.[8] The capacity of lipoprotein lipase to hydrolyze chylomicron triglycerides is normally very high, so that TG clearance is not ordinarily saturated even after a substantial fat-containing meal.[9] This presumably reflects binding of many lipase molecules to a single large chylomicron particle, yielding very rapid catalysis. By contrast, removal of chylomicron remnants by the liver is relatively slow, occuring over 15 minutes or more, and remnant clearance is generally saturated after a fat-containing meal. Thus, those lipoprotein particles found in the blood that are derived from the intestine can be considered to be remnants in the postprandial state, and probably in the postabsorptive state as well.[9]

The secretion and catabolism of VLDL follow the same general scenario as for chylomicrons, with some notable exceptions (Figure 28–2).[1] VLDL particles secreted from hepatocytes contain a single molecule of apo B-100, together with other apoproteins, including apo A-I, A-II, the three C apoproteins, and apo E. After secretion, additional apo E and the C apoproteins are acquired from HDL, and remnants are produced in the same general manner as occurs with chylomicrons, although at a considerably slower rate. VLDL particles therefore may circulate normally without appreciable hydrolysis for several minutes or more.

VLDL are known to be converted (via the action of lipases) to LDF. Previously, it was thought that human VLDL are progressively delipidated to form progressively smaller particles to ultimately yield LDL. Research in other mammals, however, showed that only a small fraction of VLDL is converted to LDL (each containing a single molecule of apo B-100). The remainder follow the pathway described for chylomicron remnants, namely uptake and endocytosis into hepatocytes. It is now recognized that, even in humans, one-half or more of VLDL particles are so metabolized and less than one-half are converted to LDL.[10] (For additional information on the fate of LDL particles, refer to Chapters 1 and 5.)

VLDL remnants isolated from functionally hepatectomized rats resemble chylomicron remnants: they are smaller than nascent VLDL (250–700 vs. 300–800 Å in diameter) and are depleted of TG and phospholipids, together with all the non-B apoproteins except for apo E.[4] Particles resembling rat VLDL remnants can be separated from the plasma of some normal humans by virtue of their reduced electro-

Figure 28-2 ✧ The Pathway of Transport of Endogenous Lipids in VLDL, and the Formation of VLDL Remnants and LDL

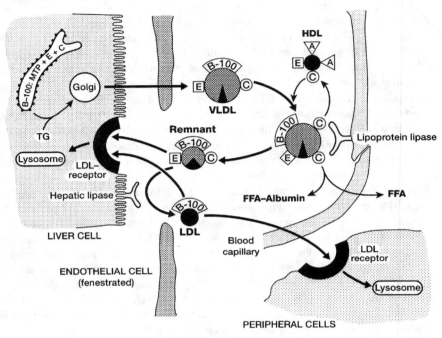

Source: *Medical Clinics of North America,* Vol. 66, 1982:321. Reproduced by permission of the publisher.

phoretic mobility (reflecting the altered apoprotein composition).[11] These apo E-enriched and apo C-depleted particles have "slow" rather than "fast" prebeta electrophoretic mobility and are smaller than the fast-migrating particles (~360 vs. 430 Å in average diameter).

In humans, partially catabolized VLDL are contained not only in the TRL (defined operationally as lipoprotein particles with a hydrated density <1.006 kg/L), but also in intermediate density lipoproteins (IDL) (with hydrated densities between 1.006 and 1.019 kg/L).[1] IDL (diameter about 280 Å) represent further delipidation products of VLDL that contain relatively more cholesteryl esters and less TG. Some IDL also contain one or more molecules of apo E. LDL particles, the final product of VLDL-delipidation, are 220–270 Å in diameter, with hydrated densities between 1.019 and 1.063 kg/L, in which apo B-100 is the sole protein component. The core of LDL is composed predominantly of cholesteryl esters.

CLINICAL RELEVANCE OF TRL REMNANT

In the 1970s, two lines of evidence led to the hypothesis that TRL remnants may have atherogenic potential. First, it was shown that the cholesterol-enriched TRL remnants that accumulate in familial dysbetalipoproteinemia, a monogenic disorder associated with accelerated atherosclerotic disease, resemble chylomicron and VLDL remnants, including enrichment in apo E relative to C apoproteins.[12] Point mutations of apo E impair binding of TRL particles to the LDL receptor in familial dysbetalipoproteinemia, and the clearance of chylomicrons as well as VLDL particles is greatly reduced.[13] Second, the cholesterol-enriched VLDL that accumulate in the plasma of rabbits and some other animals that were fed cholesterol-enriched diets were also shown to be enriched in apo E.[14] These particles have been implicated in the formation of fatty streak lesions in the arteries of such animals. Subsequently, the concentrations of IDL and small VLDL were shown to be the best predictors of the extent of spontaneous atherosclerosis developing on a standard chow diet in genetically hyperlipidemic (St. Thomas) rabbits.[15]

TRL remnants containing mainly apo B-48 accumulate at very high concentrations in apo E-knockout mice. These mice develop lipid-rich atherosclerotic lesions rapidly, even on a low-fat (chow) diet.[16] Most recently, overexpression of lipoprotein lipase in cholesterol-fed LDL-receptor-knockout mice, which dramatically reduced the concentration of TRL that resemble remnants, almost abolished lipid-rich arterial lesions (an 18-fold reduction).[17] The concentration of LDL was little affected by overexpresssion of the enzyme in these mice.

In 1979, Zilversmit proposed that postprandial TRL remnants (principally chylomicron remnants) are important atherogenic particles.[18] His proposal was based in part on studies suggesting that the remnant particles that accumulate in cholesterol-fed rabbits are derived from chylomicrons. Subsequent work showed that these particles contain primarily apo B-100 and are in fact derived from the liver.[19] Other studies have shown that small VLDL and IDL particles enter the artery wall of humans and rabbits from the blood at an appreciable rate, albeit somewhat more slowly than LDL (owing to their larger size), whereas influx of larger VLDL is much slower.[20]

Apo E-enriched TRL containing apo B-100 but not apo B-48 have been isolated from human atherosclerotic lesions obtained from femoral arteries at endarterectomy.[21] Such particles account for about one-third of the total apo B-100-containing lipoproteins that can be readily extracted from such lesions as well as lipoproteins that are bound to the connective tissue matrix.

Apo E-enriched particles, such as the beta-VLDL that accumulate in cholesterol-fed rabbits, are readily taken up by macrophages via receptors that recognize apo E (mainly the LDL receptor) without chemical modification, such as the oxidative alterations of LDL that are prerequisite to their uptake via scavenger receptors.[22] However, the apo B-48-rich remnants that accumulate in apo-E-knockout mice evidently are also taken up readily by macrophages, in a process that clearly involves apo-E-independent mechanisms. Gianturco, Bradley, and their colleagues have shown that both chylomicron-derived particles and large VLDL particles from hypertriglyceridemic subjects can be readily taken up by monocyte-macrophages by an apo-E-independent mechanism, leading to foam cell formation.[23] This uptake is mediated by a novel receptor for TRL that recognizes domains on the N-terminal one-half of apo B.[24] Oxidative modification may also promote uptake of TRL by macrophages.[25] Thus, considerable evidence suggests that some TRL particles derived from the liver or intestine can accumulate in arteries and form macrophage foam cells—a hallmark of the fatty streaks thought to be the precursor of the more advanced atherosclerotic lesions that lead to ischemic complications.

TRL may also promote atherosclerotic disease through effects upon blood coagulation and fibrinolysis. Thus, TRL may activate blood coagulation factor VII and increase secretion of plasminogen activator inhibitor-1 (PAI-1) into the blood.[26] Large VLDL particles from hypertriglyceridemic subjects, presumably related to those that are actively taken up by monocyte-macrophages, are particularly potent in stimulating PAI-1 secretion.[27] Lipolyzed TRL have been shown to activate coagulant Factor XII.[28] Such data suggest that at least some TRL particles not only promote atherogenesis, but complicating thrombotic events as well.

During the last 15 years, clinical studies in diverse populations have provided considerable support for the atherogenicity of particles that resemble remnants. Several case-control studies have found increased concentrations of certain remnant lipoproteins, particularly IDL, to be the salient lipoprotein abnormality in patients with CHD.[29–33]

Three angiographic trials have identified lipoprotein particles considered to be TRL remnants as independent risk factors for progression of coronary arteriosclerosis. In the National Heart, Lung, and Blood Institute (NHLBI) Type II Coronary Intervention Study, coronary arterial lesions were assessed angiographically over a five-year period of treatment with cholestyramine or placebo.[34] IDL concentrations, assessed by analytical ultracentrifugation, predicted progression of atherosclerotic lesions. In this study, LDL-C concentrations, also assessed by analytical ultracentrifugation, did not predict disease progression.

Lipoprotein cholesterol and TG were quantified after preparative ultracentrifugation in an intervention study of the calcium channel blocker, Nicardipine. Lesion progression over a two-year period, assessed by a quantitative coronary artery angiographic method in 335 patients, was independently associated with the concentration of remnant lipoproteins.[35] Remnant concentrations were estimated by measuring the extent of enrichment of TRL with cholesterol as compared with TG, together with the concentration of IDL-cholesterol (IDL-C). Over a period averaging 4.7 years after completion of the trial, remnant-cholesterol concentrations were also independently associated with clinical cardiovascular events: sudden death, myocardial infarction, or requirement of coronary bypass surgery or angioplasty. As with the NHLBI Type II study, LDL-C concentrations were not predictive of angiographically assessed disease progression. In addition, LDL-C concentrations did not predict subsequent clinical events, whereas HDL-cholesterol (HDL-C) concentrations predicted (inversely) both progression and clinical events.

In the Nicardipine trial, patients were selected by the number and character of their coronary lesions at baseline, not by their lipoprotein concentrations, as in the NHLBI Type II trial. These patients (272 men and 63 women) had only modestly elevated LDL-C concentrations at baseline (147 and 159 mg/dL; 3.80 and 4.11 mmol/L). By contrast, concentrations of VLDL-C (37 and 31 mg/dL; 0.96 and 0.80 mmol/L) and IDL-C (16 and 18 mg/dL; 0.41 and 0.47 mmol/L) were considerably higher than those observed in healthy young adults. Thus, these patients' lipoprotein concentrations were typical of younger CHD populations.

LDL-C, as assessed in this trial, included lipoprotein(a) [Lp(a)] but not IDL-C. In most prospective and interventional studies of lipoproteins as CHD risk factors, LDL-C assessed by the Friedewald formula or by the beta-quantification method, which involves separation of TRL at a density of 1.006 kg/L, includes IDL-C as well as Lp(a) cholesterol.

Finally, in the Monitored Atherosclerosis Regression Study, in which coronary lesions were assessed in patients randomized to lovastatin or placebo, the concentration of small VLDL (S*f* 20 to 60) predicted lesion progression.[36] In this trial, IDL-C concentrations independently predicted increased intima-media thickness of the carotid arteries.[37]

Given the limited size and power of these prospective studies, results clearly do not negate the much more extensive body of evidence that LDL-C, which includes mainly "true" LDL (1.019 $< \rho <$1.063 kg/L), is an important predictor of atherosclerotic disease and its complications. They do, however, suggest that TRL remnants, including IDL, may be particularly robust predictors of CHD risk.

Taken together, the substantial experimental animal and clinical evidence summarized here suggests that lipoprotein particles with properties of TRL remnants should be included in assessement of risk for atherosclerotic disease. Remnant lipoproteins have not been commonly measured in clinical and population studies because of the lack of practical, validated methods. It is, therefore, important to develop simple and reliable methods to assess remnant concentrations.

APPROACHES TO QUANTIFICATION OF TRL REMNANTS

Since the 1970s, several methods have been proposed to quantify remnant lipoproteins, but at this time, no generally recognized procedure has emerged that is both practical and has a sound theoretical basis. Nonetheless, some new methods have recently been developed that hold promise for useful clinical application. The various methods are summarized in Table 28–1 and are described and evaluated in the following sections.

Agarose Gel Electrophoresis

Upon electrophoresis of plasma proteins in supporting media, the prebeta component of lipoproteins, stained with a lipophilic dye, is often composed of two components with "fast" and "slow" mobilities.[38,39] In some cases, the slow component represents Lp(a), in which the apo (a) protein is in disulfide linkage to apo B-100 of LDL. Lp(a) is also found in the 1.006 kg/L density infranatant fraction of ultracentrifuged plasma (termed "sinking prebeta lipoprotein"). The TRL lipoproteins with a density <1.006 kg/L, however, may also contain a slowly migrating component, which has been shown to have all of the expected properties of VLDL remnants: smaller size and enrichment in cholesteryl esters and apo E relative to C apoproteins.[11] The slow prebeta component thus resembles the "beta-VLDL" that accumulate in plasma of patients with familial dysbetalipoproteinemia. The differences from fast-migrating VLDL are, however, less pronounced, and slow prebeta VLDL may be found in individuals with

Table 28–1 ✧ Proposed Methods to Quantify TRL Remnants*

Method	Property of TRL Assessed	Reference	Evaluation
Agarose gel electrophoresis of TRL	TRL "slow prebeta" band	11	Requires preliminary separation of TRL. Separation from "fast prebeta" band may be imprecise and arbitrary.
Quantification of IDL	Particle density (cholesterol assay)	32, 35	Requires ultra-centrifugation at two densities.
	Selective precipitation of IDL by heparin-MgCl$_2$	36	Applied to serum, but technically complex.
	Capillary isotachophoresis	37	Performance character-istics uncertain.
Cholesterol-enrichment of TRL	Cholesterol-triglyceride ratio	32	Requires preliminary ultracentrifugation of serum and apo E phenotyping.
Polyacrylamide gel electrophoresis of plasma	Mobility between VLDL and LDL	38	May be confounded by Lp(a). Performance characteristics uncertain.
Immunochemical separation of TRL-subfraction	Reactivity of TRL with monoclonal antibody to apo B-100	41, 43	Facile, but requires cholesterol assay of high sensitivity. In principle, includes all chylomicron remnants but not all VLD remnants.
Quantification of apo B-48	Specific immunoreactivity of C-terminus of apo B-48	48	Measures chylomicron remnants only.

*As applied to blood plasma from postabsorptive subjects; does not include measurements on postprandial plasma obtained after fat-containing meals.

any of the apo E phenotypes other than E 2/2, although it is more frequently found in individuals with a single ε3 and ε4 allele.

The prevalence of "double prebeta VLDL" as examined by agarose gel electro-phoresis may be as high as 50% in adult populations,[11] but this value appears to be de-pendent upon the particular technique used. Furthermore, apo E may dissociate from TRL particles during ultracentrifugation, which could affect their mobility. The dis-tinction between single and double prebeta VLDL is sometimes difficult to judge visu-ally or by scanning techniques, so that quantification of the two components may frequently be arbitrary. For these reasons, and also because the method requires ultracentrifugation to separate TRL, this approach has not been widely applied in clinical studies, even though it has a sound theoretical basis.

Quantification of IDL-C

IDL include those TRL-remnants that are immediate precursors of LDL. Originally, IDL were defined as lipoproteins of density intermediate to that of VLDL and LDL (1.019 < ρ < 1.063 kg/L) with Svedberg flotation rates of 12–20 units. IDL-C can be quantified after separation of IDL by standard sequential ultracentrifugation,[40] or by simultaneous ultracentrifugation of serum at densities of 1.006 and 1.019 kg/L, in which case the concentration of IDL-C is calculated as the difference between VLDL-C and VLDL + IDL-C.[35] Alternatively, IDL-C can be calculated as the difference between the cholesterol concentration in the "bottom" fractions obtained at these two densities.

IDL-C can also be quantified after separation of IDL from LDL by a two-step agarose electrophoretic technique.[41] In this method, IDL are selectively precipitated with heparin and $MgCl_2$ after the first step. This immobilizes IDL, but not IDL particles; the latter move toward the anode in a second electrophoretic step, after which the cholesterol in the precipitated IDL is extracted and quantified.

IDL can also be separated from VLDL and LDL by capillary isotachophoresis of serum pre-stained with a lipophilic dye or fluorescent phospholipid analog.[42] The performance characteristics of this method have not been fully described.

Based on kinetic studies of the conversion of VLDL particles to LDL, some investigators have broadened the definition of IDL to include smaller VLDL particles, so that IDL have been considered to encompass particles with S_f rates of 12–60 units,[33] which are separated from those of higher S_f rates by rate ultracentrifugation. This approach has theoretical appeal but is more demanding than the standard method of sequential ultracentrifugation; hence, it is unlikely to be applied in large-scale studies. Furthermore, it is now recognized that the sizes of nascent VLDL entering the blood vary widely, and may include some particles of S_f 20–60 and even S_f 12–20 units.

Cholesterol-Enrichment of TRL

In patients with familial dysbetalipoproteinemia and in individuals with double pre-beta VLDL, TRL are enriched in cholesterol (both free cholesterol and cholesteryl esters) relative to TG.[11] This property has been exploited to estimate TRL remnants, taking into account the fact that the average size of TRL particles generally increases with increasing TG concentration, so that the ratio of cholesterol to TG tends to fall. Philips et al. used the average ratio of cholesterol to TG at a given TG concentration in subjects with an apo E 3/3 phenotype as a baseline from which they estimated remnant-cholesterol in individual samples as a positive or negative number.[35] The estimated TRL-remnant cholesterol concentration correlated with that of cholesterol in IDL ($r = 0.47$); therefore the two values were summed to obtain an estimate for remnant-cholesterol concentration. This method appeared to have value in that the concentration of remnant cholesterol independently predicted progression of coronary atherosclerosis and ischemic cardiovascular events;[35] however, the method is evidently arbitrary in the definition of TRL-remnant cholesterol concentration and requires ultracentrifugation to separate both VLDL and IDL.

Disk Electrophoresis in Polyacrylamide Gel

With this method, lipoproteins separated according to size in a low concentration of polyacrylamide (~3%) are stained with a lipophilic dye.[43] Components migrating between VLDL and LDL, termed "midband lipoproteins," are often seen and have been reported to be more prevalent in patients with CHD.[31,44] In Japanese populations, midband lipoproteins correlate with cholesterol-TG ratios in TRL and with IDL cholesterol and TG concentrations.[31] Increased concentrations of Lp(a) may also appear as midband lipoproteins,[44] so that a midband may reflect increased concentrations of small TRL, Lp(a), or both. Since both of these lipoproteins may be atherogenic, detection and quantification of midband lipoproteins by densitometry may be clinically useful, and the method can be applied to unfractionated plasma or serum. From a theoretical standpoint, however, the lack of specificity is a serious limitation of this method.

Immunochemical Separation of Remnant-like Particles

It is now recognized that even in plasma obtained after an overnight fast, TRL remnants include an appreciable complement of chylomicron remnants derived from the intestine as well as VLDL remnants derived from the liver.[45] A monoclonal antibody (Mab) to apo B-100 has been found to be useful in separating such TRL particles from plasma. This Mab (JI-H) recognizes an epitope in the region of apo B-51.[46] It binds to LDL and most TRL, but not to a minor fraction of TRL particles containing apo B-100 that is enriched in apo E.[47] This antibody also fails to recognize chylomicron-derived particles containing apo B-48, which, as explained earlier, are essentially chylomicron remnants.

The unbound TRL particles in the plasma of fasting subjects are enriched in apo E relative to apo B and contain more cholesteryl esters and free cholesterol than those that bind to Mab JI-H; however, the average particle diameter of the unbound particles is larger than that of the bound TRL, which contain only apo B-100.[47] This larger diameter is in part due to the content of chylomicron-derived particles, but the apo B-100 particles that fail to bind to Mab JI-H are usually somewhat larger on average than the bound VLDL particles. The electrophoretic mobility of the unbound particles is reduced, as compared with the bound VLDL. Although the unbound particles consistently contain more apo E than those that bind to Mab JI-H, the ratio of apo E to C apoproteins is not invariably increased.[47,48] In normolipidemic individuals, unbound particles account for about 15% of the total apo B in TRL; this value tends to be highter in subjects with endogenous hypertriglyceridemia and familial dysbetalipoproteinemia. The affinity of the unbound particles for the LDL receptor far exceeds that of those VLDL that bind to Mab JI-H, and is comparable to that of total VLDL from individual subjects.[47] Thus, it appears that the TRL that are not recognized by Mab JI-H include not only chylomicron-derived particles (chylomicron remnants), but also apo E-enriched VLDL particles that have properties resembling VLDL remnants and which are somewhat larger than other VLDL remnants that presumably bind to Mab JI-H.

Based upon these properties of Mab JI-H, an immunochemical procedure has been devised to separate the remnant-like TRL from other plasma lipoproteins in plasma by use of an immunoaffinity matrix in which Mab JI-H and a Mab to apo A-I are bound to agarose beads.[49] When incubated with serum or plasma, almost all LDL and HDL particles, as well as the bulk of VLDL, are bound to the matrix. In this test, serum or plasma is mixed with the immunoaffinity matrix and, after incubation and sedimentation of the agarose beads, cholesterol and/or TG are measured in the supernatant fluid.[46,49] In clinical studies in Japan, the concentration of unbound cholesterol, designated "remnant-like particle cholesterol" (RLP-C), has been found to be highly correlated with that of plasmaTG.[46,49] In groups of patients with CHD, RLP-C concentrations are substantially higher than in control subjects, even when plasma TG concentrations are within normal limits.[49] RLP-C concentrations also have been found to be increased in several other clinical states, including familial dysbetalipoproteinemia[47,50] and chronic renal failure.[51]

This test, which is now being evaluated in North America, is technically facile and suitable for use in clinical studies, although it does require highly sensitive assays for cholesterol and triglycerides, owing to the large dilution of plasma when it is mixed with the immunoaffinity matrix. The test appears to have a good theoretical basis and it provides a measure of all remnants derived from chylomicrons together with particles resembling VLDL remnants. Concentrations of RLP-C in fasting plasma are low in most healthy, normolipidemic subjects (<7 mg/dL; 0.18 mmol/L).[52] In plasma from such subjects, much of the measured cholesterol is contained in the small amount of LDL and HDL that fails to bind to the immunoaffinity matrix.[47]

Other studies in subjects with elevated RLP-C concentrations have shown that the unbound lipoproteins are readily taken up by monocyte-macrophages, causing foam cell formation.[53] RLP may include the large TRL particles, found especially in hypertriglyceridemic subjects, that are readily taken up by macrophages via the apo E-independent TRL receptor to form foam cells[23] and promote secretion of PAI-1.[27] Thus, it appears that remnant particles contained in the unbound fraction have functional properties consistent with those of atherogenic lipoproteins.

Quantification of Apo B-48

Recent studies have shown that the molar concentration of apo B-48 in TRL is 5%–8% of that of apo B-100 in plasma of postabsorptive normolipidemic subjects.[54] The concentrations of apo B-48 and apo B-100 in TRL are well correlated, owing to competition between these particles for lipoprotein lipase binding and TG hydrolysis. The hepatic LDL receptor is responsible for the endocytosis of most chylomicron as well as VLDL remnants,[8] and it is reasonable to postulate that the concentration of apo B-48, representing chylomicron remnants, may be surrogate for that of VLDL remnants as well. The validity of this postulate remains untested, however, and it is known that chylomicron remnants can also be taken up by the liver by at least one other lipoprotein receptor, the LDL receptor-related protein, which is regulated independently of the LDL receptor.[8] Furthermore, the regulation of apo B-100 production by the liver is largely independent of that of apo B-48 by the intestine.

Until recently, quantification of apo B-48 has been accomplished by ultracentrifugal separation of TRL followed by denaturing polyacrylamide gel electrophoresis of apo-TRL, staining of the separated protein, and densitometry.[54] A new method, based on antibodies recognizing the conformation of the C-terminal region of apo B-48, permits quantification of apo B-48 in unfractionated plasma.[55,56] Since apo B-48, unlike apo B-100, is contained almost exclusively in TRL, this method may provide a practical approach to quantification of chylomicron remnants in clinical studies.

Quantification of TRL Remnants Postprandially

Recent studies have applied methods to quantify apo B-48 and apo B-100 in TRL as a measure of the intestinal and hepatic contributions to postprandial lipemia.[45] It has been shown that, whereas particles containing apo-48 account for most of the increase in TRL-TG postprandially, the absolute increase in particles containing apo B-100 exceeds that of particles containing apo B-48. Furthermore, the increase in TG late in the postprandial phase (6h or more after a fat-containing meal) may be contributed mainly by particles containing apo B-100. The increase in VLDL particle concentrations evidently reflects the effective competition of postprandial chylomicrons for lipoprotein lipase binding related to the larger size of chylomicrons in relation to VLDL.[57,58] However, the concentration of particles containing apo B-48 postprandially increases substantially, as expected given the saturation of remnant particle clearance. This enables evaluation of the effectiveness of hepatic clearance mechanisms, which may be related to atherogenic risk.[9,59] Therefore, future research should address not only the concentration of apo B-48 and TRL remnants more generally in the postabsorptive state, but also the response of these analytes to challenge meals.

OTHER ASPECTS OF TRL HETEROGENEITY

The composition of nascent TRL has been assessed by analysis of chylomicrons obtained from intestinal lymph and VLDL isolated from liver perfusates and Golgi apparatus-rich fractions of rat liver.[60–62] Although experiments in intact animals validate the general concept of remnant formation from chylomicrons,[63,64] the paradigm for TRL heterogeneity as related to remnant formation is based primarily upon experiments in rats in which remnant particles have been isolated after functional hepatectomy.[4] Experiments with immunoaffinity columns containing anti-apo E or anti-apo C-III have disclosed other aspects of VLDL heterogeneity, the relationship of which to remnant formation is not entirely clear. Thus in rabbits, some newly secreted VLDL apparently contain apo E whereas others lack this protein.[65] Some of the VLDL lacking apo E seem to acquire it in the course of metabolism, but those VLDL that fail to acquire apo E are metabolized more slowly and are more likely to be converted to VLDL than those that contain apo E.[65]

As in rabbits, only some human plasma VLDL contain apo E. Some, but not all, of the VLDL lacking apo E bind to heparin.[66] The apo-E-poor VLDL that do not bind heparin are larger than those that do and probably represent a form of nascent VLDL.[67] By sequential immunoaffinity chromatography four classes of VLDL can be separated: those containing apo E and apo C-III, those containing apo E but no apo C-III, those containing apo C-III but no apo E, and those lacking both apoproteins.[68] The characteristics of the second class in particular resemble those predicted for remnants. It is important to note that the immunoaffinity separations have been carried out with native plasma, with subsequent separation of VLDL subfractions. This reduces the possibility that the observed heterogeneity is an artifact of ultracentrifugation.

Apoprotein heterogeneity of TRL has also been assessed by two-site differential ELISA techniques.[69,70] This more practical approach has been used to study the relationship of lipoproteins containing both apo E and apo B to CHD risk.[71] How such measurements relate specifically to remnant lipoproteins is uncertain and for this reason they have not been considered further here.

REFERENCES

1. Havel RJ. Origin, metabolic fate, and metabolic function of plasma lipoproteins. In: Steinberg D, JM Olefsky, eds. Contemporary issues in endocrinology and metabolism, Vol. 3 New York: Churchill Livingstone, 1986:117–41.

2. Hokanson JE, Austin MA. Plasma triglyceride level is a risk factor for cardiovascular disease independent of high-density lipoprotein cholesterol level; a meta-analysis of population based prospective studies. J Cardiovasc Risk 1996;3:213–9

3. Adult Treatment Panel II. National cholesterol education program: second report of the expert panel on detection, evaluation, and treatment of high blood cholesterol in adults. Circulation 1994;89:1333–445.

4. Mjøs OD, Faergeman O, Hamilton RL, Havel RJ. Characterization of remnants produced during the metabolism of triglyceride-rich lipoproteins of blood plasma and intestinal lymph in the rat. J Clin Invest 1975;56:603–15.

5. Havel RJ. McCollum award lecture, 1993. Triglyceride-rich lipoproteins and atherosclerosis: new perspectives. Am J Clin Nutr 1994;59:795–9.

6. Havel RJ. Contrasts and similarities between the metabolism of intestinal and hepatic lipoproteins: the role of particle size. In: Windler E, Greten H, Zuckschwerdt W, eds. Intestinal Lipid and Lipoprotein Metabolism. Munich: Verlag, 1989:168–73.

7. Kane JP, Havel RJ. Disorders of the biogenesis and secretion of lipoproteins containing the B-apolipoproteins. In: Scriver CR, Beaudet AL, Sly WS, Valle DS, eds. The Metabolic and Molecular Basis of Inherited Disease, 8th ed. New York: McGraw-Hill (in press).

8. Havel RJ. Chylomicron remnants: hepatic receptors and metabolism. Curr Opin Lipidol 1995;6:312–16.

9. Havel RJ. Postprandial hyperlipidemia and remnant lipoproteins. Curr Opin Lipidol 1994;5:102–9.

10. Havel RJ. The formation of LDL: mechanisms and regulation. J Lipid Res 1984;25:1570–6.

11. Pagnan A, Havel RJ, Kane JP, Kotite L. Characterization of human very-low-density lipoproteins containing two electrophoretic populations: double pre-beta lipoproteinemia and primary dysbetalipoproteinemia. J Lipid Res 1977;18:613–22.

12. Havel RJ, Kane JP. Primary dysbetalipoproteinemia: predominance of a specific apoprotein species in triglyceride-rich lipoproteins. Proc Natl Acad Sci USA 1973;70:2015–19.

13. Stalenhoef AFH, Malloy MJ, Kane JP, Havel RJ. Metabolism of apolipoproteins B-48 and B-100 of triglyceride-rich lipoproteins in patients with familial dysbetalipoproteinemia. J Clin Invest 1986;78:722–8.

14. Mahley RW. Dietary fat, cholesterol, and accelerated atherosclerosis. In: Paoletti R, Gotto Jr AM, eds. Atherosclerosis Reviews, Vol. 5. New York: Raven Press, 1979:1–24.

15. Nordestgaard BG, Lewis B. Intermediate density lipoprotein levels are strong predictors of the extent of aortic atherosclerosis in the St. Thomas's Hospital rabbit strain. Atherosclerosis 1991;87:39–46.

16. Breslow JL. Mouse models of atherosclerosis. Science 1966;272:685–8.

17. Shimada M, Ishibashi S, Inaba T, Yagyu H, Harada K, Osuga J, et al. Suppression of diet-induced atherosclerosis in low-density-lipoprotein-receptor-knockout mice over-expressing lipoprotein lipase. Proc Natl Sci USA 1996;93:7242–6.

18. Zilversmit DB. Atherogenesis: a postprandial phenomenon. Circulation 1979;60: 473–85.

19. Havel RJ. The role of the liver in atherosclerosis. Arteriosclerosis 1985;5:569–80.

20. Nordestgaard BG, Tybjaerg-Hansen A. IDL, VLDL, chylomicrons and atherosclerosis. Eur J Epidemiol 1992;8 (Suppl.) 92–8.

21. Rapp JH, Lespine A, Hamilton RL, Colyvas N, Chaumeton AH, Tweedie-Hardman J, et al. Triglyceride-rich lipoproteins isolated by selected-affinity anti-apolipoprotein B immunosorption from human atherosclerotic plaque. Arterioscler Thromb 1994;14: 1767–74.

22. Koo C, Wernette-Hammond ME, Garcia A, Malloy MJ, Uauy R, East C, et al. Uptake of cholesterol-rich remnant lipoproteins by human monocyte-derived macrophages is mediated by low-density-lipoprotein receptors. J Clin Invest 1988;81:1332–40.

23. Gianturco SH, Ramprasad MP, Lin AH-Y, Song R, Bradley WA. Cellular binding site and membrane binding proteins for triglyceride-rich lipoproteins in human mono-cyte-macrophages and THP-1 monocytic cells. J Lipid Res 1994;35:1674–87.

24. Brown ML, Ramprasad MP, Umeda PK, Tanaka A, Kobayashi Y, Wanatabe T, et al. The human apolipoprotein B48 receptor (R): cDNA sequence , expression, and atheroscle-rosis. Circulation 1999;100 (Suppl.) I–330.

25. Whitman SC, Sawyez CG, Miller DB, Wolfe BM, Huff MW. Oxidized type IV hypertri-glyceridemic VLDL-remnants cause greater macrophage cholesteryl ester accumula-tion than oxidized LDL. J Lipid Res 1996;39:1008–20.

26. Hypertriglyceridaemia and vascular risk. Report of a meeting of physicians and scien-tists, University College London Medical School. Lancet 1993;342:781–7.

27. Stiko-Rahm A, Wiman G, Hamsten A, Nilsson J. Secretion of plasminogen activator in-hibitor-1 from cultured human umbilical vein endothelial cells is induced by very-low-density lipoprotein. Arteriosclerosis 1990;10:1067–73.

28. Mitropoulus, KA, Miller, GJ, Watts GF, and Durrington PN. Lipolysis of triglyceride-rich lipoproteins activates coagulant factor XII: a study in familial lipoprotein-lipase defi-ciency. Atherosclerosis 1992;95:119–25.

29. Avogaro P, Bittolo Bon G, Cazzolato G, Rora E. Relationship between apolipoproteins and chemical components of lipoproteins in survivors of myocardial infarction. Ath-erosclerosis 1980;37:69–76.

30. Tatami R, Mabuchi H, Ueda R, Haya T, Kametani T, et al. Intermediate-density lipopro-tein and cholesterol-rich very-low-density lipoprotein in angiographically determined coronary artery disease. Circulation 1981;64:1174–84.

31. Kameda K, Matsuzawa Y, Kuba M, Ishikawa K, Maejima I, Yamamura T, et al. Increased frequency of lipoprotein disorders similar to type III hyperlipoproteinemia in survivors of myocardial infarction in Japan. Atherosclerosis 1984;51:241–9.

32. Reardon MF, Nestel PJ, Craig IH, Harper RW. Lipoprotein predictors of the severity of coronary artery disease in men and women. Circulation 1985;17:881–8.

33. Steiner G, Schwartz L, Shumak S, Poapst M. The association of increased levels of in-termediate-density lipoproteins with smoking and with coronary heart disease. Circu-lation 1987;75:124–30.

34. Krauss RM, Lindgren FT, Williams PT, Kelsey SF, Brensike J, Vranizan K, et al. Inter-mediate-density lipoproteins and progression of coronary artery disease in hyper-cholesterolawmic men. Lancet 1987;2:62–6.

35. Philips NR, Waters D, Havel RJ. Plasma lipoproteins and progression of coronary artery disease evaluated by angiography and clinical events. Circulation 1993;88: 2762–70.

36. Mack WJ, Krauss RM, Hodis HN. Lipoprotein subclasses in the Monitored Atherosclerosis Regression Study (MARS). Treatment effects and relation to coronary angiographic progression. Arterioscler Thromb Vasc Biol 1996;16:697–704.

37. Hodis HN, Mack WJ, Dunn M, Liu C, Selzer RH, Krauss RM. Intermediate-density lipoproteins and progression of carotid arterial wall intima-media thickness. Circulation 1997;95:2022–6.

38. Carlson LA, Ericsson M. Quantitative and qualitative serum lipoprotein analysis. Part 1: Studies in healthy men and women. Atherosclerosis 1975;21:417–33.

39. Hedstrand H, Vessby B. Serum lipoprotein concentration and composition in healthy 50-year-old men. Upsala J Med Sci 1976;81:161–8.

40. Havel RJ, Eder H, Bragdon J. The distribution and chemical composition of ultracentrifugally separated lipoproteins in human serum. J Clin Invest. 1955;34: 1345–53.

41. Wikinski RLW, Schreier LE, Rosenthal SB. New method for isolating and quantifying intermediate and beta-very-low-density lipoprotein cholesterol. Clin Chem 1991;37: 1913–16.

42. Schmitz G, Möllers C. Capillary isotachophoresis of lipoproteins in human body fluids. In: Rifai N, Warnick GR, eds. Laboratory measurement of lipids, lipoproteins, and apolipoproteins. Washington DC: AACC Press, 1994:334–40.

43. Mead MG, Dangerfield WG. The investigation of "mid-band" lipoproteins using polyacrylamide gel electrophoresis. Clin Chim Acta 1974;51:173–82.

44. Tashiro J, Nishide T, Shinomiya M, Shirai K, Saito Y, Yoshida S, et al. The "midband" lipoprotein is a coronary risk factor in Japanese patients with familial hypercholesterolaemia. Scand J Clin Lab Invest 1993;53:335–8.

45. Bergeron N, Havel RJ. Assessment of postprandial lipemia: nutritional influences. Curr Opin Lipidol 1997;1:43–52.

46. Nakajima K, Okazaki M, Tanaka A, Wang T, Pullinger C, Nakano T, et al. Separation and determination of remnant-like particles in human serum using monoclonal antibodies to apo B-100 and Apo A-1. J Clin Ligand Assay 1996;19:177–83.

47. Campos E, Nakajima K, Tanaka K, Havel RJ. Properties of an apolipoprotein E-enriched fraction of triglyceride-rich lipoproteins isolated from human blood plasma with a monoclonal antibody to apolipoprotein B-100. J Lipid Res 1992;33:369–80.

48. Marcoux C, Tremblay M, Nakajima K, Davignon J, Cohn JS. Characterization of remnant-like particles isolated by immunoaffinity gel from the plasma of type III and type IV hyperlipoproteinemic patients. J Lipid Res 1999;40:636–647.

49. Nakajima K, Saito T, Tamura A, Suzuki M, Nakano T, Adachi M, et al. Cholesterol in remnant-like lipoproteins in human serum using monoclonal anti-apo B-100 and anti-apo A-I immunoaffinity mixed gels. Clin Chim Acta 1993;223:53–71.

50. Nakajima K, Saito T, Tamura A, Suzuki M, Nakano T, Adachi M, et al. A new approach for the detection of Type III hyperlipoproteinemia by RLP-Cholesterol Assay. Atheroscler Thromb 1994;1:30–36.

51. Sekihara T, Nakano T, Nakajima K. High postprandial plasma remnant-like particles-cholesterol in patients with coronary artery diseases on chronic maintenance hemodialysis. Japanese J Nephrol 1996;38:220–8.

52. Leary ET, Wang T, Baker DJ, Cilla DD, Zhong J, Warnick GR, Nakajima K, Havel RJ. Evaluation of an immunoseparation method for quantitative measurement of remnant-like particle-cholesterol in serum and plasma. Clinical Chemistry 1998;44:2490–8.

53. Shige H, Nishiwaka M, Tomiyasu K, Suzuki J, Namiki M, Yamashita T, et al. Studies for atherogenicity of remnant-like particles (RLP) from cultured cells. J Jpn Ateroscler Soc 1991;19:991.

54. Bergeron N, Kotite L, Havel RJ. Simultaneous quantification of apolipoproteins B-100, B-48, and E separated by SDS-PAGE. In: Methods in enzymology plasma lipoproteins. Part C: Quantitation. 1996;263:82–94.

55. Lovegrove JA, Isherwood SG, Jackson KG, Williams CM, Gould BJ. Quantitation of apolipoprotein B-48 in triacylglycerol-rich lipoproteins by a specific enzyme-linked immunosorbent assay. Biochim Biophys Acta 1996;1301:221–9.

56. Yamashita S, Saika Y, Nishida M, Nakagawa Y, Hirano K, Sakai N, et al. Application of a sandwich ELISA for Apo B48 and immunohistochemical detection of Apo B48 in human atherosclerotic aorta. Circulation 1999;100 (Suppl.) I-330.

57. Schneeman BO, Kotite L, Todd KM, Havel RJ. Relationships between the responses of triglyceride-rich lipoproteins in blood plasma containing apolipoproteins B-48 and B-100 to a fat-containing meal in normolipidemic humans. Proc Natl Acad Sci USA 1993;90:2069–73.

58. Björkegren J, Packard CJ, Hamsten A, Bedford D, Caslake M, Shepherd J, et al. Accumulation of large very-low-density lipoprotein in plasma during intravenous infusion of a chylomicron-like triglyceride emulsion reflects competition for a common lipolytic pathway. J Lipid Res 1996;37:76–86.

59. Karpe F, Steiner G, Uffelman K, Olivecrona T, Hamsten A. Postprandial lipoproteins and progression of coronary atherosclerosis. Atherosclerosis 1994;106:83–97.

60. Imaizumi K, Fainaru M, Havel RJ. Composition of proteins of mesenteric lymph chylomicrons in the rat and alterations produced upon exposure of chylomicrons to blood serum and serum proteins. J Lipid Res 1978;19:712–22.

61. Hamilton RL, Williams MC, Fielding CJ, Havel RJ. Discoidal bilayer structure of nascent high-density lipoproteins from perfused rat liver. J Clin Invest 1976;58:667–80.

62. Hamilton RL, Moorehouse A, Havel RJ. Isolation and properties of nascent lipoproteins from highly purified rat hepatocytic Golgi fractions. J Lipid Res 1991;32:529–43.

63. Bergman EN, Havel RJ, Wolfe BM, Bøhmer T. Quantitative studies of the metabolism of chylomicron triglycerides and cholesterol by liver and extrahepatic tissues of sheep and dogs. J Clin Invest 1971;50:1831–39.

64. Havel RJ, Yamada N, Shames DM. Watanabe heritable hyperlipidemic rabbit. Arteriosclerosis 1989; (1 Suppl) I33–8.

65. Yamada N, Shames DM, Havel RJ. Effect of LDL receptor deficiency on the metabolism of apo B-100 in blood plasma: kinetic studies in normal and Watanabe heritable hyperlipidemic (WHHL) rabbits. J Clin Invest 1987;80:507–15.

66. Campos E, Jäckle S, Chen GC, Havel RJ. Isolation and characterization of two distinct species of human very-low-density lipoproteins lacking apolipoprotein E. J Lipid Res 1996;37:1–10.

67. Fielding PE, Fielding CJ. An apoE-free very-low-density lipoprotein enriched in phosphatidylethanolamine in human plasma. J Biol Chem 1986;261:12;5233–5236.

68. Khoo C, Campos H, Judge H, Sacks FM. Effects of estrogenic oral contraceptives on the lipoprotein B particle system defined by apolipoprotein E and C-III content. J Lipid Res 1999;40:202–12.

69. Kandoussi A, Cachera C, Parsy D, Bard JM, Fruchart JC. Quantitative determination of different apolipoprotein-B-containing lipoprotein by an enzyme linked immunosorbent assay: apo B with apo C-III and apo B with apo E. J Immunoassay 1991;12:305–23.

70. Yang CY, Xie YH, Yang M, Quion JA, Gotto AM Jr. ELISA quantitation of apolipoproteins in plasma lipoprotein fractions: ApoE in ApoB-containing lipoproteins (Lp B:E) and ApoB in ApoE-containing lipoproteins (Lp E:B). J Protein Chem 1995; 14:503–9.

71. Parra HJ, Arveiler D, Evans AE, Cambou JP, Amouyel P, Bingham A, McMaster D, Schaffer P, Douste-Blazy P, Luc G, et al. A case-control study of lipoprotein particles in two populations at contrasting risk for coronary heart disease. The ECTIM Study. Arterioscler Thromb 1992;12:701–7.

Determination and Significance of Low-Density-Lipoprotein Receptors

29

Anne K. Soutar

✧   The low-density-lipoprotein (LDL) receptor is a cell surface receptor. That mediates the specific uptake by cells of lipoproteins that contain apolipoproteins B or E. After uptake, lipoproteins are delivered to the lysosomal compartment. The apolipoprotein is then degraded and the cholesteryl esters in the particle cores are hydrolyzed. The free cholesterol generated in this way is used either for new membrane synthesis, as a precursor for biosynthetic pathways, or it can be re-esterified and stored as lipid droplets.

In cultured cells, the intracellular free sterol content regulates LDL-receptor gene expression and key enzymes in cholesterol biosynthesis at the level of gene transcription; thus the main function of the receptor is to maintain cholesterol homeostasis in the cell. This also appears to be the case in the whole body, but in addition, the hepatic LDL receptor pathway *in vivo* plays a central role in regulating the concentration of cholesterol in human serum, as it is the predominant means by which LDL is removed from the circulation.[1] Furthermore, since the LDL receptor is able to recognize not only LDL itself, but also the immediate precursors of LDL in plasma, namely the remnants of very-low-density lipoproteins (VLDL remnants) and intermediate-density lipoproteins (IDL), hepatic LDL-receptor activity influences the rates of both synthesis and catabolism of plasma LDL.

The importance of the LDL receptor in human lipoprotein metabolism has been deduced from the marked increase in serum LDL concentration that occurs in those patients who have familial hypercholesterolemia (FH) and whose LDL-receptor genes have a defect that affects the protein function.[2] Numerous different mutations in the LDL-receptor gene have been found in FH patients throughout the world. Patients who are homozygous for the disorder, or those who are compound heterozygous, with two different defective alleles, frequently have a plasma cholesterol concentration that is more than four times higher than the ideal normal upper limit of 200 mg/dL (5.2 mmol/L). As a result, cholesterol is deposited in the skin and tendons (xanthomata) from an early age and, even more significantly, accelerates the formation of atherosclerotic plaques in the arterial wall. This greatly increases the risk of coronary heart disease (CHD) and, indeed, death due to coronary disease, which can occur as early as the second or third decade of life.

FH is inherited as a co-dominant disorder, and although heterozygous FH patients are less seriously affected than the very rare homozygous FH patients, they nonetheless have an approximately two-fold increase in serum LDL compared to unaffected individuals. This puts them at considerably increased risk of developing CHD in early middle age.[3] There has also been some speculation that minor genetic variation in the LDL-receptor gene could influence its level of expression and thereby contribute to milder forms of hypercholesterolemia and polygenic CHD.[4]

CLINICAL RELEVANCE

Although heterozygous FH is one of the most commonly inherited disorders of metabolism, affecting about 1 in 500 people in most populations, it is estimated to be the underlying cause in only a small fraction of all individuals with hypercholesterolemia. However, an FH patient is considered to be at greater risk of premature CHD than an individual who has the same LDL cholesterol (LDL-C) concentration due to some secondary cause, mainly because the FH patient will have been exposed to the high concentration of cholesterol from birth, whereas secondary hypercholesterolemia generally occurs only much later in life.[5] Thus, accurate diagnosis of FH is important, so that the patient receives appropriate advice and treatment, preferably before the onset of overt CHD, and so that counseling can be offered to the patient's family.

A clinical diagnosis of definite heterozygous FH is given to a patient with a serum LDL-C concentration ≥190 mg/dL (5.0 mmol/L) if certain other criteria are fulfilled:

❖   the presence of tendon xanthomata in the patient or a first-degree relative, and

❖   a positive family history of high serum cholesterol or severe premature CHD.

If these criteria are not met fully, but it is suspected that severe hypercholesterolemia is inherited, then a diagnosis of possible FH is made.[5] Not surprisingly, many patients fall into the second category, and determining whether or not they do have a heritable defect in LDL-receptor function is not always straightforward. Other factors, genetic or environmental, appear to influence the phenotype of heterozygous FH patients. For instance, the severity of the disease in FH patients differs quite widely, even among patients who have the same defect in the LDL-receptor gene.[6]

A mutation in the gene for apolipoprotein (apo) B has been identified that results in substitution of an arginine residue in the protein (Arg3500) with glutamine. This affects its ability to bind to the LDL receptor and creates a clinical phenotype very similar to that seen in patients with a defect in the LDL-receptor gene.[7] This disorder is now referred to as familial defective apo B (FDB). With the currently available lipid-lowering drugs, it is probably not critical to distinguish between FDB and FH when managing an individual patient at risk of premature CHD due to inherited hypercholesterolemia[8] but this may not always remain so.

Ideally, identification of a genetic defect in the LDL-receptor gene that affects LDL-receptor function provides the only unequivocal diagnosis of FH but, as discussed in Chapter 34, this is not yet feasible for every patient. One reason is that there are almost as many different mutations as there are FH patients in some clinics.[6] Another reason is that some potential mutations, such as those distant from the coding region or those occurring in introns, would not be detected by current methods.

Many assays have been devised to measure LDL-receptor activity or LDL-receptor protein content in human tissues or cells as a means of detecting defective LDL-receptor function. However, as discussed below, none of these assays has proven able to discriminate unequivocally between all heterozygous FH patients and the normal population.

REVIEW OF CURRENT METHODS

Measurement of LDL Receptors in Cultured Cells

Sound, reliable methods are described in the literature and, indeed, are widely used in research for measuring binding, internalization, and degradation of ^{125}I-labeled LDL by cultured cells such as human skin fibroblasts,[9] based on the pioneering work of Brown and Goldstein and colleagues.[10,11] LDL-receptor protein content of cells can also be determined by

✧ semi-quantitative immunoblotting or ligand blotting of cell extracts fractionated by polyacrylamide gel electrophoresis,[12] or

✧ radioimmunoassay of a membrane fraction of whole cell extracts.[13]

All these techniques are ideal for elucidating, for example, the effects of stimulatory or inhibitory factors of LDL-receptor gene expression in an individual cell line, but the absolute values obtained for different cell lines vary considerably, even when no defect in receptor function is suspected. This is probably because LDL-receptor expression is very sensitive to the sterol content of the cells and is barely detectable in cells that have been pre-incubated in medium containing serum.[10] Thus, cells must be pre-incubated in sterol-free medium, usually one containing lipoprotein-deficient serum (LPDS), which is prepared by ultracentrifugation of serum to remove all lipoproteins that float at a density of ≤ 1.2 kg/L. Pre-incubating cells in such a medium removes the source of the large majority of exogenous sterols, but some traces of free sterol may remain. Furthermore, pre-incubating cells with sterol-free medium stimulates the rate of cholesterol synthesis in the cell,[11] and excess newly synthesized cholesterol will also down-regulate LDL-receptor expression. Inhibitors of hydroxy-methylglutaryl-coenzyme A (HMG-CoA) reductase, a key enzyme in the pathway of cholesterol biosynthesis, can be included in the pre-incubation medium, but cultured cells will not survive long if deprived entirely of sterols. The growth rate of the cells in culture can also be affected by, for example, the presence of growth factors or other mitogens in the medium,[14–16] and this will influence the demand for cholesterol needed for membrane synthesis. Thus, the balance between synthesis and utilization of cholesterol can vary between different cells, or even between the same cells on different days, and this critically influences the absolute level of LDL-receptor gene expression.

This variability causes virtually insoluble problems for diagnosing heterozygous FH based on LDL-receptor activity in cultured cells from an individual patient. Usually, cells from a homozygous patient can be clearly identified in this way, because the residual LDL-receptor activity is almost always less than 10%–20% of normal, even when the mutant protein from both alleles retains some activity. However, the clinical phenotype of homozygous FH is normally unmistakable,[2] and there is rarely a need to assay receptor function for clinical purposes. A few patients have been described in the literature in whom a diagnosis of homozygous FH is suspected, but some doubt of that diagnosis exists because only one or neither of the parents is clearly hypercholesterolemic.[17,18] On such occasions it can be useful to assay receptor activity in the patient's cells to confirm or, in some instances, preclude, a diagnosis of homozygous FH.

Problems arise in attempting to distinguish between heterozygous FH and hypercholesterolemia due to other causes, because although the mean values for LDL-receptor activity or protein content between suspected FH and control groups clearly differ, the region of overlap between them is too great to permit unambiguous differentiation of all individuals. This overlap occurs even when the FH group comprises only patients with defined mutations in the LDL-receptor gene. This is partly because of the experimental variability described above, and partly because some mutations are less deleterious than others to the function of the protein.[19] Some mutations produce no protein at all from the mutant allele or produce one with undetectable residual activity, while others reduce only partially the LDL-receptor activity of the protein encoded by that allele. Also, cells from a heterozygous FH patient produce the normal amount of LDL-receptor protein from the unaffected allele, and thus retain half the normal level of LDL-receptor activity, apparently regardless of the defect in the mutant allele.[20,21] The result is that the activity in heterozygous FH cells can vary from 50% to 100% of a normal range that is itself quite wide, as is demonstrated by the data shown in Figure 29–1. Thus, it is not possible to confirm that a particular individual has a defect in one allele of his or her LDL-receptor gene by assaying LDL receptors in the individual's cultured cells.

Measurement of LDL Receptors in Freshly Isolated Cells

A further disadvantage of attempting to measure LDL receptors in cultured cells as a diagnostic tool is the length of time required to establish cell lines. Culturing skin fibroblasts can take many weeks before sufficient cells grow out of the biopsy for experiments to be feasible, and obtaining a skin biopsy is an invasive procedure. Lymphocytes from fresh human blood can be transformed with Epstein-Barr virus to produce immortalized lymphoblasts, and in this case sufficient cells can be obtained within three to four weeks. However, these cells grow in suspension, which makes assays of binding of LDL to the cell surface less reliable, and lymphoblasts are less well characterized in terms of their regulation of LDL-receptor expression than cultured skin fibroblasts.[23]

This inevitable delay in obtaining results from cultured cells, together with the considerable labor and cost involved in their maintenance, has led to the development of methods to measure LDL receptors in freshly isolated white blood cells by flow cytometry. In most of the methods described, non-adherent mononuclear cells have been incubated either with LDL labeled with a hydrophobic fluorescent molecule that is localized in the lipid core of the particle,[24–28] or with a specific antibody to the LDL receptor that is then detected with a second antibody conjugated to a fluores-

Figure 29–1 ✧ Comparison of LDL-Receptor Activity and Immuno-detectable LDL-Receptor Protein in Epstein-Barr Virus (EBV)-Transformed Lymphocytes in Patients with a Clinical Diagnosis of Heterozygous FH and Normolipemic Controls

LDL-receptor activity (○) was determined as the maximum rate of saturable degradation of ^{125}I-labeled LDL by cells pre-incubated for 48h in medium containing lipoprotein-deficient serum and compactin. LDL-receptor protein content (●) was determined by semi-quantitative immunoblotting of the cell extracts fractionated by SDS-polyacrylamide gel electrophoresis with monoclonal antibodies specific for the LDL receptor. A genetic defect in the LDL-receptor gene was identified in some of the heterozygous FH patients (mutation known). No genetic defect in the gene for apoB or for the LDL receptor was detected in the remaining patients (defect unknown). Data from Sun.[22]

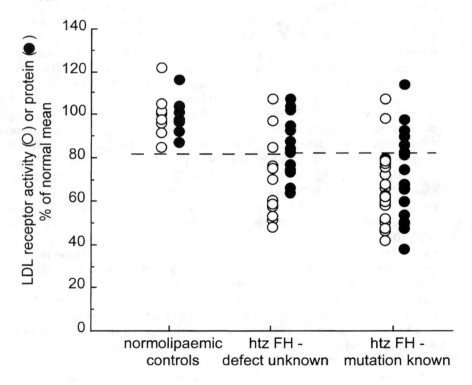

cent label.[26,29] The advantage of using labeled LDL is that only functional LDL receptors are measured, while the antibody may also bind to non-functional mutant protein on the cell surface. However, isolated LDL has a very limited shelf life, so it must be prepared frequently from fresh plasma. The level of activity in freshly isolated cells is too low to be detected, and pre-incubation for one to several days with a sterol-depleted medium has been found necessary to induce measurable LDL-receptor expression.[30] Some researchers have also found it necessary or beneficial to stimulate the cells by pre-incubating them with cytokines or mitogens, while others believe that this increases experimental variability because the cell population appears to be less homogeneous with respect to LDL-receptor expression.[26,27,31,32]

The absolute requirement for cholesterol for cell proliferation has been exploited to assess LDL-receptor activity in peripheral blood mononuclear cells (PBMCs). Freshly isolated PBMCs in which cholesterol biosynthesis is inhibited are entirely dependent on an external supply of cholesterol for growth in response to a mitogenic stimulus.[33] Low concentrations of LDL, in the range of 2–3 µg of LDL cholesterol per mL, can supply cholesterol for cells with the normal complement of functional LDL receptors. However, concentrations approximately two-fold higher are required to support the proliferation of cells with half the number of functional LDL receptors obtained from patients with heterozygous FH.[34]

In practice, freshly isolated cells are incubated in medium containing LPDS and mevinolin, a potent inhibitor of cholesterol biosynthesis, together with LDL in varying concentrations (in the range of 0–10 µg of cholesterol per mL), with or without the mitogen phytohemagglutinin in the medium. The proliferative response in the presence of different concentrations of LDL is then determined as the difference in the rate of incorporation of ^{3}H-thymidine after four days of incubation with or without the mitogen. As originally described, this method showed that there was a clear difference between control cells and cells from heterozygous FH patients.[34] However, the authors later demonstrated that the response was "normalized" in cells from heterozygous FH patients treated with lipid-lowering drug therapy,[35] suggesting that the response in cells from different patients might be affected by a variety of factors, and that the method is not likely to be totally reliable for diagnostic purposes in today's lipid clinics.

Although all the various methods have been able to show a significant difference in the mean activity between freshly isolated lymphocytes from normolipemic individuals and from patients with a clinical diagnosis of heterozygous FH, in practice all these methods suffer from the same drawback as those used for cultured cells: the region of overlap between heterozygous FH and control subjects is too great to permit discrimination in a significant number of cases. Unfortunately, these patients often will be the very ones in whom the clinical diagnosis of FH is in some doubt. One flow-cytometric study compared cells from individuals with known mutations in the LDL-receptor gene with cells from individuals with no detectable defect. This confirmed that the method could not be used to diagnose FH unequivocally in all individuals.[36] Indeed, no instances have been published in which a diagnosis of possible heterozygous FH has been confirmed or refuted by measurement of LDL-receptor activity in the patient's cells.

These problems are clearly demonstrated in a recent careful study of 384 patients with a clinical diagnosis of heterozygous FH based on serum cholesterol levels, family history, and clinical symptoms.[26] In the study, LDL-receptor-dependent binding of LDL and of anti-LDL-receptor antibody to freshly isolated PBMC was determined by flow cytometry. Based on the assay results, LDL-receptor deficiency was thought to be present in only 72% of the patients. Therefore, by this technique, the diagnosis apparently remained unconfirmed in one out of every three to four potential FH patients. In a smaller study, but one in which every possible care was taken to standardize the flow-cytometric assay of LDL binding,[31] a similar proportion of patients with a clinical diagnosis of heterozygous FH, including the presence of tendon xanthomata in the patient, was found to have LDL-receptor activity within the normal range. Only one recent study—by flow cytometry with PHA-stimulated cells—has claimed to show that there is always a clear distinction between cells from heterozygous FH and normolipemic individuals. Although their results showed no overlap, all the patients included in the study had a clinical diagnosis of definite heterozygous FH, with tendon xanthomas present in the patient or a first-degree relative.[32]

Measurement of LDL Receptors in the Whole Body

To assess whether or not variation in LDL-receptor activity between individuals significantly influences their plasma lipoprotein concentration or their risk of premature CHD, one must be able to measure LDL-receptor activity under the physiological conditions of sterol balance that exist in the whole body. Clearly, this is not possible by any of the methods described above, not even with freshly isolated lymphocytes, because to induce measurable amounts of LDL-receptor protein or activity, the cells must be deprived of all exogenous sterols. Thus, the activity measured in fully induced cultured cells will reflect the maximum genetic potential of the cells to express LDL receptors, although this is always influenced to some extent by the state of growth of the cells, as described above. It certainly will not reflect the physiologically regulated level of expression in different tissues in the whole body, where the flux of cholesterol varies in response to numerous physiological changes. Hence, there is considerable doubt that the low level of LDL-receptor activity expressed in circulating lymphocytes accurately reflects that expressed in the liver.

With the exception of malignant cells,[37] lymphocytes have little need of cholesterol for cell membrane synthesis or for biosynthetic purposes. Yet there is considerable flux of cholesterol in the liver, where cholesterol is converted to bile acids that are secreted in the bile, together with free cholesterol. The liver also secretes cholesterol-containing lipoproteins, thereby further depleting hepatocytes of cholesterol. As a result, the expression of LDL receptors is much higher in the liver than in circulating white blood cells. LDL-receptor activity in most tissues other than the liver appears to be very low, with the exception of those that synthesize steroid hormones, but these tissues normally make only a small contribution to LDL-receptor activity in the whole body in comparison to the liver.[38]

Unfortunately, any methods that can or have been devised to measure hepatic LDL-receptor expression directly, whether by immunoassay of LDL-receptor protein,[12] by measurement of binding of ^{125}I-labelled LDL to hepatic membranes,[39] or by assaying the amount of LDL-receptor mRNA,[40] require a liver biopsy. Thus, these methods are suitable only for research purposes, with strictly limited numbers of patients who are undergoing biopsy or surgery for other reasons, and not for routine clinical measurement. The potential exists for determining LDL uptake in the liver by non-invasive whole-body imaging after the administration of a trace of labeled LDL, and this has been achieved in rabbits by scintigraphy following injection of radionuclide-labeled LDL.[41] However, the much higher concentration of LDL in the human circulation would greatly reduce the sensitivity of this or any other imaging technique, as any specific binding or uptake would be superimposed on a high background.

The same limitation of lack of feasibility for routine clinical purposes applies to the indirect measurement of LDL-receptor function by determining the LDL turnover rate in the whole body. This technique relies on following the fate, in plasma, of an administered trace of autologous-labeled lipoprotein.[42] With radioactively labeled lipoproteins, specific LDL receptor-mediated uptake can be assessed by comparing the rate of removal of a trace of normal LDL with that of a trace of a chemically modified form of LDL that is not recognized by the LDL receptor but is otherwise metabolized normally.[43] More recently, measurement of LDL turnover has been made less invasive by using stable isotopes as an endogenous label, generally administered as a single dose of a deuterated amino acid[44] rather than ^{125}I-labeled lipoproteins as tracers for apo B. However, receptor-mediated uptake cannot be distinguished from non-receptor-mediated uptake by this method.

The major drawback of the procedure, one which precludes its use for routine diagnostic purposes, is that with either type of labeling technique, blood samples must be taken daily for at least 7–10 days after administering the dose, during which time the patient must consume a carefully controlled diet. In addition, the subsequent experimental procedure for sample analysis is very labor intensive, and with either an endogenous label or a radioactive trace to measure LDL turnover, a number of assumptions must be made in order to equate LDL catabolism with LDL-receptor expression.

One of the least valid assumptions that must be made, at least for FH patients, is that LDL is cleared primarily by the LDL-receptor pathway. Although the fractional rate of LDL catabolism is reduced in FH, the absolute amount of LDL cleared from the circulation each day by FH patients can actually exceed that of normolipemic individuals.[45] Clearly, alternative pathways for LDL removal exist, especially when the concentration of LDL in the circulation is high. The specificity of determining the activity of the LDL-receptor pathway in the whole body could be increased by assaying the uptake of a specific antibody to the LDL-receptor protein that is bound and internalized in the same way as a lipoprotein ligand.[46] This has been successfully carried out in rabbits,[47] but the potential problems associated with administering a foreign protein has precluded the development of this method for human subjects.

SUMMARY AND CONCLUSIONS

Although all the methods described above have been used successfully for research purposes, there is little direct evidence that they are useful for routine clinical diagnosis of heterozygous FH in a typical clinic. Several of the groups who have set up flow cytometric methods for the measurement of LDL-receptor-dependent binding of fluorescently labeled LDL state that this method is likely to be useful as an aid to diagnosis. Thus far, this technique probably provides the best discrimination between heterozygous FH patients and normal controls based on LDL-receptor activity, but no one has yet provided a clear description of cases where results from flow cytometric analysis of LDL-receptor activity in cells has changed the course of clinical management.

It should also be borne in mind that obtaining reproducible results with this method requires a high level of technical expertise, as well as specialized equipment that is expensive and may not always be available in the routine laboratory. In practice, a combination of a sound clinical examination and knowledge of the family history, supported where possible with analysis of the mutation or polymorphisms in the LDL-receptor gene,[48] provides the best diagnosis of heterozygous FH for routine clinical management. ✧

REFERENCES

1. Brown MS, Goldstein JL. A receptor-mediated pathway for cholesterol homeostasis. Science 1986;232:34–47.
2. Goldstein JL, Hobbs H, Brown MS. Familial hypercholesterolaemia. In: Scriver CR, Beaudet AL, Sly WS, Valle D, eds. The metabolic and molecular bases of inherited disease, Vol. II. New York: McGraw-Hill, 1995:1281–2030.
3. Slack J. Risk of ischaemic heart disease in familial hyperlipoproteinaemic states. Lancet 1969;ii:1380–82.
4. Pedersen JC, Berg, K. Gene-gene interaction between the low-density lipoprotein receptor and apolipoprotein E loci affects lipid levels. Clin Genet 1990;38:287–94.
5. Scientific Steering Committee on behalf of the Simon Broome Register Group. Risk of fatal coronary heart disease in familial hypercholesterolaemia. BMJ 1991;303:893–6.
6. Webb JC, Sun X-M, McCarthy SN, Neuwirth C, Thompson GR, Knight BL, Soutar AK. Characterisation of mutations in the low-density lipoprotein (LDL)-receptor gene in patients with familial hypercholesterolaemia (FH) and frequency of these mutations in FH patients in the UK. J Lipid Res 1996;37:368–81.
7. Myant NB, Gallagher JJ, Knight BL, McCarthy SN, Frostegard J, Nilsson J, Hamsten A, Talmud P, Humphries SE. Clinical signs of familial hypercholesterolemia in patients with familial defective apolipoprotein B-100 and normal low-density-lipoprotein-receptor function. Arterioscler Thromb 1991;11:691–703.
8. Maher VM, Gallagher JJ, Thompson GR, Myant, NB. Response to cholesterol-lowering drugs in familial defective apolipoprotein B-100. Atherosclerosis 1991;91:73–6.
9. Goldstein JL, Basu SK, Brown MS. Receptor-mediated endocytosis of low-density lipoprotein in cultured cells. Methods Enzymol 1983;98:241–60.
10. Goldstein JL, Brown MS. Binding and degradation of low-density lipoproteins by cultured human fibroblasts. Comparison of cells from a normal subject and from a patient with homozygous familial hypercholesterolemia. J Biol Chem 1974;249:5153–62.
11. Goldstein JL, Basu SK, Brunschede GY, Brown MS. Release of low-density lipoprotein from its cell surface receptor by sulfated glycosaminoglycans. Cell 1976;7:85–95.
12. Soutar AK, Harders-Spengel K, Wade DP, Knight, BL. Detection and quantitation of low-density lipoprotein (LDL) receptors in human liver by ligand blotting, immunoblotting, and radioimmunoassay: LDL receptor protein content is correlated with plasma LDL cholesterol concentration. J Biol Chem 1986;261:17127–33.
13. Knight BL, Preyer S, Soutar AK. Immunoassay of bovine and human low-density-lipoprotein receptors using monoclonal antibodies. Biochem J 1986;238:405–10.
14. Moorby CD, Gherardi E, Dovey L, Godliman C, Bowyer DE. Transforming growth factor-beta 1 and interleukin-1 beta stimulate LDL receptor activity in Hep G2 cells. Atherosclerosis 1992;97:21–8.
15. Nicholson AC, Hajjar, DP. Transforming growth factor-beta up-regulates low-density lipoprotein receptor-mediated cholesterol metabolism in vascular smooth muscle cells. J Biol Chem 1992;267:25982–7.
16. Chait A, Ross R, Bierman EL. Stimulation of receptor-dependent and receptor-independent pathways of low-density lipoprotein degradation in arterial smooth muscle cells by platelet-derived growth factor. Biochim Biophys Acta 1988;960:183–9.
17. Harada SM, Tajima S, Yokoyama S, Miyake Y, Kojima S, Tsushima M, Kawakami M et al. Siblings with normal LDL receptor activity and severe hypercholesterolemia. Arterioscler Thromb 1992;12:1071–8.

18. Norman D, Sun X-M, Bourbon M, Knight BL, Naoumova R, Soutar AK. Characterization of a novel defect in patients with phenotypic homozygous familial hypercholesterolemia. J Clin Invest 1999;104:619–628.

19. Soutar AK. Familial hypercholesterolaemia. In: Humphries SE, Malcolm S, eds. From genotype to phenotype. Oxford, UK: Bios, 1994:83–103.

20. Goldstein JL, Sobhani MK, Faust JR, Brown MS. Heterozygous familial hypercholesterolemia: failure of normal allele to compensate for mutant allele at a regulated genetic locus. Cell 1976;9:195–203.

21. Patel DD, Lelli N, Garuti R, Volti SL, Bertolini S, Knight BL, Calandra S. Analysis of two duplications of the LDL receptor gene affecting intracellular transport, catabolism, and surface binding of the LDL receptor. J Lipid Res 1998;39:1466–75

22. Sun X-M, Patel DD, Knight BL, Soutar AK, with the Familial Hypercholesterolaemia Regression Study Group. Comparison of the genetic defect with LDL-receptor activity in cultured cells from patients with a clinical diagnosis of heterozygous familial hypercholesterolaemia. Arterioscler Thromb Vasc Biol 1997;17:3092–101.

23. Lombardi P, de Wit E, Frants RR, Havekes LM. Characterisation of the LDL receptor in Epstein-Barr virus transformed lymphocytes. Biochim Biophys Acta 1990;1044: 127–32.

24. Lestavel DS, Benhamamouch S, Agnani G, Luc G, Bard JM, Brousseau T, Billardon C et al. Evidence of non-deficient low-density lipoprotein receptor patients in a pool of subjects with clinical familial hypercholesterolemia profile. Metabolism 1994;43:397–402.

25. Ranganathan S, Hattori H, Kashyap ML. A rapid flow cytometric assay for low-density lipoprotein receptors in human peripheral blood mononuclear cells. J Lab Clin Med 1995;125:479–86.

26. Schmitz G, Bruning T, Kovacs E, Barlage, S. Fluorescence flow cytometry of human leukocytes in the detection of LDL receptor defects in the differential diagnosis of hypercholesterolemia. Arterioscler Thromb 1993;13:1053–65.

27. Suzuki K, Hara M, Kitani A, Harigai M, Norioka K, Kondo K, Hirata F. et al. Augmentation of LDL receptor activities on lymphocytes by interleukin-2 and anti-CD3 antibody: a flow cytometric analysis. Biochim Biophys Acta 1990;1042:352–8.

28. Traill KN, Jurgens G, Bock G, Huber L, Schonitzer D, Widhalm K, Winter U et al. Analysis of fluorescent low-density-lipoprotein uptake by lymphocytes: paradoxical increase in the elderly. Mech Ageing Dev 1987;40:261–88.

29. Benhamamouch S, Kuznierz JP, Agnani G, Marzin D, Lecerf JM, Fruchart JC, Clavey, V. Determination of the LDL receptor-binding capacity of human lymphocytes by immunocytofluorimetric assay. Biochim Biophys Acta 1989;1002:45–53.

30. Bilheimer DW, Ho YK, Brown MS, Anderson RGW, Goldstein JL. Genetics of low-density-lipoprotein receptor: diminished receptor activity in lymphocytes from heterozygotes with familial hypercholesterolemia. J Clin Invest 1978;61:678–96.

31. Lohne K, Urdal P, Leren TP, Tonstad S, Ose L. Standardization of a flow-cytometric method for measurement of low-density lipoprotein receptor activity on blood mononuclear cells. Cytometry 1995;20:290–5.

32. Chan P, Edwards A, Lafreniere R, Parsons H. Improved detection of familial hypercholesterolemia by determining low-density-lipoprotein-receptor expression in mitogen-induced proliferating lymphocytes. J Lipid Res 1998;39:2261–70

33. Cuthbert JA, Lipsky PE. Provision of cholesterol to lymphocytes by high-density and low-density lipoproteins: requirement for low density lipoprotein receptors. J Biol Chem 1987;262:7808–18.

34. Cuthbert JA, East CA, Bilheimer DW, Lipsky PE. Detection of familial hypercholesterolemia by assaying functional low-density-lipoprotein receptors on lymphocytes. N Engl J Med 1986;314:879–83.

35. Cuthbert JA, East CA, Lipsky, PE. Normalization of LDL receptor function by lymphocytes of patients with heterozygous familial hypercholesterolemia after treatment with plasma-cholesterol-lowering agents. Am J Med Sci 1989;298:152–60.

36. Raungaard B, Heath F, Brorholt-Petersen JU, Jensen HK, Faergeman O. Flow-cytometric assessment of LDL receptor activity peripheral blood mononuclear cells compared to

gene mutation detection in diagnosis of heterozygous familial hypercholesterolemia. Cytometry 1999;36:52–9

37. Rudling MJ, Peterson CO. A simple binding assay for the determination of low-density lipoprotein receptors in cell homogenates. Biochim Biophys Acta 1985;833:359–65.

38. Rudling MJ, Reihner E, Einarsson K, Ewerth S, Angelin B. Low-density-lipoprotein-receptor-binding activity in human tissues: quantitative importance of hepatic receptors and evidence for regulation of their expression in vivo. Proc Natl Acad Sci USA 1990; 87:3469–73.

39. Harders-Spengel K, Wood CB, Thompson GR, Myant NB, Soutar AK. Difference in saturable binding of low-density lipoprotein to liver membranes from normocholesterolaemic subjects and patients with heterozygous familial hypercholesterolaemia. Proc Natl Acad Sci USA 1982;79:6355–9.

40. Rudling M. Hepatic mRNA levels for the LDL receptor and HMG-CoA reductase show coordinate regulation in vivo. J Lipid Res 1992;33:493–501.

41. Huettinger M, Corbett JR, Schneider WJ, Willerson JT, Brown MS, Goldstein JL. Imaging of hepatic low-density lipoprotein receptors by radionuclide scintiscanning in vivo. Proc Natl Acad Sci USA 1984;81:7599–603.

42. Shepherd J, Bicker S, Lorimer AR, Packard, CJ. Receptor-mediated low-density lipoprotein catabolism in man. J Lipid Res 1979;20:999–1006.

43. Slater HR, Packard CJ, Shepherd, J. Measurement of receptor-independent lipoprotein catabolism using 1,2-cyclohexanedione-modified low-density lipoprotein. J Lipid Res 1982;23:92–6.

44. Packard CJ. The role of stable isotopes in the investigation of plasma lipoprotein metabolism. Baillieres Clin Endocrinol Metab 1995;9:755–72.

45. Packard CJ, Third JL, Shepherd J, Lorimer AR, Morgan HG, Lawrie TD. Low-density-lipoprotein metabolism in a family of familial hypercholesterolemic patients. Metabolism 1976;25:995–1006.

46. Huettinger M, Schneider WJ, Ho YK, Goldstein JL, Brown MS. Use of monoclonal anti-receptor antibodies to probe the expression of the low-density-lipoprotein receptor in tissues of normal and Watanabe heritable hyperlipidemic rabbits. J Clin Invest 1984;74:1017–26.

47. Fitzsimmons C, Bush R, Hele D, Godliman C, Gherardi E, Bowyer DE. Measurement of the absolute number of functioning low-density-lipoprotein receptors in vivo using a monoclonal antibody. Biochem J 1995;305:897–904.

48. Soutar AK. Investigation and diagnosis of disorders of lipoprotein metabolism. In: Rapley R, Walker MR. Molecular Diagnostics. Oxford, UK: Blackwell Scientific Publications, 1993:139–68.

New Approaches to the Use of Lipoprotein Electrophoresis in the Clinical Laboratory*

30

Gerd Schmitz, Alfred Böttcher, Stefan Barlage, and Karl J. Lackner

❖ The analysis of serum lipids as well as of lipoproteins and their apoproteins has become of major importance for clinical laboratory medicine ever since large-scale international epidemiological studies suggested that disorders of lipoprotein metabolism caused cardiovascular disease.[1,2]

Fredrickson et al.[3] published a first classification of lipid disorders in 1967. They proposed a system of five hyperlipoproteinemia phenotypes based on elevations of the four major classes of plasma lipoproteins, namely chylomicrons, very-low-density lipoproteins (VLDL), low-density lipoproteins (LDL), and high-density lipoproteins (HDL). This classification system was a major breakthrough in categorizing cholesterol and triglycerides (TG) elevations into distinct and recognizable lipoprotein patterns. Today, the determination of the lipoprotein cholesterol content (LDL-C, HDL-C) has become the major clinical parameter for the assessment of an individual's risk of cardiovascular disease. Only lipoprotein(a) [(Lp(a)], which also has been found to be an independent risk factor, is usually measured by immunological methods. The Adult Treatment Panel of the National Cholesterol Education Program (NCEP) recommends that LDL-C should be used as the basis for initiation of treatment and follow-up of patients with high blood cholesterol. In addition, measurement of HDL-C is recommended as part of the initial screening.[4,5] Furthermore, the Working Group on Lipoprotein Measurement has developed guidelines for accurate and precise measurement of LDL-C and HDL-C.[6,7]

In order to obtain lipoprotein cholesterol values, the clinical laboratory generally measured serum TG, total cholesterol, and HDL-C and used the Friedewald equation[8] to estimate LDL-C. The use of this formula has some major limitations:

❖ patients must be fasting overnight to avoid the presence of chylomicrons and to enable the accurate determination of TG in the fasting state;

❖ lipemic specimens—TG > 200 mg/dL (2.2 mmol/L)—can cause some error, and values > 400 mg/dL (4.5 mmol/L) can cause major inaccuracies in the calculated LDL-C value;[9]

*This chapter is based in part on "New Approaches to the Use of Lipoprotein Electrophoresis in the Clinical Laboratory," by Naito HK, Ward KM, Schmitz G, Mollers C, Bottcher A, Ploch J, Myers GL. This chapter appeared in the 1997 edition of Handbook of Lipoprotein Testing (Washington, DC: AACC).

❖   the equation cannot be used if the patient has Type III hyperlipoproteinemia (disbetalipoproteinemia); and

❖   accuracy is dependent on accurate measurement of all three analytes—total cholesterol, TG, and HDL-C—and on the influence of biological variation of the three analytes at the time of specimen collection.

These drawbacks, as well as recommendations from the NCEP and other consensus groups, motivated the development of methods for direct measurement of LDL-C. Direct LDL-C assays, which now have become somewhat common in the clinical laboratory, often use an immunoseparation technique and, although conflicting results have been reported, the direct LDL-C measurement generally seems to demonstrate improved performance compared to the estimation technique.[10–14] For additional information on the measurement of LDL-C, refer to chapter 12.

Conventional precipitation methods for HDL-C, which became common in routine practice, also have disadvantages. They usually require a manual pretreatment step that is labor intensive, time consuming, and subject to greater variation than, for example, cholesterol measurements alone.[15,16] A major source of inaccuracy is interference resulting from incomplete precipitation of lipoproteins containing apolipoprotein (apo) B, which often occurs with hypertriglyceridemia. Chylomicrons, in particular, tend to cause greater interference problems than VLDL, depending on the method used. Increasing demand in routine clinical laboratories for full automation, lower cost per test, and faster methods with smaller sample and reagent volume requirements led to improvements in the technology, culminating in the recent development of direct and fully automated HDL-C methods, the so-called homogeneous assays. These methods are based on a one-step procedure whereby the discrimination between lipoproteins is accomplished online and the chemistry analyzer only measures HDL-C.[17,8,19] These methods are faster because the pretreatment steps are eliminated: manual addition of a precipitation reagent to the specimen, mixing, centrifugation, and decanting of the supernatant solution. Although reagents tend to be more expensive, the total cost is less due to decreased labor costs. Recently, a multi-center evaluation of a homogeneous assay for HDL-C without sample pretreatment based on the use of polyethylene glycol (PEG)-modified enzymes and α-cyclodextrin has been reported by Nauck et al., confirming that this assay did meet the NCEP precision goals, even in hypertriglyceridemic samples (up to at least 800 mg/dL; 9 mmol/L) respectively in samples with bilirubin < 10 mg/dL (0.71 mmol/L).[20] However, interference with the β-VLDL of patients with Type III hyperlipidemia has been reported far below TG concentrations of 1000 mg/dL (11.3 mmol/L).[21] For additional information on the measurement of HDL-C, refer to chapter 11.

LIPOPROTEIN ELECTROPHORESIS

Although the above-mentioned methods have mainly displaced electrophoretic methods in the clinical laboratory, some laboratories still use lipoprotein electrophoresis, e.g., for diagnosing Type III hyperlipidemia (Figure 30–1). Electrophoresis offers the advantage making the lipoprotein band patterns visible, which may aid in the identification of unusual phenotypes, such as Type III hyperlipoproteinemia (broad β dis-

Figure 30–1 ✧ Lipoprotein Patterns by Conventional Agarose Gel Electrophoresis

Patients 1, 2, and 3 have hypobetalipoproteinemia. Patient 4 has Type IIa hyperbetalipoproteinemia. Patient 5 has Type IIb hyperlipoproteinemia. Patient 7 has a normal lipoprotein profile. Note that when only two lipoprotein bands (alpha and beta) are involved (Patients 1, 2, and 3), the separation is very discrete. On the other hand, when the pre-beta lipoproteins are present (Patients 4, 5, and 7), the separation of the pre-beta band often trails off from the anodal edge of the band to the beta band.

COMPARISON OF SERUM LIPOPROTEIN ELECTROPHORETIC PATTERNS ON AGAROSE MEDIA

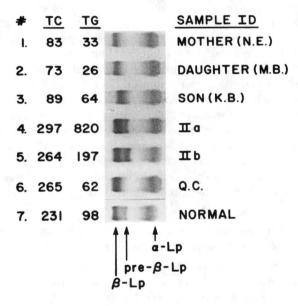

#	TC	TG			SAMPLE ID
1.	83	33			MOTHER (N.E.)
2.	73	26			DAUGHTER (M.B.)
3.	89	64			SON (K.B.)
4.	297	820			II a
5.	264	197			II b
6.	265	62			Q.C.
7.	231	98			NORMAL

α-Lp
pre-β-Lp
β-Lp

ease). Electrophoresis of plasma lipoproteins has been performed on a number of different support media, such as starch gel,[22] cellulose acetate,[23,24] paper,[25–30] agarose,[31–34] polyacrylamide gel (PAG),[35–40] and others.[41–45] Each of the media has its strengths, weaknesses, and advantages for different types of procedures. Several comprehensive reviews of electrophoretic techniques for lipoprotein analysis are available.[46–51] In addition, capillary electrophoresis (CE) and isotachophoresis (ITP) have been used to separate lipoproteins.

The most widely used technique in the clinical laboratory is still the characterization of lipoproteins using agarose gels. In 1968, Noble introduced the use of agarose gel electrophoresis and, while numerous changes in the methodology of agarose gel electrophoresis have been described, Noble's work still forms the basis for the agarose gel electrophoresis of serum lipoproteins. The resolving power of the agarose gel is greater than that of paper or cellulose acetate and the relatively clear matrix of the agarose gel allows for better quantitation of the lipoprotein fractions with the use of a scanning densitometer. Starch-gel has not been used to any great extent in the clinical laboratory. However, for the isolation of lipoproteins in large quantities, the starch-block electrophoretic technique has been useful in the research laboratory, because lipoproteins isolated by this method can be used for further immunological, chemical composition, physical-chemical, and electron microscopic studies. PAG, like starch gel, separates lipoproteins on the basis of both the electrical charge and molecular size. The molecular sieving action of the PAG slows the large VLDL band to a position between the origin and the LDL band (the reverse of the pattern seen with agarose, paper, and cellulose acetate media, in which VLDL migrates to the pre-β band). The molecular sieving effect in PAG also results in lipoprotein fractions being separated with a higher degree of resolution. PAG electrophoresis has been used extensively in the research laboratory because of its greater resolving power to separate subclasses of major lipoprotein fractions. However, this apparent advantage can become an obstacle when a large number of lipoproteins separate into so many discrete bands that it is difficult to identify the individual bands.

Noble electrophoresed serum lipoproteins for 2 h in a gel composed of 0.6% agarose, 0.5% bovine serum albumin, and 50 mmol/L sodium barbital buffer, pH 8.6. Finally the gel strip was fixed, dehydrated, and dried, and lipoprotein bands were made visible with the fat stains Sudan Black B or Oil Red O (lipoprotein content was determined by densitometry). Whereas chylomicrons did not enter the gel and stayed at the origin, three distinct bands could be determined: β (LDL), pre-β (VLDL) and α (HDL), all migrating anodally with the α band moving the greatest distance. However, several problems have been reported with these early quantitative electrophoretic methods:

✧   The heterogeneity of each lipoprotein fraction causes poor resolution, making it difficult for the analyst to precisely delineate between the lipoprotein fractions.

✧   The lipid stains have different affinities for the different classes of lipids (cholesteryl esters, free cholesterol, TG, phospholipids), which vary in their proportions in each lipoprotein class. The dye becomes more or less intense in relation to the total amount of lipids, affecting the quantitation of the lipoprotein fractions.

✧   No method has been found to calibrate the integrated peaks or dye intensity against a "gold standard" method that accurately quantitates lipoprotein concentrations. In the past, the calibration of electrophoretic methods was based on preparative or analytical ultracentrifugal data. However, the bands separated by electrophoretic techniques are not exactly equivalent to the classes separated by ultracentrifugation.

✧   A constant lipid–dye and alcohol concentration from one batch to the next, or from one electrophoretic run to the next, could not be maintained.

In addition to these problems, several factors can cause poor resolution of lipoprotein bands and make manual or automatic demarcation of one lipoprotein fraction from another very difficult:

❖   the support media used,

❖   the environmental conditions (relative humidity, room temperature),

❖   the voltage/current and electrophoretic time used,

❖   the different sizes and electronegativity of lipoproteins, which can all cause a change in their mobility or can cause an overlap of the lipoprotein bands on electrophoretograms.

Poor resolution or incomplete separation of lipoprotein fractions can lead to inaccurate quantitation of each of the lipoprotein fractions, especially the pre-β lipoproteins (VLDL) and β-lipoproteins (LDL). Adding to the problem of inaccurate lipoprotein quantitation are specimens with chylomicrons or high levels of heterogeneous VLDL, which tend to cause trailing from the application point to the α_1-globulin area, which can also create significant positive interference in the quantitation of the other lipoprotein fractions. In addition, the presence of unusual lipoproteins such as β-migrating VLDL and Lp(a) can cause biases in the quantitation of VLDL because in many systems both of these variant lipoproteins migrate to the same zone as the VLDL. Finally, changing the electronegativity of the lipoproteins can change the normal migration patterns of the electrophoretogram. For instance, physiological stress conditions (the epinephrine effect) can cause increased lipolysis of TG in adipose tissue, resulting in increased levels of free fatty acids (FFA) in the bloodstream. The FFA bind preferentially to albumin, but once albumin is saturated, the lipoproteins are their next transport vehicle. This binding changes the electronegativity of the lipoproteins and thus their migration pattern. Injecting the patient with a bolus dose of heparin can have the same effect since heparin activates the intravascular lipoprotein lipase, causing hydrolysis of the circulating TG and resulting in high concentrations of blood FFA and glycerol.

Since the original report on the use of Sudan Black B or OIL RED O, several other techniques for materialization of the lipoprotein bands have been proposed. Wieland and Seidel described a technique in which lipoproteins can be precipitated within the gel with polyanions *in situ* to facilitate their materialization under oblique light.[52] Apart from the analysis of the lipoprotein band pattern, which can be materialized by lipid staining or precipitation, the specific measurement of the lipoprotein associated cholesterol within the lipoprotein bands has been reported. For the staining of lipoprotein cholesterol, gels were incubated with a reagent consisting of cholesterol esterase (0.4 U/mL and NAD (0.5 mmol/L), cholesterol dehydrogenase (0.14 U/ml) phenazinmethosulfate (PMS, 0.03 mmol/L) and 2-(p-(iodophenyl)-3-(p-nitrophenyl)-5-phenyltetrazolium chloride (INT), 0.16 mmol/L), Tris-HCL buffer (57 mmol/L), pH 8.0. Staining results were reported to be independent of the actual composition of the lipoprotein. No interference from co-precipitated proteins in the gel, such as fibrinogen or paraproteins, exists, and the staining is insensitive to lipolysis and high FFA concentrations.[53,54] Furthermore, the measurement of Lp(a) cholesterol upon electrophoretic separation, as reported by Nauck et al.[55], instead of Lp(a) mass, offers additional advantages, including the elimination of problems associated with standardization of Lp(a) mass assays due to apo(a) polymorphism. Recently, Contois et al. reported a comparison of a quantitative determination of cholesterol in lipoprotein fractions using the Helena REP cholesterol profile system (Helena Laboratories, Beaumont, TX) to a combined ultracentrifugation/precipitation technique (β-quantification, BQ).[56] The Helena REP cholesterol profile system separates lipoproteins by agarose gel electrophoresis and quantifies cholesterol by enzymatic staining and densitometry. The data indicated that the Helena REP cholesterol profile system is able to accurately and precisely measure LDL-C, whereas HDL-C measurement did not meet the NCEP guidelines for accuracy and precision. Furthermore, a poor resolution of VLDL and LDL in some samples presented a problem, which altogether prevented recommending the assay for comprehensive lipoprotein testing in the clinical laboratory.

Capillary electrophoresis, although mainly applied to the analysis of apolipoproteins, has recently been used to characterize intact lipoproteins, especially of charge-modified lipoproteins such as *in vitro* oxidized LDL.[57] Oxidation of LDL is accompanied by an increase in electrophoretic mobility and, in addition, an increase in absorbance at 234 nm occurs, due to the formation of conjugated dienes in constituent polyenoic fatty acids, the formation of thiobarbituric acid-reacting substances, and lipid hydroxyperoxides. Both parameters—the increase in absorbance at 234 nm as well as in mobility of the modified lipoprotein particle—can be determined. Up to now, no clinical application has been validated for these assays, although oxidation of LDL particles has been proposed as a major atherogenic modification also occuring *in vivo*. Capillary electrophoresis in general offers the potential advantages of a more rapid separation and a better control of operating conditions, on-column monitoring, and a potential for automation of analysis.

ANALYTICAL CAPILLARY ISOTACHOPHORESIS OF HUMAN SERUM LIPOPROTEINS

An analytical capillary isotachophoresis (ITP) procedure has been developed for the detailed analysis of lipoproteins on commercially available capillary electrophoresis systems. The original technique was based on the specific staining of lipoproteins with the lipophilic dye Sudan Black B before performing capillary ITP.[58,59] Since Sudan Black B shows no saturation in lipoprotein staining, we looked for another lipophilic dye that was composition independent but surface area or particle size dependent. Fluorescence-tagged phospholipid analogs have been tested and NBD-ceramide was identified as a good compromise for specific labeling and quantitation of individual lipoprotein classes.[60]

After blood clotting, centrifugation, and one-minute incubation with NBD-ceramide-staining solution, serum samples are diluted with the evaluated spacer mixture and applied by pressure between leading and terminating buffer into a dimethyl polysiloxane modified fused-silica capillary (180-μm inner diameter, 20-cm length to detector). The discontinuous buffer system consists of chloride as leading-, alanine as terminating- and 2-amino-2-methyl-1,3-propanediol as common counterion. The leading buffer (pH 8.8) is supplemented with 0.35% (w/v) hydroxypropylmethyl cellulose. Under the electric field, the stained lipoproteins are separated within 6 min according to their electrophoretic mobility. The addition of non-fluorescent spacer compounds allows the discrimination of 9 individual lipoprotein subfractions monitored with laser-induced fluorescence detection (ex 488 nm; em 520 nm; see Figure 30–2).

Figure 30–2 ✧ Representative Isotachopherogram of Human Serum Obtained from a Healthy Volunteer

Serum was incubated with NBD-ceramide and subsequently separated by analytical capillary isotachophoresis. The first peak (I) represents the internal marker compound carboxylfluorescein.

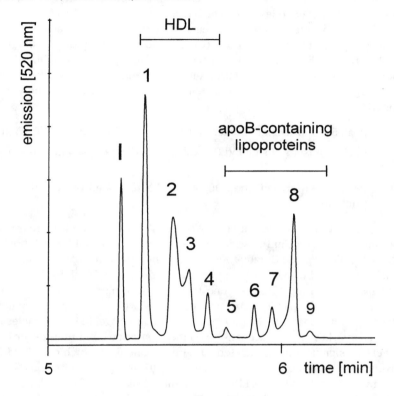

The bulk of HDL are separated into three major subfractions, which are designated as fast-(peak 1), intermediate-(peak 2 and 3) and slow-migrating HDL (peak 4) according to their electrophoretic mobility.

To further characterize these HDL subfractions, a newly developed free-solution ITP (FS-ITP)-system was used. This solution allows micro-preparative separation of human lipoproteins directly from whole plasma.[61] The fractions obtained by FS-ITP were analyzed for their lipid and apolipoprotein composition and by two-dimensional nondenaturing polyacrylamide gradient gel electrophoresis (2D-GGE).[62]

The three fractions defined in ITP differ in several relevant aspects. Fast-migrating HDL (fHDL) and intermediate-migrating HDL (iHDL) contain the bulk of HDL and apo A-I. However, compared to iHDL, fHDL have an increased ratio of LpA-I / LpA-I:A-II and an increased proportion of cholesteryl esters compared to unesterified cholesterol. The particle size of fHDL analyzed by 2D-GGE corresponds to HDL_{2a} and HDL_{2b} which is on the average larger than iHDL. However, there is considerable overlap and fHDL contains significant amounts of HDL_3. Other apolipoproteins besides apo A-I and apo A-II were not detectable, indicating that such proteins could only be present in trace amounts. Especially, no apo A-IV and only traces of apo E were found in the fHDL fractions.

Slow-migrating HDL (sHDL) contain several minor apolipoproteins such as apo A-IV, apo D, apo E, apo J and factor H. They also have an increased ratio of LpA-I to LpA-I:A-II. The presence of many different apolipoproteins suggests that this fraction may be of functional relevance, which deserves further study. The particular function of sHDL is also indicated by the presence of lecithin cholesterol acyltransferase (LCAT), cholesteryl esters transfer protein (CETP), and phospholipids transfer protein (PLTP) in this fraction. For additional information on the separation of HDL subclasses and lipoprotein particles LpA-I and LpA-I:A-II, refer to chapters 15 and 27, respectively.

The apo B-containing lipoproteins (peaks 5 to 9) can be subdivided into three functional groups:

❖ Peak 5 comprises chylomicron-derived particles and large, TG-rich, VLDL;

❖ Peak 6 consists of small VLDL and intermediate-density lipoproteins (IDL) particles;

❖ Peaks 7–9 represent the LDL, which are separated by ITP into two major subfractions.

The peak with lowest mobility is mostly small. This fraction is increased in abnormal serum samples, e.g., in the sera of patients with primary biliary cirrhosis.

Bittolo-Bon and Cazzolato[63] reported the separation of four LDL subfractions by analytical ITP of whole plasma lipoproteins, pre-stained with Fat Red 7B. The ratio of the faster-migrating LDL fractions to the slower-migrating fractions correlated inversely with LDL particle size and positively with the relative amount of electronegative LDL. This subfraction may represent atherogenic LDL particles like oxidized small dense LDL. Schlenck et al.[64] used the separation conditions described above. TG level was significantly associated with peak 5 and 6, in which peak 5 correlated positively with apo E serum concentration ($p < 0.01$) and peak 6 with apo C-III-containing lipoprotein level ($p < 0.001$). LDL-C was positively correlated to peak 7 and 8 ($0.05 \leq p < 0.01$). The fast-migrating LDL (peak 7) was positively associated with apo B and LpCIII:B ($p < 0.01$). They suggested that fast-migrating LDL may characterize small, dense LDL subfractions and the slow-migrating LDL large, buoyant LDL subfractions. For additional information of LDL subclasses, refer to chapter 16.

Lipoprotein data obtained by capillary ITP analysis were compared with routinely used precipitation procedures for HDL-C and LDL-C quantitation and turbidimetric determination of the apolipoprotein content. Calculation of cholesterol content in HDL (peak 1 to 4) and LDL (peak 7 to 9) determined by capillary ITP was assessed by applying total cholesterol concentration to the sum of relative peak areas. Peak areas are calculated by valley-to-valley integration, because a part of HDL (peak 2 and 3) co-migrates with albumin and appears as shoulder on the partially stained albumin. The correlation of HDL-C and LDL-C determined by capillary ITP and precipitation procedures is shown in Figure 30–3 for a group of 52 samples obtained from patients of our university hospital. The correlation coefficients for HDL-C and LDL-C are 0.9 and 0.91, respectively.

Beyond quantitation of HDL-C and LDL-C particles as a whole, the analytical capillary ITP technique allows further insights into plasma lipoprotein metabolism by estimation of major lipolytic enzyme activities with the help of an appropriate precursor/product concept. The ratio between precursor- and product-lipoprotein peaks influenced by a defined lipolytic enzyme allows the estimation of lipoprotein conversion rates.

Chylomicrons and large TG-rich VLDL particles are the precursors for lipoprotein lipase. Lipoprotein lipase converts this subpopulation into particles with intermediate density. In capillary ITP, peak 5 resembles mainly unhydrolyzed TG-rich lipoproteins, including chylomicrons and large VLDL, whereas IDL particles primarily migrate in peak 6. Thus, the ratio of peak 5 and peak 6 provides a rough estimate of the lipoprotein lipase activity in human plasma.

In vivo IDL particles are further metabolized by the hepatic TG lipase (HTGL) into LDL particles. Therefore, the relative distribution of VLDL/IDL and LDL particles in capillary ITP permits the analysis of HTGL activity in mixed hyperlipidemias.

Intra-plasmatic lipoprotein metabolism can be studied under postprandial conditions after an oral fat load and repetitive capillary ITP. To ascertain whether patients with borderline hyperlipidemia can still effectively metabolize oral fat, we monitored changes occurring in the lipoprotein pattern under postprandial conditions in normal subjects and in patients with Type IV hyperlipidemia and familial hypobetalipoproteinemia.[65] Analyses were made from fasting and postprandial sera 2, 3, 4, 5, and 6 h after fat ingestion. Significant differences among the analyzed patients were observed in the metabolism of apo B-containing lipoproteins, allowing the detection of metabolic disturbances in the conversion of these lipoproteins. Besides postprandial studies of plasma TG metabolism, Type III hyperlipoproteinemia can be easily detected by the presence of increased chylomicron-derived particles in capillary ITP.

Figure 30–3 ✧ Correlation Analysis of HDL and LDL Cholesterol Levels Measured by Capillary Isotachophoresis and Precipitation Procedures

HDL-C has been measured by phosphotungstic acid precipitation and LDL-C in accordance with the Lipid Research Clinics protocol. Total cholesterol levels of the sample group (n = 52) were 67–391 mg/dL (1.73–10.11 mmol/L) with a mean of 210 mg/dL (5.43 mmol/L).

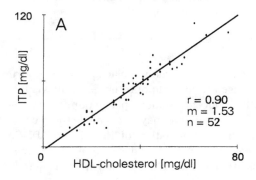
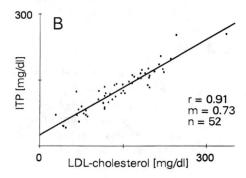

Figure 30–4 ✧ Comparison of Lipoprotein ITP Peak Areas Obtained from Male Patients with Coronary Sclerosis and from Healthy Volunteers

Black boxes represent patients with coronary sclerosis. White boxes represent healthy volunteers. Significance levels, when calculated, are indicated.

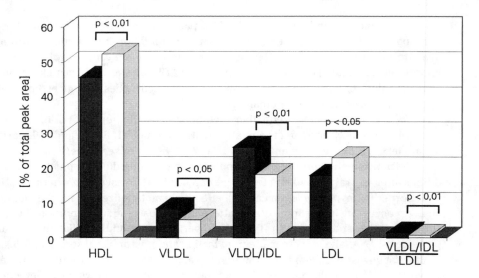

To study the value of our analytical ITP technique in separation and quantitation of atherogenic IDL particles, we analyzed a group of male patients with angiographically documented coronary heart disease (CHD) (n = 17) versus a control group (n = 22). The CHD patients had either mildly elevated or normal levels of total cholesterol and LDL-C or TG (Figure 30–4). However, compared to the control group, in the CHD group LDL-C was significantly increased and HDL-C was significantly decreased. These data are consistent with the data obtained by capillary ITP, in which the LDL peak areas were increased and the HDL peak areas were significantly reduced in the CHD group (see Figure 30–5). Furthermore, in capillary ITP the IDL subfraction in CHD patients is significantly increased, and the ratio of IDL versus LDL is also increased compared to the control group. These data give evidence for an ineffective conversion of IDL to LDL by hepatic lipase in CHD patients.

SUMMARY

The agarose gel electrophoresis technique, which has mainly replaced other support media in the clinical laboratory, has been used to make lipoprotein patterns visible and to quantitate VLDL-C, LDL-C, and HDL-C concentrations in plasma or serum. Today, however, the analytical performance of this method may not achieve the recommended goals defined by the NCEP for the determination of HDL-C and LDL-C. Therefore, the direct determination at least of HDL-C should be preferred. Subsequently, and providing that the limitations of the Friedewald equation are considered,

Figure 30–5 ✧ Comparison of Lipid Data Obtained from Male Patients with Coronary Sclerosis and from Healthy Volunteers

Black boxes represent patients with coronary sclerosis. White boxes represent healthy volunteers. Significance levels, when calculated, are indicated.

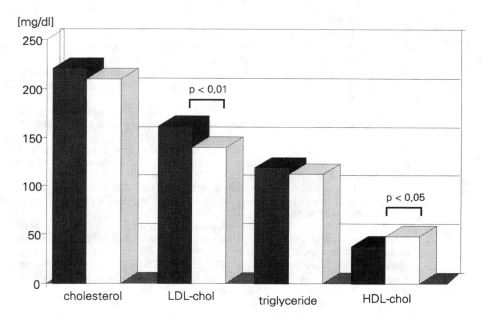

LDL-C can be calculated based on the results of total cholesterol, TG, and HDL-C values. Further improvements will be achieved by the direct LDL-C assays, which have now become common in the clinical laboratory. Therefore, the use of lipoprotein electrophoresis may be limited to the diagnosis of Type III hyperlipidemia, especially if no ultracentrifugation technique is available.

The analytical capillary ITP can be performed directly from whole serum, plasma, and other biological fluids and allows simultaneous quantitation of HDL-C and LDL-C. The precision of this 7-min procedure agrees well with that of methods currently in routine use. The technology has the advantage of also facilitating estimation of the major serum lipolytic enzyme activities, based on relative levels of large, TG-rich VLDL, cholesterol-ester-enriched VLDL remnants, and IDL particles. ✧

REFERENCES

1. Kannel WB, Castelli WP, Gordon T. Cholesterol in the prediction of atherosclerotic disease. New perspectives based on the Framingham study. Ann Intern Med 1979; 90:85–91.
2. Stampfer MJ, Sacks FM, Salvini S, Willett WC, Hennekens CH. A prospective study of

cholesterol, apolipoproteins, and the risk of myocardial infarction. N Engl J Med 1991;325:373–81.

3. Fredrickson DS, Levy RI, Lees RS. Fat transport in lipoproteins: an integrated approach to mechanisms and disorders. N Engl J Med 1967;276:34–44,94–103,148–56,215–225, 273–81.

4. The Expert Panel. Report of the National Cholesterol Education Program (NECP) expert panel on detection, evaluation and treatment of high blood cholesterol in adults. Arch Intern Med 1988;148:36–69.

5. The Expert Panel. Summary of the second report of the National Cholesterol Education Program (NECP) expert panel on detection, evaluation and treatment of high blood cholesterol in adults. JAMA 1993;269:3015–23.

6. Bachorik PS, Ross JW. National Cholesterol Education Program recommendations for measurement of low-density-lipoprotein cholesterol: executive summary. Clin Chem 1995;41:1414–20.

7. Warnick GR, Wood PD. National Cholesterol Education Program recommendations for measurement of high-density lipoprotein cholesterol: executive summary. Clin Chem 1995;41:1427–33.

8. Friedewald WT, Levy RI, Frederickson DS. Estimation of the concentration of low-density lipoprotein cholesterol in plasma, without use of the preparative ultracentrifuge. Clin Chem 1972;18:499–502.

9. McNamara Jr., Cohn JS, Wilson PWF, Schaefer EJ. Calculated values for low-density lipoprotein cholesterol in the assessment of lipid abnormalities and coronary disease risk. Clin Chem 1990;36:36–42.

10. Jialal I, Hirany SV, Devaraj S. Sherwood TA. Comparison of an immunoprecipitation method for direct measurement of LDL cholesterol with β-quantitation (ultracentrifugation). Am J Clin Pathol 1995;104:76–81.

11. McNamara JR, Cole TG, Controls JH, Ferguson CA, Ordovas JM, Schaefer EJ. Immunoseparation method for measuring low-density lipoprotein cholesterol directly from serum evaluated. Clin Chem 1995;41:232–40.

12. Harris N, Neufeld EJ, Newburger JW, Ticho B, Baker A, Ginsburg GS et al. Analytical performance and clinical utility of a direct LDL-cholesterol assay in a hyperlipidemic pediatric population. Clin Chem 1996;42:1182–8.

13. Schectman G, Patsches M, Sasse EA. Variability in cholesterol measurements: comparison of calculated and direct LDL cholesterol determinations. Clin Chem 1996; 42:732–7.

14. Rifai N, Iannotti E, DeAngelis K, Law T Analytical and clinical performance of a homogeneous enzymatic LDL-cholesterol assay compared with the ultracentrifugation-dextran sulfate-Mg2+ method. Clin Chem 1998;44:1242–50.

15. Warnick GR, Marian CC, Albers JJ. Comparison of current methods for high-density lipoprotein cholesterol quantitation. Clin Chem 1979;25:596–604.

16. Demacker PN, Vos-Janseen HE, Hijmans AG, Van't Laar A, Jansen AP. Measurement of high-density lipoprotein cholesterol in serum: comparison of six isolation methods combined with enzymatic cholesterol analysis. Clin Chem 1980;26:1780–86.

17. Naito HK, Kwak YS. The evaluation of a new high-density lipoprotein cholesterol (HDL-C) technology: selective separation of lipoproteins by magnetic precipitation. Clin Chem 1995;41:S135.

18. Sugiuchi H, Yoshinori U, Hiroaki O, et al. Direct measurement of high-density lipoprotein cholesterol in serum with polyethylene glycol-modified enzymes and sulfated cyclodextrin. Clin Chem 1995;41:717–23.

19. Cobbaert C, Mulder PG, Baadenhuijsen H, Zwang L, Weykamp CW, Demacker PN. Survey of total error of precipitation and homogeneous HDL-cholesterol methods and simultaneous evaluation of lyophilized saccharose-containing candidate reference materials for HDL cholesterol. Clin Chem 1999;45:360–70.

20. Nauck M, Marz W, Jarausch J, Cobbaert C, Sagers A, Bernard D, Delanghe J, Honauer G, Lehmann P, Oestrich E, von Eckardstein A, Walch S, Wieland H, Assmann G.

Multi-center evaluation of a homogeneous assay for HDL cholesterol without sample pretreatment. Clin Chem 1997;43:1622–9.

21. Lackner KJ, Schmitz G beta-VLDL of patients with type III hyperlipoproteinemia interferes with homogeneous determination of HDL cholesterol based on polyethylene-glycol-modified enzymes. Clin Chem 1998;44:2546–8.

22. Lewis LA. Starch-gel electrophoresis of lipoproteins. In: Lewis LA, Opplt JJ (eds.). Handbook of electrophoresis (Vol. I): Lipoproteins: basic principles and concepts. Boca Raton, FL: CRC Press, 1980;221–7.

23. Chin HP, Blankenhorn DH. Separation and quantitation of serum lipoproteins by means of electrophoresis on cellulose acetate. Clin Chim Acta 1968;20:305–14.

24. Charman RC, Landowne RA. Separation of human plasma lipoprotein by electrophoresis on cellulose acetate. Anal Biochem 197;19:177–9.

25. Iammarino RM, Humphrey M, Antolik P. Agar gel lipoprotein electrophoresis: a correlated study with ultracentrifugation. Clin Chem 1969;15:1218–29.

26. Winkelman J, Ibbott FA, Sobel C, Wybenga DR. Studies on the phenotyping of hyperlipoproteinemias: evaluation of cellulose acetate technique and comparison with paper electrophoresis. Clin Chim Acta 1969;26:33–39.

27. Lewis LA. Paper as a support media for lipoprotein electrophoresis. In: Lewis LA, Opplt JJ (eds.). Handbook of electrophoresis (Vol. I): Lipoproteins: basic principles and concepts. Boca Raton, FL: CRC Press, 1980;129–49.

28. Jencks WP, Hyatt MR, Jetton MR, Maltingly TW, Durrum EL. A study of serum lipoproteins in normal and atherosclerotic patients by paper electrophoretic techniques. J Clin Invest 1956:35:980–90.

29. Dangerfield WG, Smith EB. Investigation of serum lipids and lipoproteins by paper electrophoresis. J Clin Pathol 1955:8:132–9.

30. Lees RS, Hatch FT. Sharper preparation of lipoprotein species by paper electrophoresis in albumin-containing buffer. J Lab Clin Med 1963;61:518–28.

31. Noble RP. Electrophoretic separation of plasma lipoproteins in agarose gel. J Lipid Res 1968;9:693–700.

32. Hulley SB, Cook SG, Wilson WS, Nichaman MZ, Hatch FT, Lindgren FT. Quantitation of serum lipoproteins by electrophoresis on agarose gel: standardization in lipoprotein concentration units (mg–100 mL) by comparison with analytical ultracentrifugation. J Lipid Res 1971;12:420–33.

33. Hatch FT, Lindgren FT, Adamson GL, Jensen LC, Wong AW, Levy RI. Quantitative agarose gel electrophoresis of plasma lipoproteins: a single technique and two methods for standardization. J Lab Clin Med 1973;81:946–60.

34. Opplt JJ. Agarose gel electrophoresis of lipoproteins. In: Handbook of electrophoresis (Vol. I): Lipoproteins: basic principles and concepts. Boca Raton, FL: CRC Press, 1980; 151–82.

35. Gros M, Jurman-Gros T. Electrophoretical separation of pre-stained serum lipoproteins on cellulose acetate, agarose gel, and polyacrylamide. Clin Chim Acta 1973; 45:165–7.

36. Davis BJ. Disc electrophoresis. II. Method and application to human serum proteins. Ann NY Acad Sci 1964;121:404–27.

37. Narayan KA, Narayan S, Kummerow FA. Disc electrophoresis of human serum lipoproteins. Nature 1965;205:246–8.

38. Naito HK, Wada M. The use of polyacrylamide-gel electrophoresis for the detection of dyslipoproteinemia. In: Lewis LA, Opplt JJ (eds.). Handbook of electrophoresis (Vol. I): Lipoproteins: basic principles and concepts. Boca Raton, FL: CRC Press, 1980;183–219.

39. Pratt JJ, Dangerfield WG. Polyacrylamide gels of increasing concentration gradient for the electrophoresis of lipoproteins. Clin Chim Acta 1969;23:189–201.

40. Muniz N. Measurement of plasma lipoproteins by electrophoresis on polyacrylamide gel. Clin Chem 1977;23:1826–33.

41. Reissell PK, Hagopian CM, Hatch FT. Thin-layer electrophoresis of serum lipoproteins. J Lipid Res 1966;7:551–7.

42. Oriente P. Lipoprotein electrophoresis on cellogel: a practical method for screening hyperlipoproteinemias. Adv Exp Med Biol 1973;38:247–58.

43. Wieland H, Seidel D. Changes in the plasma lipoprotein system due to liver disease. In: Lewis AL, Opplt JJ (eds.). Handbook of electrophoresis (Vol. II): Lipoproteins in disease. Boca Raton, FL: CRC Press, 1980;79–101.

44. Nichols AV, Blanche PJ, Gong EL. Gradient gel electrophoresis of human plasma high-density lipoproteins. In: Lewis LA (ed.). Handbook of electrophoresis (Vol. III): Lipoprotein methodology and human studies. Boca Raton, FL: CRC Press, 1983;29–47.

45. Mahley RW, Weisgraber KH. Subfractionation of high-density lipoproteins in two metabolically distinct subclasses by heparin affinity chromatography and Geon-Pevikon electrophoresis. In: Report of the High Density Lipoprotein Methodology Workshop (NIH Pub. No. 79–1661). Bethesda, MD: National Institutes of Health, 1977;356–67.

46. Bachorik PS. Electrophoresis in the determination of plasma lipoprotein patterns. In: Lewis AL, Opplt JJ (eds.). Handbook of electrophoresis (Vol. II): Lipoproteins in disease. Boca Raton, FL: CRC Press, 1980;7–27.

47. Lindgren FT, Jensen LC, Hatch FT. The isolation and quantitative analysis of serum lipoproteins. In: Nelson G (ed.). Blood lipids and lipoproteins: quantitation, composition, and metabolism. New York: Wiley Interscience, 1972;181–274.

48. Lindgren FT, Adamson GL, Krauss RM. Automated quantitative lipoprotein microelectrophoresis. In: Lewis LA, Opplt JJ (eds.). Handbook of electrophoresis (Vol. I): Lipoproteins: basic principles and concepts. Boca Raton, FL: CRC Press, 1980;229–49.

49. Demacker PNM, Otvos JD, Schmitz G, Mollers C, Lombardi P, Cost B, et al. Alternative approaches to lipoprotein analysis. In: Rifai N, Warnick GR (eds.). Laboratory measurement of lipids, lipoproteins, and apolipoproteins. Washington, DC: AACC Press, 1994; 323–47.

50. Winkelman J, Wynbenga DR, Ibbott F. Quantitation of lipoprotein components in the phenotyping of hyperlipoproteinemias. Clin Chim Acta 1970;27:181–3.

51. Greenspan P, Mao FW, Ryu BH, Gutman RL Advances in agarose gel electrophoresis of serum lipoproteins. J Chromatogr A 1995;698:333–9.

52. Wieland H, Seidel D. Quantitative lipoprotein electrophoresis. In: Lewis LA (ed.). Handbook of electrophoresis (Vol. III): Lipoprotein methodology and human studies. Boca Raton, FL: CRC Press, 1983;83–102.

53. Aufenanger J, Haux P, Kattermann R. Improved method for enzymic determination of cholesterol in lipoproteins separated by electrophoresis on thin layer agarose gels. J Clin Chem Clin Biochem 1989;27:807–13.

54. Aufenanger J, Haux P, Weber U, Kattermann R. A specific method for the direct determination of lipoprotein cholesterol in electrophoretic patterns. Clin Chim Acta 1988 Oct 14;177(2):197–207.

55. Nauck M, Winkler K, Marz W, Wieland H. Quantitative determination of high-, low-, and very-low-density lipoproteins and lipoprotein(a) by agarose gel electrophoresis and enzymatic cholesterol staining. Clin Chem 199541:1761–7.

56. Contois JH, Gillmor RG, Moore RE, Contois LR, Macer JL, Wu AH. Quantitative determination of cholesterol in lipoprotein fractions by electrophoresis. Clin Chim Acta 1999;282:1–14.

57. Stocks J, Miller NE. Capillary electrophoresis to monitor the oxidative modification of low-density lipoproteins. J Lipid Res 1998;39:1305–9.

58. Nowicka G, Bruning T, Bottcher A, Kahl G, Schmitz G. Macrophage interaction of HDL subclasses separated by flow isotachophoresis. J Lipid Res 1990;31:1947.

59. Nowicka G, Bruning T, Grothaus B, Kahl G, Schmitz G. Characterization of apolipoprotein-B-containing lipoproteins separated by preparative free flow isotachophoresis. J Lipid Res 1990;31:1173–86.

60. Schmitz G, Mollers C, Richter V. Analytical capillary isotachophoresis of human serum lipoproteins. Electrophoresis 1997;18:1807–13.

61. Boettcher A, Mollers C, Lackner KJ, Schmitz G. Automated free-solution isotacho-

phoresis: instrumentation and fractionation of human serum proteins. Electrophoresis 1998;19:1110–16.

62. Boettcher A, Schlosser J, Kronenberg F, Dieplinger H, Knipping G, Lackner KJ, Schmitz G. Preparative free solution isotachopheresis for separation of human plasma lipoproteine: apolipoprotein and lipid composition of HDL fractions. J Lipid Res, in press.

63. Bittolo-Bon G, Cazzolato G. Analytical capillary isotachophoresis of total plasma lipoproteins: a new tool to identify atherogenic low-density lipoproteins. J Lipid Res 1999;40:170–177.

64. Schlenck A, Herbeth B, Siest G, Visvikis S. Characterization and quantification of lipoprotein subfractions by capillary isotachophoresis: relationships with lipid, apolipoprotein, and lipoprotein levels. J Lipid Res 1999;40:2125–33.

65. Nowicka G, Gheeraert P, Schmitz G. Monitoring of postprandial changes in the serum lipoprotein pattern by analytical capillary isotachophoresis. In: Windler E, Greten H (eds.). Intestinal lipid and lipoprotein metabolism. Munchen: W. Zuckschwerdt Verlag, 1989.

Measurement of Lipoprotein Subclass Profiles by Nuclear Magnetic Resonance Spectroscopy

31

James D. Otvos

CLINICAL SIGNIFICANCE OF LIPOPROTEIN SUBCLASSES

✧ Total plasma cholesterol (TC) has serious limitations as a risk factor for coronary heart disease (CHD). The reason is that cholesterol is found in all of the major lipoprotein classes in fasting plasma: very-low-density lipoprotein (VLDL), low-density lipoprotein (LDL), and high-density lipoprotein (HDL). As is well known,[1,2] VLDL cholesterol (VLDL-C) and LDL cholesterol (LDL-C) have positive associations with CHD (elevated concentrations confer increased risk) while HDL cholesterol (HDL-C) levels have a negative association (higher concentrations confer protection). Because patients with the same TC level are likely to have differing VLDL, LDL, and HDL concentrations (and therefore differing CHD risk), measurement of the more complex and costly "lipid panel" has become common in routine CHD risk assessment and management. This is not to say that TC has no role to play as a CHD risk factor, because many people with very high levels (> 300 mg/dL; 7.77 mol/L) or very low levels (< 150 mg/dL; 3.89 mmol/L) have risk that is adequately predicted with this information alone. There are simply many more people with intermediate TC levels for whom CHD risk cannot be accurately evaluated without measurement of the lipoproteins.

The foregoing discussion is directly relevant to the question of what clinical value would accrue from measuring lipoprotein subclass levels. As depicted in Figure 31–1, VLDL, LDL, and HDL each comprise a heterogeneous group of particles that differ in size and, in many cases, in their observed associations with CHD.[3,4] (Subclasses also differ in density and chemical composition, but we focus here on size since that is the distinguishing characteristic exploited by the nuclear magnetic resonance (NMR) analysis method described in this chapter.)

With recent advances in knowledge about the complexity of lipoprotein subclass metabolism and the mechanisms of atherogenesis,[5] it is not difficult to understand why people with the same concentrations of LDL-C and HDL-C, but with different subclass distributions, might differ significantly in CHD risk. There is, for example, abundant evidence that LDL particle size is an important determinant of CHD risk[6–11] (see Chapter 16). Several cross-sectional and prospective studies have shown that individuals who have predominantly small, dense LDL particles (subclass pattern B) are at increased risk for CHD even when levels of LDL-C are not elevated. Other studies indicate that intermediate-density lipoprotein (IDL), which is included with

Figure 31–1 ✧ Lipoprotein Subclasses Quantified by NMR

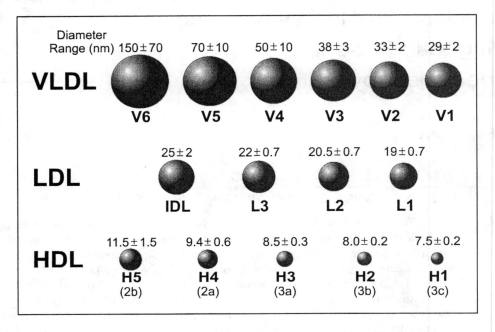

the LDL fraction measured by standard methods, may be particularly atherogenic as well.[12] Differing associations of HDL subclasses with CHD have also been noted (see Chapter 15). Of the five subclasses separable by gradient gel electrophoresis, the three largest (HDL_{2b}, HDL_{2a}, and HDL_{3a}) show the expected inverse correlation with disease incidence and severity, whereas the two smallest subclasses (HDL_{3b} and HDL_{3c}) show a positive association.[13,14]

Thus, for the same reason that TC is often an inadequate indicator of CHD risk, HDL-C levels might not accurately predict the degree of CHD protection because of variability among individuals in the relative amounts of atherogenic and anti-atherogenic subclasses. No efficient high-resolution method is available to measure VLDL subclasses, and consequently little is known about their relation to CHD risk. There is some indication, however, that increased numbers of large VLDL particles in fasting plasma predict CHD independently of lipid levels[4] and correlate with delayed chylomicron clearance rates, which are themselves independently related to CHD risk.[15,16]

LIMITATIONS OF EXISTING METHODS OF SUBCLASS MEASUREMENT

Traditional methods of measuring lipoproteins generally involve two sequential operations: *separation* of the lipoprotein to be measured, and *quantification*. The primary reason for the two steps is that quantification is based on the concentration of one or more of the chemical constituents of the particles (usually cholesterol, but sometimes other lipid or apolipoprotein moieties) that are not unique to any particular class or subclass of lipoprotein. If a particular subclass contained a distinct, measurable chemical component or had some other unique characteristic that could serve as a marker for its concentration, the separation step would not be needed and quantification could proceed directly using whole plasma.

Several important benefits would be gained by avoiding the physical separation step(s), particularly when quantifying lipoprotein subclasses. First and foremost would be significant cost savings in time and labor. Even the routine methods of HDL and LDL separation using selective chemical or immunoprecipitation are considerably more time-consuming and less automatable than TC or triglyceride (TG) measurements that do not require any fractionation.[17] Because the subclasses of a lipoprotein are so closely similar to one another in size, density, and composition, their separation is much more difficult to achieve than that of the major lipoprotein classes.[3] The techniques used most frequently for subclass fractionation (described in Chapters 15, 16, 27, 30, 32, and 33) include various types of ultracentrifugation, electrophoresis, chemical precipitation, and chromatography. They typically take several hours to several days to complete and usually achieve only partial resolution of the subclasses. Accuracy and precision are unavoidably limited by many sources of analytical variability inherent to separation procedures.

SUBCLASS QUANTIFICATION BY NMR SPECTROSCOPY

Advantages of Spectroscopic Lipoprotein Subclass Analysis

Several years ago, we proposed a spectroscopic alternative to separation-based methods of lipoprotein analysis that would make possible rapid, simultaneous quantification of several subclasses of VLDL, LDL, and HDL.[18,19] The process takes advantage of the natural proton NMR spectroscopic "signatures" of lipoprotein particles of different size. Using dedicated intermediate-field (400 MHz) NMR analyzers, automated measurement of 15 lipoprotein subclasses requires only about one minute. As might be expected of a method using no reagents and requiring minimal sample manipulation, accuracy and precision are as good or better than can be achieved by the best alternative procedures. With the measurement efficiency of the NMR process, plus the ability to analyze archived frozen (−70°C) research specimens, it is now possible to conduct large-scale epidemiological studies to examine subclass associations with CHD and other disease endpoints, and assess the impact of various treatment regimens on subclass levels and clinical outcomes. Panels of NMR subclass information (*NMR LipoProfile®*) are also available to physicians for routine clinical assessment and management of CHD risk.

Description of the NMR Method: The "Tolling of the Bells"

The basic concepts underlying NMR lipoprotein subclass analysis are simple and require no background in NMR spectroscopy to understand. Quantification is achieved in a three-step process consisting of *measurement* of the plasma NMR spectrum followed by computer *deconvolution* of the spectral data and *calculation* of the subclass concentrations. The measurement step, which is performed automatically on un-

Figure 31–2 ✧ Typical NMR Spectrum of Plasma

Shown are the plasma methyl lipid signal (shaded) and a schematic representation of lipoprotein structure, depicted as a neutral lipid core of cholesteryl ester (CE) and triglyceride (TG) surrounded by a shell consisting of phospholipid (PL) and free (unesterified) cholesterol (FC).

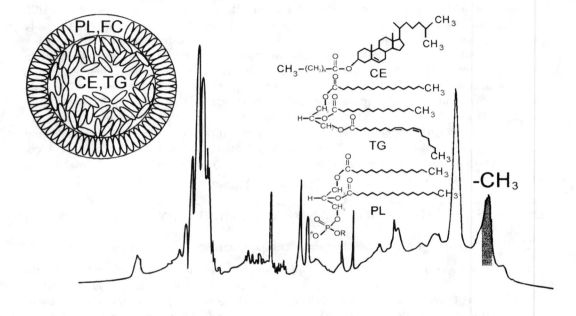

treated plasma or serum specimens (~0.5 mL), takes less than one minute. The deconvolution and calculation steps, which are performed on the digitized data using specialized analysis software running off-line on a personal computer, require just a few seconds.

A typical plasma NMR spectrum is shown in Figure 31–2, highlighting the spectral region at ~0.8 ppm containing the information used to derive the subclass concentrations. This region contains the signals emitted by the methyl group protons of the four types of lipid in the particles: phospholipid, cholesterol, cholesterol ester, and TG. Since the methyl signals from these lipids are indistinguishable from each other, they overlap to produce a bulk lipid "particle signal." The amplitude of each lipoprotein particle signal serves as a measure of the concentration of that lipoprotein, in exactly the same way that the band intensities on a lipid-stained gel measure the amounts of electrophoretically separated lipoproteins. What makes it possible to exploit the methyl lipid signal for lipoprotein subclass quantification (without separating the subclasses first) is a magnetic property specific to lipoproteins that causes the lipids in larger particles to broadcast signals that are characteristically different in frequency and shape from the lipid signals emitted by smaller particles.[20]

The simplest way to conceptualize the origin of these spectral differences is to

Figure 31–3 ✧ Lipoprotein Subclasses Behave Like Bells in the NMR Analyzer

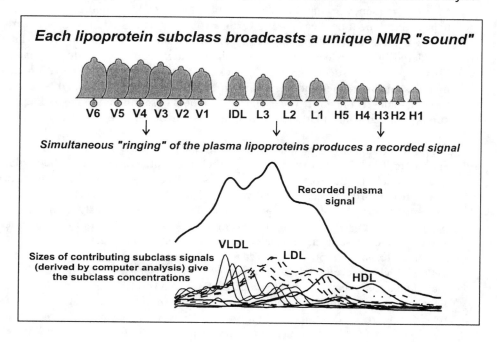

draw an analogy between lipoprotein subclasses and bells of varying size (Figure 31–3). We observe that bells of different size produce distinguishable sound signals despite being constructed of the same material. For related reasons associated with the *physical form* of lipoprotein particles, different-size subclasses broadcast distinguishable lipid NMR signals. If we strike a group of bells with equal-force blows (analogous to "exciting" the subclasses with a microsecond radiofrequency NMR pulse), we expect the amplitude (loudness) of the resultant sound signal to reflect the number of bells struck. By recording the composite signal produced by the "ringing" of all of the lipoprotein subclasses in a plasma sample, it is possible to back-calculate the concentration of each subclass using prior knowledge about the quantitative relationship between subclass concentration and signal amplitude.

This analogy makes clear that the quantitative subclass information is obtained by performing a simple NMR *measurement* (recording the signals produced by the "tolling of the subclass bells"), and then performing *calculations* that convert the subclass signal amplitudes to the desired units of concentration: cholesterol or TG mass (mg/dL or mmol/L) or subclass particle number (nanomoles of particles per liter, nmol/L). Although a large amount of information needs to be accumulated in advance about the exact relationship between the signal amplitude of each subclass and its concentration, the calculations themselves are straightforward and require only seconds.

The reason why the NMR analytical process entails a third step, *deconvolution,* is that there is no way to selectively ring only one size bell at a time. Instead, all of the subclasses in a plasma sample are stimulated simultaneously (and equivalently) by the radiofrequency excitation pulse, and they then broadcast their characteristic signals at the same time. Because the various subclass signals add together linearly to produce the recorded plasma signal, the individual subclass signal amplitudes may be calculated by linear least-squares regression using singular value decomposition.[19] This approach is successful only if there is accurate prior knowledge about the methyl signal frequency and line shape expected from each subclass in the sample. Although a substantial effort was required (see below) to obtain the needed library of subclass spectral information, the computer deconvolution step itself takes very little time.

Most of the experimental details of the NMR methodology have been published elsewhere.[18,19,21] The key to successful subclass quantification is availability of high-quality spectral data from isolated subclasses. This information, which is incorporated into proprietary analysis software (LipoMed Inc., Raleigh, NC) in the form of a reference library of subclass spectra, was obtained by laboriously isolating narrow particle size ranges of lipoprotein particles from fasting plasma of normolipidemic and dyslipidemic subjects using a combination of ultracentrifugation and agarose gel filtration chromatography. All reference spectra were acquired under the same well-defined, highly reproducible conditions (47°C, 400 MHz) used subsequently for automated analysis of patient plasma samples. For rapid through-put in high-volume settings, a system was devised to move plasma to and from the NMR magnet rapidly and reliably (Figure 31–4). With this set-up, 400 uL specimens are withdrawn by needle aspiration from a tray of plasma samples and sent to the NMR probe in a flow injection mode. After the plasma spectrum is acquired and electronically transmitted off-line for deconvolution analysis, the next sample is introduced after the probe and transfer lines are thoroughly cleaned with a wash solution.

The magnetic property of lipoproteins that gives them "bell-like" behavior is a difference in magnetic susceptibility induced by the orientational order of the phospholipids in the shell surrounding the neutral lipid core.[20] The equations describing this effect predict that every lipoprotein particle of different diameter should have a different lipid NMR signature. (The diameter referred to is that of the phospholipid shell, which does not include a contribution from the apolipoprotein(s) on the surface.) In practice, particles of closely similar diameter have NMR properties that are not sufficiently distinct to have a noticeable impact on the observed spectrum. It has been determined empirically that the resolving power of the NMR method is sufficient to allow reliable quantification of six VLDL, four LDL (including IDL), and five HDL subclasses (see Figure 31–1). It should be understood, however, that these subclasses represent groupings of particles of similar but not identical size, and that there is no implication of metabolic significance to these groupings.

Approximate diameter ranges (in nm) of the isolated subclasses serving as NMR reference standards are given in Figure 31–1. VLDL and LDL subclass diameters were measured by electron microscopy and those of HDL by polyacrylamide gradient gel electrophoresis. It is noteworthy that the IDL and LDL subclass diameters are uniformly ~5 nm smaller than estimates based on gradient gel electrophoresis measurements (Chapter 16). They are, however, in agreement with other electron microscopy data[22,23] and calculations based on detailed LDL chemical compositional informa-

Figure 31–4 ✧ Schematic Depiction of NMR Lipoprotein Subclass Analysis Using an Automated Flow-Injection Sampling Process

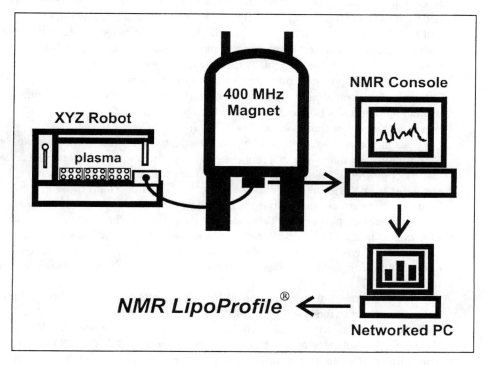

tion.[24] The HDL subclasses H5, H4, H3, H2, and H1 are closely related to the gradient gel electrophoresis subclass designations HDL_{2b}, HDL_{2a}, HDL_{3a}, HDL_{3b}, and HDL_{3c}, respectively.[25] Not represented in Figure 31–1 are chylomicrons, which are larger than the V6 subclass. By including chylomicron reference spectra in the line-shape analysis model, non-fasting specimens are analyzed as accurately as fasting samples.

Since the only basis of NMR distinction between lipoprotein subclasses is the diameter of the phospholipid shell, it is not possible to distinguish between intestinally derived chylomicron remnants and liver-derived VLDL particles of similar size. Likewise, the presence of the extra attached apolipoprotein(a) protein on lipoprotein(a) [LP(a)] particles does not affect the phospholipid shell diameter; therefore, Lp(a) and LDL cannot be distinguished by NMR. Although one might expect the methyl groups of the apolipoproteins to produce signals in the same spectral region as those of the lipids, they are significantly broader and do not appreciably contribute to the bulk lipid signal that is the basis of subclass quantification. Using the bell analogy again, the apolipoproteins on the particle surface can be likened to different designs painted on the bells to give them a distinct identity. Since the designs have no effect on the sounds the bells produce, they have no impact on the analytical measurement.

Quantification Issues

Since lipids are much easier than lipoproteins to measure directly, it is standard practice to use the amounts of cholesterol in LDL and HDL as surrogate indicators of LDL and HDL levels. As a result, LDL-C and HDL-C are the established "currencies of the realm" for CHD risk assessment, despite having certain limitations.[26,27] Chief among these is that in many people (usually those with elevated TG) LDL-C levels fail to accurately reflect LDL particle concentrations and the associated magnitude of CHD risk. This situation is created by lipid transfer and lipolysis reactions that modulate lipoprotein lipid composition and size, leading to production of particles that often contain less cholesterol than normal.[27,28]

An important distinguishing characteristic and potential clinical advantage of NMR lipoprotein analysis is that it quantifies the entire lipoprotein particle, instead of just its cholesterol. The methyl lipid signal upon which NMR quantification is based emanates from the entire collection of lipids in the particle (both those in the neutral lipid core and surface shell) and is unaffected by person-to-person variability in chemical composition, particularly that caused by core cholesterol ester-TG exchange.[29] This means that a given concentration of subclass particles will always produce the same size methyl NMR signal (and inferred concentration), even in the face of differences in lipid composition that would cause the measured cholesterol concentrations to vary.

To facilitate clinical utilization of NMR lipoprotein profiles in today's lipid-oriented world, the analysis software converts the measured NMR subclass signal amplitudes into concentration units of cholesterol or TG (mg/dL or mmol/L). It then sums the respective subclass concentrations to give values for TC, TG, LDL-C, and HDL-C. The lipoprotein → lipid conversion process assumes that for each subclass, a fixed relationship exists between NMR signal amplitude and cholesterol/TG concentration. As just mentioned, however, there is known variability in lipoprotein lipid composition, particularly in LDL, resulting from cholesterol ester-TG exchange catalyzed by cholesterol ester transfer protein (CETP).[29] The relatively minor impact this variability has on relations between NMR-calculated and chemically measured LDL-C and HDL-C values is shown in Figure 31–5. Correlation coefficients for LDL-C are typically in the 0.91–0.95 range, while those for HDL-C are between 0.93 and 0.97. To investigate whether observed discrepancies between NMR and chemical LDL-C values in Figure 31–5 were due primarily to lipid compositional differences rather than analytical error, the LDL was isolated from each plasma sample and analyzed for cholesterol and TG content. In every instance where the NMR estimate of LDL-C exceeded the measured cholesterol value by 10%, the LDL was found to be cholesterol-depleted and TG-enriched compared to normal. For patients with abnormally low amounts of cholesterol in their LDL particles, standard chemical LDL-C measurements give a falsely low impression of the amount of LDL actually present. In contrast, the NMR-calculated LDL-C values reflect the true mass concentration of LDL since they are derived from measurement of the bulk lipid LDL NMR signal.

In addition to converting measured subclass signal amplitudes to lipid concentration units, the NMR analysis software calculates average VLDL, LDL, and HDL particle sizes (nm diameter) for each sample by weighting the mass percentage of each

Figure 31–5 ✧ Relations of LDL-C and HDL-C Calculated by the NMR Method and Measured by Beta-Quantification

Each graph shows the line of identity and the measured correlation coefficient and regression equation. (To convert cholesterol values in mg/dL to mmol/L, multiply by 0.0259.)

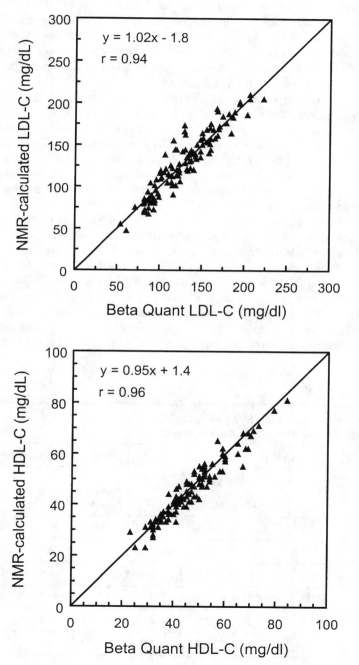

subclass by its diameter (Figure 31–1). Studies indicate that using an LDL size cut-point of 20.5 nm to distinguish individuals with mainly large LDL (pattern A, LDL size > 20.5 nm) from those with small LDL (pattern B, LDL size ≤ 20.5 nm) gives good agreement with the original gradient gel electrophoresis (GGE) LDL subclass pheno-typing method of Austin and Krauss.[6] For example, NMR analyses of over 3,400 ar-chived frozen plasma samples from the Framingham Offspring Study showed pattern B prevalences to be 36% in men and 13% in women.[30] These percentages closely match those reported in studies that used GGE LDL peak particle diameter < 25.5 nm as the basis of pattern B classification.[6,31]

Another series of calculations performed automatically by the analysis software converts NMR subclass concentrations to particle concentrations (in units of nano-moles of particles per liter), using known relations between lipoprotein particle diam-eter and core lipid volume and mass.[32] By summing the particle concentrations of the LDL subclasses (IDL, L1, L2, L3), a value is obtained for total LDL particle concentra-tion. This important variable supplies information comparable to that given by a plasma apolipoprotein B measurement, and may be anticipated to be a more discrimi-nating CHD risk factor than LDL-C.[11,26]

Split sample comparison studies show that NMR lipoprotein subclass distribu-tions agree well with those determined by electrophoretic or ultracentrifugal separa-tion methods, despite methodological differences that complicate the ability to make direct quantitative comparisons. Correlation coefficients of ~0.9 are generally seen for NMR and GGE comparisons of average HDL particle size,[19,25] while those for LDL size are somewhat lower, typically ranging from 0.7–0.9.[33] Measurement reproduci-bility of NMR lipoprotein profiles is excellent, as indicated by the data in Table 31–1. Coefficients of variation (CVs) are under 3% for the standard lipid panel variables and LDL particle concentration, and about 0.5% for average LDL (and HDL) particle size.

Table 31–1 ✧ Precision of *NMR LipoProfile* Analysis
(20 replicates of 2 plasma pools over 4 days)

Sample		NMR Lipid Panel (mg/dL)				NMR Lipoprotein Panel			
		TC	LDL-C	HDL-C	TG	LDL Particles (nmol/L)	LDL Size (nm)	Large HDL (mg/dL)	Large VLDL (mg/dL)
Pool 1	Mean	191.5	130.1	54.3	71.2	1349	20.97	43.1	24.0
	SD	3.2	2.6	1.1	2.1	24	0.11	1.3	2.2
	CV%	1.7	2.0	2.0	2.9	1.8	0.53	2.9	9.0
Pool 2	Mean	261.8	196.4	44.1	156.9	1975	21.69	27.8	67.5
	SD	4.5	3.8	0.7	3.6	35	0.10	0.9	4.8
	CV%	1.7	2.0	1.5	2.3	1.8	0.47	3.3	7.1

By comparison, CVs of ~2% are typically reported for LDL particle sizes measured by GGE.[11,31,34]

NMR LipoProfile®

To simplify and enhance clinical utilization, NMR test results are supplied to physicians in a two-page *NMR LipoProfile* report, which is organized into the four sections shown in Figure 31–6. The NMR Lipid Panel section contains the calculated values for TC, LDL-C, HDL-C and TG, along with CHD risk category boxes highlighted to show the patient's risk status according to National Cholesterol Education Program (NCEP) guidelines.[35] The Lipoprotein Panel section displays four alternative risk factors thought to have diagnostic advantages over the standard lipid panel variables:

❖ *LDL particle concentration* and *LDL size* (which in combination predict CHD risk better than LDL-C[11]),

❖ *large HDL* (sum of the H3 + H4 + H5 subclasses; the component of HDL which, unlike small HDL, confers protection against CHD[4,13,14]),

❖ *large VLDL* (sum of the V5 + V6 subclasses; the component of TG-rich lipoproteins most strongly associated with delayed chylomicron clearance and increased CHD risk[4]).

Risk categories for the Lipoprotein Panel variables are patterned after the corresponding NCEP lipid categories, with cut-points selected on a percentile equivalence basis using NMR population data from the Framingham Offspring Study.

The third section of the report contains a bar chart showing concentrations, in absolute and percentile terms, of individual subclasses, or groups of subclasses. Included are large VLDL (V5 + V6), medium VLDL (V3 + V4), small VLDL (V1 + V2), IDL, large LDL (L3), medium LDL (L2), small LDL (L1), large HDL (H3 + H4 + H5), and small HDL (H1 + H2). Finally, the Risk Assessment Panel summarizes the patient's CHD risk status as assessed by two key determinants:

❖ *increased LDL particle concentration* (> 1400 nmol/L, 50th percentile), and

❖ *atherogenic dyslipidemia,*[36] defined by the presence of at least two of the following traits: small LDL (pattern B), reduced level of large HDL (< 25th percentile), or increased level of large VLDL (> 75th percentile).

An impression of the potential clinical value of *NMR LipoProfile* data can be gained by comparing the profiles of Patient A and Patient B in Figure 31–6. Both patients are middle-aged men with virtually identical lipid panel values. According to NCEP guidelines,[35] the LDL-C levels indicate borderline-high risk, the HDL-C levels are intermediate (neither a positive nor negative risk factor), and the TG levels are desirable. Despite the close similarities in lipid levels, the subclass distributions are markedly different for the two patients, signifying important differences in lipoprotein metabolic status and CHD risk.

Based on what we know from recent clinical studies, Patient B would be assigned a significantly higher risk owing to the prevalence of small, dense LDL (pattern B)[6–11] and the fact that most of the HDL mass is found in the smallest subclasses (H1

Figure 31–6 ✧ *NMR LipoProfile* Reports of Two Patients

Note that the patients have very different lipoprotein subclass distributions, despite having comparable levels of LDL-C, HDL-C, and TG. (To convert cholesterol values in mg/dL to mmol/L, multiply by 0.0259. To convert triglycerides in mg/dL to mmol/L, multiply by 0.0113.)

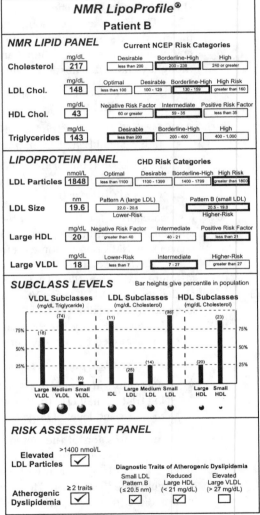

and H2), which appear to confer little (or none) of the protection offered by the larger subclasses.[4,13,14] Importantly, Patient B has a much higher (33%) concentration of LDL particles than Patient A, despite having the same LDL-C concentration—a consequence of having smaller LDL particles. The overall impression gained from the *NMR LipoProfile* of Patient B is one of high enough risk to suggest the advisability of LDL-lowering therapy, something that would not have been considered necessary based on the traditional lipid risk factors. Patient A, on the other hand, would be reassured to learn that his risk was fairly minimal.

We have observed many similar examples where an individual's lipoprotein metabolic status and associated risk of CHD were almost certainly not assessed correctly by conventional lipopoprotein cholesterol measurements. On the other hand, there are many low-risk individuals—for example, those with very low LDL-C or very high HDL-C—who would not benefit significantly from the higher-order information in the *NMR LipoProfile*. ✧

Acknowledgments: *This work was supported by NIH Grant HL-43230 and SBIR contract #200–98–0007 from the Centers for Disease Control and Prevention. The author wishes to thank Dr. Dennis Bennett, Elias Jeyarajah, Qun Zhou, and Irina Shalaurova for valuable research assistance and Drs. Lawrence Rudel and Ernst Schaefer for helpful discussions and assistance with validation studies.*

REFERENCES

1. Castelli WP, Garrison RJ, Wilson PWF, Abbott RD, Kalousdian S, Kannel WB. Incidence of coronary heart disease and lipoprotein cholesterol levels: The Framingham Study. JAMA 1986;256:2835–8.
2. Austin MA. Plasma triglyceride and coronary heart disease. Arterioscler Thromb 1991; 11:2–14.
3. Musliner TA, Krauss RM. Lipoprotein subspecies and risk of coronary disease. Clin Chem 1988;34(Suppl):B78–83.
4. Freedman DS, Otvos JD, Jeyarajah EJ, Barboriak JJ, Anderson AF, Walker JA. Relation of lipoprotein subclasses as measured by proton nuclear magnetic resonance spectroscopy to coronary artery disease. Arterioscler Thromb Vasc Biol 1998;18:1046–53.
5. Steinberg D, Witztum JL. Lipoproteins and atherogenesis: current concepts. JAMA 1990;264:3047–52.
6. Austin MA, Breslow JL, Hennekens CH, Buring JE, Willett WC, Krauss RM. Low-density lipoprotein subclass patterns and risk of myocardial infarction. JAMA 1988;260: 1917–21.
7. Griffin BA, Freeman DJ, Tait GW, Thomson J, Caslake MJ, Packard CJ, Shepherd J. Role of plasma triglyceride in the regulation of plasma low-density lipoprotein (LDL) subfractions: relative contribution of small, dense LDL to coronary heart disease risk. Atherosclerosis 1994;106:241–53.
8. Campos H, Genest JJ, Blijlevens E, McNamara JR, Jenner JL, Ordovos JM, Wilson PWF, Schaefer EJ. Low-density particle size and coronary artery disease. Arterioscler Thromb 1992;12:187–95.
9. Gardner CD, Fortman SP, Krauss RM. Association of small low-density lipoprotein particles with the incidence of coronary artery disease in men and women. JAMA 1996;276:875–81.
10. Stampfer MJ, Krauss RM, Ma J, Blanche PJ, Holl LG, Sacks FM, Hennekens CH. A prospective study of triglyceride level, low-density lipoprotein particle diameter, and risk of myocardial infarction. JAMA 1996;276:882–88.

11. Lamarche B, Tchernof A, Moorjani S, Cantin B, Dagenais GR, Lupien PJ, Després J-P. Small, dense, low-density lipoprotein particles as a predictor of the risk of ischemic heart disease in men: prospective results from the Québec Cardiovascular Study. Circulation 1997;95:69–75.

12. Hodis HN, Mack WJ, Dunn M, Liu C, Selzer RH, Krauss RM. Intermediate-density lipoproteins and progression of carotid arterial wall intima-media thickness. Circulation 1997;95:2022–26.

13. Wilson HM, Patel JC, Russe D, Skinner ER. Alterations in the concentration of an apolipoprotein-E-containing subfraction of plasma high-density lipoprotein in coronary heart disease. Clin Chim Acta 1993;220:175–87.

14. Johansson J, Carlson LA, Landou C, Hamsten A. High-density lipoproteins and coronary atherosclerosis: a strong inverse relation with the largest particles is confined to normotriglyceridemic patients. Arterioscler Thromb 1991;11:174–82.

15. Karpe F, Bell M, Bjorkegren J, Hamsten A. Quantification of postprandial triglyceride-rich lipoproteins in healthy men by retinyl ester labeling and simultaneous measurement of apolipoproteins B-48 and B-100. Arterioscler Thromb Vasc Biol 1995;15: 199–207.

16. Patsch JR, Miesenböck G, Hopferwieser T, Mühlberger V, Knapp E, Dunn JK, Gotto AM Jr, Patsch W. Relation of triglyceride metabolism and coronary artery disease: studies in the postprandial state. Arterioscler Thromb 1992;12:1336–45.

17. Working Group on Lipoprotein Measurement. NCEP recommendations on lipoprotein measurement. (NIH Publication No. 95–3044). Bethesda, MD: National Institutes of Health, 1995.

18. Otvos JD, Jeyarajah EJ, Bennett DW. Quantification of plasma lipoproteins by proton nuclear magnetic resonance spectroscopy. Clin Chem 1991;37:377–86.

19. Otvos JD, Jeyarajah EJ, Bennett DW, Krauss RM. Development of a proton nuclear magnetic resonance spectroscopic method for determining plasma lipoprotein concentrations and subspecies distributions from a single, rapid measurement. Clin Chem 1992;38:1632–8.

20. Lounila J, Ala-Korpela M, Jokisaari J. Effects of orientational order and particle size on the NMR line positions of lipoproteins. Phys Rev 1994;72:4049–52.

21. Otvos J, Jeyarajah E, Bennett D. A spectroscopic approach to lipoprotein subclass analysis. J Clin Lig Assay 1996;19:184–9.

22. Groszek E, Grundy SM. Electron-microscopic evidence for particles smaller than 250 Å in very-low-density lipoproteins of human plasma. Atherosclerosis 1978;31:241–250.

23. Rumsey SC, Galeano NF, Arad Y, Deckelbaum RJ. Cryopreservation with sucrose maintains normal physical and biological properties of human plasma low-density lipoproteins. J Lipid Res 1992;33:1551–61.

24. McNamara JR, Small DM, Li Z, Schaefer EJ. Differences in LDL subspecies involve alterations in lipid composition and conformational changes in apolipoprotein B. J Lipid Res 1996;37:1924–35.

25. Grundy SM, Vega GL, Otvos JD, Rainwater DL, Cohen JC. Hepatic lipase influences high-density lipoprotein subclass distribution in normotriglyceridemic men: genetic and pharmacological evidence. J Lipid Res 1999;40:229–34.

26. Sniderman AD, Pedersen T, Kjekshus J. Putting low-density lipoproteins at center stage in atherogenesis. Am J Cariol 1997;79:64–7.

27. Otvos J. Measurement of triglyceride-rich lipoproteins by nuclear magnetic resonance spectroscopy. Clin Cardiol 1999;22(Suppl II):21–7.

28. Packard CJ. Understanding coronary heart disease as a consequence of defective regulation of apolipoprotein B metabolism. Curr Opin Lipidol 1999;10:237–44.

29. Tall AR. Plasma cholesteryl ester transfer protein. J Lipid Res 1993;34:1255–74.

30. Otvos JD, Schaefer EJ. Unpublished data.

31. Austin MA, King M-C, Vrinizan KM, Krauss RM. Atherogenic lipoprotein phenotype. A proposed genetic marker for coronary heart disease. Circulation 1990;82:495–506.

32. Tall AR, Small DM, Atkinson D. Studies of low-density lipoproteins isolated from *Macaca Fascicularis* fed an atherogenic diet. J Clin Invest 1978;62:1354–63.
33. Otvos JD, unpublished results.
34. Festa A, D'Agostino R, Mykkanen L, Tracy R, Howard BV, Haffner SM. Low-density lipoprotein particle size is inversely related to plasminogen-activator inhibitor-1 levels: the Insulin Resistance Atherosclerosis Study. Arterioscler Thromb Vasc Biol 1999;19: 605–10.
35. The Expert Panel. Summary of the Second Report of the National Cholesterol Education Program (NCEP) Expert Panel on Detection, Evaluation, and Treatment of High Blood Cholesterol in Adults (Adult Treatment Panel II). JAMA 1993;269:3015–23.
36. Grundy SM. Hypertriglyceridemia, atherogenic dyslipidemia, and the metabolic syndrome. Am J Cardiol 1998;81(4A):18B–25B.

The Use of Ultracentrifugation for the Separation of Lipoproteins

32

Muriel J. Caslake and Christopher J. Packard

✧   Lipoproteins are complexes of phospholipid, triglyceride (TG), cholesteryl ester, and free cholesterol with apolipoproteins that mediate the transport of lipid through the bloodstream. The lipid content of particles, especially that of the hydrophobic components TG and cholesteryl ester, gives these complexes the unique property of having a density substantially less than that of most of the other constituents in plasma. Therefore, they can be prepared virtually pure by ultracentrifugation. TG-rich lipoproteins [chylomicrons and very-low-density lipoproteins (VLDL)] have a density less than that of plasma and will float under increased gravity. The other cholesterol-rich lipoproteins have densities in the range 1.006–1.21 kg/L, quite distinct from the density of proteins (about 1.7 kg/L) and that of the only other major lipid-transporting protein, albumin, which carries fatty acids. Increasing the non-protein solvent density of plasma permits the isolation of the major classes of lipoproteins in a sequential fashion (Table 32–1).

The most widely used nomenclature defines five main classes of lipoproteins based on their hydrated density.[1] Other ways of describing lipoproteins include electrophoretic mobility, apoprotein composition, and the rate of flotation through a salt solution expressed in Svedberg units (S_f).[2] These lipoproteins have proven to be structurally heterogeneous entities with differing metabolic properties and atherogenicity.

Chylomicrons are particles that have a density less than 0.94 kg/L and a flotation rate greater than S_f 400. They are the large TG-rich lipoproteins of enteric origin that carry exogenous TG into the plasma. Circulation of chylomicrons distributes dietary TG to adipose tissue and to muscle.

VLDL have a density between 0.94 and 1.006 kg/L with a flotation rate between 20 and 400 Svedberg units in a NaCl solution of density 1.063 kg/L at 26°C. VLDL is synthesized in the liver and is the endogenous TG transporter in plasma.

Intermediate-density lipoproteins (IDL) have a density greater than 1.006 kg/L but less than 1.109 kg/L with a flotation rate S_f 12–20 at solvent density 1.063 kg/L. IDL is generated from VLDL by lipolysis.

Low-density lipoproteins (LDL) consist of particles that have a density between 1.019 kg/L and 1.063 kg/L and a flotation rate S_f 0–12 at solvent density 1.063 kg/L. LDL is the product of lipolysis of IDL and is the major cholesterol carrier in plasma. Its nor-

Table 32–1 ✧ Lipoprotein Classes

Class	Density (kg/L)	S_f unit*	Diameter (nm)	Molecular Weight
Chylomicron	<0.94	>400	75–1,200	$50–1,000 \times 10^6$
VLDL	0.94–1.006	20–400	30–80	$10–80 \times 10^6$
IDL	1.006–1.019	12–20	25–35	$5–10 \times 10^6$
LDL	1.019–1.063	0–12	18–25	$2–3 \times 10^6$
HDL	1.063–1.21	$F_{1.20}$ 0–9	5–12	$65–386 \times 10^3$
Lp(a)	1.05–1.08			

*S_f Svedberg units

mal function is to deliver cholesterol to the peripheral tissues principally for the maintenance of cell membranes and to the liver to support bile acid synthesis.

High-density lipoproteins (HDL) have a hydrated density of 1.063–1.21 kg/L and float in a solvent density of 1.20 kg/L with a rate between 0 and 9 Svedberg units ($F_{1.20}$ 0–9). They are the smallest lipoprotein particles and are involved in reverse cholesterol transport—i.e., the centripetal movement of cholesterol from the peripheral tissues back to the liver.

Lipoprotein (a) or Lp(a) is a complex of LDL bound to apoprotein (a) and varies in mass between 300 and 800 kDa. Its normal function is not known but the homology with plasminogen has led to the speculation that Lp(a) might serve as the link between thrombosis and atherosclerosis. It cannot be isolated by ultracentifugation techniques alone because its density overlaps that of LDL and HDL.

Prior to embarking upon separation by ultracentrifugation, it is important to recognize the need for accurately measuring density. Anumber of centrifugal techniques are available, each of which has its own advantages and disadvantages.

DETERMINATION OF SOLUTION DENSITY

The most important requirement for reliable separations is the control and monitoring of density. There are two main methods: densitometry and refractrometry.

Densitometry

The density meter is based on the principle that the frequency of oscillation of a hollow glass tuning fork depends on the mass of any solution with which it is filled. Therefore, density measurements depend on the precise electronic measurement of the change in frequency of the tube when filled with different solutions. This is the method of choice in our laboratory; versions of this technology from Paar Scientific Ltd., London, UK, can rapidly measure the density of solutions accurately to three to six decimal places in volumes less than one mL.

Refractrometry

Refractrometry is a simple way of estimating the density of a solution of a single salt from its known correlation with the refractive index of the solution. (Such tables are found in the *Handbook of Chemistry and Physics*, CRC Press Inc, West Palm Beach, Florida, USA. However it is not such a good technique when the solution contains a mixture of salts. With an Abbe refractrometer, one drop of solution is sufficient for measurement. A monochromatic light source is required, preferably from a sodium lamp. The refractive index of solutions has been tabulated in reference 3.

CHOICE OF CENTRIFUGAL TECHNIQUE

Particles sediment or float at a rate, which is proportional to the centrifugal force applied. The viscosity of the sample solution and the physical properties of the particle also affect the sedimentation rate of each individual particle. From Stokes' Law, at a fixed centrifugal force and liquid viscosity, the sedimentation rate of the particle is proportional to its size (molecular weight) and the difference between its density and the density of the solution.

$$V = \frac{d^2(P_p -)}{18\mu} \times g$$

where, V = Sedimentation rate
d = diameter
P_p = particle density
P_l = liquid density
μ = viscosity of liquid medium
g = gravitational force

Density gradient centrifugation of lipoproteins is usually performed using salts such as NaCl, NaBr and KBr, which are known not to disrupt lipoprotein structure. Two main techniques have been applied to lipoprotein separation: rate zonal ultracentrifugation and isopycnic ultracentrifugation.

Rate Zonal Ultracentrifugation

In the rate zonal technique, a sample solution containing particles to be separated is layered under a preformed gradient. The density of the sample is adjusted to prevent mixing prior to centrifugation. Under centrifugal force, the particles float through the gradient in separate zones, each consisting of particles of a given flotation rate. To achieve a rate zonal separation, the density of the particles must be greater or less than the density at all positions along the gradient. The run is terminated before any of the separated zones reaches the top of the tube or, in the special case of cumulative flotation, when they reach the top of the tube at the end of a specific run time.

Isopycnic Technique

In the isopycnic technique, the density gradient column encompasses the whole range of densities of the sample particles. Each particle floats/sediments to the position in the centrifuge tube at which the gradient density is equal to its own density and remains there. The isopycnic technique, therefore, separates particles into zones solely on the basis of their differences in density.

In many density gradient experiments, elements of both the rate zonal and isopycnic principles may enter into the final separations. For example, the gradient may be of such a range that one component sediments to the bottom of the tube while another component sediments to its isopycnic position.

RECOVERY OF SEPARATED LIPOPROTEINS

If particles can be detected visually after centrifugation, a Pasteur pipette can be used to carefully remove the individual zones. It is best to use a drawn-out elongated glass pipette and to illuminate the centrifuge tube with a light. Touch the tip of the meniscus at the side of the tube and carefully remove the lipoprotein fraction in a stream of bubbles and transfer into a volumetric flask. Care is taken not to disturb the gradient and to place the pipette under the surface of the liquid to avoid having the lighter layer float down as the underlying solution is removed. This technique requires skill and practice but gives excellent recovery of the separated fractions.

An alternative method is the tube slicer, which holds the tube firmly between two rubber rings. A lance-shaped slicing knife is used to minimize flattening of the tube during cutting. With care, several cuts can be made at different levels of the tube. The sample is removed by piercing the tube with a needle and syringe. Tube slicers are commercially available from Beckman Instruments (High Wycombe, UK).

The entire contents of the tube may be fractionated using a fraction recovery system, which permits heavy liquid (such as Maxidens, Nycomed Pharma AS, Oslo, Norway) to be introduced at the bottom of the tube so that the contents are displaced upwards. A spectrometer and fraction collector may be used if required (Figure 32–1).

ISOLATION OF LIPOPROTEINS BY SEQUENTIAL FLOTATION ULTRACENTRIFUGATION IN A FIXED-ANGLE ROTOR

This method is valuable for the preparation of lipoproteins for compositional analysis and experimental purposes. It is dependent on operator skill and requires calculation for recovery if quantitative estimates of sample concentrations are required.

Principle: The solvent density of plasma (or lipoprotein) is adjusted to the upper limit of the fraction to be isolated, and it is then subjected to ultracentrifugation. The lipoproteins of density less than that to which the solution was adjusted float to the top, while the others sediment to the bottom. The supernatant lipoproteins are removed as described above. The residue in the tube is mixed, its solvent density is adjusted to the upper limit of the next required lipoprotein fraction, and centrifugation is repeated. By readjusting the solvent density of the infranatant to successively higher values, a sequence of lipoprotein fractions can be isolated.

Figure 32–1 ✧ Recovery of Separated Lipoproteins Using a Fraction Recovery System

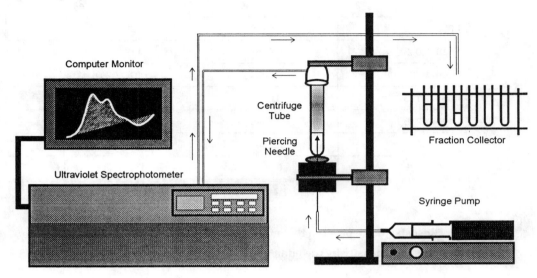

Disadvantage: Fractions overlap because particles close to the density of the solvent migrate very slowly to the upper part of the tube. Repeated washing and ultracentrifugation at the upper density may solve this. This tends to remove adsorbed plasma proteins but prolonged manipulation may lead to degradation of the lipoprotein, loss of its apolipoproteins, and poor recoveries.

Preparative Isolation of VLDL, IDL, LDL, HDL

This method is suitable for the isolation of large quantities of lipoproteins and it is convenient to start with 200 to 250 mL plasma. Isolation may be carried out using either a Ti 60 or Ti 50.2 rotor from Beckman Instruments that holds thick walled polycarbonate bottles (Beckman catalog no. 355654) with a capacity of 25 mL.

Procedure

1. Place 20 mL plasma in a polycarbonate bottle and carefully over-layer with 5 mL 0.15 mol/L NaCl.

2. If sample is not from a fasting subject and it is necessary to isolate chylomicrons, centrifuge at 20,000 rpm for 30 min at 4°C. Carefully remove the top 5 mL and replace with 0.15 mol/L NaCl.

3. Centrifuge at 40,000rpm at 10°–15°C for 20 h or 4°C for 24 h.

4. Remove upper layer of VLDL in 2.0–2.5 mL and carefully remove the next clear non-lipoprotein layer in a volume of 2.0–2.5 mL.

Table 32-2 ✧ Density Adjustment by KBr		
Density (kg/L)	*g KBr/mL*	*Lipoprotein*
1.006–1.019	0.0190	IDL
1.019–1.063	0.0658	LDL
1.006–1.063	0.0834	IDL + LDL
1.063–1.125	0.0955	HDL_2
1.125–1.215	0.1449	HDL_3
1.063–1.21	0.236	HDL
1.006–1.225	0.357	Total lipoproteins

5. Resuspend the pellet in the infranatant and measure its volume.

6. Raise the density by the addition of solid KBr according to the formula

$$x = \frac{Vo(d - do)}{1 - d\overline{v}}$$

where,   x   = amount of KBr in g
         Vo = initial volume in mL
         do = initial density (1.006 kg/L for plasma)
         d   = final density required
         v   = apparent specific volume of Kbr

Table 32–2 indicates the weights of KBr to add per mL of infranatant. This has the advantage in that the volume to be ultracentrifuged is only minimally increased

7. Place this solution in the centrifuge tubes at a volume of 20 mL and over-layer with 0.15 mol/L NaCl in 0.01% EDTA solution at the same density.

8. Centrifuge at 40,000 rpm, 10°–15°C for 20 h or 4°C for 24 h.

9. Remove upper layer as before and adjust to the appropriate density.

If HDL or total lipoproteins are being isolated, increase the centrifugation time to 48 h. This technique can be used to isolate single lipoprotein fractions or several fractions when the steps are combined to reduce time. A common use is to isolate total lipoproteins or to prepare lipid-deficient plasma.

Quantitative Estimation of VLDL, IDL, LDL and HDL in Plasma

When measurement of plasma lipoproteins for clinical purposes is required, a method giving better recovery and smaller samples is more suitable. Disposable 6.5-mL Ultraclear tubes (Beckman catalog number 344088) can be used for this purpose. The Beckman 50.3 or 40.3 rotor holds 18 such tubes and the 50.4 rotor holds 44 tubes.

1. Place 4 mL plasma in a 6.5-mL tube and over-layer with 2 mL d = 1.006 kg/L solution.

2. If it is necessary to isolate chylomicrons, centrifuge at 10,000 rpm at 4°C for 30 min.

3. Carefully remove the top 2 mL and over-layer with 2 mL d = 1.006 kg/L solution.

4. Centrifuge at 40,000 rpm and 15°C for 18 h or 4°C for 24 h.

5. Remove VLDL in top 2 mL by tube slicing or by using a Pasteur pipette.

6. Adjust the infranatant to d = 1.109 kg/L by the addition of 0.32 mL of solution at d = 1.182 kg/L.

7. Mix and transfer to a new centrifuge tube.

8. Over-layer with 1.68 mL d = 1.019 kg/L solution.

9. Centrifuge at 15°C for 18 h or 4°C for 24 h.

10. Remove IDL (d = 1.006–1.109 kg/L) in top 2 mL by tube slicing or with a Pasteur pipette.

11. Adjust the infranatant to d = 1.063 kg/L by adding 1.47 mL of solution at d = 1.182 kg/L.

12. Mix and transfer to a new centrifuge tube.

13. Over-layer with 0.53 mL solution at d = 1.063 kg/L.

14. Centrifuge at 15°C for 18h or 4°C for 24h.

15. Remove LDL (d = 1.019–1.063 kg/L) in 2 mL by tube slicing or with a Pasteur pipette.

16. Adjust the infranatant to d = 1.21 kg/L by adding 2 mL of solution at d = 1.478 kg/L.

17. Remove HDL (d = 1.063–1.21 kg/L) in 2 mL by tube slicing or with a Pasteur pipette.

In our laboratory this technique is routinely used to quantify lipoproteins according to the Lipid Research Clinic Program Manual of Laboratory Operations[4] when VLDL is isolated as in steps 1, 4, and 5. The apolipoprotein B (apo B)-containing lipoproteins in the infranatant are precipitated by adding an equal volume of sodium heparin (5×10^5 units)/MnCl$_2$ (0.092 mol/L),[5] followed by centrifugation at 10,000 rpm at 4°C for 30 min. This leaves HDL in solution. Cholesterol measurements are carried out on total plasma, VLDL, and HDL. LDL cholesterol is obtained by subtracting the HDL cholesterol (HDL-C) level from the cholesterol content in the d > 1.006 kg/L fraction. [IDL and Lp(a) are also included in this fraction].

It is possible to use this technique to fractionate subfractions of HDL. In some laboratories it is used to fractionate LDL into LDL-I (d = 1.026–1.032 kg/L) and LDL III (d = 1.040–1.054 kg/L).[6]

ISOLATION OF LIPOPROTEINS IN A FIXED-ANGLE ROTOR USING A NON-SALT SELF-GENERATING GRADIENT

Iodixanol is an inert, non-toxic density gradient medium widely used as an imaging agent in humans. It forms self-generating gradients that can be made iso-osmotic at all densities. In an initial report Graham, Higgins et al.[7] described the results of fractionating VLDL, LDL, and HDL in an iodixanol gradient after centrifugation in a vertical or near-vertical rotor for 3 h. The lipoprotein fractions were comparable in density and composition to those prepared by centrifugation in traditional salt-based gradients. Today this simple, rapid, and versatile technique is being further developed to isolate individual lipoprotein subfractions and shows potential for their preparation in a time-scale that would minimize damage.

DENSITY GRADIENT ULTRACENTRIFUGATION

The separation of lipoprotein classes by density gradient ultracentrifugation in swinging bucket rotors has gained increasing popularity in recent years. It has a major advantage over sequential ultracentrifugation: the centrifugation time is much reduced. In our experience the separation is superior to that of the fixed-angle centrifugation described above.

Principle: Density gradient ultracentrifugation depends on floating the lipoprotein particles through a gradient formed by layering solutions of decreasing density (NaCl, NaBr, or KBr) above a sample of plasma adjusted to a high density. Centrifugation in a swinging bucket rotor makes the lipoprotein float through the gradient. One of two methods may be used: discontinuous or continuous gradients.

A discontinuous gradient is prepared by layering solutions of successively lower densities one above the other. This allows the lipoproteins of different hydrated densities to be isolated as they float to the top of the tube in a cumulative fashion.

In the continuous format the lipoproteins float to a particular part of the gradient dependent on their hydrated density and are then isolated by displacement of the tube contents.

Disadvantages: This technique is time consuming and requires a high level of technical skill. Care must be taken when over-layering the gradient as the gradient is easily disturbed. The tubes must allow smooth flow of liquid down the interior surface when the gradient is constructed. Routinely we coat the inner surface with polyvinyl alcohol as described by Holmquist,[8] which allows salt solutions to gravity-feed smoothly down the sides.

Surface Modification of Swing-Out Ultraclear Centrifuge Tubes

The procedure is as follows:

1. In a round-bottomed flask dissolve 10 g polyvinyl alcohol in 250 mL distilled water while stirring and heating to achieve gentle reflux.

2. Slowly add 250 mL propan-2-ol while continuously stirring and heating until the solution is clear.

3. Cool the solution to room temperature.

4. Fill the ultracentrifuge tubes with the polyvinyl alcohol solution and leave for 15 min.

5. Remove the solution, being careful to remove all of it from the bottom of the tubes.

6. Dry overnight.

7. Fill the tubes with distilled water and let stand overnight.

8. Pour off all the water and flush each tube briefly with distilled water.

9. Tap tubes to remove excess water.

10. Leave to dry in air at room temperature.

CUMULATIVE FLOTATION ULTRACENTRIFUGATION[2]

Specific details of the separation of various subfractions of chylomicrons, VLDL, IDL, and LDL will be described, based on the original method of Lindgren et al.[2]

Isolation of Chlyomicrons $S_f > 3200$, $S_f > 1100$, $S_f > 400$

Sample Preparation

Adjust 3 mL of plasma to d = 1.065 kg/L by adding 0.254 g of NaCl.

Formation of Gradient

The density solutions and sample are carefully over layered in tubes for a Beckman SW25.3 rotor as in Table 32–3.

Run Conditions

The samples are centrifuged at 23°C for a total centrifugal force of 0.739×10^6 g min to recover a 0.5-mL fraction of $S_f > 3200$, a further 1.32×10^6 g minutes to recover a 0.5 mL fraction of $S_f > 1100$ and a further 3.384×10^6 g minutes to recover a 0.5-mL fraction of $S_f > 400$. The following formula is useful if you wish to use a rotor with a different path length (or radius):

$$RCF = 1.12 \times r \times (rpm/1,000)^2$$

where   RCF is the relative centrifugal force or g
        r is the radius of the rotor in mm
        rpm is revolutions per min

Table 32–3 ✧ Density Gradient for Isolation of Chylomicron Subfractions

Solution Number	Density (kg/L)	Volume (mL)
—	1.182	0.5 Bottom
—	plasma at 1.065	3.0
1	1.0464	1.0
2	1.0336	1.0
3	1.0271	3.0
4	1.0197	3.0
5	1.0117	3.0
6	1.0064	3.0 Top

Isolation of VLDL$_1$ (S$_f$ 60–400), VLDL$_2$ (S$_f$ 20–60), IDL (S$_f$ 12–20), LDL (S$_f$ 0–12)

Density Solutions

Stock solutions in 0.195 mol/L NaCl, 0.01% EDTA density are prepared as described and mixed to prepare six solutions as in Table 32–4. The density of the solutions should also be checked as described.

Solution at d = 1.006 kg/L: Dissolve 22.8 g NaCl, 0.2 g Na$_2$ EDTA, and 2 mL NaOH (1 mol/L) and make up to a volume of 2 L with distilled water.

Solution at d = 1.182 kg/L: Dissolve 249.8 g NaBr in 1 L of solution at d = 1.006 kg/L.

Table 32–4 ✧ Preparation of Density Gradient Solutions (d=1.0588–1.0988 kg/L)

Solution Number	Density (kg/L)	mL d = 1.006 kg/L	mL d = 1.182 kg/L
1	1.0988	50	55.78
2	1.0860	50	41.66
3	1.0790	75	53.16
4	1.0722	75	46.50
5	1.0641	75	36.93
6	1.0588	100	42.92

Sample Preparation

Plasma density is adjusted to 1.118 kg/L by the addition of 0.341 g of NaCl to 2 mL plasma. The sample is mixed well without frothing and allowed to stand at room temperature for at least 30 min before being placed in the centrifuge tube (Beckman catalog no. 344060).

Formation of Gradient

The density solutions and sample are carefully over-layered in a coated Beckman SW40 centrifuge tube as described in Table 32–5. This may be done manually, but for speed and reproducibility it is recommended that a multi-channel peristaltic pump at a speed of 1 mL/min be used.

Run Conditions

Centrifuge in an L8 Beckman ultracentrifuge that is run at 23°C at normal acceleration and zero deceleration according to the speeds and times in Table 32–6. Alternative run times may be calculated using g min. Samples are removed using specially elongated Pasteur pipettes placed on the surface of the meniscus and at the side of the tube with careful bubble formation as previously described.

Isolation of VLDL$_1$ (S$_f$ 60–400), VLDL$_2$ (S$_f$ 20–60), IDL$_1$ (S$_f$ 16–20), IDL$_2$ (S$_f$ 12–16), LDL$_1$ (S$_f$ 8–12), LDL$_2$ (S$_f$ 1.5–8)

In our laboratory we routinely use this density gradient to additionally fractionate IDL and LDL at S$_f$ 16–20, 12–16, 8–12, and 1.5–8 using a Beckman SW 40 rotor and the run

---

Table 32–5 ✧ Density Gradient Solutions for Preparation of Lipoproteins S$_f$ 0–400

Solution Number	Density (kg/L)	Volume (mL)
–	1.182	0.5 Bottom
–	plasma at 1.118	2
1	1.0988	1
2	1.0860	1
3	1.0790	2
4	1.0722	2
5	1.0641	2
6	1.0588	2 Top

Table 32–6 ✧ Conditions for Preparation of Lipoproteins S$_f$ 0–400

Fraction (S$_f$)	Speed (rpm)	Time (h/min)	$\omega^2 t$ ($\times 10^{11}$)	Sample Volume (mLs)
VLDL$_1$(60–400)	39,000	1.38	1.03	1.0*
VLDL$_2$(20–60)	18,500	15.41	2.12	0.5
IDL (12–20)	39,000	2.35	1.63	0.5
LDL(0–12)	30,000	21.10	7.52	1.0

S$_f$ Svedberg unit
*After removal of 1 mL VLDL$_1$, carefully over-layer with 1 mL of solution at d = 1.0988kg/L

conditions described in Table 32–7. Other laboratories use cumulative ultracentrifugation to isolate different subfractions of all three lipoproteins.

LDL SUBFRACTIONATION BY DENSITY GRADIENT ULTRACENTRIFUGATION

A variety of ultracentrifugation methods have been developed to identify and characterize subfractions along the LDL density spectrum. These have employed sequential separations at various densities, rate zonal ultracentrifugation, and density gradient ultracentrifugation. The procedures differ in the construction of the gradient and care should be taken when reading the literature, as there is no universal classification system and use of the terms "large," "small," "buoyant," and "dense" refer to different species dependent on the method of isolation. In addition to the LDL subfraction gradient used in our laboratory,[9] two methods of density gradient ultracentrifugation are

Table 32–7 ✧ Ultracentrifugation Conditions for VLDL$_1$, VLDL$_2$, IDL$_1$, IDL$_2$, LDL$_1$, LDL$_2$

Lipoprotein (S$_f$)	Speed (rpm)	Time (h/min)	Sample Volume (mLs)
VLDL$_1$ (60–400)	39,000	1.43	1.0*
VLDL$_2$ (20–60)	18,500	15.46	0.5**
IDL$_1$ (16–20)	39,000	1.15	0.5
(IDL$_2$ (12–16)	39,000	1.22	0.5
LDL$_1$ (8–12)	39,000	2.09	0.5
LDL$_2$ (1.5–8)	40,000	17.00	0.5

S$_f$ Svedberg unit
*Replace with d = 1.0588 density solution
**Replace with 0.5 mL d = 1.0588 density solution

Table 32–8 ✧ LDL Subfractions

	Krauss et al. [10]				Guerin et al. [11]			Griffin et al. [9]		
Class	Density (kg/L)	Peak Size (nm)	S_f*	Class	Size	Density (kg/L)	Class	Density (kg/L)	Peak Size (nm)
I	1.022–1.032	26.5–28.5	7.5–11	1	light	1.019–1.023	I	1.024–1.034	26.0
				2		1.023–1.029			
IIa	1.032–1.038	26.0–26.5	5.5–8	3	intermediate	1.029–1.039	II	1.034–1.044	25.5
IIb		25.5–26.0	5–6						
IIIa	1.038–1.050	24.7–25.5	3–5	4	dense	1.039–1.050	III	1.044–1.063	24.7
IIIb		24.2–24.7	0–4						
IVa	1.050–1.063	23.2–24.2		5		1.050–1.063			
IVb		22.0–23.2							

*S_f Svedberg units

described by Krauss et al.[10] and Guerin et al.[11] These generally agree in size and classification based on gradient gel electrophoresis. These are listed in Table 32–8.

LDL Subfraction Method in Glasgow[9]

In our laboratory we have developed a density gradient procedure that permits the separation of three LDL subfractions directly from plasma within 24 h. This has the advantage of fractionating fresh plasma (LDL has been found to be unstable during prolonged centrifugation and during freezing).

Sample Preparation

The density of plasma is adjusted to 1.09 kg/L.

Density Solutions

Stock (0.195 mol/L NaCl, 0.01% EDTA) is prepared as described and mixed to prepare six solutions as in Table 32–9. The density of the solutions should be checked as described above.

Solution at d = 1.006 kg/L: Dissolve 22.8 g NaCl, 0.2 g Na_2 EDTA, and 2 mL NaOH (1 mol/L) and make up to a volume of 2 L with distilled water.

Table 32–9 ✧ Density Solutions for LDL Subfractionation[9]

Solution Number	Density (kg/L)	mL d = 1.006	mL d = 1.182
6	1.019	100	8.5
5	1.024	100	13.6
4	1.034	100	18.6
3	1.045	100	27.8
2	1.056	100	42.9
1	1.060	100	49.3

Solution at d = 1.182 kg/L: Dissolve 249.8 g NaBr in 1 L of solution at d = 1.006 kg/L.

Formation of Gradient

The density solutions and sample are carefully over-layered in a coated SW40 centrifuge tube (Beckman catalog no. 344060) as described in Table 32–10. This may be done by hand, but for reproducibility and speed it is recommended that a multi-channel peristaltic pump at a speed of 1 mL/min be used.

Run Conditions

Centrifuge in a Beckman L8 ultracentrifuge at 23°C with slow acceleration and no deceleration for 24 h at 40,000 rpm. The gradient containing separated LDL subfractions

Table 32–10 ✧ Density Gradient for LDL Subfractions[9]

Solution number	Density (kg/L)	Volume (mL)
—	1.182	0.5 Bottom
—	plasma at 1.09	3.0
1	1.060	1.0
2	1.056	1.0
3	1.045	1.0
4	1.034	2.0
5	1.024	2.0
6	1.019	1.0 Top

Figure 32–2 ✧ The Separation of LDL Subfractions Using Density Gradient Centrifugation

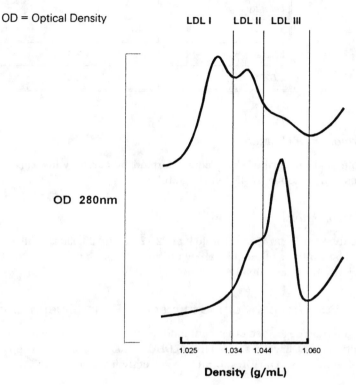

is displaced upwards as described. This procedure generates LDL subfraction profiles from which it is possible to resolve three subfractions, namely LDL-I (d = 1.025–1.034 kg/L), LDL-II (d = 1.034–1.044 kg/L) and LDL-III (d = 1.044–1.060 kg/L). A typical LDL subfraction profile is illustrated in Figure 32–2.

LDL Subfraction Method (Krauss et al.[10])

This is an equilibrium density procedure and was one of the first methods described. Application has revealed the existence of up to four discrete isopycnic LDL bands.

Sample Preparation

LDL (d = 1.009–1.063 kg/L) is isolated from plasma by sequential ultracentrifugation. The density is adjusted to 1.04 kg/L by dialysis overnight against NaBr solution of density 1.04 kg/L.

Table 32–11 ✧ LDL Gradient Formation[10]	
Density (kg/L)	Volume (mL)
1.054	2.5
LDL at d = 1.040	2.0
1.0275	2.5

Formation of Gradient

Table 32–11 describes the gradient formed by carefully layering NaBr density solutions in a Beckman SW45 centrifuge tube.

Run Conditions

The tubes are centrifuged for 40 h at 22°–24°C and 39,000 rpm in a Beckman SW45 rotor. The contents of the tube are withdrawn, beginning with the top 0.5 mL, then in six 1-mL fractions, and finally the bottom 0.5 mL.

LDL Subfraction Method in Inserm, Paris (Guerin et al.[11])

The method described is a recent modification of the original method [12] where 15 subfractions of LDL were isolated from LDL d = 1.006–1.063 kg/L. It separates VLDL, 5 LDL subfractions, and 4 HDL subfractions directly from plasma.

Sample Preparation

Plasma at a density of 3 mL is adjusted to 1.21 kg/L by adding solid KBr.

Formation of Gradient

Density solutions are NaCl/KBr, pH 7.4, and contain 0.01% sodium azide, 0.01% EDTA, and 0.005% gentamycin. A discontinuous density gradient is constructed as in Table 32–12 in a Beckman SW41centrifuge tube.

Run Conditions

Centrifuge at 15°C at 40,000 rpm for 44 h in a Beckman SWTi41 rotor. After centrifugation, gradients are collected from the top of the tube in 12 fractions corresponding to VLDL (d < 1.017 kg/L); IDL (d = 1.018–1.019 kg/L); LDL-I (d = 1.019–1.023 kg/L); LDL-II (d = 1.023–1.029 kg/L); LDL-III (d = 1.029–1.039 kg/L); LDL-IV (d = 1.039–1.050 kg/L); LDL-V (d = 1.050–1.063 kg/L); HDL_{2b} (d = 1.063–1.091 kg/L); HDL_{2a} (d = 1.091–1.110 kg/L); HDL_{3a} (d = 1.110–1.133 kg/L); HDL_{3b} (d = 1.133–1.156 kg/L); and HDL_{3c} (d = 1.156–1.179 kg/L).

Table 32–12 ◆ LDL Subfraction Gradient[11]	
Density of solution (kg/L)	*Volume (mL)*
1.24	*2.0*
plasma at d = 1.21	*3.0*
1.063	*2.0*
1.019	*2.5*
1.006	*2.5*

IDL SUBFRACTIONATION[13]

There are few methods for separating IDL into different fractions and Musliner et al. published the following in 1986.

Fractions of lipoprotein obtained by nonequilibrium density gradient ultracentrifugation are further fractionated by equilibrium density gradient ultracentrifugation to isolate two fractions of IDL at d = 1.008–1.022 kg/L and d = 1.013–1.028 kg/L.

Nonequilibrium Density Centrifugation

Sample Preparation

Lipoproteins d < 1.063 kg/L are adjusted to d = 1.21 kg/L by the addition of solid NaBr.

Formation of Gradient

Density solutions are over-layered in a Beckman SW41 tube as in Table 32–13.

Run Conditions

The tubes are centrifuged at 17°C for 6 h at 40,000 rpm and allowed to coast to a stop without braking. The contents of the tube are withdrawn by pipetting four successive 1-mL fractions followed by six successive 0.5-mL fractions.

Table 32–13 ◆ Nonequilibrium Density Gradient Ultacentrifugation[13]		
Solution Number	*Density (kg/L)*	*Volume (mLs)*
–	Sample at 1.21	4.5 Bottom
1	1.020	3.0
2	1.010	3.0
3	1.000	1.5 Top

Table 32–14 ◇ Equilibrium Density Gradient Ultracentrifugation [13]

Solution Number	Density (kg/L)	Volume (mLs)	
1	1.040	1.0	Bottom
2	1.030	3.5	
3	Sample at 1.020	3.5	
4	1.010	3.0	
5	1.000	1.0	Top

Equilibrium Density Ultracentrifugation

Sample Preparation

The density of fractions 5,6,7, and 8 from the non-equilibrium technique described above are adjusted to d = 1.020 kg/L by dialysis against four changes of NaBr solution over a 24-h period.

Formation of Gradient

The solutions are carefully layered in a Beckman SW41 centrifuge tube according to the scheme in Table 32–14.

Run Conditions

The tubes are centrifuged at 40,000 rpm for 60 h in a Beckman SW41 rotor and allowed to coast to stop without braking. The contents of the tube are withdrawn in 1-mL fractions.

RATE ZONAL ULTRACENTRIFUGATION

Advantages: Conventional sequential or density gradient ultracentrifugation is limited by the small capacity of centrifuge tubes. This can be overcome by the use of zonal rotors Ti14 and Ti15 (from Beckman Instruments) with a capacity of 665 and 1665 mL respectively. There is an added advantage in that isolation can be completed in a comparatively short time due to the much shorter path lengths.

Disadvantages: This technique requires capital investment in rotors, apparatus to load and unload the rotor, equipment to monitor and record the lipoprotein fractions as the rotor is being unloaded, and time-consuming care and maintenance of equipment due to the effects of heavy salt solutions. Also, only one sample can be fractionated in each run. The zonal rotor has been utilized to isolate fractions of VLDL, and HDL and large-scale preparations of LDL.

VLDL Isolation by Rate Zonal Centrifugation[14]

Seven fractions of VLDL are isolated on the basis of differing flotation rates. With decreasing flotation rates there is an increase in free cholesterol, cholesteryl ester, phospholipid, apo B, and a decrease in TG.

Sample Preparation

A quantity of 8 to 15 mL plasma is adjusted to d = 1.15 kg/L.

Formation of Gradient

Stock solutions of NaBr are prepared in 0.35 mmol/L EDTA, pH 7.6. A linear gradient of d = 1.0–1.15 kg/L is formed in a Beckman Ti14 zonal rotor while centrifuging at 3,500 rpm. The plasma at d = 1.15 kg/L is carefully loaded on the outside of the gradient followed by a cushion of 25 mL of solution at d = 1.15 kg/L.

Run Conditions

Centrifuge at 42,000 rpm for 45 min at 14°C. Unload the rotor at 3,500 rpm by pumping a solution of d = 1.15 kg/L through the peripheral line of the loading head. The eluate is monitored at OD280 nm and 10-mL fractions are collected to yield seven fractions of VLDL ranging from Sf 20–400 as in Table 32–15.

LDL Isolation by Rate Zonal Centrifugation

Isolation of LDL by rate zonal ultracentrifugation has been the method chosen in our laboratory to prepare LDL during metabolic studies because it can be isolated from

Table 32–15 ✧ VLDL Fractions Isolated by Rate Zonal Centrifugation

Subfraction	S_f
$VLDL_1$	424.2–181.9
$VLDL_2$	189.6–121.4
$VLDL_3$	128.7–77.7
$VLDL_4$	86.3–59.1
$VLDL_5$	69.5–41.7
$VLDL_6$	47.7–32.9
$VLDL_7$	36.6–21.4
S_f Svedberg unit	

plasma rapidly and so can be radioactively labeled and re-injected into the subject within hours of venipuncture.

Sample Preparation

The density of 50 mL plasma is adjusted to 1.3 kg/L by the addition of 15 g NaBr.

Formation of Gradient

Density solutions at 1.0 and 1.3 kg/L are prepared in 0.1 mol/L Tris-0.01% (w/v) Na_2 EDTA, pH 7.6, by the addition of NaBr. A linear gradient of d = 1.0–1.3 kg/L is formed in a Beckman Ti14 rotor while centrifuging at 3,500 rpm. Fifty mL plasma at d = 1.3 kg/L are carefully loaded onto the outside of the gradient, followed by a cushion of 25 mL of solution at d = 1.3 kg/L.

Run Conditions

Centrifuge at 45,000 rpm for 140 min at 10°C. The rotor is unloaded at 3,500 rpm by pumping solution at density d = 1.3 kg/L through the peripheral line of the loading head. The eluate is monitored at OD 280 nm and the appropriate fractions of LDL pooled. Figure 32–3 shows a typical LDL profile obtained from zonal ultracentrifugation.

HDL Isolation by Rate Zonal Centrifugation[15]

By centrifugation through a discontinuous gradient of density 1.00–1.40 kg/L, VLDL and LDL are first removed, allowing separation of HDL_2 and HDL_3 subfractions uncontaminated by other plasma proteins.

Figure 32–3 ✧ The Separation of LDL Using Rate Zone Centrifugation

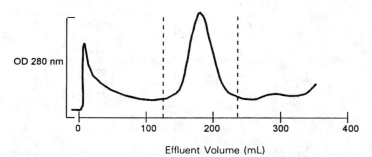

OD = Optical Density

OD 280 nm

Effluent Volume (mL)

Sample Preparation

The density of 50 mL plasma is adjusted to 1.4 kg/L by adding 26.6 g NaBr.

Formation of Gradient

Solutions at d = 1.0 and 1.4 kg/L are prepared in 0.1 mol/L Tris-0.01% (w/v) Na_2 EDTA, pH 7.6, by the addition of NaBr. A stepwise gradient of d = 1.0–1.4 kg/L is formed in a Beckman Ti14 rotor (Beckman Instruments) while spinning at 3,500 rpm. Fifty mL plasma at d = 1.4 kg/L are carefully loaded onto the outside of the gradient, followed by a cushion of 25 mL of solution at d = 1.3 kg/L.

Run Conditions

Centrifugation occurs at 45,000 rpm for 18 h at 10°C. The rotor is unloaded at 3,500 rpm by pumping solution at density 1.4 kg/L through the peripheral line of the loading head.

The eluate is monitored at OD 280 nm and the appropriate fractions of HDL pooled, HDL_2 being the first fraction to be eluted followed by HDL_3. Figure 32–4 illustrates a typical HDL profile obtained in our laboratory.

SUMMARY

The advantage of ultracentrifugation is that it separates useful entities; its disadvantage is that the isolated fractions are still heterogeneous, for instance with respect to the content of apo B, C, and E. Moreover, there is an exchange of apoproteins among the lipoprotein particles and shedding of apo E during centrifugation. Plasma contains enzymes such as cholesteryl ester transfer protein (CETP), lecithin cholesterol acyl transferase (LCAT), lipoprotein lipase (LPL), and hepatic lipase (HTGL) that modify the composition and structure of the lipoproteins. These activities are ongoing during centrifugation but effects may be minimized by carrying out procedures at 4°C or by

Figure 32–4 ✧ Separation of HDL Using Rate Zone Centrifugation

OD = Optical Density

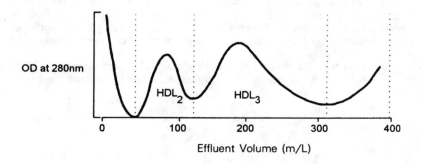

Effluent Volume (m/L)

adding inhibitors such as 1.5 mmol/L Ellman's reagent [5,5-dithiobis (2-nitro-benzoic acid)], 2 mmol/L diisopropyl fluorophosphonate, or thiomersal. Lipoproteins are susceptible to oxidative modification and it is common practice to collect blood in K_2 EDTA at a final concentration of 1 kg/L and to add 1 mmol/L Na_2EDTA to all solutions to sequester the heavy metal catalysts. ✧

REFERENCES

1. Havel RJ, Eder HA, Bragdon JH. The distribution and chemical composition of ultracentrifugally separated lipoproteins in human serum. J Clin Invest 1955;34:1345–53.
2. Lindgren FT, Jensen LC, Hatch FT. The isolation and quantitation analysis of serum lipoproteins. In: Nelson GJ (ed.). Blood, lipids, and lipoproteins: quantitation, composition, and metabolism. New York: Wiley-Interscience, 1972:181–274.
3. Mills GL, Lane PA, Weech PK. The isolation and purification of plasma lipoproteins. In: Burdon RH, Knippenberg PH (eds.). Laboratory techniques in biochemistry and molecular biology: a guidebook to lipoprotein technique. Elsevier, Amsterdam, 1984: 18–116.
4. U.S. Dept. Health, Education and Welfare. Lipid research clinics program: Manual of laboratory operations. Vol. 1: Lipid and lipoprotein analysis. Bethesda, MD: National Institutes of Health publication no. 1975:75–628.
5. Warnick GR, Albers JJ. A comprehensive evaluation of the heparin/manganese precipitation procedure for estimating HDL cholesterol. J Lipid Res 1978;9:65–76.
6. Tribble DL, van den Berg JJM, Motchnik PA, Ames BN, Lewis DM, Chait A, Krauss RM. Oxidative susceptibility of low-density subfractions is related to their ubiquinol-10 and -tocopherol content. Proc Natl Acad Sci USA 1994;91:1183–7.
7. Graham JM, Higgins JA, Gillott T, Taylor T, Wilkinson J, Ford T, Billington D. A novel method for the rapid separation of plasma lipoproteins using self-generating gradients of iodixanol. Atherosclerosis 1996;124:125–35.
8. Holmquist R. Surface modification of ultraclear centrifuge tubes. J Lipid Res 1982;23: 1249–50.
9. Griffin BA, Caslake MJ, Yip B, Tait GW, Packard CJ, Shepherd J. Rapid isolation of low-density lipoprotein (LDL) subfractions from plasma by density gradient ultracentrifugation. Atherosclerosis 1990;83:59–67.
10. Krauss RM, Burke DJ. Identification of multiple subclasses of plasma low-density lipoproteins in normal humans. J Lipid Res 1982;23:97–104.
11. Guerin M, Bruckert E, Dolphin PJ, Turpin G, Chapman MJ. Fenofibrate reduces plasma cholesteryl ester transfer from HDL to VLDL and normalizes the atherogenic, dense LDL profile in combined hyperlipidemia. Arterioscler Thromb Vasc Biol 1996;16: 763–72.
12. Chapman MJ, Goldstein S, Lagrange D, Laplaud PM. A density gradient ultracentrifugal procedure for the isolation of the major lipoprotein classes from human serum. J Lipid Res 1981;22:339–58.
13. Musliner TA, Giotas C, Krauss RM. Presence of multiple subpopulations of lipoproteins of intermediate density in normal subjects. Arteriosclerosis 1986;6:79–87.
14. Patsch W, Patsch JR, Kostner GM, Sailer S, Braunsteiner H. Isolation of subfractions of human very-low-density lipoproteins by zonal ultracentrifugation. J Biol Chem;1978: 4911–5.
15. Patsch W, Schonfeld G, Gotto AM, Patsch JR. Characterization of human high-density lipoproteins by zonal ultracentrifugation. J Biol Chem 1980;255:3178–85.

Analysis of Plasma Lipoproteins by Gel Permeation Chromatography

33

Mitsuyo Okazaki, Shinichi Usui, and Seijin Hosaki

✧   It is widely known that an increase in low-density-lipoprotein cholesterol (LDL-C) or a decrease in high-density-lipoprotein cholesterol (HDL-C) represents a major risk factor for the development of atherosclerotic arterial diseases.[1] Consequently, reliable methods for determining serum total cholesterol and cholesterol in lipoprotein fractions including chylomicrons (CM), very-low-density lipoprotein (VLDL), intermediate-density lipoproteins (IDL), LDL, and HDL are of interest for appropriate preventive strategies for atherosclerosis-dependent heart disease. In the most commonly used routine method, LDL-C concentration is estimated from the measurements of total cholesterol (TC), triglycerides (TG), and HDL-C by the Friedewald equation.[2] However, new and optimized quantitative methods for cholesterol determination in major lipoprotein classes are desirable for routine laboratory assays.

Until now, the major serum lipoprotein classes have been separated generally on the basis of differences in density by ultracentrifugation or on the basis of electrical charge by electrophoretic techniques.[3] Separation on the basis of particle size by gel permeation chromatography has also been attempted.[4,5] Heterogeneities in size within each lipoprotein class have been examined using agarose gel chromatography with fractionated lipoprotein samples obtained by ultracentrifugation.

In 1980, Hara et al.[6] successfully applied the high-performance liquid chromatography (HPLC) technique to lipoprotein analysis. In those studies, the TSKgel columns (TSKgel SW and PW type, TOSOH, Japan) were used and post-column detection of lipid components such as cholesterol,[6-8] phospholipids,[9] and TG[10] was performed by enzymatic reactions. The post-column detection method could make it possible to obtain lipoprotein profiles from a very small amount of whole serum (> 10 μL) within 60 min. Okazaki et al.[11-13] and several other investigators[14-20] have confirmed the reliability of this technique by comparing it with other established techniques. Many valuable clinical studies have also been reported based on subsequent work. Abnormal lipoproteins were detected in lecithin:cholesterol acyltransferase (LCAT) deficiency[21] and in Tangier disease.[22] A marked enlargement of HDL size in subjects with cholesterol ester transfer protein (CETP) deficiency,[23] a change in HDL size induced by drug therapy[24,25] and decreased serum HDL$_3$-C levels in liver cirrhosis[26] were reported. The differentiation of asymptomatic primary biliary cirrhosis from symptomatic cirrhosis was achieved by the HDL size in the elution profile.[27] However, these have remained as alternative methods because of the difficulties in eliminating the non-specific adsorption of lipoproteins to TSKgel materials.

In 1993, improved gel permeation columns (TSKgel Lipopropak and Lipopropak XL, TOSOH) and specifically prepared eluents (TSK eluent LP-1 and LP-2, TOSOH) were developed for quantitative separation of lipoproteins.[28] Using the new columns and eluents, a simple, rapid, and accurate quantification technique for cholesterol in major serum lipoprotein classes—CM, VLDL, LDL, and HDL—has been reported.[29–31] This automated lipoprotein analytical system has been used for routine assay of cholesterol concentration in major lipoprotein classes in Japanese clinical laboratories,[32,33] where 80–90 samples can be processed in a working day. In 2000, a good assessment of between-apparatus variation for measurement of lipoprotein cholesterol and particle size of LDL and HDL using this system has been reported by Usui et al.[34] Moreover, a new simultaneous profiling technique for lipoprotein cholesterol and TG has been performed by post-column reaction on the split effluent after separation using TSKgel LipopropakXL and TSK eluent LP-2.[35]

Gel permeation columns other than the TSKgel series have been used for lipoprotein analysis. In 1990, Kieft et al.[36] reported a rapid online measurement method for lipoprotein cholesterol by HPLC using a single column (Superose 6HR 10/30). Lipoprotein analysis using Superose 6 columns on a Pharmacia fast-protein liquid chromatography (FPLC) system has been reported by several investigators.[37–47] The FPLC system has been used as an analytical approach in combination with post-column detection of cholesterol as well as a preparative method by collecting a number of consecutive fractions for analysis of lipid components and apolipoproteins. In this technique, three separate fractions related to VLDL, LDL, and HDL can be obtained within a relatively short time. Moreover, a few approaches to determine particle size of LDL have been reported.[48,49]

In this chapter, we describe the usefulness and reliability of the gel permeation chromatography method for the separation and quantitation of the major serum lipoprotein classes and their subclasses. We also describe the application and prospective development of the chromatographic method for lipoprotein analysis in clinical laboratories as well as in research laboratories.

GEL PERMEATION COLUMNS USED FOR LIPOPROTEIN ANALYSIS

Gel permeation columns obtainable from various suppliers can be used for separating serum lipoproteins in various chromatographic systems (see Table 33–1).

Agarose Gel Column

Agarose gel columns consisting of 4% or 6% beads can be used to separate VLDL, LDL, and HDL from whole plasma and to collect their fractions. If plasma proteins are removed from samples by a single ultracentrifugation at density < 1.21 kg/L, the lipoprotein profile can be directly monitored at A_{280}. For quantitation purposes, the amount of cholesterol in each of the pooled fractions can be determined. The recovery of lipoproteins from these agarose gel columns was reported to be 89.5 ± 8.8% by Rudel and Pitts.[50] The conventional method of agarose chromatography required 5–8 mL of plasma and an elution time of over 16 h.[4,5]

Table 33-1 ✧ Gel Permeation Columns for Lipoprotein Separation

Column	Source	Lipoprotein Classes
Bio-Gel A50m	Bio-Rad Laboratories	CM, VLDL subclasses
Bio-Gel A15m	Bio-Rad Laboratories	CM+VLDL, LDL, HDL
Bio-Gel A5m	Bio-Rad Laboratories	HDL subclasses
Superose 6HR 10/30	Pharmacia Biotech	CM+VLDL, LDL, HDL
TSKgel G5000PW	TOSOH Corporation	CM, VLDL, LDL, HDL
TSKgel G4000PW	TOSOH Corporation	CM+VLDL, LDL, HDL
TSKgel G3000PW	TOSOH Corporation	HDL subclasses
TSKgel G4000SW	TOSOH Corporation	CM+VLDL, LDL, HDL
TSKgel G3000SW	TOSOH Corporation	HDL subclasses
TSKgel Lipopropak	TOSOH Corporation	CM, VLDL, LDL, HDL
TSKgel LipopropakXL	TOSOH Corporation	CM, VLDL, LDL, HDL
Fractogel 65-F	Bodman Chemicals	CM, VLDL subclasses
GF-450	DuPont	CM, VLDL subclasses

Superose 6 Column

A FPLC system has been used to separate plasma lipoproteins on a Superose 6 column.[37–47] Elution profiles monitored by A_{280} for the lipoproteins with lower density than 1.21 kg/L isolated by ultracentrifugation from 3–4 mL of plasma showed three major peaks corresponding to VLDL, LDL, and HDL. Compared to conventional agarose gel chromatography, the FPLC method greatly reduces the separation time and improves the separation of lipoproteins. März et al.[37] reported a new method for quantitation of cholesterol in VLDL, LDL, and HDL fractions by loading 20 μL of plasma on a 300-mm prepacked Superose 6 column in the FPLC system. Lipoproteins were detected at 500 nm after post-column reaction by reagents for cholesterol. The elution patterns showed three separate peaks corresponding to VLDL, LDL, and HDL, and their cholesterol values were calculated on the basis of relative peak area and TC. Analytical time per sample was 80 min. The FPLC inter-assay precision assessed by 13 consecutive analyses of a normolipidemic sample was reported to be 5.8%, 2.0%, and 1.9% for VLDL-C, LDL-C, and HDL-C, respectively. Moreover, the correlation coefficients of the FPLC method with a combined ultracentrifugation and precipitation method were reported to be 0.979, 0.978, and 0.933 for VLDL-C, LDL-C, and HDL-C, respectively. Despite a high correlation between the two methods, overestimation of LDL-C and underestimation of VLDL-C by the FPLC method was reported because 15%–20% of the VLDL fraction with density < 1.006 kg/L co-eluted with LDL. The authors asserted that the FPLC method might be a useful complement to conventional methods in selected patients' samples, because the number of analyses was only 10–20 samples per working day. The recovery of lipoproteins from this Superose 6 column was reported to be over 90%.[36,41]

TSKGel Column Series

In the HPLC technique used by Hara et al.,[12] a post-column detection method involving enzymatic reaction was adopted to obtain lipoprotein profiles directly from whole serum. Okazaki et al.[8] proposed a procedure for quantitation of cholesterol in the major lipoprotein classes (CM+VLDL, LDL, HDL_2, and HDL_3) from cholesterol-monitoring patterns obtained by loading 10 µL of whole serum on TSKgel G4000SW + G3000SW columns. The amount of cholesterol in each lipoprotein class was calculated from the relative peak area and the TC level in serum. Each area was divided by drawing a line perpendicular to the baseline at the elution volume corresponding to the following particle diameters: 30 nm, 16 nm, 10 nm, and 8 nm. A high correlation ($r = 0.83$–0.99) between the G4000SW + G3000SW column system and the ultracentrifugation method of Havel et al.[51] has been reported by Okazaki et al.[8] Comparison studies of the HPLC method using TSKgel columns with density gradient ultracentrifugation by Williams et al.,[19] with agarose gel chromatography by Carroll and Rudel,[14] and with rate zonal ultracentrifugation by Oida et al.[20] have supported the reliability of lipoprotein separation by the HPLC method. Although the recovery of lipoproteins from TSKgel materials was reported to be over 90%,[14,17–19] considerable adsorption of lipoproteins to the gel materials was found.[14,44] In 1993, this problem was resolved by developing new columns (TSKgel Lipopropak and LipopropakXL) and mobile phase solutions (TSK eluent LP-1 and LP-2) for lipoprotein separation, and Kitamura et al.[28] reported over 99.8% recovery. An automated analytical system (TOSOH) also has been developed for routine use, as described in the previous edition of this handbook.[52]

CURRENT AUTOMATED HPLC SYSTEM FOR ROUTINE USE

Principle

In order to separate all major lipoprotein classes—CM, VLDL, LDL, and HDL—simultaneously and quantitatively, a gel permeation column with separation characteristics ranging from 5 nm to 100 nm in diameter is required. The use of the new column and mobile phase solutions with post-column enzymatic reaction to obtain serial cholesterol patterns allows cholesterol concentration in all major lipoprotein classes to be quantified conveniently.

The particle diameter range of major lipoprotein classes—CM, VLDL, LDL, and HDL—was defined by Hara and Okazaki[12] as follows: CM, over 80 nm; VLDL, 30–80 nm; LDL, 16–30 nm; HDL, 8–16 nm. The identification of each lipoprotein class was based on particle diameter estimated by the elution time for each column system. This conversion was carried out using a column calibration curve, a plot of logarithm of the particle diameter of standard samples, latex beads (Magsphere, Inc.), and high-molecular-weight standards (Pharmacia) against their elution times.

The peak areas of major lipoprotein classes were obtained as follows: In most samples, the HDL peaks were clearly separated from other lipoproteins; the HDL area was obtained by drawing a vertical line from the minimum point between the LDL and HDL peaks down to the baseline (x axis). The area corresponding to the column void volume was defined as CM regardless of the presence of a peak. The areas corresponding to VLDL and LDL peaks were separated mathematically because of a continuous size distribution from VLDL to LDL, suggesting the presence of numerous subclasses in these lipoproteins. A Gaussian curve-fitting approach using computer-assisted data processing[29] was applied to separate peaks corresponding to VLDL and LDL.

The concentration of cholesterol in each lipoprotein class was calculated from its peak area using a certified reference serum as a calibrator.

Procedures

The HPLC system is modeled on the concept described above. This system consists of two pumps, one detector, one autosampler and one data processor. Although we used an analytical system (CCP & 8020) from TOSOH, similar equipment from other companies such as Waters may be available. Two connected columns (TSKgel Lipo-propakXL, 7.8 mm in diameter, 300 mm in length, TOSOH) and the TSK eluent LP-1 was used at a flow rate of 0.7 mL/min. A 5-μL aliquot of whole serum was applied to the columns with an interval of 16 min. The cholesterol in the effluent from the columns was detected at an absorbance of 550 nm after an online enzymatic reaction using a enzymatic cholesterol reagents (Determiner L TC, Kyowa Medex, Tokyo) in a reaction tube (Reaction Coil K, 0.4 mm i.d., 7.5 m in length, TOSOH) at 45°C. In an online reaction, the effluent was mixed with reagent 1 (ascorbic acid oxidase, cholesterol oxidase, peroxidase, N-ethyl-N-(3-methylphenyl)-N'-succinyl-ethylenediamine) at a flow rate of 0.263 mL/min and reagent 2 (cholesterol oxidase, peroxidase and 4-aminoantipyrine) at a flow rate of 0.087 mL/min. With other cholesterol reagent kits, the optimum reaction conditions, dimension of the reaction coil, reaction temperature, and flow rate of the cholesterol reagent might need to be modified

Analyses were carried out consecutively and automatically by placing a calibrator and test samples in the autosampler and by entering the sample numbers and concentration of TC of the calibrator into the computer. The elution time (in min) and concentration of cholesterol (mg/dL and mmol/L) for major lipoprotein classes (peak 1, CM; peak 2, VLDL; peak 3, LDL; peak 4, HDL) were reported together with the HPLC patterns using computer-assisted data processing by Kitamura et al.[29] Representative HPLC patterns and analytical data are shown in Figure 33–1. Commercial materials prepared from human pooled sera such as certified reference serum (Health Care Technology Foundation, Standard Reference Center, Kawasaki, Japan) and Determiner HDL-C reference serum (Kyowa Medex) could be used as a calibrator for this system. To establish traceability to the reference methods recommended by Centers for Disease Control and Prevention (CDC), a calibrator must have a cholesterol value that has been assigned by CDC. Furthermore, the calibrator has to have known particle diameters of LDL and HDL so as to calculate those of LDL and HDL in the test samples. Prolonged sample storage after thawing can affect the measurement of TC, LDL, and HDL sizes; therefore, reference sera should be used within one day after thawing.

Figure 33–1 ✦ HPLC Patterns Obtained Using the Current Lipoprotein
Analytical System

Samples: whole serum (5 μ l); (a) normolipidemic healthy man, TG = 59
mg/dL (0.67 mmol/L); (b) familial hypercholesterolemia (Type IIa), TG = 35
mg/dL (0.40 mmol/L); (c) patient with diabetes mellitus (Type IIb), TG = 244
mg/dL (2.76 mmol/L); (d) the same patient as c before drug treatment (Type
IV), TG = 400 mg/dL(4.52mmol/L); (e) lipoprotein lipase deficiency (Type I or
Type V), TG = 825 mg/dL(9.32 mmol/L); (f) patient with apo $E_{2/2}$ phenotype
(Type III), TG = 216 mg/dL(2.44 mmol/L). Analytical data are reported together
with the HPLC pattern.

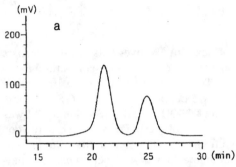

No.	Class	Elution Time min.	Elution Time nm	Cholesterol mg/dL	Cholesterol mmol/L
1	CM	—		0.0	0.00
2	VLDL	—		9.7	0.25
3	LDL	21.10	25.8	99.5	2.57
4	HDL	24.95	11.1	63.3	1.64
			TOTAL	172.5	4.46

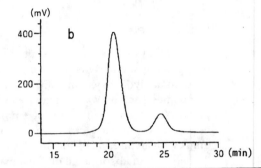

No.	Class	Elution Time min.	Elution Time nm	Cholesterol mg/dL	Cholesterol mmol/L
1	CM	—		0.1	0.00
2	VLDL	—		11.4	0.29
3	LDL	20.93	26.8	297.2	7.69
4	HDL	25.11	10.7	60.4	1.56
			TOTAL	369.0	9.54

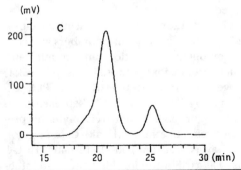

No.	Class	Elution Time min.	Elution Time nm	Cholesterol mg/dL	Cholesterol mmol/L
1	CM	—		0.0	0.00
2	VLDL	—		50.6	1.31
3	LDL	21.06	26.0	171.5	4.43
4	HDL	25.26	10.4	44.6	1.15
			TOTAL	266.7	6.90

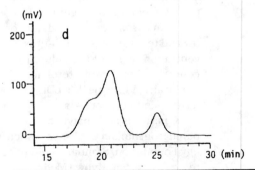

No.	Class	Elution Time min.	Elution Time nm	Cholesterol mg/dL	Cholesterol mmol/L
1	CM	—		0.1	0.00
2	VLDL	—		92.9	2.40
3	LDL	21.10	25.8	88.9	2.30
4	HDL	25.28	10.3	32.5	0.84
			TOTAL	214.4	5.54

Figure 33–1 ✧ *Continued*

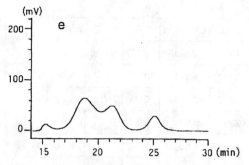

No.	Class	Elution Time		Cholesterol	
		min.	nm	mg/dL	mmol/L
1	CM	15.40	89.8	6.4	0.17
2	VLDL	18.99	40.9	96.5	2.50
3	LDL	21.46	23.8	44.3	1.15
4	HDL	25.32	10.3	23.1	0.60
			TOTAL	147.2	3.81

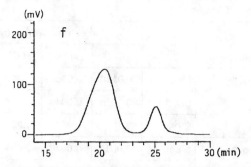

No.	Class	Elution Time		Cholesterol	
		min.	nm	mg/dL	mmol/L
1	CM	—		0.1	0.00
2	VLDL	20.58	28.8	124.7	3.22
3	LDL	—		47.3	1.22
4	HDL	25.17	10.5	39.5	1.02
			TOTAL	211.7	5.47

Reliability

The within-run precision values of cholesterol determination in each lipoprotein class and particle diameters of the identified lipoprotein classes are summarized in Table 33–2. In a recent study[34] using four HPLC apparatuses with different column-load numbers from 250 to 5000, between-apparatus imprecision values (CV), which were calculated by an analysis of variance, were 1.9% for TC, 3.1% for HDL-C, 3.0% for LDL-C, 10.5% for VLDL-C, 49.1% for CM-C, 0.6% for LDL size, and 0.8% for HDL size.

When 5 µL of whole serum was applied, a linear relationship between loaded amount of sample and peak areas of LDL and HDL was observed at serum cholesterol concentrations ranging from 7.7 to 464 mg/dL (0.2 to 12 mmol/L), and the detection limit for each peak was 0.2 mg/dL (0.005 mmol/L).

Diagnostic Applications

The World Health Organization (WHO)[53] has proposed categorizing phenotypes of hyperlipoproteinemias. Representative HPLC patterns of patients with hyperlipoproteinemias are shown in Figure 33–1.

Subjects classified to Type IIa (b in Figure 33–1), Type IIb (c in Figure 33–1) and Type IV (d in Figure 33–1) showed LDL and HDL peaks. Patients with lipoprotein lipase (LPL) deficiency (Type I by WHO, e in Figure 33–1) and almost all of Type V hyperlipidemia with TG > 0.9 mmol/L (800 mg/dl), showed CM and VLDL peaks as well as LDL and HDL peaks. A patient with apo E deficiency (pattern not shown) or all subjects with apo $E_{2/2}$ (f in Figure 33–1) presented VLDL and HDL peaks. Matsuzawa et al.[54] reported that no peak corresponding to LDL was detected for the subjects with

Table 33-2 ✧ Within-Run Precision of the Current Lipoprotein Analytical System (n = 5)

Sample[c]		Cholesterol Concentration (mmol/L)[a]					Particle Diameter (nm)[b]			
		CM	VLDL	LDL	HDL	Total	CM	VLDL	LDL	HDL
No. 1	Mean	0.0140	0.530	2.230	1.615	4.395	93.03		25.66	10.73
	SD	0.0005	0.0049	0.0045	0.0047	0.0097	0.31	ND	0.02	0.02
	CV%	3.70	0.92	0.20	0.29	0.22	0.34		0.10	0.15
No. 2	Mean	0.0011	0.057	2.934	1.514	4.505			25.88	11.32
	SD	0.0003	0.0007	0.018	0.0052	0.014	ND	ND	0.05	0.03
	CV%	27.54	1.19	0.61	0.34	0.32			0.18	0.26
No. 3	Mean	0.0026	3.635	2.277	1.048	6.963		40.81	24.21	10.25
	SD	0.0007	0.026	0.010	0.007	0.032	ND	0.06	0.02	0.01
	CV%	26.52	0.71	0.44	0.70	0.046		0.15	0.07	0.10

[a]To convert cholesterol concentration from mmol/L to mg/dL, multiply by 38.67.
[b]The data were obtained from additional analysis using column calibration curve.
[c]No. 1: Determiner HDL-C Reference serum (Lot 121AFF, Kyowa Medex, Tokyo)
No. 2:Normolipidemic subject (TG = 77 mg/dL [0.87 mmol/L])
No. 3: Hyperlipidemic subject (TG = 798 mg/dL [9.01 mmol/L])
ND = Peak not detected

apo $E_{2/2}$. This finding was clearly demonstrated by the current HPLC system for routine use, and the particle size of VLDL in a patient with apo $E_{2/2}$ was smaller than that in a patient with LPL deficiency. In contrast, a peak corresponding to HDL could not be clearly observed in rare cases such as LCAT deficiency, Tangier disease, severe hyperbilirubinemia, and primary biliary cirrhosis.[31,55]

Qualitative and quantitative information by the HPLC system can be useful for the phenotyping of hyperlipoproteinemias. In addition, Kazama et al. have recently demonstrated association of the lipoprotein cholesterol profiles by HPLC with prevalence of macroangiopathy (symptomatic cerebrovascular disease or coronary artery disease) in elderly diabetic patients.[56,57]

COMPARISON WITH OTHER AVAILABLE TECHNIQUES

Total Cholesterol

The TC concentration obtained as the sum of each lipoprotein class in this system was identical to that determined by conventional enzymatic analysis on a chemistry analyzer.[28,30] The HPLC method showed high correlation(r = 0.997) and good agreement with the reference method (Abel-Kendall) (absolute mean bias < 1.2%).[34]

Major Lipoprotein Classes

The cholesterol values in major lipoprotein classes measured by this system were found to be identical to those measured by sequential ultracentrifugation,[51] except for subjects with high concentrations of lipoprotein(a) [Lp(a)].[31,58] Results for 191 subjects with a wide range of Lp(a) concentrations (10~1630 mg/L) are shown in Figure 33–2. The values for LDL-C by HPLC were consistent with the sum of IDL-C and LDL-C measured by the sequential ultracentrifugation method. Although the values of (CM + VLDL)-C and HDL-C by the HPLC method were highly correlated with VLDL-C and (HDL$_2$ + HDL$_3$ + VHDL)-C determined by the sequential ultracentrifugation method, a qualitative discrepancy was observed between the two methods; Lp(a)-C was measured as VLDL-C by the HPLC method and as HDL$_2$-C by the sequential ultracentrifugation method (see bottom panel in Figure 33–2). In Figure 33–3, the HPLC profiles of whole sera and their fractions separated by sequential ultracentrifugation are presented for three representative cases: subject 1, hyperlipidemia with high level of IDL-C; subject 2, hyperlipidemia with low IDL-C; and subject 3, normolipidemia with high Lp(a).

Figure 33–2 ✧ Comparison of Lipoprotein Cholesterol Concentrations by the HPLC Method with Those by Sequential Ultracentrifugation

CM-C plus VLDL-C, LDL-C, and HDL-C results obtained by the current automated HPLC system compared with the equivalent values from the sequential ultracentrifugation (UC) by least-squares linear regression analysis (top panels), and difference (HPLC results minus UC results) plotted as a function of serum Lp(a) concentrations (bottom panels).

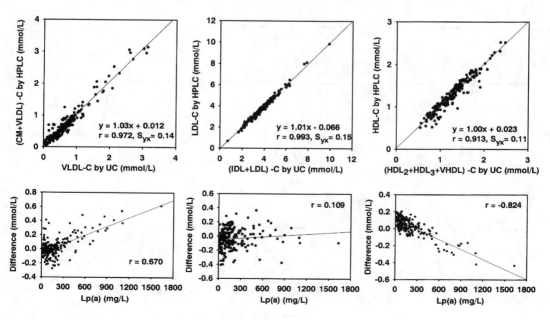

Figure 33–3 ✧ Cholesterol Profiles of Sera and their Fractions Separated by Sequential Ultracentrifugation

Subject 1, TC = 238 mg/dL (6.15 mmol/L), TG = 749 mg/dL (8.46 mmol/L), Lp(a) = 16 mg/L

Subject 2, TC = 303 mg/dL (7.84 mmol/L), TG = 439 mg/dL(4.96 mmol/L), Lp(a) = 200 mg/L

Subject 3, TC = 186 mg/dL(4.81 mmol/L), TG = 99 mg/dL (1.12mmol/L), Lp(a) = 1110 mg/L

Profiles are (a) whole serum; (b) VLDL fraction (d < 1.006 kg/L); (c) IDL fraction (d = 1.006–1.019 kg/L); (d) LDL fraction (d = 1.019–1.063 kg/L); (e) HDL$_2$ fraction (d = 1.063–1.125 Kg/L); and (f) HDL$_3$ fraction (d = 1.125–1.21 Kg/L), respectively. The elution position of LDL peak observed in each LDL fraction is presented in a vertical broken line.

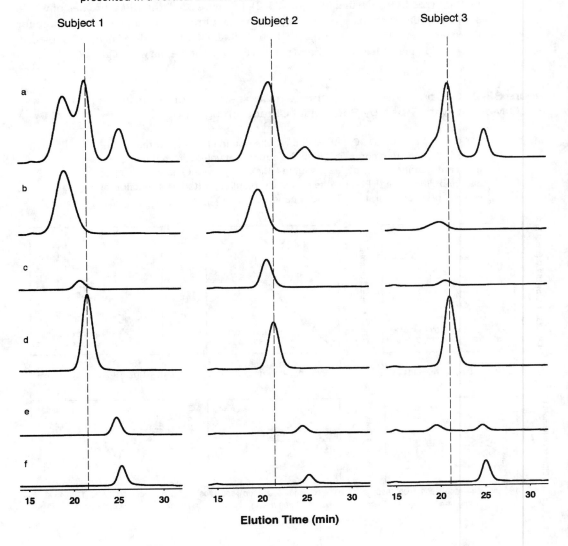

HDL-C values obtained by the HPLC method were compared with those obtained by several precipitation methods: phosphotungstate-$MgCl_2$, polyethylene glycol, and isoelectric point methods.[30,59,60] The values obtained by isoelectric point and phosphotungstate-$MgCl_2$ methods were markedly lower than those obtained by the HPLC method, while the polyethylene glycol method showed very good agreement with those of the HPLC method. The values of HDL-C (y) obtained by a direct (homogeneous) measurement method.[61] (Determiner HDL-C, Kyowa Medex) showed good correlation with those (x) obtained by the HPLC method (y = 1.016x-0.008 mmol/L, r = 0.998, n = 74).[62,63] The corresponding values (y') obtained by the phosphotungstate-$MgCl_2$ precipitation method were y' = 0.842x + 0.117 mmol/L, r = 0.987, n = 74.[63] Quantitative HPLC analysis of supernates obtained by precipitation methods revealed that the lower values of HDL-C obtained by the phosphotungstate-$MgCl_2$ method compared to those obtained by the HPLC method was because this particular commercial reagent precipitated part of HDL along with apolipoprotein-B-containing lipoproteins. This discrepancy could be minimized by using a modified reagent with lower $MgCl_2$ concentration.[63] In a comparison study with the CDC reference method, the results from the HPLC method were significantly higher (10.8% absolute mean bias) than those of the reference method, in spite of good correlation between the two methods (r = 0.998).[34]

In a method-comparison study with the LDL-C assay of Matsubara et al.[32,33] the HPLC method correlated highly with homogeneous and electrophoretic methods in usual clinical subjects but large discrepancies were observed in sera of subjects with severe lipid disorders.

SIMULTANEOUS PROFILING SYSTEM FOR LIPOPROTEIN CHOLESTEROL AND TRIGLYCERIDES

We have already developed a quantitative detection method of TG in lipoproteins and free-glycerol in serum.[64,65] Recently, we have developed a simultaneous profiling system for lipoprotein cholsterol and triglycerides, and serum-free glycerol.[35] Since the TSK eluent LP-1 is limited only to cholesterol quantification, we used the LP-2 eluent developed for cholesterol, TG, and phospholipids detection. The post-column effluent can be split into two lines, one line for cholesterol detection and the other for TG. A splitter, another detector, and pump for TG were added to the cholesterol-profiling system described above. In the simultaneous profiling system, injection volume of a sample was twice as much as in a cholesterol-profiling system. A reagent modified by Kyowa Medex was used to detect TG. Representative patterns obtained for transgenic mouse samples[66-68] are illustrated in Figure 33–4.

ANALYSES OF SUBCLASSES WITHIN MAJOR LIPOPROTEIN CLASSES

VLDL Subclasses

The degree of heterogeneity within each lipoprotein class has been examined by gel permeation chromatography. Sata et al.[4] examined the characterization of subfractions of TG-rich lipoproteins using 2% agarose chromatography. Williams and Kushwaha[69] demonstrated that CM and VLDL subclasses could be conveniently separated

Subjects: (a) wild type; (b) human CETP expressed; (c) LCAT knock-out; (d) apo E knock-out; (e) apo E knock-out + human apo E2 expressed; (f) apo E knock-out + human apo E3 expressed. Solid and broken lines show cholesterol and triglyceride profiles, respectively. Peaks at 35 min indicate free glycerol.

Sample: 200 µL of 10 times diluted plasma with eluent buffer.
Column: two connected TSKgel LipopropakXL.
Eluent: TSKeluent LP-2 (0.7 ml/min).
Reagents: Both TC and TG reagents are specially supplied from Kyowa Medex (0.35 ml/min)
Online reaction: Teflon tube (0.4 mm in diameter, 15 m in length) at 37°C.
Detection: 550 nm

The arrows show the peaks of hemoglobin in plasma samples. Vertical lines of one- and two-chain represent elution positions of LDL (25.3 nm) and HDL (11.3 nm) of a healthy human pooled serum, respectively.

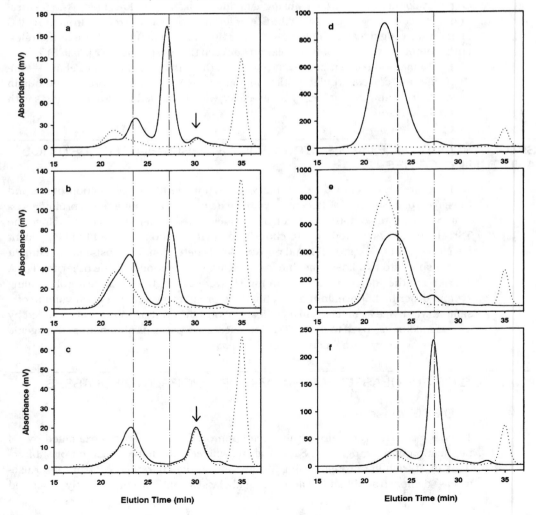

by HPLC using a GF-450 column (DuPont, USA) or a Fractgel 65-F column (Bodman Chemicals, USA). The size heterogeneity of the VLDL fraction isolated by ultracentrifugation was examined by Oida et al.[20] on HPLC with a TSKgel G5000PW column.

HDL Subclasses

Studies on HDL subclasses have been reported using a Superose 6 column in the FPLC system[38,70] as well as a TSKgel G3000SW column in an HPLC system.[18,71–73.] Okazaki et al.[71] reported that HDL in normal males and females consisted of five subclasses having the following particle diameters: 12.2 ± 0.28 nm, 11.0 ± 0.21 nm, 9.75 ± 0.18 nm, 8.67 ± 0.13 nm and 7.63 ± 0.16 nm. Characterization of HDL has been carried out in the new HPLC system[31] with four connected TSKgel LipopropakXL columns. The HDL peak was divided into seven Gaussian curves: HDL_{p1}, HDL_{p2}, HDL_{p3}, HDL_{p4}, HDL_{p5}, HDL_{p6}, and HDL_{p7} in order of particle size. The HDL_{p1} and HDL_{p2} subclasses were prominent in such subjects with high HDL-C such as those with CETP deficiency, but were negligible in normal subjects. The particle diameters of five subclasses, excluding HDL_{p1} and HDL_{p2}, were found to be identical to those of the previously reported five subclasses in the earlier HPLC system.[71] The correlations of cholesterol concentration in each subclass with the serum levels of apolipoprotein AI (apo A-I) or apo A-II showed a significant difference among subclasses.[74] Hence, the analysis of HDL subclasses by the HPLC method may be of clinical interest.

LDL and HDL Subclasses

Lipoprotein profiles obtained by the current HPLC system described above can provide information about subclasses of both LDL and HDL, simultaneously. An HPLC pattern was divided into Gaussian curves, as shown in Figure 33–5: a normal subject (a), liver cirrhosis (b), LPL deficiency (c), and CETP deficiency (d). Peak separation was performed as the following particle diameters: Peak 1, > 90 nm; peak 2, 75 nm; peak 3, 64 nm; peak 4, 53.6 nm; peak 5, 44.5 nm; peak 6, 36.8 nm; peak 7, 31.3 nm; peak 8, 28.0 nm; peak 9, 25.5 nm; peak 10, 23.0 nm; peak 11, 20.7 nm; peak 12, 18.6 nm; peak 13, 16.7 nm; peak 14, 15.0 nm; peak 15, 13.5 nm; peak 16, 12.1 nm; peak 17, 10.9 nm; peak 18, 9.8 nm; peak 19, 8.8 nm; peak 20, 7.6 nm.

Main components of the fractions isolated by sequential ultracentrifugation[51] were as follows: VLDL fraction, peak 5 (10%–30%) + peak 6 (45 %) + peak 7 (10%–25%); IDL fraction, peak 7 (40 %) + peak 8 (35%) + peak 9 (15%); LDL fraction, peak 8 (10%–30%) + peak 9 (35%–40%) + peak 10 (20%–35%) + peak 11 (5%–15%); HDL_2 fraction, peak 15 (5%–10%) + peak 16 (50%) + peak 17 (30%–40%); HDL_3 fraction, peak 17 (55%) + peak 18 (35%–40%). LDL-sized peaks within HDL_2 fraction were mainly peaks 10 and 11, which might be small-dense LDL. We defined each peak as follows: peaks 8, 9, 10, 11, 12 and 13 represent LDL_{p1}, LDL_{p2}, LDL_{p3}, LDL_{p4}, LDL_{p5} and LDL_{p6}, respectively. Peaks 14, 15, 16, 17, 18, 19 and 20 represent HDL_{p1}, HDL_{p2}, HDL_{p3}, HDL_{p4}, HDL_{p5}, HDL_{p6} and HDL_{p7}, respectively. Definition of lipoprotein subclasses by the peak separation technique is shown in Table 33–3. This approach to analysis of LDL and HDL subclasses was successfully applied to various subjects including those with lipid disorders.

Figure 33–5 ✧ Lipoprotein Subclasses in Cholesterol Profile by the Current HPLC System

Subjects: (a) a healthy young female, TC = 131 mg/dL (3.39 mmol/L), TG = 39 mg/dL (0.44 mmol/L); (b) a patient with liver cirrhosis, TC = 81 mg/dL (2.09 mmol/L), TG = 52 mg/dL (0.59 mmol/L); (c) a patient with LPL deficiency, TC = 219 mg/dL (5.66 mmol/L), TG = 1420 mg/dL (16.01 mmol/L); (d) patient with CETP deficiency, TC = 356 mg/dL (9.20 mmol/L), TG = 137 mg/dL (1.55 mmol/L)

Each peak represents a subclass, which is described in the text and Table 33–3.

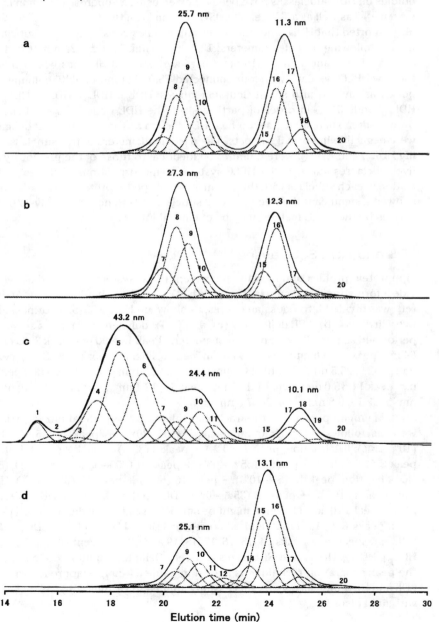

Table 33-3 ✧ Definition of Serum Lipoprotein Subclasses by HPLC Method

	Peak No	1	2	3	4	5	6	7	8	9	10	11	12	13	14	15	16	17	18	19	20
HPLC	Peak Name	Void							LDLp1	LDLp2	LDLp3	LDLp4	LDLp5	LDLp6	HDLp1	HDLp2	HDLp3	HDLp4	HDLp5	HDLp6	HDLp7
	Particle Diameter (nm)	>90	75	64	53.6	44.5	36.8	31.3	28.6	25.5	23	20.7	18.6	16.7	15	13.5	12.1	10.9	9.8	8.8	7.6
	Subclass Name		large VLDL			medium VLDL		small VLDL	large LDL	medium LDL	small LDL	very small LDL			very large HDL		large HDL	medium HDL	small HDL	very small HDL		
	Major Class	CM (>80 nm)			VLDL (30–80 nm)				LDL (16–30 nm)						HDL (8–16 nm)						
Sequential UC	d<1.006					10–30%	45%	10–25%													
	d:1.006–1.019							40%	35%	25%											
	d:1.019–1.063								10–30%	35–40%	20–35%	5–15%									
	d:1.063–1.125					+	++ Lp(a)	+			+	++ dense LDL	+			5–10%	50%	30–40%			
	d:1.125–1.21																	55%	35–40%		

Note: Two columns (TSKgel LipopropakXL) were used with eluent (TSKeluent LP-1 or LP-2) at a flow rate of 0.7 mL/min

Figure 33–6 ✧ The Effects of Lipid-Lowering Agents on Cholesterol Levels in LDL and HDL Subclasses by the HPLC Method

Subjects (n = 27) with diabetes mellitus were treated with bezafibrate (open square) and pravastatin (closed square) in a randomized cross-over design. The definition of LDL subclasses (left panel) and HDL subclasses (right panel) is in the text and Table 33–3.

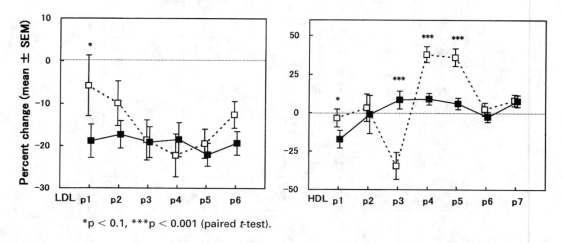

*p < 0.1, ***p < 0.001 (paired *t*-test).

We used this technique to examine the effects of two lipid lowering agents, bezafibrate and pravastatin, on lipoprotein profiles in a randomized cross-over design.[75] As presented in Figure 33–6, the percentage of change in cholesterol levels in LDL and HDL subclasses was markedly different between the two agents.

The HPLC method is more useful for analyzing LDL and HDL subclasses than non-denaturing gradient gel electrophoresis and density gradient ultracentrifugation,[76,77] because it provides quantitative and qualitative information about LDL and HDL subclasses simultaneously.

FURTHER APPLICATION OF HPLC IN LIPOPROTEIN STUDIES

Because of the high sensitivity of lipoprotein detection, the new HPLC method could be successfully applied to analyze lipoproteins of low concentration, such as unbound lipoproteins in supernates of mixtures of serum and immunoaffinity gel of antibodies to apolipoproteins,[78–82,] lipoproteins in cerebrospinal fluid,[83] and secreted lipoproteins in supernates of culture media of HepG$_2$ cells or hepatocytes of the WHHL rabbit.[84] Typical examples with cholesterol concentration ranging from 0.30 to 0.32 mg/dL (0.0078 to 0.0083 mmol/L) are shown in Figure 33–7, which illustrates remnant-like particles (RLP)[85–87] and lipoproteins in supernates of culture medium. These patterns clearly reveal that the major components of the RLP fraction from Type III dyslipidemia with apo E$_{2/2}$ are lipoproteins of intermediate size between VLDL and

Figure 33–7 ✧ HPLC Patterns Obtained from Samples with Very Low Cholesterol Concentration

Non-concentrated sample of 250 μ l for (a) unbound fraction to immunoaffinity gels (monoclonal antibodies anti-human apo B-100 and apo A-I, RLP immunoseparation reagent, JIMRO, Japan) of serum from a subject with Type III dyslipidemia with apo $E_{2/2}$; (b) and (c) supernates of conditioned medium for rat hepatocytes and HepG$_2$ cells were applied to four connected columns (TSKgel LipopropakXL, TOSOH), and eluted at a flow rate of 0.60 ml/min using TSKeluent LP-2. Cholesterol in the effluent from the column was monitored under the same conditions as the current HPLC system. The detection range of cholesterol (absorbance at 550 nm) is 6 mV (0.006 O.D.) in full scale. The arrows show the average elution positions of VLDL, LDL, and HDL for human subjects.

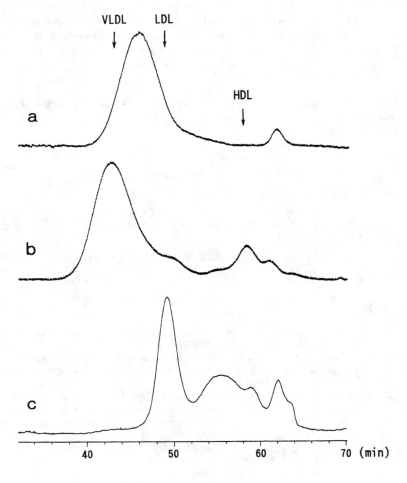

LDL, and that HepG$_2$ cells secrete both LDL and larger sized HDL, while rat hepatocytes secrete mainly VLDL. The HPLC technique provides quantitative lipoprotein cholesterol profiles for samples with cholesterol concentration as low as 1/1000 of normal plasma.

Lipoprotein profiles of various species other than humans were reported by many investigators using the Superose 6 column[36,40–42,88] and the TSKgel column series.[17,19,66–9,89–96]Lipoprotein profiles of experimental animals obtained by the simultaneous detection technique of cholesterol and TG (Figure 33–4) will be useful for studies on lipoprotein metabolism.

SUMMARY

Application of gel permeation chromatography in combination with appropriate analytical reagents can greatly facilitate studies on serum lipoprotein classes. The use of HPLC and FPLC can provide quantitative, qualitative, and diagnostic information on diseases with underlying lipoprotein abnormalities. Unlike conventional methods, the HPLC method can be used for the analysis of samples available in very small volumes or containing very low levels of lipoproteins.   ✧

Acknowledgments: The authors wish to thank Dr. A. R. Saniabadi for editing the text and Drs. M. Nakamura, K. Nakajima, Y. Matsuzawa, S. Yamashita, H. Kamido, H. Tomoike, and H. Kazama for useful discussion.

APPENDIX

The elution buffer of TSK eluent LP-2 has not been commercially available since 1998. The published components of the eluent are as follows:

50 mmol/L Tris-Acetate buffer (pH 8.0) containing 0.3 mmol/L sodium acetate and 0.005% Brij 35.

Cholesterol profiling according to our HPLC method is actually conducted in major clinical research center(s) in Japan.

REFERENCES

1. Miller GJ, Miller NE. Plasma high-density lipoprotein concentration and development of ischemic heart disease. Lancet 1975;1:16–19.
2. Friedewald WT, Levy RI, Fredrickson DS. Estimation of the concentration of low-density lipoprotein cholesterol in plasma, without use of the preparative ultracentrifuge. Clin Chem 1972;18:499–502.
3. Naito HK, Ward KM, Schmitz G, Mollers C, Bottcher A, Ploch J, Myers G. New approaches to the use of lipoprotein electrophoresis in the clinical laboratory. In: Rifai N, Warnick GR, Domimiczak MH (eds.). Handbook of lipoprotein testing. Washington DC: American Association for Clinical Chemistry Press, 1997:447–95.
4. Sata T, Havel RJ, Jonas AL. Characterization of subfractions of triglyceride-rich lipoproteins separated by gel chromatography from blood plasma of normolipidemic and hyperlipidemic humans. J Lipid Res 1972;13:757–68.
5. Rudel LL, Marzetta CC, Johnson FL. Separation and analysis of lipoproteins by gel filtration. Methods Enzymol 1986;129:45–57.

6. Hara I, Okazaki M, Ohno Y. Rapid analysis of cholesterol of high-density lipoprotein and low-density lipoprotein in human serum by high-performance liquid chromatography, J Biochem 1980;87:1863–5.

7. Okazaki M, Ohno Y, Hara I. Rapid method for the quantitation of cholesterol in human serum lipoproteins by high performance liquid chromatography, J Biochem 1981; 89:879–87.

8. Okazaki M, Itakura H, Shiraishi K, Hara I. Serum lipoprotein measurement—liquid chromatography and sequential floatation (ultracentrifugation) compared. Clin Chem 1983; 29:768–73.

9. Okazaki M, Hagiwara N, Hara I. High-performance liquid chromatography of human serum lipoproteins: selective detection of choline-containing phospholipids by enzymatic reaction. J Chromatogr 1982;231:13–23.

10. Hara I, Shiraishi K, Okazaki M. High-performance liquid chromatography of human serum lipoproteins: selective detection of triglycerides by enzymatic reaction. J Chromatogr 1982;239:549–57.

11. Okazaki M, Hara I. Lipoprotein separations by high-performance gel permeation chromatography. In: Hancock WS (ed.). CRC handbook of HPLC for the separation of amino acids, peptides, and proteins. Boca Raton FL: CRC Press, 1984:393–403.

12. Hara I, Okazaki M. High-performance liquid chromatography of serum lipoproteins. Methods Enzymol 1986;129:57–78.

13. Okazaki M, Muramatsu T, Makino K, Hara I. High-performance liquid chromatography of serum lipoproteins. In: Mukherjee KD, Weber N (eds.). CRC handbook of chromatography: analysis of lipids. Boca Raton, FL: CRC Press, 1993:101–14.

14. Carroll RM, Rudel LL. Lipoprotein separation and low-density lipoprotein molecular weight determination using high-performance gel filtration chromatography. J Lipid Res 1983;24:200–7.

15. Williams MC, Kelley JL, Kushwaha RS. Detection of an abnormal lipoprotein in a large colony of pedigreed baboons using high-performance gel exclusion chromatography. J Chromatogr 1984;308:101–9.

16. Busbee DL, Payne DM, Jasheway DW, Carlisle S, Lacko AG. Separation and detection of lipoproteins in human serum by use of size-exclusion liquid chromatography: a preliminary report, Clin Chem 1981;27:2052–8.

17. Williams MC, Stenoien CG, Kushwaha RS. Rapid method or measuring plasma low-density lipoprotein turnover using high-performance gel exclusion chromatography. J Chromatogr 1986;375:233–43.

18. Holmquist L, Carlson LA. Subfractionation and characterization of native and incubation enlarged human plasma high-density lipoprotein particles by high-performance gel filtration. Lipids 1985;20:378–88.

19. Williams MC, Kushwaha RS, McGill HC. Quantitation of baboon lipoproteins by high performance gel exclusion chromatography. Lipids 1987;22:366–74.

20. Oida K, Nakai T, Miyabo S, Krul ES, Schonfeld G. Detection of size heterogeneity of very-low-density lipoproteins by high-performance liquid chromatography, J Jpn Atheroscler Soc 1987;15:889–95.

21. Kodama T, Akanuma Y, Okazaki M, Aburatani H, Itakura H, Takahashi K et al. Abnormalities in plasma lipoprotein in familial partial lecithin:cholesterol acyltransferase deficiency. Biochim Biophys Acta 1983;752:407–15.

22. Takizawa A, Komoda T, Hokari S, Sakagishi Y, Tanaka A, Hara I. Evaluation of the particle size distribution of plasma lipoprotein in a patient with Tangier disease by high-performance liquid chromatography. Clin Chim Acta 1990;193:85–8.

23. Yamashita S, Matsuzawa Y, Okazaki M, Kako H, Yasugi T, Akioka H et al. Small polydisperse low-density lipoproteins in familial hyperalphalipoproteinemia with complete deficiency of cholesterol ester transfer activity. Atherosclerosis 1988;70:7–12.

24. Yamamoto A, Matsuzawa Y, Yokoyama S, Funahashi T, Yamamura T, Kishino B. Effects of probucol on xanthomata regression in familial hypercholesterolemia. Am J Cardiol 1986;57:29H–35H.

25. Matsuzawa Y, Yamashita S, Funahashi T, Yamamoto A, Tarui S. Selective reduction of cholesterol in HDL$_2$ fraction by probucol in familial hypercholesterolemia and hyper-HDL$_2$ cholesterolemia with abnormal cholesterol ester transfer. Am J Cardiol 1988;62: 66B–72B.

26. Okazaki M, Hara I, Tanaka A, Kodama T, Yokoyama S. Decreased serum HDL$_3$ cholesterol levels in cirrhosis of the liver. N Engl J Med 1981;304:1608.

27. Teramoto T, Kato H, Hashimoto Y, Kinoshita M, Toda G, Oka H. Abnormal high-density lipoprotein of primary biliary cirrhosis analyzed by high-performance liquid chromatography. Clin Chim Acta 1985;149:135–48.

28. Kitamura T, Ito S, Kato Y, Sasamoto K, Okazaki M. Analysis of serum lipoproteins by high-performance gel filtration chromatography. J Jpn Anal Chem 1996;41:103–6.

29. Kitamura T, Ito S, Moriyama H, Kato Y, Sasamoto K, Okazaki M. Quantitative analysis of serum lipoproteins (CM, VLDL, LDL and HDL) by high-performance gel filtration chromatography. Chromatography 1996;17:33–7.

30. Sasamoto K, Okazaki M, Muramatsu T, Yanagisawa T, Ando Y, Kamei et al. Quantitation of total cholesterol and HDL cholesterol by the HPLC method: comparison with the automated enzymatic method and the precipitation method. Jpn J Clin Chem 1996; 25:28–34.

31. Okazaki M. Clinical application of HPLC for lipoprotein analysis. J Med Technol 1996; 40:1281–92.

32. Matsubara A, Usui S, Kambe M, Okazaki M. Discrepancy of high-density lipoprotein cholesterol (HDL-C) and low-density lipoprotein cholesterol (LDL-C) values by HPLC, homogeneous and electrophoretic methods. Jpn J Clin Lab Auto 2000;25(in press). 1999;24:431 (abstract).

33. Matsubara A, Kodama K, Sugimoto K, Kambe M. Usefulness of HPLC method in measurement of serum lipoprotein cholesterol. Jpn J Med Tchnol 1997;466:1005–9.

34. Usui S, Nakamura M, Jitsukata K, Nara M, Hosaki S, Okazaki M. Assessment of between-instrument variations in a HPLC method for serum lipoproteins and its traceability to reference methods for total cholesterol and HDL-cholesterol. Clin Chem 1999; 46:63–72.

35. Usui S, Jitsukata K, Kazama H, Mizukami Y, Hosaki S, Okazaki M. Simultaneous analysis of serum lipoprotein cholesterol and triglycerides by a HPLC method. Submitted to 52nd Annnual Meeting of AACC, in San Francisco, 2000 (July 23–27).

36. Kieft KA, Bocan TMA, Krause BR. Rapid online determination of cholesterol distribution among plasma lipoproteins after high-performance gel filtration chromatography. J Lipid Res 1991;32:859–66.

37. März W, Siekmeier R, Scharnagl H, Seiffert UB, Gross W. Fast lipoprotein chromatography: new method of analysis for plasma lipoproteins. Clin Chem 1993;39:2276–81.

38. Clifton PM, MacKinnon AM, Barter PJ. Separation and characterization of high-density lipoprotein subpopulations by gel permeation chromatography. J Chromatogr 1987; 414:25–34.

39. Van Gent T, van Tol A. Automated gel permeation chromatography of plasma lipoproteins by preparative fast-protein liquid chromatography. J Chromatogr 1990;525: 433–41.

40. Maagdenberg AMJM, Hofker MH, Krimpenfort PJA, Bruijn IG, Vlijmen B, Boom H et al. Transgenic mice carrying the apolipoprotein E3-Leiden gene exhibit hyperlipoproteinemia. J Biol Chem 1993;268:10540–5.

41. Ha YC, Barter PJ. Rapid separation of plasma lipoproteins by gel permeation chromatography on agarose gel Superose 6B. J Chromatogr 1985;341:154–9.

42. Jiao S, Cole TG, Kitchens RT, Pfleger B, Schonfeld G. Genetic heterogeneity of lipoproteins in inbred strain of mice: analysis by gel-permeation chromatography. Metabolism 1990;39:155–60.

43. Lagorist L, Gambert P, Meuneier S, Morgado P, Desgres J, d'Athis P et al. Correlation between apolipoprotein A-IV and triglyceride concentrations in human sera. J Lipid Res 1989;30:701–10.

44. Cost B, Harvekes LM. Analysis of plasma lipoproteins by fast-protein liquid chromatography, In: Rifai N, Warnick GR (eds.). Laboratory measurement of lipids, lipoproteins, and apolipoproteins. Washington, DC: American Association for Clinical Chemistry Press, 1994:333–4.

45. Nyyssönen K, Salonen JT. Comparison of gel permeation chromatography, density gradient ultracentrifugation, and precipitation methods for quantitation of very-low-, low- and high-density lipoprotein cholesterol. J Chromatogr 1991;570:382–9.

46. Gerdes LU, Gerdes C, Klausen IC, Faergeman O. Generation of analytical plasma lipoprotein profiles using two prepacked Superose 6B columns. Clin Chim Acta 1992;205: 1–9.

47. Krause BR, Schork NJ, Kieft KA, Smith MP, Maciejko JJ. High correlation but lack of agreement between direct high-performance gel chromatography analysis and conventional indirect methods for determining lipoprotein cholesterol. Clin Chem 1996; 42:(12)1996–2001.

48. Scheffer PG, Bakker SJL, Heine RJ, Teerlink T, Measurement of low-density lipoprotein particle size by high-performance gel-filtration chromatography. Clin Chem 1997; 43:1904–12.

49. Scheffer PG. Bakker SJL. Heine RJ.Teerlink T. Measurement of LDL particle size in whole plasma and serum by high-performance gel-filtration chromatography using a fluorescent lipid probe. Clin Chem 1998;10:2148–51.

50. Rudel LL, Pitts LL. Male-female variability in the dietary cholesterol-induced hyperlipoproteinemia of cynomolgus monkey (Macaca fascicularis). J Lipid Res 1978;19: 992–1003.

51. Havel RJ, Eder HA, Bragden JH. The distribution and chemical composition of ultracentrifugally separated lipoproteins in human plasma. J Clin Invest 1955;34:1345–53.

52. Okazaki M, Sasamoto K, Muramatsu T, Hosaki S. Analysis of plasma lipoproteins by gel permeation chromatography. In: Rifai N, Warnick GR, Dominiczak MH (eds.). Handbook of lipoprotein testing. Washington, DC: American Association of Clinical Chemistry Press, 1997:531–48.

53. Fredrickson DS, Lees RS. A system for phenotyping hyperlipoproteinemia. Circulation 1965;31:321–7.

54. Matuszawa Y, Sho N, Kameda K, Kubo M, Hirobe K, Tarui S, et al. Characterization of lipoprotein abnormalities in type III hyperlipoproteinemia associated with apo E3 deficiency (E2/2 phenotype). J Jpn Atheroscler Soc 1984;11:1243–8.

55. Okazaki M. Analysis of dislipoproteinemia by HPLC method. J Anal Bio-Sci 1997; 20:1100–10.

56. Kazama H, Okazaki M, Araki A, Inoue J, Horiuchi T, Nakamura T, Itoh H. Examination of lipoprotein disorder in diabetes mellitus by HPLC method. J Jpn Atheroscler Soc 1998;25(sup):133(abstract).

57. Kazama H, Okazaki M, Araki A, Inoue J, Horiuchi T, Hosoi T, Itoh H. Gender difference of risk factor for macroangiopathy in elderly diabetic patients: lipoprotein profiles by HPLC method. J Jpn Atheroscler Soc 1999;26(sup):151(abstract).

58. Okazaki M, Kitamura T, Ito S, Umino M, Yamashita S, Matsuzawa Y. Comparison of quantitation of cholesterol in major serum lipoprotein classes between HPLC method and sequential ultracentrifugation method. Jpn J Clin Chem 1997;26(sup3):89c(abstract).

59. Okazaki M, Sasamoto K, Muramatsu T, Jitsukata K, Horiuchi K, Kubono K. Quantitation of HDL-cholesterol by the improved HPLC method: comparison with ultracentrifugation, precipitation, and direct methods. Jpn J Clin Chem 1995;24:245–52.

60. Sasamoto K, Okazaki M, Muramatsu T, Kawamura K, Kimura N, Kurihara-A Y et al. HPL-C analysis of HDL-cholesterol by precipitation method: comparison between different precipitation reagents. Jpn J Clin Chem 1996;25:234–42.

61. Sugiuchi H, Uji Y, Okabe H, Irie T, Uekama K, Kayahara N et al. Direct measurement of high-density lipoprotein cholesterol in serum with polyethylene glycol-modified enzymes and sulfated α-cyclodextrin. Clin Chem 1995;41:717–23.

62. Okazaki M, Sasamoto K, Mashige H. Evaluation of direct methods for HDL-cholesterol measurements by HPLC method. J Anal Bio-Sci 1996;19:389–97.

63. Okazaki M, Sasamoto K, Muramatsu T, Hosaki S. Evaluation of the precipitation and direct methods for HDL-cholesterol assay by HPLC. Clin Chem, 1997;43:1885–90.

64. Okazaki M, Komoriya N, Tomoike H, Inoue N, Usui S, Itoh S, Hosaki S. Quantitative detection method of triglycerides in serum lipoproteins and serum free glycerol by high-performance liquid chromatography. J Chromatogr B 1998;709:179–87.

65. Okazaki M, Usui S, Toriumi A, Nara M, Hosaki S, Saniabadi A, Nakano T, Nakajima K. Triglyceride contents of major lipoprotein classes by HPLC and remnant-like lipoprotein particles triglyceride by immunoaffinity method. Clin Chem 1999;45(S6):A14.

66. Tsujita M, Tomimoto S, Usui S, Komoriya N, Nara M, Okazaki M, Yokoyama S. Effect of Probucol on HDL generation and clearance in mice: *in vivo* study. Proc J C B L (Proceedings of Japanese Conference on the Biochemistry of Lipids) 1998;40:73–76.

67. Tsujita M, Tomimoto S, Okumuya-Noji K, Okazaki M, Yokoyama S. Apolipoprotein-mediated cellular cholesterol/phospholipid efflux and plasma high density lipoprotein level in mice. Biochim. Biophys. Acta, 2000;1485:199–213.

68. Ishigaki Y, Oikawa S, Tokita K, Karita A, Hara Y, Sekikawa A, Hoshi K et al. Apolipoprotein E-sendai and lipoprotein glomerulopathy: a large-scale production and its characterization. J Jpn Atheroscler Soc 1999;26(sup):108.

69. Williams MC, Kushwaha RS. Fractionation of baboon chylomicrons and very-low-density lipoproteins by high-performance liquid chromatography. J Chromatogr 1988;433:257–63.

70. Clifton PM, Barter PJ, Mackinnon AM. High-density lipoprotein particle size distribution in subjects with obstructive jaundice. J Lipid Res 1988;29:121–35.

71. Okazaki M, Hagiwara N, Hara I. Heterogeneity of human serum high-density lipoproteins on high-performance liquid chromatography. J Biochem 1982;92:517–24.

72. Kurasawa T, Yokoyama S, Miyake Y, Yamamura T, Yamamoto A. Rate of cholesterol ester transfer between high- and low-density lipoproteins in human serum and a case with decreased transfer rate in association with hyperalphalipoproteinemia. J Biochem 1985;98:1499–508.

73. Ide H, Tsuji M, Shimada M, Kondo T, Fujiya S, Akanuma Y et al. An evaluation of serum high-density lipoprotein phospholipids. Tohoku J Exp Med 1988;155:261–70.

74. Okazaki M, Nara M, Isii R, Fujii Y, Usui S, Hosaki S, Komoriya N et al. Analysis of LDL and HDL subclasses by Gaussian summation method on HPL-C profiles and its clinical significance. J Jpn Atheroscler Soc 1998;25(sup):132(abstract).

75. Okazaki M, Usui S, Kazama H, Araki A, Ito H. Analyses of LDL and HDL subclasses by a HPLC method: The effects of lipid-lowering agents on lipoprotein cholesterol profile. Submitted to 52nd AACC Annual Meeting in San Francisco, 2000 (July 23–27).

76. Austin MA, Hokanson JE, Brunzell JD. Measurement and clinical significance of low-density-lipoprotein subclasses. In: Rifai N, Warnick GR (eds.). Laboratory measurement of lipids, lipoproteins, and apolipoproteins. Washington DC: American Association for Clinical Chemistry Press, 1994:223–34.

77. Warnick GR. Measurement and clinical significance of high-density lipoprotein subclasses. In: Rifai N, Warnick GR (eds.). Laboratory measurement of lipids, lipoproteins, and apolipoproteins. Washington, DC: American Association for Clinical Chemistry Press, 1994:207–22.

78. Okazaki M, Sasamoto K, Muramatsu T, Hosaki S. Binding capacities of immunoassay reagents for remnant-like particles to LDL and HDL by the improved HPLC method. Jpn J Clin Chem 1994;23:236–42.

79. Okazaki M, Sasamoto K, Muramatsu T, Hosaki S, Fukuda Y, Nakano T, Nakajima K. Analysis of lipoprotein components in remnant-like particle (RLP) fraction by an improved HPLC method. Clin Chem 1996;42:S295.

80. Okazaki M, Sasamoto K, Muramatsu T, Nozaki S, Yamashita S, Takemura K et al. The lipoprotein analysis of RLP (remnant-like particle) by an improved HPLC method. I: Abnormally high RLP cholesterol levels. J Jpn Atheroscler Soc 1995;22:939–46.

81. Kugiyama K, Doi H, Motoyama T, Soejima H, Misumino K,Kawano H, Nakagawa O et al. Association of remnant lipoprotein levels with impairment of endothelium-dependent vasmotor function in human coronary arteries. Circulation 1998;97:2519–26.

82. Okazaki M, Usui S, Tada N, Nakano T, Nakajima K. Relation between RLP-triglyceride to RLP-cholesterol ratio and particle size distribution in RLP-cholesterol profiles by HPLC. Clin Chim Acta 2000;296:135–149.

83. Miida T, Yamazaki F, Sakurai M, Wada R, Yamadera T, Asami K, Hoshiyama M et al. The apolipoprotein E content in cerebrospinal fluid is higher in children than adults. Clin Chem 1999;45:1294–6.

84. Tanaka M, Otani H, Yokode M, Kita T. Regulation of apolipoprotein B secretion in hepatocytes from Watanabe heritable hyperlipidemic rabbit, an animal model for familial hypercholesterolemia. Atherosclerosis 1995;114:73–82.

85. Nakajima K, Okazaki M, Tanaka A, Pullinger CR, Wang T, Nakano T, Adachi M, Havel RJ. Separation and determination of remnant-like particles in human serum using momoclonal antibodies to apo B-100 and apo A-I. J Clin Ligand Assay 1996;19:177–83.

86. Nakajima K, Saito T, Tamura A, Suzuki M, Nakano T, Adachi M et al. Cholesterol in remnant-like lipoproteins in human serum using monoclonal anti-apo B-100 and anti-apo A-I immunoaffinity mixed gel. Clin Chim Acta 1993;223:53–71.

87. Nakajima K, Saito T, Tamura A, Suzuki M, Nakano T, Adachi M et al. A new approach for the detection of type III hyperlipoproteinemia by RLP-cholesterol assay. J Atheroscler Thromb 1994;1:30–6.

88. Shimano H, Yamada N, Katsuki M, Shimada M, Gotoda T, Harada K et al. Overexpression of apolipoprotein E in transgenic mice: marked reduction in plasma lipoproteins except high-density lipoprotein and resistance against diet-induced hypercholesterolemia. Proc Natl Acad Sci USA 1992:89:1750–54.

89. Okazaki M, Ohno Y, Hara I. High-performance aqueous gel permeation chromatography of human serum lipoproteins. J Chromatogr 1980;221:257–64.

90. Tanaka K, Inoue S, Ohkawa S, Asami M, Takamura Y, Murase T et al. Abnormalities of rat serum lipoproteins after partial hepatectomy. J Jpn Atheroscler 1985;13:499–506.

91. Hirai K, Ohno Y, Nakano T, Izutani K. Effects of dietary fats and phytosterol on serum fatty acid composition and lipoprotein cholesterol in rats. J Nutr Sci Vitaminol 1984; 30:101–12.

92. Iijima N, Kayama M, Okazaki M, Hara I. Time course change of lipid distribution in carp plasma lipoprotein after force-feeding with soybean oil. Bull Jpn Soc Sci Fisheries 1985;51:467–71.

93. Iijima N, Aihara M, Kayama M, Okazaki M, Hara I. Composition of carp plasma lipoproteins under starved and fed conditions. Bull Jpn Soc Sci Fisheries 1989;55:2001–7.

94. Yagyu H, Ishibashi S, Chen Z, Osuga J, Okazaki M, Perrcy S et al. Overexpressed lipoprotein lipase protects against atherosclerosis in apolipoprotein E knock-out mice. J Lipid Res 1999:40:1677–85.

95. Zhang C, Ito T, Tsuchida E, Otsu N, Yamaki M, Tomoike H. Heritable hypertriglyceridemia is associated with enhanced coronary stenosis, insulin resistance, and augmented CETP activity in WHHL rabbits. Circulation 1998;98 (Supp I):I-400.

96. Komoriya N, Zhang C Itoh T, Tomoike H. Lipoprotein profile of hypertriglyceridemic WHHL rabbits by HPLC method. J Jpn Atheroscler Soc 1997;25(sup):146(abstract).

Consideration of the Clinical Utility of Tests of Three Well-Known Genes: APOE, APOB, and LDLR

Ian N.M. Day, Steve E. Humphries, and Philip R. Wenham

✧   Over 100 years separated two events: the observation that xanthomata and coronary heart disease could be heritable,[1] and the ability to isolate the gene involved.[2] Genetic variation, some characterized, most as yet uncharacterized, underpins many of the more severe dyslipidemias, and in addition underpins polygenic variation important to setting plasma lipid concentrations in the general population. Characterizing the structure of and variation in apolipoprotein genes and other genes involved in lipid metabolism has proven valuable in our understanding of lipoprotein metabolism and has led to the development of new therapeutic approaches, such as powerful cholesterol-lowering drugs. Much research is yet to be undertaken in this field. However, except for centers with specialist research interests, gene tests are little used in lipidology.

This chapter examines potential applications where such tests could satisfy the criteria of altering disease management in some way. Such tests depend on the satisfaction of a range of performance criteria—accuracy, reproducibility, robustness, sensitivity, specificity, cost, influence—sufficient to merit their use.[3] Examples are considered with reference to these criteria.

BACKGROUND

Influence of Assays on Disease Management

Laboratory assays are traditionally categorized as having four potential influences on disease management:

1.   *Diagnosis,* e.g., amylase levels in establishing that pancreatitis is the cause of a patient's abdominal pain.

2.   *Prognosis,* e.g., low paracetamol level post-overdose indicates that conservative management will lead to spontaneous recovery.

3.   *Monitoring,* e.g., serial measure of tumor markers to assess tumor change or response to chemotherapy.

4.   *Screening,* e.g., neonatal bloodspot to identify neonates with phenylketonuria, who need a special diet to prevent mental retardation.

A fifth category, *counseling*, is particularly relevant where genetic status is concerned and should be added.

Today, the most obvious potential for the clinical use of genetic tests would be in categories 1, 2, 4, and 5. Category 3, monitoring, does not apply because we are concerned with germ line rather than somatic cell variation.

Criteria for Evaluating New Laboratory Tests

In a system of unlimited resources, any analysis that could add to a clinical evaluation in any way would be justifiable. However, because limited resources are available for health care, some system of priority and equity must evolve. Clearly, an analysis that would alter management of an important clinical condition would take priority. Frequently, most of the resources expended in clinical management pay for drugs and for clinical staff time, so the impact of a test on these aspects rather than the cost of the test itself will be the more important criterion. Therefore, certain parameters emerge as more important than others in evaluating potential laboratory tests.

Accuracy and precision are important criteria for quantitative tests. For gene tests, classification is usually qualitative rather than quantitative. However, in contrast to the typical biochemical assay used for monitoring, gene tests are not usually repeated. They may be the determinant of lifelong decisions, concerns, behavior, and lifestyle; of reproductive decisions; and of substantial counseling that may involve a whole family.

Gene tests can be problematic in many ways:

1. Laboratory techniques are susceptible to inaccuracy. Suitable reference materials and quality controls must be used.

2. Unexpected genetic variation can confound a test, e.g., a second site of variation never previously observed can give a misleading outcome that is dependent on the design of the test.

3. *De novo* mutation scanning will lead to the identification of possible gene defects never previously observed. Testing for known gene defects generally presupposes that the natural history is known, but where complex spectra of mutations occur (true for most genes), previously unknown mutations must be identified. Sometimes interpretation is clear-cut, as in the case of a premature stop codon in a haploinsufficiency disorder, such as in the low-density-lipoprotein receptor (LDLR) gene in familial hypercholesterolemia (FH); but the effect of an amino acid variation may be more difficult to predict because the natural history of that variation is unknown—it might be silent, mild, or severe—and functional tests (cellular, etc.) are usually not readily available.

Such considerations bear on the use of a gene test for diagnosis, differential diagnosis, prognosis, and counseling. Screening adds a further layer of complexity. In contrast with diagnosis and prognosis, where the patient has presented to the clinical system, screening seeks to take at-risk groups, often large numbers of individuals, and to identify a few who are at higher risk. The implications of "making patients of individuals" and of the mechanisms and politics of dealing with wide catchments of the population are substantial; in addition, there is substantial potential for a screening program to fail. The criteria of Wilson and Jungner[4] should be observed:

1. The test should be capable of identifying presymptomatic risk.

2. The test should be feasible and affordable.

3. Treatment and management should be possible.

4. Management should be affordable.

Beyond accuracy and diagnostic applicability, two important parameters for evaluating test performance are sensitivity and specificity. An insensitive test—one that failed to find most or all at-risk individuals—would not be effective; it would be inefficient, provide false reassurance, and lead to "unexpected" disease. A non-specific test would also be problematic: false positives would cause unnecessary alarm and, where there are many, an overload of follow-up tests.

Simple, cheap, high-throughput tests must be implemented. Clinical laboratories must evaluate tests in relation to equipment needed, staffing skills, turnover and turn-around time, and in relation to alternative tests that answer the same question.

In this chapter, three genes, each much vaunted in the literature for its diagnostic applicability, are explained and considered in the context of the parameters discussed above. Rather than representing a comprehensive catalog of possibilities, these tests have been chosen to illustrate the relationship between molecular genetics and the reference lipid laboratory. The basic techniques are straightforward and are not generally difficult to establish. However, any deviation from a described protocol or test can be difficult to troubleshoot for laboratorians new to analytical molecular genetics. In particular, polymerase chain reaction (PCR)[5,6] is biochemically reproducible (with the caveat that the manufacturer's DNA polymerase remains unaltered), but the thermal cycling conditions are much less reproducible due to differences in the performance (ramp times, overshoots, thermal accuracy, and precision and spatial homogeneity across the PCR block) among thermal cycler models. In consequence, PCR tends to be defined as "people's choice reaction" on a good day, but as "pretty confusing result" on a bad day. Since most post-PCR analytical procedures hinge on the yield, quality, and purity of the initial PCR, "perfect PCR" should be an important objective. PCR-based analysis of the APOE, APOB, and LDLR genes is considered below.

THE APOE GENE

Type III Hyperlipidemia, Vascular Disease, and Apolipoprotein E Defects

Type III hyperlipidemia is characterized by lipoprotein particles with properties intermediate between those of very-low-density lipoprotein (VLDL) and low-density lipoprotein (LDL). On electrophoresis, these particles appear as a broad beta band between the LDL (beta) and VLDL (pre-beta) bands. On ultracentrifugation, these particles float with the VLDL fraction ("beta-migrating VLDL"). More precise definition hinges on the measurement of cholesterol and triglyceride content of the VLDL fraction.

The intermediate nature of this lipoprotein fraction reflects its pathological origin as "remnant" particles representing partially delipidated VLDL and chylomicrons. These particles are unusually rich in apolipoprotein (apo) E, but although apo E is the usual ligand for specific receptor-mediated clearance, the apo E of patients with Type III hyperlipidemia is unable to mediate lipoprotein clearance.

The genetic basis of Type III hyperlipidemia remained obscure until apo E phenotyping by isoelectric focusing was initiated[7] and it was shown that there were several patterns marking different alleles, termed initially II, III and IV.[8] The pattern representing homozygosity for allele IV was present in Type III patients, who characteristically display palmar xanthomata and an increased incidence of early coronary and peripheral arterial disease.

The identification of the amino-acid sequence of apo E[9] and demonstration that alleles E_2, E_3, and E_4 contained at positions 112 and 158—respectively, cysteine/cysteine, cysteine/arginine and arginine/arginine—were consistent with the results of isoelectric focusing. It was further shown that most Type III patients have the E_2/E_2 phenotype. The absence of arginine at these positions appears to cause poor receptor binding and delayed clearance from the circulation, and in support of this model, chemical conversion of the cysteines to a positively charged derivative confers upon apo E_2 good receptor binding.[10] However, the E_2/E_2 phenotype occurs in an estimated 1% of the population, whereas only a small percentage (fewer than 5%) of E_2/E_2 individuals display Type III hyperlipidemia. The dyslipidemia is generally only apparent in adults, unmasked by obesity, diabetes, and aging, all of which increase VLDL secretion, and also by hypothyroidism or other disease. In hypothyroidism the conversion of intermediate-density lipoprotein (IDL) to LDL by hepatic lipase is poor. It seems likely that any secondary compromise, genetic or environmental, to IDL clearance, which is critically rate-limited by apo E_2/E_2 phenotype, could precipitate Type III hyperlipidemia.

In addition to the common variants of apo E described above, a number of rare variants have also been described. In contrast with E_2/E_2, some are dominant in their effect on plasma lipid phenotype and are associated with Type III hyperlipidemia.[11] Characterization of such variants is generally only within the scope of the research laboratory and is not considered further here.

APOE Genotype and Alzheimer's Disease

This disease, first recognized in 1907 by Alois Alzheimer, is now known to be a common disease that is the predominant cause of dementia in persons older than 65 years. Progression from mild short-term memory problems to massive loss of memory, language, and orientation incapacitates the individual. As survival to old age increases, society is faced with the future care of vast numbers of patients with dementia whose quality of life is poor.

Evidence gathered from multiplex families with late-onset dementia suggests that familial clustering was unlikely due to chance alone and, in 1991, Pericak-Vance et al.[12] used affected pedigree member analysis to show that a region of chromosome 19 was common to affected pedigree members more frequently than random chance would predict. This linkage was confirmed, but the much earlier report by Schellenberg et al.[13] of an association of a restriction fragment length polymorphism (RFLP) allele of the APOCII gene with Alzheimer's dementia did not replicate in these data. The APOCII gene is adjacent to the APOE gene on chromosome 19; the failed replication of the APOCII gene association, and the fact that apo C-II and apo E were regarded as lipoprotein components relevant to atherosclerosis, diverted attention from these genes as candidates for the Alzheimer locus. However, apo E was shown by Strittmatter et al.[14] to bind Alzheimer amyloid beta peptide, and furthermore, apo E antisera stained senile plaques and neurofibrillary tangles, prompting investigation of APOE genotype in Alzheimer's disease.

The three common isoproteins of apo E, designated 2, 3, and 4, have allele frequencies of 6%, 78%, and 16% respectively. The differences are at amino acids 112 and 158, the isoforms containing respectively, cysteine and cysteine (2), cysteine and arginine (3), or arginine and arginine (4). Many laboratories have now confirmed the association of APOE genotype with susceptibility, with APOE$_4$ marking increased risk, in family and sporadic late-onset disease in many studies in various racial groups.[15]

The effect of APOE$_4$ is dose-dependent.[16] The E4/E4 genotype has the most severe effect, advancing age of onset by about 8 years per allele, from 84 years if no E$_4$ allele is present to an age of 68 years for the E$_4$/E$_4$ genotype. APOE$_2$ seems to mark reduced risk relative to E$_3$. However, the observed associations do not prove that these genotypes are the functional feature on chromosome 19; they could simply be acting as linkage disequilibrium markers for other genetic diversity in a nearby gene, which causes the true pathological effect. However, the circumstantial evidence, the expression of apo E in the nervous system, the strong enhancement of expression in response to nerve injury, the difference in expressed isoproteins (which, at least in the cardiovascular system, confers differences in interactions, with lipoprotein receptors, for example), and differential effects of isoform-specific beta-very-low-density lipoprotein on neurite extension *in vitro*, make APOE genotype a strong candidate for representing the etiological site within this genomic region of chromosome 19. The APOE gene has thus come to the forefront for its role in a new area: the "lipidology of the nervous system."

APOB Gene and Familial Defective apo B

In 1989, Innerarity et al.[17] described a disorder called familial defective apo B-100 (FDB), involving an amino acid change of arginine to glutamine at position 3500 in the APOB gene (APOB R3500Q). This single amino acid change reduces binding of the LDL that contains apo B-Gln, resulting in the accumulation of such LDL, thus causing hyperlipidemia and atherosclerosis.

In an FDB heterozygote as much as 70% circulating LDL will be LDL-Gln. The mechanism of the effect was revealed by studying the differential binding of monoclonal antibodies and by using carbon-13 nuclear magnetic resonance,[18] which showed that the six lysine residues within the amino acid 3500 region have altered pK in the presence of Gln$_{3500}$. Lysine residues are known to be involved in the binding of apo B-100 to the LDL receptor, and because of its large effect on the conformation of the surrounding area of the protein, the substitution of arginine by glutamine at residue 3500 alters the microenvironment of the receptor-binding domain.

Individuals with FDB have been identified in the United States, Canada, Austria, the United Kingdom, Denmark, Germany, Italy, and France, but not in Finland.[19] Haplotype analysis using APOB gene polymorphisms has shown that in all but a few cases reported to date, the mutation is identical by descent, and thus almost all FDB carriers have a common ancestor. The mutation was originally identified in a patient who was moderately hypercholesterolemic.[20]

Among patients with a clinical diagnosis of FH, approximately 3% were heterozygous for the APOB-3500 mutation. Therefore, this mutation can be associated with severe hypercholesterolemia, tendon xanthomas, and a family history of premature CHD; it is thus clinically indistinguishable from FH caused by receptor defects. However, as discussed later in the section on clinical relevance, it is not always expressive as hypercholesterolemia, nor as coronary disease.

More recently, using a variety of molecular scanning techniques, other point mutations have been described. These occur within the putative LDL-receptor binding domain of APOB. Two of these have been shown to produce APOB-100 that exhibits defective binding towards the LDL receptor:

- ✧ One results in the substitution of cysteine for arginine at codon 3531 (APOB R3531C).[21]

- ✧ The other substitutes tryptophan for arginine at codon 3500 (APOB R3500W).[22]

However, to date, only a handful of individuals have been identified worldwide for either mutation.[22–25]

Low-Density Lipoprotein Receptor Gene and Familial Hypercholesterolemia

The clinical significance of the LDL receptor is described in Chapter 29.

CLINICAL RELEVANCE

APOE Gene

Diagnosis means the identification of the underlying cause of a patient's clinical condition. It is thus evident that the APOE E_2/E_2 genotype will frequently, but not always, be found in Type III dyslipidemia. In the presence of a characteristic phenotype (clinical features, plasma cholesterol, and triglyceride levels), genotype identification can add strong support to the diagnosis. However, a more precise phenotypic diagnosis is possible using lipoprotein electrophoresis, isoelectric focusing, apo E immunoblotting, ultracentrifugation, or some combination of these. In a subset of individuals such as rarer APOE gene variants, and where there are confounding features in the phenotype (for example, different glycation patterns of apo E in diabetes mellitus[26]), the genotype and phenotype methods will yield apparently discrepant results. The resolution of such discrepancies can be highly complex, more the domain of the research laboratory than of a service laboratory. Nevertheless, in most patients, the gene test for E_2/E_2 genotype would concord with phenotyping.

What practical value is the gene test? A biochemical or genetic diagnosis of Type III dyslipidemia is useful. The clinical categorization defines likely natural history (prognosis); suggests additional investigations for possible trigger conditions such as hypothyroidism, diabetes, and obesity, which may represent the primary problem; gives access to knowledge of optimal therapeutic approaches and possibility of new trials; defines potential risk to siblings; and gives the doctor and patient a clear-cut disease entity to address.

The importance of allele APOE as a susceptibility gene in the development of late onset Alzheimer's disease presents new challenges. While not relevant to conventional lipidology, it is an extremely important aspect of the "lipidology of the nervous system" and instructive to future lipidology in general. In many populations, more than 20% percent of individuals have an E_4 allele, and therefore an APOE genotype analysis predicts their risk for late-onset Alzheimer's (an odds ratio approximately 4 for one E_4 allele, and estimated near 20 for the E_4/E_4 genotype[15])—a risk ratio considerably greater than that of high-density lipoprotein (HDL) concentration as a predictor of coronary risk.

However, in contrast with coronary risk, there is no opportunity at present of averting the onset of Alzheimer's disease, and traditional clinical wisdom is that, to be justifiable, a test must offer some opportunity for management. Furthermore, in the case of APOE many people with E_4 alleles will never get Alzheimer's disease and conversely, many with Alzheimer's disease will not have any E_4 alleles. Thus APOE genotyping is unsuitable as a predictive test for Alzheimer's. Yet APOE geneotyping is in widespread use as a diagnostic test in patients with dementia, a practice that is becoming under increased criticism. A recent report suggested that APOE genotyping is only useful when applied to people who already have a clinical diagnosis of probable Alzheimer's disease.[27] The presence of an E_4 allele in such patients adds weight to the clinical diagnosis, but the absence of such an allele does not exclude it. The small increase in diagnostic confidence provided by APOE genotyping does not justify the burdens on the patient of such testing. Consequently, a consensus is now emerging among groups working in this area that APOE genotyping should not be available as a diagnostic test for patients with dementia except in research studies.[28] Needless to say, an E_4 genotype should not be reported to a patient tested for E_2/E_2 genotype in the context of dyslipidemia.

APOB Gene

Up to 6% of patients of Western European descent with the clinical characteristics of familial hypercholesterolemia carry the APOB R3500Q (29 and reviewed in 19). Genotype analysis is simple, using one of several methods, and therefore offers a diagnostic test for clinic patients with Type IIa hyperlipidemia. One question needs to be answered, however: namely, is this useful?

First, the test does not presently alter management *per se*. Management is based on cholesterol or LDL cholesterol concentrations, together with the presence of other risk factors such as age, gender, smoking, hypertension and diabetes, and would be the same whether the LDL receptor or the APOB gene were involved. In general, the R3500Q mutation is considerably less expressive in clinical terms than LDL receptor gene mutations (see 19). The majority of APOB R3500Q carriers in affected families may have cholesterol levels within the reference range, in contrast with kindreds bearing LDLR mutations. Hyperlipidemia may be less evident in childhood and have much higher coefficient of variation in adulthood,[30] and cholesterol-years, a potentially important prognostic factor, may thus be lower. It has been suggested that the effect of the R3500Q mutation on cholesterol concentrations has been overestimated among patients with ischemic heart disease and FH.[29] Cholesterol concentrations are a risk factor for ischemic heart disease, and are also one of the clinical criteria used in the diagnosis of FH, thus due to study design, carriers identified with FH may have higher cholesterol concentrations than carriers in the general population. Additionally, R3500Q homozygotes do not develop coronary disease in childhood and not even necessarily in later life, a further pointer to the lesser clinical expressivity of the mutation.[31] Counseling, necessary if gene tests are to be used, will thus be quite complex. Detection of R3500Q carriers is on these grounds less important than the detection of carriers of classical LDL receptor mutations. While it represents one simple test easily achieved, it should be considered as a small component of the overall system for FH molecular diagnostics (see below).

To date, far fewer studies have been performed on carriers of the two other functional APOB mutations. However, it has been suggested that the R3531C mutation may not be associated with hypercholesterolemia and the R3500W mutation is too rare to justify looking for it.[29] Further studies are required to see if in fact this is the case.

LDLR Gene

Genetic Diagnosis

As with many other single-gene diseases, a wide range of mutations occurs. In general, the number of different mutations accounting for the majority of FH is inversely proportional to the complexity of the target population. These mutations often differ among different populations. Founder populations, specific ethnic subsets, and smaller populations (less than 5–10 million) may have a handful of specific mutations accounting for the majority of FH. In larger, outbred and historically older (10,000 rather than 1,000 years) populations, the complexity may be one or two orders of magnitude greater.

The ease of setting up direct assays is proportional to the number of mutations, as is the cost. There must come a point at which *de novo* mutation scanning (e.g., by denaturing gradient gel electrophoresis or single-strand conformation polymorphism technique) presents an equally efficient first-line test, and in the United Kingdom we have focused our efforts on this strategy. Ultimately, oligonucleotide binding assays for thousands of different mutations (over 300 are known worldwide at present, with continued linear increment of reports) converges with *de novo* sequencing-by-hybridization using chip technology, as has been developed for the breast cancer BRCA1 gene and mitochondrial genome.[32]

Lipidologists can often recognize the proband for an FH family and make a clear-cut diagnosis on the basis of clinical and biochemical features and family history. A gene test in such individuals is confirmatory, and may have a "galvanic" effect in dietary and therapeutic compliance and stopping smoking, but despite improved life expectancy can compromise life insurance, mortgage, and employment opportunities. However, with suitable counseling, family tracing in conjunction with definitive gene tests seems sensible. Regional diagnostics laboratories in the United Kingdom undertake such complex gene tests for a variety of disorders, and it is accepted and explained to probands that a definitive mutation identification can take weeks and may prove impossible. This philosophy differs from the lipid clinic used to monitoring tests (which cost cents or dollars in contrast with hundreds of dollars for gene scanning), with guaranteed results and more rapid turn-around. Additionally, the cost of attempting to establish a direct gene test for family tracing seems high, but as a once-in-a-lifetime test, the cost is small compared to the costs of long-term drug therapy.

Deducing genotype from cholesterol values may give a genetic misdiagnosis to 10% of family members with polygenic hypercholesterolemia,[33] and physicians may not have age- and gender-specific reference ranges available or be skilled at using them. In large, complex populations there seems little option except to use this technology in central, specialized regional laboratories that maintain collections of reference mutations, stocks of many oligonucleotides, and specialized knowledge base and expertise. This approach will be most cost effective as well.

Differential Diagnosis

A frequent question asked with hypercholesterolemic patients is, "Does this patient have FH, the single gene disorder?" If family history is not available, or if the hypercholesterolemia is less profound, a secondary gene-based laboratory test following the finding of a "significantly" elevated LDL-cholesterol level would be valuable. Only in low-complexity populations is current technology capable of this.

Screening

Population screening, such as a two-tiered approach, is theoretically possible, but would not currently satisfy the criteria for a targeted screening program. If the objective were to identify phenotype risk, why not stop at total or LDL/HDL cholesterol values? A more holistic approach to coronary risk,[34] the main cause for concern, should seek to identify individuals whose global risk is beyond a cut-point defined from epidemiological surveys such as the Framingham study. Many FH gene carriers would fall well below such a cut-point for coronary risk and would be at no greater risk of rising above the cut-point than a new smoker or a new hypertensive. Additionally, in complex populations the technology currently available could not support genetic diagnosis either in sensitivity, throughput, or cost.

Screening of high-risk groups is generally applied already at the level of plasma cholesterol tests, and in this group the semantic distinction between screening, diagnosis, and genetic diagnosis (proband for family, test for family members) can become blurred.

Prenatal Diagnosis

Prenatal diagnosis for homozygous FH affecting one child per million and one couple per quarter million would be appropriate where both parents are heterozygotes. If direct mutation testing is to be applied, both parents would have to be ascertained and characterized in advance. Linkage using RFLPs or microsatellite polymorphisms[35] would also be possible, and would complement cellular assays that have been established previously, particularly for non-null mutations where the cellular assay may be uninformative.[2]

SELECTED METHODOLOGIES AND COMMENTS

APOE Genotyping

The gene test demands the analysis of two separate single-base variations in codons 112 and 158. These can be analyzed within the span of one PCR fragment, and a wide range of methods has been published. The wide range of published methods may in part reflect the fact that two sites have to be genotyped, and also that the region is quite rich in G+C bases and hence needs some care to achieve good PCR amplification of high yield and free of PCR misproducts. Many laboratories use the method of Hixson and Vernier,[36] which relies on the fact that both sites alter an *HhaI* restriction site. Six different genotype band patterns are then recognizable (see Figure 34–1). We have previously addressed every aspect of this protocol[37] to achieve robust high throughput, from sample acquisition and processing to electrophoretic typing. Sample preparation for PCR is, in our view, under-addressed.

The typical clinical chemistry analysis starts from plasma or serum separated from blood after a brief centrifugation. DNA templates suitable for PCR usually come from a multi-step purification that may take several hours. Blood is commonly the source, but most of the content of blood is red cells, which are devoid of DNA but contribute massive excesses of undesired membrane and protein and include heme, an inhibitor of PCR. Buccal wash or scrapes, in our experience, lead to simpler (2–5 min) sample preparation and high-quality DNA template in a yield sufficient to support thousands of PCRs if needed. Additionally, sample acquisition needs no venisection skill, presents lower infection hazard, and is comfortable, stable to transport, repeatable, and feasible by post. These considerations are important if genotyping is to compete with, or complement, phenotyping.

The typical district hospital laboratory could expect to receive only single or small batches of samples for analysis in any week. Thus, APOE genotyping would benefit from running in parallel with other PCR-based analyses. At present, few are in use in clinical chemistry, but this situation may change. The utility of the final common pathway of analysis enabled by PCR can be compared with the utility of adapting enzyme assays to common indicators such as NAD. Core equipment for PCR and post-PCR analysis can then be established, with cost savings and ability to offer a diverse repertoire of tests. This contrasts with unique individual phenotyping assays.

PCR technology is very different from the phenotyping methods and therefore needs separate staff training and separate equipment, with a likely startup cost of

Figure 34–1 ✧ Band Patterns of the Six Common APOE Genotypes after HhaI Restriction Digest of PCR Product, in a MADGE Format Array

Top view: schematic. Bottom view: close-up of real image.

The full format contains wells in an 8 × 12 array. Band sizes for the homozygous genotypes are as follows:

E_2/E_2: 91, 83, 63 b.p. E_3/E_3: 91, 63, 48, 35 b.p. E_4/E_4: 73, 63, 48, 35 b.p.
Heterozygotes show the bands of both relevant homozygous genotypes.

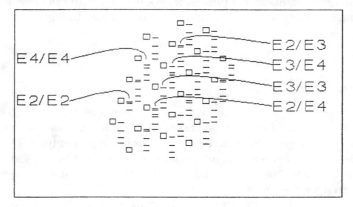

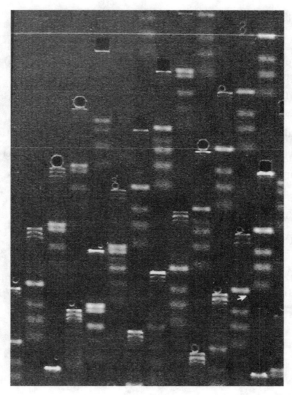

$15,000–$30,000. Thus, the decision to use APOE genotyping in a laboratory not using PCR technology is likely to be a generic one involving the potential utility of PCR throughout the entire repertoire of services offered. Clearly a central laboratory covering applications in genetic disease, infectious disease, hematology, and clinical chemistry could not operate without the technology, but a small clinical chemistry laboratory could not readily justify the need. In the right environment, APOE genotyping for E_2/E_2 can probably be made cheaper and faster than several of the phenotyping methods, and thus either competitive with or complementary to them. For rarer variants, the considerations are akin to the LDLR gene discussed below.

Protocol

GENERAL

In our experience, many apparently minor variables that do not affect many other PCR reactions affect the success of APOE gene PCR, and re-optimization may be necessary if the reaction is to be carried out in a different type of PCR machine or if different sources of reagents or template DNA prepared by a different method are to be used, even within the same laboratory. The equipment and reagents listed below were used for the current work.

EQUIPMENT

✧   deep 96-well plates (Beckman, High Wycombe, Bucks, UK)

✧   96-well Omniplates (Hybaid, Teddington, Middlesex, UK) with loose-fitting lids (Falcon, Becton Dickinson, Oxford, UK)

✧   0.5–10 μL 8-channel multi-pipette (Finnipipette, Life Sciences, Basingstoke, Hants, UK)

✧   100 μL repeater pipette (Biohit, Alpha Laboratories, Eastleigh, Hants, UK)

✧   centrifuge (Sorvall T60000B, du Pont, Newtown, CT, USA)

✧   Omnigene PCR machine (Hybaid, Teddington, Middlesex, UK)

✧   polystyrene block (10 cm × 7.5 cm)

✧   incubator (Sanyo-Gallenkamp, Leics, UK)

✧   horizontal gel electrophoresis tank (11.5 cm × 21 cm)

✧   7.5% MADGE gels (genetiX, Wimborne, Dorset, UK)

✧   UV transilluminator, charge-coupled-device camera, Imagestore 5000 frame grabber for digital images and video copy processor (UV Products, Cambridge, UK).

REAGENTS

✧   10X "polmix" (500 mmol/L KCl, 100 mmol/L Tris (pH 8.3), 0.01% gelatin, 2 mmol/L of each dNTP)

- ✧ 15 mmol/L MgCl$_2$
- ✧ dimethylsulphoxide (BDH, Lutterworth, Leics, UK)
- ✧ PCR primers (Genosys, Cambridge, UK)
- ✧ "FH49" 5'-GAACAACTGACCCCGGTGGCGG (100 pmol/μL)
- ✧ "FH50" 5'-GGATGGCGCTGAGGCCGCGCTC (100 pmol/μL)
- ✧ Taq polymerase (5 U/μL) (GibcoBRL cat. No. 18038–026)
- ✧ paraffin oil
- ✧ *HhaI*, 20,000 U/mL (New England Biolabs, Hitchen, Herts, UK)
- ✧ 10X NE buffer 4 (New England Biolabs)
- ✧ bovine serum albumin, 10 mg/mL (New England Biolabs)
- ✧ 10X Tris-borate (TBE) pH 8.3
- ✧ formamide loading buffer: 98% ionized formamide, 10 mmol/L EDTA (pH 8.0), 0.025% xylene cyanole Ff, 0.025% bromophenol blue
- ✧ 1 kilobase molecular weight marker ladder (GibcoBRL, Renfrewshire, Scotland)
- ✧ ethidium bromide, 10 mg/mL in water

DNA Templates and Pre-PCR Setup

GENOMIC DNA:

Genomic DNA was isolated from potassium-EDTA anticoagulated whole blood (either fresh or frozen at –20°C until used), using serial steps of cellular lysis with a sucrose buffer, nuclear lysis including sodium dodecyl sulphate and overnight protein digestion by proteinase K, salt precipitation of residual debris, and ethanol precipitation of DNA, as previously described.[38]

Template DNA stock was re-dissolved to approximately 0.16 mg/mL in Tris-EDTA and aliquots were placed in deep-well 96-well Beckman plates. Dilutions in water to 0.0256 mg/mL were set up in a replica array, from which 2.5 μL aliquots containing 40 ng DNA were drawn to set up either 10 or 20μL PCRs. DNA samples for this work were anonymous samples for research studies approved by local ethical committees.

MOUTHWASH DNA:

10-mL mouthwashes were in 0.9% (w/v) saline. Patients were supplied a 20-mL universal tube containing 10 mL saline and asked to draw the liquid into their mouth, swill it around for approximately 30 sec, and spit it back into the tube. Sample transit of one to three days at room temperature and/or storage at –20°C until used gave acceptable PCR template DNA.

Mouthwashes were vortexed before removal of 1 mL into an Eppendorf tube. This was centrifuged at approximately 10,000 ×g for 2 min and the supernatant removed. The pellet was then re-suspended in 400 μL of 10 mmol/L NaCl-EDTA, vortexed, and centrifuged for a further 2 min. The supernatant was again removed and the resultant pellet fully re-suspended in 100 μL of 20 mmol/L NaOH and heated to 95°C for 15–20 minutes. Before removal of a 2.5 μL aliquot for use either neat or diluted with water as template for PCR, the preparation was pulse centrifuged to pellet cell debris. A 1 in 10 dilution was made of each DNA sample and pipetted into a deep-well Beckman plate, leaving a few of the 96 wells empty (for positive/negative controls). This array was used to transfer 2.5 μL of each DNA into its corresponding coordinate of a 96-well omniplate, to the very base of the well. The empty wells on the plate were used to pipette 2.5 μL of DNA from reference genotypes or of water for negative controls. The DNAs (approximately 40 ng DNA in each well) were then allowed to dry, and the dried DNA array stored at room temperature (up to months) until required for PCR.

PCR Conditions

A total volume of 1000 μL PCR mix, sufficient for one 96-well omniplate (96 × 10 μL reactions), contained:

✧ 100 μL 10× Polmix

✧ 100 μL 15 mmol/L MgCl$_2$

✧ 50 μL DMSO

✧ 40 μL Oligonucleotide pair (FH49/50 at 20 pmol/μL each)

✧ 704 μL sterile distilled water

✧ 6 μL Taq polymerase (stock at 5 U/μL)

A volume of 10 μL of this PCR mix was pipetted into each of the 96 wells, and overlaid with an equal volume of paraffin oil. The plate was covered with a lid and centrifuged for 1 min at 1600 ×g ready for thermal cycling. The following cycling conditions were used:

✧ 95°C for 10 min

✧ 95°C for 1 min

✧ 72°C for 3 min (5 cycles)

✧ 95°C for 1 min

✧ 55°C for 1 min

✧ 72°C for 1 min (30 cycles)

Restriction Digests

The amplified DNA was then digested using 4 U of *HhaI* using the procedure illustrated below. For one 96-well plate, 260 μL digest mix was prepared as follows:

✧ sterile distilled water 91 Ll

✧ 10× NE buffer 4 130 μL

✧ 13 μL 100X BSA (10 mg/mL)

♦   26 μL *HhaI* (20 U/μL)

The digest mix was subsequently aliquotted into a column of 8 wells on a clean 96-well plate, and this then used to pipette 2.0 μL into each well of a clean plate using 8-channel multipipette. To each well, 8.0 μL of PCR product was transferred across from its identical coordinate on the PCR plate.

The plate was centrifuged at 1600 ×g for 1 min and digested in an incubator at 37°C for at least 1 h.

Microplate Array Diagonal Gel Electrophoresis (MADGE) Imaging and Analysis

After digestion, 5.0 μL of each sample was added to 2.0 μL formamide dye mix (formamide, 0.5 mol/L EDTA, 0.025% w/v of both bromophenol blue and xylene cyanol), and 5.0 μL of this mix was loaded into the well of a 7.5% MADGE gel (pre-stained in a solution of 10 μL of 10 mg/mL ethidium bromide in 100 mL 1 × TBE for 10 min) in an electrophoresis tank containing 1 × TBE. MADGE gels were prepared as described previously.[39]

Briefly, the gels are supported on glass, contain 96 2-mm cubic wells for sample loading in an 8 × 12 array, with the long axis of the array at an angle of 71.6 degrees relative to the electrodes and with the edges of the wells parallel and perpendicular to the line of electrophoresis. A 1 kb ladder was also loaded into one well of the gel. Electrophoresis was at 10 V/cm at room temperature for 45 min, after which time the gel was observed using an ultraviolet transilluminator and a digital image of the gel acquired using a ccd camera and frame grabber (see Figure 34–1).

Gene Tests for FDB (R3500Q)

This laboratory has used many methods for R3500Q genotyping. Tests often are performed on singletons or small batches. The method of forced restriction site analysis of Mamotte and van Bockxmeer[40] has proven the simplest, most comprehensive, and most robust, requiring only PCR oligonucleotides and a restriction enzyme. The method allows both a sensitive assay in which normal PCR product should cut to completion (i.e., residual undigested PCR product may represent FDB, a different mutation at the site, or failed restriction digest) and a specific assay forcing the surrounding base sequence such that only the R3500Q allele results in a restriction site. For high throughput, the method is also compatible with microplate PCR and microplate array diagonal gel electrophoresis (MADGE) devised in this laboratory.

Protocol

GENERAL

Template DNA, PCR equipment, and general procedures including PCR volumes and oligonucleotide concentrations were as above.

SPECIFIC

Conditions were identical with those of Mamotte and van Bockxmeer.[33]

✧   The upstream PCR primer was 5'-TCTCGGGAATATTCAGGAACTATTG.

✧   The "ARG" primer is 5'-GCCCTGCAGCTTCACTGAGGAC.

✧   The "GLN" primer is 5'-GCCCTGCAGCTTCACTGAGTAC.

Sensitive Assay:

In the sensitive assay for screening for FDB mutations in a set of samples, the upstream and ARG PCR primers are used. The ARG primer contains a base mismatching the native wild-type sequence (four bases away from the site of the mutation) and forces the occurrence of a *Sau*96I restriction site: any base change within this site, including the R3500Q base change, will eliminate the restriction site.

Specific Assay:

In the specific assay for confirming FDB R3500Q mutations, the upstream and GLN PCR primers are used. The GLN primer contains two bases mismatching the native wild-type sequence (at positions three and four bases away from the mutation site) and forces the occurrence of a *Sca*I restriction site, but only if the R3500Q base change is also present. Any base change within this site, including the R3500Q base change, will eliminate the restriction site.

Enzyme concentrations identical with those used above were found to be satisfactory, rather than the high concentration of *Sca*I used by the original authors.

Screening for R3500Q, R3500W and R3531C Mutations

These three mutations can all be detected reliably and easily by heteroduplex analysis.[23,41] Amplification of DNA heterozygous for a nucleotide substitution generates both homo- and heteroduplex molecules. The latter are distorted at the point of substitution and have a slower mobility than homoduplexes in polyacrylamide gels.

Protocol

This is essentially as described by Kotze et al.[42]

✧   The upstream primer is 5' GGAGCAGTTGACCACAAGCTTAGCTTGGAA 3'.

✧   The downstream primer is 5' CAGGGTGGCTTTGCTTGTATGTTCTCCGTT 3'. Conditions were identical to those of Kotze et al.

Heteroduplex bands are then identified after elextrophoresis in long (40 cm) gels of 10% polyacrylamide (w/v), 0.1% *N,N*'-methylene bisacrylamide(w/v)),containing 15% (w/v) urea.

Identification of Mutation in Samples with Heteroduplex Bands

APO B R3500Q

See protocol above.

APO B R3531C

Protocol

Perform PCR using primers and conditions described above in Kotze et al.[42] Following PCR, digest 22 μL of PCR product with 20 U of *Nsi* I.[21] In those samples carrying the R3531C mutation, two faster bands, identified by polyacrylamide gel electrophoresis, appear after digestion.

APO B R3500W

Perform PCR as outlined above. Digest the product with 20 U of *Nla* III.[43] Polyacrylamide gel electrophoresis reveals two additional smaller faster-migrating fragments in those samples carrying the R3500W substitution.

Comments on Restriction Enzyme-Based Genotyping

Specific mutations can be tested for in many ways: direct sequencing, single strand conformation polymorphism technique, denaturing gradient gel electrophoresis, chemical cleavage, oligo binding, allele-specific PCR, oligonucleotide ligation assay, restriction site assay, PCR-induced restriction site assay, mini-sequencing, fluorescence decoupling during PCR (e.g., TaqMan system, etc.). See Landegren[44] for a review of most of these techniques.

However, specific mutations can only be proven in three ways: by direct sequencing, which is very laborious; by oligonucleotide binding using an oligonucleotide specific to that mutation; or by restriction enzyme assay, where an enzyme site can be found that only cuts the mutant or where a specific site can be induced by using a mismatched PCR primer.

Oligonucleotide binding assays offer a generic system applicable to any sequence region, but considerable care is necessary in achieving informative conditions of hybridization wash stringency, i.e., carefully controlled salt concentration and temperature conditions must be established to distinguish perfect match from mismatch binding. Unless non-radioisotopic labeling is used, oligo binding is time consuming for singleton assays since the oligo must first be labeled. If non-radioisotopic labeling is used, then a suitable detection system must be available such as a colorimeter, fluorimeter, or DELFIA instrument.

For restriction enzyme analysis, it typically will be necessary to incubate the digest at 37°C (incubator, water bath, dry block, or simply program the PCR block to hold the temperature), then to perform a simple agarose or polyacrylamide gel electrophoresis followed by ethidium bromide staining, and imaging (photographic or digital imaging) during excitation on an ultraviolet transilluminator.

In our laboratory the availability of equipment makes restriction enzyme analysis the most favorable and is compatible both with singleton and large batch analysis (the latter using the MADGE system). However, the availability of different equipment in different laboratories—for example, of high capital cost systems such as DELFIA in service clinical chemistry laboratories—may lead one to choose a different method. The methods we use are simple, robust, and cheap to set up and therefore recommended for a laboratory with no adaptable systems.

Until now, we have recommended the electrophoresis-based restriction enzyme method for APOE genotype analysis. However, a method has very recently been described that uses a heteroduplex generator, which may be more reliable and less prone to misinterpretation due to incomplete digestion or inefficient PCR amplification.[45] If this technique fulfills initial expectations, it may become the method of choice in the future.

LDLR Gene Tests in FH

In all but the lowest complexity populations (e.g., founder populations, populations in isolated regions, and ethnic groups numbering less than a few million), it is unlikely that direct mutation assays will account for more than the minority of FH mutations. A few such examples are listed in Table 34–1.

Table 34–1 ✧ Common Nucleotide Variations Causing Hyperlipidemias

Gene	Sequence Change	Comments
LDLR	10kb deletion, promoter, exon 1	63% of French-Canadian FH patients
	Deletion exons 16, 17, part of 18	FH-Helsinki accounts for 56% of FH in east Finland
	Deletion 7 nt in exon 6	FH-North Karelia accounts for 34% of FH in east Finland
	Asp206Glu (exon 4)	69% of Afrikaner FH
	Asp 154 Asn (exon 4)	10% of Afrikaner FH
	Val408Met (exon 9)	15% of Afrikaner FH
	Stop 660 (TGC to TGA (exon 14)	Christian Lebanese
	Deletion codon Gly (exon 4)	35% of Ashkenazi Jews from Lithuania
APOB	Codon change Arg3500Gln	FDB is a phenocopy of FH. Estimated 1/700 in several countries in Europe. Probably origin central Europe.
APOE	E_2 allele differs from E_3 and E_4, having Cys not Arg at positions 112 and 158	Approximately 1% of individuals are E_2/E_2, and 1% of these develop Type III hyperlipidemia

The authors have recently discussed[46] the progress of Schuster and colleagues[47] in developing direct mutation multiplex tests for a range of German FH mutations. We have also set up a Web site (accessible by any standard Web browser, such as Netscape, at http://www.ucl.ac.uk/fh/) which provides a sequenced workbook containing all exons, protein sequence, functional elements, known polymorphisms, and locations of most mutations described in the literature. Many mutations remain unpublished, but this Web site has an electronic publication area to facilitate effective international communication in this field. Sites of PCR primers that have been used in our laboratory, as well as other sundry data, are also available. In addition, a searchable mutation database is provided. An excerpt from this Web site is shown in Figure 34–2.

Our view is that *de novo* mutation scanning and direct sequencing would be necessary in most geographical locations, but that this restricts the application to highly specialized laboratories that use these techniques for many genes. We recommend the use of two techniques: single strand conformation polymorphism (SSCP) and denaturing gradient gel electrophoresis (DGGE).[44] The former offers greater ease of setup; the latter is more complex to set up, but is now tending to be more favored by diagnostics laboratories due to its greater reproducibility and apparently higher sensitivity to more of the possible base variations within a PCR product. However, SSCP is considerably more reproducible if thermostatted electrophoresis apparatus is used, a feature that has long been addressed for DGGE (the typical run temperature is 60°C) but is only now being addressed by manufacturers of SSCP (the typical run temperature needed is 20°C).

The methodologies in this field are rapidly evolving, and it is impossible to discuss in detail the advantages and disadvantages of each. Instead, we recommend that a series of books, papers, and reviews[44,48–53] be used in conjunction with the Web site, which will save several weeks' time getting oriented on the sequence to set up laboratory work.

FAMILIAL HYPERCHOLESTEROLEMIA—THE FUTURE?

In broad terms, it is possible that future work will be in three areas. The first of these will involve the continued screening of populations to identify families with *de novo* mutations. However, studies of this type are now becoming more of limited interest unless large numbers of individuals are involved and the functional and clinical aspects of the mutations have been characterized, e.g., as in Graham et al.[54] The second area of work will be the development of alternative methods to detect large-scale rearrangements of the LDLR gene. The majority of these are caused by deletions of various sizes that occur along the entire length of the gene. Until now, these have generally been detected by Southern blot hybridization, which is extremely labor-intensive and tedious. Recent studies have utilized long-distance PCR as an alternative to Southern blotting. Using this technique, Kim et al.[55] have been able to amplify the entire LDL receptor gene in five fragments and identify two different deletion mutations. The third area of work and probably the most exciting involves studies of a basic molecular functional interest. Individuals who possess a primary hypercholesterolemia, but who have no apparent defect in either the LDL receptor gene or

Figure 34–2 ✧ An Excerpt of Information Available from a Web Site for LDLR Gene Mutations: Familial Hypercholesterolemia

A segment of exon 3 is shown, with a segment from the mutations table. For example, one might have used oligo FH4 as a PCR then as a sequencing primer to read through the sequence shown. One might find heterozygosity at a G base which can immediately be seen to be at nucleotide 301 (codon E80). Three mutations are known (arbitrary code number 13, 175 and 201) at this position, and they can then be looked up in more detail. The reverse process is also possible. It can be seen that E80 is in a binding domain motif, DXXSDE, increasing the likelihood that an amino acid change would have a functional effect.

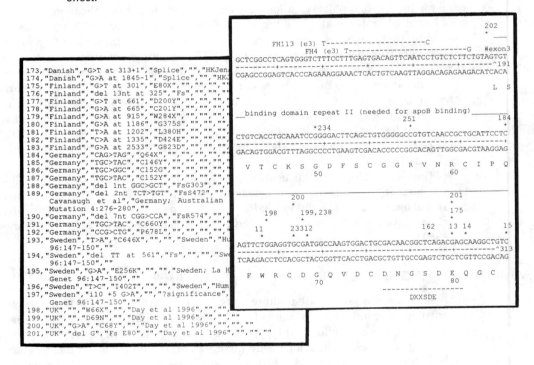

the apo B gene, are now being identified. Furthermore, alleles of the LDL receptor and apo B genes do not co-segregate with hypercholesterolemia in the families of these individuals.[56–58] Perhaps in the next edition of this book, such a third genetic locus that causes familial hypercholesterolemia will be described.

CONCLUSIONS

There is no overwhelming case to apply gene tests in the typical lipidology service. Their influence on management is relative rather than absolute. However, a well-resourced and forward-thinking clinical laboratory should gain valuable and wide-ranging experience by exploring some of the applications described in this chapter. With rapidly developing technology and a widening array of treatment options, these approaches seem likely to disseminate more widely. This will improve the quality of the "genetic" component of the service. ✧

REFERENCES

1. Fogge CH. General xanthelasma or vitilogoidea. Trans Path Soc Lond 1872;24:242.
2. Goldstein JL, Brown MS. Familial hypercholesterolemia. In: Scriver CR, Beaudet AL, Sly WS, Valle D (eds.). The metabolic basis of inherited disease, 6th ed. New York: McGraw Hill, 1989;1215–50.
3. Gowenlock AH, ed. Varley's practical clinical biochemistry, 6th ed. Oxford UK: Heinemann Medical Books, 1988.
4. Wilson JMG, Jungner G. Principles and practice of screening for disease. Public Health Papers 34. Geneva: World Health Organization, 1968.
5. Erlich HA. PCR technology principles and applications for DNA amplification. New York: Stockton Press, 1989.
6. Mullis KB, Ferre F, Gibbs RA (eds.). PCR: The polymerase chain reaction. Boston: Birkhauser, 1994.
7. Utermann G, Pruin N, Steinmetz A. Polymorphism of apolipoprotein E III: effect of a single polymorphic gene locus on plasma lipid levels in man. Clin Genet 1979;15: 63–72.
8. Zannis VI, Just PW, Breslow JL. Human apolipoprotein E isoprotein subclasses are genetically determined. Am J Hum Genet 1981;33:11–24.
9. Rall SCJ, Weisgraber KH, Innerarity TL, Mahley RW. Structural basis for receptor-binding heterogeneity of apolipoprotein E from type III hyperlipoproteinemic subjects. Proc Natl Acad Sci USA 1982;79:4696–700.
10. Weisgraber KH, Innerarity TL, Mahley RW. Abnormal lipoprotein receptor-binding activity of the human E apo21.
11. Rall SC, Mahley RW. The rprotein due to cysteine-arginine interchange at a single site. J Biol Chem 1982;257:2518–ole of apolipoprotein E genetic variants in lipoprotein disorders. J Int Med 1992;231:653–9.
12. Pericak-Vance MA, Bebout JL, Gaskell PC, Yamaoko LH, Hung WY, Alberts MJ et al. Linkage studies in familial Alzheimer's disease: evidence for chromosome 19 linkage. Am J Hum Genet 1991;48:1034–50.
13. Schellenberg GD, Deeb S, Boehnke LM, Bryant EM, Martin GM, Lampe LM, et al. Association of apolipoprotein C-II allele with familial dementia of the Alzheimer type. J Neurogenetics 1987;4:97–108.
14. Strittmatter WJ, Weisgraber KH, Huang DY, Dong LM, Salvesen GS, Pericak-Vance M et al. Binding of human apolipoprotein E to synthetic amyloid beta-peptide: isoform-specific effects and implications for late-onset Alzheimer's disease. Proc Natl Acad Sci USA 1993;90:8098–102.
15. M-S Tsai, Tangalos EG, Petersen RC, Smith GE, Schaid DJ, Kokmen E, et al. Apolipoprotein E: risk factor for Alzheimer Disease. Am J Hum Genet 1994;54:643–9.
16. Corder EH, Saunders AM, Strittmatter WJ, Schmechel DE, Gaskell PC, Small GW, et al. Gene dose of apolipoprotein-E type-4 allele and the risk of Alzheimer's disease in late onset families. Science 1993;261:921–3.
17. Innerarity TL, Weisgraber KH, Arnold KS, Mahley RW, Krauss RM, Vega GL, Grundy SM. Familial defective apolipoprotein B-100: low-density lipoproteins with abnormal receptor binding. Proc Natl Acad Sci USA 1987;84:6919–23.
18. Katz SL, Ibadah JA, Letizia JY, Thomas MT, Philips MC. A ^{13}C NMR characterization of

lysine residues in apolipoprotein B and their role in binding to the low-density-lipoprotein receptor. J Biol Chem 1988;263:13831–8.

19. Myant NB. Familial defective apolipoprotein B-100: a review, including some comparisons with familial hypercholesterolemia. Atherosclerosis 1993;104:1–18.

20. Vega GL, Grundy SM. In vivo evidence for reduced binding of low-density lipoproteins to receptors as a cause of primary moderate hypercholesterolemia. J Clin Invest 1986;78:1410–14.

21. Pullinger CR, Hennessy LK, Chatterton JE, Liu W, Love JA, Mendel CM et al. Familial ligand-defective apolipoprotein B: identification of a new mutation that increases LDL receptor-binding affinity. J Clin Invest 1995;95:1225–34.

22. Gaffney D, Reid JM, Cameron LM, Vass K, Caslake MJ, Shepherd J, Packard CJ. Independent mutations at codon 3500 of the apolipoprotein B gene are associated with hyperlipidemia. Arterioscler Thromb 1995;15:1025–9.

23. Wenham PR, Henderson BG, Penney MD, Ashby JP, Rae PWH, Walker SW. Familial ligand-defective apolipoprotein B-100: detection, biochemical features and haplotype analysis of the R3531C mutation in the UK. Atherosclerosis 1997;129:185–92.

24. Choong M-L, Koay ESC, Khoo K-L, Khaw M-C, Sethi SK. Denaturing gradient gel electrophoresis of familial defective apolipoprotein B-100 in a mixed Asian cohort: two cases of arginine^{3500} → tryptophan mutation associated with a unique haplotype. Clin Chem 1997;43:916–23.

25. Fisher E, Scharnagl H, Hoffman MM, Kusterer K, Wittmann D, Wieland H et al. Mutations in the apolipoprotein (apo) B-100 receptor binding region: Detection of apo B-100 (Arg^{3500}Trp) associated with two new haplotypes and evidence that apo B-100 (Gln^{3405} → Gln) diminishes receptor-mediated uptake of LDL. Clin Chem 1999;45:1026–38.

26. Stavljenic-Rukavina A, Sertic J, Salzer B, Dumic M, Radica A, Fumik K, Krajina A. Apolipoprotein E phenotypes and genotypes as determined by polymerase chain reaction using allele-specific oligonucleotide probes and the amplification refractory mutation system in children with insulin-dependent diabetes mellitus. Clin Chem Acta 1993;216:191–8.

27. Mayeux R, Saunders AM, Shea S, Mirra S Evans D, Roses AD et al. Utility of the apolipoprotein E geneotype in the diagnosis of Alzheimer's disease. N Engl J Med 1998;338:506–11.

28. McConnell, Koenig BA, Greely HT, Raffin TA & the Alzheimer Disease Working Group of the Stanford Program in Genomics, Ethics and Society. Nature medicine 1998;4:757–9.

29. Tybjærg-Hansen A, Steffensen R, Meinertz H, Schnohr P, Nordestgaard BG. Association of mutations in the apolipoprotein B gene with hypercholesterolemia and the risk of ischemic heart disease. N Engl J Med 1998;338:1577–84.

30. Miserez AR, Keller U. Differences in the phenotypic characteristics of subjects with familial defective B-100 and familial hypercholesterolemia. Arterioscler Thromb Vasc Biol 1995;15:1719–29.

31. Gallagher JJ, Myant NB. The affinity of low-density lipoproteins and of very-low-density-lipoprotein remnants for the low-density-lipoprotein receptor in homozygous familial defective apolipoprotein B-100. Atherosclerosis 1995;115:263–72.

32. Chee M, Yang R, Hubbell E, Berno A, Huang XC, Stern D, et al. Accessing genetic information with high-density DNA arrays. Science 1996;274:610–14.

33. Williams RR, Hunt SC, Schumacher MC, Hegele RA, Leppert MF, Ludwig EH, et al. Diagnosing heterozygous familial hypercholesterolemia using new practical criteria validated by molecular genetics. Am J Cardiol 1993;72:171–6.

34. Haq IU, Ramsay LE, Pickin DM, Yeo WW, Jackson PR, Payne JN. Lipid-lowering for prevention of coronary heart disease: what policy now? Clin Sci 1996;91:399–413.

35. Day INM, Haddad L, O'Dell SD, Day LB, Whittall R, Humphries S. Identification of a common low-density-lipoprotein receptor mutation (R329X) in the South of England: complete linkage disequilibrium with an allele of microsatellite D19S394. J Med Genet 1997;34:111–16.

36. Hixson JE, Vernier DT. Restriction isotyping of human apolipoprotein E by gene amplification and cleavage with *HhaI*. J Lipid Res 1990;31:545–8.

37. Bolla M, Haddad L, Winder AF, Humphries SE, Day INM. High-throughput method for determination of apolipoprotein E genotypes with use of restriction digestion analysis by microplate array diagonal gel electrophoresis (MADGE). Clin Chem 1995;41: 1599–604.

38. Miller SA, Dykes DD, Polesky HF. A simple salting out procedure for extracting DNA from human nucleated cells. Nucleic Acids Res 1988;16:1215.

39. Day INM, Humphries SE. Electrophoresis for genotyping: microtitre array diagonal gel electrophoresis (MADGE) on horizontal polyacrylamide (H-PAGE) gels, Hydrolink or agarose. Anal Biochem 1994;222:389–95.

40. Mamotte CDS, van Bockxmeer FM. A robust strategy for screening and confirmation of familial defective apolipoprotein B-100. Clin Chem 1993;39:118–21.

41. Henderson BG, Wenham PR, Ashby JP, Blundell G. Detecting familial defective apolipoprotein B-100: three molecular scanning methods compared. Clin Chem 1997; 43:419–23.

42. Kotze MJ, Langenhoven E, Peeters AV, Theart L, Oosthuizen CJJ. Detection of two point mutations causing familial defective apolipoprotein B-100 by heteroduplex analysis. Mol Cell Probes 1994;8:513–8.

43. Talmud PJ, Tamplin OJ, Heath K, Gaffney D, Day INM, Humphries SE. Rapid testing for three mutations causing familial defective apolipoprotein B100 in 562 patients with familial hypercholesterolemia. Atherosclerosis 1996;125:135–7.

44. Landegren U, ed. Laboratory protocols for mutation detection. Oxford: Oxford University Press, 1996.

45. Bolla MK, Wood N, Humphries SE. Rapid determination of apolipoprotein E (APOE) genotype using a heteroduplex generator. J Lipid Res 1999;40:2340–5.

46. Day INM, Humphries SE. Genetic tests for familial hypercholesterolemia. Nature Biotechnology 1996;14:1227–8.

47. Baron H, Fung S, Aydin A, Bahring S, Luft FC, Schuster H. Oligonucleotide ligation assay (OLA) for the diagnosis of familial hypercholesterolemia. Nature Biotechnology 1996;14:1279–82.

48. Orita M, Suzuki Y, Sekiya T, Hayashi K. Rapid and sensitive detection of point mutations and DNA polymorphisms using the polymerase chain reaction. Genomics 1989;5: 874–9.

49. Myers RM, Maniatis T, Lerman LS. Detection and localization of single base changes by denaturing gradient gel electrophoresis. Meth Enzymol 1987;155:501–27.

50. Vidal-Puig A, Moller DE. Comparative sensitivity of alternative single-strand conformation polymorphism (SSCP) methods. Biotechniques 1994;17:490–6.

51. Sheffield VC, Beck JS, Kwitek AE, Sandstrom DW, Stone EM. The sensitivity of single-strand conformation polymorphism analysis for the detection of single base substitutions. Genomics 1993;16Human Mutation 1992;1:445–66.

52. Hobbs HH, Brown MS, Goldstein JL. Molecular genetics of the LDL receptor gene in familial hypercholesterolemia. D, Haddad L, Bolla M, Gudnason V, Humphries S. Spectrum of LDL receptor gene mutations in heterozygous familial hypercholesterolemia. Hum Mutat 1997;10:116–27.

53. Day INM, Whittall R, O'Dell S:325–32.

54. Graham CA, McLean E, Ward AJM, Beattie D, Martin S, O'Kane M et al. Mutation screening and genotype: phenotype corellation in familial hypercholesterolemia. Atherosclerosis 1999;147:309–16.

55. Kim SH, Bae JH, Chae JJ, Kim UK, Choe S-J, Namkoong Y et al. Long-distance PCR-based screening for large rearrangements of the LDL receptor gene in Korean patients with familial hypercholesterolemia. Clin Chem 1999;45:1424–30.

56. Varret M, Saint-Jore B, Cenarro A, Marinoni JC, Civeira F, Devillers M et al. A third major locus for autosomal dominant hypercholesterolemia maps to 1p34.1–p32. Am J Hum Genet 1999;64:1378–87.

57. Haddad L, Day INM, Hunt S, Williams RR, Humphries SE, Hopkins PN. Evidence for a third genetic locus causing familial hypercholesterolemia: a non-LDLR, non-APOB kindred. J Lipid Res 1999;40:1113–22.

58. Norman D, Sun X-M, Bourbon M, Knight BL, Naoumova RP, Soutar AK. Characterization of a novel cellular defect in patients with phenotypic homozygous familial hypercholesterolemia. J Clin Invest 1999; 104: 619–28.

Matrix Effects in the Measurement and Standardization of Lipids and Lipoproteins

35

W. Greg Miller

✧   Current routine methods for lipid and lipoprotein analysis are based on enzymatic and immunologic reactions. Because pure total cholesterol (TC) or triglyceride (TG) molecules are only soluble in organic solvents, these primary standard materials are not suitable for calibration of routine assay methods. Lipoproteins can be purified, but their tertiary and quaternary structures are usually altered in the process. This structural alteration can affect their chemical reactivity in enzymatic and immunologic reactions. Consequently preparing primary aqueous-based standards for lipid testing has not been practical for most assay systems.

Pooled human serum-based secondary standards are commonly used for routine laboratory calibration. Because of changes in lipoproteins and other serum matrix components during manufacturing, serum-based secondary standards frequently have a different chemical reactivity with respect to lipid molecules than that observed for native serum specimens in routine assays. Routine laboratory methods are designed to recover analyte from human serum specimens. Routine methods do not always recover lipid analytes from matrix-modified secondary standard calibration materials. Consequently the target values assigned to serum-based calibration materials are adjusted to compensate for any altered reactivity due to matrix-modified materials. Moreover, the analytic sensitivity to matrix-modified materials is usually a unique characteristic of a specific lot of secondary calibration material and a specific routine method.

The observation of method-material matrix interactions has also been observed for quality control and proficiency testing materials as well as for pooled serum secondary calibration materials. Each of these materials is prepared using similar technology and each has similar matrix limitations. Consequently it has been difficult to develop reliable systems to monitor and verify method calibration accuracy and inter-laboratory standardization using reference materials. Most inter-laboratory, daily quality control summary programs and proficiency testing (external quality assessment) programs lack adequate serum-based materials that would allow results from different methods to be compared with each other or to a credentialed reference method. Recent research and development has produced reference materials that can be used to calibrate and assess the accuracy of methods for TC and high-density-lipoprotein cholesterol (HDL-C), TG, apolipoproteins A (apo A) and B, and lipoprotein (a) [Lp(a)].

The term "commutability" was used in 1973 by Fasce et al.[1] to refer to the ability of a processed material to show inter-assay analytical properties comparable to authentic clinical specimens. Ideally, processed materials used for routine calibration and for standardization and verification of accuracy among laboratories should be commutable with freshly collected serum specimens. In practice, processed materials frequently have assay properties that are different from those of fresh patient specimens.

If an analytical system is sensitive to the difference between an analyte's reactive properties in a processed material and in fresh human specimens, the change in measured response to that analyte is referred to as a method/material-specific matrix interaction or matrix effect.[2] The matrix effect produces a matrix-related bias in the analyte result for that processed material, which precludes using that result to establish or evaluate accuracy of results for patient specimens. Matrix effects can be unique to a single lot of processed material and a single lot of reagents used in an analytical system. It is more common for matrix effects to be consistently observed between an analytical measurement system and a processed serum-based material, although the magnitude of the matrix bias may be unique to each lot of material or reagent.

The matrix of a specimen or material has been defined differently in different contexts. The National Committee for Clinical Laboratory Standards (NCCLS) defines matrix as "all components of a material system, except the analyte."[3,4] The American Society for Testing and Materials (ASTM) defines matrix as "the principal element or elements in a sample" and defines an interference as "an effect due to the presence of a constituent or characteristic that influences the measurement of another constituent or characteristic."[5] Rej has provided a comprehensive definition of matrix as "the entire milieu or environment in which an analyte resides and all components (other than the analyte) or attributes."[6]

The (NCCLS) defines a matrix effect (or interference) as "the influence of a sample property, other than the measurand (analyte), on the measurement, and thereby on the value of the measurand;[3] and the physicochemical effect(s) (e.g., interference) of the matrix on the analytical method's ability to accurately measure an analyte."[4] These definitions do not address the condition in which the structure of the native analyte is altered in a way that affects its chemical reactivity. This condition has been observed in lipoprotein molecules as a result of purification and freeze-drying processes (see below).

With these broad definitions, a matrix interference or effect could be ascribed to any processing-induced or physiologically derived component of the material. Rej cautions that "matrix effects are often ascribed to interferences due to unknown or uncharacterized substance(s) or factor(s) in the biological specimen."[6] He suggests that matrix interferences are the result of lack of analytical specificity for the analyte, but notes that at some point a processed material may "differ so fundamentally from the normally encountered clinical specimen that the specificity of even the most robust method is unfairly challenged."

In the context of this chapter, matrix effects are considered to be analytical interferences caused by alterations in the human serum material induced by preparation and processing of that material. Processing includes human and non-human additives to the material as well as any physical or chemical changes that occur to components of the material or to the analyte as a result of the preparation or manufacturing procedure. Matrix effects in this context do not include interferences from physiological or drug-induced metabolic substances present in normal or abnormal concentrations. However, such physiological interferences are significant issues and represent analytical challenges that must be solved by acceptable field methods. Matrix effects may be caused by undefined substances in the material, but this phenomenon should not be used to arbitrarily dismiss inadequate methodologic specificity for the analyte being measured.

Although commutability between pooled-serum materials and fresh individual specimens is desirable, it is not necessary for all aspects of calibration. Secondary standard calibration materials used by a manufacturer solely to calibrate a unique analytical system do not need to be commutable with any other analytical system nor with patient specimens. In this case, any matrix bias in the calibration materials can be accommodated by assignment of a nominal analyte value such that the analytical system's response is set to produce accurate results for individual patient specimens. The process for value assignment of the secondary standard and verification of accurate results for those specimens must be linked to a credentialed reference system such as the National Reference System for the Clinical Laboratory (NRSCL) of the NCCLS (see Chapter 36).

FROZEN SERUM POOLS AS REFERENCE MATERIALS

Frozen serum pools are commonly considered to be less prone to matrix modifications than the typical freeze-dried commercial serum-based materials. However, frozen pools can be prepared following a wide range of protocols and have been reported to exhibit method- and material-specific matrix biases. The most successful frozen serum materials are prepared with great care to avoid altering lipoproteins or other serum components.[22,23] Frozen serum pools require validation of performance characteristics to ensure commutability with individual patient specimens among a group of analytic methods.

NCCLS has a guideline for preparation and validation of commutable frozen human serum pools for cholesterol.[7] Key features of this protocol include

- ❖ rapidly separating serum from red blood cells prior to clotting,
- ❖ clotting for several hours in glass containers, then separating serum from clot components,
- ❖ maintaining serum at 4°C throughout the handling period,
- ❖ mixing the pool for 18 h, then filtering to remove any aggregated material,
- ❖ aseptically dispensing the material into vials, and
- ❖ uniformly freezing the material at −70°C within 56 h of initial blood collection.

Donors were pre-screened for TC concentration and pools were prepared to achieve normal and elevated levels. Two pools were prepared by this protocol and tested for commutability among 26 instrument/reagent systems from 13 manufacturers and one reagent vendor. The expected TC value for the pools was calculated for each assay system as the weighted mean of the TC values for each individual donor unit used in each pool. All assay systems recovered the expected TC value for both pools within 1.5% with one exception for each pool. The validation data suggest that "serum pools prepared according to the guideline behave like donor samples on the systems evaluated."[7]

Fresh non-frozen or frozen human serum pools prepared to less stringent protocols are subject to deterioration of lipoprotein and other components with concomitant deleterious effects on commutability characteristics. Holding serum units or pools at refrigerator temperatures for long periods of time can degrade lipoproteins and other proteins, which creates increased levels of ammonia, free glycerol, and other molecules, can alter tertiary and quaternary structure, and can form various adducts with other serum molecules.

As early as 1976, Warnick and Albers[8] identified a difference in apparent bias between two non-enzymatic methods for TC and TG in the Lipid Research Clinics program with respect to fresh plasma specimens versus frozen serum pools. The frozen pools were prepared by the Centers for Disease Control and Prevention (CDC) using Cohn fraction and egg white supplementation for cholesterol and triglycerides respectively.

Waymack et al.[9] evaluated eight frozen human serum pools used in the CDC Lipid Standardization Program for performance in enzymatic methods for TC. Some of the pools were supplemented with human Cohn fraction serum lipid concentrates. Fresh, non-frozen individual patients' sera with Abell-Kendall value assignment were used to establish assay performance. Five of the eight frozen pools had a matrix bias that was not a function of the reagent used but of unique instrument assay parameters.

Myers et al.[10] reported that three CDC Cohn-fraction-cholesterol-supplemented frozen human serum pools showed significant matrix bias with two of 16 routine enzymatic methods for TC. Three commercial liquid-stabilized human serum pools showed matrix bias with nine of the 16 methods. For this study, non-supplemented, fresh-frozen serum pools were used as the controls for no matrix effects.

Miller et al.[11] evaluated matrix bias in pooled serum materials. Two non-frozen pools were prepared from two sets of eight freshly collected, off-the-clot individual patients' sera and tested with four routine methods. These non-frozen serum pools had no matrix effects as assessed by routine enzymatic methods. TC results were the same as the mean of the individual sera making up the pools. However, with less carefully controlled preparation conditions, frozen serum pools did exhibit matrix bias. Four frozen serum pools were prepared from a different set of off-the-clot, non-supplemented human serum that was pooled in two 3-liter bottles, frozen in bulk, thawed, remixed, aliquoted, and refrozen. One to four of these frozen human serum pools showed significant matrix bias as compared to non-frozen individual donor sera for each of four routine methods.

Tetrault et al.[12] prepared three frozen human serum pools from off-the-clot serum that was frozen, thawed, pooled, aliquoted, and refrozen. One of the pools was supplemented with an ultracentrifugally concentrated human serum low-density-lipoprotein (LDL) fraction from outdated blood bank plasma. Matrix bias was determined as the difference in apparent bias indicated by the mean of 16 fresh non-frozen patient sera versus the frozen pooled materials. All concentration values were assigned by the CDC reference methods for TC and HDL-cholesterol (HDL-C). One or more of the frozen human serum pools showed matrix bias for four of seven routine enzymatic methods for TC and for six of seven routine methods for HDL-C.

Holani et al.[13] used the College of American Pathologists (CAP) matrix effect evaluation protocol[14] to test five CAP processed freeze-dried serum pools and nine CDC supplemented frozen serum pools using three commercial enzymatic reagents for TG measurement. Twenty-four freshly collected individual sera were used as controls for no matrix bias. All specimens were assayed by the CDC chromotropic acid TG reference method and by three glycerol blank corrected commercial reagent systems adapted to a Cobas-BIO analyzer (Roche Instruments, Nutley, NJ). Results of two of the commercial reagents for both CAP and CDC proficiency testing (PT) materials were commutable with fresh sera. Results of the third reagent system were commutable with the CDC frozen pools but had a significant matrix bias for four out of five CAP freeze-dried materials.

SOURCE OF MATRIX MODIFICATIONS: TYPICAL PREPARATION OF SERUM-BASED REFERENCE MATERIALS

Serum-based reference materials can undergo a substantial number of processes during their manufacture that can change the matrix from that of native serum.[15–18] The starting material is commonly plasma collected at a commercial donor center. The plasma may be stored in liquid form or, more typically, frozen for several months prior to use. Off-the-clot serum can be used to obtain the base material, but it is more expensive than plasma due to the time delay for clotting and its special handling requirements. Plasma is defibrinated and converted to serum by addition of calcium and clotting agents. The recovered serum may undergo various additional processes, such as filtration, dialysis, ion exchange, reverse osmosis, charcoal adsorption, or lipid stripping[19] to reduce endogenous constituents to low levels.

Various spiking materials are added to the base serum pool to produce the desired composition and concentrations of analytes. Other additives may also be used to prevent microbial growth, to enhance product stability, or to enhance compatibility with an analytical system. In the case of lipid products, the common spiking materials are LDL-rich and HDL-rich fractions from human serum obtained by various modifications of the ethanol and pH precipitation procedures originally described by Cohn.[16,20] TG-rich additives are typically obtained from hen egg yolk.[17,18] Ultracentrifugation can be used to obtain concentrated lipoprotein fractions from serum when smaller quantities of additive are required.[12]

Once the pool is prepared and analytes are adjusted to desired concentrations, the material is mixed to homogeneity, filtered to 0.22 μm to remove bacteria and aggregated material, and dispensed into vials. The vials can be frozen or freeze-dried for storage and distribution. Freezing below $-50°C$ is necessary to fully crystallize water[21] and provide maximum stability of serum materials. Freeze-drying is commonly used because the materials can be stored, packaged, and shipped (usually at ambient temperatures) considerably more economically than when frozen. Substances such as sucrose are sometimes added to confer cryoprotection to lipid molecules during freeze-drying cycles.[22]

The freeze-drying process has been shown to alter the physical properties of serum materials. Rej[6,23] reported that lyophilization of an aliquot of serum produced moderate changes in osmolality, surface tension, and viscosity, and produced large changes in pH, number and size of particles, and absorbance. It is well accepted that freeze-drying produces denaturation of lipoprotein particles, which makes them difficult to resolubilize in water and increases turbidity in reconstituted specimens. Kroll et al.[24] showed that freeze-drying two serum pools decreased the recovery of TC for four routine enzymatic methods compared to freezing at $-20°C$ or $-70°C$. Marcovina et al.[25] showed a systematic decrease in recovery of apo B by seven immunologic methods after lyophilization of six human serum pools. Kroll and Chesler[26] reported that five commercial and two in-house lyophilized pooled serum materials, including National Institute for Standards and Technology (NIST) Standard Reference Material (SRM) 909, had decreased recovery of TC with the duPont ACA due to a decreased reaction rate for the enzymatic hydrolysis of TC esters in these materials. The reaction time allowed by the analyzer was adequate for fresh human specimens but too short for complete hydrolysis of the matrix-altered lipoproteins in the lyophilized materials. Noel et al.[27] and Wiebe and Bernert[28] reported that cholesteryl esterases used in some enzymatic reagents did not completely hydrolyze cholesterol arachidonate present in some processed serum materials.

Myers et al.[29] described a CAP lipid survey material formulation that more closely resembled the characteristics of native serum. The CAP lipid product was prepared from off-the-clot human serum. Serum units were assayed for TC, HDL-C, and TG and blended into pools to achieve the desired analyte concentrations. The pools were freeze-dried and showed good inter-method comparability in survey results. More recently the CAP survey program has used frozen pooled human sera collected similarly as off-the-clot serum.

Stabilized liquid lipid reference materials have been developed by several vendors using proprietary stabilization processes. The convenience of liquid materials for quality control and PT applications will stimulate further development of these products. The matrix-related nonspecificity of any new reference material requires careful investigation to establish its suitability for analytical usefulness.

IDENTIFYING MATRIX LIMITATIONS IN MATERIALS AND METHODS

Commutability of a reference material must be evaluated by comparing test results for an analyte in that material to those obtained for individual patients' specimens for the methods of interest. Each individual's serum is variable in many components, including the distribution of lipoproteins. This variability becomes greater when sera from diseased persons are included to evaluate the full analytical range for a method. Thus, a group of freshly collected patient sera will differ physiologically in composition, and these sera may exhibit some variability in chemical reactivity when assayed by a routine method with limitations in chemical specificity. When comparing the analytical performance of clinical specimens between routine and reference methods, any observations of "outliers" must be evaluated carefully, as they may represent methodological limitations of the routine method when used with patients' specimens. Because of inherent physiological variability and the analytical imprecision of measurement, an adequate number of representative freshly collected patients' specimens is essential to evaluate a material's or method's performance.

Any inference about the presence of matrix bias in a processed material must be based on a statistically sound evaluation protocol. The CAP has developed a protocol to detect the presence of matrix effects in processed materials when a reliable accuracy comparison method is available.[14] NCCLS has developed the CAP approach into a consensus guideline.[4] Briefly, the protocol involves selecting 20 or more freshly collected individual human specimens and assaying them along with the processed materials under evaluation, using the test method and a suitable comparison method. The comparison method should be the most robust method available—ideally a NRSCL-credentialed reference method, such as Abell-Kendall[30] for TC or beta-quantification for HDL and LDL cholesterol[31]; or the best-characterized consensus method available for the analyte. Regression analysis on the native patients' results from each method is used to establish a 95% prediction interval, and the processed materials are evaluated for conformance to that interval.

This protocol identifies commutability of a material but does not specifically quantitate the magnitude of any matrix bias that may be present. When used with a chemically specific reference method, this procedure can also validate the accuracy of a routine method for patients' specimens and determine whether processed materials can be used for assessment of the method's accuracy. When used with a non-credentialed comparison method, this procedure can only confirm commutability of a material between the two methods.

Rej et al.[6] have described use of correspondence analysis[32] as a statistical tool to evaluate the commutability of processed materials with authentic clinical specimens. This technique does not require an accuracy-based reference method and does not quantitate matrix bias or calibration bias. The approach is useful for evaluating commutability among materials by simultaneously comparing reactivity characteristics among several materials assayed by several analytical methods. This procedure uses a multivariate statistical analysis and produces a two-dimensional projection of the most significant analytical components. Materials and methods that have commutable reactivity characteristics cluster in the same region as clinical specimens, while materials and methods with matrix interactions are located elsewhere.

EXAMPLES OF MATRIX RELATED PROBLEMS

Koch et al. demonstrated matrix-related limitations in reference materials in 1988.[33] They documented that the accuracy of four routine TC methods for freshly collected non-frozen individual patients' sera had an average bias of $< 2.7\%$ compared to the Abell-Kendall reference method. Also assayed with each of the four methods were processed, freeze-dried serum materials intended for calibration of TC: NIST SRM 909 and three CAP Lipid Reference Materials. When the results for the reference materials were compared to the Abell-Kendall assigned target values, two of the routine methods had insignificant apparent biases ranging from -1.1% to $+2.3\%$, while the other two routine methods had significant apparent biases ranging from -9.8% to -4.8%. Those two routine methods had chemical nonspecificity for the matrix-modified reference materials, which resulted in incorrect recovery of the TC. Consequently if the materials had been used for calibration of those methods, results for patients' specimens would have been incorrect.

A CAP-sponsored conference in 1992, "Matrix Effects and Accuracy Assessment in Clinical Chemistry,"[34] reviewed the state of the art in understanding and controlling matrix interactions and its impact on method performance. At this conference, Naito et al.[35] demonstrated the possible errors in interpretation of PT results for TC using processed serum materials. They described a standardization program for TC that included 174 VA medical centers. Each center received six fresh, non-frozen, non-supplemented, pooled human serum samples and five freeze-dried, human-Cohn-fraction-supplemented, pooled human serum-based materials as used in the 1990 CAP PT program. The fresh, non-frozen serum pools were assumed to be free of any matrix interactions. Target values for the materials were set by the CDC using the Abell-Kendall method. Based on the fresh serum results, 112 laboratories (63%) met the ±3% analytical bias specifications of the National Cholesterol Education Program (NCEP), and their results were used to evaluate matrix biases in the freeze-dried processed materials. Six of eight routine methods had matrix-induced apparent biases with the lyophilized materials that ranged from −8.9% to +4.4%. Figure 35–1 illustrates the insidious nature of matrix bias using the duPont Dimension as an example. In this case, although results for patient specimens were correct, the PT results incorrectly indicated an apparent bias in results. The results from these PT materials could not be used to judge the performance of a laboratory for patient specimens.

At the CAP conference, Ross et al.[36] reported results from an extensive evaluation of matrix effects in 37 routine method peer groups in the 1989 CAP Survey PT program. A sample of 915 out of approximately 5,000 participants assayed a single, freshly collected, off-the-clot, non-supplemented, frozen, pooled serum specimen as well as the two freeze-dried, human-Cohn-fraction-supplemented, pooled human serum-based materials used in the PT program at that time. The fresh-frozen material was assumed to be free of matrix interactions. Target values for TC were assigned by both the NIST, using the definitive isotope dilution mass spectrometry method,[37] and the CDC, using the Abell-Kendall reference method.[30] Method calibration bias was determined as the difference between the peer group mean result and the definitive method target value for the fresh-frozen specimen. Method matrix bias was quantitated as the difference between the peer group mean result for a freeze-dried survey material and its definitive method target value minus the calibration bias determined from the fresh frozen serum specimen. The freeze-dried PT material used for statistical analysis had a reference method TC of 204 mg/dL (5.29 mmol/L), which closely matched the fresh-frozen serum value of 198 mg/dL (5.11 mmol/L). The participants were divided into 37 unique method groups based on instrumentation and reagent source. Of these method groups, 70% exhibited a significant matrix bias with the freeze-dried survey material using the NIST definitive method as the basis for accuracy evaluation. Ten of the analytical systems in this study had an apparently small survey bias but, because of the method-material matrix bias, actually had a significant calibration bias for the fresh-frozen serum specimen.

Lasky et al.[38] evaluated the matrix bias of PT materials used for TC assessment in eight different survey programs from four countries. They used frozen human serum pools, some of which were supplemented with human serum cholesterol concentrates, as the basis for evaluation of the processed freeze-dried materials. The Abell-Kendall reference method was used for target value assignment. Ten routine methods had acceptable performance with frozen serum pools; however, based on

Figure 35–1 ✧ Example of Matrix Effects between duPont Dimension and CAP and Proficiency Testing Materials

The ideal line is the line of identity. The patient-regression line represents mean values of triplicate measurements on each of the five fresh human specimens plotted against CDC reference-method values (duplicate measurements). The CAP-regression line represents triplicate measurements on each of the five 1990 CAP Comprehensive Chemistry Survey specimens plotted agsinst the CDC reference-method values. Data also indicate the laboratory's overall precision, mean bias on measurement of fresh human materials, and mean bias on measurement of CAP Survey materials. CV = Coefficient of variation. *Source*: Naito et al.[35] Reprinted by permission.

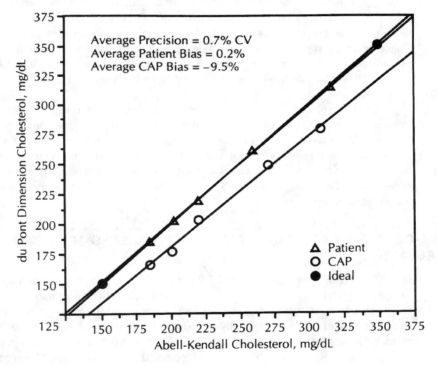

(To convert mg/dL to mmol/L, multiply by 0.0259.)

the CLIA'88 ±10% criterion, nine methods would have failed PT with one or more processed materials.

Franzini and Luraschi[39] evaluated the commutability of 24 lyophilized commercial control materials from 11 manufacturers with 107 individual patients' sera assayed by two methods using Roche Diagnostics, then Boehringer Mannheim, enzymatic TC reagents. They showed that if the lyophilized materials had been used as calibrators, seven of the materials had a matrix interaction that would have introduced a mean bias of > 3% into the patients' results.

Kroll and Chesler[40] investigated the impact of matrix modification on HDL-C methods. They measured HDL-C in serial dilutions of a fresh serum pool, two concentrations of Sigma HDL-C lyophilized control materials, and CAP lyophilized serum-based linearity materials. Eight routine laboratory methods were tested, four using dextran sulfate and four using phosphotungstate precipitating agents. Kroll and Chesler concluded that matrix modifications in the lyophilized materials affected the precipitation step and resulted in apparent non-linearity that was not observed with the fresh serum pool.

Little information is available on the matrix sensitivity of the current generation of homogeneous methods for HDL-C and LDL-cholesterol (LDL-C). Rifai et al.[41] assayed the older lyophilized CAP Survey PT materials in three labs all using the same homogeneous HDL-C method. Comparison of results to the CDC reference method indicated an apparent matrix-related bias in one of five materials. They also tested ten fresh unfrozen serum pools and eight frozen serum pools with no apparent effects. These authors reported that the homogeneous method was specific to human lipoproteins and gave erroneous results for rodent serum. It is likely all of the homogeneous HDL-C and LDL-C methods will show sensitivity to matrix alterations in reference materials.

The literature clearly demonstrates that matrix-modified serum-based materials frequently have significant method-material matrix interactions that prevent them from reliably assessing method performance with native human serum specimens. Proficiency testing results are not a reliable indicator of the true accuracy of a laboratory's results for patients' specimens. Inappropriate interpretation of PT results as an assessment of accuracy can lead to incorrect inference on the true accuracy of results for patients' specimens.

MATRIX-COMPENSATED TARGET VALUES TO ASSESS ACCURACY FOR LIPID ASSAYS

In 1994, the CAP extended the 1989 PT evaluation and included a carefully prepared fresh-frozen serum specimen in the survey materials sent to a sample of participants (approximately 700 from 7000) representing 15 peer groups in the survey program[42]. Each participant assayed the fresh-frozen specimen along with the usual survey specimens for 11 analytes including TC, HDL-C and TG. The fresh-frozen serum specimen was prepared according to specifications that formed the basis for the NCCLS guideline.[7] All materials were assayed by the CDC reference methods for lipid analytes. The participant results for the fresh-frozen serum specimen were used to evaluate accuracy vs. the reference methods and to quantitate peer group calibration bias. Likewise participant results for the PT materials vs. the reference methods quantitated the apparent survey bias. The apparent survey bias contains components from both calibration and matrix sources. The difference between apparent survey bias and actual calibration bias quantitated the matrix bias for each peer group. The results supported the earlier conclusions that matrix bias was fairly common, was quantitatively different for different peer groups, and was unique to specific method/material combinations.

Two types of PT materials were used in the 1994 CAP Survey program. One type was lyophilized serum-based multi-constituent material prepared from defibrinated plasma that was supplemented with non-human purified lipid components and other general chemistry analytes. The other material type was lyophilized off-the-clot serum prepared from units that had been stored at 4°C for up to three months and then pooled based on lipid concentrations; no supplements or other analytes were added. Significant matrix biases were noted for both types of materials with most methods. For TC, 15 peer groups were evaluated across four materials, two of each type. For TC, 93% of the supplemented multi-constituent specimens and 70% of the pooled serum specimens had significant matrix bias. For HDL-C, 14 peer groups were evaluated across four materials, two of each type. For HDL-C, 71% of the supplemented multi-constituent specimens and 86% of the pooled serum specimens had significant matrix bias. For TG, 16 peer groups were evaluated with one supplemented multi-constituent material that had significant matrix bias with 50% of methods. The magnitude of matrix bias ranged from -0.5 to 4.7% for TC, from -26.2 to 61.8% for HDL-C, and from -11.5 to 45.0% for TG.

This CAP evaluation showed that the reference method result for a PT material could not be used to evaluate the accuracy of a routine laboratory method. A matrix bias correction factor was calculated from the quantified matrix bias for each method-material combination. This transfer function was then applied to the reference method value to calculate a peer group specific matrix compensated target value for each method-material combination. This matrix-compensated target value can be used as the appropriate recovery value to indicate that a method was correctly calibrated to report accurate results for native patients' serum specimens. Table 35-1 shows selected examples of matrix compensated target values for accuracy assessment. This design offers the possibility of using a PT program to sample a large number of routine labs and reliably evaluate a method's accuracy for authentic clinical specimens. Matrix-compensated target values were applied to the individual results for all survey program participants and performance was compared to CLIA'88 target values for PT programs in 1994 (TC $\pm 10\%$; HDL-C $\pm 30\%$; TG $\pm 25\%$). The acceptable results (average per specimen) were 97.7% for TC; 93.7% for HDL-C; and 98.9% for TG.

MATRIX ISSUES IN OTHER LIPOPROTEIN MEASUREMENTS

Apolipoprotein assays present a different challenge when controlling for matrix interactions between different lots of reagents and calibrators and inter-instrument analytical variability. There are substantial method/material matrix interactions with apolipoprotein assays. However, there are no credentialed reference methods with well-established performance characteristics. Thus, the method of accuracy transfer or validation based on splitting fresh human sera is not possible.

Standardization of apo A-I and apo B accuracy is being accomplished using commutable serum reference materials, with consensus target values assigned, which are approved by the World Health Organization (WHO) and distributed to analytical method manufacturers. Thus, the state of the art depends on the continued commutability of the reference materials and the ability of manufacturers to transfer that accuracy to the secondary calibration materials provided with the assay systems.

Table 35–1 ◇ Matrix-Compensated Target Values for Cholesterol in One PT Specimen*

Peer Group (in 1994)	Survey Mean Value (mg/dL)	Matrix Bias (%)	Actual Calibration Bias (%)	Matrix-Compens ated Target Value at 95% Confidence Interval (mg/dL)
BMC 747 (now Roche/Hitachi 747)	163.6	−4.2%	0.3%	162.2–163.9
Beckman CX (now Beckman-Coulter CX)	174.7	−0.5%	3.1%	168.5–170.3
DuPont Dimension (now Dade Dimension)	154.3	−10.5%	1.2%	151.5–153.1
Kodak Ektachem (now Ortho Vitros)	168.4	1.8%	−2.8%	172.5–173.9

*Adapted from Ross et al.[42] for CAP 1994 survey specimen C-02, which had CDC reference method value 170.2 mg/dL. The matrix-compensated target value can be used to evaluate calibration accuracy for authentic clinical serum specimens.

Smith et al.[43] reported an international investigation of four non-supplemented lyophilized human serum pools by eight method principles in 140 laboratories. They found that some lyophilized materials had equivalent mean values for apo A-I among the method groups, but that all materials had significantly different apparent mean values for apo B assays.

Marcovina et al.[44] prepared three non-supplemented human serum pools for apo A-I and six such pools for apo B. Half the vials were stored frozen at −78°C and the other half were lyophilized. Each material was assayed by five method principles with a common frozen serum pool used to standardize calibration for each method. Apo A-I values were the same for frozen and lyophilized pools. Apo B values for the lyophilized pools differed from those of the frozen materials by −26% to +4%, depending on the assay method.

Albers et al.[45] reported results from an investigation of reference materials for calibration of apo A-I and B that was conducted by the International Federation of Clinical Chemistry (IFCC) Committee on Apolipoprotein Standardization. The inter-method commutability of 15 candidate reference materials for apo A-I and 11 materials for apo B were evaluated by 26 and 28 methods, respectively, in 28 laboratories in nine countries. Three non-supplemented, fresh-frozen human serum pools were used to standardize calibration among the laboratories. Ten fresh-frozen individual donor sera were used to confirm standardization with an inter-method coefficient of variance (CV) of 5% for apo

A-I and 6.3% for apo B. For the candidate materials, inter-method CVs for apo A-I ranged from 4.4% to 80.6%, with four of 15 materials having an inter-method CV <5%. For apo B, inter-method CVs ranged from 6.0% to 35.1%, with three of 11 materials ≤ 7%. Only three materials for each apolipoprotein had no turbidity and nearly normal lipoprotein patterns on electrophoresis. The most suitable candidate reference materials for apo A-I were lyophilized and those for apo B were liquid stabilized.

Subsequent work by Marcovina et al.[46] utilized linearity and parallelism evaluation to identify one material for apo A-I (inter-method CV = 3%) and one for apo B (inter-method CV = 6%) which were sufficiently commutable for use as calibration reference materials. Marcovina et al.[47] reported value assignment and use of the apo A-I reference material to standardize calibration of 30 routine methods involving 23 manufacturers. Assays of 50 fresh-frozen individual donor sera by each participant resulted in an inter-laboratory CV for each sample ranging from 2.1% to 5.6%. Similarly, the apo B reference material was value assigned and used to standardize calibration of 28 methods from 21 manufacturers. Comparison of inter-laboratory results for fresh-frozen sera gave CVs ranging from 3.1% to 6.7%, again demonstrating good commutability of the reference material. These two materials have been endorsed by the WHO as International Reference Materials for Apolipoprotein A-I and Apolipoprotein B. These materials are only available to manufacturers and select reference laboratories.

An IFCC working group is approaching the standardization of Lp(a) following an approach similar to that used for apo A-I and B. This strategy will identify commutable reference materials that can be value assigned and then used by all manufacturers to calibrate their assay systems. Phase 1 of the project has been reported by Tate et al.[48] in which 40 methods were evaluated using both pooled human sera and candidate commercial calibration materials. One-half the methods were found to be non-optimized for precision, linearity, or parallelism, based on the results for fresh and frozen pooled serum specimens. For additional information on the standardization of Lp(a), refer to chapter 17.

IMPACT OF MATRIX LIMITATIONS ON CALIBRATION AND VERIFICATION OF ACCURACY

Calibration

Calibration of lipid testing is generally provided by the analytical system manufacturer. TC, HDL-C, LDL-C and TG methods are standardized by splitting freshly collected patients' sera with a laboratory of the Cholesterol Reference Method Laboratory Network (CRMLN) sponsored by the CDC. Apo AI and B are standardized by reference to the WHO International Reference Materials. For all analytes, the manufacturer must transfer the accuracy base to a series of secondary calibration products for use in many individual laboratories to calibrate individual lots of reagents used with individual instrument systems.

Accuracy transfer to individual laboratories is a substantial analytical challenge[49,50] Manufacturing of equipment, reagents, and calibration products is performed to tolerances defined to allow the total error of the final analytical system to meet medical requirements at an acceptable cost. Manufacturing tolerances result in some degree of variability among instruments, lots of reagents, and lots of calibrators. Some variables, such as shipping and storage conditions, operating environment conditions, equipment maintenance, and operator training are beyond the control of manufacturers yet can affect the accuracy of results and must be accommodated in the total analytical system design.

The calibration material provided by an analytical system manufacturer is formulated and value assigned to compensate for any unique matrix effects such that patients' specimens assayed by that specific method are correctly traceable to national or international accuracy guidelines. Because of unpredictable matrix interactions, one cannot use calibration materials from one manufacturer with a reagent or instrument system from a different manufacturer. If one intends to mix sources of instrument, reagent, and calibrator materials, that specific combination must be validated for accuracy using one of the patient-specimen-based strategies mentioned previously and discussed in detail in Chapter 36. The validation can be performed by a material vendor or the individual laboratory.

Verification of Accuracy

The success of accuracy transfer to individual laboratories has been investigated. Kimberly et al.[51] found that approximately 20% of clinical laboratories splitting patients' sera with one of the CRMLN laboratories during 1991–92 failed to meet the NCEP 3% accuracy guideline for TC. The CAP included a fresh-frozen serum specimen in the 1994 Comprehensive Chemistry Survey, which was assayed by 570 routine laboratories[42]. Eleven of 15 peer groups had statistically significant mean calibration bias for TC versus the CDC Abell-Kendall method, with two peer groups exceeding the NCEP 3% mean bias accuracy guideline. However, 97.6% of individual laboratories had TC results within the 8.9% total error specification for an individual measurement. For HDL-C, eight of ten peer groups had significant mean calibration bias versus the CDC reference method, with two peer groups exceeding 10% bias and five exceeding 5% bias. For TG, after correcting for free glycerol, 15 of 16 methods had significant mean calibration bias versus the CDC reference method, with two peer groups exceeding 10% bias and nine exceeding 5% bias.

Individual laboratories can validate accuracy relative to the NCEP guidelines using two strategies. First is to split freshly collected individual patient specimens with one of the CRMNL laboratories to evaluate agreement with the reference methods. Protocols have been established to meet the needs of clinical laboratories. The second strategy for accuracy validation is to assay a reference material that is suitable for the lab methods and has target values traceable to the reference methods.

Because matrix interferences are commonly observed in lipid assays one must use care in selecting a reference material for accuracy validation. When carefully prepared and properly validated, frozen serum reference materials can provide commutable reference materials for accuracy validation. The pools validated by the NCCLS protocol[7] are available from NIST and have been value assigned for TC, HDL-C, LDL-C, and TG by CDC reference methods. These pools were not validated for the new homogeneous HCL-C and LDL-C methods.

Within an individual laboratory, various reference materials can be value assigned by that laboratory and then used periodically over time to check method performance. The value assignment should be performed at a time when the lab method is independently validated to meet NCEP performance guidelines using one of the techniques described above. Figure 35–2 illustrates the relationship between analytical accuracy validation and value assignment of a reference material to be used for monitoring relative accuracy on a continuing basis. This target value assignment strategy compensates for any matrix interaction that may be present between the reference materials and routine methods. As long as the matrix relationship does not change, the reference material can be used to confirm that the method calibration has been maintained relative to the time when the absolute accuracy was validated.

The primary limitation to lab-assigned target values on a reference material is change in matrix interaction between the reference material and the specific reagent lot in use. The more commutable a reference material, the more useful it is for long-term method monitoring. Frozen human serum pools provide highly reliable reference specimens to validate accuracy and troubleshoot method problems. Frozen serum pools with reference method value assignment are available from Pacific Biometrics Research Foundation (220 W. Harrison Street, Seattle, WA 98119, USA) and Solomon Park Research Laboratories (12815 N.E. 124th Street, Suite 1, Kirkland, WA 98034, USA)

Figure 35–2 ✧ Schematic of Calibration Adjustment based on Individual Patients' Sera and Matrix Compensated Value Assignment of a Reference Material for Subsequent Verification of Field (Routine) Method Accuracy

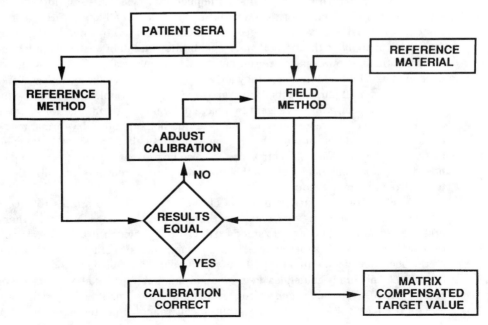

NIST SRM 909b is a two-concentration set of supplemented, freeze-dried pooled serum materials that have definitive and reference method values assigned for lipid parameters. The SRM 909b processed serum-based materials do exhibit matrix bias with various methods and must be used in conjunction with appropriate accuracy validation based on fresh sera.

Least robust as reference materials are commercially available lipid control materials. These materials are intended for process monitoring and can be very stable formulations. They frequently have significant matrix interactions with many routine methods and must be used in conjunction with appropriate accuracy validation based on fresh sera. When target values are provided, they are commonly based on minimal statistical designs and do not include accuracy traceability to the NRSCL. Consequently, value assigned quality control materials should not be used for accuracy verification.

IMPACT OF MATRIX LIMITATIONS ON PROFICIENCY TESTING

PT materials in common use exhibit such sufficiently widespread matrix interactions that PT results cannot be used to evaluate a laboratory's ability to produce accurate lipid results for patients' specimens. Ross et al.[36] reported that 70% of the enzymatic methods in use for TC exhibited non-specific matrix interaction with one or more materials used in the 1989 CAP Survey program. In the 1994 CAP Survey program, 82% of TC, 79% of HDL-C, and 50% of TG method-material combinations had significant matrix interactions.[42]

All providers of large PT programs in the United States are currently evaluating lipid assays by comparison of results to the peer-group mean. Peer-group evaluation compares an individual laboratory's result to the mean of all laboratories using the same method. Variability within a peer group can be caused by an individual laboratory's skill at applying the method and by calibration variability in the manufacturer's accuracy transfer process. Peer-group evaluation is minimally affected by the presence of matrix interactions since they are a property of the assay system and should be the same for all participants. However, there can be variable matrix bias within a homogeneous peer group if reagent lots have different matrix interactions with a PT material. Some of the newer compact analyzer methods that use dry-format reagents and membrane and filtration technology may be particularly sensitive to lot-specific matrix interactions. Variable matrix bias can also be present within a peer group composed of hybrid analytical systems that, for example, use reagents or calibration materials from different vendors.

A peer group evaluation protocol allows individual laboratories to ascertain whether they are applying a particular methodology in the same manner as other laboratories. In addition, peer group standard deviations provide a useful indicator of between lab precision for a method. Peer group evaluation does not provide information on the accuracy of a method for patients' specimens, and thus does not allow validation of NCEP accuracy guidelines. Peer group evaluation does not allow comparison of results between methods. Peer-group evaluation is not suitable for small method groups because a statistically valid group mean cannot be determined. Small peer groups cannot be evaluated against some other target value because matrix bias is likely to invalidate the comparison.

Laboratories that calibrate hybrid systems or find it necessary to adjust the manufacturer's calibration settings to meet NCEP guidelines will need to report PT results appropriately to permit useful evaluation. Appropriate reporting requires any calibration offsets from the manufacturers settings to be removed to permit comparison of PT results to the peer group mean. The method/material matrix interaction is a function of the methodology and is unaffected by calibration adjustments.

One should not report calibration-adjusted PT results with a method designation of "other." PT providers may evaluate "other" method groups against a reference-method-assigned target value, the all-method mean, or some other target value derived from the participants' results. If there are matrix-induced biases with the PT materials, reliable evaluation of the laboratory's performance will be impossible.

The most useful strategy is to report PT results after removing adjustment factors to revert to the manufacturer's original calibration settings. In this way, PT results can be compared to an appropriate peer-group target value to evaluate the laboratory's ability to correctly use the analytical system. A calibration offset does not change the matrix interaction. Thus, removing mathematical calibration adjustments prior to assaying the PT specimens or mathematically "back-calculating" the PT results to reflect the manufacturer's calibration settings does not alter the method's operational condition.

Restoration of instrument calibration settings to manufacturer's specifications for assay of PT specimens does not violate CLIA'88 regulations as long as a new calibration event with resetting of the base calibration factors is not performed. The regulations state:

⬧ "If a laboratory performs the same test using different methodologies or instruments, or performs the same test at multiple testing sites, the laboratory must have a system that twice a year evaluates and defines the relationship between test results using different methodologies, instruments, or testing sites."[52]; and

⬧ "Pertinent 'reference' . . . ranges . . . must be available to the authorized person who ordered the tests or the individual responsible for utilizing the test results."[53]

These regulations support calibration adjustments that produce the same clinical result with the same reference range for an analyte irrespective of the method or test site performing the assay. This calibration adjustment process will optimize clinical interpretation of the results. The regulations further state:

⬧ "Pertinent updates on testing information must be provided to clients whenever changes occur that affect the test results or interpretation of test results.[54]

This section, when applied to specimens received from the PT provider as the client, means the results must be reported with the calibration set such that the results can be interpreted correctly. PT results can only be interpreted correctly if they can be compared to the peer group mean. Thus the method calibration must be restored to the manufacturer's original settings and any mathematical calibration adjustments necessary for patient results to agree with a reference method removed.

An additional pertinent regulation is this one:

✧ "The laboratory must examine or test . . . the proficiency testing samples . . . in the same manner as it tests patient specimens."[55]

This regulation means that a lab cannot recalibrate the measurement system with a new set of calibration materials solely for the purpose of assaying PT specimens. However, removing the post-assay calibration adjustment factors from the PT result or simply restoring the calibration settings to the original manufacturer's values without performing a new calibration event does not change the base calibration parameters in current use for patient specimen testing. The process only removes the amount of offset required to have the method produce clinical results in agreement with a reference method and appropriate for the clinical interpretation criteria.

PT providers are restricted to peer group evaluation until PT materials are improved to the point of good commutability between routine lab methods.

The specialty program offered by Pacific Biometrics Research Foundation offers an option for PT of lipid methods. This program uses freshly collected, non-supplemented, non-frozen pooled human serum specimens that are likely to have minimal method/material matrix interactions. Target values are assigned by certified reference methods. This approach offers the possibility for reliable evaluation of accuracy. Detailed evaluation of the effectiveness of this PT program awaits publication. A similar program is available in Canada through the Canadian Reference Foundation (307–2083 Alma Street, Vancouver, BC V6R 4N6).

SUMMARY AND FUTURE DIRECTIONS IN CONTROLLING MATRIX LIMITATIONS

Matrix modifications are inherent in the current state of the art for producing large quantities of stable serum-based reference materials. Recent efforts have successfully produced moderate quantities of highly commutable frozen serum pools and other analyte-specific reference materials. Future efforts should continue to develop and validate commutable materials, perhaps utilizing the tools of molecular biology to make robust molecules for reference materials.

Standardization and calibration can be successfully performed with the current materials and analytical strategies. Authentic clinical specimens split between routine and certified reference methods continues to be the primary mechanism to both establish and verify accuracy. Although expensive, this strategy has worked successfully at the manufacturer level to achieve practical standardization of TC, HDL-C, LDL-C, and TG. A second protocol adopted for apo AI and B and in development for Lp(a) utilizes commutable reference materials with consensus target values. These materials are endorsed by the WHO and are used by manufacturers to calibrate commercial assay methods. Highly commutable frozen serum pool materials with reference method target values assigned are now available from NIST and other commercial suppliers.

Good laboratory practice requires standardized, accurate results to meet national recommendations for medical diagnosis and therapeutic intervention for lipid disorders. Accuracy transfer from manufacturers to individual laboratory instrument systems utilizes a variety of techniques and frequently uses matrix-modified materials for routine method calibration. These calibration materials are intended for use with specific assay systems and should not be used for calibration or accuracy validation of other systems. The likely presence of unpredictable matrix interactions with these materials precludes their use except as specifically documented.

Current regulations require that accuracy be independently verified at each laboratory testing location using a PT program. Consequently, analytical methods should be designed to recover analyte from the usual patient specimens as well as from available reference materials. New measurement technology must address the PT requirement as an integral part of the assay system. Robust assay characteristics must be uniformly manufactured into subsequent lots of reagents, calibrators, and other analytical components of the measurement system.

Most large PT programs use serum-based materials that are known to have matrix interactions with routine methods. The method-material matrix interactions compromise the PT material's ability to mimic the analytical performance of authentic clinical specimens. Consequently, PT results cannot be used to evaluate a routine method for its accuracy for patient specimens. The current practice of evaluating PT results by conformance to a method peer group mean value only establishes that an individual laboratory utilizes a measurement system the same as other users of that system. Peer group evaluation does not evaluate the accuracy of a laboratory for analysis of patients' specimens. Consequently, laboratories must also perform a patient specimen comparison with a certified reference laboratory or utilize a documented commutable reference material with NRSCL target values to validate accuracy and conformance with NCEP guidelines.

It would be possible to evaluate accuracy in the presence of matrix interactions if the method/material-specific matrix bias could be measured and were constant and predictable among laboratories using a particular method. The CAP tested this concept for evaluation of TC, HDL-C, and TG in the 1994 Survey Program.[42] This evaluation strategy is very promising for allowing PT to be used to assess a laboratory's accuracy for the clinically relevant patients' specimens. The alternative is to continue to develop commutable materials for use as PT and reference preparations. Some PT programs are using frozen pooled specimens from unmodified off-the-clot serum. These materials offer the possibility of evaluating accuracy among different methods and laboratories.   ✧

REFERENCES

1. Fasce CF, Rej R, Copeland WH, Vanderlinde RE. A discussion of enzyme reference materials: applications and specifications. Clin Chem 1973;19:5–9.
2. Miller WG, Kaufman H. College of American Pathologists Conference XXIII. Introduction: matrix effects and accuracy assessment in clinical chemistry. Arch Pathol Lab Med 1993;117:343–4.
3. NCCLS. Terminology and definitions for use in NCCLS documents; approved standard. NCCLS Document No. NRSCL8-A (ISBN 1–56238–359–0). NCCLS, 940 West Valley Rd., Suite 1400 Wayne, PA 19087–1898 USA. 1998.
4. NCCLS. Evaluation of matrix effects; proposed guideline. NCCLS document EP14-P

(ISBN 1–56238–345–0). NCCLS, 940 West Valley Rd., Suite 1400 Wayne, PA 19087–1898 USA. 1998.

5. ASTM Committee on Terminology. Compilation of ASTM standard definitions. Philadelphia, PA: American Society for Testing and Materials, 1990.

6. Rej R. Accurate enzyme activity measurements: two decades of development in the commutability of enzyme quality control materials. Arch Pathol Lab Med 1993;117:352–64.

7. NCCLS. Preparation and validation of commutable frozen human serum pools as secondary reference materials for cholesterol measurement procedures; approved guideline. NCCLS document C37-A (ISBN 1–56238). NCCLS, 940 West Valley Rd., Suite 1400 Wayne, PA 19087–1898 USA. 1999.

8. Warnick GR, Albers JJ. Physiological and analytical variation in cholesterol and triglycerides. Lipids 1976;203–8.

9. Waymack PP, Miller WG, Myers GL. Assay instrument-dependent matrix effects in standardization of cholesterol measurements. Clin Chem 1993;39:2058–62.

10. Myers GL, Schap D, Smith SJ, et al. College of American Pathologists–Centers for disease control collaborative study for evaluating reference materials for total serum cholesterol measurements. Arch Pathol Lab Med 1990;114:1199–1205.

11. Miller WG, Brown B, Dalby T. Cholesterol matrix effects in fresh non-frozen and frozen serum pools. [Abstract]. Clin Chem 1991;37:920.

12. Tetrault GA, Miller WG, Chinchilli VM, et al. Regional inter-laboratory standardization of determination of cholesterol, high-density lipoprotein cholesterol, and triglycerides. Clin Chem 1990;36:145–9.

13. Holani KK, Miller WG, Waymack PP. Robustness of three triglyceride reagents for matrix effects of proficiency testing materials. [Abstract]. Clin Chem 1993;39:1126.

14. Eckfeldt JH, Copeland KR. Accuracy verification and identification of matrix effects: The College of American Pathologists' protocol. Arch Pathol Lab Med 1993;117:381–6.

15. Posner A. Problems in formulating method-insensitive proficiency testing materials. Arch Pathol Lab Med 1993;117:422–4.

16. Kuchmak M, Hazlehurst JS, Olansky AS, Taylor L. Reference sera with graded levels of high-density lipoprotein TC. Clin Chim Acta 1984;144:237–43.

17. Williams JH, Taylor L, Kuchmak M, Witter RF. Preparation of hypercholesterolemic and/or hypertriglyceridemic sera for lipid determinations. Clin Chim Acta 1970;28:247–53.

18. Kuchmak M, Taylor L, Williams JH. Preparation of reference sera with desired levels of TC and TG. Clin Chim Acta 1981;114:127–35.

19. Kuchmak M, Taylor L, Olansky AS. Low-lipid-level reference sera with human serum matrix. Clin Chim Acta 1981;116:125–30.

20. Cohn EJ, Strong LE, Hughes WL Jr, et al. Preparation and properties of serum and plasma proteins IV: a system for the separation into fractions of the protein and lipoprotein components of biological tissues and fluids. J Am Chem Soc 1946;68:459–75.

21. Van Brunt N, Egensperger H, Greenberg N, Halstead R, Cassano T, Doptis P. Serum-based quality control fluids and calibrators: is there an advantage of lyophilization over vacuum drying? [Abstract]. Clin Chem 1989;35:1101.

22. Baadenhuijsen H, Demacker PNM, Hessels M, Boerma GJM, Penders TJ, Weykamp C, Willems HL. Testing the accuracy of total cholesterol assays in an external quality control program. Effect of adding sucrose to lyophilized control sera compared with use of fresh or frozen sera. Clin Chem 1995;41:724–30.

23. Rej R, Jenny RW, Bretaudiere JP. Quality control in clinical chemistry: characterization of reference materials. Talanta 1984;31:851–62.

24. Kroll MH, Chesler R, Elin RJ. Effect of lyophilization of results of five enzymatic methods for cholesterol. Clin Chem 1989;35:1523–6.

25. Marcovina SM, Adolphson JL, Parlavecchia M, Albers JJ. Effects of lyophilization of serum on the measurement of apolipoproteins A-1 and B. Clin Chem 1990;36:366–9.

26. Kroll MH, Chesler R. Effect of serum lyophilization on the rate constants of enzymatic methods for measuring cholesterol. Clin Chem 1990;36:534–7.

27. Noel SP, Dupras R, Filion AM. The activity of cholesteryl ester hydrolase in the enzymatic determination of cholesterol: comparison of five enzymes obtained commercially. Analytical Biochemistry 1983;129:464–71.

28. Wiebe DA, Bernert JT. Influence of incomplete cholesteryl ester hydrolysis on enzymic measurements of cholesterol. Clin Chem 1984;30:352–6.

29. Myers GL, Ross JW, Smith SJ, Morris CH, Triplett RB, Groff M. Evaluating lyophilized human serum preparations for suitability as proficiency testing materials for high-density lipoprotein cholesterol measurement. Arch Pathol Lab Med 1995;119:686–94.

30. Cooper GR, Smith SJ, Duncan IW, Mather A, Fellows W D, Foley T, Frantz ID, Gill JB, Grooms TA, Hynie I. Inter-laboratory testing of the transferability of a candidate reference method for total cholesterol in serum. Clin Chem 1986;32:921–9.

31. Hainline A, Karon J, Lippel K, eds. Manual of laboratory operations. In: Lipid Research Clinics Program. Lipid and lipoprotein analysis, 2nd ed. Bethesda, MD: US Dept. Health and Human Services, 1982.

32. Greenacre M. Correspondence analysis in medical research. Stat Meth Med Res 1992; 1:97–117.

33. Koch DD, Hassemer DJ, Wiebe DA, Laessig RH. Testing cholesterol accuracy: performance of several common laboratory instruments. JAMA 1988;260:2552–7.

34. Miller WG, Kaufman H, McLendon WW. College of American Pathologists Conference XXIII: matrix effects and accuracy assessment in clinical chemistry. Arch Pathol Lab Med 1993;117(4):343–436.

35. Naito HK, Yun-Sik K, Hartfiel JL, et al. Matrix effects on proficiency testing materials: impact on accuracy of cholesterol measurement in laboratories in the nation's largest hospital system. Arch Pathol Lab Med 1993;117:345–51.

36. Ross JW, Myers GL, Gilmore BF, Cooper GR, Naito HR, Eckfeldt J. Matrix effects and the accuracy of cholesterol analysis. Arch Pathol Lab Med 1993;117:393–400.

37. Cohen A, Hertz HS, Mendel J, et al. Total serum cholesterol by isotope dilution/mass spectrometry: a candidate definitive method. Clin Chem 1980;26:854–60.

38. Lasky FD, Powers DM, Hassemer DJ, Wiebe DA. Quality of fluids used in external quality control programs affects the reliable assessment of accuracy of routine methods, as documented by cholesterol. Quality Control in the Clinical Laboratory '91. Proceedings of the 7th International Symposium on Quality Control, Tokyo, June 15–16, 1991: 199–208.

39. Franzini C, Luraschi P. Commutability of control materials in cholesterol measurement. Scand J Clin Lab Invest 1993;53:51–55.

40. Kroll MH, Chesler R. Non-linearity of high-density lipoprotein cholesterol determinations is matrix dependent. Clin Chem 1994;40:389–94.

41. Rifai N, Cole TG, Iannotti E, Law T, Macke M, Miller R, Dowd D, Wiebe DA. Assessment of inter-laboratory performance in external proficiency testing programs with a direct HDL-cholesterol assay. Clin Chem 1998;44:1452–1458.

42. Ross JW, Miller WG, Myers GL, Praestgaard J. The accuracy of laboratory measurements in clinical chemistry. A study of 11 routine chemistry analytes in the College of American Pathologists Chemistry Survey with fresh frozen serum, definitive methods, and reference methods. Arch Pathol Lab Med 1998;122:587–608.

43. Smith SJ, Henderson LO, Hannon WH, Cooper GR. Effects of analytical method and lyophilized sera on measurements of apolipoproteins A-1 and B: an international survey. Clin Chem 1990;36:290–6.

44. Marcovina SM, Albers JJ, Dati F, Ledue TB, Ritchie RF. International Federation of Clinical Chemistry standardization project for measurements of apolipoproteins A-1 and B. Clin Chem 1991;37:1676–82.

45. Albers JJ, Marcovina SM, Kennedy H. International Federation of Clinical Chemistry standardization project for measurements of apolipoproteins A-1 and B. II. Evaluation and selection of candidate reference materials. Clin Chem 1992;38:658–62.

46. Marcovina SM, Albers JJ, Henderson LO, Hannon WH. International Federation of Clinical Chemistry standardization project for measurements of apolipoproteins A-1 and B. III. Comparability of apolipoprotein A-1 values by use of international reference material. Clin Chem 1993;39:773–81.

47. Marcovina SM, Albers JJ, Kennedy H, Mei JV, Henderson LO, Hannon WH. International Federation of Clinical Chemistry standardization project for measurements of apolipoproteins A-1 and B. IV. Comparability of apolipoprotein B values by use of international reference material. Clin Chem 1994;40:586–92.

48. Tate JR, Rifai N, Berg K, Couderc R, Dati F, Kostner GM, Sakurabayashi I, Steinmetz A. International Federation of Clinical Chemistry standardization project for the measurement of lipoprotein(a). Phase I. Evaluation of the analytical performance of lipoprotein(a) assay systems and commercial calibrators. Clin Chem 1998;44:1629–1640.

49. Lasky FD. Achieving accuracy for routine clinical chemistry methods by using patient specimen correlations to assign calibrator values: a means of managing matrix effects. Arch Pathol Lab Med 1993;117:412–19.

50. Gochman N, Hall S. Manufacturer's approach to transferring accuracy to multiple field installations. Arch Pathol Lab Med 1993;117:420–1.

51. Kimberly MM, Smith JS, Myers GL. Evaluation of performance criteria for clinical laboratories in the Cholesterol Reference Method Laboratory Network (CRMLN). [Abstract]. Clin Chem 1993;39:1123.

52. Federal Register, Vol. 57, No. 40 (Feb. 28, 1992), p. 7184, section 493.1709. Washington DC: U.S. Government Printing Office.

53. Federal Register, Vol. 57, No. 40 (Feb. 28, 1992), p. 7162, section 493.1109, part d. Washington DC: U.S. Government Printing Office.

54. Federal Register, Vol. 57, No. 40 (Feb. 28, 1992), p. 7162, section 493.1109, part g. Washington DC: U.S. Government Printing Office.

55. Federal Register, Vol. 57, No. 40 (Feb. 28, 1992), p. 7146, section 493.801, part b. Washington DC: U.S. Government Printing Office.

Standardization of Lipid and Lipoprotein Measurements

36

Gary L. Myers, Gerald R. Cooper, Neil Greenberg,
Mary M. Kimberly, Parvin P. Waymack, and
David J. Hassemer

✧ The National Cholesterol Education Program (NCEP) mounted a concerted national effort to identify and treat every American adult who has high blood cholesterol and who therefore has increased risk of coronary heart disease (CHD). The association between increased total cholesterol (TC), due to increased concentrations of low-density-lipoprotein cholesterol (LDL-C), and the risk of premature CHD has been well documented.[1,2] In addition, high-density lipoprotein cholesterol (HDL-C) concentrations are known to be negatively associated with CHD risk.[3,4] The association of triglycerides (TG) with the risk of CHD has been somewhat controversial.[4–7] However, growing evidence indicates that an elevated TG serum level is a marker for increased risk of CHD.[8] Combined data from 17 prospective studies[9] and the Copenhagen Male Study[10] found that a high level of fasting TG is a strong risk factor for CHD independent of other risk factors, including HDL-C. TG's effect on the estimation of LDL-C by the Friedewald equation reinforces its importance as a risk factor.[11] Data from many epidemiological and clinical studies suggest that apolipoprotein A-I (apo A-I) and apo B-100 (apo B) may have promise as predictors of CHD risk and may eventually serve as additional markers of CHD risk.[12,13] Epidemiologic studies have also established a link between high concentration of Lp(a) and an increased risk of early CHD and stroke.[14–16]

In its first report, the Adult Treatment Panel (ATP) of the NCEP established uniform decision points for identifying individuals who have increased risk of CHD.[2] The ATP's guidelines outlined a systematic approach to treatment of increased blood cholesterol that based initial case findings on TC concentrations and cholesterol-lowering therapy on LDL-C as the primary decision point.

In 1993, the second report issued by the Adult Treatment Panel (ATP II) reaffirmed that lowering TC and LDL-C concentrations reduces the risk of CHD[17] (see Chapter 5 for additional information). However, ATP II raises some new issues that distinguish it from ATP I. For the clinical laboratory, the most significant difference is the increased emphasis on HDL-C as an independent risk factor for CHD. Specifically, ATP II recommends the addition of HDL-C to initial TC testing, so that whenever serum TC is measured for assessing CHD risk, HDL-C is also measured.

All this attention to TC and the lipoproteins has focused unprecedented national attention on clinical laboratories and the need to provide reliable measurements of TC, TG, HDL-C, and LDL-C. Given the central role of cholesterol measurement in the assessment and management of CHD risk, the NCEP established the Laboratory

Standardization Panel on Blood Cholesterol Measurement to assess the reliability of cholesterol measurement in clinical laboratories and to recommend means to improve the precision and accuracy of cholesterol testing. In 1988, the Laboratory Standardization Panel[18] recommended that cholesterol measurements be standardized so that values are traceable to the Centers for Disease Control and Prevention (CDC) cholesterol reference method,[19,20] which is a modification of the Abell-Kendall method,[21] or to the National Institute of Standards and Technology (NIST) definitive method for cholesterol, which involves isotope dilution-mass spectrometry.[22] For additional information on these methods, refer to chapter 9 or to the section below entitled "Cholesterol." In 1995 a second laboratory panel, the NCEP Lipoprotein Measurement Working Group, published similar guidelines for obtaining reliable TG,[23] HDL-C,[24] and LDL-C[25] measurements.

It is not possible or practical to require that all laboratories use the same measurement methods, calibrators, and controls. Nevertheless, the demand for measurement standardization in the product of the clinical laboratory, i.e., test results, is no different than consumer's demand for standardization of commercial products available from other industrial sectors. Consumers expect that light bulbs manufactured by any of perhaps 10 different manufacturers will all fit and operate properly in lamp sockets manufactured by yet another company. For the physicians and patient consumers of laboratory data, the same degree of interchangeability is expected for serum cholesterol measurements made on a single specimen, regardless of which company manufactured the reagents or the analytical equipment used for the measurement, or where and when the measurement was made.

For *in vitro* diagnostic tests, the expectation of standardization has recently achieved the status of a legal requirement. To comply with the European Union's *In Vitro* Diagnostic (IVD) Medical Device Directive[26] (compulsory after December 2003), *in vitro* diagnostic device manufacturers will need to define the traceability of "bottle" values (assigned to their commercial calibrators) to available reference materials and reference procedures. The key point to emphasize here is that all laboratory measurements should be *traceable*, i.e., all results for a given substance should be tied to a standard that is recognized and accepted at the national, and preferably the international, level. Metrological traceability requires that a well-defined analytical base is established, to provide a common denominator that permits laboratories to compare and interchange results, to monitor analytical performance, and to ensure the continuity of true and precise measurements.

The elements required to establish a traceable measurement system and accuracy base are defined in a draft international standard, which is being prepared via collaboration between the International Organization for Standardization (ISO) and the European Committee for Standarization (CEN).[27] These elements comprise a hierarchical framework of measurement procedures and reference materials, and should include, ideally, a primary reference method (referred to as a definitive method in the United States), primary reference materials, a secondary reference method, and secondary reference materials. With the required elements in place, these transferable calibration tools can be effectively employed by the in-house calibration laboratories of IVD device manufacturers to transfer accuracy from the reference system, down the calibration hierarchy, to the measurement products, reagents, assay kits, and systems used in routine clinical laboratories. Thus, at each level of the hierarchy, through to the end-user of commercial IVD devices, calibration is performed against a standard with metrological qualities that are pre-determined by calibration against a higher-level standard. The end-product of this process is an unbroken chain of comparisons, *traceable* up the hierarchy, back to a national or international standard that is acceptable to all parties.

THE ACCURACY BASE

For each lipid, lipoprotein, and apolipoprotein, an analytical procedure must be established that is widely accepted as the universal basis for reference measurements. While it is generally accepted that a primary reference method (definitive method) establishes a true value for a substance, primary measurement techniques are not widely available to fulfill all of the requirements necessary to provide a point of reference for effective laboratory standardization. As a result, primary methods are typically used to validate more widely available secondary reference methods, which in turn are designed for broader use and application.

If reference methods are to serve as the reference point for laboratory standardization, the problem becomes how to interface the accuracy base with the laboratory community. The base must be transferable on a broad scale. The most rapid and economical means of broadening the transfer of this accuracy base and of multiplying the impact of laborious reference-method analyses has traditionally been through the use of high-quality secondary reference materials. However, this approach to standardization by assigning target values to reference materials by primary or secondary reference methods has been complicated by fluid matrix effects in some analytical systems. This phenomenon is discussed later in this chapter and is presented in greater detail in Chapter 35.

Table 36–1 summarizes the components that make up reference systems for the various lipids, lipoproteins, and apolipoproteins.

Cholesterol

The standard for accuracy in blood cholesterol measurement is the National Reference System for Cholesterol (NRS/CHOL) established by the National Committee for Clinical Laboratory Standards (NCCLS).[28] The NRS/CHOL is a unique voluntary consensus standard endorsed by professional, industrial, and government organizations. It is made up of the NIST primary reference method (definitive method), the CDC secondary reference method, and a certified pure cholesterol standard, NIST SRM 911b.

The NIST primary reference method (definitive method) is an isotope dilution-mass spectrometry procedure.[22] The CDC secondary reference method for TC is a modification of the extraction procedure of Abell, Levy, Brodie, and Kendall.[21] The method consists of saponification of a 0.5-mL serum sample with alcoholic potassium hydroxide, extraction with hexane, evaporation of an aliquot of the extract, and development of color with Liebermann-Burchard reagent (acetic anhydride, glacial acetic acid, and concentrated sulfuric acid) at 620 nm. The secondary reference method is

Table 36–1 ✧ Lipid and Lipoprotein Reference Systems

	1° Reference Method (Definitive)	1° Reference Material	2° Reference Method	2° Reference Material
Cholesterol (NRS/CHOL)	ID-MS (NIST)	NIST SRM 911b Pure cholesterol	Abell-Kendall (CDC)	CDC Frozen Pools NIST SRM 909 NIST SRM 1951a
HDL-C	Not available	Not available	UC/Heparin-Mn^{2+}- Abell-Kendall (CDC) Recommended by NCEP.	CDC Frozen Pools NIST SRM 1951a
Triglyceride	ID-MS (NIST)	NIST SRM 1595 Tripalmitin	Methylene chloride silicic acid-chromo-tropic acid (CDC). Recommended by NCEP.	CDC Frozen Pools NIST SRM 1951a
LDL-C	Not available	Not available	Beta-quantification (CDC). Recom-mended by NCEP.	CDC Frozen Pools NIST SRM 1951a
Apo A-1	HPLC-MS (CDC) (primary standard only) (Candidate)	BCR-CRM 393 Purified Apo A-I	Not available	WHO Reference Reagent SP1-01 (for manufacturers). Labeled by CDC-RIA compar-ison method.
Apo B	Not available	d = 1.030–1.050 UC purified LDL	Not available	WHO Reference Reagent SP3-07 (for manufacturers). Labeled by NWLRL-immuno-nephelometry com-parison method.

CDC = Centers for Disease Control, NCEP = National Cholesterol Education Program, WHO = World Health Organization, NWLRL = Northwest Lipid Research Laboratories, CAP = College of American Pathologists

calibrated using the NIST SRM 911b pure cholesterol material. Typical performance of the CDC secondary reference method is at a coefficient of variation (CV) of 0.4%–0.5%.

The two methods are monitored on an ongoing basis, and comparisons have demonstrated a small but persistent positive bias in the secondary reference method of +1.6% compared to the primary reference method (definitive method).[29] The results of further investigations suggest that more than half of the difference in cholesterol values determined by the two methods is from small contributions from cholesterol precursor sterols and phytosterols, which are measured by the secondary reference method.[30] Since the observed bias is consistent and quite small, the secondary reference method provides a practical basis for standardization of routine methods used in the clinical environment. The primary reference method would be impractical for use in this manner.

HDL Cholesterol

The accuracy base for HDL-C is not as well defined and complete as that for TC. A significant problem is that the lipoproteins, as a heterogeneous mixture of lipids and proteins, are not rigidly defined. As a result, significant overlap can exist in the physical properties of the major lipoprotein classes. Therefore, developing a reference system for HDL-C will require that it be precisely defined. The current operational definition of HDL-C is based on physical separation, such as ultracentrifugation or chemical precipitation.

A primary reference method (definitive method) for HDL-C does not exist. The reference point for HDL-C measurement, as recommended by the NCEP Lipoprotein Measurement Working Group,[24] is the CDC secondary reference method, a multi-step procedure involving ultracentrifugation, precipitation, and cholesterol analysis.[31] The method combines removal of very-low-density lipoprotein (VLDL) by a beta-quantification ultracentrifugation procedure, isolation of HDL-C by precipitation of apo-B-containing lipoproteins [LDL-C, intermediate density lipoprotein cholesterol (IDL-C), and lipoprotein(a)(Lp[a])] from the beta-quantification bottom fraction (d > 1.006 kg/L) by 46 mmol/L heparin-manganese (Mn^{+2}), and cholesterol analysis of the HDL-C supernate by the NRS/CHOL cholesterol reference method. The major problems with the HDL-C secondary reference method are that it is technically demanding, requires a large sample volume (5 mL), has low throughput, and needs an expensive ultracentrifuge, which may preclude its widespread use for routine standardization of HDL-C measurements. However, since this HDL-C method has served as the reference method for the epidemiologic and clinical investigations by the CDC and National Heart, Lung, and Blood Institute (NHLBI), from which CHD risk estimations and population distributions have been derived, there is considerable justification for continuing this procedure as a national reference method. Typical performance of the CDC secondary reference method for HDL-C is at a CV of 1.4%. A reduced volume modification of the HDL-C secondary reference method is under development by CDC.

LDL Cholesterol

Like HDL-C, the process of establishing an accuracy target for LDL-C is complicated due to its heterogeneity and the difficulty of precisely defining the fraction of interest. The CDC has adopted as a reference procedure for LDL-C a variation of the multi-step beta-quantification procedure used by the Lipid Research Clinics,[31] which combines separation by ultracentrifugation and chemical precipitation. In the CDC procedure, heparin-manganese precipitation is performed on the d > 1.006 kg/L serum fraction rather than on whole plasma. The CDC reference value for LDL-C is calculated as the difference in cholesterol between the measured HDL-C and the cholesterol recovered in the d > 1.006 kg/L fraction obtained by ultracentrifugation. This is the reference point for LDL-C measurement, as recommended by the NCEP Lipoprotein Measurement Working Group.[25] Typical performance of the LDL-C secondary reference method at CDC is at a CV of 0.8%–1.1% for the bottom fraction cholesterol and 1.0%–1.3% for LDL-C.

Triglycerides

The reference system for TG has two of the main components necessary for establishing a defined accuracy base, i.e., a primary and a secondary reference method. NIST has developed a primary reference method (definitive method) for TG utilizing isotope dilution-mass spectrometry (ID-MS).[32] The primary reference method (definitive method) is actually two ID-MS methods: one for total glycerides (defined as the sum of TG, diglycerides, monoglycerides, and free glycerol) and another for TG only.[32] Total glycerides are measured because this represents the analytical species that the majority of clinical laboratories measure when testing for TG. In both assays a known amount of $[^{13}C_3]$ tripalmitin is added to the serum sample, which is then processed and derivatized, and the abundance ratios of selected ions are determined.[32]

A secondary reference method for TG established at CDC in 1963, based on the method of Carlson[33,34] and the techniques of Van Handel and Zilversmit[35] and Lofland,[36] has been used as the CDC's accuracy base for its standardization programs. This is the reference point for TG measurement, as recommended by the NCEP Lipoprotein Measurement Working Group.[23] The method is complicated, requiring extraction with silicic acid and chloroform for removal of free glycerol and other interferences, filtration to remove the silicic acid particles, hydrolysis with alcoholic potassium hydroxide, and color development by metaperiodate-arsenite-chromotropic acid reagent. The extraction procedure removes phospholipids and free glycerol, but retains a minimal amount of some monoglycerides and diglycerides. In 1993 the CDC reference method was modified to replace chloroform with methylene chloride in order to eliminate the use of chloroform in the extraction step and to eliminate the need for filtration to remove the silicic acid particles. The CDC uses a triolein/tripalmitin (2:1 ratio) standard to reflect the average unsaturated/saturated TG composition in human serum. A tripalmitin standard (99.5% pure) is available from NIST, but because it is insoluble in aqueous medium, it is unsuitable for enzymatic methods. Typical performance of the secondary reference method at CDC is at a CV of 2.0%.

CDC is collaborating with members of the Cholesterol Reference Method Laboratory Network (CRMLN) to further improve the TG method by combining the hydrolysis and extraction steps of the CDC method with color development by enzymatic endpoint procedure. Since the primary reference method (definitive method) and secondary reference method for TG do not measure exactly the same analytical species, a straightforward direct comparison of the two methods is not possible. To compare the two methods one must compare a measured value from one method with an estimated result from the other. It is most appropriate to compare the NIST measured result for total glycerides to a CDC estimated result for total glycerides. The CDC estimate for total glycerides is obtained by adding the CDC secondary reference method result, which is a measure of TG plus a small amount of unremoved mono- and diglycerides, together with the CDC result for free glycerol. In order to establish the target glycerol content of serum lipid reference materials, CDC developed an isotope dilution-gas chromatography-mass spectrometry method for the analysis of serum free glycerol.[37] The NIST primary reference method (definitive method) and the CDC secondary reference method were compared using both frozen and lyophilized serum pools. There was an average bias of + 1.1% between the two methods.

Lipoprotein(a)

A lack of an adequate accuracy base has inhibited standardization of Lp(a) assays and contributed to poor performance by laboratories.[38,39,40] Significant inter-laboratory variation was observed with three different commercial methods for Lp(a), with coefficients of variation ranging from 21% for an ELISA kit to 30% for a radioimmunoassay kit.[39] This large variation is due to the varied composition specificity of antibodies and matrix effects of calibrators used to measure Lp(a) and the lack of common standards and poor assay precision. Large inter-assay variation in Lp(a) measurements may confound results in clinical studies attempting to show an association of Lp(a) with the risk of heart disease because of an inability to correctly classify subjects on the basis of their Lp(a) results. To provide useful Lp(a) measurements, a major effort is needed to develop and validate an accuracy base for standardizing Lp(a) assays. Towards this goal, the International Federation of Clinical Chemistry (IFCC) formed a Working Group for the Standardization of Lp(a) Assays. The IFCC Working Group initiated a project to select and characterize a suitable Lp(a) secondary reference material to normalize and improve comparability of Lp(a) values between different measurement systems. This was accomplished by identifying and testing suitable candidate Lp(a) secondary materials for imprecision, linearity, parallelism, and their ability to provide between-assay harmonization of Lp(a) measurements.[41,42]

Considering the major impact that the lack of comparability of data may have on the clinical interpretation of Lp(a) values, the NHLBI awarded a four-year contract to the University of Washington Northwest Lipid Research Laboratory for the standardization of Lp(a) analytical methods. As recently reported,[42] the IFCC Working Group on Lp(a), whose aim was to make available a suitable secondary reference material for Lp(a), has extensively evaluated and characterized several candidate reference materials. The best performance was obtained by a preparation in lyophilized form that has been designated as an IFCC proposed reference material (IFCC-PRM) for Lp(a).[42] The Northwest Lipid Research Laboratory actively collaborated with the IFCC Working Group by assigning an Lp(a) value to the IFCC-PRM. A monoclonal antibody-based ELISA insensitive to apo(a) size polymorphism[43] and calibrated with a purified Lp(a) preparation was used as the method for the value assignment. Based on 144 replicate analyses, a target value of 107 nmol/L was assigned to the IFFC-PRM, which is an important step toward a scientifically sound approach in reporting Lp(a) data. To evaluate to what extent the use of a common reference material would contribute to comparability of Lp(a) values, the IFCC-PRM, three quality control samples, and 30 individuals samples, encompassing a broad range of Lp(a) values and apo(a) isoforms, were sent to 15 manufacturers and six research laboratories. Among the methods evaluated, two exhibited a very high correlation with the assigned value (r = 0.999 and 0.995, respectively) with minimum bias between the obtained and the assigned value related to apo(a) size. In contrast, a highly significant apo(a) size-dependent bias for the 30 samples was observed in most systems. The among-method CV for each of the 30 samples ranged from 6% to 31%, while the among-system CV for the IFCC-PRM was only 3%. The high comparability of values obtained with two of the methods and the very low among-method CV for the reference material seem to clearly indicate the suitability of the IFCC-PRM to be used as a secondary reference material for Lp(a). However, as noted previously and confirmed by this study, the availability of a common reference preparation can only reduce the variability due to the calibration component of the different assay. The major problem in the lack of comparability of Lp(a) values is represented by the overestimation or underestimation of Lp(a) values due to apo(a) size polymorphism. Even methods that are affected by apo(a) size do not produce comparable results due to the fact that each method has a different degree of apo(a) size dependency. This means that it is possible to evaluate and standardize those methods that do not appear to be affected by apo(a) size polymorphism. Manufacturers of Lp(a) test kits should include standardization as one of their primary design goals by making available to clinical chemistry laboratories Lp(a) assays documented to be unaffected by apo(a) size polymorphism. As part of the NHLBI supported activity, the Northwest Lipid Research Laboratory is available to closely work with manufacturers or laboratories that want to develop accurate Lp(a) methods. The availability of the IFCC reference material for such assays greatly contributes to the comparability of Lp(a) values.

Apolipoproteins A-I and B

Ideally, gravimetrically weighed pure apolipoproteins should be used as primary standards in apolipoprotein analysis. However, the physical and chemical properties of purified apo B do not lend themselves to immunochemical analysis, making this approach unsuitable. Purified apo A-I can be used as a primary standard in some immunochemical techniques, and an ultracentrifugally prepared LDL fraction (d = 1.030–1.050 kg/L) that excludes intermediate-density lipoprotein or lipoprotein(a) is currently the best choice as a surrogate primary standard for apo B. A purified apo A-I has been developed by the European Bureau of Reference for use as a primary standard.[44] Reference methods for the immunochemical analysis of apo A-I and B have not been universally accepted in the scientific community. Also, determination of the protein content of LDL presents significant problems[45] that are still under investigation.

The preferred approach to establishing an accuracy base is to use an accepted and well-documented primary or secondary reference method to determine apolipoprotein mass units on a secondary reference material (SRM) in a suitable matrix base. These SRMs can then be used as calibrators to set apolipoprotein mass units on calibration materials used by manufacturers of apolipoprotein measurement kits. This process is not possible at present because there is no universally accepted reference method for analysis of apo A-I or B.[46]

Primary and secondary reference methods for proteins depend on highly accurate protein determinations with primary standards. CDC has investigated and established an enzymatic digestion, liquid chromatography, isotope dilution–mass spectrometry method to assign mass values to an apo A-I primary standard for use as a model for apolipoprotein primary standards.[47]

The IFCC Committee on Apolipoproteins, together with manufacturers of apolipoprotein diagnostic kits, began a collaborative program in 1988 to produce and evaluate SRMs for standardizing apolipoprotein measurements. In early 1989, more than 20 manufacturers and several reference laboratories evaluated 26 candidate SRMs and measured 10 frozen sera with assigned values for apo A-I and B. A lyophilized serum for apo A-I and a liquid-stabilized serum for apo B were selected as reference materials on the basis of homogeneity, stability, reproducibility, and linearity upon dilution. The World Health Organization (WHO) has accepted these two serum matrix-based materials as reference reagents: SP1–01, a lyophilized material for apo A-I, and SP3–07, a stabilized liquid preparation for apo B. Mass units have been assigned using standardized immunoassay techniques and purified apo A-I and LDL (d = 1.030–1.050 kg/L) as primary calibrators.[48,49]

NATIONAL PERFORMANCE CRITERIA

The role of TC, HDL-C, LDL-C, and TG in the assessment of CHD risk has accentuated the need for more precise and accurate laboratory measurements.[17,50] In order to properly assess the quality of analytical performance in individual laboratories, meaningful criteria to evaluate the reproducibility of measurements and the deviation from a target value are needed. CDC was the first organization to establish specific performance criteria for TC, TG, and HDL-C analysis, which were designed to improve the performance of specialized lipid laboratories participating in the CDC-NHLBI Lipid Standardization Program.[51]

In 1988, the NCEP Laboratory Standardization Panel recommended goals for both bias and precision of TC measurement.[18] Specifically, the panel recommended that, as a national goal, clinical laboratories should achieve a bias of ± 3% of the CDC reference method and an overall precision consistent with a CV of 3% or less.[18] For a single analysis, the allowable total error (imprecision plus bias) would be within ± 8.9% using $L = 0.05$ in a two-tailed test.[52] This was one of the most important recommendations from the Laboratory Standardization Panel in that it established for the first time specific national performance criteria by which clinical laboratories can judge the reliability of cholesterol assays.

Similarly in 1995, the NCEP Working Group on Lipoprotein Measurement issued national performance criteria for TG,[23] HDL-C,[24] and LDL-C.[25] The NCEP performance goals for HDL-C, LDL-C, and TG were presented in terms of allowable total error; in other words, method bias and method precision must satisfy the goals for total error.

Presented in Table 36–2 are the performance criteria for specialized lipid laboratories participating in the CDC-NHLBI Lipid Standardization Program, and the NCEP performance goals for clinical laboratories. In addition, under the Clinical Laboratory Improvement Amendments (CLIA) of 1988, the federal government has established national proficiency testing criteria for a large number of clinical analytes. The CLIA '88 evaluation criteria (total error) for TC, TG, and HDL-C are also presented in Table 36–2. Nationally accepted performance criteria for measurement of apolipoproteins by routine laboratories have not been established to date.

Table 36-2 ✧ National Performance Criteria for Lipid and Lipoprotein Measurement[a]

Analyte	CDC Standardization Criteria			NCEP Performance Criteria[b]			CLIA Evaluation Criteria[c]
	Concentration Range	Bias	Imprecision	Bias	Imprecision	Total Error	Total Error
Low TC	< 50 mg/dL (1.29 mmol/L) 50–99.9 mg/dL (1.29–2.58 mmol/L)	± 2.0 mg/dL (0.052 mmol/L) ± 3.0 mg/dL (0.08 mmol/L)	SD[e] ≤ 2.0 mg/dL (0.052 mmol/L) SD ≤ 3.0 mg/dL (0.052 mmol/L)				
TC	100–149 mg/dL (2.59–3.85 mmol/L) ≥ 150 mg/dL (3.88 mmol/L)	≤ 0.03 Rv[d] ≤ 0.03 RV	SD ≤ 4.0 mg/dL (0.10 mmol/L) CV[f] ≤ 3.0%	≤ 3% RV	CV ≤ 3.0%	≤ 9%	± 10%
TG (mmol/L)	0.00–0.99 1.00–1.99 2.00–2.49 ≥ 2.50	≤ 0.10 ≤ 0.11 ≤ 0.12 ≤ 0.05 RV	SD ≤ 0.08 SD ≤ 0.09 SD ≤ 0.11 CV ≤ 5%	≤ 5% RV	CV ≤ 5.0%	≤ 13%	± 25%
HDL-C	< 40 mg/dL (1.03 mmol/L) ≥ 40 mg/dL (1.03 mmol/L)	≤ 0.05 RV ≤ 0.05 RV	SD ≤ 1.7 mg/dL (0.044 mmol/L) SD ≤ 0.04 RV	≤ 5% RV	SD ≤ 1.7 at < 42 mg/dL (1.09 mmol/L) CV ≤ 4% at ≥ 42 mg/dL (1.09 mmol/L)	≤ 13%	± 30%
LDL-C				≤ 4% RV	CV ≤ 4.0%	≤ 12%	

[a]TC = Total Cholesterol, TG = Triglyceride, HDL-C = High-Density Lipoprotein Cholesterol, LDL-C = Low-Density Lipoprotein Cholesterol.
To convert TG values from mmol/L to mg/dL, divide by 0.0113.
[b]Performance criteria for TC recommended by the NCEP Laboratory Standardization Panel in Clin Chem 1998;34:193–201. Performance criteria for TG recommended by the NCEP Lipoprotein Working Group in Clin Chem 1995;41:1321–1426. Performance criteria for HDL-C recommended by the NCEP Lipoprotein Working Group in Clin Chem 1995;41:1427–33. Performance criteria for LDL-C recommended by the NCEP Lipoprotein Working Group in Clin Chem 1995;41:1414–20.
[c]Federal Register, February 28, 1992.
[d]RV = reference value assigned by CDC reference methods
[e]SD = standard deviation
[f]CV = coefficient of variation

TC = 0.0258

STANDARDIZATION ISSUES

When attempting to standardize laboratory measurements, one must consider factors that contribute to inaccuracy in the measurement process and affect the reliability of test results. Traditionally, major emphasis has been on analytical factors, i.e., factors that compromise accuracy during measurement. However, as efforts to control analytical imprecision and inaccuracy progress, concern has increased significantly about the effect on test results of preanalytical sources of variation, i.e., factors that operate before, during, and after blood collection and storage.[53] It is important, therefore, to carefully consider both preanalytical sources of variation and laboratory sources of error.

Preanalytical Consideration

Physicians need to understand and control, as much as possible, factors that can transiently alter a patient's usual lipid and lipoprotein concentrations.[54] Preanalytical factors include behavioral factors, the clinical state of the patient, patient preparation, and the collection, handling, storage, and shipment of patient samples.[53] Preanalytical factors are covered in detail in Chapter 8; hence, only a brief overview is given here.

Considerable variation in intra-individual biological variation has been reported in the literature. In order to obtain the best estimates of the average intra-individual biological variability (expressed as CV_b) in the concentrations in serum of TC, TG, HDL-C, and LDL-C, results from 30 studies published from 1970 to 1992 were evaluated by meta-analysis.[55]

A method based on relative range was developed to estimate the effect of biological variation on the total variation of the mean serum TC result.[56] This method can serve as a guide for determining the number of specimens required from an individual to minimize the effect of biological variation on the individual's TC result.[56] Using the meta-analysis results for CV_b and the NCEP performance goals, this method has been extended to estimate relative range goals for TG, HDL-C, and LDL-C.[56] The in-depth discussion of preanalytical variation presented in Chapter 8 includes detailed recommendations issued in 1990 by the NCEP Laboratory Standardization Panel.[52] The NCEP report does not cover apolipoproteins specifically, and although no thorough temporal studies on variation in apo A-I or apo B have been conducted, similar precautions should be taken to minimize preanalytical variation in apolipoprotein measurements.[57]

Matrix Effects of Reference Materials

The traditional approach to transfer standardization from higher-order methods and materials to field methods has been to use reference materials and calibrators that have been value-assigned by primary or secondary reference methods. This approach is based on the assumption that reference materials mimic fresh patient specimens when assayed by all methods throughout the method hierarchy. The degree to which a reference material effectively mimics patient samples is also known as *commutability*. Commutability, as defined by Rej et al., refers to the ability of a reference, survey, or quality control material to exhibit inter-assay characteristics comparable with those demonstrated by authentic clinical specimens.[58] However, studies have indicated that significant discrepancies in the measurement of cholesterol exist when some analytical systems are compared to the reference methods using lyophilized and frozen processed serum materials.[59–67] The processed materials may undergo changes that affect their assay characteristics and their commutability. The use of unprocessed fresh-frozen serum may alleviate the problems associated with matrix interactions, but even freezing appears to affect some analytical methods.[68] Matrix effects complicate standardization because different methods may produce different results for the same reference material and may yield erroneous conclusions about the performance of an analytical system. In addition to the matrix interactions affecting the cholesterol analysis, any changes in the specimen that affect the separation step may also give rise to matrix effects in the measurement of lipoproteins, including HDL-C. Efforts have been made to improve performance of materials for assessing HDL-C measurement.[69] Matrix effects in the measurement of TG have also been reported[70] (see chapter 35 for additional information on matrix effects).

Few guidelines that provide formulation specifications for preparing commutable lipid and lipoprotein reference materials exist. Published guidelines were developed before the widespread use of enzymatic assays and thus do not specifically address the problems of modern cholesterol methods.[71–74] An NCCLS Subcommittee on Cholesterol Reference Material Specifications has developed written guidelines for preparing frozen human serum pools that are commutable across different cholesterol test systems permitting proper calibration, accuracy assessment, and traceability of field methods to the NRS/CHOL.[75] The guideline provides specifications for collecting and processing raw materials to manufacture frozen serum pools and for quality assurance of the final product. In preparing serum pools, it is generally assumed that pooling of individual donor units does not contribute significantly to matrix effects in the final product. To evaluate the scientific basis of the guideline and also evaluate the pooling effect, NCCLS had two cholesterol pools prepared according to the written specifications. Two frozen serum pools using a large number of selected individual donor units of "off-the-clot" serum were prepared and characterized. The performance of the pools was assessed in terms of the degree of commutability (true response versus predicted response) relative to the individual sera that comprise the pools. The experiment was statistically designed to detect a 2% matrix bias between the predicted and true response for each instrument system evaluated. All of the instrument systems evaluated had biases less than 2%, with most systems having biases less than 1.5%.[75]

Until commutable materials free of matrix effects are routinely available, an interim approach that involves implementation of the NCEP Laboratory Standardization Panel's recommendations is to directly compare an analytical system with the cholesterol reference method through the use of split fresh patient specimens. Validating traceability by comparing split fresh patient specimens is a useful approach for both manufacturers of diagnostic systems and for clinical laboratories seeking to verify the performance of a cholesterol method. Since the same type of matrix limitations exist for lipoproteins and TG, the cholesterol experience is a good model for overall standardization.

Purified apo A-I is an acceptable primary standard. However, because of self-aggregation problems, purified apo B is not an acceptable primary standard in all immunological methods of analysis. Generally, freshly collected serum is the specimen of choice as a primary calibrator, but practical considerations of distribution and stability of the diagnostic products preclude using fresh materials. Lyophilized serum-based reference materials with assigned concentrations of apo A-I seem to adequately perform in most immunological methods.[76] However, when certain methods, including radial immunodiffusion and immunoturbidimetry, are used, systematic differences in apo B measurements occur.[49,77] Fresh-frozen serum seems to perform well in most immunological methods, if the protein epitope bound by the antibody is not sensitive to freeze/thaw cycles. Stabilized liquid preparations of whole serum appear to work satisfactorily for apo B analysis in most immunological techniques.[49,77]

There are inherent problems in maintaining stability of large quantities of frozen or stabilized liquid apolipoprotein reference materials.[77] For a given method, reagent system, or combination of instrument system and reagents, the primary responsibility for establishing and maintaining an accuracy base rests with the manufacturer, which should calibrate each lot of secondary calibrators to the appropriate WHO-IFCC Reference Reagents (SP1–01 for apo A-I and SP3–07 for apo B).

Triglycerides Measurement and Free Glycerol

The TG measurement poses a unique matrix-effect problem resulting from the contribution of free glycerol. When measuring TG, U.S. laboratories almost exclusively measure a combination of TG, monoglyceride, diglyceride, and free glycerol. It is the varying amounts of free glycerol present in samples that can cause measurement problems. The question of blanking TG analyses for free glycerol has been debated.[78–80] In a study of patients at a university hospital, the need for free glycerol blanking was evaluated, and, except in those situations in which abnormally increased glycerol is expected, no significant consequences resulted for the average individual when a glycerol blank was not used.[79]

Serum glycerol blanking does, however, become extremely important when attempting to standardize TG measurements. Glycerol content in commercially prepared materials, such as survey samples, controls, and calibrators, has been reported to be quite variable, depending on the matrix of the source material and the fortification used to increase lipid concentrations.[69, 70] Such variation in free glycerol content can make the standardization of TG measurements across the nation's clinical laboratories and the assessment of accuracy very difficult. However, with the increased use of survey samples, standardization materials and reference materials prepared from fresh off-the-clot human serum, the presence of free glycerol has been reduced to levels in the range found in patient specimens. To ensure that elevated free glycerol is not present in reference materials and survey materials, it is very important that laboratories evaluate each lot of serum materials for free glycerol content before using them for calibration or accuracy evaluation.

Comparison of glycerol concentrations for several reference serum pools determined by using different enzymatic kits sometimes produced substantially different results.[37] Thus, potential matrix effects with different enzymatic free glycerol assays must also be considered. However, all the evaluated methods provided similar results when pure aqueous standards were tested and when standard addition studies were conducted.[37]

In addition to the issue of free glycerol blanking, enzymatic methods to determine TG may also be affected by the turbidity of the specimen.[81] The effects of specimen turbidity and glycerol blanking on nine enzymatic TG methods were compared.[82] The results showed variability among the methods ranging from 6.2%–15.6%.[82] Methods using a bichromatic blank better minimized the interference from turbidity than did a reagent or serum blank, and therefore a bichromatic glycerol-blanked method was recommended to obtain a more accurate TG result for turbid specimens.[82]

LDL-C Measurement

Although the primary decision factor for patient follow-up and treatment is based on LDL-C, a routine direct assay for measuring LDL-C was not available until 1993.[83] Despite the present availability of routine LDL-C assays, most laboratories determine LDL-C by an indirect estimation reported in 1972 by Friedewald.[11] According to Friedewald, LDL-C is estimated from the formula:

LDL-C = TC – HDL-C – TG/5 (in mg/dL or TG/2.22 for mmol/L)

Because TC, HDL-C, and TG are directly measured values, the calculated LDL-C is subject to independent errors in each of the three measurements. Since considerable emphasis has been placed on standardizing TC, HDL-C, and TG measurements, it generally has been assumed that LDL-C values are standardized when TC, HDL-C, and TG values are standardized. However, as the NCEP guidelines for measurement performance were developed, it became clear that even if TC, HDL-C, and TG measurements were all within the limits of acceptable performance, LDL-C may not be within performance limits. Thus, it seems that direct measurement of LDL-C would have considerable advantage over calculation since it would be necessary to only insure the accuracy of one measurement rather than three. Various studies have shown that a direct LDL-C method gives results correlating highly with the ultracentrifugation reference method.[84]

Assessing the accuracy of the early generation direct LDL-C method or standardizing it using the conventional approach was not possible because of its documented unreliability with frozen specimens.[84,85] However the more recent homogeneous LDL-C assays that were developed and introduced in Japan do not appear to suffer from this problem.[86] To insure proper calibration, CRMLN offers a certification program for manufacturers of clinical diagnostic products used for the measurement of LDL-C.

RESOURCES AVAILABLE FOR STANDARDIZATION

The NCEP's Laboratory Standardization Panel stated that to ensure reliable cholesterol results, the measurement of cholesterol in all clinical laboratories must be traceable to a national accuracy base such as the NRS/CHOL.[18] Achieving traceability to the NRS/CHOL or the accuracy bases for TG, the lipoproteins, and the apolipoproteins will require a unified national effort involving manufacturers, government agencies, and the clinical professions. The programs and resources available to assist clinical laboratories in standardizing the measurement of lipids and lipoproteins are summarized below.

CDC-NHLBI Lipid Standardization Program

Since 1957, the CDC in collaboration with the NHLBI has been developing, evaluating, and offering the resources needed to standardize the analytical measurement of TC, HDL-C, and TG. These standardization resources were developed because many investigators interested in the relationship between serum lipid concentrations and cardiovascular disease were concerned about the reliability of lipid analyses within laboratories and the comparability of results among laboratories. Through standardization programs, the CDC has offered these resources nationally and internationally to[51]

1. epidemiologic laboratories, to ensure comparability of population studies and clinical trials;

2. lipid methodology research laboratories, to help in the development of accurate methods;

3. reference laboratories, to provide targets for proficiency testing programs;

4. reference laboratories of manufacturers of diagnostic products, through which standardization assistance can be provided to all clinical laboratories.

CDC annually standardizes laboratories supporting more than 100 studies funded by the National Institutes of Health that investigate CHD and other related factors, including diabetes, nutrition, genetics, and health issues of women and minorities.

The CDC-NHLBI Lipid Standardization Program has three major phases. Part I is the preliminary evaluation phase in which CDC reference materials and fresh patient specimens are analyzed concurrently. During this phase, a split-sample comparison with a laboratory participating in the CRMLN is made to verify comparable performance of CDC materials versus patient samples when the participant's method is used. If analytical criteria are met by the participant and significant matrix effects on CDC pools are not seen, performance is assumed to be adequate to ensure the quality of the relationship determined in the participant's laboratory between CDC's reference values and the participant's values.

Part II is the principal phase in standardization and confirms the level of accuracy and precision found in Part I as well as the laboratory's ability to achieve and maintain acceptable performance.

Part III monitors the ability of a participant laboratory to maintain acceptable performance for 12 months or longer. In this phase, CDC reference materials are distributed at quarterly intervals. To ensure representative performance on the part of the analyst, the CDC samples are provided as unknowns to the participants in all phases of standardization.

Criteria for acceptable performance in the CDC program were discussed earlier and summarized in Table 36–2. CDC standardization performance evaluations of individual laboratory results are based on fixed limits combined with target values established by the CDC secondary reference methods. In this way, standardization permits evaluation of all components of method error.

CDC has taken steps to provide standardization service for laboratories that determine LDL-C by beta-quantification. CDC has evaluated the applicability of frozen reference serum for standardizing LDL-C measurements.[87] Fresh serum was collected from 24 donors and analyzed for LDL-C by the beta-quantification method (LDL-C = bottom fraction – HDL-C). Aliquots were stored frozen at –60°C and re-analyzed at intervals for at least one year. The mean percentage change in LDL-C upon initial freezing was –1.6%. In 19 of 24 samples the change was less than 2% and showed increasing negative change with increasing VLDL-C. Over one year of storage, the HDL-C and bottom fraction-C were stable such that any further decrease in LDL-C was less than 1%. Results from this study show that beta-quantification methods can be standardized using frozen reference serum.

Following the stability studies using frozen serum, a round robin analysis of four frozen reference sera value-assigned by the CDC beta-quantification method was carried out by 28 laboratories in the CDC-NHLBI Lipid Standardization Program.[88] The participants analyzed the samples in a single run and reported duplicate results for bottom fraction and HDL-C. Using results from 28 laboratories, the mean absolute bias for all samples was 5.3% ± 6.1. In general, the bias in the LDL-C result was directly related to the bias in the bottom fraction result. This brief study indicated that standardization of beta-quantification will require standardization of the bottom fraction cholesterol

The standardization of homogeneous LDL-C enzymatic assays using frozen serum reference materials must take into consideration the apparent change in LDL-C upon freezing indicated by beta-quantification analysis. An LDL-C method can be standardized using frozen serum if it can be demonstrated that the assay does not have a different response to freezing compared to the beta-quantification procedure. If the LDL-C assay is not sensitive to freezing, then the bias (frozen vs. fresh) detected by the beta-quantification procedure becomes problematic. It is possible that frozen serum can be selected for low VLDL concentration (i.e., low TG) and thus have a minimal decrease from the initial fresh value. Some of the current generation of homogeneous LDL-C assay methodologies are subject to interference by TG, giving a TG-dependent result even in fresh serum. The magnitude of this TG effect on the accuracy for individual methodologies compared to the effect of freezing on the LDL-C reference method needs to be assessed in light of the NCEP accuracy requirement (4%) before a decision about the utility of frozen serum for standardizing homogeneous assays can be reached.

For more information, contact the Special Activities Branch, Division of Laboratory Sciences, Centers for Disease Control and Prevention, 4770 Buford Highway, NE (F25), Atlanta, GA 30341–3724; Telephone 770–488–4126; Fax 770–488–4192.

THE CHOLESTEROL REFERENCE METHOD LABORATORY NETWORK

The NCEP's medical decision points for identifying individuals who have increased risk of CHD were derived from population studies and clinical trials that were standardized by CDC. To implement a national intervention and prevention strategy based on these uniform decision points requires that all cholesterol, HDL-C, LDL-C, and TG measurements be traceable to the CDC reference methods. The problems associated with matrix effects on the accuracy of cholesterol and HDL-C[89] measurement were briefly discussed in this chapter and are discussed in more detail in Chapter 35.

Matrix effects preclude the universal use of conventional reference materials for establishing a chain of traceability from the field methods to the reference methods. Therefore, the recommended approach to assess how well a laboratory method correlates with the accuracy base is to directly compare diagnostic methods to the reference methods using fresh patient specimens.[18]

Unfortunately, the sheer number of laboratories in the United States makes standardization using fresh patient comparisons a nearly impossible task. In contrast, the number of manufacturers that provide the diagnostic methods for measuring TC, HDL-C, LDL-C, and TG is relatively small. Working with manufacturers of diagnostic methods to assist them in calibration is the most efficient way to validate traceability and to improve the measurement of these analytes in clinical laboratories. Therefore, CDC focused its efforts toward the manufacturers and developed the CRMLN, which was established to assist manufacturers in correctly calibrating their measurement systems and validating traceability to the NRS/CHOL through a certification program. It was the first network of its kind to use fresh sample comparisons as the basis of accuracy validation, and therefore serves as a model for other analytical systems that require fresh sample comparisons to validate traceability to an accuracy base.[90]

The CRMLN consists of five U.S. laboratories (listed in Table 36–3) and six interna-

---

Table 36–3 ✧ U.S. Laboratories Participating in the Cholesterol Reference Method Laboratory Network

State Laboratory of Hygiene University of Wisconsin Center for Health Sciences 465 Henry Mall Madison, WI 53706 David Hassemer, M.S. hassemer@mail.slh.wisc.edu (608) 265-1100 (x102) Phone (608) 265-1111 Fax	**Wadsworth Center for Laboratories and Research** New York State Department of Health Empire State Plaza Albany, NY 12201 Robert Rej, Ph.D. bobrej@wadsworth.org (518) 473-0117 Phone (518) 474-7824 Fax	**Pacific Biometrics Research Foundation** 220 West Harrison St. Seattle, WA 98119 Elizabeth Teng Leary, Ph.D. etl@pacbio.com (206) 298-0068 Phone (206) 298-9838 Fax
University of Washington, Department of Medicine Northest Lipid Research Laboratories 2121 N. 35th Street Seattle, WA 98103 Santica Marcovina, Ph.D. smm@u.washington.edu (206) 685-3331 Phone (206) 685-3279 Fax	**Washington University School of Medicine** Core Laboratory for Clinical Studies Box 8046 660 S. Euclid Avenue St. Louis , MO 63110 Thomas G. Cole, Ph.D. thom@imgate.wustl.edu (314) 362-3516 Phone (314) 362-4782 Fax	

Table 36–4 ✧ International Laboratories Participating in the Cholesterol Reference Method Laboratory Network

Rotterdam University Hospital "Dijkzigt" Department of Clinical Chemistry Lipid Reference Laboratory 3015 GD Rotterdam The Netherlands Christa M. Boersma-Cobbaert, Ph.D. boersma@ckcl.azr.nl 31-10-4633493 Phone 31-76-5036710 Fax	**Canadian Reference Laboratory (1996) Ltd.** 307-2083 Alma Street Vancouver British Columbia V6R 4N6 CANADA David W. Seccombe, M.D., Ph.D. seccombe@unixg.ubc.ca (604) 222-1355 Phone (604) 222-1373 Fax
Osaka Medical Center for Cancer and Cardiovascular Diseases Department of Epidemiology and Mass Examination for CVD 3 Nakamichi 1-chome Higashinari-ku Osaka 537 JAPAN Masakazu Nakamura, Ph.D. xnakamur@iph.pref.osaka.jp Minoru Iida, M.D. 81-6-6972-1181 (ext 2211) Phone 81-6-6972-7749 Fax	**H.S Raffaele** Laboratorio Analisi Cliniche Via Olgettina 60 20132 Milano ITALY Ferruccio Ceriotti, M.D. ceriotti.ferruccio@hsr.it 39-02-2643-2315 (or 2313) Phone 39-02-2643-2640 Fax **Undergoing Standardization:**
Institute of Biochemistry Department of Pathological Biochemistry Glasgow Royal Infimary 4th Floor Alexandra Parade Glasgow G31 2ER GREAT BRITAIN Chris J. Packard, Ph.D. chrispackard@compuserve.com 44-141-221-4979 (or 4322) Phone 44-141-553-2558 Fax	**Fundacíon Bioquímica Argentina** Programa de Evaluacion Externa de Calidad Calle 6 No. 1344 La Plata 1900 ARGENTINA Daniel Mazziotta, Ph.D. dmpeec@netverk.com.ar 54-21-231150 Phone 54-21-232021 Fax

tional laboratories (listed in Table 36–4). The CRMLN laboratories perform the CDC's secondary reference methods or designated comparison methods and are standardized to CDC through participation in the CDC-NHLBI Lipid Standardization Program.

Since a reference system equivalent to the NRS/CHOL does not exist for HDL-C or LDL-C, the NCEP Lipoprotein Measurement Working Group has recommended that the methods used at CDC serve as the accepted accuracy base for these analytes.[24,25] Although the CDC's reference method for HDL-C can be transferred, it is too labor-intensive and expensive to utilize in the CRMLN for providing reference analyses for fresh sample comparisons. For practical reasons, the CRMLN laboratories have chosen to utilize a "designated comparison method" (titled based on NCCLS nomenclature)[91] for establishing traceability to the CDC reference method for HDL-C. The designated comparison method employs direct precipitation of the apo-B-containing lipoproteins with dextran sulfate of 50 kDa with magnesium, followed by measurement using the Abell-Kendall reference method for cholesterol.[92–94] Only samples with TG concentrations < 200 mg/dL (1.26 mmol/L) can be used in this protocol.

For LDL-C, three of the CRMLN laboratories (Northwest Lipid Research Laboratories, Osaka Medical Center for Cancer and Cardiovascular Diseases, and Rotterdam University Hospital) have established and standardized the reference method. These laboratories serve as a first tier for manufacturer certification programs. A second tier of laboratories will standardize the reference method or designated comparison methods and will be available to work with manufacturers in method development.

The performance of all methods used in the CRMLN is monitored monthly in each CRMLN laboratory. These monthly surveys involve the analysis of CDC frozen serum reference materials. It has been shown through mathematical simulations that the most influential factor in the ability to determine the performance of an analytical system by comparison with a reference laboratory is the bias the reference laboratory has to the accepted accuracy base.[95] The CRMLN has strived to achieve the lowest possible bias to the accuracy base so that manufacturers can properly and reliably validate the traceability of their measurement systems to the CDC accuracy base. When methods are adopted in the CRMLN, whether they be the reference method or a designated comparison method, initial goals for bias have been half the target goals recommended by the NCEP. As experience is gained with the methods and performance improves, the bias goals for the CRMLN laboratories are tightened.

For TC, the CRMLN laboratories must maintain a CV of less than 2% and a bias to CDC of less than 1%. Between December 1995 and October 1999, the within-lab CV ranged from 05 to 1.3%, with an average of 0.4%. During the same period, the average bias for the CRMLN laboratories ranged from −1.3% to 0.7%, with an overall average of −0.1%.

For HDL-C, the CRMLN laboratories must maintain a bias vs. the CDC secondary reference method of ≤1 mg/dL (0.026 mmol/L) and a SD of ≤1 mg/dL (0.026 mmol/L). Between September 1998 and October 1999, the SD ranged between 0.1 and 1.3 mg/dL (0.003 and 0.034 mmol/L), with an overall average of 0.5 mg/dL (0.013 mmol/L). During the same period the average bias of CRMLN laboratories ranged between −1.8 and 1.2 mg/dL (−0.047 and 0.03 mmol/L), with an overall average of −0.2 mg/dL (0.005 mmol/L).

For LDL-C, the CRMLN laboratories must maintain a bias versus the CDC secondary reference method of ≤2%. The CRMLN does not currently have a criterion for precision for the LDL-C secondary reference method. Between September 1998 and September 1999, two of the CRMLN members (Northwest Lipid Research Laboratories and Osaka Medical Center for Cancer and Cardiovascular Diseases) were standardized as first tier LDL-C laboratories. The SD for these two laboratories during this time ranged between 0.2 and 2.2 mg/dL (0.005 and 0.057 mmol/L), with an overall average of 0.8 mg/dL (0.021 mmol/L). During this same period of time, the bias ranged between −2.7 and 2.1%, with an overall average of 0.3%.

A certification program for TG is under development and will be available in selected CRMLN laboratories. For reasons similar to those for the HDL-C method, it is impractical to use the CDC's TG reference method to provide TG reference services in the

CRMLN. The CDC and several of the CRMLN members, including H. S. Raffaele, the Canadian Reference Laboratory, the Washington University School of Medicine, and the Wadsworth Center for Laboratories and Research have collaborated to modify the reference method by combining the extraction and hydrolysis steps of the current CDC reference method with an enzymatic endpoint method for determining TG. H.S. Raffaele has a method that is accurate and precise, and has the advantages of ease in transfer and operation. CDC is working with H.S. Raffaele to perform final validation studies. When these are completed, the method will be transferred to additional CRMLN laboratories and a certification program for TG for manufacturers will be implemented.

The strategy for validating tracebility to the accuracy base for TC, HDL-C, and LDL-C for manufacturers and clinical laboratories via the CRMLN is shown in Figure 36-1.

Certification of Instrument Systems, Reagents, and Reference Materials

Manufacturers of instruments and reference materials are key to achieving standardization of TC, HDL-C, and LDL-C measurements in clinical laboratories. Manufacturers should perform comparison analyses with the accuracy base using fresh patient specimens in order to document the performance of their own complete instrument systems, reagent applications on other instrument systems, reference materials, and calibrators. To document performance and traceability to the accuracy bases, the CRMLN has adopted a methods evaluation protocol developed by NCCLS entitled "Method Comparison and Bias Estimation Using Patient Samples."[96] The comparison protocol requires analyzing a minimum of 40 patient specimens throughout the range of interest in duplicate by each method. Once evaluation of the test method has been completed and certification criteria have been met, a dated Certificate of Traceability is issued to the manufacturer stating that the analytical system, reference material, or reagent application was traceable to the NRS/CHOL under the conditions tested. This Certificate of Traceability records the bias, CV, and total error for the analytical system. Manufacturers are encouraged to re-evaluate their systems whenever a new reagent or calibrator lot is prepared or at a minimum of every two years. The CRMLN maintains a list of analytical systems, reagents, and calibrators that have met the NCEP criteria for TC, HDL-C, and LDL-C during the last two years. This list is published on the American Association for Clinical Chemistry web site at http://www.aacc.org/standards/cdc/cholesterolinfo.stm.

For more information about how to participate in the manufacturer programs, contact any one of the CRMLN laboratories listed in Tables 36–3 and 36–4 or contact the Special Activities Branch, Division of Laboratory Sciences, Centers for Disease Control and Prevention, 4770 Buford Highway NE, Atlanta, GA 30341–3724; Telephone 770–488–4683; Fax 770–488–4192.

Certification of Clinical Laboratories

The CRMLN also has a cholesterol certification program for clinical laboratories. Clinical laboratories will use either of two types of analytical systems, homogeneous or

Figure 36–1 ✧ Strategy for Validating Traceability to the Lipid and Lipoprotein Accuracy Base for Manufacturers and Clinical Laboratories

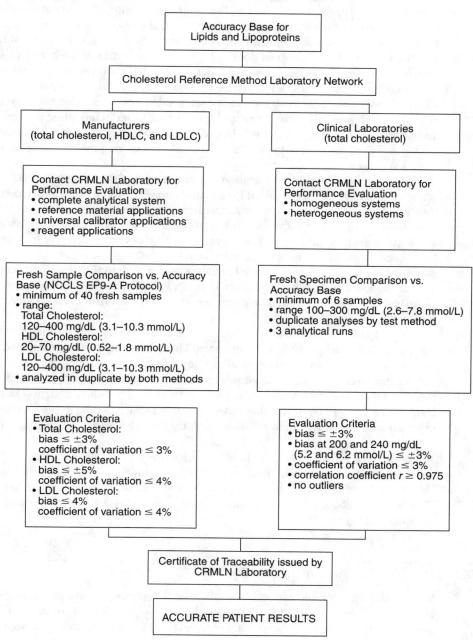

heterogeneous. In a homogeneous analytical system, the instrument, reagent, and calibrator are supplied by a single manufacturer, whereas in a heterogeneous system, each may come from different sources. For laboratories using a homogeneous system, documentation of performance and traceability to the reference method can be obtained from the manufacturer. However, the manufacturer's demonstration of traceability to the NRS/CHOL in itself does not guarantee accuracy in the hands of every eventual user. For this reason, it is recommended that laboratories using certified systems verify their system's performance by performing a direct comparison with a CRMLN laboratory using fresh patient specimens. Laboratories using heterogeneous analytical systems must assume primary responsibility for documenting performance and establishing traceability to the NRS/CHOL. In many cases, the test system used by a laboratory will be unique to that laboratory, thus requiring individual documentation of accuracy.

For practical reasons, certification of a laboratory's traceability to the NRS/CHOL is not as extensive as that required for a manufacturer. However, laboratory certification is still based on a direct comparison with the reference method using fresh patient specimens. The protocol requires that the laboratory analyze six patient specimens in duplicate in each of three runs. The TC values should cover a range that includes the NCEP recommended cholesterol decision points of 200 and 240 mg/dL (5.18 and 6.22 mmol/L).[2] Acceptable performance, indicating traceability to the NRS/CHOL, is documented by a Certificate of Traceability that is valid for six months from the date of comparison.[97] All of the CRMLN laboratories offer certification for clinical laboratories for TC.

CDC has implemented a Voice Information System to provide information about the clinical laboratory certification program. This system provides a general explanation of the CRMLN and information about how clinical laboratories can verify accuracy in cholesterol testing. It also offers physicians a regional listing of labs that have met the national performance goals to which they can send their patients' samples. Listed are clinical laboratories that have successfully participated in the certification program within the last 12 months and the dates they received a Certificate of Traceability.

For more information about how to participate in the clinical laboratory cholesterol certification program, contact any one of the CRMLN laboratories listed in Tables 36–3 and 36–4 or telephone the CDC Voice Information System at 888–232–6789. The CRMLN currently has no specific HDL-C or LDL-C certification program for clinical laboratories.

APOLIPOPROTEIN STANDARDIZATION PROGRAMS

In 1981 the CDC formed an apolipoprotein working group to standardize apolipoprotein measurements. In 1983 a large pool of lyophilized human serum (CDC-1883) was prepared and used in several international surveys to determine the sources of variability in apolipoprotein measurements as well as the utility of this lyophilized material as a reference material for apolipoprotein measurement.[98–100] In 1985 a group of expert laboratories measured CDC-1883 serum using their own analytical techniques and calibrators. Preliminary-consensus mass units for apo A-I and B were assigned to CDC-1883. The accelerated thermal stability and temporal stability over five years have shown that this material is suitable as a stable point of reference for apo A-I and B measurement. However, CDC-1883 demonstrates a matrix bias when used in certain immunological techniques to measure apo B. CDC-1883 has a labeled value of 124 mg/dL for apo A-I and is traceable to the WHO-IFCC Reference Reagent for apo A-I (SP1–01).

WHO and IFCC appointed CDC to be the repository for the WHO-IFCC International Reference Reagents for apo A-I (SP1–01) and apo B (SP3–07). WHO and IFCC appointed Dr. S. Marcovina, former Chairperson of the IFCC Apolipoprotein Working Group, to conduct the standardization and distribution program for manufacturers using an IFCC calibration protocol. This protocol covers dose-response linearity and parallelism, intercept equality of the reference materials, as well as confirmation procedures using fresh serum. WHO-IFCC International Reference Reagents are available to manufacturers of reagents and/or instrumentation for apo AI and apo B measurements, to assign target values to calibrator and quality control materials, and to evaluate new reagents and instrument performance. Additionally, the reference preparations are available to international reference laboratories that are responsible for monitoring apo A-I and apo B standardization within their countries. For clinical laboratories, the Northwest Lipid Research Laboratories offer three frozen serum pools with assigned values for apo A-I and B (traceable to the WHO-IFCC Reference Reagents) for calibration or confirmation of accuracy of their calibrators.

For more information, contact Dr. Santica Marcovina, Northwest Lipid Research Laboratories, University of Washington, 2121 N. 35th Street, Seattle, WA 98103; Telephone 206–685–3331.

The Subcommittee on Apolipoproteins of the NCCLS has prepared a proposed guideline for apolipoprotein immunoassays (I/LA 15-A). For information contact NCCLS, Wayne, PA 19087; Telephone 610–688–0100; Fax 610–688–0700.

NATIONAL PROFICIENCY SURVEYS

The Clinical Laboratory Improvement Amendments (CLIA) passed by Congress in 1988 established standards designed to improve the quality of clinical laboratory testing in U.S. laboratories that conduct testing on human specimens for health assessment or for the diagnosis, prevention, or treatment of disease. CLIA '88 mandates proficiency testing as a means to externally evaluate the quality of a laboratory's performance. Each participating laboratory is challenged in three testing events annually. In each testing event, five unknown samples for each analyte or test are provided. Those proficiency testing programs that have been approved in 1999 by the Health Care Financing Administration are listed in Table 36–5.

All of the programs offer surveys that include TC, TG, and HDL-C. However, only the College of American Pathologists, Pacific Biometrics Research Foundation, Solomon Park Research Laboratories, and the New York State Health Department offer

Table 36–5 ✧ CLIA-Approved Proficiency Testing Programs

Program	Telephone	Sample Type
American Association of Bioanalysts	800-234-5315	Liquid
American Academy of Family Physicians	800-274-7911	Liquid
Accutest	800-356-6788	Liquid
American Proficiency Institute	800-333-0958	Liquid
Medical Laboratory Evaluation (MLE)	800-338-2746	Liquid
College of American Pathologists (Surveys)	800-323-4040	Frozen Serum
College of American Pathologists (EXCEL)	800-323-4040	Liquid
Idaho Bureau of Labs	208-334-2235, Ext. 246	Liquid
New Jersey Department of Health	609-292-5605	Liquid
New York State Department of Health	518-474-8739	Frozen Serum
Pacific Biometrics Research Foundation	206-298-0068	Fresh Serum
Puerto Rico Department of Health	809-764-7735	Lyophilized
Solomon Park Research Institute	800-769-7774	Fresh Serum
Wisconsin State Laboratory of Hygiene	800-462-5261	Liquid

programs that use fresh or frozen human serum pools, thus greatly minimizing or eliminating matrix effects inherent in processed materials. Although this permits assessment of testing accuracy by comparison of survey results to a reference method target value, all proficiency testing programs continue to assess accuracy for participant performance by using peer grouping.

OTHER NON-CLIA PROGRAMS

The University of Washington's Reference Lipoprotein Analysis Basic Survey

The Northwest Lipid Research Laboratories at the University of Washington, Seattle (member of the CRMLN), conducts a quarterly survey called the Reference Lipoprotein Analysis Basic Survey (ReLABS). The goals of the program are to achieve and maintain the NCEP performance guidelines for cholesterol analysis and to standardize HDL-C, TG, LDL-C, and apo A-I and B measurements using fresh patient specimens. Participating manufacturers and clinical laboratories receive quarterly statistical reports and troubleshooting assistance. For more information, contact Northwest Lipid Research Laboratories, University of Washington, 2121 N. 35th Street, Seattle WA 98103; Telephone 206–685–3317; Fax 206–685–3279.

The Canadian Reference Laboratory's External Quality Assurance (EQA) Programs

The Canadian Reference Laboratory (CRL) (member of the CRMLN) supports the standardization of lipid testing in Canada. The CRL provides a number of EQA programs, all of which use fresh human serum as the quality control material. With the LIPID^PLUS EQA program, laboratories receive three frozen samples of human serum drawn from normolipidemic and dyslipidemic subjects. Target values are assigned using CRL's standardized secondary reference methods. Preliminary reports are distributed by fax to participating laboratories within seven days of submitting their results. More complete reports follow by mail one week later. CRL offers a full range of EQA programs for clinical laboratories. For more information, contact the Canadian Reference Laboratory (1996) Ltd., 307–2083 Alma Street, Vancouver, British Columbia V6R 4N6, Canada; Telephone 604–222–1355; Fax 604–222–1373; Web site, http://biotech. bc.ca/bcba/crl/Default.htm.

Rotterdam's Cholesterol Standardization Program

The Lipid Reference Laboratory (LRL) Rotterdam (member of the CRMLN) offers a Cholesterol Standardization Program (for TC, HDL-C, LDL-C, and apo A-I and apo B) to Dutch clinical laboratories in collaboration with the Dutch Foundation for Quality Assessment in Clinical Laboratories. Lyophilized, cryoprotected materials, and fresh frozen sera, of which the matrix is minimally modified, are sent every two months. LRL's standardized secondary reference methods assign values for serum lipids; standardization of apo A-I and B to the WHO-IFCC is based on reference preparations SP1–01 and SP3–07 respectively. In the case of serum lipids, the analytical performance of the labs is judged against the NCEP criteria for overall imprecision and bias. For more information, contact the Lipid Reference Laboratory Rotterdam, 3015 GD Rotterdam, The Netherlands; Telephone 31–10–4633493; Fax 31–76–5036710.

H.S. Raffaele's EQA Program

H.S. Raffaele (member of the CRMLN), in collaboration with Bio Rad Italy, and under the auspices of the Italian Society of Clinical Biochemistry and Clinical Molecular Biology, conducts an External Quality Assessment Program in Clinical Chemistry (PROLARIT). Program participants come from Italy, Greece, and Spain. The program is organized for six events per year, with two lyophilized materials sent per event. Target values for the lipids are assigned using H.S. Raffaele's secondary reference methods for cholesterol and the designated comparison method for HDL-C.

Table 36–6 ✧ Primary Standards		
Organization	*Telephone*	*Standard*
Public Sources		
Natl. Institute for Standards & Technology	301-975-6776	Cholesterol (99.8%): SRM 911b Tripalmitin (99.5%): SRM 1595
Commercial Sources		
Alfa Aesar (Morton Thiokol, Inc.)	800-343-0660	Glycerol (99.5+%)
Calbiochem Novabiochemicals	800-854-3417	Cholesterol (95%)
Gallard-Schlesinger	516-333-5600	Glycerol (99+%)
ICN Biomedicals, Inc.	714-545-0113	Cholesterol (99+%) Glycerol (99.5%) Triolein (95+%)
Fisher Scientific	800-766-7000	Cholesterol (95%) Glycerol (99.5%) Tripalmitin (99%)
Sigma-Aldrich	800-558-9160	Cholesterol (99+%) Glycerol (99.5%) Triolein (99%) Tripalmitin (99%)
Roche Diagnostics	800-262-1640	Glycerol (99.5%)

For more information, contact H.S. Raffaele, Laboratorio Analisi Cliniche, Via Olgettina 60, 20132 Milano, Italy; Telephone 39–02–2643–2315 (or 2313); Fax 39–02–2643–2640.

SOURCES OF STANDARDS AND REFERENCE MATERIALS

Although matrix effects and commutability issues complicate the standardization of lipid and lipoprotein measurements, reference materials still play a significant role in assessing the performance of test systems.[101] The matrix sensitivity of either a homogeneous or heterogeneous analytical system to a specific reference material should be established by concurrent analysis of fresh patient specimens. If an evaluated instrument system has been shown to be matrix insensitive or if a consistent matrix discrepancy can be documented for a particular material, then that material can be used with reasonable confidence to assess system performance. The College of American Pathologists has developed a reliable protocol for verifying ac-

Table 36–7 ✧ Secondary Reference Materials

Organization	Telephone	Reference Material(s)
National Institute for Standards and Technology	301-975-6776	web site: www.nist.gov/srm SRM 909b is a lyophilized human serum for specified constituents (cholesterol and total glycerides). SRM 1951a is a frozen human serum for evaluating the accuracy of clinical procedures for the determination of TC, HDL-C, LDL-C, and TG (triglycerides and total glyceride species). Values for TC and TG assigned by NIST definitive methods and CDC reference methods. Values for HDL-C and LDL-C assigned by CDC reference methods only; SRM 968b is a lyophilized human serum for validating methods used to determine fat-soluble vitamins, carotenoids, and cholesterol in human serum and plasma.
Centers for Disease Control and Prevention	770-488-4126	Frozen serum pools prepared from human-based material. Target values assigned by the CDC reference methods for cholesterol, TG, and HDL-C. Available, on a limited basis, through the CDC-NHLBI Lipid Standardization Program.
Solomon Park Research Laboratories, Kirkland, Washington	425-821-7005	Frozen serum pools prepared from human based material. Target values assigned by reference methods standardized by CDC.
Northwest Lipid Research Laboratories, University of Washington	206-685-3317	WHO-IFCC Reference Reagent SP1-01 for apo A-I WHO-IFCC Reference Reagent SP3-07 for apo B

curacy and demonstrating the presence of matrix interference in reference materials.[102]

The responsibility for assigning appropriate target values that are traceable to the recommended lipid, lipoprotein, and apolipoprotein accuracy base rests with the manufacturer. Calibrators provided by a manufacturer for a specific instrument system are suitable for that instrument system only and should not be assumed to be appropriate for other measurement systems unless specifically evaluated. Universal reference materials should be evaluated for each intended system application. Sources of primary standards are listed in Table 36–6 and available secondary reference materials are listed in Table 36–7. These lists are certainly not comprehensive, and more extensive information can be obtained from specific measurement system manufacturers or found in most clinical chemistry reagent catalogs.

Note: Use of trade names in this chapter is for identification only and does not constitute endorsement by the Public Health Service or the U.S. Department of Health and Human Services. ✧

REFERENCES

1. Lipid Research Clinics Program. The Lipid Research Clinics Primary Prevention Trial results. I: Reduction in incidence of coronary heart disease. II: The relationship of reduction in incidence of coronary heart disease to cholesterol lowering. JAMA 1984; 251:351–75.
2. The Expert Panel. Report of the National Cholesterol Education Program Expert Panel on detection, evaluation, and treatment of high blood cholesterol in adults. Arch Intern Med 1988;148:36–9.
3. Gordon DJ, Rifkind BM. High-density lipoprotein: the clinical implications of recent studies. New England J Med 1989;148:1311–16.
4. NIH Consensus Conference. Triglyceride, high-density lipoprotein, and coronary heart disease. JAMA 1993;269:505–10.
5. Consensus Development Conference. Treatment of hypertriglyceridemia. JAMA 1984; 251:1196–1200.
6. Stein EA, Steiner PM. Triglyceride measurement and its relationship to heart disease. Clin Lab Med 1989;9(1):169–85.
7. Austin MA. Plasma triglyceride and coronary heart disease. Arterioscler Thromb 1991; 11:2–15.
8. Grundy SM. Hypertriglyceridemia, atherogenic dyslipidemia, and the metabolic syndrome. Am J Cardiol 1998;81(4A):18B–25B.
9. Hokanson JE, Austin MA. Plasma triglyceride level is a risk factor for cardiovascular disease independent of high-density lipoprotein cholesterol level: a meta-analysis of population-based prospective studies. J Cardiovasc. Risk 1996;3:214–19.
10. Jeppesen J, Hein HO, Suadicani P, Gyntelberg F. Triglyceride concentration and ischemic heart disease. An eight-year followup in the Copenhagen Male Study. Circulation 1998;97:1029–36.
11. Friedewald WT, Levy RI, Fredrickson DS. Estimation of the concentration of low-density lipoprotein cholesterol in plasma, without use of the preparative ultracentrifuge. Clin Chem 1972;18:499–502.
12. Albers JJ, Brunzell JD, Knopp RH. Apoprotein measurements and their clinical application. Clin Lab Med 1989;9:137–52.
13. LaMarche B, Moorjani S, Lupien PJ et al. Apolipoprotein A-I and B levels and the risk of ischemic heart disease during a five-year follow-up of men in the Quebec Cardiovascular Study. Circulation 1996;94:273–8.
14. Kostner GM, Avogaro P, Cazzolato G et al. Lipoprotein Lp(a) and the risk for myocardial infarction. Atherosclerosis 1981;38:51–61.
15. Schaefer EJ, Lamon-Fava S, Jenner JL et al. Lipoprotein(a) levels and risk of coronary heart disease in men. JAMA 1994;271:999–1003.
16. Bostom AG, Cupples LA, Jenner JL et al. Elevated plasma lipoprotein(a) and coronary heart disease in men aged 55 years and younger. JAMA 1996;276:544–8.
17. The Expert Panel. Summary of the Second Report of the National Cholesterol Education Program (NCEP) Expert Panel on Detection, Evaluation, and Treatment of High Blood Cholesterol in Adults (Adult Treatment Panel II). JAMA 1993;269:3015–23.
18. Current status of blood cholesterol measurement in clinical laboratories in the United States: A report from the laboratory standardization panel of the National Cholesterol Education Program. Clin Chem 1988;34:193–201.
19. Duncan IW, Mather A, Cooper GR. The procedure for the proposed cholesterol reference method. Atlanta, GA: Centers for Disease Control, 1988.
20. Cooper GR, Smith SJ, Duncan IW et al. Interlaboratory testing of the transferability of a candidate reference method for total cholesterol in serum. Clin Chem 1986;32:921–9.
21. Abell LL, Levy BB, Brodie RB, Kendall. Simplified method for the estimation of total cholesterol in serum, and demonstration of its specificity. J Biol Chem 1952;195:357.
22. Cohen A, Hertz HS, Mendel J et al. Total serum cholesterol by isotope dilution–mass spectrometry: a candidate definitive method. Clin Chem 1980;26:854–60.

23. Stein EA, Myers GL. National Cholesterol Education Program Recommendations for triglyceride measurement: Executive summary. Clin Chem 1995;41:1321–426.

24. Warnick GR, Wood PD. National Cholesterol Education Program Recommendations for measurement of high-density lipoprotein cholesterol: executive summary. Clin Chem 1995;41:1427–33.

25. Bachorik, PS, Ross JW. National Cholesterol Education Program recommendations for low-density lipoprotein cholesterol: executive summary. Clin Chem 1995;41;1414–20.

26. European Union, Directive 98/79/EC of the European Parliament and of the Council, of 27 October 1998, on *in vitro* diagnostic medical devices, Official Journal of the European Communities, 7 December 1998, L331/1–37.

27. ISO/TC212/WG2, International Standards for Clinical Laboratory Testing and *In Vitro* Diagnostic Test Systems, prEN ISO 17511, *In vitro* diagnostic medical devices—Measurement of quantities in samples of biological origin—metrological traceability of values assigned to calibrators and control materials (November, 1999).

28. Vanderlinde RE, Bowers GN Jr, Schaffer R, Edwards GC. The National Reference System for Cholesterol. Clin Lab Med 1989;9:89–104.

29. Ellerbe P, Myers GL, Cooper GR et al. A comparison of results for cholesterol in human serum obtained by the reference and by the definitive method of the National Reference System for Cholesterol. Clin Chem 1990;36:370–5.

30. Bernert JT, Jr, Akins JR, Cooper GR et al. Factors influencing the accuracy of the National Reference System total cholesterol reference method. Clin Chem 1991;37:2053–61.

31. Hainline A, Jr, Karon J, Lippel K (eds.). Manual of laboratory operations: lipid and lipoprotein analysis (2nd ed). [HEW Pub. No. (NIH) 75–628 (rev.), U.S. Government Printing Office Publication No. 1982–361–132:678.] Bethesda, MD: National Heart, Lung, and Blood Institute, Lipid Research Clinics Program.

32. Ellerbe P, Sniegoski LT, Welch MJ. Isotope dilution mass spectrometry as a candidate definitive method for determining total glycerides and triglycerides in serum. Clin Chem 1995;41:397–404.

33. Carlson LA, Wadstrom LB. Determination of glycerides in blood serum. Clin Chim Acta 1959;4:197–205.

34. Carlson LA. Determination of serum triglycerides. J Ather Res 1963;3:334–6.

35. Van Handel E, Zilversmit DB. Micromethod for the direct determination of triglycerides in serum. J Lab Clin Med 1957;50:152–7.

36. Lofland HB, Jr. A semi-automated procedure for the determination of triglycerides in serum. Anal Biochem 1964;9:393–400.

37. Bernert JT, Jr, Bell CJ, McGuffey JE. Determination of free glycerol in human serum reference materials by isotope-dilution gas chromatography-mass spectrometry. J Chromatography 1992;578:1–7.

38. Labeur C, Rosseneu M, Henderson O. International Lp(a) Standardization. Chem Phys Lipids 1994;67/68:265–70.

39. Balbo-Enzi G, Baiocchi MR, Crepaldi G. Comparison of lipoprotein(a) assay methods in serum and in a plasminogen-free fraction. Clin Chim Acta 1993:218:83–95.

40. Albers JJ, Marcovina SM. Lipoprotein(a) quantification: comparison of methods and strategies for standardization. Current Opinion in Lipidology 1994;5:417–21.

41. Tate JR, Rifai N, Berg K et al. International Federation of Clinical Chemistry standardization project for the measurement of lipoprotein(a). Phase I. Evaluation of the analytical performance of lipoprotein(a) assay systems and commercial calibrators. Clin Chem 1998;44:1629–40.

42. Tate JR, Berg K, Couderc R et al. International Federation of Clinical Chemistry and Laboratory Medicine (IFCC) standardization project for the measurement of lipoprotein(a). Phase 2. Selection and properties of a proposed secondary reference material for lipoprotein(a). Clin Chem Lab Med 1999;37:949–58.

43. Koschinsky ML, Marcovina SM. Lipoprotein(a): structure implication for pathophysiology. Int J Clin Lab Res 1997;27:14–23.

44. Shepherd J, Rosseneu M, Vercaemst R, Colinet E, Profilis C. Purification and certifica-

tion of human apolipoprotein A-I and A-II reference materials (CRM 393 and 394). Community Bureau of Reference, 1991. (BCR Information series No. CD-NA-13393-EN-C, ISBN 92–826–2402–1.) Luxembourg: Commission of the European Communities, 1991, 78 pp.

45. Henderson LO, Powell MK, Smith SJ et al. Impact of protein measurements on standardization of assays of apolipoprotein AI and B. Clin Chem 1990;36:1911–7.

46. Albers JJ, Marcovina SM. Standardization of apolipoprotein B and A-I measurements. Clin Chem 1989;35:1357–61.

47. Barr JR, Maggio VL, Patterson DG et al. Isotope dilution-mass spectrometric quantification of specific proteins: model application with apolipoprotein A-I. Clin Chem 1996;42;1676–82.

48. Marcovina SM, Albers JJ, Henderson LO, Hannon WH. International Federation of Clinical Chemistry standardization project for measurement of apolipoproteins. III: Comparability of apo A-I values by the use of common reference material. Clin Chem 1993; 39:773–81.

49. Marcovina SM, Albers JJ, Kennedy H et al. International Federation of Clinical Chemistry standardization project for measurement of apolipoproteins A-I and B. IV: Comparability of apo B values using international reference materials. Clin Chem 1994;40:586–92.

50. Naito HK. The need for accurate total cholesterol measurement. Clin Lab Med 1989; 9:37–60.

51. Myers GL, Cooper GR, Winn CL, Smith SJ. The Center for Disease Control, National Heart, Lung, and Blood Institute Lipid Standardization Program: an approach to accurate and precise lipid measurements. Clin Lab Med 1989;9:105–35.

52. Recommendations for improving cholesterol measurement: a report from the Laboratory Standardization Panel of the National Cholesterol Education Program. (NIH Publication No: 90–2964). Bethesda, MD: National Institutes of Health, February 1990.

53. Cooper GR, Myers GL, Smith SJ, Sampson EJ. Standardization of lipid, lipoprotein, and apolipoprotein measurements. Clin Chem 1988;34:B95–105.

54. Cooper GR, Myers GL, Smith SJ, Schlant RC. Blood lipid measurements: variations and practical utility. JAMA 1992;267:1652–60.

55. Smith SJ, Cooper GR, Myers GL, Sampson EJ. Biological variability in the concentration of serum lipids: sources of variation among results from published studies and composite predicted values. Clin Chem 1993;39:1012–22.

56. Cooper GR, Smith SJ, Myers GL et al. Estimating and minimizing effects of biologic sources of variation by relative range when measuring the mean of serum lipids and lipoproteins. Clin Chem 1994;40:227–32.

57. Cooper GR, Hannon WH, Henderson LO, Smith SJ. Apolipoprotein measurements: Preanalytical issues and standardization. Proceedings of the Fourth Asian-Pacific Congress of Clinical Biochemistry. Hong Kong: Gardiner-Caldwell Communications, 1990: 392–7.

58. Fasce CF Jr, Rej R, Copeland WH, Vanderlinde RE. A discussion of enzyme reference materials: applications and specifications. Clin Chem 1973;19:5–9.

59. Greenberg N, Li ZM, Bower GN. National Reference System for Cholesterol (NRS-CHOL): problems with transfer of accuracy with matrix materials. Clin Chem 1988;34:1230–1.

60. Kroll MH, Chesler R, Elin RJ. Effect of the lyophilization on results of five enzymatic methods for cholesterol. Clin Chem 1989;35:1523–6.

61. Kroll MH, Chesler R. The effect of surfactant on the enzymatic determination of cholesterol with lyophilized materials. [Abstract]. Clin Chem 1990;36:960.

62. Lasky FD, Powers DM, Hassemer DJ, Wiebe DA. Quality of fluids used in external QC programs affects the reliable assessment of accuracy of routine methods, as documented by cholesterol. In: Kawai T, Ohba Y, Kanno T, Kawano K, Ueda K, Tatsumi E (eds.). Quality control in the clinical laboratory '91. Princeton, NJ: Excerpta Medica 1992:199–208.

63. Koch DD, Hassemer DJ, Wiebe DA et al. Testing cholesterol accuracy performance of several common laboratory instruments. JAMA 1988;260:2252–7.

64. Myers GL, Schap FD, Smith SJ et al. CAP-CDC collaborative study for evaluating reference materials for total serum cholesterol measurements. Arch Pathol Lab Med 1990; 114:1199–205.

65. Naito HK, Kwak YS, Hartfiel JL et al. Matrix effects on proficiency testing materials: impact on accuracy of cholesterol measurement in laboratories in the nation's largest hospital system. Arch Pathol Lab Med 1993;117:345–51.

66. Ross JW, Myers GL, Gilmore BF et al. Matrix effects and the accuracy of cholesterol analysis. Arch Pathol Lab Med 1993;117:393–400.

67. Waymack PP, Miller WG, Myers GL. Assay instrument-dependent matrix effects in standardization of cholesterol measurements. Clin Chem 1993;39:2058–62.

68. Miller WG, Levine J, Santulli M et al. Effect of freezings on cholesterol in individual sera. [Abstract]. Clin Chem 1990;36:965.

69. Myers GL, Ross JW, Smith SJ et al. Evaluating lyophilized human serum preparations for suitability as proficiency testing materials for HDL cholesterol measurement. Arch Pathol Lab Med 1995;119:686–94.

70. Holani KK, Miller WG, Waymack PP. Robustness of three triglyceride reagents for matrix effects of proficiency testing materials. Clin Chem 1993;39:1126.

71. Williams JH, Taylor L, Kuchmak M, Witter RF. Preparation of hypercholesterolemic and/or hypertriglyceridemic sera for lipid determinations. Clin Chim Acta 1970;28: 247–53.

72. Proksch GJ, Bonderman, DP. Use of a cholesterol-rich bovine lipoprotein to enhance cholesterol concentrations in the preparation of serum control materials. Clin Chem 1976;22:1302–5.

73. Kuchmak M, Taylor L, Williams JH. Preparation of reference sera with desired levels of cholesterol and triglyceride. Clin Chim Acta 1981;114:127–35.

74. Kuckmak M, Taylor L, Olansky AS. Low lipid level reference sera with human serum matrix. Clin Chim Acta 1981;116:125–30.

75. NCCLS. Preparation and validation of commutable frozen human serum pools as secondary reference materials for cholesterol measurement procedures; approved guideline. NCCLS document C-37A (ISBN 1–56238–392–2), NCCLS, 940 West Valley Road, Suite 1400, Wayne, PA 19087, 1999.

76. Smith SJ, Henderson LO, Hannon WH et al. Effects of analytical method and lyophilized sera on measurements of apolipoproteins A-I and B: an international survey. Clin Chem 1990;36:290–6.

77. Mei JV, Powell MK, Henderson LO et al. Method-dependent variation in the stability of apolipoprotein B in a stabilized liquid reference material. Clin Chem 1994;40:716–22.

78. Rautela GS, Stater S, Arvon DA. Assessment of the need for triglyceride blank measurements. Clin Chem 1973;19:1193–5.

79. Jessen R, Cass C, Eckfeldt J. Do enzymatic analyses of serum triglycerides really need blanking for free glycerol? Clin Chem 1990;36:1372–5.

80. Cole T. Glycerol blanking in triglyceride assays: is it necessary? Clin Chem 1990; 36:1267–8.

81. Klotzsch SG, McNamara JR. Triglyceride measurements: a review of methods and interferences. [Review]. Clin Chem 1990;36:1605–13.

82. Sampson M, Ruddel M, Elin RJ. Effects of specimen turbidity and glycerol concentration on nine enzymatic methods for triglyceride determination. Clin Chem 1994; 40:221–6.

83. Leary ET, Tjersland G, Warnick GR. Evaluation of the Genzyme immunoseparation reagent for direct quantitation of LDL cholesterol. [Abstract]. Clin Chem 1993;39:1124.

84. McNamara JR, Cole TG, Contois JH et al. Immunoseparation method for measuring low-density lipoprotein cholesterol directly from serum evaluated. Clin Chem 1995;41: 232–40.

85. Jialal I, Hirany SV, Devaraj S, Sherwood, TA. Comparison of an immunoprecipitation

method for direct measurement of LDL-cholesterol with beta-quantification (ultracentrifugation). Amer J Clin Pathol 1995;104:76–81.

86. Nakamura N, Sato S, Iida M. Comparison of LDL-cholesterol in fresh and frozen samples by five homogeneous methods in Japan. Clin Chem 1998;44:A80.

87. Waymack P, Chen W, Ethridge SF, Myers GL. Stability to freezing of low-density lipoprotein (LDL) cholesterol in serum [Abstract]. Clin Chem 1996;42:S291.

88. Waymack PW, Ethridge SF, Chen W, Myers, GL. Beta-quantification round robin for low-density lipoprotein cholesterol using frozen reference serum. Presented at the Frontiers in Lipid and Lipoprotein Research Conference. October 5, 1996, Dallas, Texas.

89. Kroll MH, Chesler R. Nonlinearity of high-density lipoprotein cholesterol determinations is matrix dependent. Clin Chem 1994;40:389–94.

90. Thienpont LM, Van Landuyt KG, Stockl D, De Leenheer AP. Four frequently used test systems for serum cholesterol evaluated by isotope dilution gas chromatography-mass spectrometry candidate reference method. Clin Chem 1996;42:531–5.

91. NCCLS. The reference system for the clinical laboratory: criteria for development and credentialing of methods and materials for harmonization of results; proposed guideline. NCCLS document NRSCL13-P (ISBN 1–56238–278–0). NCCLS, 940 West Valley Road, Suite 1400, Wayne, PA. 19087 USA, 1995.

92. Kimberly MM, Leary ET, Cole TC, Waymack PP. Selection, validation, standardization, and performance of a designated comparison method for HDL-cholesterol for use in the Cholesterol Reference Method Laboratory Network. Clin Chem 1999:45:1803–12.

93. Kimberly MM, Waymack PP, Myers GL, Cole TG, Ferguson C, Gibson D, Leary ET, Warnick GR. Comparison of precipitation methods for determination of HDL cholesterol in the cholesterol reference method laboratory network. [Abstract]. Clin Chem 1994;40:1105.

94. Kimberly MM, Waymack PP, Smith SJ. Evaluation of frozen vs. fresh samples by the designated comparison method for HDL cholesterol in the Cholesterol Reference Method Laboratory Network. [Abstract]. Clin Chem 1995;41:S136.

95. Bennett ST, Eckfeldt JH, Belcher JD, Connelly DP. Certification of cholesterol measurements by the National Reference Method Laboratory Network with routine clinical specimens: effects of network laboratory bias and imprecision. Clin Chem 1992;38:651–7.

96. NCCLS. Method comparison and bias estimation using patient samples; approved guideline. NCCLS document EP9-A (ISBN 1–56238–283–7). NCCLS, 940 West Valley Road, Suite 1400, Wayne, PA 19087 USA, 1995.

97. Centers for Disease Control and Prevention. Clinical laboratory measurements traceable to the National Reference System for Cholesterol. Morbidity and Mortality Weekly Report. U.S. Department of Health and Human Services, Public Health Service. 1994; 43:149–50.

98. Cooper GR, Smith SJ, Wiebe DA et al. International survey of apolipoproteins A-I and B measurements (1983–84). Clin Chem 1985;31:223–8.

99. Smith SJ, Henderson LO, Cooper GR, Hannon WH. An evaluation of the trends in analytical performance of international apolipoprotein A-I and B assays. Clin Chem 1988; 34:1644–6.

100. Smith SJ, Cooper GR, Henderson LO, Hannon WH. Apolipoprotein Standardization Collaborating Group: An international collaborative study on standardization of apolipoproteins A-I and B. Part I: Evaluation of a lyophilized candidate reference and calibration material. Clin Chem 1987;33:2240–9.

101. Miller WG. How useful are reference materials? [Editorial]. Clin Chem 1996;42:1733–4.

102. Eckfeldt JH, Copeland KR. Accuracy verification and identification of matrix effects: the College of American Pathologists' protocol. Arch Pathol Lab Med 1993;117:381–6.

Providing Laboratory Support for Clinical Trials, Epidemiological Studies, and *In vitro* Diagnostics Evaluations

37

Thomas G. Cole, G. Russell Warnick, and Nader Rifai

✧ The clinical laboratory plays a vital role in the partnership among academics, private industry, and government in improving the delivery and quality of health care. The opportunities for the clinical laboratory to expand medical knowledge through developing and evaluating new ideas about medical diagnostics and treatment are enormous.

Participating in clinical research can have many rewards for the clinical laboratory-based scientist. Besides the financial benefit of increasing revenue for the laboratory, there are other rewards, such as working at the cutting edge of medical science, enhancing one's career through increased visibility from consequent presentations and publications, interacting with clinical investigators, and enjoying the satisfaction that comes from contributing to progress in the field. This chapter explores the specific roles the laboratory can take to support clinical research.

Currently, hospital-based or reference laboratories have many opportunities to take part in clinical research. Research and development (R&D) expenditures by research-based pharmaceutical companies reached $24 billion in 1999, an increase of 14.1% over 1998. The percentage of domestic U. S. sales allocated to R&D increased from 11.0% to 20.8% in 1999. Among R&D expenditures, costs for clinical evaluation studies (Phases I to IV) represent the major expense, projected to be $6.5 billion in 1999. The allocation for laboratory testing has been estimated at 7.1% of total pharmaceutical R&D expenditures, which amounted to $1.7 billion in 1999. The National Institutes of Health (NIH) also support clinical research; laboratory costs are believed to account for approximately 20% of the total NIH clinical expenditure. The allocation for clinical laboratory testing is estimated to be as much as $1.12 billion.

The worldwide market for *in vitro* diagnostics has reached $20 billion in 1999, with the four largest companies being Roche Diagnostics, Abbott Laboratories, Bayer Diagnostics, and Johnson & Johnson. A 5% annual growth is predicted for this market, which should reach $22.2 billion in 2001. Diagnostics companies allocate approximately 10% of total revenues to R&D, suggesting a total annual budget of approximately $2 billion for development activities, including both in-house and outsourced research activities. Collaborations are possible in all types of laboratory venues, including hospital and referral laboratories, specialty laboratories, and even the smaller laboratories associated with physicians' offices. Given these statistics and the antici-

749

pated sustained growth in the field, the future looks promising for clinical laboratories interested in supporting various types of clinical research.

PROCESSES

Clinical Trials for the Pharmaceutical Industry

Clinical trials, by definition, involve human test subjects. The pharmaceutical industry uses laboratory data from clinical trials to develop new drugs. The U. S. Food and Drug Administration (FDA) mandates various types of trial designs (Phases I–III) before a drug can be marketed. Clinical trials are also performed to examine the dose-response relationship of a drug on clinical and biochemical end points, to characterize the pleiotropic or secondary effects of a drug, or to establish the performance of a particular drug in specific patient populations. Clinical trials also establish the safety profile of newly developed drugs by identifying a panel of biochemical markers to be used in monitoring possible side effects.

In vitro Diagnostics

Clinical laboratories play an important role in the development *in vitro* diagnostic technologies. Because the laboratories have relevant expertise, as well as access to characterized specimens and patients, their participation in the diagnostic development process can facilitate introduction of new technologies. Laboratory participation in the development process falls into four general areas:

✧ technical development,

✧ regulatory clinical trials,

✧ marketing studies, and

✧ quality assurance.

Epidemiological Studies and Clinical Trial Sub-Studies

Prospective epidemiological studies are usually conducted to characterize the incidence of chronic diseases and to identify important associations between lifestyles, diet, and biochemical markers with regard to the disease of interest. Although cross-sectional studies are useful in reporting novel observations, they are less helpful in determining whether these observations are a result or a cause of the examined disease. In contrast, prospective epidemiological studies are crucial for determining disease causality.

After the epidemiological study or clinical trial is completed and the original question resolved, the accumulated database and stored study samples from well-characterized subjects are often used to explore novel research directions and to elucidate potential methods of diagnosis or treatment. The value of the stored blood, serum, plasma, and urine samples cannot be underestimated. As novel biochemical markers are developed or as the understanding of the pathophysiology of a particular disease is improved, these baseline samples can be re-examined to establish the utility of the candidate marker and the validity of the new concept. When these precious, irreplacable blood samples are consumed, the ability to gain new information from the study will significantly diminish.

COMMON FACTORS

Clinical Trials

Clinical trials are critical activities in the development of both new drugs and new diagnostic tests. In this section the term *clinical trial* refers to any study involving humans, irrespective of the end purpose of the trial.

When new drugs are developed, trials may be prolonged and involve many specimen collections from subjects who may or may not be exposed to the drug under evaluation. First and foremost, the safety of the trial participants must be protected and their health status constantly evaluated. Such is often not the case in the development of new diagnostic tests, in which specimens are usually collected from subjects who may or may not have a particular disease or evidence a particular metabolic state. Therefore, some trials do not risk the participants' health and do not require as intense a level of monitoring.

In the United States, clinical trials are regulated by the FDA, which requires several levels of protection for study participants. First, all trials are controlled through the use of a written protocol, which the participating investigators agree to follow. Second, the protocol must be approved for use by the local Institutional Review Board (IRB), which is composed of a diverse group of physicians, medical scientists, and nonscientists from the community. (The FDA has tended in recent years to be more demanding of the evaluation processes used by the IRBs in guaranteeing the safety of the subjects in clinical trials.) Finally, each participant must give written informed consent before entering the trial. Violation of any of these points can lead to serious legal consequences.

Although some smaller clinical trials are investigator initiated and sponsored, most of the larger clinical trials are initiated by industry or government sponsors, who design, direct, and monitor the trial. Trial sponsors typically approach the clinical laboratory for participation in the trial based upon previous interactions of the sponsor with the laboratory or based on the laboratory's reputation in a specific analytical area. Participation in certain standardization programs, such as the Centers for Disease Control and Prevention/National Heart, Lung, and Blood Institute (CDC/NHLBI) Lipid Standardization Program, will be helpful in attracting trials involving lipid measurements. After the initial contact is made and confidentiality agreements are in place, the sponsor will distribute the full protocol and describe the requirements of the trial. The protocol describes the trial in detail, including the purpose, background, and design of the study.

The schedule of visits and the testing to be performed at each visit are clearly defined, allowing the laboratory to evaluate whether it is capable of meeting the requirements. At this point, the laboratory may point out errors in or suggest improvements to the study design that may not have been obvious to the sponsor. (Note that protocols provided by pharmaceutical and diagnostics sponsors tend to be complete and usually do not change significantly during the course of the set-up or performance of the trial, while those from government-sponsored studies may be more flexible and open to change as new research information becomes available.)

Once a sponsor is interested in using a particular laboratory, it will almost always perform an in-laboratory quality audit before the first contract is awarded. This audit assures the sponsor and the FDA, if necessary, that the laboratory meets the minimum requirements for performing the desired services. The audit is similar to those conducted by professional organizations such as the College of American Pathologists (CAP) for the Clinical Laboratory Improvement Amendments (CLIA) accreditation with some differences. Quality audits tend to focus more on the quality of the Standard Operating Procedures (SOP) and the level of documentation than on the specifics of laboratory analysis. The validation of the transfer of data from instruments to the laboratory information system (LIS) and to sponsor reports is closely examined. The audit mimics the type of questions typically asked by the FDA during an inspection, in order to anticipate potential problems. The findings of the audit will be discussed with the laboratory director and deficiencies must be resolved before a study is placed in the laboratory. This is an extraordinary opportunity for the laboratory to improve its documentation and performance. Some sponsors repeat the audit on a scheduled basis, while others do not.

Ideally, a contract will be signed before a trial begins; however, depending upon the relationship between the parties and the need for a rapid start, the contract may be finalized during the term of the trial. The contract should contain all the relevant information necessary to protect the interests of both parties and to also guarantee that the necessary work will be done to the satisfaction of regulatory bodies, such as the FDA. The protocol and payment schedule are usually included in the contract, as they define the scope of the work to be done, the testing schedule, and the sponsor's cost. All points of the contract are negotiable and all issues must be resolved before the contract is signed.

A particularly troublesome point for academic-based laboratories is the specification regarding right of publication. In most instances, the laboratory does not have the right to publish study results, since it lacks ownership of the data, particularly if the sponsor initiated the trial or if the trial was blinded. On occasion, the laboratory may co-author publications with the sponsor or a writing group, particularly if a sub-study has been conducted (see below). In such instances, it is important to establish the conditions for publication in advance and to have them described explicitly in the contract.

The laboratory will be liable for inspection or audit by the FDA for years after the clinical trial is completed. These audits, like those of the sponsor's quality assurance department, are more rigorous than those required by CLIA. Complete and consistent documentation is critical. Basically every process, including pre- and post-analytical processes, must be controlled by an SOP, much as CLIA requires for analytical processes, and each SOP must be followed rigorously. Every process must be verified, signed, and dated. For drug trials, source documentation (instrument printouts, photos of gels, etc.) must be retained for FDA inspection for either two years after the drug wins approval or for two years after an Investigational New Drug (IND) application is withdrawn. Because the laboratory may not be aware of either event and because data from many trials may be commingled, data retention and retrieval can become burdensome. One option is to retain all source documentation for the longest period during which review might occur. This policy may be less costly than the alternatives, such as the separation of all data as they are produced. Each laboratory should set its policy based on its ability to live with the consequences: paper, paper, paper. For *in vitro* diagnostic products, the FDA requires retention of data and source materials for two years; for tumor marker and pathology reports, 10 years.

Laboratory accreditation under CLIA is a minimum requirement for drug trials; it is preferred for *in vitro* diagnostics trials. However, since all clinical laboratories that perform more than CLIA-waived testing require CLIA accreditation, such a requirement becomes moot. CLIA also dictates the requirements for laboratory personnel who will perform the analytical work for clinical trials. Among the personnel records that should be maintained are professional certifications, résumés or curriculum vitae for all laboratory personnel, and training records. In addition, a variety of other study-related information must be retained where appropriate: relevant agreements and contracts, case report forms for study subjects, as well as all study-related worksheets and computer printouts. The quality control processes and the quality assurance plans followed by laboratories servicing both types of trials will be similar and will be those typically used in most clinical laboratories. The extended length of time over which a drug trial is usually conducted and the fact that the data are often evaluated longitudinally require the laboratory to have demonstrable long-term stability.

In contrast to clinical trials, epidemiological studies and clinical trial sub-studies are usually initiated by investigators interested in advancing medical science rather than promoting the development of a product for monetary gain. These investigators usually approach the appropriate sponsor, i.e., the government for an epidemiological study or a pharmaceutical company for a sub-study, to obtain financial support for the project. The tests performed for an epidemiological study or a clinical trial sub-study are often tests that are not routinely performed in a clinical laboratory for patient care, and consequently do not fall under the purview of CLIA regulations. Often the tests will have only recently moved from academic research laboratories into clinical laboratories and are performed under different concepts of quality assurance by analysts who may not be trained medical technicians or technologists.

FACTORS SPECIFIC FOR EACH TYPE OF ACTIVITY

Clinical Trials for the Pharmaceutical Industry

Several factors distinguish clinical trials performed to develop a new drug from those performed to develop a new diagnostic test. Most, but not all, drug trials are conducted at multiple sites, following a protocol that requires multiple specimen collections over an extended time and continual monitoring of the health of the trial participants. Therefore, the laboratory supporting a drug trial must be able to provide a variety of tests that evaluate the safety and efficacy of the new potential drug, and do so daily, with rapid turn-around. In contrast, *in vitro* diagnostics trials generally do not require extended interaction with the trial participants, thereby reducing the concern for participant safety to the process of specimen collection only until recently, if approved by the IRB, well-characterized specimens collected for purposes other than the trial may be used without identifying or contacting trial participants. However, a recent guideline from the FDA may require informed consent for all specimens used in clinical trials for the *in vitro* diagnostic industry.[1]

A thorough knowledge of the steps involved in developing new drugs is necessary to successfully support clinical trials for the pharmaceutical industry. In the United States, the process is closely monitored by the FDA. The process typically begins with the identification of chemicals that may have a desired biological activity; these are then further evaluated for clinical usefulness. These chemicals may be the result of sophisticated molecular design efforts, modifications of known drug structures, or even serendipity. Current technology allows the rapid screening of as many as 100,000 compounds with the hope of finding a few that can be developed into a drug. A rule of thumb: only one of 5,000 compounds tested will ever reach the market as an approved drug. An interesting interactive description of the new drug discovery and development phases may be found at *http://www.searlehealthnet.com/pipeline.html.*

Candidate drugs are tested in animals in the pre-clinical phase of development, which evaluates biological activity and safety as well as establishes pharmacokinetic and pharmacodynamic parameters. The pre-clinical phase is relatively short, lasting from weeks to a year or more, and involves at least two animal species. If the candidate drug still looks promising, the FDA is notified, the data are examined, and the drug company then submits an IND application.

With FDA approval, the candidate drug will be tested in 20 to 80 *healthy* human volunteers in a Phase I or "First in Man" clinical trial. Phase I is used to establish early evidence of effectiveness, dose ranges, and acute safety. In addition, the absorption, distribution, and elimination of the drug are established by measuring drug levels in the body. Phase I trials usually last several months to one year.

Phase II studies are conducted on several hundred volunteers, each of whom has the disease of interest. These studies, which may last several years, investigate the effectiveness of the candidate drug against the disease and establish the profile of short-term side effects.

The final step before FDA approval is the Phase III trial, which may involve several hundred to thousands of volunteers, at several sites, who have the targeted disease. Phase III establishes the long-term safety and effectiveness of the candidate drug and may last three years or more. The drug company then submits a New Drug Application (NDA) that includes all data on the candidate drug and may be several hundred thousand pages in length. If, after several meetings and rounds of questioning, the FDA deems the drug safe and effective, the drug is approved for sale. (A summary of this process is available at *http://www.fda.gov/cder/handbook/develop.htm.*)

In some situations, the drug company or the FDA will request Phase IV studies to gather additional information about the drug after its release or to increase the number of labeled indications for the drug. For some drugs, e.g., anti-HIV drugs, the approval process is placed on an abbreviated "fast track." In addition, the availability of well-characterized subjects and archived specimens allows for a variety of substudies to be conducted after the initial trial is completed (see below).

On average, the entire process for drug development, from discovery to FDA approval, may cost as much as $500 million and take 12 to 15 years.[2] Two factors drive the process to reduce development time: the drug is protected by patent for only 20 years, and the typical income for a successful drug is about $1 million per day.

If the submission of the NDA is delayed for one month by a problem in the laboratory, the company may lose $30 million of income! This is truly a situation where "time is of the essence," and the importance of timely problem resolution and of providing a clean data set immediately at the end of clinical trial cannot be overemphasized.

The FDA does not have specific requirements for laboratories that perform the analytical work for clinical trials. However, as a contractor to the drug company sponsoring the clinical trial, the laboratory has, by referral, responsibilities under the FDA's Good Clinical Practice (GCP) regulations.[3] GCP is in place to meet the FDA's primary concern, which is to protect the welfare of the trial participants.

On occasion, a sponsor will request that the laboratory perform the clinical trial testing under the FDA's Good Laboratory Practice (GLP) regulations.[4] Such a request appears reasonable, since no one wants testing that is less than "good"; however, GLP by statute applies specifically to non-clinical trials, i.e., those that do not involve human subjects. GLP has specific requirements that go far beyond those of CLIA and that carry the force of law. Although the application of GLP to the routine testing conducted in the typical clinical laboratory would be onerous and would not necessarily improve the quality of the testing performed, the concepts behind GLP are desirable. Therefore, the analytical work should be performed under the "essence of GLP," which embodies the concepts, but not the specific requirements, of GLP. This level of improved accountability over standard clinical laboratory work has been termed "glp" or "GLP-lite" and is being requested by more and more sponsors over time. Be aware that if a sponsor requires that analytical work be performed under the tenants of "good laboratory practice," this terminology may be interpreted as meaning "the legally defined GLP" rather than "glp" and should be clarified prior to signing the contract.

Most analytical work for clinical trials is performed by large, often international, laboratories that specialize in these services. Large laboratories, such as Covance Central Laboratories, Covance, Indianapolis, IN, USA, associated with a clinical research organization (CRO) and the large referral chains such as LabCorp, Burlington, NC, USA and Quest, Teterboro, NJ, USA, generally provide an extensive test menu and pre- and post-analytical services such as national courier capabilities that cannot be easily matched by smaller laboratories. Nevertheless, there are many opportunities for smaller laboratories to compete successfully by identifying an appropriate specialty or niche.

Most of the laboratory testing for clinical trials is done either to establish the safety profile of a drug or to establish its efficacy against a target disease. Safety testing (general organ panels, hematology, and urinalysis) generally involve high-volume, low-profit tests. Efficacy testing involves measuring a biomarker that varies in relation to exposure to the drug. For instance, the change in concentration of low-density lipoprotein cholesterol (LDL-C) is often determined to establish the effectiveness of a potential lipid-lowering drug. In ideal situations, the biomarker may serve as a surrogate endpoint in the clinical trial, thereby reducing the need for costly long-term outcomes trials. Esoteric testing, such as determination of LDL particle size or the tendency for LDL to oxidize, performed to establish efficacy, often will have a higher margin of profit, particularly if the assays are only offered by a small number of laboratories. Some trials also include highly specialized testing, such as kinetic turn-over studies, performed in order to establish the mechanism of drug action. Esoteric and specialty testing is often performed in external research laboratories under subcontract to the trial's central laboratory, similar to a clinical trial sub-study.

Clinical trials establishing the efficacy of lipid-altering drugs generally span several months to years and may involve only modest changes in lipoprotein and apo-lipoprotein concentrations. As a result, analytical systems for the detection of these small changes must be accurate and, more importantly, reproducible, over long periods of time. The availability of standardization programs for the measurement of lipids and lipoproteins (CDC/NHLBI Lipid Standardization Program) and apolipo-proteins (ReLabs, Seattle, WA, USA, Northwest Lipid Research Laboratories, Seattle, WA, USA [see Chapter 36]) has allowed external verification of analytical stability and accuracy. Such may not be true for analytes measured in epidemiological studies or clinical trial sub-studies where new tests are transitioning from the research laboratory environment into the clinical laboratory.

The pre-clinical phase of drug development requires safety and efficacy testing on animal-derived specimens. This provides an opportunity for laboratories with experience in animal testing, but may challenge the human-oriented hospital-based or reference laboratory. This type of testing is highly specialized; assays optimized for use on human-derived specimens may not behave as anticipated on animal-derived specimens and will need to be validated for the particular species being investigated, particularly if immunoassays are used.[5,6]

A laboratory that excels in toxicology or therapeutic drug testing will have an advantage in supporting pharmacokinetic trials. Laboratories with expertise in methods development might be interested in developing new assays to measure efficacy indicators. Such work is highly specialized, but can be very rewarding. The areas of molecular diagnostics and pharmacogenomics, for example, are rapidly growing and will probably continue to do so in the foreseeable future, creating new opportunities in related disciplines.

The handling and reporting of laboratory data in supporting clinical trials differ from those required for patient care. Although the same analytical processes may be used on similar specimens, the data are used for very different purposes. Patient care testing is usually ordered with the intent to use the results for either diagnosis of disease or monitoring of treatment. The laboratory results are interpreted in the context of the clinical status of the patient and once a clinical decision is made, the results are entered into the patient record, perhaps never to be seen again. In contrast, the data from a clinical trial have a very different use and fate. The data may be interpreted initially and then reside in a database for years before being submitted to a variety of longitudinal or cross-sectional statistical tests. If the measurement represents an indicator of efficacy, each data point may be closely scrutinized in relation to other results in the database. Trends might be identified and questions are likely to arise whether an observed trend is due to the effect of the drug or to analytical drift. Answers will be needed years after the analytical runs have been performed. Therefore, quality control and quality assurance data must be readily available for many years and demonstrable long-term stability of assays is critical.

The laboratory must provide the sponsor with a complete and clean data set as soon as possible after the trial is completed. To do so requires that error prevention and detection schemes be utilized throughout the trial. *Prevention* of an error is more efficient and cost effective than identifying and correcting errors, particularly those discovered long after they occur. Errors are most readily prevented by proactive means, carefully reviewing the various laboratory processes to identify potential problem areas and then by writing detailed SOPs and by implementing a quality improvement program (QIP).

Despite the best intentions and SOPs, errors are likely to occur in the data set, often as a result of the laboratory getting erroneous information from the clinical sites. Therefore, error detection systems must be in place and used routinely. Typical systems involve the use of an "extremes check" program on an analyzer to identify values outside reasonable limits, such as a very high cholesterol, e.g. 500 mg/dL. A "delta checking" routine often identifies specimens that may have errors by immediately comparing the current test result to the previous result for that subject, thus allowing for quick resolution. The two values must agree within limits related to the expected biological variability for the analyte. Flagged values are examined by a supervisor or senior technologist for possible error. This process is extremely powerful, since it uses the subject's previous status as the basis for comparison, rather than that derived from a population distribution.

Other delta checks, such as comparing the current value to initial baseline values, are used as required by the sponsor. Such schemes require a flexible computer system. Identifying and correcting errors in real time and not waiting for the end of the trial is critical, since the data set will be as clean as possible at all times and time is saved at the end of the trial. Delays in submission to the FDA translate into delayed approvals and delayed revenues for the sponsor. As errors are detected and flaws in the various processes identified, the final step in the QIP is to modify the SOPs when possible to prevent such errors in the future.

Clinical trial data must be reported to a variety of recipients. Reports must be sent daily to clinical sites, so that participant safety is monitored in a timely manner. Copies of these reports are often also sent to the sponsor. Traditionally, rapid turnaround time is attained through overnight express courier services, which are expensive but provide a permanent report, or by fax, which must be followed by a mailed permanent report. Computer-to-computer data transfer eliminates the problems associated with distribution of paper reports and can be instantaneous. As electronic data transmission becomes more secure, direct transfer of data from the laboratory to the clinical sites over the Internet becomes feasible.

The information contained in the laboratory report is critical to the success of the study. In addition to the information typically contained in reports from hospital or reference laboratories, sponsors often request specific information related to that particular clinical trial. Situations of subject inclusion or exclusion are often provided to the clinical site by the laboratory by way of the report. For instance, subjects may be accepted into the trial based on the stability of the LDL-C concentration, which must fall within defined limits over a two-week period. As a convenience to personnel at the clinical site and to reduce the number of potential errors, such calculations may be provided on a laboratory report, with the notation whether the subject is eligible for entry into the study. Similarly, protocol violations, such as specimens being collected outside of a defined window of time, may be noted. A sponsor may also require immediate notification of a clinical site of any laboratory value that varies from the baseline value by a fixed or relative amount. The variation may not be large enough to constitute a medical alert situation, but might still have importance for a particular trial. Finally, some double-blind trials require the suppression of certain information at various times in the trial to maintain the blind status, such as LDL-C concentration in a trial of a new cholesterol-lowering drug. The variations can seem endless. Meeting these needs of the sponsor requires a responsive information system department and an LIS that is flexible and readily programmed, especially since each trial will have its own set of unique variables.

For the laboratory to sustain success in servicing clinical trials, it will, at a minimum, need to offer high-quality testing services. In addition, the laboratory should offer as many ancillary services as possible. Generally, drug companies prefer to work with a single full-service laboratory than to send specimens to a variety of locations or to use multiple local laboratories.[7] Possible services include providing

- the operations manual for use in the trial;

- visit-specific kits for collection of specimens and shipment back to the laboratory;

- preprinted color- and bar-coded labels;

- color-coded flow diagrams for complex processes;

- auto-inventory system with a "just-in-time" delivery of supplies so clinical sites do not have to warehouse large volumes of supplies;

- customized reports in the format desired by the sponsor (one size does *not* fit all)—i.e., progress reports, data, laboratory results (fax, hard copy, electronic);

- customized data transfer—i.e., internet, e-mail, CPU-to-CPU, file server;

- long-term storage of records and frozen specimens; and

- competent, real-time customer service.

In vitro Diagnostic Trials

The development process for *in vitro* diagnostics generally follows a fairly common pattern. The first stage can be designated discovery, i.e., conceptualizing a new technology. The discovery might take place in the head of a creative laboratorian, through experiments conducted in a research or clinical laboratory, or in the diagnostic manufacturer's internal research laboratory. Associated with discovery are proof of concept and intellectual property issues. In preliminary studies, an idea must be shown to have some likelihood of actually working before a decision to undertake the large costs associated with the development process can be made.

A concept that uniquely represents new art and is not an obvious conclusion from prior technology may be patentable. Patenting a new development seems to be perceived negatively by some; i.e., there is a common perception that a patent might lock up or limit the use of the new technology. In truth, however, patenting can actually encourage development and eventual introduction of promising new technologies.

The cost of bringing a new diagnostic method to market is very high, requiring years of effort and millions of dollars in research and development costs. In diagnostics much of this cost is incurred in obtaining FDA clearance, which is usually essential for commercialization. Companies, which must gain a financial return in order to survive, cannot justify investing the huge amounts of capital required to commercialize a method unless there is an exclusive or proprietary right. In the absence of a patent giving a proprietary position, any single company would usually forego the cost of taking a new technology through the development process, because there would be no assurance of priority in the market and a reasonable return on the investment. In the absence of a patent another company could simply copy the new technology, saving much of the development cost and thus undercutting the price.

Clearly, patenting not only protects initial research investment costs and therefore promotes the commercialization and use of new technologies; patented technology licensed to industry can also generate income for the inventor and the institution, which in turn can fund additional future research.

The next stage in the development process typically involves perfecting and fine-tuning the concept and putting it into a working device. The result might be a new chemistry reagent, an instrument, or a complete new analytical system. This development stage can require many months or years of effort depending on the complexity and the resources applied. Many concepts are abandoned during this stage; what appears to be a good idea might not actually work well in practice. During this stage, a clinical laboratory might get involved; for example, to determine if a prototype developed in the research environment actually functions in a real laboratory setting.

The next stage of development might be pilot scale production, which can have two purposes. The first is to demonstrate that the device can be produced consistently and reliably and with acceptable cost parameters. A second purpose is to produce devices for use in subsequent evaluation and regulatory studies. The regulatory studies for submission to FDA and other regulatory bodies typically must include at least three separate production lots to demonstrate that consistency of production. Pilot scale production also helps realistically determine the cost of production and eventual pricing of the device.

With early production devices available, laboratory or clinical studies for regulatory submission can be undertaken. (See Chapter 38 for more detail about the FDA clearance process.) The regulatory studies are often, and in certain cases must be, outsourced, that is, conducted by an organization other than the manufacturer. Instruments and reagents for use in hospital and referral lab settings often undergo clinical studies in the environments in which they eventually will be used. The majority of new diagnostic devices are cleared by the FDA through the 510(k) provision, which requires demonstrating substantial equivalence of a new method to an existing method already on the market. Newer and more novel *in vitro* diagnostic technologies might be cleared under the pre-market application (PMA) provision, which requires more extensive studies to demonstrate efficacy and safety. Because the clinical laboratories are using the current methods and have ready access to characterized specimens, clinical trials are often outsourced to laboratories. In other cases the manufacturer might obtain characterized specimens from the laboratory. Studies might be retrospective, i.e., conducted on archived frozen specimens selected from previously sampled populations. In other instances the laboratory might be required to recruit new subjects meeting certain established criteria. Laboratories are also called upon to provide access to patient populations to establish reference ranges for new analytes or methods for the regulatory submission.

Devices for use outside the laboratory, for near-patient testing or point-of-care use (e.g., at the bedside, in wellness programs, or in the physician's office), are generally subjected to clinical trials in their usual operating environment. For example, devices intended for direct sale to consumers, the over-the-counter (OTC) market, must be tested in the field with subjects representative of eventual consumers. However, even these clinical trials might be managed and coordinated by personnel from a clinical or specialty laboratory. Thus, many opportunities exist for laboratorians to become involved in the studies leading to regulatory submissions.

As clinical studies are completed, the regulatory submission is prepared and sent to the FDA or other appropriate regulatory body. Concurrently with the clinical studies and submission, the manufacturer could be scaling up the production process and building an inventory for eventual distribution. During this pre-clearance period, devices might be distributed in markets that do not require prior clearance, e.g., for research purposes or in other jurisdictions.

The timeline for FDA clearance is somewhat uncertain, especially with new or highly novel technologies. The FDA and other regulatory bodies are in the often difficult position of "walking a tightrope," i.e., allowing useful new technologies to reach the market without excessive delay while at the same time keeping from the market devices that might cause harm. Steps have been taken in recent years to facilitate and streamline the FDA regulatory process. In addition there is now a major effort to harmonize regulatory requirements for *in vitro* diagnostics internationally. Diagnostic companies with experienced regulatory staff and incremental progress in technologies can anticipate with some certainty the clearance timelines. On the other hand smaller and newer companies and those with highly novel technologies must often cope with unpredictable timelines for clearance. In these instances the time from submission to clearance can be one of anxious waiting. In the interim before clearance, devices might be subjected to additional testing in clinical laboratories, another opportunity to be involved in the development process.

With the necessary regulatory clearances in hand, a device can be marketed; a market launch will usually occur. Prior to the launch, devices typically will have gone through successive levels of evaluation for marketing purposes. A limited first level is often termed an alpha study: one or a few sites evaluate an early stage of a system. The next stage involves beta sites, usually a few sites evaluating a later production stage of the system. Clinical laboratories and scientists with expertise and reputation with a particular class of analytes, a system, or technology, will have an advantage in competing for such studies. The diagnostic companies tend to minimize risk by working with laboratories that have an established reputation and track record. Clinical laboratorians involved in the evaluations will likely have opportunities to submit publications and/or make presentations regarding their experience with the device, an excellent opportunity to establish a reputation that can lead to more collaborations in the future.

In many cases even after the launch, marketing departments will initiate additional studies to study or emphasize certain features of a diagnostic product. In some instances the objective might be to make the product more widely known by exposure to influential laboratorians. New studies might be initiated to support additional regulatory submissions for device modifications or for new or expanded claims. After the launch and distribution begins, the attention of the diagnostic company turns to sales, expanding distribution, and technical support. Each of these activities can lead to additional collaborations between clinical laboratories and industry. For example, a technical problem might arise with a device, prompting queries from customers and motivating the manufacturer to contract a study to identify a fix. In other instances the manufacturer might be interested in developing new application specifications for a reagent used on a different instrument.

Clinical laboratories might also become involved in studies primarily related to quality assurance issues. A manufacturer might contract with a clinical laboratory to assign target values on calibration or reference materials. Laboratories with particular expertise and a reputation for accuracy compete for these types of studies. Laboratories with on-line reference methods or well-characterized procedures traceable to accepted reference methods are able to provide a useful service in this type of work and thereby contribute to improvements in the overall accuracy of testing.

In order to be competitive for diagnostics industry outsourcing, laboratories must be meticulous about maintaining not only the usual laboratory protocols and SOPs, but also about study-specific protocols and records. All analytical methods and procedures should be fully documented, inspected, and updated as necessary. The current study should be fully documented in such aspects as technical protocols, specimen processing, subject records, and data processing. An important aspect of record keeping is a document control system, which indexes all relevant protocols and records. As noted earlier in this chapter, industry sponsors often conduct a site audit prior to selecting sites or initiating a study and again during and at the completion of clinical trials. The FDA has the right to and sometimes does inspect laboratories performing studies for regulatory submissions, especially those involving a PMA. In recent cases clearances have been delayed for months and even years while issues of inadequate record-keeping at a laboratory site are resolved. Needless to say, a site that delays a clearance due to inadequate documentation or performance is not likely to gain repeat business.

In certain instances, for example, pre-clinical animal studies in pharmaceutical drug development, such as those described previously, requirements are spelled out by law—the so-called GLP regulation. In the case of *in vitro* diagnostic development, the requirements do not have legal status, but are nevertheless equally important. Sponsors will generally request evidence of professional competence; for example, current laboratory certifications by organizations such as the College of American Pathologists, the Joint Committee for Accreditation of Hospitals, or the Committee for Office Laboratory Accreditation.

Appropriate project management tools are important in conducting studies. Studies can be broken down into the specific steps and sequences for coordination and management using available project management software on the computer. Provisions for communicating among staff and with the industry sponsor (for example, regularly scheduled meetings and progress reports) are also important. Laboratory personnel must be clear about the sponsor's expectations. Get clear and detailed study protocols before beginning. Remain in close communication with the sponsor's study manager, the clinical research associate, or other assigned liaision. Be candid about mistakes or other problems with the sponsor; the sooner the sponsor is aware of a problem, the less the potential for compromising the study. There should be an established mechanism for documenting errors and a quality assurance committee should meet regularly to review and fix recurring problems.

Professional associations and other resources can be accessed for information and training in the process of conducting *in vitro* diagnostic studies. (FDA resources are detailed in Chapter 38.) Various organizations have informative websites and/or conduct training:

✧ The Regulatory Affairs Professional Society (RAPS) can be reached at *www.raps.org*.

✧ The Association of Clinical Research professionals (ACRP) has a website at *www.acrpnet.org;* its journal, *The Monitor*, can be accessed there.

✧ Commercial organizations such as Barnett International (*www.barnettinternational.com*) deliver seminars in conducting diagnostic and other types of regulatory trials.

✧ The Health Instrument Manufacturers Association (HIMA) has staff members with expertise in regulatory clearance issues.

✧ Applied Clinical Trials is accessible at *www.pharmaportal.com*.

✧ The Medical Device and Diagnostic Industry journal can be accessed at the website *www.devicelink.com/mddi.about.mddi.html*.

EPIDEMIOLOGICAL AND CLINICAL TRIAL SUB-STUDIES

Epidemiological studies usually involve tens of thousands of individuals who will be followed for many years. An example of the typical design is the Physician's Health Study—a randomized, double-blind, placebo-controlled trial of aspirin and beta-carotene in the primary prevention of heart disease and cancer conducted among 22, 071 U. S. male physicians aged 40–84 years. Participants were followed for over a decade, had no prior history of cardiovascular disease or cancer, and were randomly assigned to one of four treatments: 325 mg of aspirin on alternate days, 50 mg of beta-carotene on alternate days, both, or neither. Before randomization, baseline blood samples were obtained from participants and questionnaires were sent annually to elicit information on risk factors and incident health events. The obtained blood samples were carefully archived and stored in small aliquots in liquid nitrogen. During the follow-up years, participants started developing cancer and cardiovascular disease. Using a nested case-control design study, the cases being the subjects who developed the disease (myocardial infarction, for example), and the controls matched from among those who remained free of the same disease during the follow-up period, the examination of biochemical markers in samples collected at baseline when all the participants were healthy will enable the identification of new markers of risk for future myocardial infarction.

Historically, the concentrations of biochemical markers from epidemiological studies were measured in small research laboratories. For example, samples for the measurement of interleukin-6, zinc, and methymalonic acid were split into aliquots and sent to three different researchers in various institutions who were known experts in these respective areas. Although this practice was deemed acceptable in terms of the quality of the data generated, significant portions of the sample were wasted due to the division of the sample and the use of instrumentation that require large sample volume.

Instrumentation in the clinical laboratory has advanced considerably over the past two decades. Most modern automated analyzers require no more than 15 uL for the determination of a complete lipoprotein profile (total cholesterol, triglycerides, high-density lipoprotein cholesterol, and LDL-C), for example. Special cups to minimize dead volume (~35 uL) and evaporation are also commercially available. In addition, much of the equipment that was once only used in research laboratories, such as gas chromatography/mass spectrometry, high-performance liquid chromatography, isoelectric focusing, atomic absorption spectrometry, and ELISA, are currently available in sophisticated academic clinical laboratories. This represents an excellent opportunity for clinical laboratories that possess such technologies and that can handle samples with small volumes to provide specialty testing for these studies. The appropriate clinical laboratory could provide the research epidemiologists with a one-stop-shop where the concentrations of cholesterol, selenium, adhesion molecules, carotenes, cotinine, and estriol could be determined simultaneously using the most sophisticated equipment, not normally available in research laboratories, and the smallest sample volume possible, and applying rigid quality control/quality assurance practices.

As in clinical trial testing, providing laboratory services for epidemiologic studies is profitable. However, in this case the laboratorian is more active in helping researchers choose the appropriate biochemical markers and in determining their integrities in stored samples. Often, novel assays must be developed to measure certain markers. Furthermore, the laboratorian plays an important role in interpreting results. The results from these important studies are usually published in prestigious journals and lead to changes in clinical practice or public health policies. Because of his/her significant role, the laboratorian usually authors or co-authors all the resulting reports.

The requirements for providing testing for epidemiological studies are different from those needed for servicing clinical trials. All testing for epidemiological studies is done in large batches and usually accomplished in weeks or months. In contrast, clinical trials could go on for several years and the laboratory must maintain the same assays and equipment and demonstrate minimal change in assay characteristics throughout the study. In addition, laboratories that perform clinical trials should be able to generate patient results daily in a specific format and communicate with various centers when issues arise. Therefore, these laboratories usually have a fairly sophisticated LIS and a large support staff.

The strength of the laboratory that supports epidemiological studies, however, lies in its ability not only to provide testing for routinely measured analytes such as cholesterol, testosterone, and microalbumin, but also to develop, evaluate, and maintain a large number of specialty tests. Results are usually sent to the investigators electronically in an agreed-upon format. These laboratories also should maintain CLIA accreditation and CDC/NHLBI certification for lipid testing, as well as participate in proficiency testing surveys.

The latter presents a particular challenge since many of the measured analytes are in transition from the research laboratory to the clinical laboratory and are not included in the CAP or other survey materials. The best validation at this point is to standardize the assay condition to minimize imprecision and variability between duplicates and among runs. The laboratory, with time, develops expertise in several areas, for example, chromatography and ELISA, and becomes knowledgeable in determining and assessing the performance of a particular assay. Expertise develops not in a particular assay but in a technology, which is a very different mindset from that for routine established analytes.

Another important issue is that analyte stability after prolonged storage under various conditions. For valid conclusions to be made from the analytical data, the analyte stability must be validated. The stability could either be assessed from the literature or in most cases could be established by looking at the frequency distribution of about 100 stored samples and compared to that of an equal number of fresh samples from the same type of population.

TESTING FOR SUB-STUDIES OF CLINICAL TRIALS

Clinical trials provide a unique opportunity for sub-studies that are designed to answer specific questions using the trial's study population. For example, the Cholesterol and Recurrent Event (CARE) trial was originally designed to address whether pravastatin decreases the incidence of recurrent coronary events in 4159 subjects who already suffered myocardial infarction and had normal lipid levels.[8] Half the participants received 40 mg/d pravastatin and the other half received a placebo; all subjects were followed for five years. After completing the original study, a sub-study was designed in a nested case-control fashion to address whether inflammatory markers could predict the incidence of recurrent events and to explore the possible interaction between pravastatin and these markers. This sub-study revealed that inflammatory markers (CRP, SAA, and TNFalpha) can predict recurrent coronary events and could be used for the risk stratification of these patients into high- and low-risk groups.[9,10,11] More importantly, this substudy also demonstrated that pravastatin has anti-inflammatory characteristics, a finding that is perhaps more important for the sponsor than the original objective of CARE trial.

This information was learned in a remarkably short period of time with minimal expense, because the time-consuming part of the study, subject recruitment and specimen collection, had already been completed. Only access to blood samples and the clinical database were necessary. Pharmaceutical companies are recognizing more and more the importance and potential benefit of sub-studies. Therefore, particular attention is now being paid to the appropriate storage and archiving of clinical study samples.

In contrast to the original clinical trial, testing for sub-studies is done in a batch mode and in a very similar fashion to that described above for epidemiological studies. Since the cost of substudies is minimal compared to those of the original trial, investigators can afford to ask more daring questions to explore the prognostic utility of a novel marker or to implicate another in the initiation of a disease process. Therefore, the laboratory must possess or be able to add to its armamentarium of tests highly novel markers such as matrix metaloproteinase and mannose-binding protein to enable investigators to reach new frontiers. This form of translational research, the transfer of assays from the research laboratory bench to the routine clinical laboratory, is embraced by both the NIH and the pharmaceutical industry. The same concerns regarding the small sample volume for epidemiological studies, expressed above, apply here as well.

SUMMARY

Clinical and research laboratories of all types will find many opportunities for involvement in clinical trials. Government-sponsored clinical research, pharmaceutical drug development, and development of in-vitro diagnostics methods all require reliable laboratory testing. Clinical laboratory scientists cannot only benefit their institutions by participating in such research but also gain personal and professional benefit and satisfaction through their support of these research initiatives. ✧

REFERENCES

1. Guidance for FDA Staff Regulating *In Vitro* Diagnostic Device (IVD) Studies. US Department of Health and Human Services FDA, Center for Devices and Radiological Health. December 17, 1999.
2. Priorities in laboratory testing: speed, flexibility and customization. Supplement to R&D Directions 1999;May:1–18.
3. Code of Federal Regulations, Title 21, Chapter 1, Parts 50, 56, and 312.
4. Code of Federal Regulations, Title 21, Chapter 1, Part 58.
5. Clinical chemistry of laboratory animals. Clin Chem News (Suppl.), October 1992, 1–24.
6. Weingand KW, Daggy BP. Quantitation of high-density-lipoprotein cholesterol in plasma from hamsters by differential precipitation. Clin Chem 1990;36:575.
7. Cole, TG. The role of the central clinical laboratory in the development of drugs for the treatment of cardiovascular disease by the modification of lipoprotein concentrations. Am J Cardiol 1998;81:75F–77F.
8. Sacks FM, Pfeffer MA, Moye L et al. Rationale and design of a secondary prevention trial of lowering normal plasma cholesterol levels after acute myocardial infarction: the Cholesterol and Recurrent Events trial. Am J Cardiol 1991;68:1436–46.
9. Ridker PM, Rifai N, Pfeffer MA, Sacks F, Braunwald E, for the Cholesterol and Recurrent Events (CARE) investigators. Long-term effects of Pravastatin on plasma concentration of C-reactive protein. Circulation 1999;100:230–5.
10. Ridker PM, Rifai N, Sacks F, Pfeffer M,, Moye LA, Goldman S, Flaker GC, Braunwald, for the Cholesterol and Recurrent Events (CARE) Investigators. Inflammation, Pravastatin,

and the risk of coronary events after myocardial infarction in patients with average cholesterol levels. Circulation 1998;98:839–44.

11. Ridker PM, Rifai N, Pfeffer MA, Sacks F, Braunwald E, for the Cholesterol and Recurrent Events (CARE) investigators. Persistent elevation of tumor necrosis factor-alpha and increased risk of recurrent coronary events following myocardial infarction. Circulation (in press).

Regulatory Aspects of Lipid and Lipoprotein Measurements

38

Carol C. Benson and V. Michelle Chenault

✧   The Food and Drug Administration (FDA) is an agency of the United States federal government authorized by Congress to test, inspect, approve, and set safety standards for drugs, chemicals, foods and food additives, cosmetics, consumer products, and medical devices. FDA was first formed as a separate law enforcement agency in 1927 and was known as the Food, Drug, and Insecticide Administration.

The Federal Food, Drug, and Cosmetic Act (FFD & C) of 1938 established safety and purity standards and provided for inspection and legal remedy. The FFD & C has since been expanded and amended to cover animal drugs, medical devices, the premarket approval process, the burden of proof to remove unsafe products from the market place, provisions for clinical investigations and post-market surveillance, and procedures for reclassification of devices and other authorities.

On May 28, 1976, FDA began implementing its specific authority to regulate medical devices through the Medical Device Amendments to the FFD& C Act. FDA's Center for Devices and Radiological Health (CDRH) is the agency that helps ensure that medical devices are safe and effective. Additional authority to regulate devices was provided in the Safe Medical Devices Act of 1990 (SMDA), which was amended in 1992. (SMDA requirements are extensive and the reader is encouraged to contact FDA for more specific information.)

The FFD & C Act was most recently amended by the Food and Drug Administration Modernization Act of 1997. The Modernization Act contained provisions related to all products under FDA's jurisdiction and summarized each device-related section of the Modernization Act in "plain English." The term "medical device," for instance, is defined as an instrument, apparatus, implement, machine, contrivance, implant, in vitro reagent, or other similar or related article, including any component, part, or accessory, that is

✧   recognized in the official National Formulary, or the United States Pharmacopeia, or any supplement to them;

✧   intended for use in the diagnosis of disease or other conditions, or in the cure, mitigation, treatment, or prevention of disease in man or other animals; or

✧   intended to affect the structure or any function of the body of man or other animals, and which does not achieve its primary intended purposes through chemical action within or on the body of man or other animals and which is not dependent upon being metabolized for the achievement of any of its principal intended purposes. [12]

Many different products are regulated as medical devices. Examples include wheelchairs, X-ray machines, pacemakers, glucose test kits, and cholesterol test kits. The following pathways are used to get products to market for commercial distribution:

❖ Premarket Notification (510[k])—the manufacturer demonstrates that the device is substantially equivalent to a predicate device.

❖ Premarket Approval (PMA)—the manufacturer provides reasonable assurance of safety and effectiveness under conditions of intended use(s). Advisory panel review is required of all original submissions prior to marketing.

❖ Investigational Device Exemptions (IDE)—the device is considered to be still in the developmental stages; clinical investigation data is submitted and a judgment is made regarding whether the investigational device constitutes significant risk or non-significant risk.

Manufacturers may also submit a humanitarian device exemption (HDE) application for a humanitarian use device (HUD). FDA developed and issued a final rule to carry out the provisions of the Safe Medical Devices Act of 1990 regarding HDEs in 1996. This regulation provided an incentive for the development of devices for use in the treatment or diagnosis of diseases affecting fewer than 4,000 individuals per year in the United States. An HDE application is similar to a PMA but is exempt from the effectiveness requirements of a PMA.

Review of these applications described above is performed in the Office of Device Evaluation in CDRH. The majority of submissions for lipid and lipoprotein devices are premarket notification (510[k]) applications. For further information regarding the type of application that is appropriate for a device, contact the Division of Small Manufacturers Assistance (DSMA). Web address is (*http://www.fda.gov/cdrh/dsma/dsmamain.html*). DSMA can also be reached by phone at 800-638-2041 or by FAX at 301-443-8818.

SOURCES OF INFORMATION FOR PREPARING SUBMISSIONS TO FDA

The **Code of Federal Regulations (CFR)** codifies the general and permanent rules published in the Federal Register. The CFR is subdivided into 50 titles, each title is divided into chapters, and each chapter is divided into sections that cover specific regulatory areas. For example, in vitro diagnostic devices are addressed in Title 21, chapter 1, part 809.[3] Subpart A contains the general provisions and limitations of exemptions, subpart B contains the labeling regulation, and subpart C contains the general requirements for manufacturers and producers of in vitro diagnostic products and the restrictions on the sale, distribution, and use of Analyte-Specific Reagents (ASR).

The **regulations specific to in vitro diagnostic devices** for measuring lipids and lipoproteins are found in part 862 and in part 866 of Title 21. [3] Each regulation contains (a) the identification of the analyte and (b) the classification of the analyte. Examples of regulations specific to lipids are as follows:

✧   cholesterol—21 CFR 862.1175

✧   triglycerides—21 CFR 862.1705

✧   low-density lipoproteins—21 CFR 866.5600.

Additional information is available on the FDA home page (*http://www.fda.gov*). The Center for Devices and Radiological Health site contains a search form for a list of releasable 510(k)s and premarket approvals. Also, the product classification database, listed by either medical specialty or name of device, can be searched for product information. The MedWatch program can be accessed from the home page (or reached by phone at 1–800-FDA-1088) to obtain safety or continuing education information, or to voluntarily report adverse reactions and medical product problems.

Technical and regulatory assistance that can help small manufacturers comply with FDA requirements for medical devices is available from DSMA.

Specific guidance documents are available to help manufacturers determine the types of studies and performance goals recommended for specific devices. Sources include the FDA www page, DSMA, and Facts-On-Demand (1–800–899–0381). A guidance document specific for lipid determinations, for example, is "Guidance for 510(k)s on Cholesterol Tests for Clinical Laboratory, Physician's Office Laboratory, and Home Use."[4] Devices that are intended for home use are addressed in several guidance documents, for example:

✧   NCCLS Document GP14, Labeling of Home Use In Vitro Testing Products[5];

✧   HHS Publication, Write It Right, Recommendations for Developing User Instruction Manuals Used in Home Health Care [6], and

✧   FDA Document 97–4224, In Vitro Diagnostic Devices: Guidance for the Preparation of 510(k) Submissions, Appendix C, Points to Consider Regarding Labeling and Premarket Submissions for Home-Use In Vitro Diagnostic Devices.

In addition to the sources of information listed above, FDA communicates with manufacturers by reviewing protocols and scheduling meetings to discuss issues with the manufacturer. A highly effective means of obtaining FDA input is to schedule a meeting with the FDA staff prior to conducting clinical studies.

510(K) PREMARKET NOTIFICATION (PMN) PROCEDURES

An overview of the 510(k) PMN procedures is presented in a question and answer format.

Q.   When is a 510(k) PMN required?

A.   According to 21 CFR 807.81, a PMN submission is required at least 90 days before the introduction or delivery for introduction into interstate commerce for commercial distribution of a device intended for human use that meets any of the following three criteria:

- ✧ the device is being introduced for the first time, i.e., it is not the same type as a device that was in commercial distribution before May 28, 1976;

- ✧ the device is being introduced for the first time by a person required to register;

- ✧ the device is one that is already in commercial distribution and is about to be changed or significantly modified. For a modified device follow the guidance document, "When to Submit a 510(k) for a Change to an Existing Device (1/13/97)."

Q.   What information should be submitted?

A.   According to 21 CFR 807.87, each 510(k) PMN submission shall contain the following information:

- ✧ the device name, both the trade name and the common or usual name

- ✧ the establishment registration number, if applicable, of the owner or operator submitting the premarket notification submission

- ✧ the class in which the device has been placed under section 513 of the Act

- ✧ the action taken by the person required to register

- ✧ proposed labels, labeling and advertisements sufficient to describe the device, its intended use, and the directions for its use

- ✧ a description of how the device is similar to and or different from other products of comparable type in commercial distribution, accompanied by data to support the statement

- ✧ a 510(k) summary as described in 21 CFR 807.92 or a 510(k) statement as described in 21 CFR 807.93

- ✧ a statement that the submitter believes that all data and information submitted are truthful and accurate and that no material fact has been omitted

- ✧ an Indications for Use statement for which a substantially equivalent determination is sought

- ✧ any additional information regarding the device requested by FDA that is necessary for the FDA to make a substantial equivalency determination. A request for additional information will advise the 510(k) submitter that there is insufficient information contained in the original 510(k) submission for a substantial equivalent determination to be made. In this instance the 510(k) submitter may: (a) submit the requested data or a new 510(k) containing the requested information, or (b) submit a PMA application in accordance with section 515 of the FD&C Act. If the additional information is not submitted within 30 days following the date of the request, the FDA may consider the 510(k) to be withdrawn.

Q.   What is the appropriate format?

A.   According to 21 CFR 807.90, each 510(k) PMN submission shall be submitted in duplicate with the designated "510(k) Notification" in the cover letter. Electronic submissions are also accepted. For more information about electronic submissions, please refer to general information about CDRH on the FDA home page at *http://www.fda.gov/cdrh/general.html.*

Q.   Is a guidance document available for preparing a 510(k) PMN for an in vitro diagnostic device?

A.   For help in preparing a 510(k) PMN, HHS Publication FDA 97–4224, In Vitro Diagnostic Devices: Guidance for the Preparation of 510(k) Submissions is available on the FDA home page or by contacting DSMA. The appendices to this document are as follows:

✧   Appendix A. Sample Premarket Notification Submission/Clinical Chemistry

✧   Appendix B. 510(k) Response Letters

✧   Appendix C. Points to Consider Regarding Labeling and Premarket Submissions for Home-Use In Vitro Diagnostic Devices

✧   Appendix D. CDRH Document Retrieval Systems

✧   Appendix E. Premarket Submission Cover Sheet and Instructions

✧   Appendix F. 510(k) Elements List

✧   Appendix G. 510(k) Refuse to Accept Procedures #K943

✧   Appendix H. 510(k) Checklist for Acceptance Decision

✧   Appendix I. Premarket Notification Review Program #K86–3

✧   Appendix J. In Vitro Diagnostic Devices 510(k) Exemption List

✧   Appendix K. Points to Consider for Review of Calibration and Quality Control Labeling for In Vitro Diagnostic Devices

✧   Appendix L. PMA/510(k) Triage Review Procedures #G943

✧   Appendix M. PMA/510(k) Expedited Review #G94–2

✧   Appendix N. 510(k) Status Request Form

✧   Appendix O. Premarket Notification Regulation 21 CFR Part 807 Subpart E

✧   Appendix P. Third-Party Review Program.

Q.   What information and data are needed in support of a substantial equivalence claim?

A.   The following information should be considered in submitting data in support of a substantial equivalency claim:

✧   Be sure (a) a similar in vitro diagnostic device was marketed prior to May 28, 1976, or (b) a similar in vitro diagnostic product is currently being marketed legally in the U.S.

✧   Provide the identity of the similar in vitro diagnostic product.

✧   Include performance claims made for your product, e.g., accuracy, precision, sensitivity, specificity, expected values, etc.

❖ State intended use of all test results.

❖ State what methodology was used in performing tests.

❖ Indicate which reagents and materials comprise the device.

❖ Specify the type of in vitro diagnostic device, e.g., control, calibrator, finished component, reagent, instrument, etc.

Q. Where are the 510(k) PMN applications sent?

A. The applications should be sent to the following address by a method such as registered mail, which provides proof of delivery:
Document Mail Center (HFZ-401)
Center for Devices and Radiological Health
Office of Device Evaluation
Food and Drug Administration
9200 Corporate Blvd.
Rockville, Maryland 20850 USA

Q. What happens next?

A. FDA sends a letter stating that the application was received and assigns a 510(k) number.

Q. When can the device be commercially marketed?

A. The device can be commercially marketed upon the receipt of a specific letter (order) from FDA that finds the device substantially equivalent (SE) to a legally marketed "predicate" device.

Review of 510(k) Submissions

Administrative

Upon receipt, the 510(k) document undergoes an administrative review. This review is conducted to determine if the submission contains the information required, including the scientific material necessary to conduct a complete technical and scientific review. In general, the document is checked to determine if the following items are included:

❖ a Truthful and Accurate statement as required by 21 CFR 807.87(j)

❖ a 510(k) summary or statement as required by 21 CFR 807.92 or 21 CFR 807.93, respectively

❖ a draft of the labeling (also known as the package insert), as required by 21 CFR 809.10, to be included with the commercially marketed device

❖ labels that are used for the outside of the box or package, the vials, the bottles or containers for reagents, controls, and standards.

If standards and or controls are sold as a part of the device or kits or these materials are to be used exclusively with the device or reagents, labeling for these materials should be included in the submission.

Critical administrative elements for a submission include

✧ the cover letter or Center for Devices and Radiological Health Cover Sheet;

✧ applicant's name and street address;

✧ contact person, if different from applicant, or if there is a contact person in addition to the applicant;

✧ telephone and fax numbers of applicant or contact;

✧ signature of applicant;

✧ addresses of manufacturing sites;

✧ table of contents with page numbers of the Truthful and Accurate statements, the 510(k) summary or statement and any other attachments and appendices;

✧ labeling and labels for the candidate device;

✧ labeling for the predicate device; and

✧ date of application.

If critical elements are missing, the sponsor is contacted and the items are requested. An incomplete submission may delay the technical and scientific review.

Technical and Scientific

The technical and scientific review of all submissions consists of

✧ an examination of the principle of the method and references provided;

✧ an evaluation of the precision and accuracy data summary, and analytical and/or clinical (diagnostic) sensitivity and specificity;

✧ a review of the items identified as possible interferences;

✧ an assessment of the lowest detectable concentration, stability, and storage information provided for the reagents and the sample matrices;

✧ a review of information on the procedure used to perform the assay or use the device or instrumentation;

✧ a review of pre-analytical and laboratory sources of error

Statistical evaluation includes an analysis of the mean, standard deviation, and coefficient of variation for each level used in the within-run and run-to-run or within-run precision studies. The technical and scientific information included in the labeling for the candidate device will be compared with the data in the predicate device for consistency and scientific validity.

The technical and scientific review is based upon the intended use of the device. Generally, the technical and scientific review of quantitative tests intended for use in clinical and physicians' office laboratories includes the precision results near the medical decision points, and accuracy. For lipid/lipoprotein measurement devices, the statistical data are evaluated to assess the imprecision and bias with respect to current National Cholesterol Education Program (NCEP) guidelines. A detailed summary of the national performance criteria for lipid and lipoprotein measurements is presented in Chapter 36, hence only a brief overview is presented here (Table 38–1).

It is highly recommended that manufacturers participate in the certification programs conducted by the Cholesterol Reference Method Network Laboratory (CRMLN) in conjunction with the Centers for Disease Control and Prevention (CDC) for TC, HDL-C, and LDL-C. Upon successful completion of this evaluation, the manufacturer is awarded a Certificate of Traceability, which states the conditions of the evaluation and the total error calculation. Submission of this data precludes the requirement for sponsors to include raw data to support the precision and accuracy in the premarket notification document.[8] For additional information on CRMLN, refer to chapter 36.

For Physician's Office Laboratory (POL) tests that are quantitative or qualitative, data from three POL sites are reviewed. The educational level of the users of these devices in the POL setting should be representative of a non-laboratory user. The range of the clinical samples should span the medical decision points.[9] Demographic information should be provided to ensure that male and female samples from a representative population were obtained for the evaluation.

For POL-use devices that are quantitative and intended for use with venous specimens, the FDA reviews the Certificate of Traceability for tests conducted at the manufacturing site or at a clinical laboratory using aliquots of venous samples split between the test site and a CRMLN laboratory. For quantitative POL devices that use only venous specimens, aliquots split between the POL site and the CRMLN are not required.

For POL devices that are qualitative, and/or factory calibrated, and/or self-contained, or intended only for use with fresh fingerstick samples, the CRMLN comparison studies should include venous specimens analyzed by the CRMLN laboratory and paired fingerstick specimens collected concurrently and analyzed by the test device. Alternatively, the manufacturer may submit comparison data using another reference or comparison method with a description of the study conducted. The la-

Table 38–1 ✧ Overview of National Performance Criteria for Lipid and Lipoprotein Measurements[7]

Analyte	Coefficient of Variation (CV)	Allowable Total Error (%)	NCEP Bias Criteria
Total cholesterol (TC)	≤ 3%	≤ 8.9% (for a single analysis)	≤ 3%
High-density lipoprotein cholesterol (HDL-C)	≤ 4% at ≥ 42 mg/dL (1.09mmol/l) as of 1998	≤ 13%	≤ 5%
Low-density lipoprotein cholesterol (LDL-C)	≤ 4%	≤ 12%	≤ 4%
Triglyceride (TG)	≤ 5%	≤ 15%	≤ 5%

beling should include the type of comparison study performed and the method of establishing traceability. (Additional considerations for these devices are discussed in the section Special Considerations—Home Use or Point-of-Care-Use Devices, below.)

Two levels of controls are recommended: one in the normal range and one near the cutpoints for intervention. Analytical data for these materials are reviewed. Data for the calibration material are reviewed to assure that the materials are assigned values traceable to reference standards. With respect to cholesterol, for example, calibrator values should be assigned by procedures traceable to the National Reference System for Cholesterol (NRS/CHOL). Primary calibration material consisting of a known mass of unesterified cholesterol of known purity is available from NIST (National Institute of Standards and Technology) as standard reference material (SRM) 911a with a certificate of analysis.[8]

The Decision-Making Process

The substantial equivalent (SE) determination is based on an assessment of risk to the patient associated with the use of the device. If the risk of device use is low and predictable, a low level of premarket review may be acceptable for clearance. If the risk is high or unknown, more data are required and a more intense review of the data is necessary. These factors are reflected in the following questions used by FDA reviewers in determining substantial equivalency:

✧ Does the in vitro diagnostic device have the same intended use as a currently marketed device (sometimes referred to as a "predicate device"), e.g., Lp(a), cholesterol, triglyceride?

✧ Does the in vitro diagnostic device have the same technological characteristics, e.g., turbidimetric, antigen/antibody?

✧ If new technological features are present—e.g., DNA probe, monoclonal antibody—are new questions raised regarding safety and effectiveness?

✧ What types of data are needed to substantiate a substantial equivalency claim?

Additionally, FDA reviewers will use the following questions to assess whether an in vitro diagnostic device that includes technological changes is substantially equivalent to a predicate device:

✧ Does the in vitro diagnostic device pose the same type of questions about safety and effectiveness as the predicate device?

✧ Are there accepted scientific methods for assessing the impact of technological changes on safety and effectiveness, e.g., accuracy, specificity, sensitivity, precision, and expected values?

On March 20, 1998, the Center for Devices and Radiological Health (CDRH) announced the availability of a guidance document on the FDA web site: "The New 510(k) Paradigm—Alternatives to Demonstrating Substantial Equivalence in Premarket Notification Submissions." In this guidance, two alternatives to the traditional approach of demonstrating substantial equivalence are discussed. They are the special 510(k) and the abbreviated 510(k) submissions.

Special Considerations

New Matrices

When a new matrix is to be used on a previously cleared device, a new premarket notification is required. The comparative performance characteristic data submitted will undergo additional scientific and technical review. The sponsor should provide a summary of the study conducted to obtain the data using the new matrix. The data should consist of values that span the medically significant clinical range, samples at the lowest detectable concentration point, and linearity data. Literature references regarding the new matrix are also helpful to support the submission.[10] For additional information on matrix effects on the performance of tests, refer to chapter 35.

New Intended Uses/Indications for Use

When a new intended use or indication for use is claimed for a previously cleared device, a new premarket notification is required. Additional data are needed to substantiate the claim. A summary of the study conducted should be provided. This summary should include the type, number and range of samples analyzed, and the end point or links to the clinical symptoms or diagnosis that support the new intended use or indication for use. The appropriate statistical studies, e.g., regression studies or T-test, or appropriate non-parametric tests or ROC analysis, should be performed to support the data. For example, lipid and lipoprotein devices are traditional screening devices that help to identify persons at risk from cardiovascular disease.

If the intended use or indication for use is being changed to a claim for monitoring a treatment of a disease, additional studies are needed to demonstrate that the device detects the change due to the treatment and is precise and accurate at the action point(s). In addition, studies are needed to demonstrate that the treatment causes no interference in the device's performance. The results of the studies should be presented in the labeling. Manufacturers are advised to contact FDA for additional information regarding specific cases.

IVD Clinical Study Design

Ultimately, marketing approval of the device is a based upon the design and implementation of the IVD clinical study. The data generated by the clinical study must support the claims that the sponsor intends to make for the marketed device and the clinical utility of the device. If prior to initiating the clinical study the company is unsure of a particular parameter for the device, feasibility studies may be needed. Pilot or feasibility studies can and should be conducted to resolve such issues such as device design, operating specification, better definition of patient populations, and device indications.[11]

Pre-Investigational Device Exemptions (Pre-IDE) and Investigational Device Exemptions (IDE) Submissions

Studies for in vitro diagnostic devices (IVDs) such as lipid tests raise different issues than in vivo or implanted devices. These studies usually do not involve filing an IDE application. New lipid devices that do not have commercially marketed predicates and need the collection and evaluation of clinical data to demonstrate their safety and effectiveness may be covered under an IDE application and classed as a non-significant risk (NSR) device. Even if a device presents no significant risk, it is best to review the protocol or investigational plan with the Office of Device of Evaluation (ODE).

FDA recommends the submission of a pre-IDE application. These submissions may consist of a draft clinical protocol, a proposal for pre-clincial testing, pre-clinical test results, or other test results for which the sponsor wishes to obtain preliminary FDA review and comment in order to facilitate the IDE application process. The pre-IDE submissions may also include protocols for foreign studies when those studies will be used to support future marketing applications to be submitted to FDA. These submissions are held in confidence just as the IDE applications are considered confidential. Sponsors are encouraged to meet with the FDA prior to submitting the application for pre-IDE or IDE review.

Section 520(g) of the Federal Food, Drug, and Cosmetic Act (Title 21 of the United States Code), as amended, authorizes the FDA to grant an investigational device exemption (IDE) to a researcher using a device in studies undertaken to develop safety and effectiveness data for that device when such studies involve the use of human subjects. These studies are covered by the IDE regulations at 21 CFR 812. An approved IDE application permits a device that would otherwise be subject to marketing clearance to be shipped lawfully for the purpose of conducting a clinical study. An approved IDE application also exempts a device from certain sections of the Act, e.g., misbranding under section 502; registration, listing and premarket notification under section 510; performance standards under section 514; premarket approval (PMA) under section 515; banned devices under section 516; records and reports under section 519; restricted devices under section 520(e); good manufacturing practices under section 520(f) and color additive requirements under section 706.

All clinical investigations of devices not exempt from the IDE requirements must have an approved IDE. Investigations that are not exempt from the IDE regulation are subject to differing levels of regulatory control. The IDE regulation distinguishes between significant risk (SR) and non-significant risk device studies and procedures for obtaining an IDE differ accordingly. The sponsor of the device initially makes the determination of whether or not a device study presents a significant risk. A significant risk device is defined as one that

❖ is intended as an implant and presents a potential for serious risk to health, safety, or welfare of a subject;

❖ is for use in supporting or sustaining human life and represents a potential for serious risk to the health, safety, or welfare of a subject;

❖ is for a use of substantial importance in diagnosing, curing, mitigating, or treating disease or otherwise preventing impairment of human health and presents a potential for serious risk to the health, safety, or welfare of a subject; or

✧   otherwise presents a potential for serious risk to a subject.

A proposed study is then submitted to an Institutional Review Board (IRB) for review. If the IRB agrees with the sponsor that the device study presents a non-significant risk, no IDE submission to FDA is required prior to the initiation of the clinical trial. A sponsor of a significant risk device investigation must obtain IRB and FDA approval before beginning the study.

Once it is determined that the device is an SR device that is not exempt from the requirements of 21 CFR 812, the company must begin planning the submission of an IDE application. The key element of the application is an investigational plan. This plan should include

✧   the purpose of the investigation,

✧   the study protocol,

✧   a risk analysis describing the risks to humans and how these risks will be minimized,

✧   a description of the device,

✧   labeling,

✧   monitoring procedures,

✧   consent materials,

✧   IRB information, and

✧   a description of where the study will be conducted.

The IDE application must also include a description of the methods, facilities, and controls used for manufacture, processing, packing, and storage, and information regarding the quality control used in device manufacture.

Upon the receipt of an IDE application, sponsors are notified in writing of the date that FDA received the original application and the IDE number assigned. Within 30 days from the date of receipt, FDA will approve, approve with conditions, or disapprove an IDE application. In cases of disapproval, a sponsor may respond to the deficiencies and/or request a regulatory hearing.[3,12]

Premarket Approval (PMA)

In 1976, the Medical Device Amendments to the Federal Food, Drug and Cosmetic Act (the Act) established three regulatory classes for medical devices. Each class is based upon the degree of control necessary to ensure that the various devices are safe and effective.

The highest degree of regulatory control is applied to Class III devices: those that support or sustain human life or are of substantial importance in preventing impairment of human health or present a potential unreasonable risk of illness or injury. This is because information about Class III devices is insufficient to satisfy regulations for performance standards (Class II) or general controls (Class I) and therefore cannot provide reasonable assurance that the device is safe and effective for the intended use.

Under Section 515 of the Act, all Class III devices are subject to premarket approval requirements—the required process of scientific review to ensure their safety and effectiveness. An approved PMA (Premarket Approval Application) is a private license for marketing a particular medical device. A Class III device that fails to meet the PMA requirements is considered to be adulterated under Section 501(f) and cannot be marketed.

A PMA requires information on various types of product design, bench and animal testing (preclinical), clinical data, and manufacturing. Some of this information is reviewed more than once, first when submitted as a report to an IDE and later in the process, when submitted in the PMA. As part of PMA Reengineering, CDRH is seeking to remodel PMA review to increase efficiency and effectiveness. Manufacturers, for instance, may submit a modular PMA that can be compiled, over time, to make a complete submission.

The modular concept or approach for data development, submission, review, and closure breaks the contents of a PMA into well-delineated components. Reports of each component are submitted as soon as the sponsor has performed the testing and analyses, even during the IDE. FDA reviews each module as soon as it is received. This allows more rapid closure when the last components are submitted because much of the review work has already been done. Interested persons should consult the FDA/CDRH staff in the Office of Device Evaluation early in the PMA process. Additional information is available on the FDA website at *http://www.fda.gov/cdrh/pmat/modpmat.htm.*

The following information is required under 21 CFR 814 for a PMA application:

✧ general information (device generic name, trade name, applicant's name and address);

✧ indications for use

✧ device description

✧ alternative practices and procedures

✧ marketing history

✧ adverse effects of the device on health

✧ summary of studies

✧ conclusions drawn from the studies

The summary of studies should include an abstract of any data, information, or report described in the PMA under 814.20(b)8ii, and a summary of nonclinical and clinical studies or investigations conducted by or for the applicant. This section should be subdivided into nonclinical and clinical studies. The subsections should include subheadings for such items as subject selection and exclusion criteria, study population demographics, safety data, effectiveness data, and patient discontinuation. FDA strongly recommends contacting the agency for additional information regarding the submission of a device for premarket approval.

The timeframes and the processes for reviewing and filing a PMA are covered in 21 CFR 814.4 and will not be outlined in detail here. The review of a premarket application involves a four-step process:

✧   an administrative and limited scientific review by FDA staff to determine completeness ("filing review");

✧   in depth-scientific and regulatory review by appropriate FDA scientific and compliance personnel ("in-depth review");

✧   review and recommendation by the appropriate advisory committee ("panel review"); and

✧   final deliberations, documentation, and notification of the FDA approval decision.

FDA must review a PMA within 180 days after receiving an application that is accepted for filing. FDA notifies the applicant by letter of its decision and a Federal Register notice announces the decision and the availability of a summary of safety and effectiveness data on which the decision was based. The notice gives the applicant and other interested persons an opportunity for administrative review of the FDA approval or denial action.[13]

Home Use (OTC) or Point-of-Care Devices (POC)

Manufacturers should conduct comparison studies in which a statistically significant number of samples are tested at different sites to establish total error, accuracy, and imprecision.

Quantitative devices should meet NCEP guidelines for accuracy and precision. Consumer field evaluation studies should be performed as outlined in the document "Guidance for 510(k)s on Cholesterol Tests for Clinical Laboratory, Physician's Office Laboratory, and Home Use." The study design should include three geographically distinct sites, with a total of 200–400 subjects using a consistent protocol, to permit data pooling. Evaluations for OTC devices are to be conducted by having "representative" consumers perform the test at local sites and comparing the consumer's result directly with the reference method performed at a CRMLN laboratory using a paired venous sample obtained concurrently from each consumer. The analytical results should cover the clinically significant range of the test.

Determine the sample size prior to initiating the study. The number depends on the precision (width of the confidence intervals) claimed for specificity and sensitivity. The misclassification rate determined by the device should be calculated and submitted with the application. (Contact the DSMA for further information about these devices.)

When performing the test, the subjects should follow directions on the package insert for the device; they should not be coached or given additional training on device use.

The evaluation should mimic the actual use conditions as closely as possible. The consumer sample should represent a mix of intended users of varying ages, occupations, and educational levels, and the ethnic diversity should reflect that of the general population. All demographic data should be included in the submission. Results from the field study should show the number of subjects in each of the NCEP classifications (i.e., desirable, borderline, and high). The analysis should include an estimation of the misclassification rate by comparing the device result with the reference method result.

Labeling should include the information on misclassification rate and should contain a statement of accuracy. In addition, provide data that show the effects of various technique anomalies, such as variations in the sample volumes and hematocrit ranges. Include concerns specific to home users, exclusion criteria for patients, and specific instructions about the device.[4] Finally, evaluate the label for reading grade level and comprehension and revise if necessary.

CLIA CATEGORIZATION DETERMINATION

Congress passed the Clinical Laboratory Improvement Amendments (CLIA) in 1988 establishing quality standards for all laboratory testing to ensure the accuracy, reliability and timeliness of patient test results regardless of where the test was performed. The amendments define a laboratory as any facility that performs laboratory testing on specimens derived from humans for the purpose of providing information for the diagnosis, prevention, treatment of disease, or impairment of, or assessment of health.[14]

The responsibilities for categorizing commercially marketed in vitro diagnostic tests are being transferred from the CDC to FDA. CDRH was scheduled to fully assume the CLIA categorization functions on or about January 31, 2000.

Regulations codified at 42 CFR 493.17, implementing CLIA, Public Law 100–578, require the categorization of specific laboratory test systems, assays, and examinations by level of complexity. There are three levels of complexity: waived, moderate, and high. With the exception of waived tests, the test systems are scored for complexity and categorization based on seven criteria as follows:

✧   knowledge

✧   training and experience

✧   reagents or materials preparation

✧   characteristics of operational steps

✧   calibration, quality control, or proficiency testing materials

✧   troubleshooting and maintenance

✧   interpretation and judgment

The level of complexity is determined by assigning scores of 1, 2, or 3 within each criterion. Test systems scoring a total of 12 or fewer points are given a moderate complexity rating while those scoring 13 points or greater will be given a high-complexity rating.

The third category of complexity, the waived tests, are exempt from CLIA. The waived tests are defined in the regulation as simple laboratory examinations and procedures that are

♢   cleared by FDA for home use; or

♢   employ methodologies that are so simple and accurate as to render the likelihood of erroneous results negligible; or

♢   pose no reasonable risk of harm to the patient if the test is performed incorrectly.[15]

The OTC cholesterol test is an example of a waived test.

More information can be obtained from the CLIA web page at *http://www. fda.gov/cdrh/CLIA/*. In addition, questions and comments may be sent by electronic mail to *clia@cdrh.fda.gov* or by voice mail to 301–827–0496; your call should be returned within two working days.   ♢

REFERENCES

1. An Introduction to Medical Device Regulations. U.S. Department of Health and Human Services, Public Health Service, Food and Drug Administration, Center for Devices and Radiological Health. HHS Publication FDA 92–4222.
2. The Safe Medical Devices Act of 1990 and the Medical Device Amendments of 1992. U.S. Department of Health and Human Services, Public Health Service, Food and Drug Administration, Center for Devices and Radiological Health. HHS Publication FDA 93-4243.
3. Code of Federal Regulations, Title 21, Parts 800–1299, revised as of April 1, 1999.
4. Guidance for 510(k)s on Cholesterol Tests for Clinical Laboratory, Physician's Office Laboratory, and Home Use. U.S. Department of Health and Human Services, Public Health Service, Food and Drug Administration, Center for Devices and Radiological Health, Division of Small Manufacturers Assistance. Publication 605. Revised July 13, 1995.
5. National Committee for Clinical Laboratory Standards. Labeling of Home-Use-In Vitro Testing Products, approved guideline. NCCLS Document No. GP-14, ISBN 1–56238–299–3. Wayne, PA: NCCLS, 1996.
6. Write It Right, Recommendations for Developing User Instruction Manuals for Medical Devices Used in Home Health Care. U.S. Department of Health and Human Services, Public Health Service, Food and Drug Administration, Center for Devices and Radiological Health. Rockville, MD: August 1993.
7. Meyers GL, Cooper GR, Henderson LO, Hassemar DJ, Kimberly MM. Standardization of lipid and lipoprotein measurements. In: Rifai N, Warnick GR, Dominiczak MH (eds). Handbook of Lipoprotein Testing. Washington DC: AACC Press, 1997:230.
8. Recommendations for Improving Cholesterol Measurement. A Report from the Laboratory Standardization Panel of the National Cholesterol Education Program. U.S. Department of Health and Human Services, Public Health Service, National Institutes of Health. NIH Publication 90–2964, February 1990.
9. National Committee for Clinical Laboratory Standards. Method comparison and bias estimation using patient samples; approved guideline. NCCLS document EP9-A, ISBN 1–56238–283–7. Wayne, PA: NCCLS, 1995.
10. National Committee for Clinical Laboratory Standards. Evaluation of matrix effects; proposed guideline. NCCLS document EP14-P, ISBN 1–56238–345–0. Wayne, PA: NCCLS, 1998.
11. Protocol for Conduct of a Clinical Investigation. Code of Federal Regulations 21 CFR 54.120.

12. Investigational Device Exemptions Manual. U.S. Department of Health and Human Services, Public Health Service, Food and Drug Administration, Center for Devices and Radiological Health. HHS Publication FDA 92–4159.

13. Premarket Approval (PMA) Manual. U.S. Department of Health and Human Services, Public Health Service, Food and Drug Administration, Center for Devices and Radiological Health. HHS Publication FDA 97–4214.

14. CLIA. Public Law 100–578.

15. Code of Federal Regulations. Title 42, Part 493.

Appendix:
Lipid and Lipoprotein Values

Lipid and lipoprotein values for white and black males and females by age. Data presented as mean and 5–95 percentile values in mg/dL (Tables I.A–IV.A) and in mmol/L (Tables I.B–IV.B).

Source: Hainline A, Karon J, Lippel K, eds. *Manual of Laboratory Operations*, Lipid Research Clinics Program, and *Lipid and Lipoprotein Analysis*, 2nd ed., Bethesda, MD: U. S. Department of Health and Human Services, 1982.

Table I.A ✧ Plasma Total and Lipoprotein Cholesterol and Triglyceride Mean and Percentile Values (mg/dL) for White Males, by Age

				Cholesterol in					
Age in Years	N	Cholesterol (mg/dL) X (5–95 % tile)	Triglycerides (mg/dL) X (5–95 % tile)	HDL (mg/dL) N	X (5–95 % tile)	LDL (mg/dL) N	X (5–95 % tile)	VLDL (mg/dL) N	X (5–95 % tile)
0	(10)	143	63						
1	(36)	150	73						
2	(49)	158	55						
3	66	151 (110–193)	53 (28–84)						
4	77	159 (115–221)	52 (29–89)						
5	72	156 (113–203)	56 (26–88)						
6	278	158 (120–201)	54 (31–96)	66	56.0 (38–72)	61	95.0 (69–129)	61	6.9 (0–16)
7	275	159 (122–195)	55 (29–107)						
8	332	162 (121–206)	56 (29–101)	68	55.6 (39–73)	65	90.5 (65–123)	64	9.6 (0–21)
9	294	161 (123–203)	58 (30–111)						
10	455	159 (127–196)	58 (29–105)	94	57.3 (38–76)	87	96.8 (64–131)	90	10.4 (2–23)
11	409	162 (124–211)	57 (29–106)						
12	572	160 (121–203)	68 (34–125)	144	55.9 (39–75)	139	95.4 (64–129)	138	9.0 (1–19)
13	411	153 (115–195)	71 (35–143)						
14	426	152 (114–195)	73 (35–134)	129	49.2 (34–69)	129	95.5 (57–130)	127	10.7 (0–25)
15	508	149 (111–194)	74 (34–134)						
16	639	149 (113–192)	77 (35–146)	160	45.6 (30–62)	160	93.2 (64–129)	160	13.5 (2–27)
17	417	150 (110–204)	79 (39–160)						
18	238	152 (113–199)	81 (39–155)	67	43.7 (32–60)	66	99.3 (62–142)	66	13.8 (2–25)
19	173	154 (114–196)	85 (44–172)						
20–24	882	166.5 (124–218)	100.3 (44–201)	118	45.4 (30–63)	118	103.3 (66–147)	118	13.7 (1–28)
25–29	2042	182.2 (133–244)	115.8 (46–249)	253	44.7 (31–63)	253	116.7 (70–165)	253	17.4 (3–36)
30–34	2444	192.2 (138–254)	128.3 (50–266)	403	45.5 (28–63)	403	126.4 (78–185)	403	21.3 (5–48)
35–39	2320	201.3 (146–270)	144.9 (54–321)	371	43.4 (29–62)	371	133.2 (81–189)	372	24.1 (3–56)
40–44	2428	206.5 (151–268)	151.4 (55–320)	383	44.3 (27–67)	385	135.6 (87–186)	384	25.5 (5–56)
45–49	2296	212.2 (158–276)	151.7 (58–320)	325	45.4 (30–64)	325	143.9 (98–202)	326	24.4 (5–51)
50–54	2138	212.7 (158–277)	151.8 (58–320)	340	44.1 (28–63)	340	142.3 (89–197)	340	26.8 (8–62)
55–59	1621	213.9 (156–276)	141.4 (58–286)	261	47.6 (28–71)	261	145.8 (88–203)	261	21.6 (3–49)
60–64	905	213.0 (159–276)	142.3 (58–291)	131	51.5 (30–74)	131	146.3 (83–210)	131	18.9 (3–44)
65–69	750	212.6 (158–274)	136.7 (57–267)	105	51.1 (30–78)	105	150.4 (98–210)	105	19.7 (0–45)
70+	850	206.8 (151–270)	129.8 (58–258)	119	50.5 (31–75)	119	142.9 (88–186)	119	17.0 (0–38)

Table I.B ✧ Plasma Total and Lipoprotein Cholesterol and Triglyceride Mean and Percentile Values (mmol/L) for White Males, by Age

				Cholesterol in					
Age in Years	N	Cholesterol (mmol/L) X (5–95 % tile)	Triglycerides (mmol/L) X (5–95 % tile)	HDL (mmol/L) N	X (5–95 % tile)	LDL (mmol/L) N	X (5–95 % tile)	VLDL (mmol/L) N	X (5–95 % tile)
0	(10)	3.70	0.71						
1	(36)	3.89	0.83						
2	(49)	4.09	0.62						
3	66	3.91 (2.85–5.00)	0.60 (0.32–0.95)						
4	77	4.12 (2.98–5.72)	0.59 (0.32–1.01)						
5	72	4.04 (2.93–5.26)	0.63 (0.29–0.99)						
6	278	4.09 (3.11–5.21)	0.61 (0.35–1.08)	66	1.45 (0.98–1.87)	61	2.46 (1.79–3.34)	61	0.18 (0–0.41)
7	275	4.12 (3.16–5.05)	0.62 (0.33–1.21)						
8	332	4.20 (3.13–5.34)	0.63 (0.33–1.14)	68	1.44 (1.01–1.89)	65	2.34 (1.68–3.19)	64	0.25 (0–0.54)
9	294	4.17 (3.19–5.26)	0.65 (0.34–1.25)						
10	455	4.12 (3.29–5.08)	0.65 (0.33–1.19)	94	1.48 (0.98–1.97)	87	2.51 (1.66–3.39)	90	0.27 (0.05–0.60)
11	409	4.20 (3.21–5.46)	0.64 (0.33–1.20)						
12	572	4.14 (3.13–5.26)	0.77 (0.38–1.41)	144	1.45 (1.01–1.94)	139	2.47 (1.66–3.34)	138	0.23 (0.03–0.49)
13	411	3.96 (2.98–5.05)	0.81 (0.40–1.62)						
14	426	3.94 (2.95–5.05)	0.83 (0.40–1.51)	129	1.27 (0.88–1.79)	129	2.47 (1.48–3.37)	127	0.28 (0–0.65)
15	508	3.86 (2.88–5.02)	0.84 (0.38–1.51)						
16	639	3.86 (2.93–4.97)	0.87 (0.40–1.65)	160	1.18 (0.78–1.61)	160	2.41 (1.66–3.34)	160	0.35 (0.05–0.70)
17	417	3.89 (2.85–5.28)	0.89 (0.44–1.81)						
18	238	3.94 (2.93–5.15)	0.92 (0.44–1.75)	67	1.13 (0.83–1.55)	66	2.57 (1.66–3.34)	66	0.36 (0.05–0.65)
19	173	3.99 (2.95–5.08)	0.96 (0.50–1.94)						
20–24	882	4.31 (3.21–5.65)	1.13 (0.50–2.27)	118	1.18 (0.78–1.63)	118	2.68 (1.71–3.81)	118	0.36 (0.03–0.73)
25–29	2042	4.72 (3.44–6.32)	1.31 (0.52–2.81)	253	1.16 (0.80–1.63)	253	3.02 (1.81–4.27)	253	0.45 (0.08–0.93)
30–34	2444	4.98 (3.57–6.58)	1.45 (0.57–3.01)	403	1.18 (0.73–1.63)	403	3.27 (2.02–4.79)	403	0.55 (0.13–1.24)
35–39	2320	5.21 (3.78–6.99)	1.64 (0.61–3.62)	371	1.12 (0.75–1.61)	371	3.45 (2.09–4.90)	372	0.62 (0.08–1.45)
40–44	2428	5.35 (3.91–6.94)	1.71 (0.62–3.62)	383	1.15 (0.70–1.74)	385	3.51 (2.25–4.82)	384	0.66 (0.13–1.45)
45–49	2296	5.50 (4.09–7.15)	1.71 (0.66–3.70)	325	1.18 (0.78–1.66)	325	3.73 (2.54–5.23)	326	0.63 (0.13–1.32)
50–54	2138	5.51 (4.09–7.17)	1.72 (0.66–3.62)	340	1.14 (0.73–1.63)	340	3.69 (2.31–5.10)	340	0.69 (0.21–1.61)
55–59	1621	5.54 (4.04–7.15)	1.60 (0.66–3.23)	261	1.23 (0.73–1.84)	261	3.78 (2.28–5.26)	261	0.56 (0.08–1.27)
60–64	905	5.52 (4.12–7.15)	1.61 (0.66–3.29)	131	1.33 (0.78–1.92)	131	3.79 (2.15–5.44)	131	0.49 (0.08–1.14)
65–69	750	5.51 (4.09–7.10)	1.54 (0.64–3.02)	105	1.32 (0.78–2.02)	105	3.90 (2.54–5.44)	105	0.51 (0–1.17)
70+	850	5.36 (3.91–6.99)	1.47 (0.66–2.92)	119	1.31 (0.80–1.94)	119	3.70 (2.28–4.82)	119	0.44 (0–0.98)

Table II.A ✧ Plasma Total and Lipoprotein Cholesterol and Triglyceride Mean and Percentile Values (mg/dL) for White Females Not Taking Hormones, by Age

Age in Years	N	Cholesterol (mg/dL) X (5–95 % tile)	Triglycerides (mg/dL) X (5–95 % tile)	Cholesterol in					
				HDL (mg/dL) N	X (5–95 % tile)	LDL (mg/dL) N	X (5–95 % tile)	VLDL (mg/dL) N	X (5–95 % tile)
0	(6)	148	82						
1	(31)	156	70						
2	(33)	152	65						
3	57	160 (118–201)	63 (32–110)						
4	59	155 (108–196)	59 (34–94)						
5	86	162 (126–195)	56 (28–93)						
6	253	165 (129–205)	57 (32–95)	58	50.1 (28–68)	53	100.5 (66–124)	50	9.8 (1–23)
7	220	160 (124–202)	61 (32–112)						
8	297	166 (129–209)	61 (34–104)	60	55.7 (37–75)	55	100.0 (67–142)	54	10.6 (1–25)
9	261	163 (120–205)	63 (32–110)						
10	417	163 (127–205)	66 (35–116)	100	51.5 (34–72)	99	98.1 (70–140)	99	11.8 (2–23)
11	338	161 (126–200)	73 (36–126)						
12	536	161 (124–203)	79 (38–132)	102	53.0 (37–69)	101	97.7 (68–133)	101	10.6 (1–23)
13	344	155 (122–192)	79 (43–136)						
14	441	157 (120–198)	79 (38–138)	122	51.0 (34–70)	120	93.5 (60–129)	120	10.6 (2–23)
15	553	155 (119–199)	74 (39–127)						
16	675	155 (121–197)	71 (37–120)	165	52.8 (35–77)	165	95.2 (57–138)	164	12.3 (3–26)
17	351	158 (119–202)	70 (40–113)						
18	193	157 (116–199)	75 (39–126)	53	53.2 (37–74)	53	101.8 (58–143)	53	11.1 (0–24)
19	137	162 (123–212)	79 (40–135)						
20–24	778	164.1 (122–216)	72.4 (36–131)	96	52.2	96	98.1	96	11.9
25–29	1329	170.7 (128–222)	74.7 (37–145)	181	56.0 (37–81)	181	106.0 (70–151)	181	12.0 (2–24)
30–34	1569	175.4 (130–231)	78.5 (39–151)	233	55.4 (38–75)	232	108.9 (67–150)	233	10.8 (0–25)
35–39	1606	184.4 (140–242)	86.3 (40–176)	241	54.7 (34–82)	242	118.8 (76–172)	240	14.4 (1–35)
40–44	1583	193.8 (147–252)	98.4 (45–191)	244	57.1 (33–87)	244	125.1 (77–174)	244	13.9 (3–29)
45–49	1515	202.5 (152–265)	104.5 (46–214)	249	57.7 (33–86)	247	129.7 (80–187)	247	16.8 (2–38)
50–54	1257	212.7 (162–285)	114.8 (52–233)	177	60.1 (37–89)	177	146.1 (90–215)	177	16.4 (0–37)
55–59	1112	230.5 (173–300)	125.0 (55–262)	172	59.1 (36–86)	172	151.8 (95–213)	172	21.2 (2–51)
60–64	723	230.8 (172–297)	127.0 (56–239)	111	62.0 (36–91)	111	156.3 (100–234)	111	17.6 (0–40)
65–69	593	232.8 (171–303)	131.3 (60–243)	101	60.5 (34–89)	101	161.6 (97–223)	101	17.6 (0–40)
70+	748	228.1 (169–289)	132.4 (60–237)	127	60.1 (33–91)	127	148.9 (96–207)	127	16.2 (0–52)

Table II.B ✧ Plasma Total and Lipoprotein Cholesterol and Triglyceride Mean and Percentile Values (mmol/L) for White Females Not Taking Hormones, by Age

| | | | | Cholesterol in | | | | | |
Age in Years	N	Cholesterol (mmol/L) X (5–95 % tile)	Triglycerides (mmol/L) X (5–95 % tile)	HDL (mmol/L) N (5–95 % tile)	X	LDL (mmol/L) N (5–95 % tile)	X	VLDL (mmol/L) N (5–95 % tile)	X
0	(6)	3.83	0.93						
1	(31)	4.04	0.79						
2	(33)	3.94	0.74						
3	57	4.14 (3.06–5.21)	0.71 (0.36–1.24)						
4	59	4.02 (2.80–5.08)	0.67 (0.38–1.06)						
5	86	4.20 (3.26–5.05)	0.63 (0.32–1.05)						
6	253	4.27 (3.34–5.31)	0.64 (0.36–1.07)	58	1.30 (0.73–1.76)	53	2.60 (1.71–3.21)	50	0.25 (0.03–0.60)
7	220	4.14 (3.21–5.23)	0.69 (0.36–1.27)						
8	297	4.30 (3.34–5.41)	0.69 (0.38–1.18)	60	1.44 (0.96–1.94)	55	2.59 (1.74–3.68)	54	0.28 (0.03–0.65)
9	261	4.22 (3.11–5.31)	0.71 (0.36–1.24)						
10	417	4.22 (3.29–5.31)	0.75 (0.40–1.31)	100	1.33 (0.88–1.86)	99	2.54 (1.81–3.63)	99	0.31 (0.05–0.60)
11	338	4.17 (3.29–5.31)	0.83 (0.41–1.42)						
12	536	4.17 (3.21–5.26)	0.89 (0.43–1.49)	102	1.37 (0.96–1.79)	101	2.53 (1.76–3.44)	101	0.28 (0.03–0.60)
13	344	4.02 (3.16–4.97)	0.89 (0.49–1.54)						
14	441	4.07 (3.11–5.13)	0.89 (0.43–1.56)	122	1.32 (0.88–1.86)	120	2.42 (1.55–3.34)	120	0.28 (0.05–0.60)
15	553	4.02 (3.08–5.15)	0.84 (0.44–1.44)						
16	675	4.02 (3.13–5.10)	0.80 (0.42–1.36)	165	1.37 (0.91–1.99)	165	2.47 (1.48–3.57)	164	0.32 (0.08–0.67)
17	351	4.09 (3.08–5.23)	0.79 (0.45–1.28)						
18	193	4.07 (3.00–5.15)	0.85 (0.44–1.42)	53	1.38 (0.96–1.92)	53	2.64 (1.50–3.70)	53	0.29 (0–0.62)
19	137	4.20 (3.19–5.49)	0.89 (0.45–1.53)						
20–24	778	4.25 (3.16–5.59)	0.82 (0.41–1.48)	96	1.35	96	2.54	96	0.31
25–29	1329	4.42 (3.32–5.75)	0.85 (0.42–1.64)	181	1.45 (0.96–2.10)	181	2.75 (1.81–3.91)	181	0.31 (0.05–0.62)
30–34	1569	4.54 (3.37–5.98)	0.89 (1.44–1.71)	233	1.43 (0.98–1.94)	232	2.82 (1.74–3.89)	233	0.28 (0–0.65)
35–39	1606	4.78 (3.63–6.27)	0.98 (0.45–1.99)	241	1.42 (0.88–2.12)	242	3.08 (1.97–4.46)	240	0.37 (0.03–0.91)
40–44	1583	5.02 (3.81–6.53)	1.11 (0.51–2.16)	244	1.48 (0.86–2.25)	244	3.24 (1.99–4.51)	244	0.36 (0.08–0.75)
45–49	1515	5.25 (3.94–6.86)	1.18 (0.52–2.42)	249	1.49 (0.86–2.23)	247	3.36 (2.07–4.84)	247	0.44 (0.05–0.98)
50–54	1257	5.64 (4.20–7.38)	1.30 (0.59–2.63)	177	1.56 (0.96–2.31)	177	3.78 (2.33–5.57)	177	0.42 (0–0.96)
55–59	1112	5.97 (4.48–7.77)	1.41 (0.62–2.96)	172	1.53 (0.93–2.23)	172	3.93 (2.46–5.52)	172	0.55 (0.05–1.32)
60–64	723	5.98 (4.46–7.69)	1.44 (0.63–2.70)	111	1.61 (0.93–2.36)	111	4.05 (2.59–6.06)	111	0.46 (0.03–1.17)
65–69	593	6.03 (4.43–7.85)	1.48 (0.68–2.75)	101	1.57 (0.88–2.31)	101	4.19 (2.51–5.78)	101	0.46 (0–1.04)
70+	748	5.91 (4.38–7.49)	1.50 (0.68–2.68)	127	1.56 (0.86–2.36)	127	3.86 (2.49–5.36)	127	0.42 (0–1.35)

Table III.A ✧ Plasma Total and Lipoprotein Cholesterol and Triglyceride Mean and Percentile Values (mg/dL) for White Females Taking Hormones, by Age

Age in Years	N	Cholesterol (mg/dL) X (5–95 % tile)	Triglycerides (mg/dL) X (5–95 % tile)	Cholesterol in					
				HDL (mg/dL)		LDL (mg/dL)		VLDL (mg/dL)	
				N	X (5–95 % tile)	N	X (5–95 % tile)	N	X (5–95 % tile)
15–19	167	169.0 (121–231)	106.3 (49–200)	19	-----	19	-----	20	-----
20–24	788	179.2 (131–236)	105.3 (55–176)	101	54.7 (34–79)	101	108.3 (62–163)	101	15.2 (1–30)
25–29	855	183.6 (141–236)	110.4 (57–191)	132	56.1 (35–83)	132	115.9 (72–169)	132	15.3 (2–36)
30–34	579	188.5 (139–246)	115.8 (58–206)	97	58.0	95	117.4	95	15.6
35–39	406	194.4 (146–249)	126.0 (56–241)	50	57.0	50	118.9	50	20.4
40–44	466	199.4 (152–258)	128.9 (58–238)	63	61.1	63	124.8	63	17.2
45–49	627	209.4 (155–276)	129.6 (53–260)	71	65.6	71	127.3	72	19.0
50–54	729	218.1 (164–283)	130.0 (62–238)	70	67.6	70	119.7	70	18.7
55–59	577	218.1 (164–283)	126.5 (62–238)	60	70.8	60	132.5	60	19.2
60–64	341	224.4 (172–285)	126.0 (57–240)	32	70.4	32	136.6	32	13.5
65–69	224	222.5 (173–279)	129.5 (60–234)	25	76.1	25	126.4	25	15.6
70+	132	215.9 (160–274)	121.1 (60–216)	10	-----	10	-----	10	-----

Table III.B ✧ Plasma Total and Lipoprotein Cholesterol and Triglyceride Mean and Percentile Values (mmol/L) for White Females Taking Hormones, by Age

Age in Years	N	Cholesterol (mmol/L) X (5–95 % tile)	Triglycerides (mmol/L) X (5–95 % tile)	Cholesterol in					
				HDL (mmol/L)		LDL (mmol/L)		VLDL (mmol/L)	
				N	X (5–95 % tile)	N	X (5–95 % tile)	N	X (5–95 % tile)
15–19	167	4.38 (3.13–5.98)	1.20 (0.55–2.26)	19	-----	19	-----	20	-----
20–24	788	4.64 (3.39–6.11)	1.19 (0.62–1.99)	101	1.42 (0.88–2.05)	101	2.81 (1.61–4.22)	101	0.39 (0.03–0.78)
25–29	855	4.76 (3.65–6.11)	1.24 (0.64–2.19)	132	1.45 (0.91–2.15)	132	3.00 (1.86–4.38)	132	0.39 (0.05–0.93)
30–34	579	4.87 (3.60–6.37)	1.31 (0.65–2.33)	97	1.50	95	3.04	95	0.40
35–39	406	5.04 (3.78–6.45)	1.43 (0.63–2.72)	50	1.48	50	3.08	50	0.53
40–44	466	5.16 (3.94–6.68)	1.46 (0.65–2.72)	63	1.58	63	3.23	63	0.45
45–49	627	5.42 (4.01–7.15)	1.47 (0.60–2.94)	71	1.70	71	3.30	72	0.49
50–54	729	5.65 (4.32–7.23)	1.47 (0.64–2.80)	70	1.75	70	3.10	70	0.48
55–59	577	5.65 (4.25–7.33)	1.44 (0.70–2.69)	60	1.83	60	3.43	60	0.50
60–64	341	5.81 (4.46–7.38)	1.43 (0.64–2.71)	32	1.82	32	3.54	32	0.35
65–69	224	5.76 (4.48–7.23)	1.47 (0.68–2.64)	25	1.97	25	3.27	25	0.40
70+	132	5.59 (4.14–7.10)	1.37 (0.68–2.44)	10	-----	10	-----	10	-----

Table IV.A ✧ Plasma Total Cholesterol and Triglyceride Mean and Percentile Values (mg/dL) for Black Males and Females, by Age

		MALES			FEMALES	
		Cholesterol (mg/dL)	Triglycerides (mg/dL)		Cholesterol (mg/dL)	Triglycerides (mg/dL)
Age in Years	N	X (5–95 % tile)	X (5–95 % tile)	N	X (5–95 % tile)	X (5–95 % tile)
0	(0)			(2)	124	86
1	(2)	139	49	(6)	154	52
2	(4)	154	52	(5)	160	43
3	(8)	149	46	(7)	167	51
4	(3)	164	64	(4)	147	68
5	(8)	166	45	(8)	183	51
6	97	164 (128–213)	53 (33–94)	102	172 (138–216)	57 (29–108)
7	52	167 (116–208)	49 (33–75)	60	170 (126–216)	52 (27–82)
8	103	167 (129–218)	54 (28–96)	100	172 (124–226)	54 (31–90)
9	74	168 (135–200)	53 (33–81)	68	176 (133–235)	60 (33–100)
10	118	167 (126–206)	53 (29–95)	131	169 (128–211)	60 (39–97)
11	68	167 (133–191)	52 (30–81)	65	168 (131–213)	61 (33–92)
12	120	171 (127–216)	63 (32–100)	128	161 (121–203)	68 (37–109)
13	88	159 (124–195)	58 (33–90)	70	167 (120–219)	70 (37–112)
14	91	157 (115–195)	58 (32–98)	80	161 (120–205)	66 (38–110)
15	138	154 (110–200)	59 (28–97)	150	166 (129–211)	64 (34–121)
16	200	157 (120–199)	57 (31–102)	192	162 (120–206)	59 (32–95)
17	126	156 (118–208)	65 (32–122)	83	166 (124–208)	62 (36–107)
18	(38)	163	65	(23)	167	66
19	(12)	160	60	(6)	166	55
20–29	97	178.5	81.3	129	178.1 (125–234)	71.3 (36–127)
30–39	178	191.6 (138–253)	106.9 (42–224)	291	186.4 (132–243)	76.4 (38–140)
40–49	167	206.9 (148–267)	126.1 (52–294)	188	201.8 (145–267)	95.1 (43–175)
50–59	70	206.5	142.2	80	215.5	102.1
60+	46	220.7	108.5	48	233.6	115.4

Table IV.B ✧ Plasma Total Cholesterol and Triglyceride Mean and Percentile Values (mmol/L) for Black Males and Females, by Age

Age in Years	N	MALES Cholesterol (mmol/L) X (5–95 % tile)	Triglycerides (mmol/L) X (5–95 % tile)	N	FEMALES Cholesterol (mmol/L) X (5–95 % tile)	Triglycerides (mmol/L) X (5–95 % tile)
0	(0)			(2)	3.21	0.97
1	(2)	3.60	0.55	(6)	3.99	0.59
2	(4)	3.99	0.59	(5)	4.14	0.49
3	(8)	3.86	0.52	(7)	4.33	0.58
4	(3)	4.25	0.72	(4)	3.81	0.77
5	(8)	4.30	0.51	(8)	4.74	0.58
6	97	4.25 (3.32–5.52)	0.60 (0.37–1.06)	102	4.46 (3.57–5.59)	0.64 (0.33–1.22)
7	52	4.33 (3.00–5.39)	0.56 (0.37–0.85)	60	4.40 (3.26–5.59)	0.59 (0.31–0.93)
8	103	4.33 (3.34–5.65)	0.61 (0.32–1.08)	100	4.46 (3.21–5.85)	0.61 (0.35–1.02)
9	74	4.35 (3.50–5.18)	0.60 (0.37–0.92)	68	4.56 (3.44–6.09)	0.68 (0.37–1.13)
10	118	4.32 (3.44–4.95)	0.60 (0.33–1.07)	131	4.38 (3.32–5.47)	0.68 (0.41–1.09)
11	68	4.32 (3.44–4.95)	0.59 (0.34–0.92)	65	4.35 (3.39–5.52)	0.69 (0.37–1.04)
12	120	4.43 (3.29–5.59)	0.71 (0.36–1.13)	128	4.17 (3.13–5.26)	0.77 (0.42–1.23)
13	88	4.12 (3.21–5.05)	0.65 (0.37–1.02)	70	4.33 (3.11–5.67)	0.79 (0.42–1.27)
14	91	4.07 (2.98–5.05)	0.65 (0.36–1.10)	80	4.17 (3.11–5.67)	0.75 (0.43–1.24)
15	138	3.99 (2.85–5.18)	0.66 (0.32–1.09)	150	4.30 (3.34–5.47)	0.72 (0.38–1.37)
16	200	4.07 (3.11–5.15)	0.64 (0.35–1.15)	192	4.20 (3.11–5.34)	0.67 (0.36–1.07)
17	126	4.04 (3.06–5.39)	0.74 (0.36–1.38)	83	4.30 (3.21–5.39)	0.70 (0.41–1.21)
18	(38)	4.22	0.74	(23)	4.33	0.75
19	(12)	4.14	0.68	(6)	4.20	0.75
20–29	97	4.62	0.92	129	4.61 (3.24–6.06)	0.81 (0.41–1.44)
30–39	178	4.96 (3.57–6.55)	1.21 (0.48–2.53)	291	4.83 (3.42–6.29)	0.86 (0.43–1.58)
40–49	167	5.36 (3.83–6.92)	1.42 (0.59–3.32)	188	6.23 (3.76–6.92)	1.08 (0.49–1.98)
50–59	70	5.35	1.61	80	5.58	1.15
60+	46	5.72	1.23	48	6.05	1.30

Index

A

reference materials *Continued*
  traceability to, 718
  triglyceride testing, 211
reference ranges for cholesterol, lipoprotein choles-
     terol, and triglycerides, 786*t*–793*t*
refractometry, density measurement, 627
Regression Growth Evaluation Statin Study
     (REGRESS), 107
Regulatory Affairs Professional Society (RAPS), 762
regulatory agencies. *See* Food and Drug Administra-
     tion (FDA)
remnant particles
  atherogenicity of, 79
  coronary heart disease (CHD) risk and, 16
  defined, 5
  metabolism, 5–6, 11, 78*f*, 79
  triglyceride metabolism and, 209
  triglyceride-rich, 565–577
  very-low-density lipoproteins (VLDL), 567–568,
     568*f*
renal failure, 172
renal insufficiency, 83*t*
renal replacement therapy
  apolipoprotein levels, 395
  lipoprotein (a) levels, 364–365
  LpA-I:A-II and, 557
resins, 85*t*, 88–89, 90*t*
retinol, 443
reverse cholesterol transport
  high-density lipoprotein (HDL) metabolism, 8, 9*f*,
     14
  phospholipids in, 522
risk factors
  atherosclerosis, 34–35, 103–104
  cardiovascular disease, 63*t*, 127–134
    C-reactive protein, 66–67, 66*t*
    comparison of, 69–70
    homocysteine (Hcy), 62–65, 63*t*, 64*t*
  coronary heart disease (CHD), 64*f*, 81*t*, 82*t*
  coronary stenosis, 339, 340*f*
  management, primary care and specialty centers,
     118
  myocardial infarction, 41, 42*f*
  pancreatitis, 81*t*
  risk prediction and, 53–54
  thrombogenesis, 40–41, 40*t*
  total cardiovascular risk, 109–111
Roche Diagnostics, 234, 256, 742*t*
Roche Diagnostics kinetic TC procedure, 194
Roche Diagnostics LightCycler, 409

Roche Diagnostics Reflotron desktop analyzer,
     267–268
Rural Health Promotion Project, 66*f*, 67

S

Safe Medical Devices Act of 1990, 767
Scandinavian Simvastatin Survival Study (4S), 104,
     127, 135
scavenger receptor A, 441
scavenger receptor BI (SR-BI), 14–15, 401
Schistosomiasis, 523*t*
schizophrenia, 51*t*
Scottish Intercollegiate Guidelines Network (SIGN),
     136, 137*f*
screening. *See* testing and screening
Second National Health and Nutrition Examination
     Survey, 166
selenium, 443, 449
serum total cholesterol. *See* cholesterol
Sheffield Risk and Treatment Table, 151–152
sickle cell anemia, 55–56
Sigma-Aldrich, 742*t*
simvastatin, 88, 91, 450, 559
sitostanol, 430
smoking
  antioxidants and CHD risk, 443
  cardiovascular risk and, 132
  F2-isoprostanes and, 466
  high-density lipoprotein cholesterol (HDL-C) lev-
     els, 313
  lipid disorders, secondary cause of, 83*t*
  lipid profile, behavioral variations in, 168–169
  low-density lipoprotein (LDL) oxidation,
     atherosclerotic risk and, 449
  LpA-I, LpA-I:A-II and, 558
  as risk factor
    atherosclerosis, 35
    coronary heart disease (CHD), 77, 82*t*
    thrombosis, 40, 40*t*, 41
  total cardiovascular risk, 110–111
Solomon Park Research Institute, 740*t*, 743*t*
sphingomyelin (SPH), 522*f*, 531*f*
sphingophospholipids, 521
St. Thomas Atherosclerosis Regression Study
     (STARS), 107, 132
standard material, defined, 199
standardization of measurements, 199–201
  apolipoproteins, 738–739